SP Pvt. Ltd.

# Breeding Field Crops I
# *Practices*


***by***

**V.L. Chopra**

*Chancellor, Central University of Kerala*
*(Formerly) Member Planning Commission, Govt. of India*
*Secretary (DARE) Govt. of India and*
*Director General, Indian Council of Agriculture Research*
*Member, Science Council Consultative Group of International*
*Agric. Research (CGIAR)*



**2019**

**Studium Press (India) Pvt. Ltd.**

# Breeding Field Crops I
## *Practices*


First Published 2014 (Studium Press LLC, USA)



ISBN (Vol. 1) : 978-93-85046-56-8
ISBN (Vol. 2): 978-93-85046-57-5
ISBN (Set): 978-93-85046-55-1

*Published by:*

**Studium Press (India) Pvt. Ltd.**
*4735/22, 2nd Floor, Prakash Deep Building*
*(Near Delhi Medical Association)*
*Ansari Road, Darya Ganj, New Delhi-110 002*
*Tel.: + 91-11-43240200-15 (15 lines); Fax: 91-11-43240215*
*E-mail: pubdir@studiumpress.in*

*Printed in India*

# List of Contributors

**Ali, Masood:** Indian Institute of Pulses Research, Kanpur, India.

**Asthana, A.N.:** Formerly Director, Indian Institute of Pulses Research, Kanpur, India.

**Bandyopadhyay, A.:** National Research Centres, (NRC) on Groundnut, Junagargh, Gujarat, India.

**Dhillon, B.S.:** Punjab Agricultural University, Ludhiana, India.

**Dua, R.P.:** Indian Institute of Pulses Research, Kanpur, India.

**Govila, O.P.:** Formaly at the Indian Agricultural Research Institute, Delhi, India.

**Kapur, Raman:** Indian Institute of Sugarcane Research, Lucknow, India

**Khadi, B.M.:** Agricultural Research Station, Dharwad Farm, Karnataka, India.

**Kulkarni, V.N.:** Agricultural Research Station, Dharwad Farm, Karnataka, India.

**Kumar, P.R.:** Formerly Director, NRC on Rapeseed & Mustard, Bharatpur, India.

**Kumar, Shiv:** Indian Institute of Pulses Research, Kanpur, India.

**Manivel, P.:** National Research Centre, (NRC) on Groundnut, Junagargh, Gujarat, India.

**Mishra, S.P.:** Formerly at Indian Institute of Pulses Research, Kanpur, India.

**Prassanna, B.M.:** Formerly at the Indian Agricultural Research Institute, New Delhi, India.

**Raj, K. Giri:** University of Agricultural Sciences, Dharwar, Karnataka, India.

**Rao, N.G.P.:** Formerly Chairman, Agricultural Scientist Recruitment Board, ICAR, New Delhi, India.

**Rao, V.S.:** Formerly at the Agarkar Research Institute, Pune, India.

**Siddiq, E.A.:** Directorate of Rice Research, Hyderabad, India

**Tiwari, S. Prakash:** Formerly Director, NRC Soybean, Indore, India.

**Viraktamath, B.C.:** Directorate of Rice Research, Hyderabad, India.

# About the Editor

Educated at the University of Delhi, the Indian Agricultural Research Institute (IARI) and the University of Edinburgh, Chopra has been associated with IARI in various capacities that include active research in basic and applied genetics, Headship of the Genetics Division, National Professorship of the ICAR and founder of the Biotechnology Centre. He has published extensively in scientific journals of high repute and impact. His scientific standing has been recognized by national and international science academies and he is elected Fellow of the Indian National Science Academy, the Indian Academy of Science, the National Academy of Sciences India & the National Academy of Agricultural Sciences. He has also been elected to Fellowship of the European Academy of Science, Arts & Humanities, Paris and The World Academy of Science (TWAS), Trieste. In the arena of international agricultural research, Chopra was member of the Research Council of the CGIAR and on the Boards of Trustees of IRRI, ICRISAT and CIMMYT.

Chopra has held key positions in the Govt. of India including that of Secretary (DARE) & Director General, ICAR and Member, Planning Commission. Currently, he is Chancellor of the Central University of Kerala and Chairs the Science Advisory Committee to the Chief Minister of Jammu & Kashmir.

Chopra is a much decorated scientist and science administrator; his major Awards include Padma Bhushan by the Govt. of India, Aryabhata Medal by Indian National Science Academy, Dr. B.P. Pal Memorial Award by National Academy of Agricultural Sciences, Outstanding Achievement in Research in Science & Technology Award by FICCI, Om Prakash Bhasin Award & the Borlaug Award. He has been President of the International Genetics Federation and the National Academy of Agricultural Sciences.

# Preface

One of the biggest tangible benefits that application of science and technology has given to the world is the enhanced genetic production potential of crops that feed the human population and provide livelihood opportunities to very large numbers. This benefit is most manifest in the developing countries whose growing population would have been subjected to greater miseries if this benefit had not accrued. India is often cited as a country that has made a remarkable success of its plant breeding efforts. Many, specially the students of plant breeding, are interested in the details of 'what' and 'how' of the achievements made. However, a book containing information on the wide range of components that are necessary for breeding exercise is not available. This volume attempts to cover this gap.

Breeding Field Crops 1 deals with the following aspects of major field crops of the Indian sub-continent: area, production and productivity trends; origin, evolution, taxonomy and breeding systems; genetic resources relevant to breeding requirements; methods employed to develop improved varieties and hybrids; successful cultivars, their characteristics and recommended areas for cultivation; seed production requirements and strategies; future outlook.

Published first as 'Breeding Field Crops' in 2001, the book has been out of print for some time now but has retained demand both among teachers and students of the plant breeding discipline. This new version, titled 'Breeding Field Crops 1: Practices' is brought out as a twin to 'Breeding Field Crops 2: Advances'. The latter summarizes advances made in breeding of field crops post 2001. The two volumes will provide a comprehensive coverage of the subject and can be read independently, concurrently or sequentially to obtain the required insight.

**New Delhi** **V.L. Chopra**

# Table of Contents

# 1

# Rice

## 1. INTRODUCTION

Rice is the second most important food crop of the world. Over 150 million ha are planted to rice worldwide with a production of around 375 million tonnes. Feeding more than one half of the world's population, over 90% of rice is produced and consumed in Asia. Average daily intake of rice provides 20-80 per cent of dietary energy and 12-17 per cent of dietary protein for Asians. Compelled by the realization that there was no alternative to steady production growth of rice to keep pace with population growing at an alarming rate, serious crop improvement research was started about a Century back. With a very few exceptions the entire rice world has been suffering from chronic food deficiency until the advent of plant type-based high yielding varieties in the mid sixties. Extensive adoption of these varieties has enabled many countries in Asia to achieve self-sufficiency in food and to sustain it since then. As for India, the largest rice growing country in the world with long history of rice cultivation, rice production and yield have more than doubled during the last four decades culminating in sustained self-sufficiency and surplus for adequate buffer stocking and limited export (Fig. 1). The spectacular transformation being witnessed all over the rice world today in the varietal scenario is due to progressively knowledge-infused breeding research solidly based on and blended with the rich experience and material wealth carefully built over the decades. Meeting the future challenge of feeding the growing billions will, however, depend on more and more innovations in breeding research.

## 2. ADAPTABILITY

There is hardly any crop plant that grows under as diverse agroclimatic conditions as rice does. Geographical distribution of rice growing areas

V.L. Chopra (Ed.): Breeding Field Crops I: Practices, Studium Press (LLC), USA.

extends from 50º North in Central Czechoslovakia on the equator to 35º South in Australia. The growing conditions vary from below sea level in Kuttanad region of Kerala (India) to as high an altitude as 2000 m in the Himalayas, extreme water regimes ranging from highly drought-prone uplands (<50 mm rainfall) to flood prone/deepwater lowlands,

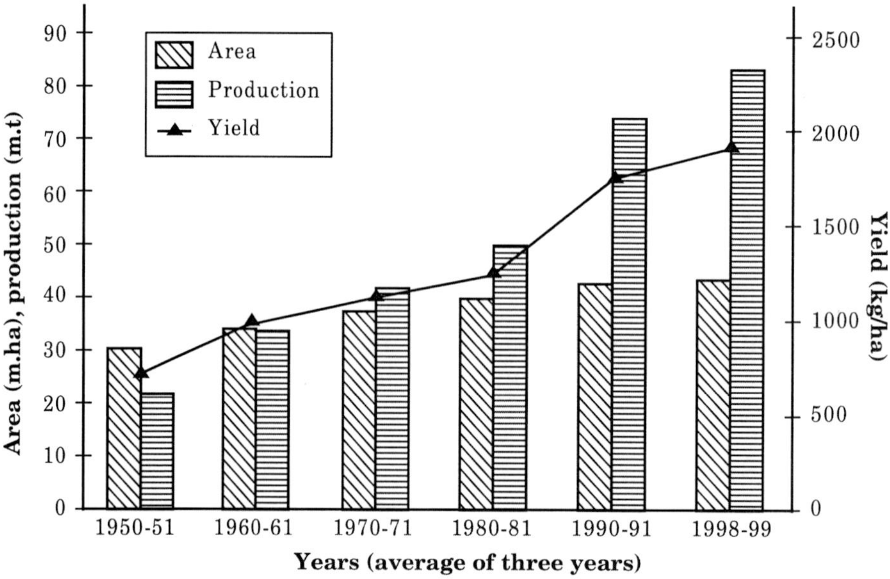


**Fig. 1:** Area, production and yield of rice in india

(2-3 m depth), temperature in the range of 33ºC in West Pakistan to 17ºC in North Japan and soil reaction from acidic (pH<4) to alkaline/saline soils (pH>11 and Ec>4.0). Given its adaptation to such a wide range of growing conditions, defining of typical "rice climate" would not be easy. Nevertheless, conditions relatively optimal for high productivity and normal growth are deep non-injurious soils, enough water, high temperature and ample solar radiation throughout the growing season.

## 3. ORIGIN AND ANTIQUITY

*Oryza sativa* and *O. glaberrima* are the only cultivated species in the genus *Oryza,* which comprises 22 valid species. Based on pan-tropical and wide distribution of *Oryza* species, it is speculated that the Gondwana Super Continent, which is believed to have got fractured during early Cretaceous period (130 million years ago) into the present day Africa, South America, South and South-east Asia, Australia and Antartica, the species also drifted along to form distinct geographical habitats

(Chang, 1976). Using genetic diversity, historical and archeological evidences and geographical distribution, centres of origin and centres of diversity of *O. sativa* and *O. glaberrima* have been nearly identified. Rice researchers are in agreement that the large belt extending from northeast hills in India to the mountain ranges of the mainland Southeast Asia and Southwest China could be the primary centre of origin of *O. sativa,* while Niger River Delta in Africa as the primary centre of origin of *O. glaberrima* (Porteres, 1956). Niches that provided conducive environment for ecogenetic differentiation facilitated by migration, natural and human selection became the centres of diversity of the cultivated species. The foothills of the Himalayas, Chattisgarh area of Madhya Pradesh, Jeypore Tract of Orissa in India, Myanmar, northern parts of Thailand, Yunnan Province of China etc., are some of the centres of diversity for Asian cultigens, as are swampy upper Niger River Basin and some areas around Guinean coast for the African rice. In all probability, the cultivars were first domesticated in the centres of diversity, where conditions were congenial for planting rice.

It is difficult to precisely define the time of origin and domestication of the cultivated rice. It is speculated that it might have originated around 10 million years back from the wild/weedy progenitor species by a series of mutations, intercrossings and natural selection. On the basis of archeological and historical evidence the period of its domestication has, however, been approximated. The assessment that *O. sativa* was domesticated between 7000 and 10000 years ago appears to be quite reasonable given the fact that the oldest remains of Asian cultivated rice found in East China and Northern India date back to 7000 years and that grain samples of wild rice excavated at Non Nok Tha in Northern Thailand are more than 6000 years old. The African rice, believed to have been domesticated at least 3500 years later, has been inferred from various evidences, found in the Niger basins around 1500 B.C. and in Guinea 400 years later.

## 4. TAXONOMY AND SPECIES RELATIONSHIPS

Rice belongs to the genus *Oryza* of the tribe *Oryzae* of the family Graminae. The 22 recognized species including the Asian and African cultivated rices constituting the genus are broadly grouped into four complexes *viz., Sativa, Officinalis*, Ridley and *Meyeriana* (Table 1). The Sativa complex comprises the cultivated species *O. sativa* and *O. glaberrima* and their weedy/wild ancestors *viz.*, perennial rhizomatous *O. longistaminata, O. barthii* (formerly *O. breviligulata*) and *O. stapfii, O. rufipogon* (*O. perennis* sub sp. *balunga*), *O. nivara* and *O. sativa f spontanea* respectively. *Oryza cubenesis (O. glumaepetula),* endemic to Cuba and adjoining Islands is yet another constituent species of this complex. It is also a *perennis* subspecies corresponding to the African *(O. longistaminata)* and Asian *(O. rufipogon)* species, but with no sign of evolving further into cultivated forms as happened in Asia and Africa. The cultivated species while having many agrobotanical traits in common are distinguishable on a few key characteristics such as glume size, number of secondary panicle branches (rachii), panicle thickness etc.

**Table 1:** Species complexes in the genus Oryza and their genomic groups

| *Complex/Species* | *Ploidy* | *Genome* | *Distribution* |
|---|---|---|---|
| ***Sative complex*** | | | |
| *O. sativa* | Diploid | AA | World wide |
| *O. glaberrima* | Diploid | $A^g$ | Africa |
| *O. barthii* | Diploid | $A^g$ | Africa |
| *O. longistaminata* | | $A^g$ | Africa |
| *O. nivara* | Diploid | AA | Tropical Asia |
| *O. rufipogon* | Diploid | AA | Tropical Asia |
| *O. mesidionalis* | Diploid | AA | Tropical Australia |
| *O. glumaepetula* | Diploid | AA | South America |
| ***Officinalis complex*** | | | |
| *O. officinalis* | Diploid | CC | Tropical Asia to New Guinea |
| *O. eichingeri* | Diploid | CC | Hast and West Africa |
| *O. rhizomatis* | Diploid | CC | Sri Lanka |
| *O. minuta* | Tetraploid | BBCC | Philippines, Papua New Guinea |
| *O. punctata* | Diploid | BB | |
| | Tetraploid | BBCC | Africa |
| *O. latifolia* | Tetraploid | CCDD | Latin America |
| *O. alta* | Tetraploid | CCDD | Latin America |
| *O. grandiglumis* | Tetraploid | CCDD | South America |
| *O. australiensis* | Diploid | EE | Australia |
| ***Meyeriana complex*** | | | |
| *O. granulata* | Diploid | F | South & Southeast Asia |
| *O. meyeriana* | Diploid | F | Southeast Asia |
| *O. brachyantha* | Tetraploid | FF | Africa |
| *O. schlechten* | Tetraploid | — | New Guinea |
| ***Ridleyi complex*** | | | |
| *O. longiglumis* | Tetraploid | — | New Guinea |
| *O. ridleyi* | Tetraploid | — | Southeast Asia |

The species relationship as understood from cytological investigations reveal that the genus includes diploid (*O. sativa, O. glaberrima* and their wild relatives, *O. officinalis, O. australiensis* and *O. punctata*) with 2n = 24 chromosomes and tetraploid (*O. minuta, O. latifolia, O. alta, O. malamphuz haensis, O. grandiglumis, O. longiglumis, O. punctata* and *O. ridleyi*) with 2n = 48 chromosomes species. Genome analysis done on the basis of chromosome pairing behaviour and fertility in interspecific hybrids has made possible to group them under six distinct genomes designated as A, B, C, D, E, and F (Table 2). Relatively inter compatible cultivars and their wild relatives constitute 'A' genome. The subscripts denote subgroups, which have basically the same genome but exhibit in hybrid combinations some detectable differences in meiotic behaviour and fertility Status (Chang, 1964).

**Table 2:** Genomic classification of rice Species

| *Genome* | *Genomic constitution* | *Species* | *Distribution* |
|---|---|---|---|
| A | AA | *O. sativa, O. nivara, O. rufipogon* (Formerly *O. balunga*) *O. sativa f. spontanea* | Asia |
| | $A^1A^1$ | *O. longistaminata, O. stapfii* | Africa |
| | $A^RA^R$ | *O. glaberrima, O. barthii* (Formerly *O. breviligulata*) | Africa |
| | $A^{Rd}A^{Rd}$ | *O. glumaepetula* (Formerly *O. cubmsis*) | America |
| C | CC | *O. officinalis, O. eichengeri* | Asia |
| B&C | BBCC | *O. minuta, O. punctata* Asia | |
| C&D | CCDD | *O. latifolia, O. alta, O. grandiglumis* | America |
| E | EE | *O. australiensis* | Australia |
| F | FF | *O. brachyantha* | Africa |

Cultivated rice is a secondarily balanced polyploid derived from an ancestral graminaceous species with a basic chromosome number of 5. During the evolutionary process two of the chromosomes were duplicated resulting in two types of plants *viz.*, 2n = 14 and 2n = 10. The amphidiploid of the cross between the two variants (2n =12) resulted in the cultivated rice and its wild ancestors with 2n = 24 chromosomes.

## 4.1. Evolution of Cultivated Rices

One topic that has interested rice scientists deeply for long is the phylogeny of the cultivated rices. Sampath and Rao (1951) were among the first to trace the evolutionary pathway of *O. sativa* based on geographical distribution of related species, cytomorphological features and sexual affinity. Years of investigation by various workers in India and Japan has led to the thesis that *O. perennis* (possibly *preperennis* now extinct) was the common ancestor of both the cultivated species. Parallel evolution aided by minor chromosomal rearrangements and a series of micro and macro mutations followed by natural selection might have resulted in Asian (*O. rufipogon*) and African (*O. longistaminata*) *perennis*. This, through a single step macro mutation and natural selection, had possibly led to loss of rhizomatous nature to give rise to weedy annuals *O. nivara* and *O. barthii* respectively. Intervention of man at this stage, through intensive selection for higher yield and early maturity, had led to the evolution of the first cultivated form *viz.*, *O. sativa* in Asia and *O. glaberrima* in Africa from the respective weedy annuals (Fig. 2). The evolutionary pathway of both the cultivated species suggests them to be of monophyletic origin. *O. sativa f spontanea* and *O. stapfii* occurred as segregating populations or hybrid swarms respectively in Asia and Africa. *O. sativa f spontanea* is a derivative from continued intercrossing between *O. sativa* and its putative progenitor species (*O. rufipogan* and *O. nivara*), while *O. stapfii* is the corresponding hybrid swarm resulting from intercrossing of *O. glaberrima* and *O. longistaminata* with *O. barthii.*

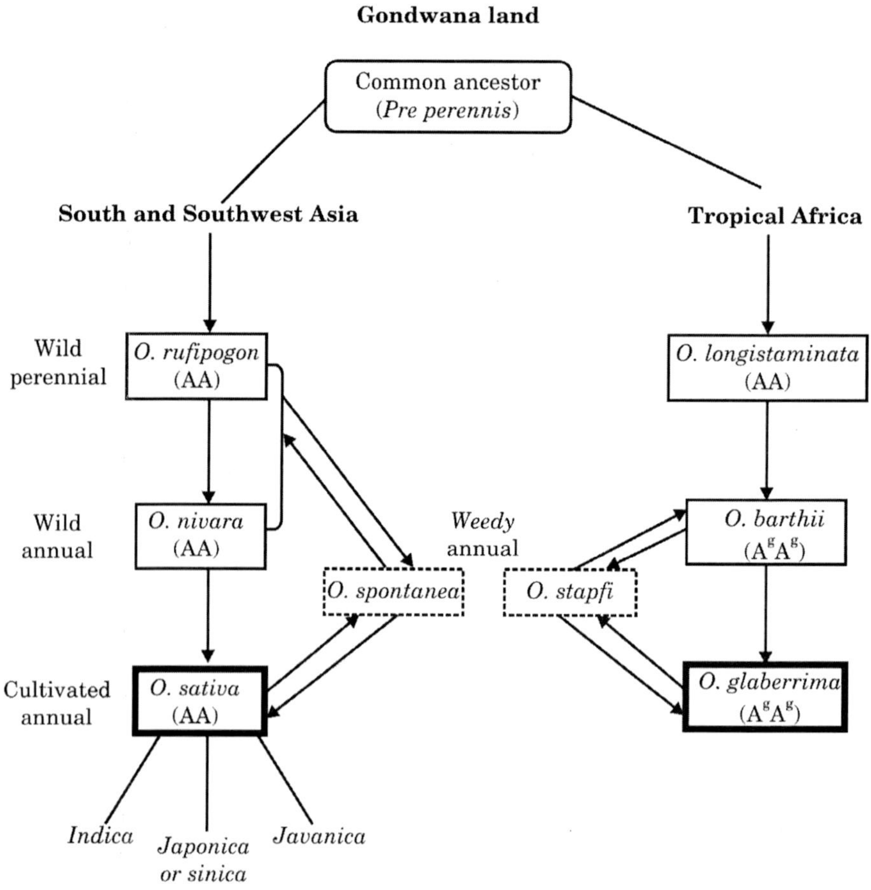


**Fig. 2:** Evolutionary pathways of Asian and African cultivated rices.

The annual ancestral form of the Asian cultigen appears to have originated during the Neothermal period (15000-10000 BC) along the southern and northern slopes of the Himalayas. Alternating periods of drought and pronounced temperature, Variation might have accelerated the development of the annual forms in the Northeastern India, Northern southeast Asia and Southern China. Early cultigens were *indicas* (Swaminathan, 1984).

### 4.1.1. *Subspecific differentiation of Asian cultivated rice*

Subsequent to its origin and domestication, the Asian cultivated rice differentiated into three eco-geographic races or subspecies *viz.*, *indica, japonica (sinica),* and *javanica. Indica* rices are well adapted to, and occur in the humid regions of tropical and subtropical Asia (India, southern China, Vietnam, Thailand, Myanmar, the Philippines, Bangladesh, Sri Lanka etc.,), while *japonicas* to subtropical and temperate regions (Korea, Japan, North China etc.,) and *javanicas* to the equatorial region in Indonesia. Evolution of the subspecies was primarily achieved by natural and human selection in different environments. Most differentiation occurred in the region extending from the southern foothills of the Himalayas to Vietnam and on the northern borders of the mountain ranges in Southwest and South China.

Increasing aridity on the northern border of the Himalayas and its associated mountain ranges in mainland Southeast Asia possibly forced early settlers in China to move east and southward in search of more humid areas conducive for planting rice. With peoples' migration plants also dispersed, thus accelerating the ecogenetic diversification process. Inside China along a branch of the River Brahmaputra, a race adapted to temperate conditions was evolved from the primitive *indica* rices. This was what is now known as *Japonica* by the Japanese and *sinica* by the Chinese. Tall large grain types on the other hand taken to the Indonesian Islands from the east coast of South Asia got differentiated to become *javanica* rice (Swaminathan, 1984). This hypothesis is corroborated by the view that aus-like and aman-like rices from eastern India moved northward and eastward had probably evolved into *japonica* and *javanica* races respectively. Characteristic features of these subspecies are given in Table 3.

**Table 3:** Characteristic features of the subspecies of *O. sativa*

| ***Character*** | ***Japonica*** | ***Javanica*** | ***Indica*** |
|---|---|---|---|
| Grain shape | Short | Long | Narrow |
| Length of 2nd leaf blade | Short | Long | Long |
| Angle between 2nd leaf and stem | Small | Small | Large |
| Texture of plant parts | Hard | Hard | Soft |
| Angle between flag leaf and stem | Medium | Large | Small |
| Flag leaf | Short, narrow | Long, wide | Long, narrow |
| Tiller number | Large | Small | Large |
| Tiller habit | Erect | Erect | Spreading |
| Leaf pubescence | None | Little | More |
| Glume pubescence | Dense | Dense | Sparse |
| Awns | Usually absent | More prominent | Less prominent |
| Threshability | Difficult | Difficult | Easy |
| Panicle length | Short | Long | Medium |
| Panicle branching | Few | Many | Medium |
| Panicle density | High | Moderate | Moderate |
| Panicle weight | Heavy | Heavy | Light |
| Plant height | Short | Taller | Tall |
| Grain (spikelet) | Short | Long | Long |

Modified from Nayar (1973)

The genetic affinity between the three subspecies as studied from chromosome pairing behaviour, $F_1$ sterility and $F_2$ segregation pattern reveal *indica-japonica* to show the least compatibility as compared to *indica-javanica* and *javanica-japonica* crosses. The genetic differences between *indica* and *japonica* have been explained through genic (Oka, 1953; 1974) and chromosomal (Sampath, 1962; Henderson *et al.,* 1959) models. The chromosomal model attributes the inter-varietal group sterility to cryptic structural differences (duplication, deletion, inversion etc.). At genic level different hypotheses have been advanced. Morinaga and Fukushima (1956) explained the sterility as due to imbalance of gene groups brought together in crosses of the *indica* and *japonica* varietal groups differentiated from each other by accumulation of gene mutations. Hsu (1945) concluded the intervarietal $F_1$ sterility as due to complimentary genes carried by the putative ancestral forms. Oka (1953; 1974) proposed that a series of duplicate genes designated as 'gametk development' genes governed gamete fertility. When parents carrying these genes in dominant or recessive state at different loci are crossed, the $F_1$ would produce gametes homozygous recessive for more than one gene resulting in sterility. For instance, where $F_1$ is highly fertile but segregants in the $F_2$, and subsequent generations remain sterile, he assumes operation of "duplicate fertility" gene, whose double recessive combination leads to pollen sterility. Siddiq and Swaminathan (1968) suggest that differentiation of the two subspecies preceded through a series of systematic mutations affecting diagnostic characteristics brought together in a cluster probably under the influence of disruptive selection. According to them, disturbed genetic coherence rather than major chromosomal differences may be responsible for semisterility and skewed segregation ratios observed in the *indica/japonica* hybrid progenies. The recent findings of Japanese workers suggest the $F_1$ sterility in the inter-subspecific hybrid to be due to absence of a few Mendelian sterility neutralizing (wide compatibility) genes (Ikehashi and Araki, 1986).

Differentiation is not restricted to the three subspecies. Over the centuries combined forces of natural and human selection, diverse agro-climate, agro-ecological Isolation, cultural practice etc., have led to continued diversification of the Asian cultivars, resulting in many overlapping varietal groups. Such a rich diversity with unlimited variability is of great value as feedstock for progressive improvement of rice.

## 5. FLORAL BIOLOGY

Precise knowledge of floral biology, which includes structural and functional aspects of rice flower is essential for breeders to plan and execute breeding strategies. Rice is a self-pollinated crop, although outcrossing to an extent of 6.8% has been reported in some varieties under certain conditions (Sahadevan and Namboodiri, 1963). Higher outcrossing is however, found in wild relatives of rice with *O. longistaminata* showing total outcrossing (100%) and *O. sativa f spontanea* about 50%.

Inflorescence of rice is a terminal panicle with single flowered spikelets. The panicle has a main axis, on which primary branches are borne. Secondary branches are borne towards the basal region of the primary branches. Tertiary branches, if any, are seen at the base of the secondary branches. Much of the variability for spikelet number is due to Variation in the number of secondary branches. The spikelet consists of two short sterile lemma, a normal fertile lemma and palea. The fertile lemma is either awnless or short or long awned (Fig. 3). The fertile lemma and palea enclose the sexual organs *viz.*, six stamens arranged in whorls and a pistil at the centre. The stamen consists of bilobed anthers borne on slender filaments, while the pistil consists of ovary, style and feathery bifid stigma.

Reproductive phase starts with panicle initiation, which occurs about 35 days before panicle emergence. In photosensitive varieties panicle initiation starts uniformly at a fixed time irrespective of date of planting during the regular season, while in photosensitive varieties, depending on the duration of the variety, panicle initiation starts 35 days before heading of a crop planted in any season or time. Complete emergence of panicle from flag leaf sheath takes place within a day. Days to complete

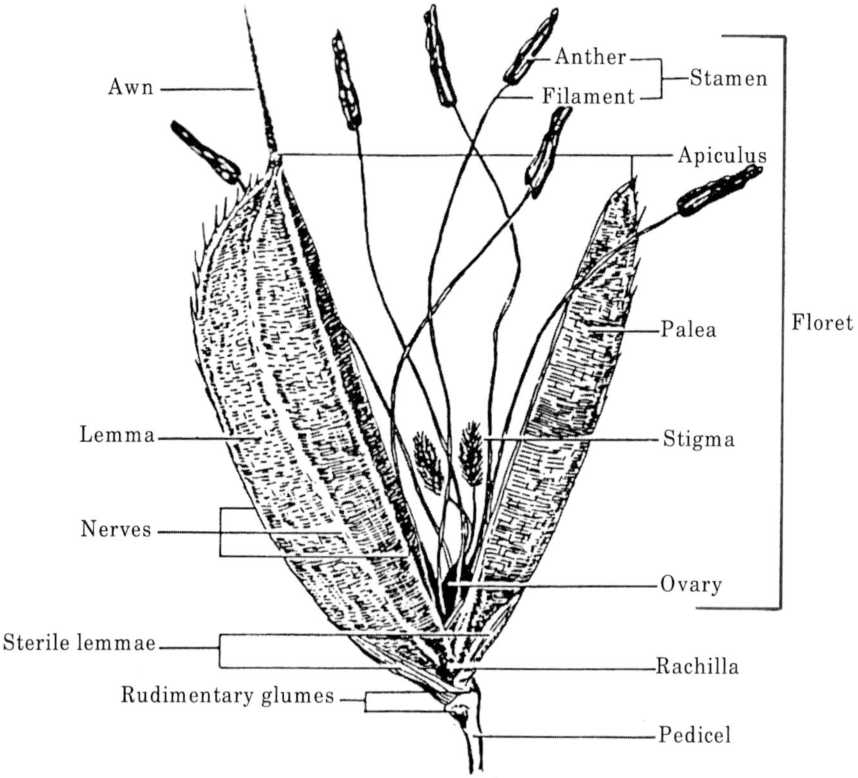


**Fig. 3:** Parts of spikelet (from Chang and Bardenas, 1965).

heading varies with the variety, the range being between 5-15 days. Anthesis (spikelet opening and dehiscence of anther) occurring immediately after the panicle emergence, follows a specific pattern, in which spikelets on the primary branch followed by spikelets on the secondary/tertiary branches at the corresponding position of the panicle open (Fig. 4). The lower most secondary/tertiary branches open last. Thus completion of anthesis on a panicle takes about 7 days. From anthesis, the panicle takes around 30 days to grain maturity in tropical rices and 35 to 45 days in temperate rices.

The process of anthesis is greatly influenced by weather conditions. The spikelets generally open on a sunny day between 10 AM and 2 PM, the maximum blooming being between 10 and 11 AM. About six days before heading, pollen grains mature and the flag leaf swells indicating the approach of booting stage. At the time of anthesis, lemma and palea get separated, filaments of stamens elongate and protrude out and anthers dehisce releasing the pollen. Most of the pollen is shed on the protruded Stigma of the same spikelet or neighbouring spikelets of the same plant, thus causing self- pollination. After 20-30 minutes of anthesis, anthers wither out and the spikelet closes leaving the stamens sticking out from the seams of lemma and palea. The pollen remain viable for not more than 3-5 minutes, while stigma is receptive for 2-3 days from the day of opening. Under tropical conditions, all the spikelets on a panicle complete flowering within 7-10 days and following fertilization, ovary starts developing into a caryopsis.

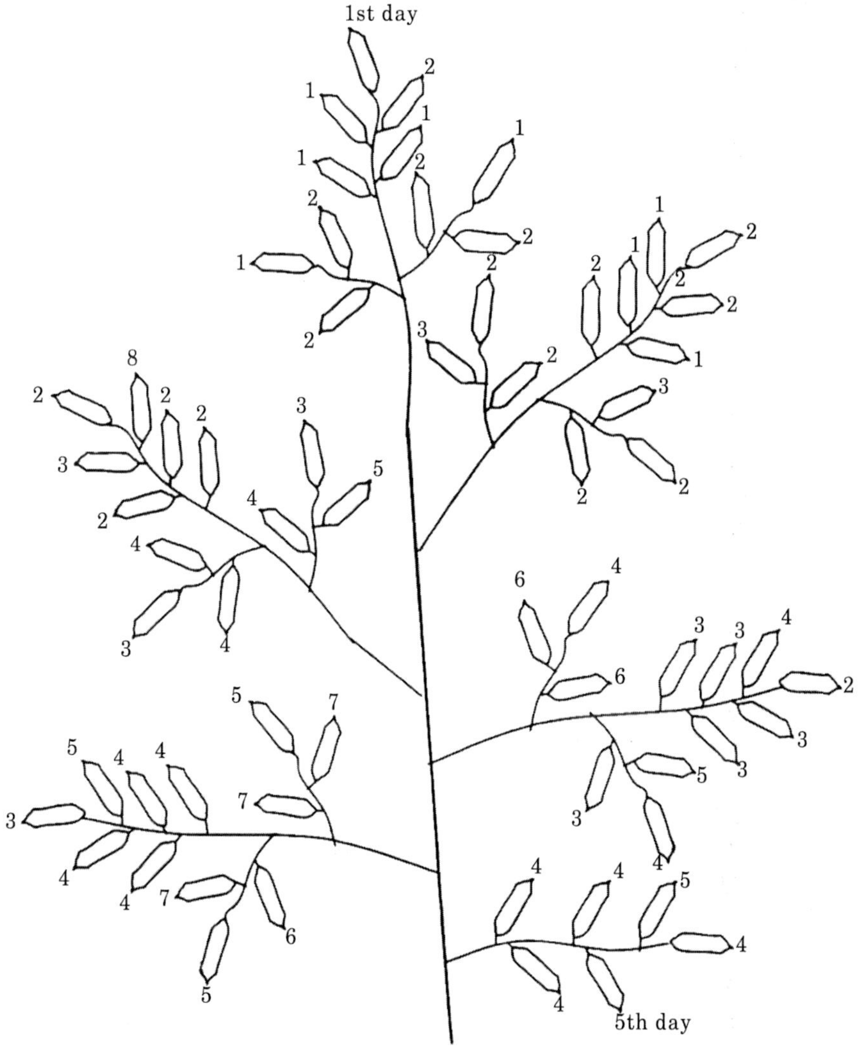


**Fig. 4:** Flowering order within a panicle

## 6. HISTORY OF RICE BREEDING

Systematic rice breeding was initiated at the beginning of the 20th century. Early breeding in tropical Asia was aimed at improvement of locally adapted popular varieties largely by pureline selection. Selection and evaluation process was confined to a single centre in each region, as breeders then had no idea about the significance of multilocation testing and as a result very large number of improved varieties were under commercial cultivation. Indonesia was the first country, where multilocation testing was started with the objective of reducing the number of varieties. Its successful experience not only prompted many countries to follow suit but also made the breeders realize the need for improving the method of varietal testing. Whereas the use of statistical parameters such as variance and standard error helped improve field testing technique, application of the principles of randomization and analysis of variance that decide on field plot design, enabled evaluation of test entries more accurately. Rediscovery around this period of Mendel's laws of inheritance, in spite of its potential for unfolding new variability could hardly change breeding-selection approaches, as breeders relied excessively on pureline selection. Nevertheless, it helped understand the mode of inheritance of scores of agrobotanic traits and floral biology as well as acquire emasculation-pollination skills, which proved valuable when recombination breeding assumed importance.

Irrespective of the method of selection, emphasis of breeding in the beginning was for improvement of traits other than yield. The traditional rice exporting countries like Burma and Thailand, for instance, placed their breeding thrust on improvement of grain quality, while breeding for resistance to rice blast, the only killer disease known then, received importance all over Asia. Identification of CO 4, a pureline selection from the local variety 'Anaikomban' found resistant to the disease served as the donor to develop the most popular variety CO 5, by hybridization. Breeding for high yields was confined to lowland varieties, as breeders believed late maturing varieties to yield more. Thus, single location selection/evaluation under low levels of nutrient management with emphasis largely on improvement of traits other than yield was the general breeding practice until the end of the World War II.

Rice breeding in India was started in 1911 at Dacca (now in Bangladesh) and in the following year at Coimbatore in the old Madras province. Recognizing the importance of rice to India's economy, the Indian Council of Agricultural Research, founded in 1929, sponsored, rice breeding projects in all the major rice growing states and as a result the country had as many as 82 research stations exclusively for rice research by 1950. It was around this period that ICAR's landmark decision led to the establishment of the Central Rice Research Institute at Cuttack, Orissa in 1946 for addressing problems of national importance. More organized breeding research that followed at central and state levels led to the release of more than 450 improved varieties all of which, except 27 cross bred varieties, were pureline selections from popular local varieties. Among varieties that remain popular till now, MTU 1, MTU 15 and HR 19 of Andhra Pradesh; Chin 7 of West Bengal; Kolamba strains of Maharashtra; GEB 24, CO 25, ASD 1 of old Madras Province; T141 and SR 26B of Orissa; Basmati 370 of Punjab and T1366 of Uttar Pradesh are important. Breeding for adverse growing conditions assigned to specific regional centres had also led to the development of varieties, which have hardly any alternative even today. They include among many ARC 353-648 of Assam; DWP-1311 of Andhra Pradesh; ADT 17, PTB 15 and PTB 16 of Madras Province FR13A and FR 43B of Orissa; Hybrid 84 of West Bengal for deepwater and flood-prone areas; Kalarata 1-24 and Bhurarata 4-10 of Bombay Province, SR 26B of Orissa; Chin 13 and Chin 19 of West Bengal for saline conditions and AKP 1, AKP 3, BCP 2 and BCP 5 of Andhra Pradesh; ASD 4, ASD 18 and PTB 18 of Madras Province; BAM 15 of Orissa; N 22 of Uttar Pradesh; Chin 25 and Chin 27 of West Bengal for drought-prone situations. Resistance breeding against biotic stresses led similarly to the development of CO 25 against blast and MTU 15, TKM 6, SLO 12, and CH 47 against stem borer. There are many more time-tested varieties that came out of resistance breeding. Inspite of such an impressive record of breeding achievements the fact remains that the efforts made for yield improvement were of no consequence as compared to what had been done for catering to other agro-ecological and socio-economic needs.

It was immediately after the World War II, when food grain supply became far short of the demand and threatened the world community, that Food and Agriculture Organization (FAO) founded the International Rice Commission (IRC) within the FAO frame-work to find ways of increasing rice production. The IRC recognized non-lodging habit, fertilizer responsiveness, early marurity and wide adaptability as the important varietal characteristics for achieving higher and stable yields. Accordingly, the FAO launched several regional network projects such as Cataloguing and Maintenance of Rice Genetic Stocks, *Indica-Japonica* Hybridization, Cooperative Varietal Trials, Wide Adaptability Test, Variety-Fertilizer Interaction in *indica* varieties, Uniform Blast Nursery and International Training Programme in Rice Breeding during 1950-1956.

The International Cooperative was instrumental in cataloguing major rice varieties of the world and establishing centres for maintenance and exchange of germplasm. The ambitious *indica/japonica* hybridization programme launched in 1952 was the earliest international effort to explore the possibilities of breaking the yield barrier in *indica* rices. Relatively higher yielding ability of *japonicas* believed then to be due to their non-lodging habit and responsiveness to higher levels of fertilizer, was what prompted the formulation and execution of this massive programme in Asia. Extensive hybridization programme with CRRI at Cuttack as the primary hybridization centre and countrywide screening of the segregating material lasting for 10 years proved a major disappointment. Except for three varieties *viz.*, ADT 27, an early maturing type found suitable for *Kunwai* season in Tamil Nadu and two medium late maturing types *viz.*, Mahsuri and Malinja identified in Malaysia that became widely popular in India and Malaysia respectively, the project hardly yielded any good variety combining the desirable features of *japonica* and *indica*. Partial sterility and skewed segregation towards parental types have been attributed to low frequency of stable fertile recombinants. Had the breeders been careful to choose tropical *japonica* parents, instead of temperate *japonica* types like Norin 6, Norin 8, Norin 16, Rikue 12, Asahi etc., the genetic hurdle could have been averted. The realization that inter-subspecific hybridization strategy would not yield anything substantial led to the abrupt termination of the project, which nearly coincided with the advent of the short statured *indica* variety Taichung (Native) 1 (T(N)1) and *'Ponlai'* varieties (Taichung 65, Tainan 3 etc.). Taichung (Native) 1 that heralded the era of plant type-based high yielding varieties is a derivative of the cross between the spontaneous dwarf mutant Dee-Geo-Wu-Gen and the Taiwanese tall variety Tsai-Yuan-Chung. The early maturing dwarf variety well adapted to round-the-year cultivation provided the base for developing the 'plant type' concept and development of a series of high yielding dwarf varieties including the miracle yielder IR 8.

An important development that accelerated breeding research at global level was the establishment of the International Rice Research Institute (IRRI) in the Philippines in 1960 by the Ford Foundation and Rockefeller Foundation in cooperation with the government of the Philippines. Breeding activities began in 1961-62 with the sole objective of evolving non-lodging varieties with high yields, which led to the release of IR 8, the widely adopted miracle yielder suited to irrigated ecology and IR 5, a semi tall variety bred for less favourable environments. It was IR 8 that provided the momentum for development of a series of high yielding dwarf varieties, which included IRRI bred IR 20, IR 26, IR 36, IR 42, IR 64, IR 72 etc., besides a large number by the National

Agricultural Research Systems (NARS). Thrust of the breeding research has been changing over the years with yield, quality and disease-pest resistance receiving successively priority attention in the case of irrigated rice, while yield maximization and adaptation to moisture stress and submergence in rainfed rice. Involving actively the NARS, most of the thrust area research programmes were sponsored and coordinated by IRRI. The multidisciplinary Genetic Evaluation and Utilization (GEU) programme initiated in 1974, while broadening the breeding efforts at IRRI and NARS, led simultaneously to the launching of global testing network called International Rice Testing Programme (IRTP). The programme, later renamed as International Network for Genetic Enhancement of Rice (INGER), involving over 75 countries and no less than 1000 scientists facilitated free exchange of germplasm (improved and unimproved) among the participant countries by IRRI's germplasm bank to an unprecedented scale. This one activity not only brought visibility to IRRI but enabled NARS to benefit the maximum. Several varieties named by IRRI were from IRTP/INGER nurseries. In the recent years IRRI, in partnership with NARS and Advanced Research Institutes in the developed world, is engaged in strategic research towards achieving food-nutrition security on a sustainable basis. Search for new yield thresholds through hybrid technology, new plant type, development and application of biotechnology-genetic engineering tools for adding value and finding solution to still unsolved biotic and abiotic stresses and functional genomics are important among them. Continued enrichment and maintenance of the gene bank which remains the 'gene source' for breeders all over, is the most laudable activity of IRRI.

It is the unique combination of short stature, non-lodging habit with profuse tillering and upright foliage, photo-insensitivity, high fertilizer responsiveness and early maturity in the new plant type that has helped break the centuries long yield barrier of the tropical rices. Short duration coupled with period bound maturity has made possible to raise 2-3 crops a year and increasing thereby the total productivity by 2-3 times over the late maturing, season bound traditional tall varieties. The impact of the plant type-based high yielding varieties is evident from various indicators. Many chronically rice deficit countries have become self-sufficient and some with sizeable surplus within 10-15 years of their introduction. Growth of rice (paddy) production in Asia has risen to 540.62 million tonnes by 1997-98 from 292.17 in the triennium ending 1971, while productivity from 2381 kg/ha in 1971 to 3900 kg/ha in the triennium ending 1997-98. Yield and production have registered from two times increase in India to four times increase in countries like Indonesia and the Philippines during the corresponding period. Largely development of high yielding varieties and their extensive adoption enabled many countries in Asia to register high and steady production growth.

As for India, more than 550 high yielding dwarf varieties have been released for all the major ecologies, the maximum being for irrigated environment. Evolution of varieties for different ecologies at such a rapid pace has been possible because of the coordinated network approach conceived and adopted at national level for material generation and multilocation testing. The realization that the entire growth has been on account of lopsided attention given to irrigated rice, prompted at national and international levels a shift in breeding emphasis towards long neglected rainfed ecologies, which account for 50% at global level and 55% in India. Rainfed ecology being the most complex and diverse, eco-regional models were conceived by IRRI for characterizing such ecologies and addressing the problems unique of them. The Rainfed Lowland and Rainfed Upland Consortia—the multicountry projects are close to finding solution to the problems of handicapped ecologies in Asia. The impact of this, coupled with national initiative, is seen today in the steadily increasing productivity and production in the predominantly rainfed eastern part of India.

Ever since the development of the dwarf high yielding varieties, breeders all over have been looking for technologies that would help raise further the genetic ceiling to yield. Of the two strategies contemplated *viz.*, tailoring of physiologically still more efficient plant type and exploitation of hybrid vigour, the latter has become a reality since the development in the late seventies of commercially viable hybrid rice technology in China. Its extensive adoption over 18 million ha (55% of the rice area) has helped China add annually 20 million tonnes to the national rice production making thereby the chronically food deficit country self sufficient. The knowledge gained from the experience and material support form IRRI and China, proved handy fifteen years later for India to develop hybrid technology suited to its agro-climatic conditions. The success stories of China and India have motivated a few more countries in the region to initiate hybrid rice research.

Thus the nine decade long history of rice breeding comprises three major phases *viz.*, the period of tall varieties with slow yield growth till early fifties, the period of semi-dwarf varieties breaching the yield barrier since mid sixties and the period of hybrid technology marking the second yield breakthrough since eighties. The current breeding emphasis at IRRI and a few other countries like China, Japan and India include (i) tailoring of new plant type varieties capable of yielding 15-20% higher than the best variety available (ii) engineering future rice varieties with novel genes conferring resistance to major insect pests and diseases and (iii) improving nutritional value of rice through conventional and molecular breeding approaches.

## 7. BREEDING APPROACHES

Genetic variability is the feedstock for improvement in the desired direction of crop plants, no matter what breeding approach is resorted to. Rice is one of the few crop plants endowed with rich genetic diversity. In the decades long history of rice breeding, natural and induced variability have been effectively exploited for its improvement. The pace of improvement has, however, depended on the shift in breeding priority and selection approaches followed at different points of time. Broadly the breeding approaches include (a) introductions (b) pureline breeding (c) recombination breeding (d) mutation breeding (e) heterosis breeding and (f) cellular and molecular breeding. The breeding priority has changed over the decades from purification of landraces placing emphasis on early maturity, consumer quality and blast resistance to recombining of desired traits through hybridization and recombinant DNA technology giving emphasis to high yield and value addition. Significantly none of the breeding/selection approaches has outlived its utility, as evident from the fact that the age old pureline selection remains still relevant and appropriate strategy to find solution to some of the most challenging problems breeders confront today.

### 7.1. Introductions

Introduction is the oldest and simplest method of meeting varietal needs of a given situation as well as an effective means to enlarge and enrich genetic variability. Varieties found popular for a given growing condition in another country or a state/region within a country are introduced and evaluated in replicated trials under similar conditions to assess yield performance and adaptability. It is not necessary that all the introduced varieties would get acclimatized to the new environment and become acceptable to the farmers and consumers to justify more systematic investigations on their level of resistance to major pests and diseases and quality features. In the process of evaluation, there is often scope for selection under the new environment and such selections invariably prove successful varietal introductions.

There are many examples of successful exotic and state to state introductions. The variety 'Swama', for instance, developed in Andhra Pradesh has become popular in Orissa, Madhya Pradesh, Bihar, U.P. and West Bengal. In the early fifties, several Chinese varieties were introduced for cold/hill ecologies in Himachal Pradesh, Kashmir and Uttar Pradesh. Among them the notable introductions include China 1039, China 988, Shenei, Ch 45, Kaohsuing 22 and Kaohsuing 27. In the recent past Mahsuri from Malaysia, Taichung (native) l, Taichung 65 and Tainan 3 from Taiwan and IR 8 from the Philippines have become popular all over the tropical rice world and opened the gateway to green revolution. International Network for Genetic Enhancement of Rice (INGER) has proved an excellent vehicle to take advantage of exotic varieties/ breeding lines. More than their direct introduction as varieties after extensive testing, they are being used as parental lines in cross breeding programmes. Introduced varieties have thus played an important role in not only contributing to the productivity growth but also in strengthening the rice breeding research in many countries including India. There are many examples of our own varieties like Jaya, Rasi, Sona etc., being adopted in several countries and similarly India has introduced varieties such as BG 380-2 from Sri Lanka and IR 20, IR 36, IR 50 and IR 64 from IRRI, the Philippines.

### 7.2. Pureline Breeding

It literally means purification of highly heterogeneous farmer grown local varieties to uniform height, maturity and other agrobotanic traits. This simple breeding/selection approach had its strength in the early years of breeding in the rich variability readily available in thousands of strains and mixtures grown then as farmer varieties. The process of purification starts either at the farmer's field or farmer strains raised at experimental farm. Seed harvested from promising plants are raised in successive generations as panicle or plant progenies till they become uniform and stable. Following seed increase, the chosen best line(s) is intensively evaluated in replicated yield trial having the local variety as the check for at least 3-5 years for ascertaining their stability of yield performance in the target environment. The best performing entry *vis-a-vis* the breeding objective is identified for general cultivation after evaluating for consumer quality. Earlier, as the test locations were restricted to one or two research stations, identification of varieties with wide adaptability was not possible and as a result varietal multiplicity became inevitable. By end of the World War II the rice world had several hundred improved varieties developed mainly by pureline selection. Some of the World's best varieties remaining still popular and widely cultivated are pureline selections. Prized quality rice varieties like GEB 24, Mozhagolukulu (BCP1) and Basmati 370 of India; Khao Dawk Mali of Thailand; C 28-16 of Burma; Saline tolerant varieties like SR 26 B and Nonabokra; pest resistant varieties Ptb 18, Ptb 33 CO 43, CO 44 and Latisail etc.; deepwater rices FR 13 and other popular varieties like Manoharsali, T 141, Neang Mas are pureline selections. Some of the varieties evolved by pureline selection since the introduction of dwarf varieties are listed in Table 4.

**Table 4:** Varieties developed through pureline selection (1966-1998)

| *Variety* | *State* | *Year of release* | *Selection from* | *Ecosy-stem* | *Grain type* |
|---|---|---|---|---|---|
| Janaki | Bihar | 1983 | Chenab Rice | SDW | LB |
| Sugandha | Bihar | 1983 | Cuttack Basmati | IRM | MS |
| Rajasree | Bihar | 1987 | — | RSL | MS |
| Sudha | Bihar | 1987 | — | DW | LB |
| Kamini | Bihar | 1991 | Katari | IRM | MS |
| Birsa Gora | Bihar | 1992 | Gora | RUR | LB |
| Vaidehi | Bihar | 1995 | Beldar | SDW | LB |
| Kolhapur | Gujarat | 1971 | — | IRM | MS |
| T3 | H.P. | 1973 | Type 3 | HRIR | LS |
| CSR6 | Haryana | 1991 | | SCR | LS |
| Taraori Basmati | Haryana | 1996 | Local Basmati | SCR | LS |
| Giza 14 | Jammu & Kashmir | 1965 | Giza 14 | HRIR | SB |
| Ranbhir Basmati | Jammu & Kashmir | 1994 | Basmati S 370-90-95 | HRIR | LS |
| Manila Paddy | Karnataka | 1970 | C4-63 | IRE | MS |
| Suvarna Modan | Kerala | 1976 | ARC 11775 | RWR | MS |
| Vytilla 2 | Kerala | 1980 | Cheruvippu | IRM | MB |
| Mata Triveni | Kerala | 1990 | Triveni | IRE | SB |
| Patel 85 | Madhya Pradesh | 1981 | IR 8 | IRM | LS |
| Safri 17 | Madhya Pradesh | 1984 | Safri | RSL | LS |
| Tuljapur-1 | Maharashtra | 1972 | Lalsal 140-31 | RUR | LB |
| Improved Ambemohar | Maharashtra | 1978 | Local | IRE | SB |
| Jalgoan 5 | Maharashtra | 1978 | Local | IRE | MS |
| Sindewahi -1 | Maharashtra | 1988 | Local | IRSA | LS |
| Terua | Maharashtra | 1989 | MAU Sel-9 | IRE | LS |
| BAM-6 | Orissa | 1986 | Ratna Chudi | RSL | MS |
| SR 26B | Orissa | 1988 | Kalambanka | RSL | LB |
| FR13A | Orissa | 1988 | Kalambanka | SDW | LB |
| T-90 | Orissa | 1988 | — | RSL | LS |
| T-141 | Orissa | 1988 | — | IIRM | MS |
| T-1242 | Orissa | 1988 | — | RSL | LB |
| AU-1 | Tamilnadu | 1976 | IR8 | IRE | SB |
| JJ-92 | Tamilnadu | 1993 | Dwarf Basmati | IRE | LB |
| Majhera 3 | Uttar Pradesh | 1968 | Jaulia | RUR | LS |
| Madhukar | Uttar Pradesh | 1969 | Gonda | SDW | MS |
| Jalmagna | Uttar Pradesh | 1969 | Badhan | SDW | SB |
| VL Dhan 206 | Uttar Pradesh | 1983 | Bamni | HRUR | MS |
| Jalanidhi | Uttar Pradesh | 1993 | Goanath | DW | LB |
| Jaladhi-1 | West Bengal | 1981 | Kalakher sail | DW | LB |
| Jaladhi-2 | West Bengal | 1981 | Local tall *indica* | DW | LB |

**Table 4:** (*Contd...*)

**Table 4:** (*Contd...*)

| *Variety* | *State* | *Year of release* | *Selection from* | *Ecosystem* | *Grain type* |
|---|---|---|---|---|---|
| Sabita | West Bengal | 1986 | Boyan | SDW | LS |
| Matangini | West Bengal | 1989 | Kajallata | SDW | SB |
| Panke | West Bengal | 1989 | — | RUR/IRE | LB |
| Jitendra | West Bengal | 1994 | Land race | DW | LS |
| Jala prabha | West Bengal | 1996 | Composite | DW | SB |

Rice ecologies, RUR: Rainfed Upland Rice; RSL: Rainfed Shallow Land; SDW: Semi Deep Water; DW: Deep Water; HRIR: Hill Rice Irrigated; IRE: Irrigated Early Duration; IRM: Irrigated Medium Duration; IRSA: Irrigated Saline Alkaline Tolerant Grain types LB: Long bold; SB: Short bold; LS: Long slender; MS: Medium slender

Pureline approach, although is the earliest breeding methodology, is found still relevant, when recombination breeding and other approaches are found slow and less effective to find varietal solution to special situations. For instance, breeding for higher yield without compromising on the prized quality features as in Basmati 370 in India and Khao Dawk Mali in Thailand and for higher yield without losing adaptability to stress as in varieties of saline soils and deep and semi deep water ecologies has been possible hither to by pureline method only. Taroari Basmati from traditional basmati varieties grown around Karnal (Haryana); Jalapriya, Jitendra, Jogon-17, Nalini, etc., bred for deep and semi-deep water conditions and Lunishri for saline water conditions are some of the recently released pureline varieties. The lines bred by this way and named varieties are not necessarily 'purelines' in strict sense of the word and as defined by Johansson (1903) because they tend to show variation for many traits when raised in different environments. They are 'pureline' varieties for the environment under which they were selected.

### 7.3. Genetics of Important Traits

Precise knowledge of genetics is as important as variability for directed crop improvement. Mode of inheritance that reveals how simple or complex a trait is genetically, enables breeders to plan breeding/selection strategies for improving a trait of their interest. Rice is one of the few crop plants wherein, genetics of a large number of agrobotanic traits, and their linkage relationships have been studied and systematically documented (refer to Rice Genetics Newsletter 1989 onwards for details and updated Information).

Broadly, the findings of many decades reveal that complex traits like yield and yield components, tolerance/resistance to abiotic stresses and majority of quality indices are polygenically controlled and most of the morpho-physiological traits and resistance to biotic stresses are oligogenically controlled (Table 5).

### 7.4. Collection, Conservation and Use of Germplasm

Rice germplasm comprising over 1,50,000 cultivars and large accessions of 22 wild species is one of the richest among crop species. The richness largely contributed by the Asian cultivated rice *O. sativa,* is due to subspecific differentiation and subsequent dispersal to different parts of the world facilitated by human migration, and human and natural selection under diverse biophysical and socio-economic conditions. Sizeable of this rich diversity was collected by the NARS long before the advent of the high yielding varieties in the mid sixties and is being maintained. National and international efforts for massive collection and conservation, motivated by the apprehension that a limited number of high yielding varieties would soon replace thousands of land races nurtured by nature and man for thousands of years were, however, made much later in the early seventies. The systematic collection compaign, mainly coordinated by IRRI since 1972, had led to the *ex situ* conservation of over 1,00,000 accessions in gene banks. Of these, about 50,000 were collections from Asia and Africa through the joint efforts of NARSs and several international institutions including IRRI, HTA, WARDA, IBPGR, FAO, IRAT, OSTROM, Japanese Agencies etc. Nearly the entire global collection is being conserved under long and medium term storage at IRRI's International Rice Germplasm Centre (IRGC) and partly duplicated collections in China, India, Japan and the USA. The indigenous collections along with limited exotic germplasm, are being conserved in the national gene banks in the major rice growing countries. Indian germplasm exceeding 30,000, is being conserved at the National Bureau of Plant Genetic Resources (NBPGR) under the ICAR at Delhi.

Evaluation is the bridge between conservation and utilization. The accessions characterized and catalogued at various gene banks, especially at IRGC (IRRI) are being evaluated for detailed passport information on their economic value. The valuable gene sources broadly include diverse resistance genes against biotic/abiotic stresses, yield and quality traits etc., The study of germplasm has also helped breeders to know potential geographic areas for specific genes of their need. For

**Table 5:** Genetics of economically important traits in rice

***I Genetics of morpho-physiological traits***

| ***Trait*** | ***Mode of inheritance*** | ***Gene (s) involved*** | ***Reference(s)*** |
|---|---|---|---|
| Awning | Awning dominant over awnlessness<br>Trigenic with cumulative effect | Full Awn : *An-1, An-2, An-3*<br>Med : *An-1, an-2, an-3*<br>short : *an-1, An-2, An-3*<br>Awnless : *an-1, an-2, an-3*<br>*An-4(t)* | Nagao and Takahashi (1963)<br>Sastry and Seetharaman (1980) |
| | Awn development mono/digenic dominant | *Ana, Anb, l-Ana, l-Anb* | Sato and Tsukasaki (1984)<br>Prasad and Seetharaman (1991) |
| Panicle type | Dense panicle dominant over normal panicle | *Dn-1, Dn-2* and *Dn-3* | Nagao and Takahashi (1963)<br>Futsuhara *et al.* (1979) |
| | Lax panicle dominant over normal | *lax* | Yu *et al.* (1992) |
| | Spreading panicle | *spr-1, Spr-2, Spr-3(t), spr-a, Spr-b* | Sano and Eiguchi (1980)<br>Nadaf *et al.* (1992) |
| Earliness | Earliness dominant over lateness | *Ef-1,ef-2(t),ef-3(t),ef-4(t), Ef-x(t), Ef-y(t), Ef(t)* | Tsai (1991d)<br>Sato *et al.* (1992) |
| Growth habit | Spreading growth habit dominant over erect growth habit | *er* | Takahashi *et al.* (1968) |
| Photosensitivity | Monogenic dominant or recessive | *Se-1, se-2, Se-3(t), se-4(t), Se-5, se-6(t), se-7(t)* | Yanagihara *et al.* (1995)<br>Tsai (1995) |
| Grain type | Polygenic, Mono/digenic | short grain *(kr1)*<br>Long grain *(kr2)* | Prasad and Seetharaman (1991) |
| | | Long grain *LK-f, LK-g, lk-i-1, lk-i-2* | Takamura (1994), Kato and Takeda (1992) |
| | | Minute Grain - Mi | Takeda and Kato (1992) |

**Table 5:** (*Contd...*)

**Table 5:** (*Contd...*)

| ***Trait*** | ***Mode of inheritance*** | ***Gene (s) involved*** | ***Reference(s)*** |
|---|---|---|---|
| Semi dwarfing | Tallness dominant over dwarfness | *sd-1, sd-2, sd-3, sd-4, sd-5, sd-6(t), sd-7(t), sd-8(t)* | Nakamura *et al.* (1995)<br>Tsai (1994a)<br>Tanaka *et al.* (1992) |
| Whole seed - dormancy | Two complementary /dominant genes | *Sdr-a and Sdr-b* | Takahashi (1962) |
| Hüll imposed dormancy | | *Dh-1(t) and Dh-2(t)* | Shenoy (1993) |
| Grain shattering | Monogenic recessive/dominant | *sh-1, sh-2, Sh-3, sh-4* | Nakamura *et al.* (1995) |
| Hard threshability | Monogenic dominant | *Th* | Eiguchi (1990) Kumar and Sharma (1982) |

***II. Genetics of disease resistance***

| ***Disease*** | ***Mode of inheritance*** | ***Gene symbol (s)*** | ***Reference(s)*** |
|---|---|---|---|
| Bacterial leaf blight (*Xanthomonas campestris.pv oryzae* | Mostly monogenic dominant and rarely recessive or digenic complementary | *Xa-1, Xa-2, Xa-3, Xa-10*<br>*Xa-14* Against Japanese and Philippines races | Ogawa and Yamamoto (1986)<br>Ogawa *et al.* (1978) |
| | | *Xa-3, Xa-4, xa-5, Xa-6, Xa-7, xa-8, Xa-10, Xa-11, Xa-12, xa-13, Xa-14, xa-15, xa-16, Xa-17, Xa-18, Xa-21, xa-19, xa-20* Against Tropical Asian races | Sidhu *et al.* (1978)<br>Singh *et al.* (1983)<br>Yoshimura *et al.* (1983)<br>Khush *et al.* (1989)<br>Ikeda *et al.* (1990) |
| RTBV (Rice Tungro Bacilliform Virus) | Polygenic | | Taura *et al.* (1989)<br>Shahjahan *et al.* (1990) |

**Table 5:** (*Contd...*)

**Table 5:** (*Contd...*)

| ***Disease*** | ***Mode of inheritance*** | ***Gene symbol (s)*** | ***Reference(s)*** |
|---|---|---|---|
| RTSV (Rice Tungro Spherical Virus) | Monogenic recessive (*Source*: Utrimerah) | *tsv-u* | Shahjahan *et al.* (1991) |
| | Three complementary recessive genes (*Source*: Kataribhog and Pankari 2003) | *tsv-2* | |
| | Two dominant genes with complementary interaction | *Tvv-a, Tuv-b* | Toriyama (1967) |
| Stripe disease | Complementary | *Str-a, Str-b* | Hayano-Saito *et al.* (1993) |
| Grassy stunt virus | Monogenic dominant | *Gsv* | Khush and Ling (1974) |
| Black streaked dwarf virus | Monogenic dominant | *Bsv* | Morinaka *et al.* (1969) |
| Hoja blanca virus | Monogenic dominant | *Hbv* | Khush *et al.* (1994) |
| Yellow dwarf disease | Monogenic dominant | *Ydv* | Morinaka *et al.* (1970) |
| Brown leaf spot | Monogenic recessive | *bl-l, bl-2, bl-3, bl-4, bl-5, bl-6* | Nagao and Takahashi (1963)<br>Takahashi *et al.* (1968)<br>Yoshimura *et al.* (1992) |
| *Helminthosporium oryzae* | Monogenic dominant | *He* | Nagai and Hara (1930) |
| *Cercospora* leaf spot | Monogenic dominant | *Ce,,* | Jodon and Chilton (1946) |
| Panicle blast | Monogenic dominant | *PBR* | Fujii *et al.* (1995) |
| **Blast** | Monogenic or digenic | *Pi-1, Pi-3, Pi-5(t), Pi-6(t),* | Kiyosawa (1972) |
| (*Pyricularia oryzae*) | dominant/recessive | *Pi-7(t), Pi-ll(t), Pi-2, Pi-a, Pi-b, Pi-f, Pi-i, Pi-k* | Hsieh (1976)<br>Mackill and Bonman (1992)<br>Wang *et al.* (1994)<br>Tanksley *et al.* (1993) |
| Yellow leaf spot | Monogenic recessive | *ysl* | Takahashi *et al.* (1968) |
| *Sderotium oryzae* | Mono-digenic duplicate | *Sc-1, Sc-2* | Hashioka (1951) |
| Iron deficiency chlorosis | Monogenic recessive | *ic* | Reddy *et al.* (1989) |
| Zebra necrosis | Monogenic recessive | *zn* | Kinoshita and Takamure (1984) |

**Table 5:** (*Contd...*)

**Table 5:** *(Contd...)*

| | | | |
|---|---|---|---|
| | ***III. Genetics of insect pest resistance*** | | |
| ***Insect pest*** | ***Mode of inheritance*** | ***Gene (s) involved*** | ***Reference(s)*** |
| Brown planthopper (*Nilaparvata lugens*) | Monogenic dominant or recessive<br>Rarely di or tri genic complementary | *Bph-1, bph-2, Bph-3, bph-4, bph-5, opn-o, opn-7, bph-8, Bph-9* | Athwal *et al.* (1971)<br>Martinez and Khush (1974)<br>Sidhu and Khush (1979)<br>Khush *et al.* (1985)<br>Nemoto *et al.* (1989) |
| Green leafhopper (*Nephotettix virescens*) | Monogenic dominant or recessive | *Glh-1, Glh-2, Glh-3, glh-4, Glh-5, Glh-6, Glh-7 and glh-8* | Athwal *et al.* (1971)<br>Siwi and Khush (1977)<br>Rezaul Karim and Pathak (1982)<br>Ghani and Khush (1988) |
| Zigzag leafhopper (*Recilia dorsalis*) | Monogenic dominant | *Zlh-1, Zlh-2, Zlh-3* | Angeles *et al.* (1986) |
| Rice gall midge (*Orseolia oryzae*) | Monogenic or digenic dominant rarely, recessive duplicate | *Gm-1, Cm-5, Gm-2, Gm-6, Gm-3, Gm-7(t), Gm-8(t), Gm-4, Gm-9(t), Gm-10(t), Gm-11(t).* | Chaudhary *et al.* (1986)<br>Katiyar *et al.* (1996)<br>Kumar *et al.* (1998)<br>Reddy *et al.* (1997)<br>Srivastava *et al.* (1993) |
| White backed planthopper (*Sogatella furdfera*) | Monogenic dominant or recessive | *Wbph-1, Wbph-2, Wbph-3, wbph-4, Wbph-5, Wbph-6* | Sidhu *et al.* (1979)<br>Saini *et al.* (1982)<br>Hernandez and Khush (1981)<br>Wu and Khush (1985)<br>Minshaoki *et al.* (1991) |
| Striped stem borer (*Chilo suppressalis*) | Polygenic (Giza-14)<br>Monogenic recessive (TKM-6) | *Sb* | Dutt *et al.* (1986) |
| Stern maggot | Monogenic dominant | *Sm* | Athwal and Pathak (1972) |

**Table 5:** *(Contd...)*

**Table 5:** (*Contd...*)

***IV. Genetics of traits related to hybrid breeding***

| ***Trait*** | ***Mode of inheritance*** | ***Gene(s) involved*** | ***Reference(s)*** |
|---|---|---|---|
| Genie male sterility | Monogenic recessive | *ms-1, ms-2, ms-3, ms-4, ms-5, ms-6, ms-7, ms-8, ms-9, ms-W, ms-11, ms-12, ms-13, ms-14, ms-15, ms-16, ms-17* | Ko and Yamagata (1989)<br>Shibuya (1973) |
| Photoperiod sensitive male sterility | Monogenic recessive or digenic duplicate | *pms-1*<br>*pms-2* | Zhang *et al.* (1993) |
| Photoperiod sensitive male sterility | Monogenic recessive | *pgma* | Wang *et al.* (1991) |
| Pollen fertility restoration | Dominant genes with digenic complementary or duplicate action | *Rf-1, Rf-2, Rf-3, Rf-4*<br>*Rf-a, b, c, d* | Yu *et al.* (1992)<br>Shinjo and Sato (1994a, b)<br>Teng and Shen (1994)<br>Maekawa (1982) |
| Wide compatibility | Monogenic | *S-5'* | Ikehashi *et al.* (1991)<br>Kumar and Virmani (1992) |
| Hybrid sterility | Mono or digenic | *S-1*, 5-2, 5-3, 5-4, S-5, 5-6, S-7, *S-8*, 5-9, 5-30, *S-11(t), S-12(t)*, S-13, *S-14(t), S-15*, S-16, | Sano *et al.* (1979)<br>Sano *et al.* (1994)<br>*Wanetal.* (1994a) |
| Temperature sensitive male sterility | Monogenic recessive | *tms-1, tms-2 and tms-3(t)* | Yang *et al.* (1992)<br>Maruyama *et al.* (1991)<br>Borkakati and Virmani (1996) |
| Elongated upper most internode | – | *eui* | Maekawa and Kita (1983) |
| ***A. Hybrid sterlity*** | | | |
| 1. Gametophytic $F_1$ sterility (*sativa x sativa*) | Duplicate gene action | *s-a-1, s-a-2, s-c-1, s-c-2, s-d-1, s-d-2, s-e-1* | Oka (1974) |

**Table 5:** (*Contd...*)

**Table 5:** (*Contd...*)

| ***Trait*** | ***Mode of inheritance*** | ***Gene(s) involved*** | ***Reference(s)*** |
|---|---|---|---|
| 2. Sporophytic $F_2$ sterility (*sativa* x *sativa*) | Duplicate genes | *S-A-1, S-A-2, S-B-1, S-B-2* | Oka (1978) |
| 3. Sterility due to sporo-gametophytic interaction (*sativa* x *glaberrima*) | Complementary | *Sa-1 and S-1, Sa-2 and S-2, Sa-3 and S3, Sa-4 and S-4* | Sano *et al.* (1979)<br>Sano (1985) |
| (*sativa* x *sativa*) | | *Sn-5, Si-5 and Sj-5* | Ikehashi and Awki (1986) |
| ***B. Hybrid weakness*** | | | |
| *indica* x *indica* | Complementary | *Hwa-1 and Hwa-2* | Oka (1957b) |
| *japonica* x *japonica* | Complementary | *Hwc-1 and Hwc-2* | Sato and Hayatihi (1983) |
| Ac-451 x Ac-521 | Complementary | *hwb-1, hwb-2* | Oka(1957b) |
| A *japonica* cv x Thai Waxy cv. | Complementary | *hwd-1, hwd-2* | Okuno (1985) |
| ***C. Chlorosis*** | | | |
| *A. japanese*. cv x *japonica* cv. | Complementary | *hca-1, hca-2* | Sato *et al.* (1984) |

***V. Genetics of traits related to abiotic stress***

| ***Trait*** | ***Mode of inheritance*** | ***Gene(s) involved*** | ***Reference(s)*** |
|---|---|---|---|
| Cold tolerance at seedling stage | Monogenic dominant or digenic complementary | *Cts-1*<br>*Cts-2 (t)* | Kwak *et al.* (1984)<br>Nagamine (1991) |
| Deep water tolerance | Duplicate genes | *dw-1, dw-2, dw-3* | Ramaiah and Ramaswami (1941)<br>Eiguchi *et al.* (1993) |
| Tolerance to salt stress and drought | Recessive | *sal-T* | Tanksley *et al.* (1993) |
| Leaf rolling under drought stress | Monogenic recessive | *Mt)* wv | Singh and Mckill (1989) |

instance, Indian subcontinent has been found to be the richest for sources of resistance to pests and diseases, while West Africa, Southern Asia and South America for tolerance to adverse soils. Significantly, the rarest resistance gene against grassy stunt virus was found in an *O. nivara* accession from India. Similarly for BPH and gall midge, most valuable genes have come from the Indian subcontinent. It is the growing genetic resources and their unrestricted flow among the rice growing countries facilitated by the IRRI that has truly accelerated rice-breeding research in Asia.

## 7.5. Recombination Breeding

Recombination breeding consisting of controlled crossing between parents of choice followed by pedigree or mass-pedigree selection in the segregating generations for targeted trait(s), is the widely employed approach in rice improvement. Unlike the pureline selection, which is limited to identification of the best in the naturally available variability, recombination breeding is a device to generate variability and recombine desired characters for any given situation. The device is used in different forms depending on the breeding goal and genetics of the trait(s) to be recombined. In breeding for quantitatively inherited traits like yield and tolerance to complex abiotic stresses for instance, straight single cross followed by selection through pedigree or modified pedigree methods is the usual practice, while for simply inherited mendelian character, depending on the agronomic potential of the parents, either single cross or backcross followed by pedigree selection is preferred. If the breeding objective is to combine a set of traits that make a variety unique or ideal to a given situation or need 'convergent breeding' approach is followed. This involves stepwise addition of constituent traits. Varieties with multiple resistance either to different insect pests and diseases or resistance to different races/biotypes of a pest and varieties of basmati quality, which is the combination of a unique set of quality indices are good examples of products of 'convergent breeding'. In a way, the ongoing worldwide effort to breed varieties for the major rice ecologies that requires stepwise accumulation of the desirable characteristics that would combine high and stable yield, adaptability and acceptable quality is also a convergent approach (Fig. 5).

Backcross breeding is resorted to when a simply inherited trait is to be selectively transferred to an otherwise good agronomic base. It can

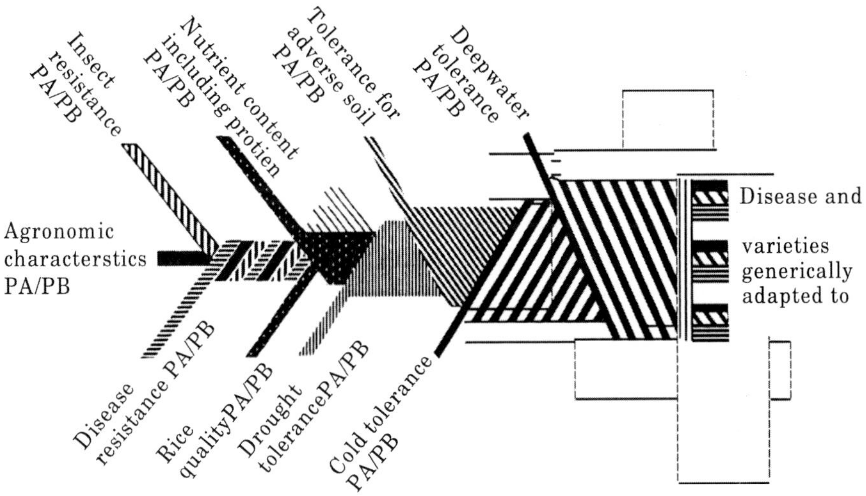


**Fig. 5:** A model of convergent improvement

be illustrated in the transfer of grassy stunt virus resistance gene *(Gsv)* from *O. nivara* into IRRI's advanced breeding line (Khush, 1984). When the transfer is from an unthrifty donor source as the above one, it is necessary to go for several backcrosses of the recurrent parent with the recipient variety. This method is routinely used in hybrid breeding for development of cytoplasmic male sterile lines. The method would prove quicker, if the donor parent is also a good agronomic base. Successful inroduction of bacterial leaf blight resistance gene *(Xa 21 and Xa 4)* into Pusa 44, the most popular high yielding variety in Punjab, is a good example to show the potential of backcross breeding. Also, this breeding approach is effective to break tight linkages between desirable and undesirable traits.

The selection methodology employed also varies depending on the genetic control of the target trait, field/laboratory facilities, man power and conduciveness of the environment for effective selection. Pedigree method is followed for improvement of both qualitative and quantitative traits in situations, where land/laboratory facilities and manpower are adequate, while modified pedigree or mass pedigree method of selection becomes inevitable when selection environment is not appropriate to discriminate desirable genotypes from undesirable ones. Under such situations the segregating populations are bulked upto 4-5 generations right from $F_2$ followed by pedigree selection. When breeding objective for instance, is incorporation of resistance to a particular insect pest, of variable incidence under field conditions and no method or facility is available for screening under artificial epiphytotic conditions, bulking of segregating populations is continued until the right screening environment occurs. This practice holds good for breeding for drought resistance as well. This is the general practice in IRRI's upland rice improvement programme (IRRI, 1987). The whole strategy of early generation bulking is a practice for yet another situation, wherein either $F_2$ population itself is too small or the likelihood of loss of valuable segregants is high under harsh target environments like salinity and drought. In the latter case, $F_2$ is raised under optimal condition and $F_3$ raised from bulked $F_2$ is screened under the stress.

While dealing with crosses involving tall and dwarf parents, it is important to minimize the inter-plant competition, in the absence of which talls would suppress the dwarfs, especially under rich fertilizer management conditions. As the prospective talls and dwarfs are recognizable from seedling height differences, they could be sorted out and transplanted separately.

### 7.5.1. *Approaches for accelerated generation advance and selection*

One of the major limitations of recombination breeding is the long period required for fixing genotypes with desired character combinations. More complex the trait is genetically, the longer the time it requires to get fixed. It would be all the more difficult and time consuming, if such traits are to be incorporated in long duration varieties. Various techniques have been developed to reduce the breeding/selection cycles as briefly discussed below.

### 7.5.2. *Single seed descent (SSD) method coupled with rapid generation advance (RGA)*

Well suited to breeding long duration photosensitive varieties, this approach is widely used by the IRRI and NARS (Ikehashi and Hille Ris Lambers, 1979). Instead of taking one crop a year of a long duration photosensitive variety under field condition, three crops can be taken by SSD-RGA strategy. In breeding for lowland and deep water ecologies, this strategy is proving handy.

Pedigree and mass pedigree including SSD methods of breeding have their own unique advantages and preference. But their relative efficacy in terms of frequency of desirable genotypes is yet to be ascertained.

More than the selection method, it is the choice of parents, GXE interaction, sample size, genetic drift, changes in gene frequency due to inbreeding etc., that determine the probability of recovering desired genotypes.

### 7.5.3. *Doubled haploidy approach*

Anther culture derived doubled haploidy is yet another rapid method of realizing homozygous recombinants from $F_1$ hybrids. It has potential use in self-pollinated crops like rice because of the advantage of recovering homozygous lines in the very next generation itself and enhanced selection response due to presence of additive genetic variance alone in doubled haploid population (Snape *et al.,* 1988). Besides shortened breeding cycle, it offers high probability of recovering desired genotypes in very small populations. This approach has been refined to suit rice and is being employed at IRRI in breeding for tolerance to cold, salinity etc., in collaboration with NARS. Inspite of such unique advantage, the strategy is not in wide use, largely on account of very low frequency of regenerants, especially in *indica* rices.

### 7.5.4. *Shuttle breeding and selection under divergent environments*

Shuttle breeding involves raising of breeding populations alternatively at two agroclimatically diverse environments for two different purposes *viz.*, (i) practicing selection at one centre and advancing generation at the other to take advantage of its favourable weather and (ii) selection and generation advance at both the centres.

### 7.5.5. *Selective diallel mating and recurrent selection*

There are some characters, which can not be easily bred through single cross/backcross breeding and pedigree/modified pedigree selection approaches, because their expression is governed exclusively by either minor genes or weak major genes in association with strong minor gene complexes. Resistance to stem borer, leaf folder, sheath blight etc., are some such characters. As yet no strong source of resistance has been found aganist these pests, though sources of moderate resistence, believed to be governed by non-mendelian genes with small effect, are known to exist. Recurrent selection that involves repeated intercrossing among selected source parents and among their progenies and practicing selection successively is a proven approach in cross pollinated crops to selectively pool desirable genes with small effect. The successive cycles of intermating among the selected recombinants followed by selection facilitate directed accumulation of desirable genes in the segregants, while enhancing the probability of breaking undesirable linkages (Jensen, 1978). This method, which has many a potential advantage has been used in self-pollinated crops like rice. The major limitation has been the lack of an easy mechanism for random intermating. However, genetic male sterility could be effectively used for this purpose. There are good prospects of making use of such mating systems to breed varieties with desired level of tolerance to pests, against which only moderate resistance sources are available as well as with durable resistance to certain diseases like blast, which are also largely governed by minor genes, possibly in association with major genes.

### 7.5.6. *Recurrent selection*

Availability of genetic male steriles in sorghum had led to the proposition that they could facilitate recurrent selection. In the case of rice, it became a possibility following the induction of genetic male sterile mutants (Fujimaki *el al.,* 1977). This development enabled Fujimaki (1978) to suggest the practice of male sterile based recurrent selection and male sterile-based backcross breeding (MSBC).

A model of Male Sterility Facilitated Recurrent Selection (MSRS) proposed by Ikehashi and Fujimaki (1980) as illustrated in Fig. 5 consists of a breeding Programme starting with the development of a 'Foundation population'. The population, which is constituted to ensure segregation for male sterility is derived from sources like biparental, double and polycrosses, is grown in isolation to facilitate outcrossing between male sterile and fertile segregants. In this process, random mating is achieved by collecting seeds from male sterile segregants, while mass selection is simultaneously operated by selecting uniformly for days to flowering. To minimize the possibility of losing heterozygosity, intensive selection for highly heritable characters is avoided. In the selection phases of the recurrent cycles, seeds are collected from self-fertile plants to develop $S_1$ progenies. Part of the seed is reserved for later use. while the rest is used for progeny testing. As the $S_1$ progeny lines would segregate for male sterility, it is difficult to assess their agronomic potential. But other traits, including disease/pest resistance, tolerance to abiotic stresses, grain quality, plant type etc., can be evaluated from the $S_1$ progeny. The results of $S_1$ progenies evaluation indicate that $S_1$ lines with desirable agronomic traits be selected. The process of recurrent selection is discontinued when lines of promise and of practical value are obtained. If not, $S_1$ lines superior in some agronomic traits are marked and the

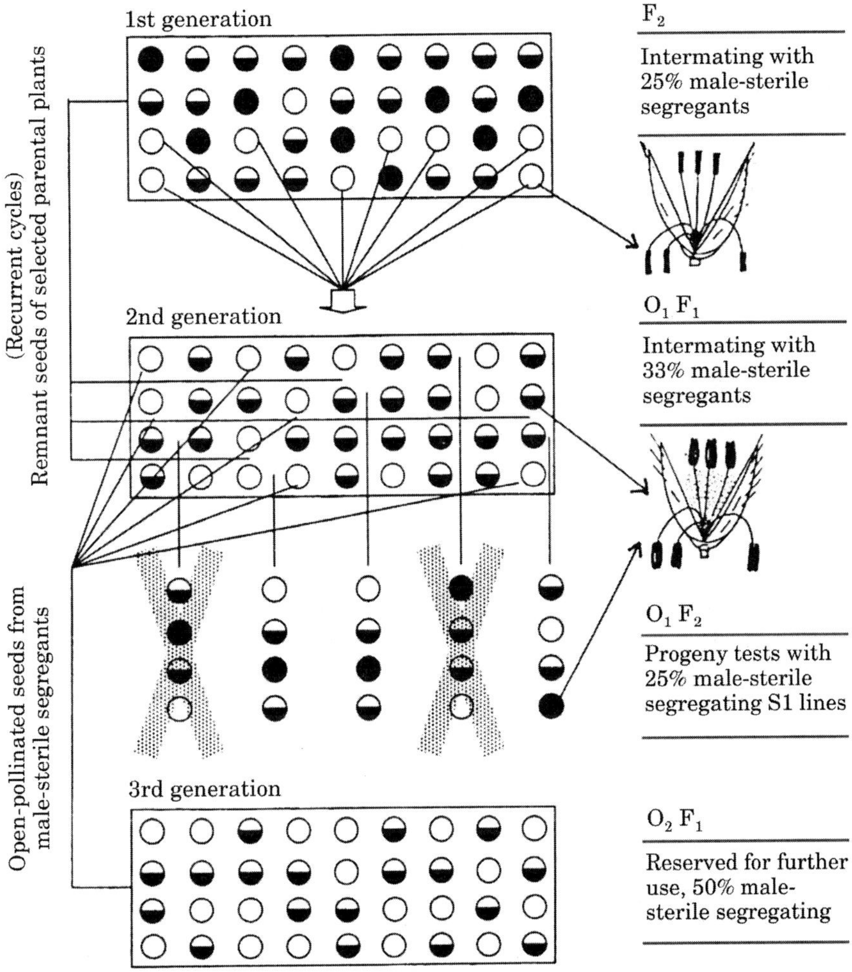


**Fig. 6:** Procedure for male sterlity facilitated recurrent selection in rice (Ikehashi and Fujimaki, 1980)

earlier reserved seeds of their parent plants are mixed to compose another foundation population for further recurrent cycles by intermating and selection. This technique appears suitable for improving complexly inherited multiple disease resistance or polygenically controlled horizontal/field resistance. An easily adoptable model had been suggested by Ikehashi and Fujimaki (1980). By linking MSRS or MSBC with rapid generation advance (RGA) the system can be made much more effective and rapid.

The strategy of bulk method of selection has been diversified following development of various techniques like single seed descent (SSD), rapid generation advance (RGA) and male sterile-facilitated recurrent selection/backcross approaches. These techniques ensure maximum genetic variability with least cost and shortest period when a trait of interest is controlled by sexually transmitted recessive genes. In other cases, one would need a large $F_2$ or to wait for later generations until half the population manifests the homozygous recessive trait. SSD coupled with RGA would help to come out with such a population in the shortest period. Rapid generation advance is a way of growing bulk population while major aim of SSD is to attain homozygosity prior to pedigree selection. RGA is to shorten the breeding generations by reducing the growth duration of the population. For breeding of photoperiod sensitive rice in the tropics, three generations can be raised by RGA approach. It helps attain homozygosity with minimum effort. The SSD method proposes that a single seed should be harvested from each $F_2$ plant to grow $F_3$ population and the same procedure is repeated until $F_5$–$F_6$ generation.

#### 7.5.7. *Synthetic approach for higher yield, stability and varietal longevity*

Durability and stability of performance are as important for the success of a variety as its inherent yield potential. These attributes depend largely on the level of heterozygosity and heterogenity ensured at the time of the release of a variety for general cultivation. Normally these are achieved through varietal mixtures and composites, which offer required level of plasticity under fluctuating growing conditions. On this premise a breeding-selection approach that would lead to development of a phenotypically homogeneous mixture ensuring desired level of genetic heterogenity and heterozygosity has been described by Das *et al.* (1990). The scheme involving both bulk population and pedigree breeding/selection strategies as illustrated in Fig. 7 starts with a base or original population chosen in the $F_3$ or $F_4$ stage, which looks nearly homogeneous and promising from productivity angle. Single plant selections made on the basis of their agronomic potential are raised as progeny rows as also as a mixed bulk and continued for 3-4 generations resulting in phenotypically homogeneous and homozygous progeny rows. Maintained as inbred lines, these are randomly mixed into several synthetic populations and evaluated in replicated trials as against the original and successively built bulk populations for yield and stability. The synthetic population(s) that performs the best, outyielding the original bulk as well as the progeny rows, is selected for commercial exploitation.

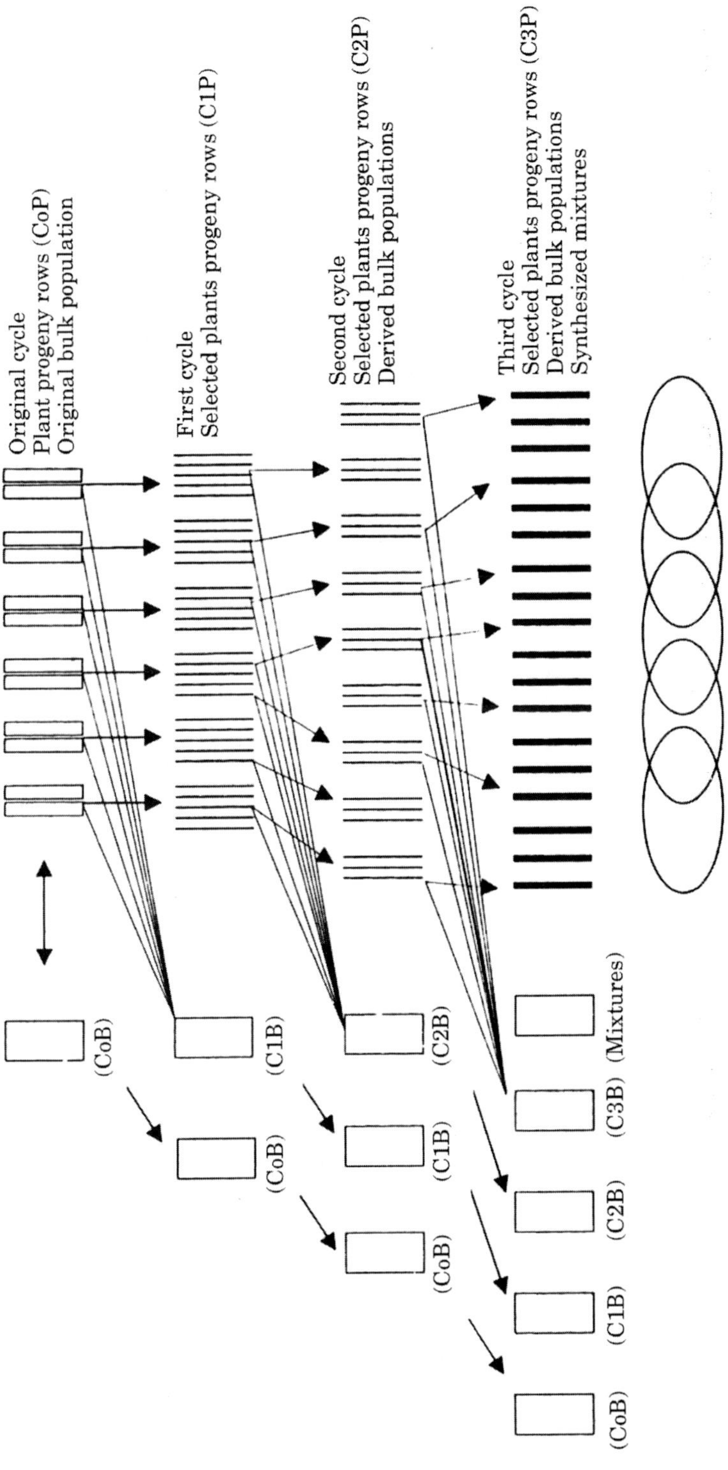


**Fig. 7:** Procedure for bulk population and pedigree method (Das *et al.*, 1990)

## 7.6. Breeding for Yield Enhancement

### 7.6.1. *Inter-varietal hybridization*

As discussed elsewhere, *indica-japonica* hybridization as a breeding strategy to increase the genetic yield level of tropical rices was started in the early 50's under the massive FAO sponsored programme. Relatively non-lodging habit of *japonica* varieties under higher fertilizer management conditions and hence high yields, which *indica* rices lacked was the basis for launching this programme. Study of segregating generations of crosses in different countries hardly yielded any tangible results except four varieties ADT 27, (India), Malinja and Mahsuri (Malaysia) and Circina (Australia). High pollen sterility and persistent spikelet sterility in the advanced generations, attributed later to differences between *indica* and *japonica* varieties, low recombination frequency and resultant skewed segregation rendered the ambitious project a failure. Breeders in India and elsewhere thought that if *japonica* relatives more compatible to tropical situation had been used instead of the typical temperate *japonicas,* the outcome would have been altogether different as demonstrated by breeders at the Central Rice Research Institute (Rao and Nagaraju, 1974). When short statured *japonicas* grown in south Japan, where climatic conditions are similar to that of Taiwan, problems earlier met with crosses involving truly temperate *japonicas* could be overcome with ease. It appeared that varieties that are adapted to mild temperate conditions would be more compatible to those adapted to extremely cold temperate zone. This fact was proved when tropical *japonica* varieties from Taiwan such as Taichung 65, Tainan 3, Kaohesing 18 and Herunchu introduced respectively in Karnataka, Kerala and Uttar Pradesh proved a great success from productivity performance angle, though their adoption could not be sustained on account of their poor consumer quality.

The major success story of *indica-japonica* hybridization is from Korea. A programme was launched in 1960's to combine non-lodging habit and high fertilizer responsiveness (contributing to high yield potential) as well as resistance to blast disease found in high yielding dwarf *indica* varieties with grain quality and adaptation to low temperature of *japonicas,* through inter subspecific hybridization. To overcome spikelet sterility and combine all the desired characteristics, the $F_1$ hybrid was backcrossed to the semidwarf *indicas.* Of many derivatives obtained therefrom the line Suweon 213 (jukara/TNl/ IR8) was named Tongil in 1971. Tongil by and large had majority of the desired traits. But its grain and consumer qualities were less acceptable as compared to that of the traditional *japonicas.* Also, its spectrum of resistance to rice blast and bacterial leaf blight as well as tolerance to low temperature conditions was not up to the expected level. Nevertheless, Tongil provided the base for developing the concept of 'bridge parent' and evolving still higher yielding and better adapted 'Tongil type varieties' (Fig. 8). Among the bridge parents, IRI 317 (Jinhaung/IR2622) proved to be the best combiner and using it, as many as 18 *indica-japonica* (Milyang 30, Suweon 284, Milyang 42 and IR 338 etc.) varieties could be developed and released for general cultivation. Their contribution to Korea's rice production-productivity advance was quite significant. Korean rice breeders always prefer to use genotypes of Tongil plant type as one of the parents to improve Korea's rices in view of its excellent morphophysiological frame and non-lodging habit derived originally from Dee-Gee-Woo-Gen derivatives like IR 8 and T (N)1.

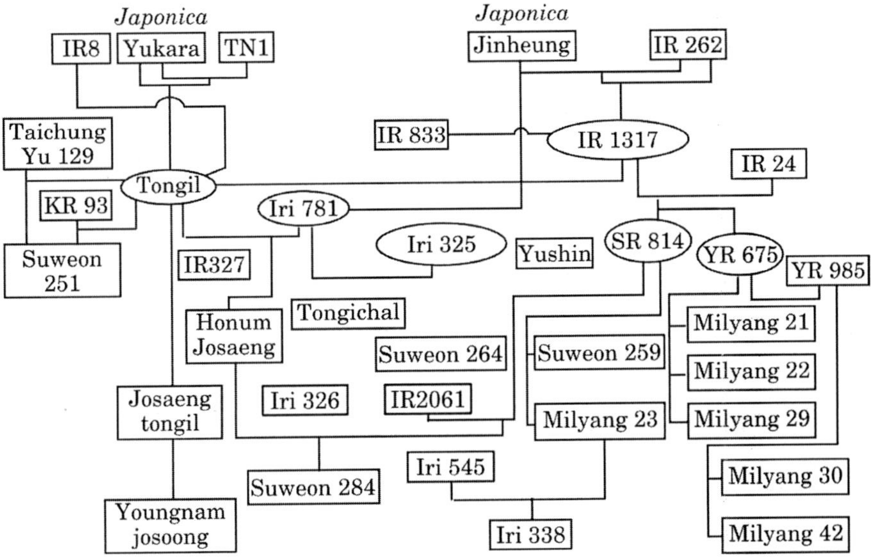


**Fig. 8:** Bridge improvement from *japonica-indica* crosses

Korean breeders could overcome the problem of $F_1$ sterility and grain quality besides ensuring desired plant stature. The strategy of backcrossing or topcrossing with *indica* parent as against the earlier Japanense practice of backcrossing with *japonica* parents has been found more rewarding in overcoming the problem of $F_1$ sterility.

The *indica* and *japonica* varieties to be used in the crossing programe were short statured, but their non-allelic nature and different genetic constitution became evident from the $F_2$ population, which showed normal distribution for height, thus making selection process for semidwarf stature difficult. This was overcome by backcrossing or topcrossing with semi dwarf *indica,* which gave in the $F_2$ ($BC_1$ $F_2$) two different families : one showing distribution for height within the desired height range and the other which showed a wide range of variation. When semidwarf plants selected for other desirable agronomic features in the same family are backcrossed/topcrossed again with semidwarf parents, distribution for plant height in the $BC_2$ $F_2$ and subsequent selfed generations would be the same as that of the recurrent semidwarf *indica* parent. This simple strategy has enabled Korean breeders to completely recover semidwarf plant types in any *indica-japonica* cross.

Recovering segregants with eating quality features acceptable to Korean people has been yet another problem, that breeders had encountered in the inter-subspecific crosses, wherein parents vastly differed in their physico-chemical properties of starch. Indicas have high amylose (>25%) and high gelatinization temperature (GT) and in crosses involving them, selection of genotypes with the targeted amylose content and GT would require chemical screening of a very large population with very low probability of recovering such types in combination with other desirable characteristics. Korean scientists have successfully experimented with alternative strategy of using short statured waxy lines in high yield background in crosses with a low amylose parent of desired plant type recovered from *indica-japonica* crosses. Using these lines in an efficient breeding/selection scheme a procedure has been designed and used to select high yielding dwarf lines of desired amylose level and blast-resistance without involving, at any stage, chemical analysis. The scheme involves a cross between a blast resistant *indica* variety used as the donor for resistance and the carrier semidwarf waxy line. The $F_1$ is backcrossed to the waxy line. The $BC_1F_1$ is subjected to screening against blast and the resistant ones are studied at flowering stage for waxy plants by pollen test. If the plant so selected is not of desired agronomic potential, it is successively backcrossed to the waxy line till desired plant type is recovered. Such plants are crossed at this stage with the dwarf low amylose line called amylose restorer. The hybrids (RF) are tested for blast resistance and survivors are grown through harvest. At $F_2$ ($RF_3$ seed) seed selection is done for nonwaxy endosperm and then for blast resistance through nursery. By $RF_4$ homozygosity for blast resistance and nonwaxiness combined with the amylose of AR line is attained as schematically represented in Fig. 9.

| ***Generation*** | ***Procedure*** | ***Treatment*** |
|---|---|---|
| Parent | wxwxrr* x WxWxRR<br>↓ | 1st cross |
| $F_1$ | wxwxrr x WxwxRr<br>↓ | Backcross |
| $BC_1F_1$ | wxwxrr wxwxRr Wxwxrr WxwxRr<br>X 0 X 0<br>0 X<br>↓ | Test for resistance<br>Select for donor<br>Select for wx |
| $BC_1F_1$ | wxwxRr x WxWxrr (AR)** | Cross for amylose restoration |
| $RF_1$ | wxwxRr<br>↓ | Test for resistance<br>Select for donor |
| $RF_2$ | WxWxRr_ WxWR_ wxwxR-Wx_rr wxwxrr<br>0 0 0 X X<br>0 0 X<br>↓ ↓ | Test for resistance<br>Select for donor<br>Select for Wx |
| $RF_3$ | Segregating Segregating<br>0 0 | Test for resistance<br>Select for donor<br>Select for Wx |

*Caular, **Amylose restorer

**Fig. 9:** Breeding for blast resistance assuming that a dominant gene is responsible for resistance.

The success of inter-subspecific hybridization involving all the three subspecies of *O. sativa viz., indica, japonica* and *javanica* has once again aroused interest among rice breeders during the last 10-15 years as they believe it to be a reliable means of tailoring still more efficient plants capable of breaching yield potential of currently cultivated dwarf varieties. The new found enthusiasm is on account of two important research findings *viz.*, (i) Use of more compatible tropical *japonicas* as parents instead of temperate ones would offset the problem of $F_1$ hybrid sterility and (ii) discovery of simply inherited wide compatibility (WC)) gene(s) that helps overcome sterility in the immediate and subsequent generations of *indica / japonica* crosses. The WC genes now in the genetic background of several improved varieties and parental lines of popular hybrids are enabling development of still higher yielding varieties and hybrids. Dr. Gurudev Khush at IRRI and rice breeders at IARI, Delhi have successfully bred new plant type varieties and hybrids capable of yielding 10-15% higher than even popular hybrids. Extensive adoption of such *indica / japonica* derived varieties and hybrids would greatly help countries to increase rice production.

### 7.6.2. *Semidwarf varieties*

If the *indica-japonica* hybridization attempted successfully in the late 1930s in the USA and later in tropical Asia is considered a transition from the traditionally followed intra-varietal hybridization for raising yield level, development of short statured varieties that exploit the spontaneous dwarf mutant Dee-Gee-Woo-Gen is the landmark in the history of rice breeding. The semidwarf varieties characterized by non-lodging habit and hence response to higher doses of fertilizer, photo-insensitivity coupled with earliness enabling its cultivation possible round the year, upright foliage facilitating better utilization of solar energy and high leaf area index enabled the entire tropical Asia to achive a major yield breakthrough in the mid sixties. Taichung (Native) 1 a derivative of the cross between the spontaneous dwarf mutant Dee-Gee-Woo-Gen (DGWG) and the traditional tall variety Tsai-Yuan-Chung released in 1949-50 was the first dwarf variety. Its spectacular yield potential attracted the attention of plant breeders and plant physiologists alike to conceptualize plant type. No one knows for certain the origin of DGWG except the fact that it was cultivated by farmers in Taiwan prior to 1950. In spite of the pondering efforts to develop a semidwarf variety, it was the IRRI developed IR 8 released much later that heralded truly the 'Green Revolution' in tropical Asia. Using largely Taichung (Native) 1 and IR 8 as the donors for dwarf stature and high yield potential, breeders all over have developed hundreds of high yielding varieties. As of today, about 90% of the dwarf varieties under cultivation in tropical Asia are based on DGWG gene. From breeders point of view, use of DGWG source for yield improvement has unique advantages. Inheritance of dwarf stature as a simple monogenic recessive, despite the fact that height is a polygenically controlled trait enables fixation of the desired plant types along with several other desirable features like photo-insensitivity and earliness, which are strongly associated with the dwarf stature. Increased grain to straw ratio to 40-50% *as* against 30-35% of the traditional tall with no major change in biomass production, upright foliage with delayed senescence allowing more time for grain filling are some of the desirable physiological features that favour high yields. Wide adaptability conferred by photoinsensitivity and short duration enabling multiple cropping have made dwarf varieties popular not only in Asia but also in Africa and Latin America. Being a panicle number type, unlike the traditional talls varieties that are designated as 'panicle weight' type, selection criteria for yield potential is population performance and not that of individual plant. Panicle number per unit area with optimum grain number per panicle and test grain weight are being used as reliable criteria for selection. A variety possessing around 400 panicles per square metre with average grain number in the range of 125-150 grains and thousand grain weight of 25 g is estimated to yield around 8 tonnes/ha. Some of the varieties of varied maturity group widely popular in the major rice ecologies are given in Table 6.

**Table 6:** Improved varieties popular in the irrigated and rainfed ecologies in India

| *Group* | *No. of varieties* | *Popular varieties* |
|---|---|---|
| ***Irrigated ecology:*** | | |
| Early and Mid early | 135 | Vikas, Pusa, 2-21, Pusa 33, Pusa 873, Khitish, Telia Hamsa Adt 36, Asd 16, Asd 17, Sarya, Prasad, Saket 4, Pusa 169. |
| Medium | 93 | Jaya, Vikram, Prabhat, Siva, CO44, IR20 Ponni, Sarjoo 52, Sujatha, IR-8, Pusa 44. |
| Hills | 20 | Himdhan, Himalaya 741, VCK 39, VL 8. |
| Basmati quality | 2 | Pusa Basmati 1 |
| ***Rainfed ecology*** | | |
| Upland | 46 | Armada, Akashi, Govind, Prasanna, Aditya, Tulasi, Kalyani II, Kaiinga III, Sattari, Vanaprabha, Birsadhan 101 and Birsadhan 201. |
| Shallow Iowland | 26 | Swarnadhan, Savithri (Ponmani) Manasarovar, Swarna, Salivahana, Lakshmi, Pranava, Ranjit. |

Although the potential of DGWG gene is widely recognized, inter varietal sterility barrier never allowed its use in the improvement of temperate and American *japonica* rices. Tongil series of varieties developed in Korea using the DGWG dwarfing gene source are the only exception as elaborated elsewhere. Use of three distinctly different dwarfing gene sources has helped Japan to improve signficantly the productivity and production of temperate *japonica* rice. Using Jikokku, a native dwarf, several high yielding varieties like Hoyku, Kokumasari, Reihou, Nishihomare, Minaminishiki etc., have been developed to suit the growing conditions of southern Japan. Similarly, most of the popular high yielding varieties in northern Japan such as Akhihikari, and Kochiliki have been developed by use of the variety Remei, a gamma ray induced mutant from the variety Fugiminori and a spontaneous mutant Shirosoubon. Test of allellism reveals Reimei and Jikokku to have the same dwarfing gene ($d_1$) as in DGWG.

In the USA, it was largely the induced dwarf that played the major role in the improvement of rice in California either as direct mutant cultivars or as sources of dwarfing gene for cross breeding. Popular varieties such as Calrose 76 and M 101 are monogenic recessive dwarf mutants from Calrose and Terso respectively. Genetic investigations suggest them also to carry the $d_1$ gene like that in DGWG.

Thus, irrespective of the varietal group/ecotype, economically exploited dwarfing gene is $d_1$ although dwarfing genes non-allelic to DGWG are available. The problem of 'genetic vulnerability' of the very widely employed $d_1$, gene aside, need for broadening genetic base for plant type and under-standing the physiological potential of already known non-allelic sources such as $d_2$, $d_3$ and $d_4$ for further raising the yield ceiling *per se* and productivity under different patterns of intercropping and cultural systems deserve emphasis.

### 7.6.3. *New plant type*

Ever since the evolution of short statured varieties that have helped break the centuries-old genetic yield barrier, rice scientists have been engaged in designing still more efficient morpho-physiological frame to look for next quantum jump in yield. Early attempt in search of exploitable variability for physiological components that directly or indirectly contribute to yield were not successful. Hardly any donor source that would have helped alter the sink-source equilibrium could be found. On the strength of experience and experimental findings, breeders/geneticists believe that genetic yield level of rice could be raised by 20-25% through enhancement of biomass from the present level of 20 t/ha without change in harvest index. On the basis of extensive analysis of growth characteristics and yield potential, IRRI scientists have modelled a new plant type capable of yielding 12.5 t/ha as against 10 t/ha obtainable in the presently available dwarf varieties for the irrigated ecology.

The strategy envisages increasing the biomass per unit area and hence grain yield by planting less profuse tillering but high panicle weight genotypes at high density by manipulating crop geometry. The model genotype has been tailored by recombining chosen morphophysiological features of tropical *japanicas* and *indicas* (Fig. 10). The new plant type thus designed is characterized by the following features.

- Semidwarf habit, 5-6 productive tillers, sturdy stem and dark green upright foliage
- Heavy panicles with high grain number (200-250) and high test grain weight (around 25 gm/1000 grains)
- More foliar growth during crop establishment
- Less foliar growth and enhanced translocation of assimilates from leaf to stem during late vegetative and reproductive phases
- High and descending concentration of tissue N from top to the base of plant canopy.

- Increased capacity of stem to store assimilates
- Improved reproductive sink capacity with prolonged period of ripening
- Increased harvest Index (>0.6).

Simultaneous efforts to design a new plant type initiated in the late seventies at the Indian Agricultural Research Institute (IARI) through slightly different approach and character association has led to a new plant type capable of breaching the yield levels of IR 8 or Jaya. The breeding strategy has been to initially exploit the rich variability available in *indica* itself and depending on the need, to use variability from the other subspecies of *O. sativa* later. The designer plant combines moderate (8-10/hill) and highly synchronous tillering, around 100 cm height with extraordinarily high culm strength, average grain number/ panicle (around 175) average test grain weight of 25 gm, high N uptake and high tissue N in the photosynthetically most active canopy region, thin husk and slightly longer grain filling period. Among the lines in advanced stages of testing, Pusa 1021, Pusa 1286, Pusa 1077 series are promising. Donors used for developing the new plant type by IRRI and IARI are listed in Table 7.

**Table 7:** Donors for various traits being used for developing new plant type by IARI

| *Triat* | *Indica/tropical Japonica* |
|---|---|
| Short stature | IR5, MD2, Sheng Nung 89-366 |
| Sturdy stem | Gharbaran, Pusa 44-37, Sengkeu, Sipapak, Sirah Bareh |
| Heavy panicle | G1291, G1298, Daringan, Djawa serang, Ketan Gebat |
| Prolonged grain filling | IR65740-AC1-3, IR65601-10-1-2, BG380, BG90-2, Dariangan |
| Photosynthetic efficiency | AC4491, Mahsuri, Ptb10, T141, NS1281, T90, Bam3 |
| Translocation efficiency | Ptb10 |
| Low photorespiration | B76, Patnai 23 |
| Slow leaf senescence | G110, Pusa 1021, Pusa 1266 and some *indica / Japonica* derivatives |
| High dry matter production | Swarnaprabha, Intan, Pankaj, Manasarovar, |
| High density grains | Badshabhog, Roupsail |
| High harvest index | Vijaya, T141 |

### 7.6.4. *Yield enhancement by identifying and using still untapped yield genes*

No practical genetic enhancement of yield could be achieved since the release of the miracle variety IR 8 in the sixties because of the breeding strategy that continues to excessively rely on the potential of the dwarf donor source ($Sd_1$ of Dee-Geo-Wu-Gen) and ignores the importance of tall parents with potential for high grain/biomass yields. The fact that over 500 high yielding varieties evolved in India during the last three decades have genetic background of only a few tall traditional varieties and one dwarfing gene source suggests how narrow the genetic base is for yield. The talls are chosen as parents on the basis of their popularity in different regions of the country and phenotype rather than diversity of their yield genes. Keeping this in view, research has been initiated to identify tall landraces with diverse and still unexploited yield genes and pool/pyramid the hormonious ones by convergent recombination breeding for evolving varieties with higher yield ceiling. Lodging, because of weak culm, does not allow tall statured landraces to express their inherent yield potential and precludes their choice as parents. Use of some device that prevents lodging and thereby enables assessment of their relative potential is one way of identifying talls that are likely to carry diverse yield genes. Extent of genetic divergence of land races from the improved modern varieties could be yet another means to choose the candidate varieties.

**Fig. 10:** A model of a new plant type

Mapping populations developed from crosses involving such landraces and high yielding varieties like IR 8 and IR 64 are now being used to identify microsatellite marker associated QTLs relating to yield and yield components at national and international levels. It is proposed to pool the newly found yield genes from the candidate varieties by convergent breeding using microsatellite linked QTLs as markers in the selection process.

Earlier efforts to map QTLs relating to yield and its major components enabled detection of about 70 QTLs, which included 16 for grain yield, 19 for grains/panicle, 9 for tillers/plant and 25 for grain weight. It was further shown that some chromosomal regions are more active than others in controlling the expression of the QTLs and such regions are largely found on chromosomes 1, 2, 4/5 and 8. Concentrated distribution of stable QTLs for yield and yield components may have important implications in rice breeding (Qifa Zhang and Sibin Yu, 2000). The findings of work underway at the Directorate of Rice Research, Hyderabad along with those of earlier workers (Xiong *et al.,* 1988; Lu *et al.,* 1996; Xio *et al.,* 1996; Causse *et al.,* 1994; Li *et al.,* 1996; 1997; Wu *et al.,* 1996; Yu *et al.,* Lin *et al.,* 1997) are expected to provide a firm base for mounting knowledge-driven breeding research towards development of varieties with higher yield thresholds.

The use of germplasm, inspite of its recognition as the feed-stock for crop improvement, has been limited for improvement of critical simply inherited-traits. Because of agronomically inferior appearance, wild species have been considered unfit as potential donor sources for improvement of quantitatively inherited traits like yield and its major components dissuaded. However, Lawrence and Frey (1976), showed that segregants in backcross generations of crosses between cultivated oats *Avena sativa* and its wild relative *A. sterillis* yield significantly higher (29%) than the recurrent cultivar parent. Recently the Carnell group has discovered two new QTLs *(Yld 1-1* and *Yld 2-1)* in *O. rufipogon* having potential of increasing rice yields by 17-20% (Xio *et al.,* 1996; Tanksley and McCouch, 1997). It appears that presence of such rare yield-related QTLs in the progenitor species and not so much in the cultivars could be due to compatibility and Isolation restrained gene flow from the wilds to cultivars. More than the nature-influenced gene flow, it is the man directed flow that might have left primitive landraces of cultivated rice with valuable but still unutilized yield related genes. Convinced of this logic, the ongoing research in search of new yield genes has been extended to closely related wild species as well.

### 7.6.5. *Pathway engineering for yield enhancement*

In the past yield levels have been improved through modification of regulatory processes governing life cycle and partitioning of resources and not through improvement of the efficiency of major metabolic processes. Increases in crop photosynthesis resulting in higher biomass and grain yield have been through promotion of both leaf area and leaf longevity under improved agronomic management. Very little has been done to enhance photosynthesis by manipulation of key photosynthetic enzymes. Recent research findings reveal the possibilities of redirecting the biosynthetic pathways through gene transfer technology to make the plants produce larger quantities of natural products like starch and lipids. Manipulation of starch content in cereals requires precise understanding of the regulatory mechanism underlying its biosynthesis. In the pathway, AGPase activity and formation of ADP glucose are considered as the rate-limiting steps. One pioneering development in this area of research is the demonstration of over production of starch in potato by splicing of genetically engineered ADP glucose diphosphorylase is not appropriate. Use of such a strategy in rice requires precise knowledge on the level of regulation of the enzyme which is very sensitive to different modes of regulation at the level of gene expression and enzyme activity. An attempt is now being made in some of the leading laboratories to explore the possibilities of engineering starch biosynthetic pathway of rice.

### 7.7. Breeding for Disease/Pest Resistance

Rice harbours about 100 pests, of which atleast 20 are considered economically important. The pest problem has assumed serious proportions only after the introduction and extensive cultivation of high yielding dwarf varieties. Year round cropping, increased genetic homogenty and favourable crop canopy have facilitated many of the minor pests to become major ones and the major pests to produce strains of varied virulence/viruliference to cope with the changing severity of selection pressure. As for diseases, besides age old problem of blast and brown spot, rice crop suffers today from viral (rice tungro virus, grassy stunt virus, ragged stunt virus etc.), bacterial (bacterial leaf blight and bacterial leaf streak) and a few additional fungal (sheath blight and sheath rot) diseases. Strainal variation now established in bacterial leaf blight (BLB) and grassy stunt virus (GSV) in addition to the known races of blast pathogen have made the disease management increasingly difficult. The story with insect pests is similar. Added to the long known stem borer and gall midge, rice has become highly vulnerable to some of the little known insects such as planthoppers, leafhoppers, leaf folder, hispa etc. Also biotype variation in gall midge and BPH has made management of these insect pests, through the strategy of host plant resistance, more difficult.

### 7.7.1. *Resistance to diseases*

Except for a few such as sheath blight, sheath rot and grassy stunt virus-II, resistance gene sources are availabe for all the major diseases and their races/pathotypes (Table 8). Knowledge of genetics of resistance (Table 5) coupled with techniques for effective screening under field as well as artificial epiphytotic conditions have enabled breeders to utilize these sources for development of large number of high yielding varieties with specific and multiple resistance to the diseases (Tables 8-11).

**Table 8:** Gene sources for resistance to biotic stresses resistance to insect pests

| ***Resistance gene*** | ***Donor source*** |
|---|---|
| ***Brown planthopper*** | |
| *Bph.1* | Mudgo, Balamavee, CO 10, CO 20, MTU 15, TKM.6 |
| *Bph.2* | ASD 7, Ptb 18, Ptb21, Ptb 33, Madayal, Dikwee 328, Malkora |
| *Bph.3* | Ptb 21, Ptb 33, Rathu Heenati, Gangal, Muthumanikam, Homamawee, Ptb.19 |
| *Bph.4* | Babawee, Senawee, Hotel Samba, Sulai, Thirissa, Lexham Sambha. |
| *Bph.5* | ARC 10550 |
| *Bph.6* | Swarnalata |
| *Bph.7* | T12 |
| *Bph.8* | China Saba, Col.5. Thailand |
| *Bph.9* | Pokkali, Kaharamana, Balanmawee. |
| ***Green leafhopper*** | |
| *Glh.1* | Pankhari 203, ARC 10313, ARC 7320 |
| *Glh.2* | ASD 7, Tendeng, Sefa, Badal-2 |
| *Glh.3* | IR 8, Chiknal, Laki 659 |
| *Glh.4* | Ptb 8, ARC 7012 |
| *Glh.5* | ASD 8, Bhawalia, Bazal |
| *Glh.6* | TAPL 796 |
| *Glh.7* | Maddai Karuppan |
| *Glh.8* | DV85 |
| ***White-backed planthopper*** | |
| *Wbph.1* | N 22, Senawee, Siam Garden, Oha |
| *Wbph.2* | ARC 10239, Chempan |
| *Wbph.3* | ADR 52, Chai Anaser |
| *Wbph.4* | Podiwi - A8 |
| *Wbph.5* | N. Diang Marie |
| *Wbph.6* | Bian-Gu, Da-Hua-Gu, Da-qi-Gu. |
| ***Zigzag leafhopper*** | |
| *Zlh.1* | Rathu Heenati |
| *Zlh.2* | Ptb 21 |
| *Zlh.3* | Ptb 33 |
| ***Gall midge*** | |
| *Gm.1* | W1263, Eswarakora, Usha, Samridhi, NHTA-8 |
| *Gm.2* | Surekha, IET 6286, RP435-107 |
| *Gm.3* | RP2068-18-3.5, Bhumansan |
| *Gm.4* | Abhaya, Bhumansan |
| Gm.5 | ARC 5984, Banglei |
| Gm.6 | Dukong. 1 |

**Table 8:** (*Contd...*)

**Table 8:** (*Contd...*)

| ***Resistance gene*** | ***Donor source*** |
|---|---|
| *Gm.7(k) and Gm.8 (k)* | Bhumansan |
| *Gm.9 (k) and Gm. 10 (k)* | NHTA-8 |
| *Gm.7 (k), Gm. 9, Gm.11 (k)* | T 1432 |
| ***Bacterial leaf blight*** | |
| *Xa-1* | Kogyoku, IR22, IR29, IR30, Java 14 |
| *Xa-2* | Te-tep, Rantai Emas-II |
| *Xa-3* | Zenith, Sateng, Java.14 |
| *Xa-4* | TKM 6, IR.20, IR.22 |
| *Xa-5* | DZ.192, IR.1545-339 |
| *Xa-7* | DV 85 |
| *Xa-8* | PI 231129 |
| *Xa-10* | Cas 209 |
| *Xa-11* | RP 9-3, IR8, Elwe |
| *Xa-12* | Kogyoku, Java 14 |
| *Xa-13* | BJ I, Chinsurah Boro. II |
| *Xa-14* | T(N)1 |
| *Xa-15* | M 41 |
| *Xa-16* | Te-tep |
| *Xa-17* | Asominori |
| *Xa-18* | Toyonishiki |
| *Xa-19* | Xm.5 |
| *Xa-20* | Xm.6 |
| *Xa-21* | *O. longistaminata* |
| **Blast** *(Pyricularia oryzae)* | |
| *Pi.1* | LAG 23 |
| *Pi.Z*[5] | 5173 |
| *Pi.3, Pi.ta* | Pai-kan-tao |
| *Pi.5(t), Pi.7(t)* | Moroberekan |
| *Pi.6(t)* | Apura |
| *Pi.8(t)* | IRAT13 |
| *Pi.9(t)* | *O. minuta* |
| *Pi.10(t)* | Tongil |
| *Pi.11(t)* | Zhaiyeing |
| **Rice tungro virus** | Latisail, Vikramarya, Utrimerah, Kataribhog, Gundil Kuning, Jimbrug.<br>Ptb 18, Ptb 21, ARC 10599, ARG 14320 |

**Table 9:** List of important disease/insect pest resistant varieties of India

| ***Disease/insect*** | ***Resistant varieties*** |
|---|---|
| Blast | IR 64, Vani, Sasyasree, Improved Sona, Rasi, Rasmi, Pinakini, VLK 39, Tikkana, VL8, Rajarajan, IR 36, Swarnadhan, NLR 9672, Pant Dhan 10, VL Dhan 221, K332, K 333 |
| Bacterial leaf blight | Ajaya, PR 110, PR 113 |
| Rice tungro virus | Srinivas, Vikramarya, IR 20, Pankhari 203, Kataribhog. |
| Brown planthopper | Sonasali, Manasarovar, Vajram, Krishnaveni, Chaitanya, Nagarjuna, Pavizam, Chandana, Pratibha, CO 42, Nagarjuna, HKR 120, Karthika, Aruna, Rasmi, Jyoti, Makom, Remya, Ananga, Daya, Kanaka, |

**Table 9:** (*Contd...*)

**Table 9:** (*Contd...*)

| ***Disease/insect*** | ***Resistant varieties*** |
|---|---|
| Green leafhopper | Vikramarya, Lalat, Khaira |
| Gall midge | Karna, Lalat, Sarasa, Abhaya, Kavya, Ruchi, Kshira, Sneha, Divya, Bhuban, Phalguna, Surekha, Shakti, Vibhava, Pothana, Mahaveer, IR 36, Dhanyalakshmi |
| WBPH | HKR 120 |
| Stern borer | Ratna, Sasyasree, Vikas |
| Sheath blight | Manasarovar, Pankaj, Swarnadhan |

**Table 10:** Varieties with resistance to more than one insect pest/disease

| ***Variety*** | ***Resistance*** |
|---|---|
| IR 36, Rasi | Blast, Brown spot |
| Vikramarya | Blast, RTV |
| Swarnadhan, Pankaj, Radha | Blast, Sheath blight |
| CNM 539 | Blast, Brown spot and RTV |
| Suraksha, Shaktiman | GM, BPH, WBPH, blast |
| Lalat | GM, BPH, GLM |
| Rasmi | GM, BPH |
| Daya, Samalei | GM, BPH, GLH |
| Ananga | BPH, GM |
| Kshira | GM, BPH, WBPH, GLH, RTV |

**Table 11:** Multiple resistant rice varieties developed at IRRI and India

| ***Variety*** | ***Disease/insect reaction*** | | | | | | | |
|---|---|---|---|---|---|---|---|---|
| | ***Blast*** | ***BLB*** | ***RTV*** | ***CSV*** | ***GLH*** | ***BPH*** | ***SB*** | ***GM*** |
| IR5 | MS | S | S | S | R | S | MR | S |
| IR8 | S | S | S | S | R | S | S | S |
| IR20 | MR | K | S | S | R | S | MR | S |
| IR22 | S | K | S | S | S | S | S | S |
| IR24 | S | S | S | S | R | S | S | S |
| IR26 | MR | R | MR | S | R | R | MR | – |
| IR28 | R | R | R | R | R | K | MR | S |
| IR32 | MR | R | R | R | R | R | MR | R |
| IR36 | MR | K | R | R | R | R | MR | R |
| IR38 | MR | R | R | R | R | *K* | MR | R |
| IR42 | MR | R | R | R | R | R | MR | R |
| IR46 | MR | R | R | R | R | R | MR | R |
| IR50 | S | R | R | R | R | R | S | – |
| IR54 | MR | K | R | R | R | R | MR | – |
| IR58 | MR | R | R | R | R | R | *S* | – |
| IR60 | MR | R | R | R | R | R | MR | – |
| IR62 | MR | R | R | R | R | R | MR | – |
| IR64 | MR | R | R | R | R | R | MR | – |
| IR66 | MR | R | R | R | R | R | MR | – |
| IR68 | MR | R | R | R | R | R | MR | – |
| IR72 | MR | R | R | R | R | R | MR | – |
| Suraksha | R | | | | | R | R | |

**Table 11:** (*Contd...*)

**Table 11:** *(Contd...)*

| *Variety* | *Disease/insect reaction* | | | | | | | |
|---|---|---|---|---|---|---|---|---|
| | *Blast* | *BLB* | *RTV* | *CSV* | *GLH* | *BPH* | *SB* | *GM* |
| Shaktiman | | | R | | | | R | |
| Lalat | R | | | | | R | | R |
| Ananga | | | | | | R | | R |
| Rasmi | R | | | | | R | | R |
| Daya | R | | | | | R | | R |
| Kshira | R | | | | | R | | R |
| Bhuban | | R | | | | R | | R |

R = Resistant; S = Susceptible; MR = Moderately resistant

In the case of blast pathogen, resistance is required at seedling and late vegetative phase against leaf blast and at reproductive phase against neck blast. High percentage correlation between resistance to leaf and neck blasts, however, suggests the possibility of their being governed by the same gene(s). There are in all 12-15 resistance genes located at 7 different loci and the resistance conferred by single dominant mendelian gene is invariably highly race specific. The racial spectrum varies from region to region and so is the distribution of critical resistance genes. In India, for instance, *Pi1(t), Pi2(t), Pi4(t)* are the critical resistance genes and their distribution varies with the region/ecology. Largely because of region specific race composition, development of varieties with desired level of resistance has become difficult. Additionally, frequent breakdown of resistance following appearance of more virulent strain(s) has prompted breeders to contemplate various gene deployment strategies to effectively manage/contain the disease.

Sequential release of varieties with matching resistance gene is the widely employed strategy. Practice of 'Varietal mosaic' *i.e.*, planting varieties carrying different resistance genes is yet another approach found effective in disease endemic areas. If this could be structured in a more planned and precise manner, *vis-a-vis* region, the disease buildup can be brought down appreciably within a short period. Multiline concept, is theoretically a sound strategy. But practical problems have never allowed it to find a place, as happened with wheat. Instead, pyramiding of all the resistance genes relevant to a given region is a more practicable approach. This too, however, could not be made use of until molecular marker aided tools became handy. Recent studies carried out in India under the Asian Rice Biotechnology Network coordinated by IRRI, reveal that right combination of resistance genes confers enhanced level of resistance to blast and bacterial leaf blight (Sridhar *et al.*, 1999a 1999b). Blast resistance genes are highly location specific. Test lines carrying the genes *Pi1* (t), Pi2 (t) and Pi4 (t) singly are resistant at one or two locations only. But in combinations of 2 or 3 they broaden the spectrum of resistance. For instance, in the case of blast pathogen, resistance genes in combinations have been shown to express wide spectrum resistance (Table 12). Of the four gene combinations studied, the one with Pi1 (t) and Pi4 (t) was susceptible to the disease at Jagadalpur, Almora and Jorhat. The combination Pi1 (t) + Pi2 (t) proved resistant at all locations except one, while PiM (t) + Pi2 (t) was found effective at all the six test locations (Table 13). In the case of bacterial leaf blight, Xa21, Xa4, individually conferring moderate level of resistance to the pathotype II in India, express very high level of resistance when they are together. Similarly, though a gene ($Xa_4$, $Xa_5$, $Xa_{13}$) is ineffective singly against the disease, its combination with another resistance gene ($Xa_4 + xa_s$; $Xa_4 + xa_{13}$; $xa_5 + xa_n$; $Xa_4 + xa_5 + xa_n$) confers resistance. The observed effect presumably because of interaction of quantitative complementation between resistance genes thus convincing that the strategy of gene pyramiding is better and more efficient than the multiline or sequential release approaches for effectively managing pathogens that exist in multiple races.

**Table 12:** Resistance reaction of donor sources alone and in combinations at different locations against rice blast.

| *Line* | *Resistance gene* | *Location* | | | | | |
|---|---|---|---|---|---|---|---|
| | | *Cut-tack* | *Jagdnl-pur* | *Ambika-pur* | *Almora* | *Jorhat* | *Suttur* |
| C101 LAG | Pi 2 *(t)* | 5 | 2 | 1 | 5 | 1 | 1 |
| C101 ASI | *Pi 2 (t)* | 5 | 3 | 2 | 4 | 3 | 4 |
| C101 PKT | *Pi 4 (t)* | 5 | 5 | 5 | 4 | 4 | 5 |
| BL 122 | *Pi 1 (t)+Pi 2 (t) 1* | 1 | 3 | 1 | 2 | 1 | 4 |
| BL142 | *Pi 1 (t)+Pi 4 (t) 2* | 2 | 5 | 1 | 4 | 5 | 1 |
| BL245 | *Pi 2 (i)+Pi 4 (t) l* | 1 | 2 | 1 | 1 | 3 | 1 |

**Table 13:** Reaction of near isogenic lines carrying bacterial leaf blight resistance genes singly and in combination.

| *Line/Variety* | *Resistance gene* | *BLB reaction** |
|---|---|---|
| IRBB 3 | $Xa_3$ | 7 |
| Malaghkit Sungsong | $Xa_3$ | 5 |
| IRBB 4 | $Xa_4$ | 7 |
| IRBB 5 | $Xa_5$ | 5 |
| IRBB 13 | $xa_{13}$ | 5 |
| IRBB 21 | $Xa_{21}$ | 1** |
| ÄY 4-5-2 | $Xa_4 + xa_5$ | 3 |
| NH 8-15-1-5 | $Xa_4 + x_{13}$ | 3 |
| NH 11-21-1-3 | $xa_5 + Xa_{21}$ | 1 |
| NH 12-27-2-4 | $xa_5 + Xa_{21}$ | 1 |
| NH-15-51-1-3 | $\mathrm{xa}_{13} + Xa_{21}$ | 1 |
| NH 21-37-1-1 | $Xa_4 + xa_5 + xa_{13}$ | 3 |
| NH 24-10-1-3 | $Xa_4 + xa_5 + Xa21$ | 1 |

*on 0-9 SES scale
**Moderate resistance to pathotype II

### 7.7.2. *Breeding for field resistance against rice blast*

Unexpected and frequent breakdown of resistance characteristic of major gene controlled vertical or specific resistance is causing heavy crop losses. This has prompted rice breeders to insulate varieties with horizontal or field resistance that remains effective over prolonged period and extended areas and environments favourable to the disease. Field resistance is race non-specific and generally of polygenic nature as evident from the fact that off-spring of a cross between varieties with different levels of moderate resistance show continuous variation. In some varieties a similar pattern is mani-fested due to presence of more than one major genes. High level of field resistance found in some of the Japanese upland varieties falls into this category (Shinoda *et al.,* 1971). To evaluate minor gene controlled field resistance, it is necessary to exclude the effect of major gene-controlled resistance as both the components contribute to what is observed as resistance at field level. Progress of leaf blast was studied on two sets of varieties—one set having a particular major gene, while the other without that major gene. Whereas the difference in blast incidence between the two sets of varieties is ascribed to true resistance, the difference between varieties within each set is attributed to field resistacne. Ezuka *et al.* (1969 a and b) have proposed two methods to assess the field resistance specifically: one by confining the comparison to resistance between varieties of a group carrying the same true resistance gene and the other by making an artificial inoculation with the most virulent strain of the fungus capable of knocking down all the test varieties. The former method is useful for tests under field condition or blast nursery, while the latter can be done under glasshouse conditions free from natural infection. It is, however, essential to consider the true resistance of the test varieties for objective evaluation of field resistance. Ezuka *et al.* (1969b) screened in blast nursery as many as 412 varieties grouped on the basis of their content of true resistance along with the susceptible check. Assessment of disease severity in each group in comparison to the susceptible check, revealed the varieties to fall under five different categories *viz.*, highly resistant(rr), resistant(r) intermediate(m) susceptible(s) and highly susceptible(ss). The observed difference also clearly suggest the level of field resistance available in each of them.

Nezeki (1967) evaluated field resistance in glasshouse by seedling inoculation of all suspected varieties with most virulent fungal strain and graded the field resistance on the basis of ratio of the number of susceptible type lesions to the total number of lesions. Yunoki *et al.* (1970a) have recommended the following steps to assess field resistance:

- Select fungal strain virulent to all the test varieties
- Grow the seedlings under excessive dose of nitrogen
- Adjust the concentration of the inoculum to 10 – 25 × $10^4$ spores/ml.
- Inoculate the seedlings at $7^{th}$ leaf stage
- Evaluate field resistance by number of susceptible type lesions.

The findings have been in good agreement with those obtained by Ezuka *et al.* (1969b) under field conditions.

The field resistance, considered to be race non-specific, is polygenically controlled and such resistance is hardly influenced by shift of races due to mutation or otherwise. Polygenic resistance, though more stable and maintainable for long, is far more difficult to breed than breeding major gene controlled resistance. The polygenic resistance identified in different sources may not be the same. By intercrossing, the polygenes conferring resistance to diverse spectrum of races can be accumulated and thereby attain steadily increased level of field resistance. The ideal approach, however would be combining field resistance with true resistance to have stable and durable resistance to the blast disease. But the problem the breeders would face is that breeding lines can not be tested for field resistance unless the race or races matching the true resistance are obtained (Ezuka, 1969b). There are two approaches to overcome this problem *viz.*, (i) select and use a fungus mutant matching the true resistance under controlled glasshouse conditions as suggested by Kiyosawa *et al.* (1975) and (ii) using an indirect evaluation method developed by Asaga and Higashi (1973). They successfully attempted to combine high field resistance available in the variety Yamabiko with true resistance *(Pi 2(t))* of Toride 1. The *Pi 2(t)* gene derived from the Indian variety TKM 1 is effective against all fungal races in Japan. Segregants without *Pi 2* (t) in the $F_3$ of the cross were tested for field resistance either under field or glasshouse condition. The field resistance was estimated by comparing the identified plants with segregants having *Pi 2* (t) gene. The effort finally led to the development of lines combining the true resistance of Toride-1 and field resistance of Yamabiko as schematically shown in Fig. 11.

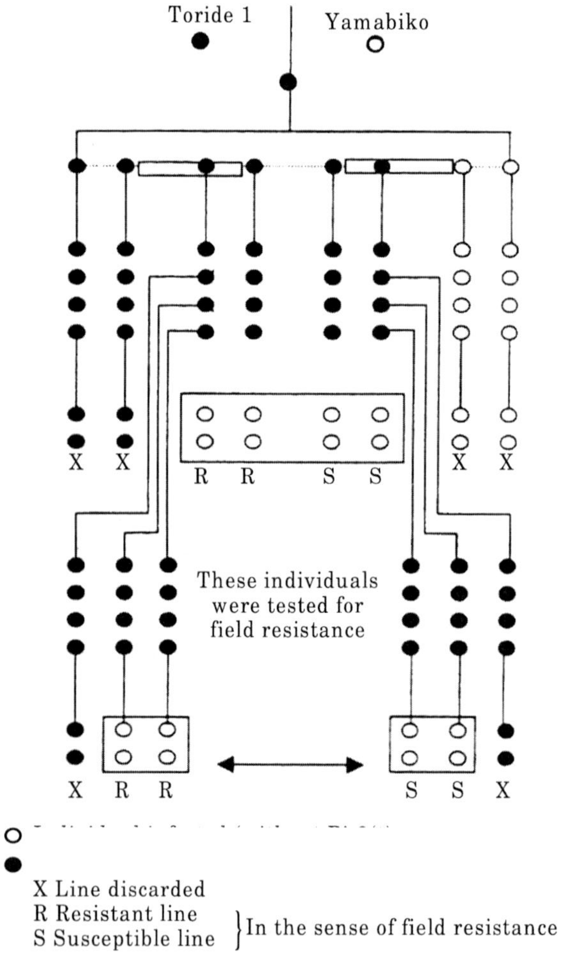


**Fig. 11:** Procedure for evaluating field resistance for blast in segregating generations

### 7.7.3. *Resistance to insect pests*

There are more than one dozen major insect pests, of which stem borer, brown planthopper, gall midge and leaf folder are most serious. Unlike stem borer, which is known for long all over the rice growing parts of the world, BPH, WBPH, leaf folder and gall midge assumed serious pest proportions after the introduction and extensive adoption of high yielding varieties. As a pest and vector of grassy stunt virus, BPH is quite destructive, serious epidemics in India, the Philippines, Indonesia and Vietnam during 1973-1976 had caused crop losses valued at US $ 400 million. Gall midge, confined to small pockets until recently, is now spreading into several non-endemic areas as the most destructive pest.

Serious outbreaks such as the one in 1986 in the state of Andhra Pradesh (India) can cause losses to the tune of over US$ 10 million. Leafroller is yet another pest that has assumed serious pest proportions like hoppers. Inspite of effective host resistance and chemical measures available, the pest management has become increasingly difficult because of biotype variation in gall midge and BPH, pesticide resistance and resurgence of BPH and lack of source of strong resistance to stem borer and leaf roller. Nevertheless taking advantage of sources of resistance and moderate resistance (Tables 8-9) and use of appropriate gene deployment strategies, several varieties combining specific and multiple resistance have been evolved (Tables 10-11).

As for gene deployment, strategies such as sequential release matching the appearance of new viruliferous strains and 'varietal mosaic' in the case of BPH and biotype/region specific release of resistant varieties against gall midge and multiple resistance against more than one pest/biotype have greatly helped minimize the crop losses due to pests.

Identification of the first resistance gene *(Bph1)* in the variety TKM 6, against BPH and its transfer into the variety IR 26 provided a great relief to the farming community all over, when the pest was causing heavy crop losses. The relief was for a very short period as IR 26 and other varieties carrying the same gene, like IR 28, IR 30 and IR 34, succumbed to the pest in a couple of years in Indonesia and India suggesting possible appearance of a new biotype. Using alternate resistance gene(s) identified in Ptb 18 *(bph 2),* four varieties *viz.*, IR 32, IR 36, IR 40 and IR 42 were released in the Philippines, Indonesia and Vietnam. In the subsequent 3-4 years the bph2-conferred resistance also brokedown in parts of the Philippines and Indonesia following the appearance of yet another biotype (biotype 3). The strugggle between the breeder and the pest continued, leading to the discovery and use of still stronger gene sources such as *Bph 3* and *Bph 4* from Rathu Heenati and Balawee to develop IR 56, IR 60 and IR 72. Although no such biotype variation could as yet be established in south Asia, existence of a more viruliferant biotype required a different approach called the strategy of 'varietal mosaic' in the endemic areas. Release of several resistant varieties such as Krishnaveni, Chaitanya, Jyothi, Sonasali, Kanakam etc., using diverse sources of resistance like Ptb 10, Ptb 18, Ptb 21 and ARC 5984, has helped greatly to bring down the frequency of pest outbreaks and thereby reducing crop losses.

For gall midge, which is a serious constraint to rice production in several Asian countries, Identification and use of biotype-specific resistance proved rewarding. As of today existence of as many as five distinct biotypes has been established along with their area of occurrence and potential sources of resistance as briefly indicated below :

| | | |
|---|---|---|
| Biotype 1 | : | Not capable of damaging rice varieties carrying resistance gene either from Eswarakora or Siam 29/ Leung 152. It is found in Andhra Pradesh (Warangal) and Madhya Pradesh (Raipur). |
| Biotype 2 | : | Capable of damaging varieties carrying Eswarakora gene but not Siam 29/Leung 152 gene. It is found in Orissa. |
| Biotype 3 | : | Capable of damaging Siam 29/Leung 152 gene but not Eswarakora. It is found in Bihar (Ranchi) and Andhra Pradesh (Jagtiyal). |
| Biotype 4 | : | Capable of damaging varieties carrying both Eswarakora and Siam 29/Leung 152 genes. It is found in Andhra Pradesh (Srikakulam) and Maharashtra (Sakoli) |
| Biotype 5 | : | Not capable of damaging both Eswarakora and Siam 29/ Leung 152 gene but capable of damaging varieties carrying the gene from Ptb 10. It is found in Kerala (Mancompu) |
| Biotype 6 | : | Not capable of damaging Eswarakora but is capable of damaging Siam 29/Leung 152 and Ptb 10. It is found in Manipur (Wangbai). |

The sources of resistance against the five biotypes and varieties evolved using them have been summarized in Table 8.

The breeding strategy in respect of pests like stem borer and leafroller, against which there are no strong sources of resistance in use of moderate resistance found in varieties like TKM 6 for the former and like Ptb 12, Darukasail, ARC 11128 etc., for the latter in selective diallel mating adopting recurrent selection. The slow progress has necessitated transgenic approach in such cases as detailed elsewhere. Considering the fact that single pest-specific resistance would hardly help reduce the crop losses appreciably in otherwise multi-pest prone rice growing areas, emphasis of breeding strategy has shifted from specific to multiple resistance since last two decades. Many of the varieties under cultivation today, as a result, are resistant to more than one pest/biotype (Tables 10-11). Molecular tagging of biotype-specific resistance genes in respect of BPH and gall midge and availability of cloned genes have placed breeders in more comfortable position to tailor varieties with desired combination of resistance genes against the target pests and their biotypes/pathotypes.

## 7.8. Breeding for Tolerance to Unfavourable Conditions

More than 70% of the rice area suffers from one or the other biophysical constraints to normal growth and development of the crop. The entire rainfed rice, accounting for about 50% of the global rice area with varied moisture regimes as in uplands, lowlands and deepwater areas, injurious soils due to acidity/alkalinity and salinity across ecologies and extreme temperature broadly constitute the less favourable environments. Each of these environments is complex in nature and is characterized by more than one constraint. Whereas moisture stress, impoverished soil, weed infestation and P deficiency constitute the problem environment in the upland rice ecology, continuous anoxic condition due to stagnant flood water, submergence, intermittent drought, and low light are the constraints that characterize the lowland ecologies. In the coastal areas and irrigation commands respectively, salinity and sodicity are the limitations. Low temperature is the problem in high altitude areas. Yield losses and value of production foregone are quite considerable due to various abiotic stresses (Table 14). Of the two broad research remedies pursued to minimize the crop losses *viz.*, (i) development of varieties to suit the stress environment and-(ii) improvement of the stress environment to suit the available varieties, the former *i.e.*, breeding for adaptation to the stress environments has been the most preferred.

**Table 14:** Yield losses due to some abiotic stresses in South Asia

| *Component* | *Yield loss (kg/ha)* | *Value of production forgone ($ million)* | *% value forgone* |
|---|---|---|---|
| Upland/drought blast | 162.7 | 751.5 | 113.3 |
| Drought at anthesis | 58.2 | 268.7 | 4.0 |
| Drought at seedling stage | 50.9 | 235.2 | 3.5 |
| Cold at seedling stage | 8.4 | 38.6 | 0.6 |
| **Soil factors** | | | |
| Coastal saline/acidic soil | 32.7 | 151.0 | 2.3 |
| Alkaline | 12.7 | 58.8 | 0.9 |
| Iron/Mn toxicity | 1.8 | 8.2 | 0.1 |
| Iron deficiency | 1.6 | 7.6 | 0.1 |

Varietal tolerance is the most reliable and cost effective strategy, but breeding for tolerance to such hostile environmnets is not easy not only because of complex nature of the stress environment but also because of different mechanisms conferring tolerance in respect of each of the component indices. The nature of their genetics is also complex. It is believed that the component traits of adaptive value for a given stress environment are inherited as a co-adapted complex evolved and sustained by natural and human selection over hundreds of years. In view of such a complex character combination contributing to a high level of adaptability, recombining them intact with high yield and desired quality is a challenging task. It requires a focussed and aggressive breeding research. Of the various breeding strategies, pureline selection in the native varieties well adapted to a given stress environment as a short term approach and cross breeding as a long term approach are receiving priority attention. Augmented research initiatives and international efforts through exclusive national networks/ecoregional consortia approaches have led to development of a wide range of high yielding varieties for the various rainfed and other stress ecologies. The level of success achieved towards finding varietal solution to such harsh environments in India is quite encouraging. Among the various factors contributing to the success of breeding for adaptation to these environments, site characterization, identification and use of appropriate donor sources (Table 15), breeding emphasis for the most important one or two key constraint(s) (for instance, drought tolerance for upland rice, submergence and drought tolerance for lowland rice, salinity/ sodicity tolerance for coastal areas and irrigation commands respectively) and development and use of reliable and rapid screening techniques are important. Breeding for tolerance to drought, salinity and submergence is briefly discussed below :

**Table 15:** Promising sources of desired traits for breeding drought tolerant varieties

| *Trait* | *Sources* |
|---|---|
| High drought tolerance with good root system | Moroberekan, OS4, OS6, E425, 20A, Lac23, 63-83, Seratus Malam, Arias Halus, Khao Lo, Khao Youth, Padi Tatakin, KU86, Ku-70-1, Kinandang Patong, Salummpikit, Azucena |
| Moderate drought tolerance and early maturity | Black Gora, Brown Gora, Kalakeri, Bala, Lalnakanda, N 22, IAC 25, Dular |
| Improved drought tolerance and good recovery ability | 1ET 1444, IR43, IR4575 selection (semidwarf), C22, UPLR-5, IR6023-10-1-1 (Intermediate tall) |

### 7.8.1. *Drought tolerance*

Moisture stress at any stage of crop growth causes significant yield reduction. Escape, avoidance and tolerance are the three mechanisms by which rice copes with drought environment. Upland varieties, in general, survive either through 'escape' mechanism facilitated through early maturity or 'avoidance' mechanism by the stress induced root elongation to reach moisture zones. Tolerance mechanism operates through curtailing transpiration losses by leaf rolling, early stomatal closure and cuticular resistance. Yet another important mechanism is the rapid recovering ability, when moisture is replenished after prolonged drought. Since most of the indices of stress resistance are independently inherited, there is good scope for recombining them by convergent breeding. Despite the availability of good sources of resistance to drought (Table 14), largely for want of rapid and reliable screening techniques, the pace of progress in breeding for tolerance is hindered for long. Recently, many new screening techniques have been developed (Maurya and O Tool, 1986) and among them an IRRI-developed mass screening technique, which takes into account absolute grain yield under the stress, relative grain yield and percent spikelet fertility has been found quite effective in practical breeding.

Most important step in breeding for drought tolerance is continuous upgrading of breeding lines using donors possessing different mechanisms of tolerance, keeping in view the fact that tolerance is stage specific too. The ongoing breeding efforts in India, Bangladesh, Indonesia, Thailand, the Philippines and some of the African countries have led to evolution of several varieties combining high yields and moderate to high level of tolerance to the stress (Table 16). Nevertheless, the pace of progress is not to the desired extent in view of (a) highly complex nature of drought tolerance and inadequate understanding of its genetics (b) lack of strong donor sources of tolerance at reproductive phase and (c) genetic barriers to obtaining desired recombinants at high frequency, especially in crosses involving geographically isolated genetic resources.

**Table 16:** Improved upland varieties with drought resistance in South east Asia

| ***Country*** | ***Varieties*** |
|---|---|
| Bangladesh | Kataktara (DA2), Panbira (DA 12), Dharial (DA 14), Dular (DA 22), Marichbati (DA 24), Hashikalmi (DA 26) |
| India | Aradhana, Parijat, DR 02, CR 146-224, CR146-225, CR 156-207, Bala, Jamuna, Pusa 2-21, UPR 82-1-7 |
| Indonesia | Gama 87, IET 1444, IR 36 |
| Philippines | Milpa 14, HBDA-2, BPI 1-48 (MI-48), Azmil 26, C 22, UPLRI 3, UPLRI 7 |

### 7.8.2. *Submergence tolerance*

Submergene is as serious and important a physical constraint as drought in rainfed lowland ecologies. Submergence tolerance is defined as the ability of rice crop to survive under complete submergence for as many as 10 days. Submerged rice due to flash floods or excessive rain caused inundation without effective drainage in the low-lying areas, occurs at any stage of crop growth. The underlying mechanisms of tolerance to submergence are (i) ability to survive under water without any growth until after drainage and (ii) escape from submergence by growing along with rising water level and remaining above the flood waters by stem or leaf elongation. A set of morpho-physiological traits listed by Hilleris Lambers *et al.* (1986) affect submergence tolerance, by building up or conserving carbohydrate reserves before or during flooding and or by maintaining physical structure during Submergence and/or avoiding submergence by emerging above the water.

Screening techniques for assessing relative tolerance to submergence now used in breeding programmes in Asia include (i) evaluation at seedling stage under simulated conditions in the greenhouse for germplasm/pedigree/RGA populations or selective seed bed method for $F_2$ and bulk populations before transplanting as practiced at IRRI (ii) screening in artificial tanks at different stages of growth for segregating populations and breeding lines as is being followed in India, Srilanka and Bangladesh and (iii) testing under typical field environment large volumes of breeding populations as in Indonesia and Thailand. Scoring for relative tolerance is done on the basis of two important parameters *viz.*, percentage survival of plants immediately after draining the water and recovering ability of stressed plants about 10 days after draining. However, due to laborious nature of such screening/evaluation techniques, breeders are developing and studying the effectiveness of relatively simple parameters such as survival rate of seedlings in darkness (This approach is based on the assumption that submergence tolerance may be the ability of the plant to cope with lack of assimilation, which happens to be one of the consequences of darkness). Though varietal differences do exist for this trait, its relationship to actual submergence tolerance is yet to be precisely related as opined by HilleRis Lambers *et al.* (1986).

Genetics of submergence tolerance is equally complex, being dependent ön several component traits. Nevertheless, tolerance as understood from the behaviour of widely used submergence tolerant landraces like FR 13A, FR 43B, Kurkaruppan and Goda Heinati, has been reported to be dominant with atleast one major gene active (Mohanty *et al.,* 1982). Experience of other breeders that the trait is transferable with ease, lends support to the above findings.

Inspite of years of breeding efforts, majority of the popular varieties in the flood-prone lowlands are still either traditional varieties or improved versions of the same by pureline selection. Among them, the most important are hybrid derivatives involving donor sources like FR 1SA, FR 43B and Kurkaruppan. Although there are some improved varieties such as Madhukar, they are still not as tolerant and adapted to submergence as the donor varieties. A lot more research efforts are, therefore, needed to combine high level of tolerance with high yield potential. The regional Rainfed Rice Lowland Consortium coordinated by IRRI is addressing these issues.

### 7.8.3. *Salinity tolerance*

Salt stress is one of the major yield destabilizing factors in the coastal areas and irrigation commands. Unlike coastal salinity, which remain nearly static in area, inland salinity is on the increase due to faulty water management in the canal irrigated areas. Progress achieved in the varietal front is hardly encouraging. Very limited choice of varieties suited to the stress is the most serious constraint to production growth. Majority of the popular varieties still under cultivation in salt affected areas are pureline selections from well adapted traditional varieties. The dismal progress of varietal improvement for this stress environment is attributable to poor understanding of the nature of the stress, inadequate understanding of the mechanism and genetics of tolerance and lack of reliable screening techniques.

The salt stress in the coastal areas is not the same as that in the irrigation commands and waterlogged lowlands. The former is saline due largely to sodium chloride and sodium sulphate, while the latter is alkaline (sodic). Their composition and level of severity vary with salts involved and their proportions. The tolerance is growth stage-specific and its genetics is index specific. Such information is not even taken into consideration while identifying donor sources, planning breeding/ selection strategies and choosing screening techniques. Mechanism of tolerance of NaCl salinity in majority of the donor sources is through relatively high retention of Na and Cl in roots than in shoots. In some, especially the most tolerant ones, tolerance is either through pronounced exclusion or compartmentation of Na at cellular/tissue level in association with rapid pace of growth. In tolerant sources like Taipei 309, it appears to be through higher tissue tolerance of Na content in the shoot due to either osmotic adjustment or compartmentation, while mitigation of high Na content in shoot is due to faster growth rate in the universally used donor variety Pokkali. By and large, ability of a plant to regulate either Na uptake or selective accumulation of K, translocation of salts from root to shoot and ionic balance (ratio of Na to macro/micro nutrients) rather than just absorbed Na content determine the level of tolerance (Siddiq *et al.,* 1999).

All genetic investigations have so far been without fully understanding and taking into consideration the complex nature of the stress and diverse mechanisms governing it. Findings of the past 20 years uniformly suggest that tolerance, as measured by different indices, is polygenically controlled with the nature of gene action varying with the index (Table 17). Most of the findings on genetics have been on the basis of studies using NaCl as the stress, which could be relevant to salinity but not necessarily to sodicity. Because of such serious lacunae in basic information, breeding for salt tolerance still remains a hit and miss method only. Whatever has been achieved so far in breeding for salt stress, is largely by screening breeding populations either in hotspots or in the lysimeter/microplots under artificially created stress conditions. Marker associated quantitative trait loci (QTLs) relating to key indices of tolerance now under development are expected in the coming years to facilitate greatly the breeding efforts.

**Table 17:** Genetics of salt tolerance in rice

| *Index* | *Mode of inheritance* | *Reference(s)* |
|---|---|---|
| Panicle sterility | Dominant, Trigenic | Akbar and Yabano (1977) |
| Shoot length, dry weight of shoot & root; Na & Cl content in shoot. | Polygenic, Predominently additive | Akbar *et al.* (1986) |
| Days to flowering; plant height; tiller number, spikelets/panicle, fest grain weight, dry matter accumulation | Polygenic, additive and dominance effects | Narayanan and Srirangasamy (1991) |
| Low Na to K ratio | Polygenic, additive and dominance effects. | Gregorio and Senadhira (1993) |
| IRRI's tolerance score | Polygenic, major influence of monogenes | Mishra *et al.* (1998) |
| Seedling shoot growth | Six basic genes interacting in varied combinations. | Ajay Garg and Siddiq (in press) |
| Shoot proline accumulation | Predominently non additive | |
| Shoot ionic ratio | Dominance-recessiveness not clear. | |

## 7.9. Breeding for Cooking and Nutritive Quality

Cooking quality of rice is determined by physico-chemical properties of starch, while nutritive quality is judged by protein content and its quality, vitamins and minerals. The quality traits have been in-depth researched to understand their genetics and breeding behaviour (please see the Monograph 'Rice Chemistry and Technology' by Juliano, 1985 for various indices and methods of their evaluation). Among the starch characteristics, amylose content determines the relative stickiness or dryness of cooked rice. Varieties having high amylose (>25%) content characteristic to Indian varieties *(indica)* cook dry and flaky, while those of low amylose (<15%) characteristic to Japanese and Korean varieties *(japonica)* cook sticky. Majority of the popular varieties worldover are of intermediate amylose (≈ 23%). The highly prized *basmati* rices have amylose content around 22%. The glutinous or waxy types used mostly for preparation of rice cakes have practically no amylose, the entire starch fraction being amylopectin. Gelatinization temperature (alkali digestion score) determines resistance to cooking. The soft cooking *japonica* rices are of low gelatinization temperature (GT), while relatively hard cooking *indicas* are of high GT. One other important cooking quality index is gel consistency, which determines how long cooked rice would remain soft. Varieties of medium and low gel consistancy (largely associated with medium and low amylose) and the medium and low GT are the most preferred, as they remain soft for long hours after cooking. High volume increase and optimum water uptake are other desirable features. Aroma, determined by 2 acetyl 1-pyrolline, and extra kernel alongation (= 2 times) with least swelling are the key characteristics that qualify *basmati* quality. From traders' point of view, percentage milling outturn (rice obtainable per unit quantity of paddy milled), head rice recovery (%unbroken) and colour of rice are important. Thus the indices that determine consumer quality are many. Except for a few like aroma, nearly all the indices of quality follow complex polygenic inheritance making breeding/selection very difficult for evolving varieties for varied consumer sections (Table 18).

Nutritive quality is as important as cooking quality for tropical countries, where it is the primary source of dietary protein, vitamins (B10) and minerals, (Fe, Ca, Zn etc.,). Rice accounts for 40% of the protein consumed on an average in Asia, the range being between 17 and 60%. In spite of its having biologically rieh protein in terms of digestibility and aminoacid profile, rice suffers on account of its inherently low protein content and milling loss of as much as 15%. Breeding for high protein content, unlike in other cereals, does not have any adverse effect on protein quality. However, it follows a quadratic relationship with grain yield and as a result, beyond 9-10% protein, grain yield tends to decline. Limited investigations to understand the complex genetics of protein content reveal it to be a polygenic trait governed predominantly by non-additive and additive gene action.

**Table 18:** Genetics of various indices of quality in rice

| ***Characteristics*** | ***Mode of inheritance (predominant gene action)*** |
|---|---|
| ***Physical features*** | |
| Grain length | Polygenic (Somrith, 1974) |
| Grain shape (L/B ratio) | Polygenic (Somrith, 1974) |
| Waxy rice | Monogenic recessive *(wx)* |
| Chalkiness (whitebelly/ | Monogenic recessive *(wb / we)* |
| white centre) | Polygenic (Chang and Li 1980) |
| ***Cooking behaviour*** | |
| Water adsorption | Polygenic/non-additive (Zaman *et al.,* 1987) |
| Volume expansion | Polygenic/non-additive (Zaman *et al.,* 1987) |
| Kernel elongation | Polygenic/non-additive (Sood *et al.,* 1982) |
| Amylose content | Oligogenic+modifiers<br>Polygenic/non-additive gene action (Puri and Siddiq, 1982) |
| Geletinization temperature | Oligogenic+modifiers (McKenzie and Rutger, 1983); Polygenic-additive gene action (Kabion, 1965; Stensil, 1986; Somrith *et al.*, 1979)<br>Polygenic/additive gene action (Puri and Siddiq, 1982); Oligogenic+modifier (Chang and Li 1980) |
| Gel consistency | Polygenic/additive gene action (Zaman *et al.,* 1985) |
| Aroma | Monogenic recessive (Sood and Siddiq, 1979) complimentary 2-3 genic interaction (Singh and Mani, 1987; Tripati and Rao, 1979). |
| ***Nutritive quality*** | |
| Protein content | Polygenic/non-additive and additive gene action (Sood and Siddiq, 1986); dominance of additive effects (Chang and Lin, 1974) |

High amylose partially dominant; High GT partially dominant;
High water absorption & volume expansion dominant
Low kernel elongation over-dominant; Low protein partially dominant.

Beyond limited research efforts to improve the protein content, very little has been done to correct other nutrient deficiencies. Rice lacks vitamin-A and is deficient in iron and zinc and lipids etc. Rectification of such deficiencies is important for nutrition security. Besides looking for natural variability for high iron and zinc uptake, concerted effort is underway to genetically engineer rice to increase the content of iron. Gene sources for high iron (Milagrosa, Jalmagna, Tong Lan, Mo Mi, Azucina, Xu Bue Nuo) and zinc (Conjay Roozy, Zuchem, Banjaiman, Xua Bue Nuo) content have been successfully used in cross breeding by IRRI to evolve iron and zinc rich, high yielding lines like IR 68144-2B-2-2-5 now under extensive testing for yield performance and iron zinc content.

For β-carotene (precursor of Vitamin-A), no reliable gene source has as yet been found. Taking advantage of the fact that incomplete pathway leading to biosynthesis of β-carotene exists in rice, scientists have successfully engineered rice by splicing the missing genes from the

*Erwinia uredevora* and daffodil *(Narcissus* sp) to make it produce β-carotene in the endosperm (Xudong Ye *et al.*, 2000). The transgenic is under intensive testing for stability of expression, biosafety and agronomic potential in developing countries including India.

Consumer quality received due importance in our breeding agenda right from the day of the introduction of high yielding dwarf varieties, which have involved in their ancestry exotic parental sources of relatively poor grain/cooking quality. Very large number of varieties released since then are of fine type with relatively better starch characteristics. Among them IRRI-developed IR 64, IR 72, IR 74 and BPT 5204 etc., of India are quite popular.

### 7.9.1. *High yielding basmati rice*

Among the worlds' highly prized rices, aromatic rices of the Indian sub-continent called *'Basmati'* are important. Differing distinctly from typical *indica* or *japonica* varieties, traditional *basmati* rices are characterized by super fine grain, pleasant aroma, extra elongation of kernel and soft texture of cooked rice. Endemic to north and northwestern part of the subcontinent, these high quality rices are otherwise very poor yielders. The breeding efforts to combine the quality of traditional *basmati* varieties in the background of high yielding dwarf varieties took more than two decades. It was by stepwise convergent breeding approach, that the key characters of complex genetics were brought together to evolve the world's first high yielding dwarf *basmati* variety Pusa Basmati-1 (Table 19). The breeding methodology consisted of crossing the high yielding dwarf variety Taichiung (Native)1 with the traditional *basmati* rice variety *Basmati 370* and repeated back-crossing with the donor parent and selection in the backcross $F_2$ generation. The varieties/ elite lines evolved and selected therefrom were top-crossed with appropriate parents, keeping in view the character deficiency at every stage and subjected to intensive selection at field level for plant type and yield potential, and at laboratory level for the quality traits. Rapid screening techniques such as mild alkali (2.4% KOH) test for aroma, actual cooking of small seed samples of selected plants for kernel elongation and alkali score, gel consistency and amylose content for texture and cohesiveness of cooked rice were developed and used althrough. Understanding of the complex genetics of the key characteristics was of great help in systematically planning the breeding/ selection strategies. Pusa Basmati-1 commanding high premium in the domestic and international market yields 50-100% more than the

**Table 19:** Quality characteristics of Pusa Basmati-1

| *Variety* | *Kernel traits* | | | *Milling traits* | | |
|---|---|---|---|---|---|---|
| | *Length (mm)* | *Breadth (mm)* | *L/B ratio* | *Hulling (%)* | *Milling (%)* | *Head rice recovery (%)* |
| Pusa Basmati-1 | 7.36 | 1.70 | 4.13 | 72.5 | 66.0 | 52.0 |
| Basmati 370 | 6.93 | 1.86 | 3.73 | 79.6 | 67.9 | 46.2 |
| Karnal Local | 7.07 | 1.80 | 3.93 | 77.0 | 66.0 | 38.2 |

| *Variety* | *Other quality traits* | | | | |
|---|---|---|---|---|---|
| | *Alkali value* | *Amylose content (%)* | *KLAC (mm)* | *KER* | *Aroma* |
| Pusa Basmati-1 | 6.0 | 22.3 | 15.17 | 2.07 | present |
| Basmati 370 | 6.2 | 22.10 | 12.80 | 1.85 | present |
| Karnal Local | 5.4 | 23.21 | 14.25 | 2.01 | present |

KLAG — Kernel length after cooking
KER — Kernel elongation ratio

traditional *basmati* varieties without compromising on quality. The variety has provided a strong agronomic base for breeding still higher yielding varieties with improved milling characteristics.

## 8. HETEROSIS BREEDING

Heterosis in rice was reported first by Jones (1926) followed by many confirming its existence to an exploitable level for grain yield as extensively reviewed by Virmani and Edwards (1983). The role of cytoplasm in causing male sterility in rice was reported way back in the fifties (Sampath and Mohanty, 1954; Katsuo and Mizushima, 1958). Yet, none could translate such information and subsequent findings including the first usable cytoplasmic genetic male sterility-fertility restoration system developed by Shinjyo and Omura (1966) by substituting nuclear genes of the *japonica* variety Taichung 65 into the cytoplasm of the *indica* variety Chinsura Boro II into commercially viable hybrid rice technology. This was probably due to strict self-pollinating nature of the crop and the attendant difficulties of commercial hybrid seed production. It was the persistent effort of Chinese scientists that ultimately led to the successful development of the hybrid rice technology by late seventies. The first commercially usable CMS line was developed in China in 1973 from a spontaneous male sterile plant isolated in a population of the wild rice *O. sativa f.spontanea* on Hainan Island (Yuan, 1977). Discovery of this source designated as 'Wild Abortive' or 'WA' type, is considered a landmark in the history of rice breeding. China released the first hybrid for commercial cultivation in 1976 (Yuan, 1977). Subsequently using WA-based CMS lines V 20A, Zhen-Shan 97A etc., several heterotic hybrids *viz.*, Nan-You 2, Nan-You 6, Shan-You 2, Shan-You 6 and Wei-You 6 were released for general cultivation. Yield advantage of 15-20% over the best inbred varieties (6.5 t/ha as against 5.4 t/ha) proved the key factor for wide adoption of the hybrid technology. Area under hybrid rice increased as a result to 55% (18 million ha) of the rice area contributing 57% to the total rice production by 1985. Following the success of hybrid rice in China, the International Rice Research Institute (IRRI) augmented research to evolve hybrids ideally suited to tropical environment. Development of stable male sterile lines in the tropical varietal background by IRRI has facilitated intensive hybrid breeding research there and a few countries like India, the Philippines, and Vietnam. India, which launched a mission mode network project on hybrid rice in 1989 has made significant progress and earned the distinction of being the second country after China to make hybrid technology a field reality.

## 8.1. Principle Breeding Approaches and Methodology

Procedure for developing hybrids is quite different from that employed for conventional breeding. In hybrid breeding, yield genes are assembled and exploited under heterozygous condition in the first filial ($F_1$) generation. On the contrary, conventional recombination breeding involves selective accumulation of yield related genes that perform well under homozygous condition year after year. Generally, rice hybrids are developed by using either cytoplasmic-genetic male sterility (CMS) or environment sensitive genic male sterility (EGMS) Systems. Of these, the former is widely utilized, while efforts are still underway to refine the photoperiod sensitive and temperature sensitive genic male sterility systems.

### 8.1.1. *The CMS-based three-line approach*

Development of stable male sterlity system is the pre-requisite for commercial hybrid seed production. Among different kinds of male sterility system known in rice, cytoplamic-genetic male sterility based 3-line approach has proved most stable and commercially viable as is the case with traditional hybrid crops. In this system male sterility results from interaction between sterility factor present in the cytoplasm and those in the nucleus. Absence of the sterility-inducing factor (gene) either in the cytoplasm or nucleus makes a line male fertile. This system involves a CMS (A-line), a maintainer (B-line) and a restorer (R-line). A CMS line is maintained by crossing it with its B line. The A and B lines are similar in all respects except that the former is male sterile and the latter male fertile. The restorer line possesses dominant fertility restoring gene(s) and hence when crossed with a CMS line, produces a fertile $F_1$ hybrid. Since the system involves the use of three (A, B and R) lines, hybrids developed by using this method are called three-line hybrids. The genetic basis of the three-line system is as illustrated in Fig. 12.

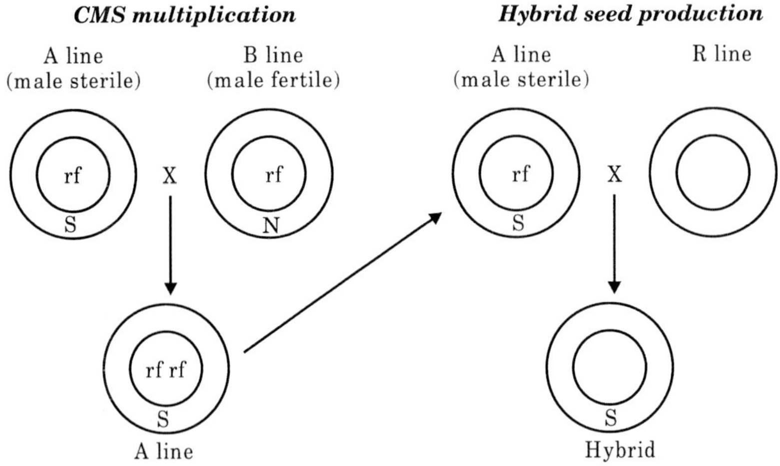


**Fig. 12:** Schematic description of cytoplasmic-genetic male sterility system

Three factors are crucial for the commercial success of hybrid rice technology. They are high standard heterosis, stable male sterile source and efficient package for obtaining high seed yields. Extent of yield heterosis has been reported to be as high as 370%, but realizable standard heterosis (yield advantage in comparison to the best standard variety) estimated across countries on population basis is in the range of 18 to 36% only (Table 20). In the high yielding varietal background, even average Standard heterosis of 10-15% would amount to an additional yield advantage of 1.0-1.5t/ha.

As for the male sterility source, China continues to exploit till now the 'WA'-based male sterile lines such as V 20 A, Zhen Shan 97A etc., in respect of *indica* and Chinsurah Boro II cytoplasm-based 'WU' 10 for *japonica* because of their high stability, combining ability and percentage outcrossing. When the same parental lines were found not

**Table 20:** Extent of standard heterosis observed in different countries

| *Country* | *Period* | *Yield (kg/ha)* *Hybrid* | *Check* | *Yield advantage over check (%)* | *Reference* |
|---|---|---|---|---|---|
| China* | 1981-1990 | 6342 | 4649 | 36 | Mao, 1992 |
| India** | 1994-1998 | 6820 | 5290 | 29 | DRR, 2000 |
| IRRI | 1986-1993 | 5280 | 4475 | 18 | Virmani *et al.*, 1993 |
| Philippines | 1990-1993 | 7630 | 6358 | 20 | Virmani *et al.*, 1993 |
| Vietnam | 1990-1993 | 6050 | 4690 | 29 | Virmani *et al.*, 1993 |
| Malaysia | 1990-1993 | 5530 | 4254 | 30 | Virmani *et al.*, 1993 |

*In commercial cultivation
**In on-farm trials

ideally suitable for tropical environment, IRRI successfully converted a few varieties well adapted to the tropics with the Chinese 'WA' cytoplasmic source. Among them IR58025A and IR62829A have been found highly promising. This development at IRRI prompted many, especially India, to accelerate hybrid rice-research using the two CMS lines to start with. The effort has led to the identification of several heterotic combinations, some of which hâve been released for general cultivation. Extensive work has been done to optimize hybrid seed production and multiplication of A-line. The package capable of yielding 2-3 ton seed/ha includes optimal R to A ratio (2R : 10A) and B to A (2B : 8A) row ratio, staggered planting for synchronization of flowering, GA3 (45g/ha) application, supplimentary pollination measures as detailed by Virmani *et al.* (1997) and favourable locations and seasons.

Hybrid rice breeding broadly covers (i) development of parental lines (ii) seed production of parental lines and experimental hybrids and (iii) evaluation of hybrids for agronomic performance. For the efficient development of parental lines, the breeding material is grouped into different nurseries *viz.*, source nursery, testcross nursery, backcross nursery and CMS evaluation nursery. The genetic base of the material used in hybrid rice breeding should be as wide as possible. The hybrids developed should be critically evaluated for yield performance and accessory characters through multilocation testing before releasing them for general cultivation.

Source nursery is constituted of elite breeding lines, notified varieties, introduced exotic material, CMS and EGMS lines. Crosses are made between CMS line and selected lines in the source nursery and thèse are called 'test-crosses'. Testcross $F_1$'s are evaluated to identify potential maintainers (the genotypes that produce completely male sterile $F_1$) and restorers (those genotypes which produce fertile $F_1$ progeny). The maintainers are backcrossed to the respective $F_1$S to convert them into new CMS lines and thèse are evaluated in the 'backcross nursery'.

Generally 5-6 backcrosses would be adequate for conversion of a maintainer into a new CMS line. The restorers are retest-crossed and hybrids therefrom are evaluated in unreplicated observational yield trial (OYT). Those found promising in OYT are evaluated in the Preliminary Yield Trial (PYT) at the station before nominating the consistently best performing ones to the three-tier National Hybrid Rice Trials as detailed elsewhere. The outline of CMS-based hybrid breeding is schematically represented in Fig. 13.

Evaluation of hybrids is done at national level by the concerned countries and at international level by IRRI. In India, hybrids developed at different hybrid rice research network centres and those received from IRRI and private companies are evaluated at the network and other voluntary centres following a three-tier system of testing. Promising hybrids identified by the participating institutions are nominated for evaluation in the Initial National Hybrid Rice Trial (IHRT) conducted at more than 20 locations. Superior hybrids, atleast one fourths, identified in the IHRT are promoted to Advanced Variety Trial-1-Irrigated Ecology (AVT-1-Irrigated) and tested along with the test entires from conventional breeding at a large number of locations. The most promising few hybrids and varieties are promoted to AVT-2 for further intensive testing in replicated trial under two level of N. Besides yield, the entries are screened simultaneously for disease-insect pest resistance and quality attributes. This system of testing has helped identify hybrids appropriate for different regions/ seasons. As many as 13 hybrids, developed by public and private sector institutions, are commercially cultivated in India (Table 21). Among these, the hybrids KRH-2, PHB-71, Sahyadri, Narendra Sankar Dhan-2, PA-6201 and DRRH-1 have wide adaptability. They have a yield advantage of 1.0 to 1.5 t per hectare over the check varieties. Some of the IRRI bred hybrids such as IR 58025A/IR 29723, IR 58025A/IR 21567, IR 62829A/IR 29723, IR 58025/IR 34686 have also been found promising in several countries including in India.

### 8.1.2. *Parental line improvement for enhanced level of heterosis*

Development of hybrids utilizing cytoplasmic-genetic male sterility system involved identification of restorers and maintainers from a large number of elite lines. The frequency of restorers and maintainers among the available elite *indica* lines is around 25% and 10% respectively. Unlike in *indica* it is difficult to find good restorers in the *japonica* germplasm. More than 75% of the elite lines tested have turned out to be either partial restorers or partial maintainers, which

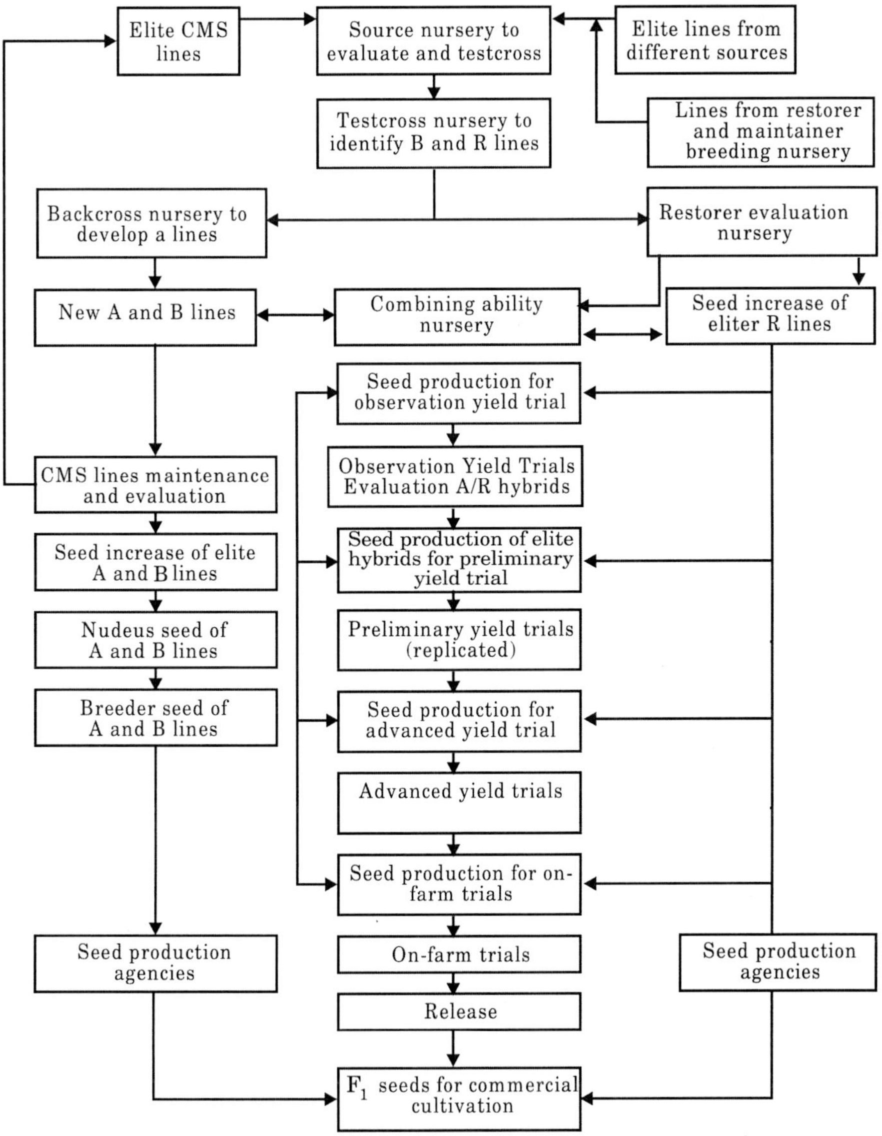


**Fig. 13:** Outline of hybrid rice breeding using CMS system

are not usable in commercial hybrid breeding. Dependence on the inbred breeding programme on a continual basis for new elite lines would hardly help improve the situation. In order to improve the efficiency of hybrid rice breeding, it is essential to augment it with an exclusive parental line improvement programme so that a large number of usable lines are available for developing more and better heterotic hybrids.

**Table 21:** Hybrids under cultivation in India

| *Name of the hybrid* | *Year of release* | *Duration (days)* | *Yield in hybrid* | *OFT (t/ha) Check* | *Yield adv. over check (%)* | *Released for the state of* |
|---|---|---|---|---|---|---|
| APHR-1 | 1994 | 130-135 | 7.14 | 5.27 (Chaitanya) | 35.4 | Andhra Pradesh |
| APHR-2 | 1994 | 120-125 | 7.52 | 5.21 (Chaitanya) | 44.2 | Andhra Pradesh |
| MGR-1 | 1994 | 110-115 | 6.08 | 5.23 (IR 50) | 16.2 | Tamil Nadu |
| KRH-1 | 1994 | 120-125 | 6.02 | 4.58 (Mangala) | 31.4 | Karanataka |
| CNRH-3 | 1995 | 125-130 | 7.49 | 5.45 (Khitish) | 37.4 | West Bengal |
| DRRH-1 | 1996 | 125-130 | 7.30 | 5.50 (Tellahamsa) | 32.7 | Andhra Pradesh |
| KRH-2 | 1996 | 130-135 | 7.40 | 6.10 (Jaya) | 21.3 | Karnataka |
| Pant Sankar Dhan-1 | 1997 | 115-120 | 6.80 | 6.20 (Pant Dhan-4) | 9.7 | Uttar Pradesh |
| CORH-2 | 1998 | 120-125 | 6.25 | 5.20 (ADT 39) | 20.2 | Tamil Nadu |
| ADTRH-1 | 1998 | 115-120 | 7.10 | 4.90 (ASD-18) | 44.9 | Tamil Nadu |
| Sahyadri | 1998 | 125-130 | 6.64 | 4.89 (Jaya) | 35.8 | Maharashtra |
| Narendra Sankar Dhan-2 | 1998 | 125-130 | 6.15 | 4.94 (Sarjoo-52) | 24.5 | Uttar Pradesh |
| PHB 71* | 1997 | 130-135 | 7.68 | 6.14 (PR 106) | 28.0 | Haryana, UP, TN |

*Private bred hybrid released by CVRC; OFT = on farm trial

Improved gene pool with higher frequency of restorers and maintainers can be developed by different approaches. The most common is through establishing specific restorer and maintainer breeding programme by meticulously planned R × R and B × B crosses. By this, it is possible to combine desirable traits from different parents, besides increasing the frequency of restorers and maintainers. Another effective method of improving parental lines is genetic male sterility-facilitated recurrent selection, which not only broadens the genetic base of parental lines but also helps in the accumulation of desirable genes.

Parental lines are improved by effecting single, double or multiple crosses among genetically diverse maintainers or restorers followed by pedigree selection. The choice of parents for the crossing should be such that they are of complementing types so as to meet various breeding objectives. The most commonly used approaches are R × R, partial restorer × R, partial maintainer × R and B × B crosses. For R × R and B × B crosses, promising lines having complementary traits are used so that probability of isolating desirable plants in the segregating generations is high. Some partial restorers or partial maintainers having exceptionally good traits can also be crossed with good restorers to obtain segregants having restorer genes coupled with desirable floral traits. The frequency of restorers in such cases will be relatively low, which necessitates rigorous selection in large populations and resorting to backcrossing in certain cases. The material so generated is test/top-crossed in advanced generations using good CMS lines to assess their restoring and combining ability.

As for the improvement of restorers and maintainers by genetic male sterility facilitated recurrent selection, genetically diverse restorers, having useful traits, are crossed with the genetic male sterile line of a restorer background. $F_1$'s are grown and equal quantity of $F_1$ seed produced from each cross is pooled to raise the $F_2$ generation. The population is subjected to random mating and seed set on male sterile plants is used to grow the next generation. After 3-4 cycles of random mating, the fertile plants are selected and handled by pedigree method to extract useful derivatives. Selected ones are test-crossed to the CMS lines to confirm their restoring and combining abilities. Similar procedure is followed for improving the maintainer lines. This strategy has been found quite rewarding for broadening the genetic base of the parental lines. Detailed procedures for parental line improvement have been outlined by Virmani *et al.* (1997).

### 8.1.3. *EGMS-based two-line approach*

The discovery of environment sensitive genic male sterility (EGMS) wherein alteration of male sterility/fertility is conditioned by environmental factors such as photoperiod or temperature, has led to the development of two-line breeding system. The lines, which respond to day length changes are called photosensitive genic male steriles (PGMS). The first PGMS source was reported by Shi (1981) in the *japonica* cultivar Nong-Ken 58. This variant remains male sterile under long day (>14 hr) conditions and turns male fertile under short day (< 13.75 hr) conditions. PGMS lines are effectively utilized in those regions, where day length differences are quite distinct.

The genetic source, wherein alteration of male fertility/sterility is controlled by change in temperature is called thermosensitive genic male sterility system (TGMS). In the tropics, where consistent temperature differences are found at different altitudes or during different seasons in the same location, the TGMS system is ideal for developing two-line hybrids. Unlike the CMS system, the TGMS system does not require a maintainer line for multiplication of male sterile line. Whereas a TGMS line at sterile phase and a male fertile parent are required to produce hybrid seed, TGMS line is maintained by growing under low-temperature conditions, which facilitates its reversion to fertile phase.

The first TGMS line Annong-IS was isolated as a spontaneous mutant in China (Tan *et al.,* 1990). The second TGMS source reported by Maruyama *et al.* (1991), was a gamma ray induced mutant from the Japanese variety Remei. This source is characterized by no seed set at 31/24ºC, partial seed set at 28/21ºC and füll seed set at 25/15ºC. Following the discovery and use of the two TGMS sources, and their derivatives in China, Japan, and (IRRI) many new sources have been identified and developed into usable lines (Table 22). Genetic investigations reveal that TGMS, like PGMS, is monogenic recessive and there are four putative genes *viz., tmsl, tms2, tms3* and *tms4* (Siddiq and Jauhar Ali, 2000).

**Table 22:** PGMS and TGMS sources identified developed in China, Japan, India, USA and at IRRI

| *Line* | *Varietal group* | *Developed through* | *Origin* | *Fertility-induction condition* |
|---|---|---|---|---|
| ***PGMS*** | | | | |
| Nongken 585 | *japonica* | Spontaneous mutation | China | Day length lower than 13.75 h |
| EGMS | *japonica* | | USA | Day length lower than 13 h |
| X88 | *japonica* | Cross breeding | Japan | Day length lower than 13.75 h |
| M 201 | *japonica* | EMS treatment | Louisiana | Day length 12 h |
| ***TGMS*** | | | | |
| Annong S | *indica* | Spontaneous mutation | China | Temperature below 27°C |
| Hennog S | *indica* | Cross-breeding | China | Temperature below 29°C |
| 5460 S | *indica* | Irradiation | China | Temperature below 29°C |
| R59TS | *indica* | Irradiation | China | Temperature below 29°C |
| IR32364-20-1-3-2 | *indica* | Irradiation | IRRI | Temperature below 28°C |
| Norin PL 12 | *japonica* | Irradiation | Japan | Temperature below 28°C |
| IVA | *indica* | Cross-breeding | China | Temperature below 24°C |
| Dianxin 1A | *japonica* | CMS | China | Temperature below 22°C |
| SM-3 | *indica* | Spontaneous mutation | India | Temperature below 22°C |
| SM-5 | *indica* | Spontaneous mutation | India | Temperature below 22°C |
| JP-2 | *indica* | Spontaneous mutation | India | Temperature below 26°C |
| JP-38 | *indica* | Spontaneous mutation | India | Reverse TGMS, Temperature above 30.5°C |

The PGMS/TGMS-based two-line System has the following advantages over the conventional CMS-based three-line system.

- There is no need of maintainer line for seed multiplication of the male sterile line and hence the seed multiplication is less cumbersome.

- Any fertile genotype can be used as male parent with no need to have a restorer gene and hence the choice of male parents is wide for developing two-line hybrids.
- The negative effects of sterility-inducing cytoplasm are not encountered.
- The TGMS/PGMS trait can be transferred to any desired genetic background without any restriction thus providing wider genetic and cytoplasmic base among the male sterile lines.
- The system is ideal for developing inter sub-specific hybrids as there is no need of restorer genes in the male parent.

For developing two-line hybrids, well characterized PGMS/TGMS lines are available. In China, breeders have extensively used well-known restorers with high combining ability to develop two-line hybrids (Lu *et al.,* 1998). Some of the popular two-line hybrids developed and commercially cultivated in China are listed in Table 23.

**Table 23:** Two-line hybrid rice combinations in commercial production and regional trials in China

| *Hybrid* | *Cross* | *Subspecies* | *Status* |
|---|---|---|---|
| 70 You 9 | 70015/Wanhul 9 | *japonica* | Commercialized |
| E Jing-Za No. 1 | N5088S/R187 | *japomca* | Commercialized |
| Hua-Jing-Za No. 1 | N5088S/1514 | *japonica* | Commercialized |
| Liang-You-Pei-Te | Peiai 64S/Tequing | *indica* | Commercialized |
| Pei-Za-Shan-Qing | Peiai 64S/Shanqing 11 | *indica* | Commercialized |
| Pei-Liang-You 288 | Peiai 645/288 | *indica* | Commercialized |
| Pei-Za 77 | Peiai 64S/77 Zhan | *indica* | Regional trial |
| Liang-You 681 | Shuguang 612S/681 | *indica* | Regional trial |

*Source*: Lu *et al.* 1998

In India, under the Hybrid Rice Network, TGMS-based two-line hybrid breeding has been intensified along with CMS-based 3-line breeding at selected centres. More than 30 TGMS lines, developed indigenously or introduced from IRRI, have been physiologically characterized for their Critical Sterility Point (CSP) and Critical Fertility Point (CFP). Among them, seven lines combine many of the desirable characteristics (Table 24) and they are being utilized to develop two-line hybrids, some of which are in advanced stages of evaluation for yield performance. Preliminary results indicate that some promising two-line hybrid have yield advantage of 5-10% over the three-line hybrids. For large scale commercial exploitation, ideal locations and periods for hybrid seed production and multiplication of TGMS lines have been identified.

**Table 24:** Promising TGMS lines identified in India

| *Location /TGMS Une* | *CST (°C)* | *CFT (°C)* | *Remarks* |
|---|---|---|---|
| ***Hyderabad*** | | | |
| DRIRTG-1 | ≥25 | ≤23 | Good outcrossing |
| DRIRTG-2 | >25 | ≤22 | Good outcrossing |
| DRIRTG-3 | ≥25 | ≤22 | Good outcrossing |
| MLTG-4 | ≥24 | ≤22 | Good outcrossing and early duration |
| ***Coimbatore*** | | | |
| TS-29 | ≥25 | ≤22 | Good outcrossing |
| ***Pantnagar*** | | | |
| UPRI 95-140 | ≥27 | ≤24 | Good plant type |
| UPRI 95-167 | ≥26 | ≤23 | Good plant type |

## 9. MUTATION BREEDING

Mutation breeding is a potential tool to generate additional variability and it has been successfully exploited to improve many crop plants including rice. In crops, where limitation of genetic variability is a constraint to progressive improvement, mutation breeding is considered relevant even today, particulary for selective rectification/improvement of one or two simply inherited traits in otherwise well-adapted and highly productive varieties.

Use of induced mutagenesis for improvement of rice was started in India in the thirties (Ramaiah and Parthasarathy, 1936). But it received importance as a potential breeding tool in the late sixties and seventies only. During this period, worldwide interest, facilitated by support from the International Atomic Energy Agency (IAEA) enabled generation of knowledge and material of theoretical and practical value.

A wide array of physical and chemical mutagens has been evaluated on rice and based on their relative efficiency (mutation rate in relation to undesirable biological effects) and effectiveness (gene mutations/unit dose), X-rays, gamma rays, and fast neutrons among physical mutagens and Ethyl methane sulphonate (EMS), Nitroso methyl urea (NMU) and sodium azide among chemical mutagens have been found to be potent for inducing point mutations. Information generated on relative mutagen sensitivity of rice varietal groups, optimum dose range and post mutagen treatment handling greatly helped breeders to be more precise in the choice of mutagens and the method of mutagen treatment etc., for practical mutation breeding. In general, *japonicas* are more sensitive than *indica* and *javanica* types. Gamma rays are found to be relatively more efficient than fast neutrons, though the latter exhibits higher effectiveness as compared to gamma rays. With regard to chemical mutagens, EMS has proved more effective than radiation (Siddiq and Swaminatham, 1966). Sensitivity of genotypes to mutagens is greatly influenced by several factors, among which seed moisture content, hydrogen ion concentration, temperature and presoaking treatments are important. Based on extensive experimentation, the dose range recommended by the PAO/ IAEA for inducing mutations in rice by chemical mutagens has been summarised in Table 25.

**Table 25:** Dose ranges of chemical mutagens recommended

| ***Mutagen**** | ***Dosage (%)*** | |
|---|---|---|
| | ***indica*** | ***japonica*** |
| Ethyl methane sulfonate | 0.5-1.25 | 0.5-1.0 |
| Nitroso-methyl urea | 0.01-0.02 | 0.01 |
| Nitroso ethyl urea | 0.01-0.02 | 0.01 |
| Ethylene imine | 0.02-0.04 | 0.03 |

*Seeds presoaked in water for 20 hr. treated in the mutagen solution for 8 hr. at 28°C ± 2°C *Source*: Siddiq (1985)

During the last four decades a wide array of economically useful point mutations affecting plant height, leaf, panicle, grain type has been recovered. Some of them have been either released directly as mutant varieties or used as donor sources for improving specifie characters (Table 26). Among the notable mutants were early maturing Reimei of Japan, RD 15 of Thailand, dwarf statured fertilizer responsive Jagannath of India, Calrose 76 of the USA and blast resistant and glutinous RD 6 of Thailand (Micke *et al.,* 1987).

The mutagen treated seed is grown as $M_1$, generation adopting close spacing so as to minimize the effect of intrasomatic selection. Seed harvested either plantwise or paniclewise from $M_1$ is raised as $M_2$ generation as progeny rows and scored for mutation frequency and spectrum. It is important that screening environment of $M_2$ as well as $M_3$ be created *vis-a-vis* the breeding objective. For instance, if the objective is for resistance to a specifie biotic stress, the $M_2$, and $M_3$ should be screened against such a disease/insect pest. The variants selected are raised in the $M_3$ generation, and those breeding true are considered as mutants and studied further for their economic utility. The evaluation is always done in comparison to standard check varieties.

Although no significant progress could be made in respect of quantitatively inherited traits through induction of polygenic variability, intensive study has provided information of great basic value. For instance, it has been brought out that the mean of the induced variability

**Table 26:** Mutant varieties of economic importance

| *Name of the mutant variety* | *Year of release* | *Country of development* | *Treatment and parent var.* | *Mutational improvement* |
|---|---|---|---|---|
| ***Early maturity*** | | | | |
| SH 30-12 | 1957 | Republic of China | X-rays | High yield and short growing period |
| T-20-74 | 1957 | -do- | X-rays | -do- |
| RD-15 | 1978 | Thailand | 15 kr $\gamma$-rays | Ten days early maturing with better drought tolerance |
| Kashmir Basmati | 1977 | Pakistan | 25 kr $\gamma$-rays (Basmati 370) | Early maturing; suitable to be grown in Azad Kashmir at 600-1500 m altitude (30% higher yield than coarse vars. grown there) |
| PARC-2 | 1973 | Philippines | 40 kr $\gamma$-rays (IR 8) | Five-ten days early in matuity; slightly narrower grains with less chalkiness; Highly acceptable to consumers and growers |
| IRATOM 38 | 1971 | Bangladesh | $\gamma$-rays (IR 8) | Thirty days earlier than IR 8 |
| IRATON 24 | 1971 | -do- | -do- | Twenty days earlier than IR 8 |
| IIT 48 | 1972 | India | Ethylene oxide (0.3%/8 hr) | One week earlier than parent with fine grain and higher test grain weight. |
| IIT60 | 1972 | India | EMS (0.5%/8h at 20°C) | One month earlier than parent with same yield potential. Early maturing and high yielding; resistant to cold and blast |
| Nucleoryza | 1976 | Hungary | Fast neutrons (1000 rod) (Cesariot) | Early maturing and high yielding; resistant to cold and blast |
| ***Dwarf stature and non-lodging*** | | | | |
| Reimie | 1966 | Japan | $\gamma$-rays (Fujiminori) | Short culmed and lodging resistant under high fertilization; widely adapted and higher yielder than the parent |
| Jagannath | 1970 | India | X-rays (T-141) | Fertilizer-responsive and high yielding |
| Calrose 76 | 1976 | USA | $\gamma$-rays (Calrose) | Short statured and otherwise same as the parent variety |
| Irat 13 | 1978 | Ivory coast | $\gamma$-rays (63X-83) | Dwarf and non-lodging |
| Milyang 10 | 1970 | Korea | 25 kr $\gamma$-rays (Palkweng) | Short statured and non-lodging; moderately resistant to leaf blast |

**Table 26:** (*Contd...*)

**Table 26:** (*Contd...*)

| *Name of the mutant variety* | *Year of release* | *Country of development* | *Treatment and parent var.* | *Mutational improvement* |
|---|---|---|---|---|
| ***Grain quality*** | | | | |
| Shwe War Tua | 1975 | Burma | 25 kr γ-rays (IR 5) | Improved grain quality, high yields, slightly early |
| RD6 | 1977 | Italy | 20 kr γ-rays (Khao Dawk Mali 105) | Glutinous endosperm and improved blast resistance |
| Delta | 1970 | France | γ-rays (Cesariot) | Long grain with high yield potential |
| PARC-1 | 1970 | Philippines | 40 kr γ-rays (IR-8) | Narrower and longer grains with less chalky abdomen Resistance to biophysical stresses |
| Fulgente | 1973 | Italy | 25 kr X-rays (Maratelli) | Blast resistant with high productivity |
| ***High yield*** | | | | |
| BPI-121-407 | 1972 | Philippines | γ-rays (BPI-121) | High yield potential |
| *Hybrid mutant varieties* | | | | |
| YH-1 | 1963 | Republic of China | Selection from Z(N)1 × Sh-30-21 | High yield and short growing period |
| Hybrid mutant-25 | 1973 | India | 50 kr g-rays (Jhona 349 × Z(N) 1) | Early maturing dwarf with high yield and adaptability; high protein (12.3%) and high lysine (4.07%). |
| M7(C1967) | 1977 | USA | *Calrose 76 X* CS-M3 | Short statured, high yielding than parents |
| Kagahikhan | 1973 | Japan | *Mutant of Koshihikari* (γ-rays) X Fukei 72 | Early with improved grain quality and taste |
| Hayanikai | 1976 | Japan | Reimei X Toyonishki | Non-lodging |
| Matsukoname (Fukei No. 90) | 1973 | Japan | — | — |
| Fujihikai | 1977 | Japan | (Fukei 71 × Fukei 67) X Koshilikai X R 151 | Photoinsensitive and early maturing, (100 days), most suited to intensive crop rotation |
| Akihikari | 1976 | Japan | Toyonishiki x Reimie | Short and stiff culm with high yield potential |

for a quantitative trait would be moving in the direction opposite to its previous selection history.

## 10. CELLULAR AND MOLECULAR BREEDING

Advances in cell and molecular biology have opened up new application opportunities for accessing novel variation and for adopting more precise ways of selection of traits of interest. Genetic engineering and biotechnology tools hold great promise in expanding the scope of rice breeding for introgression of genes across the barriers of sexual incompatibility and expediting the process of variety development. Some of the path-breaking developments in rice biotechnology include production of sporophytic plants with gametic chromosome number from microspore culture, plant regeneration from protoplasts of *japonica* and *indica* rices, transgenic rice using *Agrobacterium*-mediated transformation, construction of comprehensive molecular maps of rice genome, mapping and tagging of genes of economic significance, particularly for resistance to major diseases and insect pests of rice using DNA markers and application of maker assisted selection and molecular characterization of biodiversity in pest, pathogen and rice germplasm.

Rice with a diploid chromosome complement of 24 and most compact genome size of 4.3 Mb is now the most favoured cereal both for genome analysis and genetic transformation studies, the developments and understanding of which are expected to usher in agro innovations in future rice improvement. A molecular insight into the rice genome (rice genomics) can help improve even other cereal crops like maize, sorghum, wheat and barley.

The new capabilities in rice breeding through application of biotechnology tools of relevance are: anther culture, wide hybridization, genetic engineering and DNA marker technology. Both genetic engineering and wide hybridization are expected to help in enlarging the gene pool by accessing variation beyond cultivated rice germplasm and anther culture and DNA markers in increasing the selection efficiency and compressing the breeding cycle.

### 10.1. Tissue Culture in Rice Improvement

Tissue culture is an all embracing term to denote *in vitro* culture of gametic cells, tissues, organs and isolated protoplasts. The promising tissue culture techniques that have relevance to rice breeding are (i) anther culture for speed and efficiency in breeding a variety, (ii) somatic cell culture for efficient screening of large cell populations for variants resistant to biotic and abiotic stresses and (iii) embryo culture to rescue hybrid embryos in interspecific and intergeneric crosses for transfer of useful traits from alien taxa. Another important area of application of tissue culture is the recovery of novel genetic variants by somaclonal variation in regenerated plants in tissue culture (Larkin and Scoweroft, 1981) and gametoclonal variation in anther/pollen derived plants (Evans, 1984). The area of relevance and application of tissue culture are summarized in Table 27.

**Table 27:** Areas of relevance and possible applications of tissue culture in rice

| ***Culture technique*** | | ***Areas of application*** |
|---|---|---|
| 1. Anther culture | (a) | *Varietal improvement*<br>— Shortening the breeding cycle.<br>— Increasing selection efficiency.<br>— Gametoclonal variation.<br>— Production of chromosomal variants.<br>— Genetic mutations. |
| | (b) | *Interspecific hybridization*:<br>Development of and substitution lines. |
| 2. Somatic cell and tissue culture | (a) | *In vitro* selection and somaclonal variation for tolerance to salt stress and aluminium toxicity, high lysine and protein, disease resistance. |
| | (b) | Micropropagation of cytosterile stocks. |
| 3. Embryo culture | | — Interspecific and intergeneric hybridization. |
| 4. Protoplast culture | | — Genetic transformation.<br>— Somatic hybridization for production of hybrids. |

## 10.2. Anther Culture

Production of doubled haploids (DH) through anther culture is a rapid approach to attain homozygosity that can shorten the time required to develop a cultivar. Anther culture as a tool in rice breeding has several other advantages besides providing the quickest method of fixation of homozygous lines. It increases selection efficiency and facilitates early expression of recessive gènes. Application of anther culture in rice improvement has contributed to more than 100 new rice cultivars in China (Meifang, 1992) and over 42 cultivars in Korea. Exploitation of gametoclonal variation induced in anther culture has resulted in the development of a cultivar, Dama in Hungary (Hezsky *et al.,* 1991).

The doubled haploids from $F_1$ anther culture increase the selection efficiency. This is probably the most important advantage of anther culture. It discriminates genotypes better due to absence of dominance effects. As compared to $F_2$ population, fewer DH plants are sufficient to select for desired recombinants. Anther culture has potential application in wide crosses as well to develop substitution and addition lines (Chu, 1982).

Over the years, the technique of anther culture has been considerably improved particularly for *japonica* rice. Efforts to improve anther cultivability of *indica* rices have not as yet met with desired success due to strong genotype influence and media interaction.

Use of anther culture in rice breeding is limited by low response of most of the *indica* rices. Nevertheless, concerted research efforts have resulted in hundreds of doubled haploid lines from *indica* × *indica* and *indica* × *japonica* hybrids, which were field evaluated for desirable traits like earliness, semi-dwarf stature and good grain quality. Some anther-derived lines from *Basmati* hybrids developed at IARI combining desired grain quality, high yield and non-lodging plant type did perform well in yield trials. Anther culture as a means of realizing the vigour manifested in $F_1$ hybrids in the subsquent segregating generations through diploidization of favourable gametic combinations has been demonstrated. Shortening the time taken to breed a variety by rapid attainment of homozygosity, and breeding photoperiod sensitive long duration rices, and temperate rices, where a single generation a year is only possible are other advantages of the anther culture technique. Further, production of doubled haploids is a rapid way of developing mapping populations for construction of genetic linkage maps for traits of interest.

## 10.3. Tissue Culture and Somaclonal Variation

Variation induced in *in vitro* culture provides another option for rice improvement. The basic advantage of somatic cell culture is the ability to screen myriads of cells, in effect plants, to increase the probability of identifying rare variants. The effectiveness of cell selection and exploitation of genetic modifications induced in cell cultures (somaclonal variation) largely depend on the ability to regenerate plants from selected cell variants and the stability of expression of the trait at cellular as well as plant levels.

Salt tolerant rice plants have been obtained through *in vitro* selection from tissue cultures (Zapata and Abrigo, 1986). Lines with increased lysine and protein content as well as and tolerance to aluminium toxicity have been identified through *in vitro* selection (Chaleff and Carlson, 1975; Abrigo *et al.,* 1985). Phytotoxin resistant cell lines have been obtained for bacterial leaf blight, brown spot and sheath blight diseases (Ling *et al.,* 1986).

## 10.4. Wide Hybridization

In addition to the two cultivated species of rice, *O. sativa* and *O. glaberrima,* there are 21 wild species in the genus *Oryza.* The diploid or tetraploid wild species belong to six different genomes as detailed elsewhere. While wild species belonging to AA genome can be easily crossed with cultivated species, embryo rescue needs to be used for obtaining hybrids between cultivated and distantly related species of other genomes. A number of useful genes have been introgressed into cultivated rice from the wild germplasm. Transfer of resistance to grassy stunt virus from *O. nivara* (Khush, 1977), brown planthopper from O. *officinalis* (Khush and Jena, 1990) and bacterial leaf blight from O. *longistaminata* are some of the important examples of wide hybridization in rice improvement.

Diversification of sources of cytoplasmic male sterility is another important objective of wide hybridization. New cytosterile stocks alternative to the widely used WA have been developed using male sterility inducing cytoplasm from *O. rufipogon* and *O. nivara* through substitution backcrossing (Dalmacio *et al.,* 1995; Hoan *et al.,* 1997).

## 10.5. Development of Monosomic Alien Addition Lines

In wide hybridization, $F_1$ hybrids between species belonging to different genomes of the genus are completely sterile and are good source for production of monosomic addition lines (MAALS). Progenies advanced through embryo rescue technique and backcrossing to recurrent parent have led to recovery of plants with normal chromosome complement plus addition of one chromosome of 5 wild species at IRRI. These are with 12 chromosomes of *O. officinalis,* 11 of *O. latifolia,* 8 of *O. australiensis,* 6 of *O. minuta* and 7 of *O. brachyantha*. MAALS are useful in RFLP mapping to detect introgression of useful genes from wild species and are additional sources of genetic variation.

## 10.6. Genetic Transformation

Advances in recombinant DNA technology have provided new means for mobilizing genes within and across plant and animal kingdom. It is now possible to identify, isolate and transfer genes into rice plant, 110 matter what the source is. Transformation of rice is being done through various techniques, which include protoplast mediated DNA uptake, microprojectile electroporation and *Agrobacterium* mediated transfer. The process of genetic transformation accomplishes the same objectives as plant breeding *i.e.*, transfer of one or a few genes from one organism to the other. Genetic engineering techniques are more precise and not limited by sexual compatibility between donor and recipient variety.

First transgenic cereal to be developed was rice using protoplast-based transformation system (Toriyama *et al.,* 1988). Biolistic techniques are increasingly used for rice transformation as they circumvent genotype specificity (Christou *et al.,* 1991). Using biolistics, co-transformation of a number of genes is possible and opens the possibility of transforming rice with genes for a whole biosynthetic pathway. A major breakthrough in rice genetic engineering, however, has been the demonstration of successful *Agrobacterium* mediated transformation in rice (Hei *et al.,* 1994). The key to rice transformation is critical tissue culture parameters for regeneration.

With the feasibility of genetic engineering using *Agrobacterium,* biolistic particle gun and protoplasts, efforts are on to introduce traits previously unavailable to rice breeders. Primary targets are in the area of improving pest and disease resistance and herbicide tolerance. Transgenic rices carrying insecticidal protein gene from *Bacillus thuringiensis,* chitinase gene from bacterial and other sources and bacterial leaf blight resistance gene, Xa 21 from *O. longistaminata* have been developed. Engineered rice with better nutritional quality (vitamin A and iron), submergence tolerance and male sterility are expected to be available for breeders soon.

Many applications of genetic engineering will involve expression of the introduced gene tissue specific or stage specific. Refinements in genetic engineering to meet these requirements demand research on regulation of gene expression through use of appropriate promoters. List of useful genes transferred and the progress to date in rice improvement research using gene transfer techniques are detailed in Tables 28 and 29.

### 10.7. DNA Marker Technology

Differences in the genomic DNA between potential parents in a genetic cross can be detected by studying variations in the nucleotide sequence polymorphisms. There are several molecular tools such as restriction fragment length polymorphism (RFLP), simple sequence repeats (SSR) and amplified fragment length polymorphism (AFLP) markers for detecting such variations. Polymorphism can be used in genetic analysis because at a given allelic locus they show mendelian inheritance. This characteristic makes it possible to estimate the genetic distance between each polymorphism and construct genetic maps based on DNA markers.

Progress has been made in tagging and mapping many agriculturally important genes with molecular markers, which form the basis for

**Table 28:** List of useful genes transferred into rice

| *Sl. no.* | *Useful trait* | *Target pest* | *Novel gene* | *Rice sub-species transformed* | *Reference(s)* |
|---|---|---|---|---|---|
| 1 | ***Insect pest resistance*** | | | | |
| | *Bt*-δ-endotoxin | Stem borer | *Cry1A (b)* | *indica, japonica aromatic iranian* | Fujimoto *et al.* (1993), Datta *et al.* (1998), Alam *et al.* (1998), Ghareyazie *et al.* (1997) |
| | *Bt*-δ-endotoin | Stem borer | *Cry 1A(b) and Cry 1A(c)* | *japonica* | *Cheng et al.* (1998) |
| | *Bt*-δ-endotoin | Stem borer | *Cry 1A(c)* | *indica* | Nayak *et al.* (1997) |
| | *Bt*-δ-endotoin | Stem borer | *Cry 2A* | *indica, basmati* | Maqbool *et al.* (1998) |
| | Potato protease inhibitor II | Leaf folder | *Pin II* | *japonica* | Duan *et al.* (1996) |
| | Cowpea trypsin inhibitor | Leaf folder | *CP Ti* | *japonica* | Xu *et al.* (1996) |
| | Corn cystatin | | *CC* | *japonica* | Irie *et al.* (1996) |
| | Oryza cystatin | | *Oc* | *japonica* | Hosoyama (1995) |
| | Snowdrop lectin | BPH | *GNA* | *japonica* | Rao *et al.* (1998) |
| | Cysteine proteinase | Nematode | *OC-IΔD86* | african *indica* | *Vainetal.* (1998) |
| 2 | ***Disease resistance :*** | | | | |
| | Xa 21 | BLB | *Xa 21* | *japonica* | Wang *et al.* (1996) |
| | Xa 21 | BLB | *Xa 21* | *indica* | Tu *et al.* (1995) |
| | Chitinase gene | Blast | *Chi 11* | *indica* | Lin *et al.* (1995) |
| | Grapevine stilbene | | | *japonica* | Stark *et al.* (1997) |
| | Synthase gene | Capsid Brome mosaic virus diseases | *RNA-2, 3 genes from BMV* | *japonica* | Huntley *et al.* (1996) |

**Table 28:** *Contd...*

**Table 28:** *Contd...*

| *Sl. no.* | *Useful trait* | *Target pest* | *Novel gene* | *Rice sub-species transformed* | *Reference(s)* |
|---|---|---|---|---|---|
| | Coat protein gene | Rice dwarf virus | Outer coat protein *(S8)* gene of RDV | *japonica* | Zheng *et al.* (1997) |
| | Coat protein gene | Rice tungro spherical virus | RTSV coat protein genes | *indica*<br>*japonica* | Sivamani *et al.* (1999) |
| | RNA polymerase gene | Rice yellow mottle virus | RNA-dep. RNA polymerase of RYMV | African *indica* | Pinto *et al.* (1999) |
| 3 | ***Abiotic stress resistance*** | | | | |
| | LEA protein gene etc. | Salt and drought | *PSCS* | *japonica* | *Zhu et al.* (1997) |
| | | | *HVA 1 (LEA* 3) | *japonica*<br>*basmati* | Xu *et al.* (1996)<br>Jain *et al.* (1996) |
| | | | *CodA* | *japonica* | Sakamoto *et al.* (1998) |
| | | | *Ade* | *japonica* | Capell *et al.* (1998) |
| | | | *GPAT* | *japonica* | Yokoi *et al.* (1998) |
| 4 | ***Nutritional quality*** | | | | |
| | | Vit, A - (β carotene | Crt 1 | *japonica* | Burkhardt *et al.* (1997) |

Ade, arginine decarboxylase, Coda, Choline Oxidase gene from a soil bacterium *Anthrobacter globiformis;* HVA1, Barley late embroyogenesis-abundant (LEA-3) protein gene; OC IΔD86, an engineered cysteine proteinase inhibitor *(Oryza cystatin* -IΔD 86) gene; PSCS, Δ′-Pyrroline-5-carboxylase synthetase; RTSV, rice tungro spherical virus; RYMV, rice yellow mottle virus.

**Table 29:** Progress in rice genetic transformation

| *Sl. no.* | *Trait* | *Candi-date gene cloned* | *Chimeric gene const-ructed* | *Rice trans-formed* | *Green house trials* | *Field trials* | *Breeding line with novel genes* |
|---|---|---|---|---|---|---|---|
| 1. | Herbicide resistance *(bar)* | X | X | X | X | X | X |
| 2. | Sheath blight resistance (*Chitinase, gluconase*) | X | X | X | X | X | |
| 3 | Bacterial blight resistance (Xa21) | X | X | X | X | X | X |
| 4 | Yellow stemborer resistance (*Cry IA(b); Cnj IA (c)*) | X | X | X | X | X | |
| 5. | Tungro (RTSV) resistance (*cp*) | X | X | X | X | X | |
| 6. | Tungro (RTBV) resistance *(cp)* (*arf4, rt*) | X | X | X | X | | |
| 7. | Ragged stunt virus resistance (*seg. 10*) | X | X | X | X | X | |

marker assisted selection (MAS). DNA markers have enhanced the scope of improving the efficiency of conventional plant breeding through indirect selection for the trait of interest linked to the marker. Among the various molecular markers developed, RFLPs are the most reliable as they are numerous and codominant and distributed all over the genome complement. With the aid of RFLPs each gene (trait) can be linked to one or more markers and by following the segregating pattern of the trait and markers in crosses, it is possible to tag the gene(s). Tagging facilitates indirect but precise selection for the gene of interest.

Using RFLP markers genetic maps have been constructed and rice is the most extensively analyzed crop species by RFLPs. A rice genome map based on RFLPs has been developed at the Cornell University, USA in collaboration with IRRI (Causse *et al.,* 1994). In parallel, a rice genetic map using ca 2300 DNA markers including 1500 cDNA markers has been developed by the Rice Genome Research Programme (RGP) in

Japan (Kurata *et al.*, 1994). The availability of comprehensive molecular genetic maps in rice has facilitated tagging of many genes of economic importance with DNA markers.

DNA markers have several potential applications in rice improvement. These include germplasm characterization, assessment of genetic diversity, tracking the gene through segregating generation and marker assisted selection. Pyramiding of genes, conferring the same phenotype, is important as the gene transfer by MAS is precise and faster, especially when the trait is difficult to select on the basis of phenotype. Similarly when a number of genes governing the expression of same phenotype like resistance to a disease or an insect pest, pyramiding of such genes in the variety is facilitated easily by use of markers. MAS has been successfully deployed in rice for pyramiding of blast and BLB resistance genes as elaborated elsewhere.

Availability of high density molecular map of rice has facilitated studies on genome oganization, gene mapping, marker-aided selection, and map-based cloning. Rice has become a model for genome research among the cereals and monocots because of its small genome size, synteny with other cereals and well established classical linkage and molecular genetic maps.

## 11. CONCLUSIONS

Rice production growth has so far kept pace with the increasing demand. This encouraging trend and rice availability at stable and affordable price for all the sections of the society should not give the wrong signal that the world's rice production problems have been solved. Given the fact that rice consuming population will increase by additional 80-100 million every year, that the growth of total rice area is slowing down and that many of the favourable growth factors of the 70s and 80s have started shrinking, meeting the rice needs of the coming decades is going to be the most challenging task. It is estimated that the world's unmilled rice production has to increase by about 65% by 2030 to keep pace with the population growth and income induced demand for food. It would require productivity level to reach about 8.0 t/ha in the irrigated areas and about 4.0 t/ha in the rainfed areas. If the statistics is to be believed that over 77% of the production increase made during 1965-67 — 1992-94 has come from higher yield and increased cropping intensity, the key to achieving the projected production goal in order to remain food-nutrition secure, lies in continuously raising the genetic yield level with desired level of stability and value addition.

## 12. ACKNOWLEDGEMENTS

The authors wish to thank Dr. N.P. Sharma, Head, Biotechnology and Dr. M.S. Ramesha, Scientist, Hybrid Rice, Directorate of Rice Research, Hyderabad, for their kind help in preparing this chapter.

## REFERENCES

Abrigo W.M., Novero, A.U., Coronel, V.P., Cabuslay, G.S., Blanco, L.C. and Parao, ET. (1985). Somatic cell culture at IRRI in Biotechnology in International Agricultural Research, *Philippines Manila Int. Rice Res. Instt.,* (1985): 149–158.

Asaga, K and Higashi, T. (1973). A testing method for incorporating field resistance to blast with resistance derived from foreign rice varieties (In Japanese). *Jpn. J. Breed.* 23: 152–154.

Causse, M.A., Fulton, T.M., Cho, G.Y., Ahn, S.N., Chunwonges, J., Wu, K., Xiao, J., Yu, Z., Ronald, P.C., Harrington, S.E., Second, G., McCouch, S.R. and Tanksley, S.D. (1994). Saturated molecular map of the rice genome based on an inter-specific back cross population. *Genetics*, 135: 1251–1274.

Causse, M.A., Fulton, T.M., Cho, Y.G., Ahn, S.N., Chunwongse, J., Wu, K., Xiao, J., Yu, Z., Ronald, P.C., Harrington, S.E., Second, G., Mc Couch, S.R. and Tankslay, S.D. (1994). Saturated molecular map of the rice genome on an inter-specific backcross population. *Genetics,* 138: 1251–1274.

Chaleff, R.S. and Carlson, T. *In vitro* selection of mutants of higher plants. *In:* Genetic manipulations with plant material. Ledoux, L. (*Ed.,*). Plenum press. New York. pp. 351–363.

Chang, T.T. (1964). Present knowledge of rice genetics and cytogenetics. International Rice Research Institute, Philippines. p. 95.

Chang, T.T. (1976). The origin, evolution, cultivation, dissemination and diversification of Asian and African rices. *Euphytica,* 25: 435–441

Christen, P, Ford, T.L. and Kofron, M. (1991). Production of transgenic rice (*Oryza sativa* L.) Plants from agronomically important *indica* and *japonica* varieties *via* electric discharge particle acceleration of exogenous DNA in to immature zygotic embryos. *BioTechnology,* 9: 957–962.

Chu, C.C. (1982). Anther culture of rice and its significance in distant hybridization, pp. 47-53. *In*: Polland, L.R. (*Ed.*) Rice tissue culture Conference. IRRI, Los Banos, Philippines.

Dalmacio, R., Brar D.S., Ishii, T, Sitch, L.A., Virmani, S.S. and Khush, G.S. (1995). Identification and transfer of a new cytoplamic male sterility source from *Oryza percniiia* in to *indica* rice (O. *sativa*). *Euphytica,* 82: 221–225.

Das, S.R., Mukherjee, B.K. and Siddiq, E.A. (1990). Synthesis and evaluation of morphologically homogeneous populations for high yield in rice. In Extended summary, Proc. Int. Symp. on Rice Research: New Frontiers, DRR, Hyderabad. p. 99

Evans D.A., Sharp, W.R. and Medina Filho, H.P. (1984). Somaclonal and gametoclonal. *Variation Amer. J. Bot.,* 71(6): 759–774.

Ezuka A, Vunoki, X, Sakurai, Y., Shinoda, H. and Toriyama, K. (1969a). Studies on varietal resistance to rice blast 1. Tests for genotype of "true resistance" (In Japanese, English Summary) Bull. *Chugoku Agric. Exp. Stn. Ser. E.,* 4: 1–31.

Ezuka A, Yunoki, T., Sakurai, Y., Shinoda, H and Toriyama, K. (1969b). Studies on the varietal resistance to rice blast. 2. Tests for field resistance in paddy fields and upland nursery beds (In Japanese, English Summary) Bull. *Chugoku Agric. Exp. Stn. Ser. E.,* 4: 33–53.

Fujimaki, H. (1978). New techniques in backcross breeding for rice improvement. Proc. Symposium on methods of crop breeding. Oct. 1977, Tokyo pp. 56–67.

Fujimaki, H., Hiraiwa, S., Kushibuchi, K. and Tanaka, S. (1977). Artificially induced male sterile mutants and their usage in rice breeding. *Jpn. J. Breed.,* 27: 70–77.

Hei, Y., Ohta, S., Komari, T. and Kumashiro, T. (1994). Efficient transformation of rice (*Oryza sativa* L) mediated by Agrobacterium and sequence analysis of the boundaries of T-DNA. *Plant J.,* 6: 271–282.

Henderson, M.T., Yeh, B.P. and Exner, B. (1959). Further evidence of structural differentiation in the chromosomes as a cause of sterility in intervarietal hybrids of rice, *Oryza sativa* L. *Cytologia,* 24: B415–422.

Hezsky, L.E., Li, S.N., Kiss, E., Simon-Kiss, I., Lokos, K and Binh, D.Q. (1991). *In: In vitro* studies on rice in Agriculture and Forestry. Vol. 14. Rice, Bajaj, Y.P.S. (*Ed.*), Springer-Verlag, Berlin, Heidelberg, New York. pp. 619–641.

Hille Ris Lambers, D., Gomosta, A.R. and Kupleanchankul, T. (1986). Screening for submergence tolerance. In Progress in rainfed and lowland rice. International Rice Research Institute P.O. Box 933, Manila, Philippines. pp. 177–200

Hoan, N.T., Sarma, N.P. and Siddiq, E.A. (1997). Identification and characterization of new sources of cytoplasmic male sterility in rice. *Plant Breeding,* 116: 547–551.

Hsu, K.J. (1945). On sterility resulting from crossing different types of rice. *Indian J. Genet. Plant Breed.,* 5: 51–57.

Ikehashi, H and Fujimaki, H. (1980). Modified bulk population method for rice breeding. Innovative Approaches to Rice Breeding, IRRI, Manila, Philippines. pp. 163–182.

Ikehashi, H. and Araki (1986). Genetics of F1 sterility in remote crosses of rice. In Rice Genetics. International Rice Research Institute, Manila, Philippines. pp. 119–130.

Ikehashi, H. and Lambers, H.R. (1979). An integrated international collaborative programme in the use of rapid generation advance in rice. *In.* Proc. of the 1978 International deep water rice Workshop, IRRI, Los Banos, Laguna, Philippines.

International Rice Research Institute (1987). Annual Report for 1986, IRRI, Manila, Philippines.

Jena, K.K. and Khush, G.S. (1990). Introgression of genes from *Oryza officinalis* Well ex Watt to cultivated rice, *O. sativa* L. *Theor. Appl. Genet.,* 80: 737–745.

Jensen, N.F. (1978). Composite breeding methods and the DSM System in cereals. *Crop Sci.,* 18: 622–626.

Johannsen, W. (1903). Uber Erblichkeit in population and in reinen Linien. G. Fischer, Jena, p. 68.

Jones, J.W. (1926). Hybrid vigor in rice. *J. Am. Soc. Agron.,* 18: 424–428.

Juliano, B.O. (1985). (*Ed.*) Rice Chemistry and Technology. Revised edition St. Paul, M.N. American Association of Cereal Chemistry.

Katsuo, K. and Mizushima, U. (1958). Studies on the cytoplasmic difference among rice varieties, *Oryza sativa* L I. On the fertility of hybrids obtained reciprocally between cultivated and wild varieties. *Jpn. J. Breed,* 8: 1–5 (In Japanese).

Khush, G.S. (1977). Disease and insect resistance in rice. *Advances in Agronomy,* 29: 265–341.

Khush, G.S. (1984). Breeding rice for resistance to insects. *Protection Ecology,* 7: 147–165.

Kiyosawa, S., Kushibuchi, K and Watanabe, S. (1975). Recent trends and problems in breeding for blast resistant varieties and its investigation. (In Japanese) Nogyo Oyobi Engei). *Agric. Hortic.,* 50: 25–30, 258–262, 377–380, 629–635.

Kurata, N., Nagamura, Y., Yamamoto, K., Karushima, Y., Sue, N., Wu, J., Antonio, B.A., Shomura, A., Shimizu, T, Lin, S.Y., Inoue, T, Fukuda, A., Shimano, T, Kuboki, Y, Toyoma, T, Miyamoto, Y, Kirihara, T, Hayasaka, K., Miyao, A., Monna, L., Zhong, H.S., Tamura, Y, Wang, Z.X., Momma, T., Umchara, Y, Yano, M., Sasaki, T. and

Minobe, Y. (1994). A 300 Kilobase interval genetic map of rice including 883 expressed sequences. *Nature Genetics,* 8: 365–372.

Larkin, P.J. and Scoweroft, W.R. (1981). Somaclonal Variation — a novel source of variability from cell culture for plant improvement. *Theor. App. Genet.,* 60: 197–214.

Li, Z.K., Pinson, S.R.M., Stansel, J.W. and Park, W.D. (1995). Identification of two major genes and quantitative trait lob (QTLs) for heading date and plant height in cultivated rice *(Oryza sativum L.). Theo. Appl. Gen.,* 91: 374–381.

Lin, H., Qia, H., Zhuang, J., Lu, J., Min, S., Xiong, Z., Huang, N. and Zhang, K. (1996). RFLP mapping of QTLs for yield and related characters in rice (*Oryza sativa* L.). *Theor. Appl. Gen.,* 92: 920–927.

Ling, D., Vidya Sekharan, F., Borromeo, E.S., Zapata, F.J., and Donghua, M. (1986). *In vitro* screening of rice germplasm for resistance of brown spot disease using phytotoxin. *Acta. Genet. Sin.,* 13: 194–200.

Lu Xinggui, Virmani, S.S. and Yang, R.C. 1998. Advances in two-line hybrid rice breeding. (Virmani, S.S., *Ed*). *In*: Advances in Hybrid Rice Breeding IRRI, Philippines. pp. 89–98.

Lu, C., Shen, L., Tan, Z., Yu, Y., Aei, P., Chen, Y. and Zhu, L. (1996). Comparative mapping of QTLs for agronomic traits of rice across environments using a double haploid population. *Theor. Appl. Gen.,* 93: 1211–1217.

Maruyama, K., Kato, H. and Araki, H. 1991. Thermosensitive genetic male sterility induced by irradiation. *In*: Rice Genetics II, IRRI, Manila, Philippines. pp. 227–232.

Maurya, D.M. and O'toole, J.C. 1986. Screening upland rice for drought tolerance. *In*: Progress in upland rice research, IRRI, Manila, Philippines. pp. 245–261.

Meifang L.I (1992). Anther culture breeding of rice at CAAS. *In:* Zheng, K. and Murashige, T. Antherculture for Rice Breeders. Hang zhou, China. pp. 75–85

Micke, A., Donini, B. and Malyzynski, M. (1987). Induced mutations for crop improvement – A review. *Tropical Agriculture (Trinidad),* 64: 259–278.

Mohanty, H.K., Suprihatno, B., Khush, G.S., Coffman, W.R. and Vergara, B.S. (1982). Inheritance of submergence in deep water rice.. *In*: Proc. of 1981 International Deepwater Rice Workshop, Bangkok, Thailand, IRRI, Manila, Philippines. pp. 121–131

Morinaga T. and Fukushima, E. (1956). Cytogenetical studies on *Oryza sativa L.* VIII. Backcross progenies of the interspecific hybrids of Oryza. *Cytologia,* 21: 165–178.

Nayar, N.M. (1973). Origin and cytogenetics of rice. *Adv. Geenet.,* 17: 153–292.

Nezeki, H. (1967). On some problems in rice breeding for blast resistance with special reference to Variation of blast fungus (In Japanese). *Recent Adv. Breed.,* 8: 71–78.

Oka, H.I. (1953). Phylogenetic differentiation of the cultivated rice plant VI. The mechanism of sterility in the intervarietal hybrid of rice. *Jpn. J. Breeding,* 2: 217–224.

Oka, H.I. (1974). Analysis of genes controlling F, sterility in rice by the use of isogenic lines. *Genetics,* 77: 521–534.

Porteres, R. 1956. Taxonomic agrobotanique der riz cultives *O. sativa* Linne. *O. glaberrima* Steudel. *J. Agr. Trop. Bot. App.,* 3: 341–384.

Qifa, Zhang and Sibin, Yu. (2000). Molecular marker-based gene tagging and its impact on rice improvement *In*: "Rice Breeding and Genetics (*Ed.* Nanda, J.S.) pp. 241–268, Oxford & 1BH Publishing Co. Pvt. Ltd., New Delhi, India.

Rao, M.J.B.K. and Nagaraju, M. (1974). International rice. *Comm. Newslet.,* 23: 41.

Sah'aadevan, P.C. and Namboodiri, K.M.N. 1963. Natural crossing in rice. *Proc. Indian Acad. Sci. Sect.,* B58: 176–185.

Sampath, S. (1962). The genus *Oryza:* Its taxonomy and inter-relationships. *Oryza,* 1: 1–29.

Sampath, S. and Mohanty, H.K. (1954). Cytology of semi-sterile rice hybrid. *Curr. Sci.,* 23: 182–183.

Sampath, S. and Rao, M.B.V.N. (1951). Inter-relationships between species in the genus *Oryza. Indian J. Genet. Plant Breeding*, 11: 14–17.

Shi, M.S. (1981). Preliminary report of later *japonica* natural 2-lines and applications. *Hubei. Agric Sci.*, p. 7.

Shinijyo, C. and Omura, T. (1966). Cytoplasmic male sterility and fertility restoration in rice, *Oryza sativa L.* Sci. Bull. *College Agric. Univ. Ryukyus*, 22: 1–57

Shinoda, H., Toriyama, K., Sekiguchi, Y. and Yunoki, T. (1971). Linkage group of newly found blast resistant gene Pi-2 (In Japanese) Chugoku. *Agric. Res.*, 43: 1–2.

Siddiq, E.A. and Swaminathan, M.S. (1966). Induced mutations in relation to the breeding and phylogenetic differentiation of *Oryza sativa. In*: Mutations in Rice Breeding. *Int. Atomic Energy Agency Tech. Rep.*, 86: 25–52.

Siddiq, E.A. and Swaminathan, M.S. (1968). Mutational analysis of racial differentiation in *Oryza sativa* L. *Curr. Sci.*, 37: 451–452.

Siddiq, E.A. Garg, A.K. and Jauhar Ali. (1999). Breeding for salt tolerance in rice. Paper presented in the "Indo-U.K. Soil Salinity Project" Workshop held at Karnal.

Siddiq, E.A., and Jauhar Ali. (2000). Innovative male sterility System for exploitation of hybrid vigour in crop plants. 1-Environment sensitive genic male sterility system. *Proceedings of Indian National Science Academy B*, 65(5): 320–339.

Snape, J.W., Sitch, A., Simpson, E. and Parker, B.B. (1988). Tests for presence of gemetoclonal Variation in barley and wheat doubled haploids produced using the *Hordeitm bulbosum* system. *Theor. Appl. Genet.*, 75: 509–513.

Sridhar, R., Reddy, J.N., Singh, U.D. and Agrawal, P.K. 1999a. Usefulness of combinations of bacterial blight resistance genes at Cuttack. *IRRN*, 24(2): 24–25.

Sridhar, R., Singh U.D., Agrawal, P.K., Reddy, J.N., Chandrawanshi, S.S., Sanger, R.B.S., Bhatt, J.C., Ratnaiah, Y. and Row, K.V.S.R.K. 1999b. Usefulness of blast resistance genes and their combinations in different blast endemic locations in India. *IRRN*, 24(2): 22–24.

Swaminathan, M.S. (1984). Rice in 2000 A.D. Indian National Science Academy, New Delhi. p. 22.

Tan, Z.C., Li, Y.Y., Chen, L.B. and Zhou, G.Q. (1990). Studies on ecological adaptability of dual purposc line Annong S-l. *Hybrid Rice*, 3: 35–38.

Tanksley, S.D. and McCouch, S.R. (1997). Seed banks and molecular maps: Unlocking genetic potential from the wild. *Science*, p. 277.

Toriyama, K., Arimoto, Y., Uchimiya, Y. and Hinata, K. (1988). Transgenic rice plants after direct gene transfer in to protoplasts. *Bio / Technology*, 6: 1072–1074.

Virmani, S.S. and Edwards, I.B. 1983. Current Status and future prospects for breeding hybridnee and wheat. *Adv. Agron.*, 36: 145–214.

Virmani, S.S., Viraktamath, B.C., Casal, C.L., Toledo, R.S., Lopez, M.T. and Manalo, J.O. (1997). Hybrid rice breeding manual. International Rice Research Institute, Manila, Philippines, p. 151.

Wu, P., Zhang, G. and Huang, N. (1996). Identification of QTLs controlling quantitative characters in nee using RFLP markers. *Eupbytica*, 89: 349–354.

Xiao, J., Grandillo, S., Ahn, S.N., McCouch, S.R., Tankskey, S.O., Li J. and Yuan, L. (1996). Genes from wild rice improved yield. *Nature*, 384: 223–224.

Xiong, L., Wang, S., Liu, K., Dai, X., Saghai Maroof, M.A., Hu, J. and Zhang, Q. (1998). Distribution of microsatellite and AFLP markers on molecular linkage map in rice. *Acta Botanica Sinica*, 40: 605–614.

Xudong, Ye., Salin Al-Babill, Andreas Kloti, Jing Zhang, PaolaLucca, Peter Beyer, Ingo Potrykus (2000). Engineering the provitasnia A (?-Carotene) Biosynthetic pathway into (Carotenoid-Free) Rice Endosperm. *In Science* 287: 303–305.

Yu, Z., Mackill, D.J., Bonman, J.M., McCouch, S.R.. Guklerdoni, E., Notteghem, J.L. and Tanksley, S.D. (1996). Molecular mapping of genes Hor resistance to nee blast (*Pyncularia grisea* Sa cc). *Theor. Appl. Gen.*, 93: 859–863.

Yuan, L.P. (1977). The execution and theory of developing hybrid rice. *Chinese Agricultural Science*, lB: 27–31 (In Chinese).

Yunoki, T, Ezuka, A, Sakurai, Y, Shinoda, H. and Toriyama, K. (1970). Studies on the varietal resistance to rice blast. 3. Testing method for field resistance on young seedlings grown in green house (In Japanese, English Summary) Bull. *Chugoku Agric. Exp. Stn. E.*, 6: 1–19.

Zapata, F.J. and Abrigo E.M. (1986). Plant regeneration and screening for long term NaCl-stressed rice callus. *Intl. Rice Res. News lett.*, 11 : 24–25.

# 2

# Wheat

## 1. INTRODUCTION

Wheat is the second most important food crop in India, after rice, both in terms of area and production. The record production in the country during the last few years has enabled India to attain the position of being the second largest producer of wheat in the world. With an area of around 11 per cent under wheat in the world, India contributes 12 per cent to the world wheat basket. China is the largest producer of wheat with 13 per cent of the area and 19 per cent of the total world produce (Table 1).

**Table 1:** Major wheat producing countries of the world

| *Country* | *Area ('000 ha)* | | | *Production ('000 m.t).* | | | *Productivity (kg/ha)* | | |
|---|---|---|---|---|---|---|---|---|---|
| | *1995* | *1996* | *1997* | *1995* | *1996* | *1997* | *1995* | *1996* | *1997* |
| China | 28861 | 29611 | 30000 | 102211 | 110569 | 122600 | 3541 | 3734 | 4087 |
| India | 25700 | 25122 | 26000 | 65767 | 62620 | 69000 | 2559 | 2493 | 2654 |
| U.S.A. | 24664 | 25466 | 25729 | 59400 | 62192 | 68761 | 2408 | 2442 | 2673 |
| Russia | 23909 | 25707 | 25000 | 30118 | 34900 | 44180 | 1260 | 1358 | 1767 |
| France | 4742 | 5040 | 5116 | 30879 | 35949 | 33928 | 6512 | 7132 | 6632 |
| Canada | 11133 | 12626 | 11407 | 25017 | 29802 | 24270 | 2247 | 2360 | 2128 |
| Germany | 2579 | 2594 | 2728 | 17763 | 18922 | 19867 | 6888 | 7293 | 7283 |
| Turkey | 9400 | 9350 | 9500 | 18015 | 18515 | 18650 | 1916 | 1980 | 1963 |
| Australia | 9211 | 11337 | 10839 | 16504 | 23702 | 18554 | 1790 | 2091 | 1712 |
| Ukraine | 5479 | 5892 | 5540 | 16273 | 13547 | 17377 | 2970 | 2299 | 3137 |
| World | 219718 | 231175 | 226945 | 543614 | 586036 | 609566 | 2474 | 2535 | 2686 |

*Source*: FAO Year Book, 1999

The success story of wheat in India during the last 30-35 years is unparalleled in the history of any other country. Up to 1965-66, breeding

V.L. Chopra (Ed.): Breeding Field Crops I: Practices, Studium Press (LLC), USA.

efforts did not result in a substantial yield improvement due to lack of suitable genotypes which can respond to fertilizer and irrigation. At that time, India was depending on large scale imports to feed the growing population, a situation described as "ship to mouth". Then came the era of semi-dwarf wheats which became an instant success and contributed to the "wheat revolution". The new genotypes triggered off complementary package of technologies, services and public policies which gave birth to what was termed as "green revolution" by William Gaud of U.S.A. in 1968. India never looked back from this stage. The wheat production in India which was just 6.4 m. tons in 1950 has progressively increased to 68.7 m.t. in 1997. There was a slight reduction in production during 1998, but the 1998-99 season was another year of record production of wheat which crossed 70 m.t. During the corresponding period the area under wheat increased from 10 m. ha. to 25.4 m. ha. Although part of the production increase can be accounted for by increase in area, there was also an increase in productivity from 6.5 q/ha to 25.7 q/ha (Table 2; Fig. 1).

**Table 2:** Area, production and productivity of wheat in India

| *Year* | *Area (m.ha)* | *Production (m.t)* | *Productivity (q/ha)* | *Year* | *Area (m.ha)* | *Production (m.t)* | *Productivity (q/ha)* |
|---|---|---|---|---|---|---|---|
| 1950 | 9.8 | 6.4 | 6.5 | 1980 | 22.2 | 31.8 | 14.4 |
| 1960 | 13.4 | 10.3 | 7.2 | 1981 | 22.3 | 36.3 | 16.3 |
| 1961 | 12.8 | 11.0 | 8.5 | 1982 | 22.1 | 37.4 | 16.9 |
| 1962 | 13.3 | 11.8 | 8.1 | 1983 | 23.6 | 42.8 | 18.2 |
| 1963 | 13.6 | 10.9 | 7.9 | 1984 | 24.7 | 45.5 | 18.4 |
| 1964 | 13.5 | 9.9 | 7.3 | 1985 | 23.6 | 44.1 | 18.7 |
| 1965 | 13.5 | 12.3 | 9.1 | 1986 | 23.0 | 47.0 | 20.5 |
| 1966 | 12.8 | 10.4 | 8.3 | 1987 | 22.8 | 45.6 | 20.0 |
| 1967 | 12.8 | 11.4 | 8.9 | 1988 | 22.6 | 45.1 | 20.0 |
| 1968 | 15.0 | 16.5 | 11.0 | 1989 | 24.1 | 54.1 | 22.4 |
| 1969 | 15.9 | 18.7 | 11.7 | 1990 | 23.5 | 49.8 | 21.2 |
| 1970 | 16.6 | 20.1 | 12.1 | 1991 | 24.2 | 55.1 | 22.8 |
| 1971 | 17.9 | 23.2 | 13.0 | 1992 | 23.3 | 55.7 | 23.9 |
| 1972 | 19.1 | 26.4 | 13.8 | 1993 | 24.4 | 57.2 | 23.2 |
| 1973 | 19.5 | 24.7 | 12.7 | 1994 | 25.1 | 59.8 | 23.8 |
| 1974 | 18.6 | 22.1 | 11.6 | 1995 | 25.7 | 65.6 | 25.6 |
| 1975 | 18.2 | 24.1 | 13.3 | 1996 | 25.1 | 65.6 | 24.9 |
| 1976 | 20.1 | 28.3 | 14.1 | 1997 | 26.0 | 69.0 | 26.7 |
| 1977 | 20.8 | 29.1 | 14.0 | 1998 | 26.7 | 65.9 | 24.7 |
| 1978 | 21.5 | 31.8 | 14.8 | 1999 | 27.4 | 71.0* | 26.0 |
| 1979 | 22.2 | 35.0 | 15.8 | | | | |

* Provisional, Data compiled from several sources like: Reports of the Centre for Monitoring Indian Economy, Bombay and Reports of Directorate of Economics and Statistics, Ministry of Agriculture, Govt. of India.

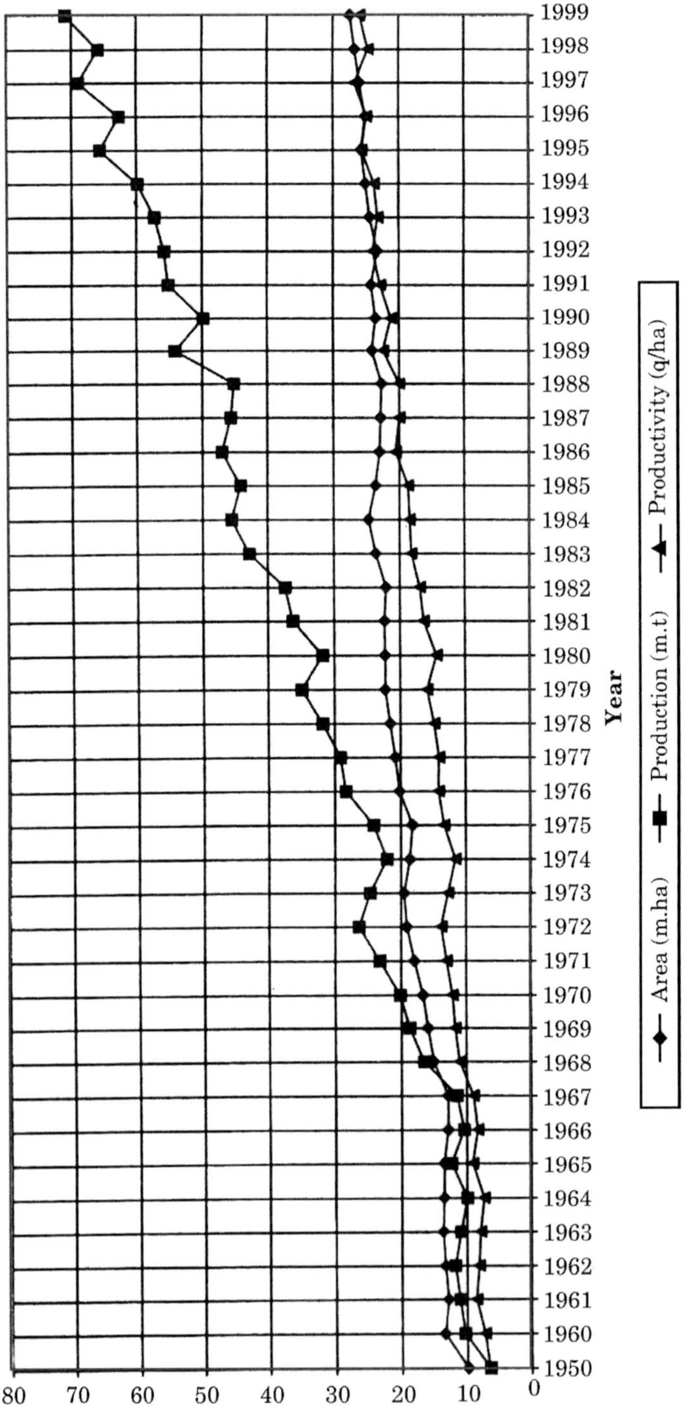


**Fig. 1:** Trends in area, production and productivity of wheat in India

## 2. WHEAT CULTIVATION IN INDIA

The wheat growing regions lie between 11º N to 35º N latitude and 72º E to 92º E longitude. They represent diverse agroclimaric conditions and a great diversity and range of soil and climatic conditions. Wheat is grown on plains, river valleys, plateaus, as well as on hills, at altitudes ranging from sea level to 3000 m above mean sea level. The soils range from light to heavy, from deep to shallow, from poor to high in fertility. Varying levels of soil and atmospheric drought occur in these areas and wheat is grown on soils having a sufficient moisture supply or under artificial irrigation and under a regime of heavy fertilizer dose to conditions of low nutrients. The length of the crop season varies from 3.5 to 4.5 months depending on the severity of winter temperatures. The rainfed wheat in India, unlike many western countries, depends on residual moisture after the recession of monsoon. Even where winter rains are received, they are not more than 100 mm during the crop season. In many parts of the country, crop has to mature before the onset of hot winds of summer or premonsoon showers. As Howard stated "wheat production in India is a gamble with temperature". The sowing time ranges from middle of October to as late as end of December in hills and north India and the crop is harvested from end of February to middle of June. In the higher elevations, wheat is grown as a summer crop from May to October.

The major wheat producing area in country lies between 20°N to 30°N comprising the states of Punjab, Haryana, Uttar Pradesh, Madhya Pradesh, Bihar, Rajasthan, West Bengal and Maharashtra. The Indo-Gangetic plains comprising of the states of Punjab, Haryana, Uttar Pradesh and Rajasthan together account for nearly 85% of total wheat production in the country (Table 3). The regional variations in productivity arise due to the extent of irrigation and coverage of semidwarf varieties, temperatures during the crop season and the farmers' adoption of improved technology.

India is probably one of the few countries in the world where three wheat types are grown. The major area of about 90% is under bread wheat *(Triticum aestivum* L. em Thell.), about 8 percent under durum or macaroni wheat (*T. turgidum* var. durum) and the remaining under dicoccum or emmer wheat (*T. turgidum* var. dicoccum). Bread wheat is grown in all the wheat growing areas. Durum wheat is largely grown in Central and Peninsular India mostly under poor to high in fertility. Varying levels of soil and atmospheric drought occur in these areas and wheat is grown on soils having a sufficient moisture supply or under rainfed, residual moisture conditions, although it is now being introduced into irrigated areas. In recent years, semidwarf durum wheat varieties have also become popular in the north India, particularly in Punjab and Haryana. The dicoccum wheat is grown in Maharashtra and Karnataka on an area of about 0.5 m. ha.

**Table 3.** Major wheat producing states in India

| *State* | *Area (m.ha)* | *Production (m.t)* | *Productivity (kg/ha)* | *Area under irrigation (%)* |
|---|---|---|---|---|
| Bihar | 2.1 | 4.18 | 1990 | 88.4 |
| Gujarat | 0.8 | 1.95 | 2438 | 79.9 |
| Haryana | 2.2 | 8.62 | 3918 | 98.3 |
| Himachal Pradesh | 0.38 | 0.64 | 1684 | 17.6 |
| J&K | 0.25 | 0.50 | 2000 | 24.2 |
| Madhya Pradesh | 4.51 | 8.34 | 1849 | 68.1 |
| Maharashtra | 1.02 | 1.12 | 1098 | 68.7 |
| Punjab | 3.36 | 14.47 | 4306 | 97.1 |
| Rajasthan | 2.77 | 6.88 | 2483 | 94.6 |
| Uttar Pradesh | 9.23 | 23.17 | 2510 | 92.5 |
| West Bengal | 0.37 | 0.80 | 2162 | 89.3 |
| Others | 0.39 | 0.34 | — | — |
| All India | 27.36 | 71.01 | 2593 | 86.8 |

Data of 1998-99; *Source:* Ministry of Agriculture, Govt. of India

Depending on the season in which wheat is grown, the varieties are distinguished as spring wheats and winter wheats. This classification is mostly used in western countries where wheat is grown both in winter and summer. The winter wheats have a long period of growth and require lower temperatures in early stages of growth. They are sown in September or October, pass through the winter covered under snow, come to flowering in spring and mature during summer months of June-July. The spring wheats are of shorter duration, they do not require cold temperatures in early growth stages and are sown in April or May and harvested in August or September. All wheat varieties grown in India in major wheat producing areas are spring types although they are grown in the winter or *rabi* season. There are small isolated areas in the northern hills where some winter wheat is grown, but its production is very limited and does not contribute much to the national production.

## 3. INTRODUCTION AND USE OF WHEAT IN ANCIENT INDIA

The north-western end of Indian subcontinent, the fold between Hindukush and Himalaya is regarded as the secondary centre of origin of hexaploid wheat (Vavilov, 1926). From here wheat transmigrated to east in three routes (Hosono, 1954). The second route which started from Afghanistan through the Khyber pass to cross the plains of Punjab and the basin of Ganga and Yamuna, skirting the Himalayas to reach upper Myanmar, is the most important one, as along this route wheat became human staple food. Along the second line of migration, *T. sphaerococcum* seems to have arisen as a spontaneous mutant at around 2500 B.C., in Afghanistan or north western parts of the Indian subcontinent from where it moved eastward (Zevan, 1978,1980).

Archaeological excavations from many parts of India revealed carbonized wheat grains from Harappan period (2300-1750 B.C.). Such carbonized grains have been recovered from Mohenja-daro and Chanhu-daro in the Sindh Valley and Harappa in Punjab; from the Atranjikhera site of Etah district in Uttar Pradesh (2000-50 B.C.); chalcolithic Sites in Madhya Pradesh at Nevadatoli-Maheshwar (1600-1450 B.C.) and Kayatha culture in Ujjain district of Madhya Pradesh (1900 B.C.); and at Sonegaon (1340-1290 B.C.), Inamgaon (1370-1025 B.C.) and Ter in Osmanabad district of Maharashtra. Critical evaluation of the samples from Mohenja-daro, Nevadatoli-Maheshwar, Ter and Chirand sites revealed that the dimensions more closely resembled *T. sphaerococcum* (Vishnu-Mittre, 1974). The earliest ones are estimated to be from c. 3500 B.C. It therefore appears that *T. sphaerococcum* was the wheat of ancient India that had wide-spread cultivation in the North and varieties of this species were reportedly under cultivation in parts of Punjab till the early 1940's. However, this species has been gradually replaced by the bread wheats and is no more under cultivation (Kulshrestha, 1985).

The use of wheat in recorded history of India is post-Rigvedic since it does not find any mention in this great epic (Prakash, 1961), indicating that it was not a major food of the Aryans. Evidence collected from the excavations at Mehrgarh, Mohenjadaro-Chirand, Nevadtoli-Maheshwar, Sonegaon-Inamgaon show beyond doubt that wheat was eaten by the inhabitants living there. It probably formed their staple food. It seems that art of cultivation of wheat and taste for its consumption perished with those cultures, but wheat picked up once again after more than 1500 years at the time of compilation of Yajurved (1500-800 B.C.). It does not appear to have become a major food grain until about 12th Century A.D. because many of the scriptures before this period mentioned wheat as an inferior grain and food of the condemned people. Wheat is mentioned among the five common grains in Vishnudharmottara (9-11 Century A.D.) (Randhawa, 1980). Many wheat-based recipes have been described in Manasollasa (1126-1135 A.D.) and Bhojan Kutuhal (c. 1600 A.D.) which indicates that wheat became a major food grain from this period (Kulshrestha, 1985).

## 4. TAXONOMY, ORIGIN AND EVOLUTION

Wheat is a member of the tribe Triticeae Dumort (Hordeae Benth.), a festucoid tribe of the family Poaceae (Gramineae), that is of great economic importance to humankind. The tribe forms a distinct natural group characterized by a compound spike, laterally compressed spikelets with two glumes, single starch grains and fairly large chromosomes in multiples of seven. It contains three major cereals - barley *(Hordeum),* rye *(Secale)* and wheat *(Triticum)* - that have been used since prehistoric times. Several other members of the tribe are important as forage and pasture grasses. The genera *Triticum, Aegilops, Secale, Agropyron* and *Haynaldia* are distinct and form a natural subtribe the Triticinae, within the tribe Triticeae.

Schulz (1913) grouped all the species of wheats in three natural groups, einkorn, emmer and dinkel wheats. Sakamura (1918) established that the three natural groups of wheats form a polyploid series with chromosome numbers n = 7, 14 and 21, respectively. Genome analysis, the determination of evolutionary relationships on the basis of chromosome pairing in hybrids, was elegantly and exhaustively applied by Kihara and his colleagues to understand the evolutionary and species relationships in the *Triticum* (reviewed by Lilienfeld, 1951). These studies indicated that allopolyploidy was involved. Accordingly, the genomic formulae AA, AABB and AABBDD were given to the three groups. Sears and Okomoto (1956) and Sears (1966) showed that the genomes were not as highly differentiated as originally thought and that each chromosome of hexaploid wheat has a homoeologue in each other genomes to which it is closely related genetically. These studies revealed that wheat evolution followed a system of diploid divergence and polyploid convergence. Okomoto (1957) and Riley and Chapman (1958) discovered that meiotic pairing in hexaploid wheat is sufficiently suppressed by a gene or genes *(Ph1)* on the long arm of chromosome 5B that allows only homologues to pair; in the absence of chromosome 5B, considerable pairing occurs between homeologues. Thus the polyploid wheats were shown to be more auto- than allopolyploid but to behave cytologically like diploids and thereby to maintain a high level of fertility and stability. Although several other minor genes for promotion or suppression of pairing were discovered on other chromosomes, *Ph1* is considered the critical pairing control gene, that switches the pairing from original polyploid to a pairing level characteristic of diploids.

In addition to the classical genomic analysis several other methods like study of karyotypes using Feulgen-stained, Giemsa C-banded or

N-banded somatic chromosomes, *in situ* hybridizations, immunological reactions, biochemical procedures, DNA hybridizations and Restriction Fragment Length Polymorphism (RFLP) have been employed for resolving some of doubtful or difficult aspects. The relative advantages and disadvantages of each of these techniques has been reviewed by Kimber and Sears (1987).

### 4.1. A Genome Donor

From the strong morphological similarities between diploid wheat, *T. monococcum* and tetraploid wheat, *Triticum turgidum* and from the chromosome pairing observed in hybrids between them it has been shown that A genome of the polyploid wheat must have come from *T. monococcum.* Archaeological evidence (Helbaek, 1959) has established that *T. turgidum* was taken into cultivation at least as early as *T. monococcum* (about 8000 B.C.) and hence there seems to be no doubt that the diploid wheat that contributed the A genome to the tetraploid wheat was the wild form *T. aegilopoides* or *T. thoudar* (Riley, 1965). Recently, using molecular approaches, it was concluded that A genome of *T. monococcum* was derived from *T. aegilopoides,* and A genome of *T. timopheevii, T. dicoccum* and *T. aestivum* was contributed by *T. urartu* (Dvorak, 1988; Dvorak *et al.,* 1990). It has also been shown that only six of the seven chromosomes of the A-genome of bread wheat were derived from its A genome progenitor and the 4A chromosome has an unknown origin (Kimber and Sears, 1987).

### 4.2. D Genome Donor

McFadden and Sears (1944,1946) and Kihara (1944) independently established that the source of D genome of hexaploid wheat was *Ae. squarrosa* (*Triticum tauschii*). Since cultivated forms of emmer, a tetraploid, were in existence by the time hexaploid appeared around 6000 B.C., a cultivated emmer probably contributed the A and B genomes to the hexaploid wheat. Evidence for genes for waxiness and other characters (Tsunewaki, 1966) and the phenotype of tetraploids extracted from the hexaploid wheat by Kerber (1964) and others lends strong support to this theory. Using a repeat DNA clone pASI isolated from *Ae. squarrosa,* D genome of bread wheat was shown to be closely related to that of *Ae. cylindrica* and *Ae. squarrosa* than to *Ae. ventricosa* and *Ae. crassa* (Rayburn and Gill, 1986,1987).

### 4.3. B Genome Donor

Efforts to identify the origin of B genome failed to give conclusive results. There are several species which have been suggested as the donor of B genome using different criteria. These are *Ae. bicornis, Ae. longissima, Ae. searsii, Ae. sharonensis* and *Ae. speltoides*. Pathak (1940), Sarkar and Stebbins (1956) and Riley *et al.* (1958) put forward the hypothesis that *T. speltoides* had contributed either the whole or a greater part of it. Chromosome banding (Shands and Kimber, 1973), *in situ* hybridization (Gerlach *et al.,* 1978), isozyme studies (Belea and Fejer, 1980) and chromosome pairing studies (Kimber and Athwal, 1972) have failed to establish *Ae. speltoides* as the B genome donor. A group of species belonging to *Ae. longissima* which were given the species status of *Ae. searsii* was considered as the B genome donor by Feldman (1979) because of its compatible morphology and relatively frequent pairing of its chromosomes with those of the B genome. Also, the distribution of the latter species overlaps that of both wild emmer and wild einkorn. Nath *et al.* (1983, 1984) reported that DNA-hybridization data support *T. searsii* as the source of B genome. Detailed analysis of the A and B genome donors is given by Kerby and Kuspira (1988) and Kerby *et al.* (1988).

On the basis of their having the genomic constitution AA, AABB, and AABBDD all of the wild and cultivated wheats are classifiable into three species, *T. monococcum, T. turgidum* and *T. aestivum,* except the tetraploid *T. timopheevii* and hexaploid *T. zhukovskyi.* The former has the genome AAGG and the latter AAAAGG. *T. timopheevii* has a wild form, *T. araraticum,* which grows fairly widely in southeast Asia and a cultivated form that is grown in only Caucasus region. *T. zhukovskyi* is a cultivated form which grows only in the Caucasus and arose as an amphiploid of the cross *T. timopheevii* × *T. monococcum* (Upadhya and Swaminathan, 1963). Wagenaar (1961) considered the G genome to be a modified B genome and the sterility in *turgidum* × *timopheevii* hybrids to be due to complementary gene action, which could not be confirmed by Feldman (1966). *T. speltoides* was proposed as the G genome donor by Shands and Kimber (1973), but Nath *et al.* (1985) provided evidence from DNA hybridization data that G genome is derived from *Ae. speltoides.* The cytoplasm of *T. timopheevii* was also shown to be equivalent to that of *Ae. speltoides* (Ogihara and Tsunewaki, 1988). Gill and Chen (1987) studied N-banding patterns of mitotic and meiotic chromosomes in *T. durum* and *T. timopheevii* and in hybrids between them. It was shown that chromosome 4 of diploid wheat was present in *timopheevii,* but absent in durum. Based on these observations and other evidences, it was concluded that *timopheevii* originated as an allotetraploid from *Ae. speltoides* x *T. monococcum* hybrid. *T. durum* originated from *T. timopheevii* with introgression from an unknown diploid species, which contributed the distinctive cytoplasm, chromosome 4B and additional chromosome segments. Therefore it is possible that *T. turgidum* and *T. timopheevii* have a common origin. Using DNA hybridization of repeat sequences, it was shown that *Ae. speltoides* is closely related not only to G genome of *T. timopheevii* but also to the B genome of *T. durum* and *T. aestivum* (Dvorak and Zhang, 1990). Thus the nuclear and cytoplasmic data now agree that G genome was contributed by *Ae. speltoides* whereas B genome of durum and aestivum might have been contributed by an unknown or extinct species in the evolutionary lineage of *Ae. speltoides*. Similar results were obtained by Talbert *et al.* (1991).

With the better knowledge about the genomic and evolutionary Status of wheat, several revisions in the nomenclature of *Triticum* species have been proposed (see Morris and Sears, 1967, for review). Since two *Aegilops* species contributed to the evolution of hexaploid wheat, it was suggested that species belonging to Sitopsis section of *Aegilops* be merged into the genus *Triticum*.

Also, since the different tetraploid and hexaploid species have been shown to cross easily and produce fertile hybrids, most of them have been merged into single species. A comparison of different classifications of the genus *Triticum L.* has been given by Miller (1987). The classification suggested by Kimber and Sears (1983) is given in Table 4.

**Table 4:** Genome formulae of the species of *Triticum*

| ***Species*** | ***Genome*** | ***Synonyms*** |
|---|---|---|
| ***Diploids*** | | |
| *T. monococcum* L. | A | *T. boeoticutn, T. urartu* |
| *T. speltoides* (Tausch) Grene. x Richter | S | *Ae. speltoides* |
| *T. bicorne* Frosk. | S | *Ae. bicarnis* |
| *T. longissimum* (Schwemf. & Muschli in Muschli) Bowden | S | *Ae. longissima*<br>*Ac. sharonensis* |
| *T. searsii* (Feldman & Kislev) Feldman, comb.nov. | S | *Ae. searsii* |
| *T. tripsacoides* (Jaub & Spach) Bowden | Mt | *Ae. mutica* |
| T. *tauschii* (Coss.) Schmal. | D | *Ae. squarrosa* |
| *T. comosum* (Sibth. & Sm.) Richter | M | *Ae. comosa, Ae. heldrechii* |
| *T. uniaristatum* (Vis) Richter | Un | *Ae. uniaristata* |
| *T. dichasians* (Zhuk.) Bowden | C | *Ae. caudata* |
| *T. umbellulatum* (Zhuk.) Bowden | U | *Ae. umbellulata* |
| ***Polyploids*** | | |
| *T. turgidum* L. | AB | *T. carthlicum, T. dicoccoides,*<br>*T. dicoccon, T. dicoccum,* |

**Table 4:** (*Contd...*)

**Table 4:** (*Contd...*)

| *Species* | *Genome* | *Synonyms* |
|---|---|---|
| | | *T. durum, T. polonicum* |
| *T. timpheevii* (Zhuk.) Zhuk. | AG | *T. araraticum* |
| *T. zhukovsky* Men. & Er. | AAG | *T. timopheevii* var. Zhukovskyi |
| *T. aestivum* L. | ABD | *T. compactum. T. macha, T. spelta, T. sphaerococcum, T. vavilovii* |
| *T. ventricosum* Ces. | DUn | *Ae. ventricosa* |
| *T. crassum* (4x) (Boiss.) Aitch & Hensl. | DM | *Ae. crassa* |
| *T. crassum* (6x) (Boiss) Aitch & Hensl. | DDM | *Ae. crassa* |
| *T. syriacum* Bowden | DMS | *Ae. crassa* ssp. vavilovii, *Ae. vavilovii* |
| *T. juvenale* Thell. | DMU | *Ae. juvenalis* |
| *T. kotschyi* (Boiss.) Bowden | US | *Ae. kotschyi, Ae. peregrina Ae. variabilis* |
| *T. ovatum* (L.) Raspail | UM | *Ae. ovata* |
| *T. triaristatum* (4x) Willd.) Codr. & Gren. | UM | *Ae. triaristata* |
| *T. triaristatum* (6x) (Willd.) Godr. & Gren. | UMUn | *Ae. triaristata* |
| *T. macrochaetum* (Schuttl. & Huet. et Duval-Jouve) Richterl | UM | *Ae. biunciaüs, Ae. lorentii* |
| *T. columnare* (Zhuk.) Morris & Sears | UM | *Ae. columnaris* |
| *T. triunciale* (L.) Raspail | UC | *Ae. triuncialis* |
| *T. cylindricum* Ces. | CD | *Ae. cylindrica* |

## 4.4. Origin Within the Polyploid Groups

The most primitive among the tetraploids are the *T. turgidum* var. dicoccoides (some refer to the original species of the tetraploids as subspecies or convarieties) and *T. araraticum,* the wild form of *T. timopheevii.* It is possible that the *timopheevii* and *dicoccoides* were taken into cultivation at almost the same time, about 8000 B.C. *T. dicoccoides* subsequently gave rise to cultivated emmers which then spread rapidly, Durum presumably originated from emmer by an accumulation of mutations that reduced the toughness of the glumes to a point that free-threshing was attained. The gene 'q' however, remains unchanged. The turgidum group differs very little from the durums. The polonicums are characterized by long glumes that are governed by a single gene. The carthlicums are the only tetraploids with Q gene. It has been suggested that this group might have been a secondary tetraploid originating from the cross of tetraploid and hexaploid. The extracted tetraploids from hexaploids, the isozyme patterns etc. confirm this hypothesis.

At the hexaploid level, the principal differences among the groups of cultivated varieties are due to single genes. Since no hexaploid has been found in wild, it is presumed that this group arose under domestication.

The genetic relationships of the hexaploid types are as follows :

| | | | | |
|---|---|---|---|---|
| *spelta* | qq | cc | SS | |
| *macha* | qq | CC | SS | |
| *aestivum* | QQ | cc | SS | free threshing, tough rachis |
| *compactum* | QQ | CC | SS | compact spike |
| *sphaerococcum* | QQ | cc | ss | compact spike, spherical seed |

From the evidence available so far, the evolution of cultivated wheat can be summarized as follow (Fig. 2).

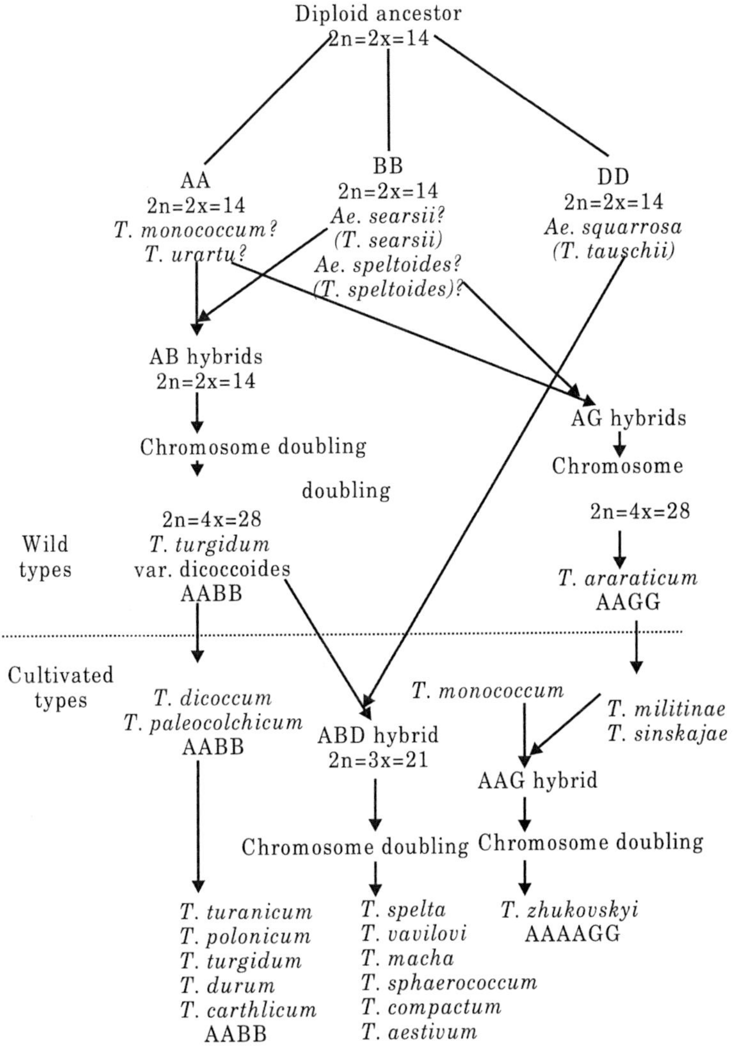


**Fig. 2:** The proposed sequence of origin of cultivated wheats

## 5. FLORAL BIOLOGY

The inflorescence of wheat is the so-called ear or head - a compound distichous spike, whose primary axis bears two opposite rows of lateral spikelets and single terminal spikelet. The main axis or rachis is a sinuous, notched structure and has numerous internodes with narrow base and broader apex. The whole axis has a zig-zag appearance. In some of the wheats, the main axis is tough and does not break even when threshed. In other species the axis is brittle and breaks down when the grains are ripe.

The unit of the spike is the spikelet. Each spikelet is a condensed reproductive shoot consisting of two subtending sterile bracts or glumes, enclosing two to five florets, borne alternately on a short axis called rachilla. The typical glume is boat-shaped with rounded base. Each flower possesses two bracts, lemma and palea, opposite to each other. Within each floret are three stamens with large anthers and a pistil bearing two styles with feathery Stigma branches. There are two delicate ovate lodicules which are considered to be modified perianth structures. Wheat stamens are small and sagitate and produce about 1000-4000 pollen grains per anther. Each pollen grain consists of an outer sculptured layer, the exine, mostly made of sporopollenin, a tough carotenoid substance, and an inner layer the intine composed of cellulose. A nuclear division produces a two-celled structure, which can now be called the pollen grain. One nucleus divides again to form two lenticular, thin-walled cells, the sperm cells. Wheat pollen is shed in this three-celled condition. The unilocular carpel of wheat, like in other grasses, has one ovule and two plumose styles with feathery stigma branches (Fig. 3). A detailed description of morphological and anatomical characters of wheat plant parts is given in Lersten (1987).

Glumes of different varieties differ in the firmness of attachment to the rachis, in the tightness with which they clasp the mature kernels and in size relative to size of the kernels. These characters cause varieties to differ in their resistance to shattering. Wheat spikes also differ in their shape, length, width and degree of compactness. The glume shape, colour and tip also differ. These spike and glume characters are quite constant and are frequently used as descriptors in classification of wheat species and varieties.

Florets at anthesis are forced open by the swelling of the lodicules. Stamen filaments elongate at a great speed, reaching three times their original length in about 3 min. The stamens thus quickly exert and expose the anthers. Stigmas are receptive for 4 to 5 days under different conditions, but pollen is viable for only 15 to 30 min. This short viability of pollen is typical of the plants in which pollen is shed in the three-nucleate stage.

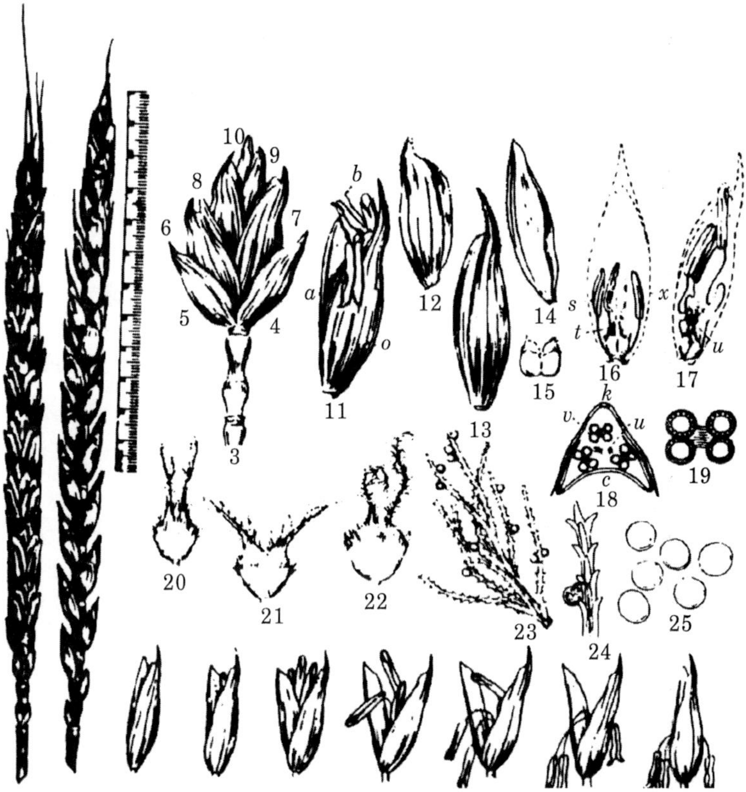


**Fig. 3.** Wheat inflorescence, spikelet, and pollination. *1,* Spike dorsiventral view; *2,* Spike lateral view; *3,* Spikelet on naked rachis; *4,* Upper glume; 5, Lower glume; *6-10,* Progressively smaller florets of a spikelet; *11,* Floret anthesis in lateral view; *12,* Glume; *13,* Lemma; *14,* Palea; *15,* Lodicules; *16,* Unopened floret showing stamen *(s)* and pistil *(t),* and outline of palea and lemma (*x*); *17,* floret at anthesis with pistil *(u)* and elongating stamen filaments; *18,* Floret cross-section showing position of palea (c), lemma *(k),* stamen *(v)* and Stigma *(w)*\ *19,* Anther cross-section showing four locules and central connective; *20-22,* Appreance of pistil before, during, and after anthesis; *23,* Pollen on stigma branches; *24,* Pollen germinating on stigma branch; *25,* Spherical pollen grains. Each has one pore (not shown); *26-32,* Florets from before to after anthesis (26 to 31 take 2 to 5 min, 31 to 32 take 20 to 25 min).

(Reproduced with permission from American Society of Agronomy, Madison, Wisconsin, USA)

Wheat normally is self-pollinated. In adverse climatic conditions, when the anthers fail to dehisce, cross pollination may occur, depending on availability of air borne pollen. Cross pollination does not exceed

0.5-1.0 per cent, as most of the pollen is shed before the anther comes out of the glumes. In other situations, the filament may not elongate at all and the pollen is deposited in the florets resulting in cleistogamous behaviour.

A wheat grain is a caryopsis, a small, dry, indehiscent, one-seeded fruit with a thin pericarp. It consists of a germ or embryo and an endosperm. The shape of the grain can be ovate, elliptical or oval. The embryo occupies about 1/6 to l /4 or more of the dorsal area. The embryo lies at an angle to the dorsal surface of the grain. The lower end, where the root tip is located, projects slightly beyond the attachment region, where the kernel was attached to the base of the floret. The surface of the wheat grain is smooth except at the stigmatic end where there is a tuft of persistent hairs known as the brush. The colour of the grains varies from reddish brown (red) to white or amber. Expression of the colour is affected by texture of the endosperm.

## 5.1. Hybridization Technique

Hybridization or crossing between two plants is an important aspect of wheat breeding. This is the most often used method for creating variability to combine desirable characteristics from different varieties. Crossing in wheat is simple but laborious. Since the flower is bisexual, it is necessary to emasculate or remove the anthers from the spike that has to be pollinated. The flower maturity starts from the middle of the spike and extends in either direction. There can be a difference of 1-2 days in maturity between the middle and the extreme spikelets. Hence, depending on the condition of the spike, one or two spikelets from either side and the terminal spikelet are removed before emasculation. Within each spikelet, the two lateral ones are bigger and the inner ones are smaller and also mature later. The spike which has to be crossed is selected at a stage when the anthers of the middle spikelets are fully grown and still green, indicating that they will ripen in a day or two. The median florets are removed by holding them with a forceps and pulling them downward and outward. This leaves only the outermost florets of each spikelet. The awns are cut slightly below the glumes which helps in the removal of anthers. After emasculation the ear is normally covered with a butter-paper bag to prevent natural pollination. Pollination is effected by placing a freshly opened anther into the emasculated floret or dusting pollen (Fig. 4). After pollination, the bag is again kept on the pollinated spike to avoid any foreign pollen. The bag may be removed after a few days, or kept till maturity.

To perform large number of crosses, a slightly modified method, called the '"twirl method" has been developed. In this method, the spike that

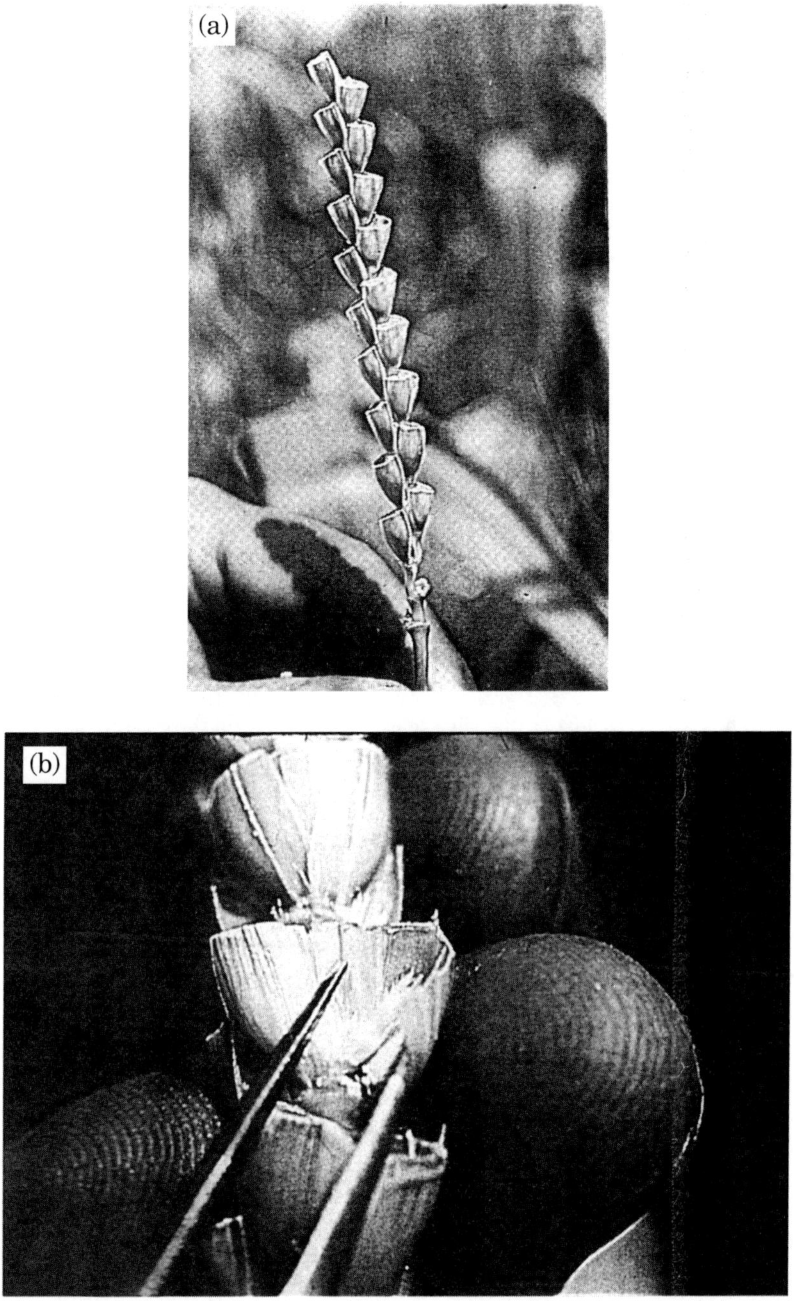


**Fig. 4:** (*Contd...*)

**Fig. 4:** (*Contd...*)

**Fig. 4:** Hybridization technique in wheat. (a) The spike to be emasculated is cut a little below the awns to expose the anthers; (b) Anthers are removed from each of the florets and the spike is bagged to avoid cross pollination; (c) The emasculated spike is pollinated after 2 days by rotating a spike from a plant with which it has to be crossed and the bag is closed; (d) Details of the date crossing, female parent and male parent are recorded on a label. One label is kept inside the bag and one label is tied to the peduncle

has to be used as female, is emasculated as in the previous case, but the glumes are cut deeper, so that the stigma is slightly exposed. For pollination, a spike is selected which is ready to anthesce. This can be easily judged by inspecting a few florets of a spike and selecting those which have yellow-coloured anthers. The awns are cut and the spike is kept erect in sun for sometime to allow the filaments to elongate and the anthers to dehisce. At an appropriate stage the spike is inverted carefully and rotated around the previously emasculated spike while still in the glassine bag. The pollen grains are thus deposited on the stigmatic surface. This avoids the tedious procedure of placing anthers or pollen manually in each of the florets.

In both cases, a label is kept inside the bag and one is kept outside the bag tied to the peduncle. Details like the female and male parents used in the cross, date of pollination etc. are mentioned on this label.

## 6. WHEAT BREEDING IN INDIA

### 6.1. Early Breeding Work

Prior to the commencement of wheat improvement work, the wheat crop in general consisted of a mixture of different varieties, belonging to *T. aestivum, T. durum, T. sphaerococcum, T. dicoccum* and *T. turgidum* (Howard and Howard, 1910). These mixtures, usually known as "sorts" were classified on the basis of grain characters, such as red or amber colour, hard or soft grain etc. irrespective of other botanical characters (Pal, 1966). Prominent among these sorts were the Sharbati, Dara, Saphed pissi, Chandausi, Karachi choice white, Hard Red Calcutta, Lal kanak, Lal pissi etc. in *aestivum* group; Haura, Bansi, Kathia, Jalalia, Jamali, Gangajali, Khandwa, Malvi etc. in *durum* group and Khapli, Popatia and Samba in *dicoccum* group.

Reference is made in literature to some isolated work in wheat selection having been carried out in India during the last quarter of the 19th Century (Howard and Howard, 1910), and production of "pedigree seed" of selected wheat varieties such as Muzaffarnagar white, Buxar white and the selected pissi wheats. Reports are also available of selection work carried out at Kanpur in 1880-81, of the attempts made in 1887 at Nagpur to produce pedigree Haura wheat using the selection method adopted in England by Hallet in 1857 and of the selection for grain and ear size made at Poona from 1903-05.

Wheat improvement work on systematic lines commenced only during the first decade of $20^{th}$ Century. The period between 1905-1962 can be divided into 3 distinct phases and is well documented by Pal (1966). Poineering work was done by the husband and wife team of Albert Howard and Gabriella Howard beginning from 1904, at the then Imperial (now Indian) Agricultural Research Institute at Pusa, Bihar, (which was shifted to New Delhi after the devastating earthquake in 1930), by utilizing a System of selection from single plants which enabled them to produce several wheat varieties like Pusa 4, Pusa 6 and Pusa 12. These varieties were popular not only in India but also in South Africa, Rhodesia and Hungary (Howard and Howard, 1910, 1928). Pusa 4 (NP 4), a selection from the local sort Mundia (= awnless) was rated as one of the best quality wheats in the world. It won the first prize successively from 1916 to 1920 in international grain exhibitions. It had a wide adaptability in India and was also grown on considerable area in New South Wales, Queensland and Western Australia even as late as 1939 (Pal, 1966). Work on similar lines conducted at other centres resulted in the production of improved types like Type 8, Type 8A, Type 9, Type 9D, and Type 11 selected by T. Milne at Lyallpur in Punjab (now in Pakistan), C13 (K13), K 53 and K 54 at Kanpur in Uttar Pradesh (the latter two varieties were selected by A.K. Mitra from Jhansi local and Azamgadh local, respectively) and Ao 13, Ao 49, Ao 68, Ao 85, Ao 88 and Ao 90 at Nagpur in Madhya Pradesh (now in Maharashtra) selected by Geoffrey Evans, Ekdania 69 selected at Institute of Plant Industry at Indore, and Bansi, Motia, Gulab etc. in Bombay, Maharashtra.

The second phase consisted of varieties developed through hybridization of these pure lines which resulted in varieties like NP 52, NP80-5, NP 100, NP 101, NP 120, NP 125, NP 165, PbC 281, PbC 518, PbC 591, PbC 273, Niphad 4, Ao 113, Ao 115, Jay, Vijay, etc. in different parts of the country. Poineering efforts were made in this period by Ch. Ramdhan Singh at Lyallpur, Dr. B.P. Pal at Pusa and later at Delhi, Dr. R.B. Ekbote at Powerkheda (Madhya Pradesh), and by Dr. B.S. Kadam at Niphad (Maharashtra).

The third phase consisted of crosses of Indian wheats with exotic varieties mainly with the objective of breeding for disease resistance, which resulted in varieties NP 700 and NP 800 series, Kenphad wheats, PbC228, PbC250, PbC253, Hyll, Hy38, Hy65, Arnej 206, Arnej 614 etc. Several exotic varieties like Federation, Chinese White, Kononso, Thatcher, Kenya C10854 (E 220), Kenya 48E(L.1) (E114), Democrat, Charter, Timstein, Gabo, Hofed, and Bobin were used in development of these varieties.

Work on improvement of durum wheat was started in the then Bombay State and Central Piovinces during 1930s. Exotic varieties like Gaza (E931), Arabian durum (E2025), Egypt 8626 and E 2158 and dicoccum were used in crosses with Indian durum selections, which resulted in varieties like Jay and Vijay, Bijaga Yellow, N 59 etc. Use was also made of other tetraploid species of wheat for durum improvement (Deodikar *et al.,* 1983).

In spite of these efforts, there was no real breakthrough in wheat productivity during this period. Efforts to produce lodging resistant varieties suitable for intensive agriculture were not successful due to non-availability of suitable genetic stocks and selection criteria (Rao, 1972).

### 6.2. The Semidwarf Wheat Era

The semidwarf wheat varieties developed in Mexico by Norman Borlaug and his colleagues using the Norin 10 dwarfing genes, *Rht-B1* and *Rht-D1* (formerly known as *Rht1* and *Rht2)* attracted the attention of Indian wheat breeders. During 1965-66, a bold policy decision was taken to introduce the semidwarf spring wheats and 200 metric tonnes of Sonora 64 and 50 metric tonnes of Lerma Rojo were obtained during 1965 for extensive trials. In the following year, another 13,000 metric tonnes of wheat was imported for large scale testing on farmers' fields. These varieties immediately became popular with the farmers because of their high yields, in spite of their red grain, in contrast to the amber grain preferred in the market. Simultaneously, search was on for amber grained types and varieties like Kalyan Sona, Sonalika, Choti Lerma and Safed Lerma were released during 1967. These varieties spread like wild-fire and triggered off what is described as "wheat revolution" in India. These varieties also acted as catalysts for a whole lot of production technologies like irrigation and fertilizer consumption. Wheat cultivation spread to unconventional areas where it was not an important crop earlier. Within 10 years of introduction of these semidwarf wheats, wheat area increased from 12.6 to 20.1 m hectares, production from 10.4 to 28.3 m. tonnes and productivity from 8.3 to 14.1 q/ha. Although there has been a marginal increase in area since then, further improvement in yield and disease resistance, and increase in the irrigation potential and spread of semidwarf varieties provided the much required enhancement of production levels.

The post-green revolution breeding programmes were mostly concentrated towards further improvement in yield, selection for adaptability to different agroclimatic conditions, and improvement of disease resistance particularly for rusts. The strategy was to cross some of the Indian wheat varieties with the semidwarf wheat varieties from Mexico to combine the grain characters and *chapati* making qualities of local wheats with the photo-insensitivity, disease resistance and input responsiveness of dwarf types. Most of these wheat varieties were commonly referred to as single gene dwarf and two gene dwarf based on the plant height in the field, but they carry either of the genes and not both. The difference in height arises due to the greater effect of Rht2 than Rht1 in reducing the height. It was thought that further reduction in height may lead to still higher yields. Varieties like Hira and Moti were developed which were called as "triple dwarfs", with very short plant height due to the additive action of *Rht-B1* and *Rht-D1*. However, these did not become popular because of difficulty in manual harvesting of wheat. Moreover, the straw is a source of cattle feed and adequate quantity of straw is equally important to the farmers.

Even after the advent of semidwarf bread wheats, durum wheat improvement was restricted to Central and Peninsular India and was mostly directed to development of tall plant types suited for rainfed conditions.Varieties like Meghdoot, Jairaj, A-9-30-1 were developed from crosses of indigenous material. The improvement of tall durum wheats did not contribute much yield advantage in Central and Peninsular India and the situation can be compared to pre-semidwarf era in bread wheat improvement. Although HD 4502 (Malavika) was released for PZ, it did not become popular. The outbreak of Karnal Bunt in the NWPZ, and identification of stripe rust resistant durum varieties led to development of semidwarf durum varieties for North India. Varieties like Raj 1555 for Central Zone and PBW 34, PBW 215, DWL 5023 and more recently PBW 233 for North Western Plains Zone were released for cultivation.

The dicoccum wheats which are grown in Karnataka and Maharashtra are of tall stature and lodge when irrigated. A programme was initiated at Dharwad and Pune to develop semidwarf dicoccum wheats. This has resulted, first time in the world, in the release of semidwarf dicoccum wheats DDK 1001 and DDK 1009 in 1996 and 1998, respectively. Their impact is still to be assessed.

## 6.3. Contribution of Breeding to Yield Improvement

The contribution of breeding efforts to productivity improvement in wheat is best assessed by yield levels in North Western Plains Zone (NWPZ), the most productive region in the country. Nagarajan *et al.* (1998) observed that small gain has been obtained in wheat after every 5-10 years. At the time of release of Kalyan Sona in 1967, the yield levels were about 4.2 t/ha and this variety and Sonalika occupied large areas in different parts of the country till about 1977. The next jump was made by the release of varieties like WL 711 and Arjun (HD 2009) in 1975, which resulted in a marginal yield gain of five per cent. These two varieties dominated NWPZ during 1970s, till they were replaced by HD 2329 because of its greater adaptability, short stature and other agronomic advantages. There was a period of yield plateauing between 1975-85 when only marginal improvement in yield levels were witnessed. With the release of Veery lines carrying 1B/1R translocation during late 1980s and early 1990s, another spurt in wheat yields was witnessed. These varieties have shown definite yield superiority over other varieties under diverse environmental conditions and several of them have been released for different agroclimatic conditions. These varieties pushed up the yield levels to 52 q/ha. in the North Western Plains Zone. The more recent genotypes like PBW 343, UP 2338 and WH 542 derived from further crosses with Veery genotypes, but still carrying the 1B/1R translocation, have higher yield potential of up to 55 q/ha. Considering only important varieties, there is a genetic yield gain of 1% annually. Another important contribution of the Indian programme is that since 1977 the breeding efforts have been able to bring about genetic diversity. During 1967-77 only two varieties, Sonalika and Kalyansona, occupied large areas. Today as many as 25 varieties cover sizable area across the country. Although the yield improvement has not been dramatic in other parts of the country, even the small yield gains have been responsible for overall productivity increase in the country.

In contrast to this, the yield under rainfed conditions is still stagnant, an can be compared to the pre-semidwarf period of bread wheat breeding. Although several lines have been tested, none of them have proved promising and no significant advance has been made in yield. The varieties like C306 an NI 5439 in bread wheat and A-9-30-1 and Bijaga yellow in durum wheat are still among the top yielding varieties.

## 6.4. Organization of Wheat Research In India

The wheat improvement programme in India today is one of the biggest national programmes in the world. Until I960, wheat improvement work was done in isolation in different states by individual breeders. The need for more interaction among them was realized and a Cooperative Research Programme was initiated in 1961. This was later converted into a All India Coordinated Wheat Improvement Project in 1965, covering all the disciplines, under the auspices of the Indian Council of Agricultural Research, the apex body for agricultural research in India. In 1978 this programme was given the Status of Directorate of Wheat Research, with its headquarters originally at New Delhi, and shifted in 1990 to Karnal, Haryana, 130 km north of New Delhi. Considering the agroclimatic conditions of the wheat growing regions, and the disease spectrum, the country has been delineated into six wheat zones (Fig. 5). Based on the different cultural practices and requirements of the individual zones, following production conditions have been identified for breeding varieties: Rainfed timely sown, irrigated timely sown and irrigated late sown. At present, there are 29 centres functioning under this project, spread over the six wheat zones (Fig. 6). In addition, about 30 voluntary centres assist the programme by way of conducting various experiments on breeding, agronomy and pathology. To address specific needs, special trials for very high altitude, saline/alkaline soils and very late sown conditions are also conducted.

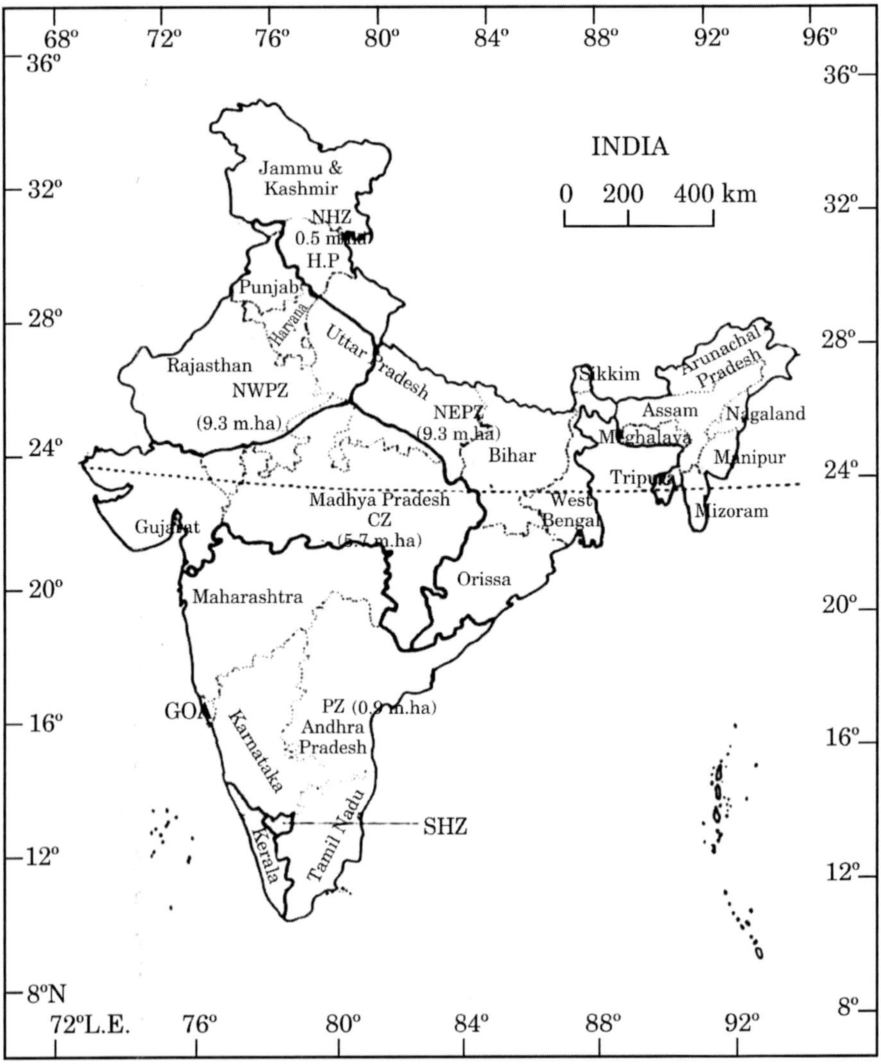


**Fig. 5:** Mega-environments of wheat testing and growing in India, (Broken lines are state boundaries; dark lines are zone boundaries; NHZ=Northern Hill Zone; NWPZ=North Western Plains Zone; NEPZ=North Eastern Plains Zone; CZ=Central Zone; PZ=Peninsular Zone; SHZ=Southern Hill Zone;Figures in parentheses indicate the area of wheat in each zone)

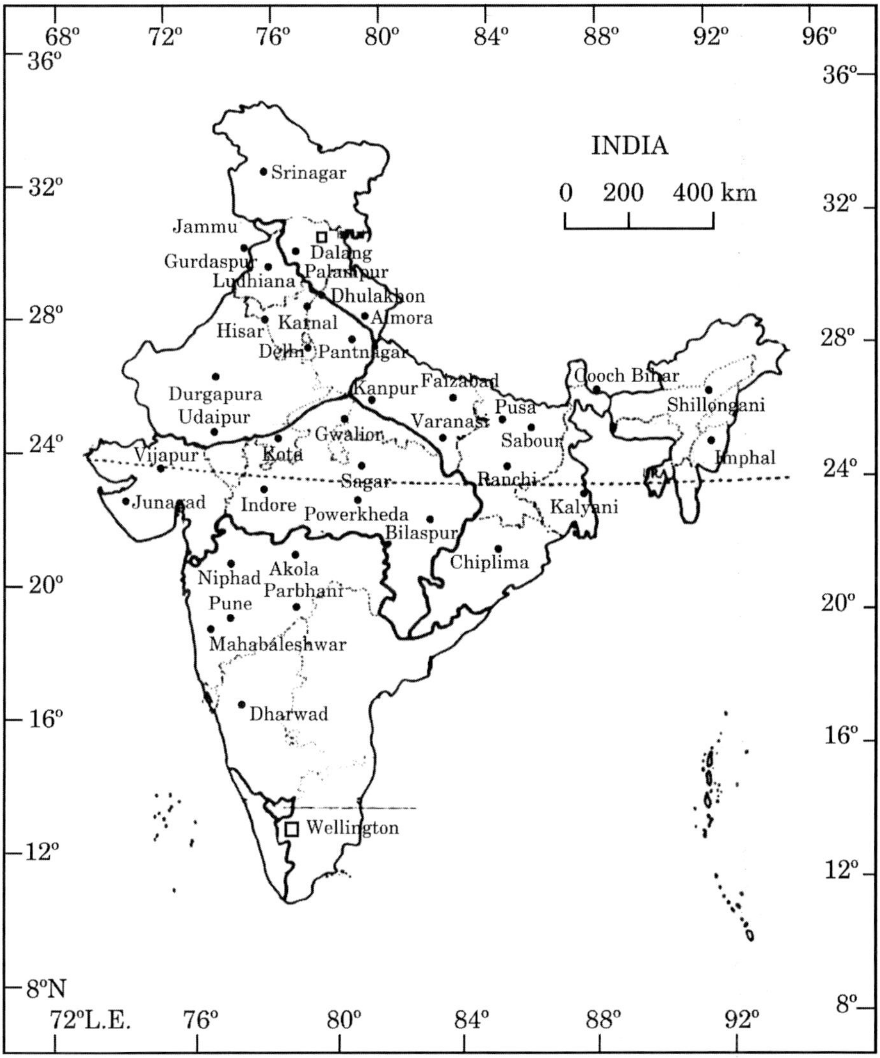


**Fig. 6:** Major centres of wheat research and testing in India

The organization of the wheat evaluations and release for commercial cultivation is given in Fig. 7.

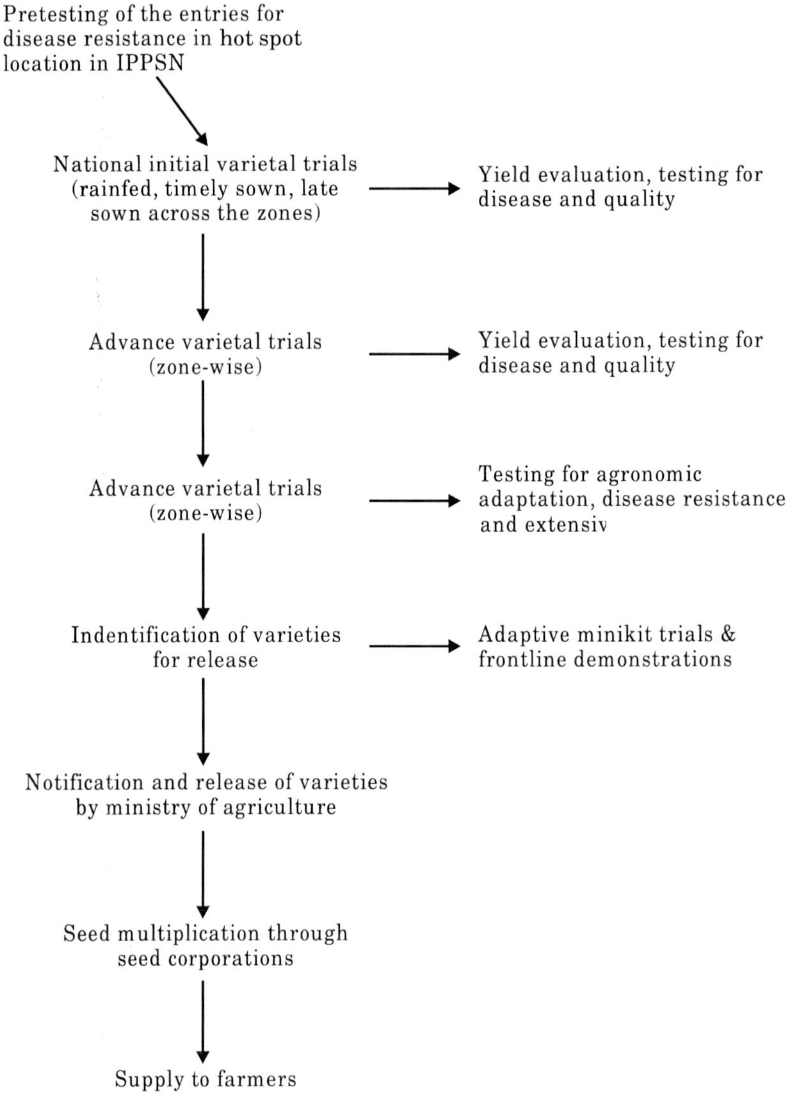


**Fig. 7:** Methodology of testing wheat entries in the AICWIP

So far, more than 180 varieties have been released in different wheat zones and for various production conditions. Not all of them have become popular and about 65-70 varieties occupy sizable areas. Details of the most important varieties which are presently under cultivation are given in Table 5.

In addition to these yield evaluation trials, several nurseries are planted across the country. The National Genetic Stock Nursery (NGSN) consists of elite materials drawn from national and international

**Table 5:** Parentages and ecological adaptation of important wheat varieties presently under cultivation in India

| *Variety* | *Parentage* | *Developed by* | *Year of release* | *Area of adaptation* |
|---|---|---|---|---|
| CPAN 3004 | GLL/AUST II61-157//CNO/NO/3/VEE | DWR, Karnal | 1992 | NWPZ; I,TS |
| DL 788-2 | DL230-16/HD 2278 | IARI, New Delhi | 1997 | CZ; I,TS |
| DL 803-3 (Kanchan) | HUW 202/ /K 7537/HD2160M | IARI, New Delhi | 1994 | NWPZ; I,TS |
| DWR 162 | KVZ/BUHO//KAL/BB | UAS, Dharwad | 1993 | PZ, I,TS |
| GW 173 | TW275-7-6-10/LOK1 | GAU, Vijapur | 1993 | CZ, I,LS |
| GW 190 | VEE/3/BB'S'/SONALIKA/ / ARJUN | " | 1993 | CZ,I,TS |
| GW 273 | CPAN 2084/VW 205 | " | 1997 | CZ,I,TS |
| GW 496 | HD 2285/4/CNO/NO//CC/INIA66/3/KAL/BB | GAU, Junagadh | 1990 | Gujarat; I,TS |
| HD 2189 | 36896/CJ54//P4160E/3/SN63//MY54/N 10B//LR64/3/TAC'S'/4/LR64//TZPP/ Y54 | IARI, New Delhi | 1979 | PZ, I,TS |
| HD 2285 | 36896/ /CJ54/P4160E/3/HUAR/4/KAL 'S'/NP852/4/PJ'S'/P14//KT54B/3/K65/ 6/HD2160/7/SL'S'/7NP852/4/PJ'S/ P14// KT54B/3/K65/5/2*SKA | " | 1985<br>1992 | NWPZ<br>I,LS,VLS |
| HD 2329 | Sl'S'/NP852/4/PJ'S'/P14//KT54B/3/ K65/5/SKA/6/UP262 | " | 1985 | NWPZ, I,TS |
| HD 2380 | HD 2135 'S'/SKA/3/TOB/CNO 'S'/ /B/4/ NAI60*2//TT/SN64/3/LR64/SN64/5/ HD2160/HD2170 | " | 1989 | NHZ R&IL; PZ, I,TS |
| HD 2402 | HD2177//CNO67/BB/3/HD2160/4/ HD2236 | " | 1988 | NEPZ I,TS |
| HD 2028 | HD1949/HD2160 | " | 1989 | NWPZ I,TS |
| HD 2643 | VEE'S'//HD 207/HD 2329 | " | 1996 | NEPZ; IR,LS |
| HD 2687 | CPAN 2009/HD 2329 | " | 1999 | NEPZ; I,TS |
| HD R77 | PTZ/2*HD 2204 | " | 1990 | NEPZ R,LS |
| HI 977 | GLL/AUSTII61-157/ /CNO/NO/3/ Y50E/3*KAL | IARI, Indore | 1988 | PZ, I,LS |
| HI 1077 | GLL/AUSTII61-157//CNO/NO/3/ KAL/BB3*KAL | " | 1989 | CZ,I,TS |

**Table 5:** (*Contd...*)

**Table 5:** (*Contd...*)

| *Variety* | *Parentage* | *Developed by* | *Year of release* | *Area of adaptation* |
|---|---|---|---|---|
| HS 240 | AURORA//KAL/BB/3/WOP/4/PVN | IARI, Shimla | 1989 | NHZ, R,IL, TS |
| HS 365 | HS 207/SONALIKA | IARI, Shimla | 1997 | NHZ R,TS |
| HUW 234 | NP826/CNO//SPRW/3/NP826/CNO | BHU, Varanasi | 1984 | NEPZ, I,LS |
| HW 2004 | C306*7/TR380-14*7/3AG14 | IARI, New Delhi | 1997 | CZ, R,TS |
| K 88 | VEE/WL711 | CSAUAT, Kanpur | 1991 | NEPZ, I,TS |
| K 9006 | CPAN 168/HD 2204 | " | 1994 | NEPZ, I,TS |
| K 9107 | K8101/K 68 | " | 1994 | NEPZ, I,TS |
| K 9465 | B 1153/CB85 | " | 1997 | NEPZ, R,LS |
| KRL 1-4 | KHARCHIA 65/WL 711 | CSSRI, Karnal | 1995 | Saline soils in all zones |
| Lok 1 | S 308/S 331 | LOK BHARATI | 1981 | CZ, I,TS&LS |
| ACS 2496 | VEERY #5 (SERI) | MACS-ARI, PUNE | 1991 | PZ, I,TS |
| NDW 1012 | PARANA#2//JUP/BJY'S'/3/VEE#5'S'/ JUN'S' | NDUAT, Faizabad | 1997 | NEPZ, I,TS |
| PBW 154 | HD2160/HD2177 | PAU, Ludhiana | 1989 | NWPZ, LTS |
| PBW 226 | C591/RN//JN/3/CHR/HIRA | " | 1989 | NWPZ, LTS |
| PBW 299 | BB/KAL//WL711/PBW65 | " | 1992 | NWPZ, I,TS |
| NDW 1014 | HAN'S' | " | 1997 | NEPZ, I,LS |
| PBW 343 | ND/V1944/ /KAL/ /BB/3/YACO'S'/4/ VEE#5 | " | 1995 | NWPZ, I,TS |
| Raj 1482 | NAPO/TOB'S//8156/KAL/BB | RAU, Durgapura | 1982 | NWPZ, LTS |
| Raj 3077 | HD2177/3/CNO67/BB//HD2160/4/ RAJ1482/5/BB//INIA66'S'/NAPO | " | 1990 | NWPZ, LTS&LS |
| Raj 3765 | HD 2402/VL 639 | " | 1994 | NWPZ, I,LS |
| Raj Laxmi (HP 1731) | LIRA 'S'/PRL'S/TONI | IARI, Pusa | 1994 | NEPZ I,TS |
| HP 1633 (Sonali) | TH*6/Tf / /6*SONALIKA | IARI, Pusa | 1992 | NEPZ, I,LS |
| Sonalika | MIDA-U/K117A//2*TH/3/FN/4*TH/4/ AN/5/B//LR/6/B4946-A4-18-1/Y53//3* Y50 | JT | 1967 | Plains of India, I,TS&ILS |
| Sujata | SEL C306 | IARI, Indore | 1983 | CZ,R,TS NEPZ, |
| UP 262 | S308/BJ 66 | GBPUA&T, Pantnagar | 1977 | I,TS |

**Table 5:** (*Contd...*)

**Table 5:** (*Contd...*)

| *Variety* | *Parentage* | *Developed by* | *Year of release* | *Area of adaptation* |
|---|---|---|---|---|
| UP 2338 | UP 368/ VL 421 / /UP 262 | " | 1993 | NEPZ, I,TS |
| UP 2425 | HD 2320 /UP 2263 | " | 1999 | NWPZ, I,LS |
| VL 616 | SKA/P46 | VPKAS, Almora | 1986 | NHZ, ES CZ,I,TS |
| WH 147 | PJ'S'/P14//Kt54B/3/C286/C273/4/S339 PV18 | HAU, Hisar | 1977 | |
| WH 283 | HD1981/RAJ821 | " | 1984 | NWPZ, I,TS |
| WH 542 | JUP/BJY'S'//URES | " | 1992 | NWPZ, I,TS |
| WH 896 | STN'S'/WH 852 | " | | |
| HS 1097-17 (Girija) | Cajemi 60/3/SPO/MTA//MQ/2*RNW | IARI, Shimla | 1973 | NHZ(H) IL, TS |
| NI 5439 | RFPM80/3*NP 710 | MPKV, Niphad | 1973 | PZ, R&IL, TS |
| K 7410 (K, Poorvi) | CNO'S'//SN 64/KLRE/3/8156/4/KAL | CSAUAT, Kanpur | 1979 | NEPZ, I &I L, TS |
| K 8027 (Maghar) | NP875/4/N10B/Y53//Y50/3/KT54B/5/2 | " | 1988 | NEPZ, R, TS |
| HUW 206 (Malaviya 206) | KVZ/BUHO//KAL/BB | BHU, Varanasi | 1955 | NEPZ, R, TS |
| WL 711 | S 308/CHRIS//Kalyansona | PAU, Ludhiana | 1979 | NWPZ, I, TS |
| UP 301 | Lerma Rojo 64/Sonora 64 | GBPUA & T, Pantnagar | 1969 | PZ, I, TS |
| C 306 | Regent 1974/CSK3//2*C591/3/C217/ N14//C281 | HAU, Hisar | 1965 | NWPZ R, TS |
| Bijaga Yellow(d) | Mysore local/Gaza | UAS, Dharwad | 1965 | Karnataka R, TS |
| A-9-30-1(d) | A206/Gaza | GAU, Arnej | 1970 | CZ, R, TS |
| Raj 1955(d) | COCORIT/RAJ 911 | RAU, Durgapura | 1982 | CZ, I, TS |
| PDW 215 (d) | RAJ911//AA'S'/D#2E/3/DWL5002 | PAU, Ludhiana | 1991 | NWPW, I, TS |
| HI 8381 (d) | JP69'S'/AA'S'//FGO'S' | IARI, Indore | 1993 | CZ, I, TS |
| HI 8498 (d) | RAJ 6070/RAJ 911 | IARI, Indore | 1997 | CZ, I, TS |
| PDW 233 (d) | YAV'S'/TEN'S' | " | 1997 | PUN, I, TS |

(d) = durum; JT = Joint release
I = Irrigated; R = Rainfed; TS = Timely sown; LS = Late sown
PUN = Punjab

programmes with passport data of characters for which it is useful. This nursery serves as a crossing block and many breeders use this material in their crossing programme. Special nurseries like Drought and Heat Tolerance Nursery (DHTSN), Quality Component Screening Nursery (QCSN), Yield Component Screening Nursery (YCSN), Salinity/ Alkalinity Screening Nursery (SSN) are planted for identifying superior genotypes for the respective characters.

Another important feature of the Indian programme is the use of summer nursery facilities at Wellington in the South and at Dalang Maidan (Lahul Spiti) in the Himalayas. These stations not only help in advancing the generations and accelerate the breeding programmes, but also act as testing centres for various biotic stresses like rusts. This approach of growing wheat in plains and hills also helps in solving the problem of photosensitivity of the material and has been the key to the success of CIMMYT semidwarfs across the world. Shuttle breeding programmes are also organized for addressing regional problems. One such activity between Karnal, Varanasi and Faizabad deals with development of leaf blight tolerant genotypes.

## 7. BREEDING METHODOLOGY

The major objectives in wheat breeding are: improvement of productivity, stabilizing yield levels by minimizing losses due to biotic and abiotic stresses and providing grain of acceptable quality for consumption and processing into products. Heyne and Smith (1967) emphasized the balance between art and science in wheat breeding. Today increased emphasis is placed on science at all stages in a breeding programme and the breeder is equipped with an armoury of techniques to draw upon. Still there is an art component to breeding particularly since the breeders practice visual selection of material. A wheat breeder has to practice the art, living with his lines from planting to harvest and be able to decide how the material selected will perform as a variety. However, a creative breeder has to be equipped with all the knowledge of modern science in relation to the wheat plant, particularly the inheritance and heritability of the characters and the expression of the character in diverse environments.

### 7.1. Yield Improvement

Wheat is naturally self-pollinated. So, most of the basic methods described for self-pollinating crops apply to wheat (Allard, 1960; Hayes, Immer and Smith, 1955; Leonord and Martin, 1963). These can be classified as line or pedigree method and bulk method. All other procedures involve the principles of these two approaches.

It has been realized that progress in further improvement is going to be slow using conventional approaches because of the inherent limitations of self-pollination, like i) rapid fixation of genotypes, ii) restriction of recombination, iii) preclusion of exchange between plants that prevent emergence of desirable gene constellations. Joshi and Dhawan (1966) emphasized the need for reorienting the breeding methodology for breeding self-pollinated crops. They suggested several approaches to bring faster and more stable improvement for turning the green revolution into an ever-green revolution. These include (i) collection, evaluation and utilization of germplasm from diverse sources, (ii) choice of appropriate parents using biometrical approaches, (iii) exploitation of segregating generations from chosen crosses by selecting superior pure lines equalling or surpassing the yield of $F_1$ hybrids or biparental mating for releasing locked-up genetic variability, and (iv) utilization of component breeding.

## 7.2. The Pedigree or Line Method of Selection

Important feature of this method are the detailed study of individuals during the segregating generations and the records kept so that parent-progeny relations can be followed. In this method, the $F_2$ plants are space planted normally at 10 cm distance, so that record of individual plants can be kept. Some characters with high heritability can be selected at this stage, such as rust resistance, height, maturity, seed size and morphological characters. The progency of each $F_2$ plant is sown as $F_3$ progeny rows. The size of each $F_3$ progeny is decided by the resources available and 2-3 rows are normally planted. Selection from $F_3$ onwards is based on line performance. The $F_3$ lines that are considered for further progeny tests are studied on the basis of individual plants. Two to 10 plants per line will be retained and their progeny are grown for the $F_4$ generation. In the $F_4$ generation evaluation and selection can be made on the basis of the family. Any line that is phenotypically homogeneous can be harvested in bulk and the progeny can be used for yield testing. If necessary, the $F_5$ generation can be handled similar to the $F_4$ generation (Fig. 8).

During the segregating generations, artificial disease and insect epidemics can be created to select resistant lines and plants. The $F_2$ or $F_3$ generation can be grown in areas with abiotic stresses, like drought, salinity/alkalinity, or soil borne diseases to select resistant plants or lines.

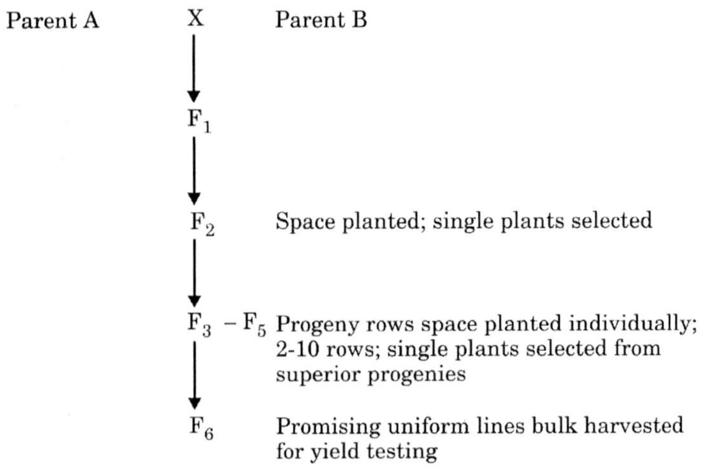


**Fig. 8:** Scheme for pedigree or line method of breeding wheat

## 7.3. Bulk Method

This method was originally proposed by Nilsson-Ehle and has several variations. The segregating generations are handled as bulks and not as single plants, up to about $F_6$ generation. Selection of spikes or plants in $F_6$ or $F_7$ generation will provide relatively homozygous lines (Fig. 9). Although this procedure requires minimum labour and cost, it is necessary to carry on with a large quantity of seed to give an adequate representation to genotypes, since both superior and inferior genotypes will be included. This could be an effective method for selecting genotypes with resistance to abiotic stresses, so that all susceptible plants are eliminated. Knott (1989) also suggested this precedure for selecting stem rust resistant lines using a system of bulk and mass selection. If stem rust can be developed in a severe form, the $F_2$ can be selected on the basis of boldness of seed as, under high infection of stem rust, the seed will be shrivelled and the healthy seed will come only from resistant plants. This will ensure greater proportion of resistant plants in the succeeding generations.

## 7.4. Modified Bulk Method

A variation or combination of line and bulk method is being followed in recent years by CIMMYT and also some centres in India. In this method, the $F_2$ and $F_3$ generations are space-planted. Spikes from promising plants are selected and bulked. From $F_4$ the material is treated as in

| | | |
|---|---|---|
| Parent A | X | Parent B |
| | ↓ | |
| | $F_1$ | |
| | ↓ | |
| | $F_2$ | Space planted; single plants/spikes selected and bulked |
| | ↓ | |
| | $F_3$ | Same as in $F_2$ |
| | ↓ | |
| | $F_4$ | Space planted; single plants/spikes selected and harvested individually |
| | ↓ | |
| | $F_5$ | Space planted; single plants selected |
| | ↓ | |
| | $F_6$ | Preliminary yield trial |
| | ↓ | |
| | $F_7$ | Space planting of superior progenies based on yield trial; for further purification single plants selected |
| | ↓ | |
| | $F_8$ | Individual plant progeny are planted; selected progeny bulk harvested |
| | ↓ | |
| | $F_9$ | Yield testing to continue |

**Fig. 9:** Scheme for modified bulk method of breeding

pedigree method. This modification of bulk method provides an opportunity to the breeder to exercise his skill and judgement in selecting superior plant types in early generations, but avoids the time and labour required in pedigree method.

Several studies have been conducted to improve the efficiency of early generation selection. Yield testing in early generations has not yielded consistent results. Even then, most breeders will not like to spend time and effort on extensive early generation testing. The use of early generation testing for yield has been discussed in detail by Knott (1987) who came to the conclusion that none of the methods demonstrated consistent advantage in increasing the efficiency of selection to warrant the extra efforts. These problems have led to consider efforts towards rapid production of homozygotes by procedures such as single seed descent (SSD) and anther culture and to postpone yield testing on such material. These methods help in identifying lines that are better than the parents, rather than identify the best possible segregate of the cross.

## 7.5. Population Improvement

In cross pollinated crops like maize, population improvement using recurrent selection is a regular procedure. This procedure is less practiced in self pollinated crops because of the difficulty in making several crosses. As a routine, however, even in wheat, a modification of recurrent selection is practiced. Breeders select lines that are promising for some characters and recycle them into the crossing programme. Gilmore (1964) suggested use of cytoplasmic or genetic male sterility in a reciprocal recurrent selection programme in cereals, while Sorrels and Fritz (1982) suggested use of dominant male sterile gene, for facilitating crossing. Based on biometrical analysis of gene action governing yield and its component characters, random intermating of early generation material has been suggested by many workers as a way of breaking linkage blocks and increasing genetic variability before enforcing selection. However, there are very few centres where this is practiced as a routine breeding methodology. Jensen (1970) proposed a diallel selective mating system which involves crossing a group of parents, intercrossing the $F_1$s, selecting among the new $F_1$s and $F_2$s and intermating the selected plants (Fig. 10). This method overcomes the limitations of pedigree method, helps in genetic upgradation of the population and at the same time provides progeny for commercial varieties. This scheme also allows for incorporating multiple parents either from germplasm or from breeding programmes into a central gene pool and application of mass and recurrent selection throughout. This method has been shown to be effective for increasing the mean yield and its components (Pawar *et al.,* 1990).

## 7.6. Rapid Attainment of Homozygosity

Because of the limitation of early generation testing for yield, wheat breeders have been interested in ways that can cut down on the time taken to reach homozygosity so that emphasis can be placed on testing the homozygous lines rather than the efforts on producing them. Two

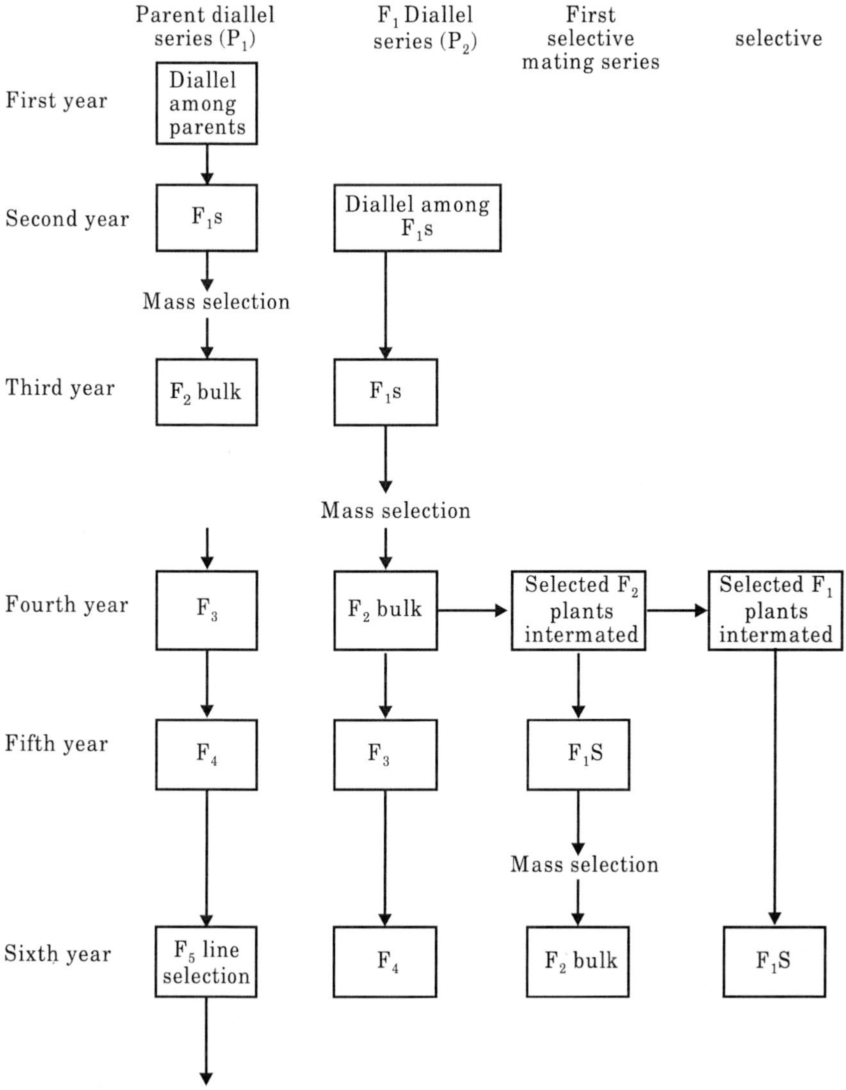


**Fig. 10:** Scheme for diallel selective mating system

approaches proposed are: (i) single seed descent, and (ii) production of haploid plants either by wide crosses or anther culture, followed by chromosome doubling.

## 7.7. Single Seed Descent Method

In the single seed descent method, a single seed is taken from each plant of the $F_2$ generation, and the seeds are grown to produce next generation. The $F_2$ plants selected for SSD can be either random or can be selected for characters that have high heritability. The objective is to reduce the amount of material carried from one generation to the next and speed up generation advance. Crosses can be advanced for any number of generations using SSD. In the final generation, the plants are spaced to provide sufficient seed to begin testing of the homozygous lines. Care should be taken to select sufficient number of plants in $F_2$ to provide a reasonable number of SSD derived lines, because at each generation, some plants can be lost due to various reasons. Evidence from several studies (Knott and Kumar, 1975; Pawar *et al.,* 1995) suggest that the SSD is a useful procedure particularly when heritability is low and early generation selection is ineffective. The relative efficiency of alternative methods like mechanical mass selection, earhead selection, simplified pedigree selection of bulking at $F_3$ stage has been reviewed by Singh and Pawar (1998) and they strongly advocated these methods for wheat improvement. The various methods must be considered as complementary to each other and a method combining merits of two or more system will be more effective.

## 7.8. Doubled Haploid Production

Doubled haploids have the potential to speed up generation advance even more. Two methods are widely used (i) culturing immature anthers in a tissue culture medium that allows the pollen grains to develop into haploid plants. The frequency of haploid plants from pollen grains is variable and large number of anthers need to be cultured, and (ii) cross wheat plants with a wild species and allow development of haploid embryos. In the earlier years, *Hordeum bulbosum*, a wild relative of barley, was crossed with wheat plants for production of haploids. However, it has been found that several wheat varieties cannot be crossed to this species, because embryos and endosperm fail to develop (Zenkteller and Straub, 1979), because they lack the crossability genes. In recent years, wheat x maize crosses have been extensively used to produce haploid embryos. The maize chromosomes are eliminated in the first two to three division cycles to produce haploid wheat embryos (Laurie and Bennett, 1988; Comeau *et al.,* 1988). The immature embryos are cultured on a medium to produce haploid plants.

The wheat material that can be used for this purpose can be either from $F_1$, $BC_1$ or $F_2$ generation. Although several breeding programmes in the West have turned to this method for developing wheat varieties, in India so far, this method is not used because many breeding stations lack expertise and facilities to carry out the *in vitro* culture on a large scale.

## 7.9. Backcross Breeding

This method is a modification of the line or pedigree method but is important in certain situation like improvement of one or more highly heritable characters in an otherwise promising variety. It differs from other methods in that one rarely gets a transgressive segregate, but has advantage of being the most rapid and inexpensive method for achieving short term goals in wheat breeding. This method was proposed by Harlan and Pope (1922) and was used in several countries. This method is particularly useful for transferring single genes for resistance to disease. When a particular variety becomes susceptible to say rust disease due to evolution of virulent pathotypes, a backcross programme canbe quickly initiated to introduce a gene that confers resistance to the new pathotype and the variety can be replaced by the new version. The speed with which the backcross derivative can be developed will depend on the nature of the gene. If a dominant gene is involved, at each backcross stage resistant plants can be selected in field for further backcrossing. If a recessive gene is involved, each backcross generation has to be interspersed with a selfing generation to recover the homozygous recessive plants, before further backcrossing can be done. Quite often, if both the donor and the recurrent parent are good genotypes, limited backcrosses, say 2 or 3 canbe made, before effecting selection. If 5 to 6 backcrosses are given, most of the recurrent parent genotypes will be recovered and there will be no scope for improvement except for the character governed by the gene that has been transferred. A programme of incorporation of genes for rust resistance in the Indian wheat varieties was initiated at the IARI Regional Station, Wellington, and several near isogenic lines (NILs) have been developed (Menon, Fers. Comm.). Some of them like HW 2004 (backcross line of C 306 carrying Lr24) and HW 2044 (backcross line of PBW 226) have been released for cultivation, to replace the existing varieties. Similarly, NILs carrying *Rht-B1* and *Rht-B3* genes have been developed in some of the tall Indian wheats.

## 7.10. Mutation Breeding

The variability found in nature is due to accumulation of natural mutations that have occurred during the evolution of crop plants. With the discovery of mutagenic agents, both physical and chemical, plant breeder has the scope of inducing variability and use it in his breeding programme. Several physical mutagenic agent like X-rays, $\gamma$-rays, fast neutrons, thermal neutrons and chemicals like EMS, DES, MNUA, ENUA, MNU, ENU have been used to produce useful mutations (review in Konzak, 1987). The term mutation breeding was originally applied only to the induction and selection of a mutant which was increased and used directly as a cultivar. The assumption was that single, simply inherited characters could be induced in a genotype without severely affecting the rest of the genotype. The concept has now been expanded to include the combination of traits from two or more mutants in the same background to indirectly develop new varieties. In mutation cross breeding, mutant traits are recombined with those from other germplasm. In India, mutation breeding experiments were conducted in wheat during the 1960s. However, this approach has not been used in the later years. Using $\gamma$-rays, ambers grained mutants of Sonora 64 and Lerma Rojo were produced and released as Sharbati Sonora and Pusa Lerma, respectively. More recently, mutants have been reported to overcome the necrotic genes which interfer in production of successfull crosses. A non-necrotic genetic stock of the highly adapted variety for rainfed conditions, C 306, has been reported. It was not possible to use this variety carrying *Ne1* gene in crosses with some exotic varieties carrying *Ne2* gene, because hybrids become necrotic due to complementary gene action and failed to set seed. The non-necrotic mutant will enable this useful agronomic base to be used as a parent in the breeding programme.

## 7.11. Hybrid Wheat

Hybrid wheat research has been going on ever since Wilson and Ross (1962) reported that interaction of *T. timopheevii* cytoplasm and *T. aestivum* nucleus resulted in complete and stable male sterility without any adverse effects on plant development and growth. Several reviews have been published on the status and prospects of hybrid wheat and the readers interested in this aspect may refer to these. Although the system exist, there have been several limitations to its use for commercial hybrid seed production. Some of them are:

a. Every time a heterotic hybrid is to be developed, the parents have to be first converted into male sterile and restorer lines for producing hybrid seed. This may take several rounds of backcross, by which time the varietal improvement may have resulted in higher yields, and the hybrid vigour may not compensate for the extra cost involved.

b. The male sterile and restorer lines may behave differently in different environments.

c. The hybrid seed yield will depend largely on the amount of outcrossing that can occur on the male sterile plants. This will be conditioned by the amount of pollen dispersed in air. Being a naturally self pollinated crop, wheat has the tendency to release the pollen before the anther is extruded. It is necessary to identify genotypes that have a greater anther extrusion and longer anthers and longer receptivity of the stigma.

Because of these problems, hybrid wheat based on CMS system has not been an economic proposition, in spite of the fact that several private companies in USA and Canada have invested substantial funds for this purpose.

A more recent alternative approach for producing hybrid wheat is through the use of chemicals that induce male sterility. These are referred to as Chemical Hybridizing Agents (CHAs) and circumvent several of the problems associated with cytoplasmic genetic male sterility system in wheat. To produce hybrid seed, one of the parents to be used is treated with the chemical at an appropriate time and the resulting male sterile plants are pollinated by wind pollination from alternating, untreated plants of the other variety. Several chemical companies have synthesized and evaluated the potential CHAs. Many of them have been patented and are not available for free-use. The requirements of a CHA are :

a. It should be able to induce complete or near complete male sterility without reducing female fertility.

b. It should be systemic or persistent to sterilize both early and late tillers.

c. The sterilizing capacity should be stable over a long period of time, to allow large areas to be sprayed before pollination can take place.

d. The chemical should have minimal effect on other parts, growth and development, *i.e.*, have least toxic effects.

e. It should be highly stable over environments

The advantages of CHAs are :

a. There is no need of developing male sterile and restorer lines. Any two varieties which produce economic heterosis can be used to produce the hybrid seed.

b. CHAs eliminate most of the problems associated with seed increase of parents. In a cytoplasmic-genetic male sterility restoration system, one needs to maintain the male steriles by using maintainer lines in separate fields, for maintaining purity.

Research on hybrid wheat in India has been initiated only during the last 3 years and several chemicals are being tried for their efficiency in inducing male sterility. It may take another 4-5 years before commercial hybrids will be available, if current research activities yield practicable solutions to various problems associated with the hybrid wheat production (Mahajan *et al.,* 1998).

## 7.12. Use of Cytogenetics in Wheat Improvement

The discovery that wheat is an allohexaploid with three homoeologous genomes led to extensive cytogenetic research in wheat. Among the polyploid crop plants, wheat is the most worked out cytogenetically and is a model for other polyploids. Sears (1954,1966) produced a series of aneuploids like monosomics, nullisomics, trisomics, tetrasomics, ditelosomics, nulli-tetra compensating lines etc. in the hexaploid wheat Chinese Spring and they formed the basis of several cytogenetic studies. In India, monosomics were developed in the variety C 591 (Swaminathan *et al.,* 1968) and Kalyan Sona. Using the nulli-tetra compensating lines, the 21 chromosomes of wheat have been grouped into the three genomes A, B and D and numbered from 1 to 7. These aneuploids enabled extensive genetic analysis of various morphological and economic characters and they are more recently used in molecular analysis of wheat. Several genes have been allocated to individual chromosomes and chromosome arms using these stocks. They are reviewed every five years with annual supplements and are published in the form of "Catalogue of Gene Symbols for Wheat" (Mclntosh *et al.,* 1998). The monosomics have been used to develop inter-varietal substitution lines which have been of immense value in understanding the contribution of individual chromosomes in different backgrounds.

## 7.13. Alien Gene Transfer in Wheat

An alien gene can be considered as one which is transferred to wheat from a related species. The genus *Triticum* contains several species which differ in their ability to cross with either the tetraploid (*T. turgidum*) or with hexaploid wheat (*T. aestivum*). Wheat can also be crossed to the related genera like *Agropyron, Elymus, Elytrigia* (=*Agropyron*), *Haynaldia, Hordeum* and *Secale.* More than 300 hybrids involving 47 species of *Triticum* have been developed and have been reviewed by Sharma and Gill (1983) and Jiang *et al.* (1994). The wild relatives of wheat are adapted to a broad range of environmnets and carry a large reservoir ot useful genes for wheat improvement. Initially they were considered primarily as sources of disease resistance. But several species have been found to have genes for high protein, cold tolerance, salt tolerance, drought tolerance, lodging resistance, early maturity and even yield.

The success in transfer of alien genes to wheat will depend on several factors like the degree of crossability and amount of pairing between the alien chromosome and wheat chromosome. The wild relatives of wheat can be classified into primary, secondary and tertiary gene pools on the basis of their genomic constitutions.

The primary gene pool consists of the tetraploid species and the A and D genome donors. Transfer of genes from tetraploid wheats to hexaploids is relatively simple because two genomes A and B are common. There are several examples of this type, like transfer of rust resistance from lumillo durum to Marquillo (Hayes *et al.,* 1920), from Yaroslav emmer to bread wheats Hope and H 44 (McFadden, 1930), and transfer of stripe rust resistance from *T. dicoccoides* to *T. aestivum* (Grama and Gerechter-Amitai, 1974). However, sometimes, the transfer may not be successful, because of suppressors in D genome as has been found while transferring leaf rust resistance from durum to bread wheat (Kerber and Green, 1980). Transfer from einkom wheats is also possible, but the hybrid embryos need to be cultured *in vitro* for getting hybrid plants. Often the tetraploids can be used as bridging species. Using this procedure, stem rust resistance from *T. monococcum* was transferred to bread wheat (Kerber and Dyck, 1973; Knott, 1979). The D genome donor, *T. tauschii* was also used to transfer leaf rust resistance genes to bread wheat (Kerber and Dyck, 1969; Dyck and Kerber, 1970; Cox *et al.,* 1993).

The secondary gene pool consists of *Triticum* and *Aegilops* species carrying at least one genome in common with wheat. These can be used to transfer useful genes by direct crosses and selection, if the gene is located on homologous genome. If the gene is on a nonhomologous chromosome, cytogenetic manipulation is required, as for tertiary gene pool described below.

For transferring desirable genes from species belonging to tertiary gene pool with genomes nonhomologous to those of wheat, ingenious techniques have been developed. With the application of embryo rescue techniques, hybrids between several species and genera have been successfully obtained. One such technique is the production of alien addition or substitution line carrying the chromosome on which the desired gene is located. This can by done by crossing the alien species with wheat and crossing either the polyhaploid $F_1$ plant or the amphiploid with the wheat parent. Repeated backcrosses to the wheat parent will result in production of alien addition line. The addition lines can be crossed with monosomics in wheat to produce alien substitution lines. Kota and Dvorak (1985) and Zhang *et al.* (1992) gave alternate methods for production of alien substitution lines. The agronomic suitability of the alien substitution line will depend upon how much compensation is provided by the alien chromosome to the missing wheat chromosome. Substitution of entire alien chromosome can often lead to some additional undesirable traits.

Once the alien addition line or substitution line is produced, the desired gene has to be transferred to the wheat chromosomes. Sears (1956) used ionizing radiations to produce translocations between a wheat chromosome and an alien chromosome from *Ae. umbellulata (T. umbellulatum,* UU) carrying a gene for leaf rust resistance. Wheat plants carrying monosomic addition of *umbellulata* chromosome were developed. The monoisosomic plants were irradiated with x-rays prior to meiosis and the pollen was used to cross with a susceptible wheat variety. Leaf rust resistant progeny were examined cytologically and plants carrying the translocation were identified. One line, designated Transfer *(Lr9)* was found to be resistant to several leaf rust pathotypes across the world. A leaf rust resistant line of Sonalika, Sonali, was developed in India carrying *Lr9,* at the IARI Regional Station, Pusa, Bihar. Recently, a pathotype of leaf rust virulent on this gene has been isolated from Wellington (Anonymous, 1999).

The discovery of genetic control of chromosome pairing in wheat opened up new approaches to transfer genes from alien homoeologous chromosomes into wheat by manipulating the *Ph1* gene. The simplest way is to produce wheat x alien species crosses that lack the *Ph1* gene, like a monosomic for chromosome 5B. Progeny lacking the 5B will have a high level of pairing and recombinants can be recovered from backcrosses of these plants with wheat. A more elegant method involves the use of alien chromosome substitution lines (Sears, 1972). By use of nullisomic 5B-tetrasomic 5D genotype, plants can be obtained which lack 5B but are monosomic for both an alien chromosome and a wheat homoeologue. In this way, induced recombination can be directed from a single alien chromosome, known to carry a required gene, to a specific wheat chromosome. Joshi and Singh (1979) crossed monosomic 5B of C 591 with Russian rye. One plant with 28 chromosomes showed extensive pairing. By backcrossing to C 591, plants with resistance to all three wheat rusts were obtained.

Use of species that suppress the activity of *Ph1,* like *Ae. speltoides (T. speltoides)* and *Ae. mutica (T. tripsacoides)* can be used to facilitate homoeologous recombination. Dvorak (1977) produced hybrids between these species and wheat by using embryo culture. By backcrossing the hybrids to wheat, leaf rust resistance from *T. speltoides* was transferred to wheat. These species were also used to transfer desired genes from other alien species. Riley *et al.* (1968) crossed an addition line of wheat carrying chromosome from *Ae. comosa (T. comosum)* with *T. speltoides* to induce homoeologous pairing. The hybrid is crossed and backcrossed to wheat and selection made for the desired character. This stock was called "Compair" and had stripe rust resistance derived from *T. comosum.*

Although a number of wheat alien transfers have been produced, very few varieties carrying these have found commercial use. Most do not compensate for the loss of wheat genome or carry with them other undesirable characters. The most successful recombinant stocks are the 1BL.1RS translocations, which have been used for wheat improvement in several countries, including India. The short arm of 1R carries genes for leaf rust (Lr26), stem rust (*Sr31*), stripe rust (*Yr9*) and powdery mildew (*Pm8* and *Pm17*) resistance along with genes for high adaptability and yielding ability (Rajaram *et al.,* 1983). However, these stocks are also not without drawbacks, as they cause the dough to become sticky due to secalin loci, resulting in poor dough quality of the flour.

## 8. BIOTIC STRESSES

Intensive agricultural practices under which wheat is grown have resulted in several biotic and abiotic problems (Table 6). Among the biotic stresses, the rusts—stem, leaf and stripe rust—caused by *Puccinia graminis* Pers. f. sp. *tritici, P. recondita* Rob. ex Desm. f. sp. *tritici* and *P. striiformis* f. sp. *tritici,* respectively, are the most important and next only to yield improvement. Breeding for rust diseases is the major activity of wheat breeders in the country. The importance of prevalent rust has changed over the years. During 1960s stem rust was the major problem and breeding efforts were directed towards controlling this disease. During 1970s, stem rust continued to be the major biotic problem followed by leaf rust and stripe rust. During 1980s stem rust almost became negligible, occurring only in the Central and Peninsular India and its place has been taken by the leaf rust and stripe rust. The situation continues to remain so at present. Leaf rust is important throughout the country, while stem rust is restricted to Central and Peninsular India and the stripe rust to the colder climates of North India.

**Table 6:** Biotic and abiotic stresses of wheat in India

| *Zone* | *Biotic stresses* | *Abiotic Stresses* |
|---|---|---|
| Northern Hill Zone | Stripe rust; Leaf rust; Powdery mildew; Hill bunt, Loose smut | Salinity/alkalinity |
| North Western Plains Zone | Stripe rust; Leaf rust; Karnal bunt; *Fusarium* head Scab (in durum); Loose smut; Flag smut; Powdery mildew; *Phalaris Minor,* Aphids; Brown wheat mite; Army worm; Cutworm; Stem borer | Salinity/alkalinity |
| North Eastern Plains Zone | Leaf rust; Stripe rust; Loose smut; Foliar blight; Powdery mildew; Cereal cyst nematode; Ear cockle disease; *Phalaris minor* | Salinity/alkalinity |
| Central Zone | Leaf rust; Stem rust; Foliar blight; *Sclerotium* foot rot; Termite; Stem borer; Cutworm | Moisture stress; high temperatures during the entire growth period |
| Peninsular Zone | Leaf rust; Stem rust; *Sclerotium* foot rot; Foliar blight | Moisture stress; high temperatures during the entire growth period |
| Southern Hill Zone | Stem rust; Leaf rust; Stripe rust; Powdery mildew; *Septoria* Glume blotch | |

Note: Most important factors are indicated in bold

## 8.1. Epidemiology of Wheat Rust in India

Poineering work was done during the 1950s and 1960s by K.C. Mehta, at Shimla, who identified that in spite of the absence of alternate hosts, rusts perpetuate in the hills of North India and Southern India. These studies proved that chief source of rust infection is through overwintering/oversummering of uredospores in sub-Himalayan ranges particularly central Nepal in the North and Nilgiri and Pulney hills in South. The epidemiology of wheat rusts in India demonstrated the role of cyclonic storm on the spread of rust in the country (Nagarajan and Joshi, 1984). The first build up of leaf rust takes place in the plains of Karnataka in South India and in foot hills of Bihar and eastern part of Uttar Pradesh in the north. The rust population from southern foci moves northward towards Maharashtra and Madhya Pradesh and the population from North moves south and finally both merge together. Stem rust on the other hand has a unidirectional movement from south to North. The cyclonic currents originating from Bay of Bengal and/or the ketabolic air currents between hills and plains lift the inoculum and introduce it as far as central India. The stripe rust is confined to the cooler parts of North India and is introduced from northern hills by ketabolic wind current and gets established in the plains along the foot hills. It is totally absent from south India except for the hills of Tamilnadu, but it cannot establish in plains due to high temperatures prevailing during the crop season.

The rusts occur as physiological races or biotypes which differ in their infection on specific hosts, called as *differential hosts.* Flor (1942) established the genetic system of host-parasite interaction for linseed rust and it has been since found operating for a number of diseases. According to this hypothesis, for each resistance gene in the host, there is an avirulence gene in the pathotype. Resistance or low infection type (LIT) occurs when a resistance gene in the host is matched by an avirulence gene in the pathogen. All other combinations produce a high infection type (HIT) or susceptible reaction. Although there are several exceptions, a simplified interaction model is presented below :

| ***Pathogen*** | ***Host*** | | |
|---|---|---|---|
| | ***RR*** | ***Rr*** | ***rr*** |
| PP | LIT | LIT | HIT |
| Pp | LIT | LIT | HIT |
| pp | HIT | HIT | HIT |

LIT = Low infection type; HIT = High infection type

Using this interaction, 45 Sr genes for stem rust resistance, 47 Lr genes for leaf rust resistance and 28 Yr genes for stripe rust resistance have been identified from different sources (Mclntosh *et al.,* 1998). These are called the major genes or specific resistance genes or vertical resistance genes because of their effectiveness in producing a resistance reaction in response to infection by a particular pathotype of rust. These are effective throughout the life of the plant and are identified on the basis of reaction on wheat seedlings. The biotypes of rust were originally identified on the basis of their infection types on the wheat varieties with a combintion of genes. However, with the understanding of the genetic basis, they are identified nowadays in relation to the known genes for resistance and are called as pathotypes. Nagarajan *et al.* (1983) developed a binary system of classification of rusts.

### 8.1.1. *Breeding for rust resistance*

It has been a common observation that the life of a variety in the field is not more than 5 years, particularly when the resistance genes are used in isolation, one at a time. Whenever a resistant variety is identified, it slowly gathers ground and tends to occupy large areas.

This phase of increase in the area is called the boom. Because of selection pressure, the pathogen mutates to develop virulent pathotypes which can overcome the resistant gene. These new pathotypes which are in low frequency initially, get selected and gradually increase in frequency. In other words, there is a response of the pathogen whenever there is an increase in the level of host resistance. The frequency of these pathotypes may increase over the years and create an epidemic that affects the crop badly. This is referred to as the bust or burst. The breeders try to incorporate additional resistance genes to circumvent the virulence, before additional pathotypes arise and the cycle continues. Shifts in the pathotypes and evolution of virulences of all three rusts, as a consequence of the host genotype have been reported (Bahadur, 1986; Sawhney, 1998). The evolution of leaf rust pathotypes can be taken as a model for such a situation.

Pathotypes of race group 104 and 12 of leaf rust which were predominant during 1970s declined in frequency and were overtaken by pathotypes of race 77 group in 1990s. The use of Gabo and Timstein both carrying *Lr10* and *Lr23* led to the evolution of 77A and 77A-1 with virulence to *Lr10*. Similarly, virulence for *Lr23* appeared in 1974 and nine pathotypes were reported in 1994. Frequency of pathotypes with virulence to *Lr23* increased from 46.3% in 1991 to 81.6% in 1996. The wide spread cultivation of Veery lines carrying *Lr26* gene for leaf rust resistance resulted in evolution of eight pathotypes with virulence for *Lr26* and their frequency increased from 7.8% in 1991 to 23.9% in 1996. Pathotypes with combined virulence for both *Lr23* and *Lr26* (104-2, 77-5, 77-6) have evolved resulting in susceptibility of most of the current bread wheat varieties to leaf rust (Sawhney, 1998). Interestingly, however, the durum wheats also containing *Lr23,* have shown resistance to these pathotypes, suggesting the presence of additional genes (Honrao and Rao, 1996). So far, 26 pathotypes of leaf rust, 9 pathotypes of stem rust and 11 pathotypes of stripe rust have been reported since 1970.

For increasing the effective life of a variety and avoiding frequent epidemics of rusts several approaches have been suggested. These are: pyramiding of genes, multilines, gene cycling and regional deployment of resistance genes. For pyramiding resistance genes, the aim is to develop multigene resistant varieties with 3 to 5 genes in one background. This is considered to increase the effective life span of a variety, because pathotypes virulent against all the genes do not evolve so easily and frequently. By systematically evaluating the pathotypes, resistance genes can be identified and incorporated by a simple backcross programme. Gene cycling ensures a temporal delay in the use of a resistance gene. This discontinuity minimizes the evolution of complex virulences and increases the utility of vertical resistance genes. In this method, once a variety becomes susceptible, use of the variety and the gene involved is discontinued. Instead of pyramiding more resistance genes, the use of the gene that has become susceptible is discontinued for some time, resulting in the reduction in the frequency of virulences matching this gene. The multiline approach was proposed originally by Jensen (1952) and was suggested by Borlaug (1958) as an effective way of controlling rusts. When an agronomically superior variety becomes susceptible, multilines can be bred to prevent epidemics. A multiline is a mixture of 6-7 components that are agronomically similar but differ with respect to specific gene for resistance. A multiline tends to be better insured in the field, as the adjoining plants will be different and there is spatial hurdle for the disease spread. This can delay the occurence of epidemic conditions, by which time the crop can mature and yield losses are reduced. Since multilines are developed by backcrossing, no yield improvement is expected. It is aimed at providing more yield stability rather than yield enhancement. In India, four multilines were released for commercial cultivation. These are: MLKS11, KSML 3, KML 7406 (Bithoor) and SKAML 1 in late 1970 and early 1980. However, because of continuous development of better-yielding varieties, developing multilines was not relevant. The problem of seed purity of the components and difficulties faced in certification of seed are also important aspects responsible for the loss of interest in this approach.

Gene deployment aims at creating genetic diversity in a large geographical area. This will erect a spatial hurdle to the spread of virulences from one area to another. Joshi and Nagarajan (1977) proposed three distinct epidemiological zones for leaf rust in the Indo-Gangetic plains. Similarly, Reddy and Rao (1979) suggested three zones for the whole country - Central plains (A), Northern Himalayas (B) and Southern Nilgiri and Pulney Hills (C). They proposed stronger genes *Lr9* and *Lr29* or *Lr10* and *Lr15* for zone A, 3-gene combinations like *Lr1* + *Lr10* + *Lr16* or *Lr3 (Ka)* + *Lr10* + *Lr17* for zone B, and *Lr3 (Ka)* + *Lr10* + *Lr17* for zone C.

In view of the vulnerability of race-specific (vertical) genes for resistance, and ineffectiveness of many of the identified genes, several other schemes have been proposed for providing durable resistance to rusts. It became evident that lower degree of resistance was not easily overcome by the pathogen and appeared to be more durable (Parlevliet, 1985). Race nonspecific resistance, often under the control of several genes with minor effects, appears to be more durable. This resistance manifests in the occurrence of fewer pustules, a longer time for sporulation and lesser spore production, resulting in a slow rusting type of situation. More recently, attention is focussed on the Adult Plant Resistance (APR) genes. These genes, as the name indicates, express themselves at adult plant stage. The seedlings show a susceptible reaction, but at the adult plant stage they govern different levels of resistance. They do not provide absolute resistance to the rusts, but help in keeping the infection levels low, so that epidemic conditions do not arise and the crop is not lost completely, when a new virulence emerges. The present strategy is to combine the major, specific resistance genes and the APR genes in a single variety, so that even if a virulence overcomes the major gene, the APR genes will ensure a lower level of infection. This will give the breeders time to develop resistant varieties to new pathotypes.

Gene postulation studies have indicated that Indian varieties carry a diversity of specific resistance genes for leaf rust and also some unknown adult plant resistance genes that provide durable resistance. The currently grown wheat varieties carry *Lr1,- Lr3, Lr10, Lr13, Lr14a, Lr23, Lr26, Lr34* either singly or in combination of 2 or 3 genes and some additional Adult Plant Resistance (APR) genes other than *Lr13* and *Lr34* (Sawhney *et al.*, 1992; Nayar *et al.*, 1994). *Sr1, Sr5, Sr1 a, Sr8, Sr9b, Sr11, Sr24* and *Sr31* for stem rust and *Yr2, Yr9* and *Yr18* for stripe rust have also been postulated. This is one of the reasons why the rust epidemics have become a thing of the past.

Another important aspect of wheat rust management in India is the close monitoring of the rust virulences in the country. By planting Rust Trap Nursery, consisting of varieties with different genetic constitutions for resistance genes, in all the wheat growing areas, it is now possible to identify evolution of new pathotypes, before they increase in prevalence. This nursery fore-warns the breeder of the likely pathotypes to look for hosts resistant to these pathotypes. This will enable the plant breeders to quickly include the resistant varieties in the crossing programme before the virulence increases in frequency.

Karnal Bunt caused by *Neovossia indica* (Mitra) Mundkar (=*Tilletia indica*) was first detected in India in 1931 (Mitra, 1931) and was considered a disease of minor importance till 1970. During mid 1970s, it became a major problem and severe epidemics started occuring, coinciding with shift to high yielding semidwarf varieties in irrigated and high fertilizer input farming. Karnal Bunt has been reported in many states including the major wheat growing areas of Punjab, Haryana, J & K, Uttar Pradesh, Delhi, parts of Bihar and West Bengal, Himachal Pradesh and Rajasthan. Depletion of organic matter content in the soil and changes in wheat production technology are some of the reasons ascribed for increase in Karnal Bunt incidence (Nagarajan *et al.,* 1997). The Central and Peninsular Zones are so far free from this disease. The outbreak of Karnal Bunt has been linked to the release of varieties like Arjun, WG 357, WG 277, WL 711 and UP 262 (Singh, 1986). The epidemiology of Karnal Bunt has been reviewed by Nagarajan *et al.* (1997). The teliospores released by KB infected grains are deposited in the soil and on the seed. In congenial conditions, these teliospores produce primary sporidia that are dispersed in splash and produce large quantities of secondary conidia. These infect the lower leaves and produce a second crop of spores and get dispersed to higher leaves. Once they reach flag leaf, they get deposited in the sheath by dew or a drizzle, get lodged in the inflorescence and produce microsporidia (Fig. 11). One of the immediate strategies adopted was to introduce durum wheat, the compact spikes of which provided tolerance to Karnal Bunt. Using artificial inoculation methods, varieties resistant to Karnal Bunt have been identified. Durum variety PDW 215 and triticale TL 1210 showed immunity. Bread wheat varieties like W 485, W 1786, WL 6975, HD 29, HD 30, HP 1531, ISWRN 191, and ISO 227-5 were found promising for Karnal Bunt resistance. Cultivation of durum wheat in Punjab and other resistant varieties of bread wheat released since mid 1980s enabled the national programme to contain the KB severity over north west India (Gill *et al.*, 1993).

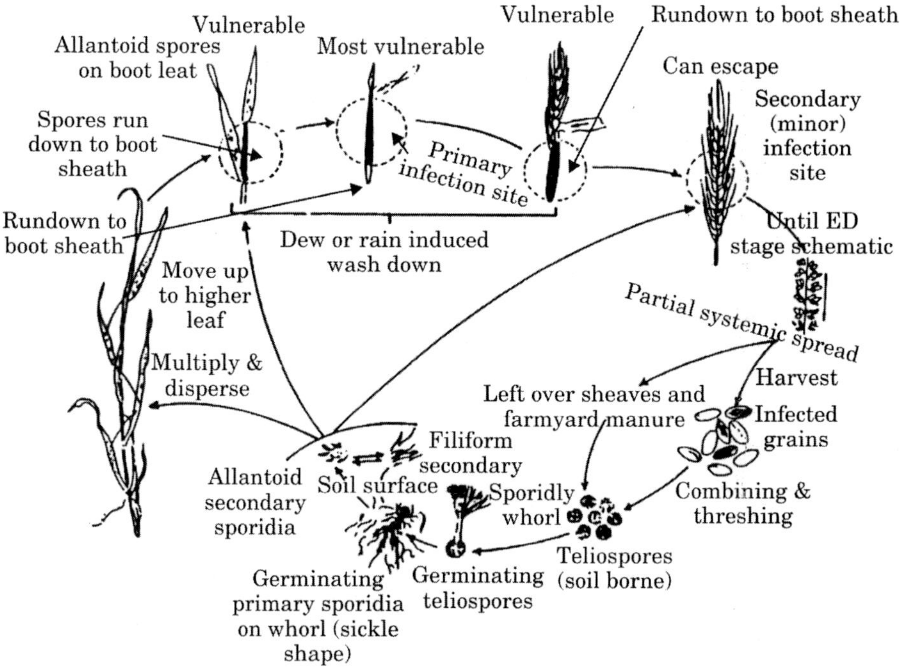


**Fig. 11:** Pathogenicity cycle of *Tilletia indica.* (Reproduced with permission from Nagarajan, 1997)

The leaf blight diseases caused by *Helminthosporium* sp. and *Alternaria* sp. are other diseases of importance particularly in the North-East Zone, Hill Zones and Tarai regions of North West Plains Zone, where the humid climate favours the development of these diseases. The extent of crop losses can be up to 35% when upper 2-3 leaves are affected and can lead to total yield loss in susceptible varieties. Unfortunately not many genetic stocks are available with resistance to these diseases. A shuttle breeding programme between Karnal, Faizabad and Varanasi has been initiated to develop leaf blight resistant varieties.

Loose smut of wheat caused by *Ustilago nuda* is another disease which is particularly important in the humid areas of North India. It is not prevalent in Central and Peninsular India. During late 1960s, the severity was high when varieties like C306, C591, Sonora 64 and Lerma Rojo were grown. The disease severity diminished with the release of varieties like Kalyan sona, but increased again with the withdrawal of Kalyan Sona from cultivation (Basant Ram and Arora, 1981) and up to 10% severity was reported in isolated areas. No organized breeding programme for breeding for loose smut resistance exists, as it is easily controlled by hot water treatment, sun drying or Vitavex treatment.

Biological control measures using *Trichoderma* sp. and *Gliocladium* sp. are being tried to control loose smut and Karnal Bunt. Studies have indicated that they are not as effective as chemicals but they hold promise in reducing the use of chemicals, by complementation with bioagents or their metabolites/culture filtrates. The bioagents can be used when disease severity is low and a combination of bioagents and chemicals when the disease is high (Sharma and Kumar, 1998).

Other minor fungal diseases which occur in different parts of the country are: powdery mildew in hills, Head scab in Punjab and *Fusarium* root rot in hot environments of south India.

Among the insect pest, the cereal cyst nematode disease caused by *Heterodera avenae,* was first recorded in India in 1958 and was termed as molya disease (Vasudeva, 1958). It is a major problem in parts of Rajasthan, Haryana, Uttar Pradesh and Jammu and Kashmir in loamy and sandy loam soils. Yield losses due to CCN have been estimated to be around 60 m. Rupees in 1970 in Rajasthan state alone (Van Berkem and Sheshadri, 1970). At least five biotype have been reported from this state.

Weeds are another major problem particularly in the North Western Plains Zone. The most important weed is *Phalaris minor* which is rampant in many parts of this zone and severely affects the wheat yields, not only because of depletion of soil moisture and nutrients but also because it is not possible to mechanically uproot the weed in early stages as it is indistinguishable from wheat. Weedicides like Stomp and Isoproturon have been recommended for control, but the tolerance build up by this weed due to indiscriminate use of weedicide is creating concern. Agronomic managements like Furrow Irrigation Raised Bed Sowing (FIRBS) of wheat have been found to be effective in controlling the weed population.

## 9. ABIOTIC STRESSES

In most parts of the country wheat crop has to be harvested before the rise in temperature during April. In many parts of Peninsular and Central India, the temperatures at sowing time are also high. Hence the crop has to face high temperatures at sowing as well as grain filling stage. With erratic winter in this area the possibility of early heading and premature senescence of the crop are also a common feature. Through multilocational and multiseasonal testing a number of genotypes with heat tolerance have been identified.

Nearly 3.0 m. ha. of land in India is saline, which spreads over the North Western Plains Zone and irrigated areas of Peninsular Zone where sugar cane is the dominant crop. Varieties like KRL1-4, KRL 19 and Raj 3077 have been developed which show better performance in such suppressive soils.

## 10. BREEDING FOR QUALITY

The primary use of wheat in India is for domestic consumption and nearly 90 per cent of wheat consumption in India is in the form of *Chapati* and other home-made products like *Pitri, Nan, Tandoori, Parotha* etc. Hence the quality of released varieties was mostly assessed for *chapati*-making. Most of the released varieties have good to excellent *chapati* making properties. Moreover, *chapati* making is an art by itself and the quality of the grain is not the sole factor. With the rapid urbanization and changing food habits, the demand for instant foods and processed products has steeply increased.

Durum wheat, when it was under cultivation in Central and Peninsular India, was also domestically consumed in the form of *chapatis.* The *Chapati* made out of durum wheat is less pliable and has a shorter shelf-life than that from bread wheat. Since this was grown as a rainfed crop, the volume of production was not high to attract attention for value addition. With the introduction of durum wheat in the main bread wheat area of North India, there is now a marketable surplus. Popularization of durum wheats in irrigated areas in Central and Peninsular India can also result in surplus durum wheat in future which can become an export commodity because of price advantage in the international market. Even in the domestic market the pasta industry has picked up and breeding of quality durums has become a necessity.

The quality of wheat grain is determined by the quality and quantity of starch and non-enzymatic storage protein which constitute the gluten of wheat. Gluten is one of the most intricate naturally occurring protein complexes. Wheat is the only cereal which has gluten and this makes it unique in terms of processing possibilities into different products. The flour of wheat when agitated with water makes a cohesive mass of dough which can be moulded to make several products. Flour components like starch, minerals, lipids and proteins play a significant role in shaping the product, but it is the viscoelastic strength of the protein that determines the quality of end product. The components of wheat storage proteins are shown in Fig. 12.

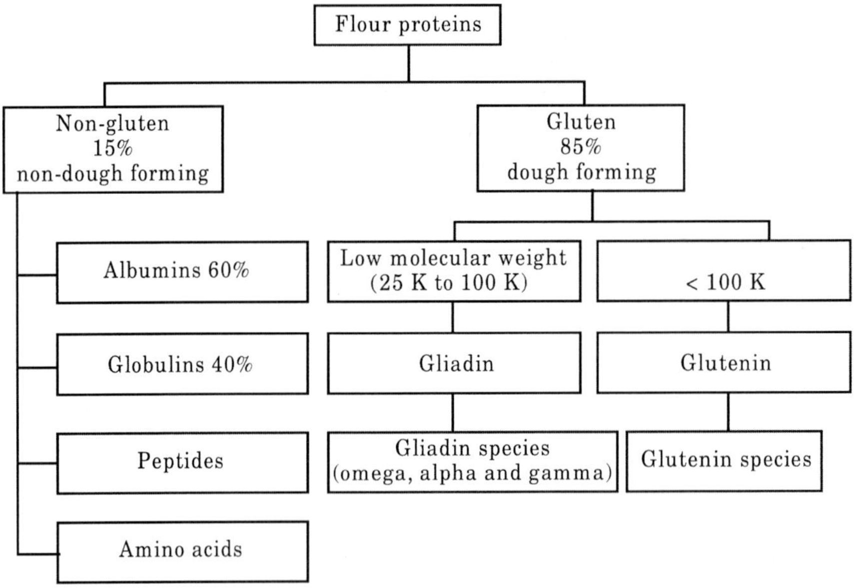


**Fig. 12:** Composition of wheat storage proteins

It is only during the last few years that some attention is paid to in-depth analysis of these parameters. The quality requirements for different end products are specific (Table 7).

**Table 7:** Threshold values of quality traits for different bread wheat products

| ***Product*** | ***Quality traits*** | | | |
|---|---|---|---|---|
| | ***Grain texture*** | ***Protein %*** | ***Semimentation value (ml.)*** | ***Water absorption (%)*** |
| Bread | Hard | >12.5 | 60-70 | 62 |
| Biscuit | Soft | <10.0 | 30-40 | 23 |
| Chapati | Medium | 10-12 | 35-50 | 65 |

***Source :*** Dr. B.K. Misra, DWR, Karnal

A flour of good quality for bread making should have high water absorption, a medium to medium-long mixing requirement, a small to medium oxidation requirement, satisfactory mixing tolerance and dough handling properties, and good loaf-volume potential. It should also yield a loaf that has good internal crumb grain and colour. The durum wheat is not useful for bread making because its gluten is tough and not easily extensible. Durum wheat is used for preparation of many pasta products like Spaghetti, macaroni, noodles and semolina. The quality of durum grain for processing is largely determined by its protein content, hardness of grain, low yellow berry, high β-carotene content and low lipoxidase activity which tends to decolorize the yellow pigment. The quality of pasta is assessed by the cooking time, cooked weight, firm bite, and low starch in the cooking water.

Wheat gluten consists of two major protein types: gliadin which confers extensibility to dough and glutenin, which confers elasticity. When fractionated according to Charge by acid-polyacrylamide-gel electrophoresis (APAGE), the gliadins are separated into α-, β-, γ-, and ω-gliadins. There is considerable variation in gliadin banding patterns of varieties and this is often used to identify varieties and varietal mixtures.

When glutenins are fractionated on SDS-PAGE they form two groups: the High Molecular Weight Glutenin Subunits (HMW-GS) and Low Molecular Weight Glutenin Subunits (LMW-GS) (Payne and Corfield, 1979). There is a wide variation among varieties in electrophoretic patterns of both HMW-GS and LMM-GS (Payne *et al.,* 1981).

In case of bread wheat, the viscoelastic properties of dough are to a great extent determined by High Molecular Weight Glutenin Subunits (HMW-GS), which are polymeric structure composed of two groups of different molecular weight. They are coded by two tightly linked genes *Glu 1-1* and *Glu 1-2* respectively located on the long arm of homeologous group 1 chromosomes and are designate as *Glu-A1-1, Glu-A1-2, Glu-B1-1, Glu-B1-2, Glu-D1-1, Glu-D1-2* (Payne *et al.,* 1983; Harberd *et al., 1986;* Payne, 1987; Shewry *et al.,* 1992). Several alleles have been identified at each of these loci and they cause considerable variation in the bands observed on SDS-PAGE (Lawrence and Shepherd, 1980; Payne *et al.,* 1983; Sreeramulu and Singh, 1984). A numbering system has been proposed for these bands (Payne and Lawrence, 1983). The role of HMW-GS in determining the bread making quality of bread wheat has been studied in detail (Payne *et al.,* 1979). Subunit 2 encoded by *Glu-D1-1a* and subunit 12 encoded by *Glu-D1-2a* are associated with poor bread making quality, whereas subunit 5 encoded by *Glu-Dl-ld* and subunit 10 encoded by *Ghi-D1-2b* are associated with good bread making quality. In durum wheat, Pogna *et al.* (1990) found that HMW-GS encoded by *Glu-B1-1a* and *Glu-B1-2a* determine larger SDS sedimentation volumes and higher gluten elasticity than subunits 6+8 (encoded by *Glu-B1-1d* and *Glu-B1-2a)* and 20 (encoded by *Glu-B1-e).*

The LMW-GS are encoded by genes on the short arm of homoeologous group l chromosomes and are given the gene symbols *Glu-B2, Glu-A3, Glu-A3, Glu-D3, Glu-B4* and *Glu-B5.* Allelic Variation has been reported for some of the genes (Gupta and Shepherd, 1990). Not much information is available on the role of LMW-GS on the technological properties of bread wheat, although they are known to interact with HMW-GS. Some alleles were shown to have large effects on dough resistance and extensibility.

The gliadins are encoded by genes on the short arm of homoeologous group 1 and 6 chromosomes. The ω- and γ-gliadins are coded by genes on group 1 chromosomes and are closely linked to the LMW glutenin genes. The α- and β-gliadins are coded by genes on short arm of chromosome 6 (Jackson *et al.,* 1983; Payne *et al.* 1984). Allelic Variation has been reported at many of these loci (Mclntosh *et al.,* 1998). Metakovskyi and Baboev (1992, a,b), and Metakovskyi and Branlard (1998) observed several novel alleles in *T. boeoticum, T. monococcum* and some French varieties. The varieties having γ-gliadin component designated as γ-45 were shown to have better pasta making quality, as compared to γ-42 types. Subsequent studies (Pogna *et al.,* 1988, 1990) revealed that the allelic variation associated with LMW-GS was responsible for this difference, and that the γ-gliadins serve only as genetic markers for the LMW-GS. The glutenin composition of Indian bread wheat varieties showed that many of them have the required quality parameters (Table 8). The analysis of Indian durum varieties revealed considerable Variation in the LMW-GS (Rao *et al.,* 1998).

Realizing the need and importance of developing wheat varieties with superior quality, the All India Coordinated Project has initiated special quality trials since two years. From the experience gained from

**Table 8:** Quality parameters of selected indian bread wheat varieties

| *Variety* | | | *Farinograph values* | | | | | *HMW-Glutenins* | | | |
|---|---|---|---|---|---|---|---|---|---|---|---|
| | ***Protein*** *(%)* | ***Wet gluten*** *(%)* | ***Sed. value*** *(ml.)* | ***Dough dev. time B'*** *(min.)* | ***Stability 'CD'*** *(min)* | ***Degree soften 'E'*** | ***Water absorp.*** *(%)* | ***Glu-D1*** | ***Glu-A1*** | ***Glu-B1*** | ***Glu score*** |
| C 306 | 10.71 | 26.9 | 44 | 4.1 | 3.3 | 60 | 75.0 | 2+12 | N | 20 | 4 |
| Raj 3077 | 11.99 | 21.5 | 51 | 1.6 | 4.6 | 88 | 61.0 | 2+12 | 2* | 7+8 | 8 |
| K 8804 | 13.58 | 32.1 | 46 | 1.2 | 9.7 | 25 | 65.5 | 5+10 | 1 | 7 | 8 |
| HUW 234 | 10.41 | 21.4 | 41 | 4.4 | 4.2 | 78 | 67.0 | 2+12 | 2* | 7+8 | 8 |
| GW 173 | 12.43 | 27.4 | 41 | 3.2 | 2.3 | 120 | 72.0 | 2+12 | 2* | 6+8 | 6 |
| WH 542 | 11.61 | 23.3 | 42 | 5.2 | 3.6 | 85 | 72.6 | 5+10 | N | 7+9 | 7 |
| PBW 343 | 11.15 | 28.6 | 39 | 4.3 | 6.1 | 110 | 70.0 | 5+10 | 1 | 7+9 | 9 |
| CPAN 3004 | 10.31 | 18.5 | 44 | 2.2 | 6.8 | 45 | 61.5 | 5+10 | 1 | 7+9 | 9 |
| NI 5439 | 14.51 | 37.2 | 51 | 3.7 | 12.0 | 45 | 62.0 | 2+12 | N | 17+18 | 6 |
| HI 977 | 14.50 | 36.2 | 65 | 7.5 | 18.0 | 40 | 63.5 | 5+10 | 2* | 17+18 | 10 |

analyzing several wheat samples from all parts of the country, locations which give maximum expression of quality parameters and enable differentiation of the wheat genotypes have been identified. The idea is that if a superior quality wheat can be identified, even if it is unable to compete in yield with the best variety, it should be possible to give price premium to the farmer and make quality wheat available to the industry for processing.

### 10.1. Nutritional Quality

The wheat grain is rich in carbohydrates and is a source of energy for the people who consume it. However, it is deficient in some essential aminoacids, particularly lysine. Efforts to improve this character have largely failed because of the negative correlation between protein content and lysine. Triticin, a minor component of the wheat endosperm is rich in lysine. This component belongs to the legumin super family of proteins and is also present in some of the cereals like rice and oats (Shewry *et al.,* 1994). Efforts are being made to transfer the triticin gene constructs for high level of expression using transgenic approach (Singh *et al.,* 1998).

## 11. MOLECULAR CYTOGENETICS AND BREEDING

The genome of hexaploid wheat is estimated to contain 18.1 picograms (pg) of DNA per haploid nucleus (Bennett, 1972), which amounts to about $16 \times 10^6$ kilobase pairs (kb). More than 75% consists of repeated DNA sequences and about 20% of low-copy number of unique sequences (Smith and Flavell, 1975; Flavell and Smith, 1976; Ranjekar *et al.,* 1976). Genome mapping in wheat has progressed slower in comparison to other crop like rice, *Brassica,* tomato, mainly because of the large genome, triplicate nature of loci, and low amount of polymorphism due to close evolutionary history of hexaploid wheat. An International Triticeae Mapping Initiative (ITMI) was initiated in 1990 to develop high density genetic maps of wheat. Several approaches like use of wild diploid wheats of A and D genomes, synthetic hexaploids developed through crossing of durum wheat with *Aegilops squarrosa,* and *durum-dicoccoides* substitution lines have been utilized to increase the polymorphism levels. Through this vast network of research activity, a number of molecular markers have been placed on the wheat chromosomes using the aneuploid Stocks. Detailed RFLP maps and cytogenetically based physical maps are available for all homoeologous groups. Apart from RFLP, other techniques like, RAPD, SSR, ISSR,

SCAR, STS, AFLP, DAF and AP-PCR are available for identification of markers linked to economically important characters. Using one or the other of these techniques markers have been identified for several genes, particularly for the disease resistance genes (reviewed by Ranjekar *et al.,* 1998).

Techniques are also available now to identify introgression of alien chromatin into wheat by *in-situ* hybridization (GISH and FISH) using repeat probes. These methods refine the cytogenetic analysis and have been used in wheat for identifying introgression of DNA from rye and other genera of the Triticeae. Thus, molecular cytogenetics has given another dimension to wheat genome analysis and introgression of alien genes into wheat.

Molecular breeding is the use of molecular markers as an indirect selection criterion for tracking economically important genes/gene blocks. Of particular interest is QTL mapping for manipulating quantitative characters. The molecular markers are useful because of their environmental neutrality, tissue nonspecificity and ubiquitous nature. These are particularly useful for pyramiding of genes for resistance, and managing tissue-specific characters.

## 12. GERMPLASM RESOURCES

As mentioned earlier, prior to the advent organized breeding programme, varieties grown in India consisted of several mixtures. Because of their long-time adaptation in local environments, they carry useful genes. The rapid encroachment of improved varieties has led to erosion of this native germplasm. Realizing the need for preserving this valuable gene pool, the National Bureau of Plant Genetic Resources (NBPGR) has organized planned explorations and nearly 3000 local varieties have been collected. Several of these possess specific traits of breeding value (Gautam *et al.,* 1998) both for yield components and disease resistance. Several breeding stations like those at Ludhiana, New Delhi, Kanpur, Almora, Indore, Powarkheda, Vijapur, Arnej, Pune and Dharwad have maintained these local material over the years. An Indian National Plant Genetic Resources System (IN-PGRS) has been designed to link National Active Germplasm Sites (NAGS), with medium-term storage facilities at DWR. More systematic evaluations of these accessions is necessary and the data base needs to be utilized by the breeders. Recently, NBPGR initiated a system of registration of genetic Stocks of crops including wheat and so far 12 wheat genetic stocks have been registered. Among these are Hindi 62, a genetic stock for heat tolerance and Kharchia local a useful genotype for salinity tolerance. This will help in protecting the Indian wheat germplasm in the context of international laws such as Intellectual Property Rights (IPR) and Plant Variety Rights (PVR). The characterization of this germplasm using molecular approaches is required to be taken on a priority basis, which will help in identifying diverse germplasm for improving the wheat breeding programme in the country. For example, in a diversity analysis of tetraploid wheats using RAPD approach, Pujar *et al.* (1999) found that Indian local durum varieties and dicoccum varieties formed separate clusters from the more recent varieties, indicating their genetic divergence.

## 13. FUTURE STRATEGIES

Not with standing the significant achievements in wheat production in the country, there is no cause for complacency. The challenges ahead are heavy, but not unsurmountable with the potential available in the country. It is expected that the population of India will be about a billion by 2000 A.D., and with present growth rate of 1.6% it is estimated to reach 1.3 billion by 2020 A.D. The per capita availability of wheat has more than doubled in the last 30 years, from 79.1 g/day to 185.4 g/day. Assuming a 20 per cent increase in per capita availability of wheat, India has to produce 75 m.t. of wheat by 2000 A.D. and over 109 m.t. by 2020 A.D. This poses a challenge of producing extra 40 m.t., which requires a growth rate of 1.8 per cent/year as against the current 1%. To achieve this, the current national average has to increase from 2700 kg/ha to 4200 kg/ha (Nagarajan, 1998).

### 13.1. Bridging the Yield Gap

Part of this increase can come through bridging the gap between the potential yields and realized yields. The present day varieties have a yield potential of 7 t/ha in Punjab, but the state average is only 4.23 t/ha. The front-line demonstrations in farmers' fields have indicated that there is a yield gap of at least 1 tonne in NWPZ and 1.5 tonnes in NEPZ. Tapping of potential yields in these zones can add about 25 m.t. to production. A similar situation exists even in Central and Peninsular India where the demonstrations have indicated potential yield of 4.5 t/ha using the available technology, whereas the average productivity of these zones is 2.4 t/ha and 1.7 t/ha, respectively. Bridging the existing yield gap in various mega-environments through judicious planning, timely supply of inputs, and attractive pricing can boost productivity and production.

## 13.2. Yield Improvement in Sub-Optimal Environments

It has been realized that there is not much scope for increasing the productivity in favourable environments, because maximum exploitation has already taken place. Any further improvement has to come from those areas where yield improvement has not taken place. Last 30 years of breeding work has not been successful in making any headway in improving the yield levels in the rainfed and warm environments, particularly in central and peninsular India, where the crop is exposed to higher temperatures throughout the crop cycle. There is a need to breed genotypes with tolerance to heat and short growing period to fit in this situation. Special screening methods, like Membrane thermostability (MTS) can be used as selection criteria for heat tolerance in glass house conditions. This approach will permit identifying the breeding material for further validation in field tests.

Similarly, in a large area of Indo-Gangetic plains, wheat is sown as late as middle of December. For this area, effort should be focussed on developing short duration varieties which can germinate and establish at low temperature, have early growth vigour and heat tolerance at maturity. There is an urgent need to strengthen breeding programme to develop better genotypes specifically suited to saline and sodic soils, and for the cold region in the upper reaches of the Himalayas. This will contribute to overall production increase, by addressing specific microlevel needs.

So far, wheat breeding is taking place as an isolated activity. There is a need to develop system oriented research. Wheat is a component of several cropping systems. To increase cropping system efficiency and total production of wheat, it is necessary to develop wheat varieties that will fit into these micro-ecological situations. Selection of early generation material under these systems will be a better approach to identify superior genotypes.

## 13.3. Breaking the Yield Barriers

To further increase the productivity levels, novel and innovative approaches are required. The result of such approaches will take time to yield results and hence, they should be initiated at the earliest. Developing hybrid wheat using male gametocides is one such activity receiving high priority. Hybrids with 20 percent or more heterosis have to be produced, if the current yield barriers are to be surmounted.

Studies have indicated that the increase in yield of semidwarf wheats has resulted from reduction in height and better partitioning of photosynthate, resulting in high harvest index (HI), and not due to increase in biomass (Kulshrestha and Jain, 1982). Since there appears to be a limit to increase the HI, further progress can be made only by increase in biological yield and maintaining the HI (Knott, 1987). Donald (1968) who pioneereed research on architecture of crop plants suggested that ideal wheat plant should have short, strong stems; a few small erect leaves; a large erect ear; awns and a single culm. At least 5-6 yield component characters like number of grains/m$^2$, greater 1000-grain weight, more grains/spike and/or more spikes/m$^2$ are to be brought harmoniously in one background from diverse sources to attain yield levels of 7 to 8 t/ha. Future wheat breeding approach, therefore, may have to identify parameters which can be used as selection criteria in developing superior genotypes.

To create and add new variability, wide crosses offer a vast potential. The wild progenitors and related genera offer a vast reservoir of useful genes. Although many of them have been considered as sources of resistance to biotic stresses, not much attention has been paid to utilize them for yield related characters. The need for developing genetic stocks with superior yield components like photosynthetic efficiency, higher total biomass, greater tillering, more spikelets/spike, more grains/spike, better hectolitre value using related species has been emphasized and several of them have been shown to be promising (Nagarajan *et al.*, 1998). The potential of winter and spring wheat crosses has been widely demonstrated by the release of Veery lines. These gene pools of winter and spring wheats have remained genetically isolated due to their different growth requirements and this variability has to be harnessed in Indian wheat programme. There are centres in Almora and Shimla where the winter wheats flower under natural conditions. These centres can attempt crosses between elite winter and spring wheats and segregating material can be supplied to other centres for selection in their respective agroclimates to make best use of the increased variability.

## 13.4. Breeding for Quality

With satisfactory production levels now achieved, it is necessary to improve the quality of wheat grain, be it for domestic processing or for export. With the changing life styles and rapid urbanization, more people will be looking for processed foods. A systematic programme for breeding quality wheats needs to be undertaken to bring together desirable combinations of HMW glutenin, LMW glutenin and gliadin components in suitable backgrounds. A premium price for such quality wheats and an effective mechanism to segregate them at the market level either for export or for value addition is essential.

### 13.5. Durum Wheat Improvement

The future thrust of durum programme will be to develop genotypes with superior yield, heat tolerance, disease resistance, freedom from yellow berry, better semolina recovery, high protein and β-carotene content. Durum has a better scope for export than bread wheat, because of premium price in international market. The incidence of yellow berry in durum wheat produced in Punjab is very erratic and can effect the acceptance for export. It is necessary to address this problem and select genotypes with stable expression, if the Indian durum wheat has to compete at International level. The durum wheat in Central India is picking up and exportable surplus may be available in future, but the pricing policy has to change to make it remunerative to the farmer.

### 13.6. Use of Biotechnology Approaches in Breeding

The wheat biotechnology work in India is still in its infancy and is dependent on short-term Government funding in a few selected laboratories. The use of marker aided selection for pyramiding of genes for disease resistance, particularly those for adult plant resistance, and for abiotic stresses has a vast potential. Some identified laboratories with expertise in molecular biology and biotechnology should function in close association with the breeders, for which sustained funding should be provided. It is hoped that, with the current level of international research, in the near future, molecular breeding will be routinely used for developing varieties with novel traits.

Development of transgenic wheat has only recently been achieved in the country. This approach will be useful for selective improvement of characters deficient in otherwise acceptable varieties, using gene constructs. Centres with good tissue culture facilities should also develop the dihaploid route using maize-wheat hybridization, to handle large number of crosses and speed up varietal development through rapid attainment of homozygosity. Molecular tools like FISH and GISH will also be useful in a wide hybridization programme, for identifying introgression of alien genome into wheat. India should also try to collaborate with the wheat genomics project currently underway in foreign laboratories to access the information generated and derive benefit of the research in developing better varieties for the country.

## REFERENCES


Allard, R.W. (1960). Principles of plant breeding. John Wiley & Sons, New York, U.S.A.

Anonymous, (1999). Mehtaensis. DWR Regional Station, Shimla, India.

Bahadur, P. (1986). Physiological specialization in wheat rusts. *In*: Joshi, L.M., Singh, D.V. and Srivastava, K.D. (*Eds.*) Problems and progress of wheat pathology in South Asia. Malhotra Publishing House, New Delhi, pp. 69–91.

Basant Ram and Arora, P.C. 1981. Smuts of wheat in India. *In*: Joshi, L.M., Singh, D.V. and Srivastava, K.D. (*Eds.*) Problems and progress of wheat pathology in South Asia, Malhotra Publishing House, New Delhi, pp. 124–161.

Belea, A. and Fejer, O. (1980). Evolution of wheat (*Triticum* L.) in respect to recent research. *Acta Agron. Scient. Hungary*, 29: 306–315.

Bennett, M.D. (1972). Nuclear DNA content and minimum generation time in herbaceous plants. *Proc. Roy. Soc. London Ser. B.,* 181: 109–135.

Borlaug, N.E. (1958). The use of multilinear or composite varieties to control airborne epidemic diseases of self-pollinated crop plants. *In*: Proc. Ist Int. Wheat Genet. Symp., Winnipeg, Canada, pp. 12–27.

Comeau, A.A. Plourde, C.A. St-Pierre and Nadeau, P. (1988). Production of doubled haploid wheat lines by wheat x maize hybridization. *Genome*, 39(1): 482.

Cox, T.S., Raupp, W.J. and Gill, B.S. 1993. Leaf rust resistance genes Lr 41, Lr 42 and Lr 43 transferred from *Triticum tauschii to* common wheat. *Crop Sci.,* 34: 339–343.

Deodikar, G.B., Patil, V.P. and Rao, V.S.P. 1979. Breeding for Indian *durum* and *dicoccum* wheats by interspecific and intergeneric hybridization with 4n *Triticum* species. *Indian J. Genet.,* 39: 114–125.

Donald, C.M. (1968). The breeding of crop ideotypes. *Euphytica*, 17: 384–403.

Dvorak, J. (1977). Transfer of leaf rust resistance from *Aegilops speltoides* to *Triticum aestivum. Can. J. Genet. Cytol.,* 19: 133–141.

Dvorak, J. (1988). Cytogenetical and molecular inferences about the evolution of wheat. *In*: Miller, T.E. and Koebner, H.M.D. (*Eds.*) Proc. 7th Int. Wheat Genet. Symp., pp. 187–192.

Dvorak, J. and Zhang, H.B. 1990. Variation in repeated nucleotide sequences sheds light on the phylogeny of wheat B and G genomes. *Proc. Nat. Acad. Sci. USA*, 87: 9640–9644.

Dvorak, J., Resta, P. and Kota, R.S. (1990). Molecular evidence on the origin of wheat chromosome 4A and 4B. *Genome*, 33: 30–39.

Dyck, P.L. and Kerber, E.R. (1970). Inheritance in hexaploid wheat of leaf rust resistance and other characters derived from *Aegilops squarrosa. Can. J. Genet. Cytol.,* 12: 175–180.

Feldman, H. (1966). Identification of unpaired chromosomes in F1, hybrids involving *Triticum aestivum* and *T. timopheevi. Can. J. Genet. Cytol.,* 8: 144–157.

Feldman, M. (1979). New evidence for origin of B genome of wheat. *In*: Ramanujam, S. (*Ed.*) Proc. 5th Int. Wheat Genet. Symp., New Delhi, pp. 120–132.

Flavell, R.B. and Smith, D.B. (1976). Nucleotide sequence organization in the wheat genome. *Heredity*, 37: 231–252.

Flor, H.H. (1942). Inheritance of pathogenicity of *Mclampsora Uni. Phytopathology*, 32: 653–662.

Gautam, P.L. Mittal, S.K. and Kochhar, S. (1998). Wheat genetic resources management and use in the national PGR System. *In*: Nagarajan, S., Singh, G. and Tyagi, B.S. (*Eds.*) Wheat: Research Needs Beyond 2000 A.D., Narosa Publishing House, New Delhi, pp. 39–50.

Gerlach, W.L., Appels, R., Dennis, E.S. and Peacock, W.J. (1978). Evolution and analysis of wheat genomes using highly repeated DNA sequences. *In*: Ramanujam, S. (*Ed.*) Proc. 5th Int. Wheat Genet. Symp., New Delhi, pp. 81–91.

Gill, B.S. and Chen, P.D. 1987. Role of cytoplasm specific introgression in the evolution of the polyploid wheat. *Proc. Nat. Acad. Sci. USA*, 84: 6800–6804.

Gill, K.S., Sharma, I. and Aujla, S.S. (1993). Karnal Bunt and wheat production. PAU Press,

Gilmore, E.C. (1964). Suggested method of using reciprocal recurrent selection in some naturally self-pollinated species. *Crop Sci.,* 22: 1033–1035.

Grama, A. and Gerechter-Amitai. (1974). Inheritance of resistance to stripe rust *(Puccinia striiformis)* in crosses between wild emmer *(Triticum dicocoides)* and cultivated tetraploid and hexaploid wheat II. *Triticum aestivum. Euphytica,* 23: 393–398.

Gupta, R.B. and Shepherd, K.W. (1990). Two-step one dimensional SDS-PAGE analysis of LMW subunits of glutenin. I. Variation and genetic control of the subunits in hexaploid wheat. *Theor. Appl. Genet.,* 80: 65–74.

Harberd, N.P, Bartels, D. and Thompson, R.D. (1986). DNA restriction fragment Variation in the gene family encoding high molecular weight (HMW) glutenin subunits in wheat. *Biochem. Genet.,* 24: 579–596.

Harlan, H.V. and Pope, H.N. (1922). The use and value of backcrosses in small grain breeding. *J. Hered.,* 13: 319–322

Hayes, H.K., Immer, E.R. and Smith, D.C. (1955). Methods of plant breeding. McGraw-Hill Book Co., New York, U.S.A.

Hayes, H.K., Parker, J.H. and Kurtzweil, C. (1920). Genetics of rust resistance in crosses of *Triticum vulgare* with varieties of *T. durum* and *T. dicoccum. J. Agr. Res.,* 19: 523–542.

Helbaek, H. (1959). Domestication of wheat in the old world. *Science*, 130: 365–372.

Heyne, E.G. and Smith, E.S. (1967). Wheat breeding, *In*: Quinsenberry, K.S. and Reitz, L.P. (*Eds.*) Wheat and Wheat Improvement, 1st Ed. American Society of Agronomy, Madison, Wisconsin, USA. pp. 269–306.

Honrao, B.K. and Rao, V.S. (1996). Sources of resistance to race 77 of leaf rust *(Puccinia recondita* f.sp. *tritici)* in durum I. seedling resistance. *Cereal Rust and Powdery Mildews Bullentin*, 24: 39–43.

Hosono, S. (1954). The classification and distribution of wheat. *In*: Kihara, H. (*Ed.*) Studies on wheat, Kyoto Univ., Kyoto, Japan.

Howard, A. and Howard, G.L.C. (1910). Wheat in India: Its production, varieties and improvement, Thacker Spink & Co., Calcutta, p. 128.

Howard, A. and Howard, G.L.C. (1928). The improvement of Indian wheat. A brief summary of investigation carried out at Pusa from 1905 to 1924 including an account of the Pusa hybrids. *Bull. Pusa Agric. Res. Inst.,* 171: 26.

Jackson, E.A., Holt, L.M. and Payne, P.I. (1983). Characterization of high molecular weight gliadin and low molecular weight glutenin subunits of wheat endosperm by two dimensional electrophoresis and chromosomal location of their controlling genes. *Theor. Appl. Genet.,* 66: 29–37.

Jensen, N.F. (1970). A diallel selective mating System for cereal breeding. *Crop Sci.,* 10: 629–635.

Jensen. N.F. (1952). Intervarietal diversification in oat breeding. *Agron. J.,* 44: 30–34.

Jiang, J., Friebe, B. and Gill, B.S. (1994). Recent advances in alien gene transfer in wheat. *Euphytica*, 53: 199–212.

Joshi, A.B. and Dhawan, N.L. (1966). Genetic improvement in yield with special reference to self-fertilizing crops. *Indian J. Genet.,* 26A: 101–113.

Joshi, B.C. and Singh, D. (1979). Introduction of alien variation into bread wheat. *In*: Ramanujam, S. (*Ed.*) Proc. 5th Int. Wheat Genet. Symp., New Delhi, India. pp. 342–348.

Joshi, L.M. and Nagarajan, S. (1977). Regional deployment of Lr genes for brown rust management. *In*: Gupta, A.K. (*Ed.*) Proc. Ist National Seminar Genet. *Wheat Improv.,* pp. 87–92.

Kerber, E.R. (1964). Wheat: Reconstitution of the tetraploid component (AABB) of hexaploids. *Science*, 143: 253–255.

Kerber, E.R. and Dyck, P.L. (1969). Inheritance in hexaploid wheat of leaf rust resistance and other characters derived from *Aegilops squarrosa*. *Can. J. Genet. Cytol.*, 11: 639–647.

Kerber, E.R. and Dyck, P.L. (1973). Inheritance of stem rust resistance transferred from diploid wheat (*Triticum monococcum*) to tetraploid and hexaploid wheat and chromosome location of the gene involved. *Can. J. Genet. Cytol.*, 15: 397–409.

Kerber, E.R. and Green, G.J. (1980). Suppression of stem rust resistance in hexaploid wheat, cv. Canthatch by chromosome 7DL. *Can. J. Bot.*, 58: 1347–1350.

Kerby, K. and Kuspira, J.L. (1988). Cytological evidence bearing on the origin of B genome in polyploid wheats. *Genome*, 30: 36–43.

Kerby, K. Kuspira, J.L. and Jones, B.L. (1988). Biochemical data bearing on the relationship between the genome of *T. urartu* and the A and B genomes of polyploid wheat. *Genome*, 30: 576–581.

Kihara, H. (1944). Discovery of the DD-analyser, one of the ancestors of vulgare wheats. *Agric. Hort. (Tokyo)*, 19: 889–890.

Kimber, G. and Athwal, D.S. (1972). A reassessment of the course of evolution of wheat. *Proc. Nat. Acad. Sci. U.S.A.*, 69: 912–915.

Kimber, G. and Sears, 1983. Assignment of genome Symbols in the Triticeae. *In*: Sakamoto, S. (*Ed.*) Proc. 6th Int. Wheat Symp. Kyoto., Kyoto, Japan, p. 1195–1196.

Kimber, G. and Sears, E.R. (1987). Evolution in the genus *Triticum* and the origin of cultivated wheat. *In*: Heyne, E.G. (*Ed.*) Wheat and Wheat Improvement, 2nd edition, American Society of Agronomy Madison, Wisconsin, U.S.A.

Knot, D.R. and Kumar, J. (1975). Comparision of early generation yield testing and a single seed descent procedure in wheat breeding, *Crop. Sci.*, 15: 295–299.

Knott, D.R. (1979). The transfer of genes for rust resistance to wheat from related species. *In*: Ramanujam, S. (*Ed.*) Proc. 5th Int. Wheat Genet. Symp. New Delhi, India, pp. 354–357.

Knott, D.R. (1987). The application to breeding procedures of wheat. *In*: Heyne, E.G. (*Ed.*) Wheat and Wheat Improvement, 2nd Edition, American Society of Agronomy, Madison, Wisconsin, USA.

Knott, D.R. (1989). The wheat rusts - breeding for resistance. Springer - Verlag, Germany, p. 201.

Konzak, C.F. (1987). Mutation breeding. *In*: Heyne, E.G. (*Ed.*) wheat and wheat improvement, 2nd Edition. American Society of Agronomy, Madison, Wisconsin, USA. pp. 428–443.

Kota, R.S. and Dvorak, J. (1985). A rapid technique for substituting alien chromosomes into *Triticum aestivum* and determining their homoeology. *Can. J. Genet. Cytol.*, 27: 549–558.

Kulshreshtha, V.P. (1985). History and ethnobotany of wheat in India. *Journ. Agric. Trad. ed de Bot. Appl.*, XXXII: 67–71.

Kulshreshtha, V.P. and Jain, H.K. (1982). Eighty years of wheat breeding in India: Past selection pressures and future prospects. *Z. Pflanzenzuchtg.*, 89:19–30.

Laurie, D.A. and Bennett, M.D. (1988). The production of haploid wheat plants from wheat x maize crosses. *Theor. Appl. Genet.*, 76: 393–397.

Lawrence, G.J. and Shephered, K.W. (1980). Variation in glutenin protein subunits in wheat. *Aust. J. Biol. Sci.*, 33: 221–233.

Leonard, W.H. and Martin, J.H. (1963). Cereal crops. Chapter 16. The McMillan Co., New York, USA.

Lersten, N.R. (1987). Morphology and anatomy of the wheat plant. *In*: Heyne, E.G. (*Ed.*). Wheat and Wheat Improvement, 2nd edition. American Society of Agronomy, Madison, Wisconsin, USA. pp. 36–75.

Lilienfeld, F.A. and Kihara, H. (1951) Genome-analysis in *Triticum* and *Acgilops*. Concluding review. *Cytologia*, 16: 101–123.

Mahajan, V, Singh, K. and Kelkar, R.G. (1998). Possibility of using CHA route in developing wheat hybrids. *In*: Nagarajan, S., Singh, G. and Tyagi, B.S. (*Eds.*) Wheat : Research needs beyond 2000 A.D. Narosa Publishing House, New Delhi, pp. 101–106.

McFadden, E.S. (1930). Successful transfer of emmer characters to vulgare wheat. *J. Am. Soc. Agron.,* 22:1020–1034.

McFadden, E.S. and Sears, E.R. (1944). The artificial synthesis of *Triticum spelta. Rec. Genet. Soc. Am.,* 13: 26–27.

McFadden, E.S. and Sears, E.R. (1946). The origin of *Triticum spelta* and its free-threshing hexaploid relatives. *J. Hered.,* 37: 81–89, 107–116.

Mclntosh, R.A., Hart, G.E., Devos, K.M., Gale, M.D. and Rogers, W.I. (1998). Catalogue of gene symbols for wheat. Proc. 9th Int. *Wheat Genet. Symp.* 5: 235.

Metakovsky, E.V. and Baboev, S.K. (1992a). Polymorphism and inheritance of gliadin polypeptides in *T. monococcum* L. *Theor. Appl. Genet.,* 84: 971–978.

Metakovsky, E.V. and Baboev, S.K. (1992b). Polymorphism of gliadin and unusual gliadin alleles in *Triticum boeoticum. Genome*, 35: 1007–1012.

Metakovsky, E.V. and Branlard, G. (1998). Genetic diversity of French common wheat germplasm based on gliadin alleles. *Theor. Appl. Genet.,* 96: 209–218.

Miller, T.E. (1987). Systematics and evolution. *In*: Lupton, F.G.H. (*Ed.*) Wheat Breeding: Its scientific basis. Chapman and Hall, U.K. pp. 1–30.

Mitra, M. 1931. A new bunt of wheat of India. *Ann. Biol.,* 18: 178–179.

Morris, R. and Sears, E.R. 1967. The cytogenetics of wheat and its relatives. *In*: Quisenberry, K.S. (*Ed.*) Wheat and Wheat Improvernent. First Edition. American Society of Agronomy, Madison, Wisconsin, USA. pp. 19–87.

Nagarajan, S. (1998). Perspectives on wheat demand and research needs. *In*: Nagarajan, S., Singh, G. and Tyagi, B.S. (*Eds.*) Wheat: Research Needs Beyond 2000 A.D. Narosa Publishing House, New Delhi, pp. 39–50.

Nagarajan, S. and Joshi, L.M. (1984). Epidemiology in the Indian subcontinent. *In*: Roelfs, A.P. and Bushnell, W.R. (*Eds.*) Cereal rust. Vol. II. Academic Press, New York. pp. 371–399.

Nagarajan, S., Aujla, S.S., Nanda, G.S., Sharma, I., Goel, L.B., Kumar, J. and Singh, D.V. 1997. Karnal bunt *(Tületia indica) of* wheat –A review. *Rev. Plant Path.,* 76: 1207–1214.

Nagarajan, *S.,* Nayar, S.K. and Bahadur, P. (1983). The proposed brown rust of wheat *(Puccinia recondita* f.sp. *tritici)* virulence monitoring system. *Curr. Sci.,* 52: 413–416.

Nagarajan, S., Tyagi, B.S. and Singh, G. (1998). Extent of genetic diversity in Indian wheats: The inadequacy to break yield barrier. *In*: Gupta, P.K. (*Ed.*) Genetics and Biotechnology in Crop Improvement, Rastogi Publications, Meerut, India, pp. 276–282.

Nath, J. MeNay, J.W, Paroda, C.M. and Gulati, S.C. (1983). Implication of *Triticum searsii* as the B genome donor to wheat using DNA hybridization. *Biochem. Genet.,* 21: 745–759.

Nath, J., Hanzel, J.J., Thompson, J.P. and McNay, J.W. (1984). Additional evidence implicating *Triticum searsii* as the B genome donor of wheat. *Biochem. Genet.,* 22: 37–50.

Nath, J., Thompson, J.P. and Gulati, S.C. (1985). Identification of the G genome donor to *Triticum timopheevi* by DNA hybridization. *Biochem. Genet.,* 23: 125–137.

Nayar, S.K., Tandon, J.P., Kumar, J., Prashar, M., Bharadwaj, S.C., Goel, L.B. and Nagarajan, S. (1994). Basis of rust resistance in Indian wheats, Res. Bull. No. 32. Regional Station, Directorate of Wheat Research, Shimla.

Ogihara, Y. and Tsunewaki, K. (1988). Chloroplast DNA diversity and evolution in *Triticum* and *Aegilops. In*: Miller, T.E. and Koebner, R.M.D. (*Eds.*) Proc. 7th Inter. Wheat Genet. Symp., Cambridge, UK, pp. 127–138.

Okomoto, M. (1957). Asynaptic effect of Chromosome V. *Wheat Inf. Serv.,* 5: 6.

Pal, B.P. (1966). Wheat. Indian Council of Agricultural Research, New Delhi, India. p. 370.

Parlevliet, J.E. (1985). Resistance of the non-race-specific type. *In*: Roelfs, A.P. and Bushnell, W.R. (*Eds*.). The cereal rusts Vol.2. Academic Press, Orlando, U.S.A. pp. 497–521.

Pathak, N. (1940). Studies in cytology of cereals. *J. Genet.,* 39: 437–467.

Pawar, I.S., Paroda, R.S., Yunus, M. and Singh, S. (1995). A comparison of three selection methods in two wheat crosses. *Indian J. Genet.,* 45: 345–357.

Pawar, I.S., Singh, S. and Yunus, M. (1990). Studies on selective intermating in bread wheat. *Crop Improv.,* 17: 68–69.

Payne, P.I. (1987). Genetics of wheat storage proteins and the effect of allelic Variation in bread making quality. *Ann. Rev. Plant Physiol.,* 38: 141–153.

Payne, P.I. and Corfield, K.H. 1979. Subunit composition of wheat glutenin protein isolated by gel filtration in a dissociating medium. *Planta*, 145: 83–88.

Payne, P.I. and Lawrence, G.J. (1983). Catalogue of alleles for the complex gene loci, *Glu-A1, Glu-B1* and *Glu-D1* which code for high molecular weight subunits of glutenin in hexaploid wheat. *Cereal Res. Comm.,* 11: 29–35.

Payne, P.I., Corfield, K.G. and Blackman, J.A. (1979). Identification of a high molecular weight subunit of glutenin whose presence correlates with bread making quality in wheats of related pedigree. *Theor. Appl. Genet.,* 55: 153–159.

Payne, P.I., Holt, L.M. and Law, C.N. (1981). Structural and genetical studies on the high-molecular-weight subunits of wheat glutenin. Part I. Allelic Variation in subunits amongst varieties of wheat (*Triticum aestivum*). *Theor. Appl. Genet.,* 60: 229–236.

Payne, P.L., Jackson, E.A., Holt, L.M. and Law, C.N. (1984). Genetic linkage between endosperm protein genes on each of the short arms of chromosome 1A and 1B in wheat. *Theor. Appl. Genet.,* 67: 235–243.

Payne, P.L., Holt, L.M., Thompson, R.D., Bartels, D. Harberd, N.P., Harris, P.A., and Law, C.N. (1983). The high molecular weight subunits of glutenin: Classical genetics, molecular genetics and the relationship of bread making quality. *In*: Sakamoto, S. (*Ed.*) Proc. 6th Int. Wheat Genetics Symp., Kyoto, Japan, pp. 827–834.

Pogna, N.E., Autran, J.C., Mellini, F., Lafiandra, D. and Feillet, P. (1990). Chromosome IB-encoded gliadin and gluten in subunits in durum wheat: Genetics and relationship to gluten strength. *J. Cereal Sci.,* 11:15–34.

Pogna, N.E., Lafiandra, D., Feillet, P. and Autran, J.C. (1988). Evidence for a direct causal effect of low molecular weight subunits of glutenins on gluten viscoelasticity in durum wheat. *J. Cereal Sci.,* 7: 211–214.

Prakash, O. (1961). Foods and drinks in ancient India, Munshi Lal Manohar Lal, New Delhi.

Pujar, S. Tamhankar, S.A., Rao, V.S., Gupta, V.S., Naik, S. and Ranjekar, P.K. (1999). Arbitrarily primed PCR based diversity assessment reflects hierarchial groupings of Indian tetraploid wheat genotypes. *Theor. Appl. Genet.,* 99: 868–876.

Punjab Agricultural University, Ludhiana, India, p. 153.

Rajaram, S., Mann, C.H.E., Ortiz-Ferrera, G. and Mujeeb-Kazi, A. (1983). Adaptation, stability and high yield potential of certain 1B/1R CIMMYT wheats. *In*: Sakamoto, S. (ed.) Proc. 6th Int. Wheat Genet. Symp., Kyoto, Japan, pp. 613–621.

Randhawa, M.S. (1980). A History of Agriculture in India, Vol. I, Indian Council of Agricultural Research, New Delhi, India, pp. 1–288.

Ranjekar, P.K., Dhaliwal H.S., Rao, V.S., Gupta, V.S. and Tiwari, R. (1998). Molecular biology approaches to wheat improvement in India - Present status and future strategies. *In*: Nagarajan, S., Singh, G. and Tyagi, B.S. (*Eds*.). Wheat: Reasearch Needs Beyond 2000 A.D. Narosa Publishing House, New Delhi, pp. 145–160.

Ranjekar, P.K., Pallota, D. and Lafontaine, J.G. 1976. Characterization of repetitive DNA in barley and wheat. *Biochem. Biophysica Acta*, 425: 30–40.

Rao, M.V. (1972). Varietal improvement. *In:* Ramanujam, S. (*Ed.*) Wheat Research in India. Indian Council of Agricultural Research, New Delhi, India, pp. 22–60.

Rao, V.S., Oak, M.D., Tamhankar, S.A., Gupta, V.S. and Ranjekar, P.K. (1998). Study of glutenins and gliadins in Indian durum wheats. Proc. 9th Int. Wheat Genet. Symp. Vol. 4: 259–261.

Rayburn, A.L. and Gill, B.S. (1986). Molecular identification of D genome chromosomes of wheat. *J. Hered.,* 77: 253–255.

Rayburn, A.L. and Gill, B.S. (1987). Use of repeated DNA sequence as cytological markers. *Amer. J. Bot.,* 74: 574–580.

Reddy, M.S.S. and Rao, M.V. (1979). Genetic strategy for wheat leaf rust control in Indian subcontinent. *In*: Ramanujam, S. (*Ed.*) Proc. 5th Int. Wheat Genet. Symp., New Delhi, India, pp. 1066–73.

Riley, R. (1965). Cytogenetics and evolution of wheat. *In*: Hutchinson, J.B. (*Ed.*) Essays on crop plant evolution, Cambridge University Press, U.K. pp. 103–118.

Riley, R. and Chapman, V. (1958). Genetic control of cytologically diploid behaviour of hexaploid wheat. *Nature (London)*, 182: 713-715.

Riley, R., Chapman, V. and Johnson, R. (1968). The incorporation of alien disease resistance in wheat by genetic interference with the regulation of meiotic chromosome synapsis. *Genet. Res.,* 12: 199–219.

Riley, R., Unrao, J. and Chapman, V. (1958). Evidence on the origin of B genome of wheat. *J. Hered.,* 49: 91–98.

Sakamura, T. (1918). Kurze Mitteilung über die Chromosomenzahlen und die verwan-schafts-verhaltnisse der Triticum-Arten. *Bot. Mag.,* (Tokyo) 32: 151–154.

Sarkar, P. and Stebbins, G.L. (1956). Morphological evidence concerning the origin of the B genome in wheat. *Amer. J. Bot.,* 43: 297–304.

Sawhney, R.N. (1998). Genetic analysis of wheat rust interaction and strategies to breed for durable resistance. *Indian J. Genet.,* 58: 391–416.

Sawhney, R.N., Sharma, J.B. and Sharma, D.N. (1992). Genetic diversity for adult plant resistance in near-isogenic lines and Indian wheats. *Plant Breeding*, 109: 248–254.

Schulz, A. (1913). Die Geschlichte *der* kultivierten *Getreide* L. Neberts Verlag, Halle, Germany.

Sears, E.R. (1954). Aneuploids of common wheat. *Missouri Agric. Exp. Stn. Res. Bull,* p. 572.

Sears, E.R. (1956). The transfer of leaf rust resistance from *Aegilops umbellulata* to wheat. *Brookhaven Symp. Biol.,* 9: 1–21.

Sears, E.R. (1966). Nullisomic-tetrasomic combination in hexaploid wheat. *In*: Riley, R. and Lewis, K.R. (*Eds.*) Chromosome manipulations in plant genetics. Oliver & Boyd, London, pp. 9–45.

Sears, E.R. (1972). Chromosome engineering in wheat. *Stadier Genet. Symp.,* 4: 23–28.

Sears, E.R. and Okomoto, M. (1956). Genetic and structural relationships of nonhomologous chromosomes in wheat. In. Proc. Inter. Genet. Symp., Tokyo, Cytologia Suppl. pp. 332–335.

Shands and Kimber, G. (1973). Reallocation of the genomes of *Triticum timopheevii* Zhuk. *In*: Sears, E.R. and Sears, L.M.S. (*Eds.*) Proc. 4th Int. Wheat Genet. Symp., Missouri, Columbia, USA, pp. 101–108.

Sharma, A.K. and Kumar, J. (1998). Biological control of wheat dieases-unfolding new opportunities. *In*: Nagarajan, S., Singh, G. and Tyagi, B.S. (*Eds.*) Wheat: Research Needs Beyond 2000 A.D. Narosa Publishing House, New Delhi, pp. 191–198.

Sharma, H.C. and Gill, B.S. (1983). Current Status of wide hybridization in wheat. *Euphytica*, 32: 17–31.

Shewry, P.R., Hoolford, N.G. and Tatham, A.S. (1992). High molecular weight subunits of wheat glutenin. *J. Cereal Sci.,* 15: 150–120.

Shewry, P.R., Tatam, A.S., Haiford, N.G., Barker, J.H.A., Hannepal, U., Gallois, R, Thomas, M. and Kries, M. (1994). Opportunities for manipulating the seed protein composition of wheat and barley in order to improve quality. *Transgenic Research*, 3: 3–12.

Singh, D.V. (1986). The bunts of wheat. *In*: Joshi, L.M., Singh, D.V. and Srivastava, K.D. (*Eds*.). Problems and progress of wheat pathology in South Asia. Malhotra Publishing House, New Delhi, pp. 124–161.

Singh, N.K., Sailesh, G., Kumar, A., Sarita Puri, N., Singh, D.T., Garg, G.K, Nayal, S., Gaur, A.K. and Srinivas, S. (1998). Improvement in the nutritional quality of wheat through genetic engineering. *In*: Gupta, P.K. (*Ed*.) Genetic and Biotechnology in Crop Improvement, Rustogi Publications, Meerut, India. pp. 158–168.

Singh, S. and Pawar, I.S. (1998). Recent advances in breeding self pollinated crops. *In*: Gupta, P.K., Singh, S.P., Balyan, H.S., Sharma, P.C. and Ramesh, B. (*Eds*.) Genetics and Biotechnology in Crop Improvement. Rustogi Publications, Meerut, India, pp. 255–275.

Smith, D.B. and Flavell, R.B. (1975). Characterization of the wheat genome by naturation kinetics. *Chromosoma*, 50: 223–242.

Sorrels, M.E. and Fritz, S.E. (1982). Application of the dominant male-sterile allele in the improvement of self-pollinated crops. *Crop Sci.,* 22: 1033–1035.

Sreeramulu, G. and Singh, N.K. (1994). High Mr glutenin subunits of Indian wheat cultivars: Association of subunits 5+10 with 1BL/1RS translocation. *J. Cereal Sci.,* 20: 217–225.

Swaminathan, M.S., Chopra, V.L., Joshi, B.C. and Singh, D. (1968). Development of a monosomic series in an Indian wheat and Identification of nullisomic lines. *Wheat Inf. Serv.,* 27: 19–20.

Talbert, L.E., Magyar, G.M., Levin, M., Blake, T.K. and Moylan, S.L. 1991. Molecular evidence for the origin of the *S* derived genomes of polyploid *Triticum* species. *Am. J. Bot.,* 78: 340–349.

Tsunewaki, K. (1966). Comparative gene analysis of common wheat and its ancestral species *H. waxiness*, growth habit and awnedness. *Jpn. J. Bot.,* 19: 175–229.

Upadhya, M.D. and Swaminathan, M.S. (1963). Genome analysis in *Triticum zhukovskyi,* a new hexaploid wheat. *Chromosoma*, 14: 589–600.

Van Berkem, J.B. and Seshadri, A.R. (1970). Some important nematode problems in India. X Int. Nematology Symp., Pescara, Italy, pp. 136–137.

Vasudeva, R. (1958). Annual Report of the Indian Agricultural Research Institute, New Delhi, India.

Vavilov, N.I. (1926). Studies on the origin of cultivated wheats. *Bull. Appl. Bot. Genet. Plant Breed.,* 16: 1–248

Vishnu-Mittre, (1974). Palaeobotanical evidence in India, *In*: Hutchinson, J.B. (*Ed*.) Evolutionary studies in world crops, Cambridge University Press.

Wagenaar, E.B. (1961). Studies on the genome constitution of *Triticum timopheevi* Zhuk. I. Evidence for genetic control of meiotic irregularities in tetraploid wheat. *Can. J. Genet. Cytol.,* 3: 47–60.

Wilson, J.A. and Ross, W.M. (1962). Male sterility interaction of *Triticum aestivum* and *T. timopheevii* cytoplasm. *Wheat Inf. Serv.,* 14: 29–31.

Zenkteller, M. and Straub, J. (1979). Cytoembryological studies on the process of fertilization and the development of haploid embryos of *Triticum aestivum* (2n=42) after crossing with *Hordeum bulbosum* (2n=14). *Z. Pflanzenzuchtg,* 82: 36–44.

Zevan, A.C. (1978). The prehistoric spread of wheat in Asia, *In*: Ramanujam, S. (*Ed*.) Proc. 5th Intern. Wheat Genet. Symp., New Delhi, India, pp. 103–107.

Zevan, A.C. (1980). The spread of wheat over the old world since the neolithicum as indicated by its genotype for hybrid necrosis. *Journ. d'Agric. Trad. et bot. Appl.,* 27: 19–53.

Zhang, Y, Luo, M., Yen, C. and Yang, J. (1992). Chromosome location of a new cross ability gene in common wheat. *Wheat Inf. Serv.,* 75: 36–40.

# 3

# Maize

## 1. INTRODUCTION

Maize (*Zea mays* L.; 2n = 20) is an important cereal crop of the world. It has worldwide significance as human food, animal feed and as a raw material for the manufacture of hundreds of industrial products. The products include corn starch, maltodextrins, corn oil, corn syrup and products of fermentation and distillation industries.

The suitability of maize to diverse environments is unmatched by any other crop. It is grown from 58°N to 40°S, from below sea level to altitudes higher than 3000 m, and in areas with 250 mm to more than 5000 mm of rainfall per year (Shaw, 1988; Dowswell *et al.,* 1996). Most of the crop is, however, grown in the warmer parts of temperate regions and in humid-subtropical climate, and the greatest production is in areas having the warmest month isotherms from 21° to 27°C and a frost-free season of 120- to 180-day duration.

Maize is the only cereal that can be harvested and used at various stages of plant development. In developed countries, maize is used more as an animal feed, and in the developing world, generally, more as human food. In India, about 55% of maize produced is used for food purposes, about 14% as livestock feed, 18% as poultry feed, 12% in wet milling industry (for example, for starch and oil production) and 1% as seed.

## 2. TRENDS IN AREA, PRODUCTION AND PRODUCTIVITY

About 480 mmt of maize is produced worldwide per year on nearly 130 m ha in temperate, tropical and sub-tropical regions, compared to

V.L. Chopra (Ed.): Breeding Field Crops I: Practices, Studium Press (LLC), USA.

totals of 531 mmt of wheat and 350 mmt of rice (CIMMYT, 1994; Rosegrant *et al.,* 1995). The yield of maize per unit area is higher than wheat and rice, the other major cereal crops. The major maize-growing countries include USA, China, Mexico, Brazil, Argentina, India, Indonesia, the Philippines and Thailand. Worldwide, maize production continues to increase but at a slower rate than in earlier years. The demand in 2020 is predicted to reach about 138% of the demand in 1995 (Rosegrant *et al.,* 1995; USDA, 1996). At present, the industrialized world uses more maize than the developing world, but forecasts indicate that by 2020, developing countries will demand more maize than the industrialized world (Duvick, 1998). The projected increase in area will certainly not be large enough to satisfy the projected demand. Increasing emphasis must be, therefore, placed on significantly enhancing productivity per unit area, particularly in the maize-growing countries in the developing world. The average maize productivity is 2.4 t/ha in developing countries compared to 5.9 t/ha in the developed world (CIMMYT, 1994).

In India, maize was cultivated in 6.04 m ha during 1998-99, and its production and productivity were 10.8 mmt and 1785 kg/ha as an average of all seasons, respectively. Major maize cultivation is carried out during monsoon *(kharif)* season (5.53 m ha), which is characterized by natural vagaries of monsoon. Maize is also cultivated during winter *(rabi)* season (0.51 m ha) which provides better climate. The average productivity during the winter season is 2875 kg/ha as compared to 1684 kg/ha during monsoon season. The area under maize cultivation increased from 3.30 to 6.04 m ha and the irrigated area from 12 to 23% since 1949-50. The productivity has risen from 0.6t/ha in 1949-50 to 1.7 t/ha at present (Anonymous, 1999). Progress made in production and productivity of wheat and rice in India are well-known, documented and appreciated. It is worth mentioning that maize productivity has increased as much as rice productivity, in spite of a shift of better managed area from maize to rice.

Maize productivity is relatively higher in the states of Karnataka, Andhra Pradesh Bihar, Punjab and Himachal Pradesh which account for about 30 per cent maize acreage. Maize is cultivated under better environments in these states and most maize area is under hybrids. In Andhra Pradesh, Karnataka and Bihar, there is sizable area under maize cultivation during winter season wherein full-season hybrids (100-110 days) are grown under irrigation. In Rajasthan, Gujarat, Uttar Pradesh and Madhya Pradesh (covering about 55-60% of total area), maize is cultivated under relatively poor environments and has lower productivity. In these states, most of the maize area is under composites.

## 3. TAXONOMY

Maize belongs to the tribe Maydeae of the family Poaceae. Maize and teosinte [*Zea mexicana* (Schrad.) Kuntze] are usually classified as domestic and wild species, respectively, of the genus *Zea*. Tribe Maydeae comprises seven genera which are recognized, namely Old and New World groups. Old World group comprises *Coix* (2n = 10/20), *Chionachne* (2n = 20), *Sclerachne* (2n = 20), *Trilobachne* (2n = 20) and *Polytoca* (2n = 20), and New World group has *Zea* and *Tripsacum*. The wild and domestic diploid *Zea* species, namely *Zea mays, Z. diploperennis, Z. mexicana* and *Z. luxurians* (n = 10) cross freely and their hybrids are fully fertile. In contrast to the annual trait of these diploids, there is a perennial tetraploid (n = 20) species (Z. *perennis*), which is now extinct in the wild, but is still maintained in culture. Its tetraploidy appears to be of recent origin and its perennialism probably of ancient derivation from an ancient *Zea* ancestor that was both perennial and diploid. The genus *Tripsacum* (Gamma grass) and/or its ancestors have a different basic chromosome number of x = 9. *Tripsacum* includes at least five diploid (n = 18) and four tetraploid (n = 36) species which are all perennial. They are of diverse morphology and adapted to a wide variety of habitats throughout much of the New World. Maize and *Tripsacum* cross with difficulty, and their $F_1$ hybrids are only partially female fertile and completely male sterile (Galinat, 1988).

## 4. ORIGIN AND EVOLUTION

Although the exact origin of modem maize plant is still debated by some botanists, the most likely ancestor of maize is believed to be teosinte (*Zea mexicana*), which is a wild grass in Mexico and Guatemala. Maize is generally believed to have originated from teosinte more than 8000 years ago in Central America, particularly Southern Mexico (Randolph, 1959; Galinat, 1992). As a result of centuries of modifications by humans, the present-day maize bears little resemblance to its ancestor. The American Indians recognized the advantages of maize centuries ago as they developed new strains adapted to diverse climatic conditions. The Mayan culture of Central America deserves credit for the evolution of present-day maize.

The transformation of maize from teosinte involved evolutionary forces such as mutation, hybridization, genetic drift and selection, aided by the activities of human beings, who selected useful variants out of large populations of teosinte and concentrated them into isolated evolutionary pools. This resulted in differentiation of maize into over 300 races. The races gradually got adapted to different agro-climatic regions in the Americas away from the centre of origin. Some workers suggested the multi-center origin of maize (Randolph, 1959; Kato, 1976,1984) on the basis of wide diversity with respect to cytological, morphological and physiological characteristics and their early widespread distribution. Galinat (1988) extended this concept by suggesting a hypothesis of two-stage origin of maize. Initially, there was inadvertant selection within teosinte and later, there was genetic construction of maize by deliberate selection of its key traits such as (i) paired female spikelets in maize in comparison with solitary spikelets in teosinte; (ii) many-ranked ear and tassel (which is unique to maize in the entire tribe Maydeae, in comparison with a two-ranked central spike in teosinte) and (iii) non-shattering rachis (cob) in maize in comparison with shattering cob in teosinte. There was an enhancement and stabilization of such key traits in maize, together with a suppression and destabilization of the teosinte ones.

On the basis of morphological data, several authors suggested that there has been extensive gene flow between maize and teosinte and that the genetic constitution of teosinte has been greatly altered by maize germplasm. Recent molecular studies confirm that there is a two-way gene flow, but at a low level. Consequently, maize and teosinte maintain distinct genetic constitutions despite sporadic introgression (Doebley, 1990). Doebley and his colleagues, on the basis of molecular analyses, suggested that only five regions of the genome accounted for most of the variation between maize and teosinte, and this was consistent with Beadle's (1972) earlier hypothesis (Doebley and Stec, 1991; Doebley, 1992). Transfer of teosinte-cytoplasm-associated miniature trait from the wild teosintes such as *Z. perennis, Z. diploperennis* and *Z. luxurians* was also found in some inbred lines of maize (Newton and Courtney, 1991).

## 5. FLORAL BIOLOGY

Maize is a monoecious plant, that is, the sexes are partitioned into separate pistillate (ear) and staminate (tassel) inflorescences. It has a determinate growth habit and the shoots terminate in inflorescences bearing staminate or pistillate flowers (also called florets in grasses). The main shoot terminates in a branched staminate tassel. The tassel is formed by a many-ranked central (uppermost) spike and several two-ranked lateral branches arranged in an usually loose panicle. Maize is generally protandrous, that is, the male spikelets mature earlier than the female spikelets. The flowers are organized into paired spikelets, one member being pedicellate and other sessile. Within each male spikelet, there are usually two functional florets, although development of the lower floret may be delayed slightly in comparison to the upper floret. Each floret contains there anthers and each anther produces about 2500 pollen grains (Kiesselbach, 1949). The pollen grains are very small, barely visible to the naked eye, light in weight, and easily carried by wind. The wind-borne nature of the pollen and protandry lead to cross-pollination, but there may also be about 5 per cent self-pollination.

The female inflorescence or ear terminates one or more lateral branches (shanks) usually borne about half-way up the main stalk. Because the internodes of the shanks are condensed, the ear remains permanently enclosed in a mantle of many husk leaves. Thus, the plant is unable to disperse its seeds in the manner of a wild plant and instead it depends upon human intervention for seed shelling and propagation.

Sex determination in maize is a complex process involving an interplay between genetic determinants, environment and hormones (Dellaporta and Calderon-Urrea, 1984). Unisexuality of flowers is achieved by the process of selective arrest and abortion of the inappropriate organ primordia within a bisexual floral meristem. Masculinizing genes [such as *tassel seed2 (ts2)]* are required for gynoecial abortion, feminizing genes [such as *Anther ear 1 (An1)* and *Silkless (Sk1)]* arrest stamen development, and both types also control secondary sexual traits involving morphological characteristics of floral tissues.

## 6. MAIZE GENETICS

Maize is an extensively characterized crop among the higher plants for both qualitative and quantitative inheritance. The genetic variability in maize has been systematically studied, with the result that more is known about the genetics and cytology of maize than any other plant. Detailed studies in maize led to the identification of genetic variants for more than 1000 loci and, depending on tests of allelism and supporting data, more than 600 loci have been unequivocally documented. These loci, related to a variety of biosynthetic pathways, chemical constituents, agronomically important traits and development have been mapped on the 10 chromosomes. A large number of loci have also been identified and mapped for proteins, enzymes, restriction fragment length polymorphisms (RFLPs) and more recently, simple sequence repeats (SSRs) or microsatellites, that are detected on the basis of segregation of polymorphic alleles under electrophoretic conditions. Nearly 80 loci concerning different isozymes have been reported.

Maize continues to serve as one of the model genetic organisms among higher plants for exploring phenomena such as transposition and paramutation, and for exposition of genetic theories that are of considerable relevance to breeding of crop plants in general and cross-pollinated plants in particular. The discovery of mobile genetic elements or transposons in maize by Barbara McClintock (1950) is a major milestone in genetics, as it highlighted the significance of dynamic genome and opened up new vistas in analysis of mutation and gene regulation (Peterson, 1987). Element systems such as *Activator/Dissociation (Ac/Ds), Suppressor-Mutator (Spm)* and *Mutator (Mu)* have also been more thoroughly analyzed at genetic and molecular levels. These transposable element systems have also been serving as very powerful tools in isolating a variety of agronomically important genes, including those controlling disease resistance, endosperm quality, plant development, sex determination, male fertility etc., *via* transposon tagging in maize (Shepherd, 1987) and other crop species (Sundaresan, 1996). With the discovery of active transposons in maize breeding populations and genetic stocks (Peterson, 1987, 1999; Prasanna and Sarkar, 1997), increasing attention is also being paid towards understanding the possible role of active transposons in generating genetic variability in breeding populations.

## 7. GENETIC RESOURCES

### 7.1. Races

Sturtevant (1899) classified maize into six kernel types (flint, dent, flour, pop, pod and sweet), but Anderson and Cutler (1942) were the first to stress the need for a more natural classification of variability. They defined 'race' as a group of related individuals with enough characteristics in common to permit their recognition as a group. Wellhausen *et al.* (1951) published the results of a comprehensive study on the races of maize in Mexico. In a series of publications that followed, a number of workers contributed to the development of the racial concept in maize, particularly through analyses of races in Central and South America, the USA, India and other parts of the world. There is at present a bewildering complex of natural geographical races in maize (Goodman and Brown, 1988). The most productive race, the US Corn Belt Dent, is a hybrid of northern flints and southern dents. Similarly, a wide array of maize germplasm is available in tropical maize-growing countries. These germplasm have evolved in conformity with specific agro-ecological forces including stresses. Important racial complexes include Tuxpeno, Cuban Flints, Tuson, ETO and Coastal Tropical Flints and these have been extensively used worldwide.

A large body of information is also available on the chromosome constitutions of races of maize. The most comprehensive study was carried out by McClintock *et al.* (1981), through detailed cytological analysis of chromosome knob pattern of 1532 collections from Central and South America and the USA. On this basis, they suggested the possible influence of the clearly recognizable knob complexes on the evolution of maize in the Americas.

## 7.2. Diversity in Indian Germplasm

India also harbours diverse maize germplasm (Singh, 1977; Wilkes, 1981). Impressed by the diversity of maize in the North Eastern Himalayan (NEH) region, Anderson (1945) considered maize to have an ancient Asiatic origin, and an early trans-Pacific migration to South America. Subsequent studies by a number of workers, including Stonor and Anderson (1949) and Suto and Yoshida (1956), showed that landraces with primitive characteristics do exist in the Himalayan region. Dhawan (1964) rechristened such landraces as 'Sikkim Primitives'. Subsequently an extensive collection of germplasm from the entire NEH region was made by researchers at the Indian Agricultural Research Institute, New Delhi. Mukherjee *et al.* (1971) showed that the two primitive Sikkim maize strains (Sikkim Primitive-1 and Sikkim Primtive-2) were different from the primtive Mexican races Nal-Tel and Palomero Toluqueno. Singh (1977) made an extensive study and classified maize germplasm primarily from the NEH region, which was published in the monograph 'Races of Maize in India'. He classified the Indian races under four categories: (i) Primitive group; (ii) Advanced or Derived group; (iii) Recent introductions; and (iv) Hybrid races. The National Gene Bank at New Delhi houses about 6000 indigenous accessions primarily from the NEH region. However, systematic and comprehensive evaluation of this germplasm for agronomically useful traits and utilization of promising races in the maize breeding programmes has not been carried out.

Besides races, there are several local varieties, named usually after the region where they were predominantly cultivated. Important locals include Jaunpur, Jullundhar, Anantnag, Hyderabad, Coimbatore, Rudrapur, Chamba, Basi, Sathi, Malan and Sikkim. Studies, carried out during 1957-1980, on the nature of genetic variability in the Indian germplasm were summarized by Mukherjee (1989). Salient findings were: (i) Crosses of Indian × Indian germplasm gave yield superiority of 24-43 per cent, whereas Indian × US dent germplasm outyielded local varieties by 58 per cent (Dhawan and Singh, 1961); (ii) Highest yielding single cross hybrids were obtained from crosses between Indian × USA germplasm followed by USA × USA and Indian x Indian germplasm, thus highlighting the significance of genetic divergence for obtaining higher yields (Ahloowalia and Dhawan, 1963); and (iii) dent x flint crosses involving Indian and Caribbean, and Indian and US germplasm showed highest expression of heterosis over better parent (47-54%) (Mukherjee and Dhawan, 1970).

Since the indigenous germplasm has evolved in balance with the prevalent agro-ecological forces, these are expected to possess better adaptation. These materials have been successfully used to develop populations, heterotic pools and hybrids. For instance, Ganga Safed-2, a double top-cross hybrid, which is being commercially cultivated since 1962 because of good stable performance, has Rudrapur Local (CM600) as its male parent.

### 7.3. Wild Relatives

Virtually all breeding stocks, germplasm accessions, and wild or weedy crop relatives contain untapped alleles or allelic combinations that could be used in malize breeding, with adequate investment in wide hybridization and marker-assisted selection. For resistance breeding in particular, there must be greater and more systematic efforts to utilize local races as well as relatives of maize. As a wild form of maize that is subjected to stresses in the natural environment, teosinte should be a perfect source of genes imparting resistance/tolerance to a variety of biotic and abiotic stresses. Nault and Findley (1982) demonstrated the utility of a perennial teosinte (*Zea diploperennis*) for transfer of resistance to Maize Chlorotic Dwarf Virus (MCDV) to maize.

## 8. BREEDING OBJECTIVES

Breeding objectives depend upon various factors like the requirements of the farmers, market forces, production levels, constraints and cropping patterns in different agroclimate regions. It is important for the breeder to clearly define the objectives by keeping in view the present as well as future needs. The major objectives of maize breeding and the achievements, with particular reference to the Indian maize programme, are discussed below.

### 8.1. Grain Yield

Grain yield is the most important and complex trait. It is quantitatively inherited, and its expression is influenced by several yield components and other traits. The salient components of maize yield are number of ears, kernel rows, kernels per row, test weight and shelling percentage. Important physiological traits influencing grain yield include nutrient uptake, photosynthesis, translocation, sink size, transpiration and respiration. Grain yield also depends on maturity-duration, standability and resistance to biotic and abiotic stresses.

The relative performance of cultivars of different eras in the USA have shown that higher grain yield of recently developed hybrids was accompanied by longer duration and grain filling period (early flowering and delayed senescence), rapid grain filling, increased sink size (more kernels per unit area), larger kernels and reduced barenness, higher harvest and shelling indices, shorter plant and tassel, upright leaves, shorter anthesis-silking interval, better standability, better disease and insect-pest resistance, and enhanced tolerance to abiotic stresses (Crosbie and Mock, 1981; Russell, 1991; Duvick, 1992). Two important features of the present-day hybrids are their ability to respond to high nitrogen and their suitability f or cultivation under high plant density. Yield can also be improved through indirect selection for yield components (Singh *et al.,* 1986; Malhi and Khehra, 1987; Malta and Coors, 1987). For instance, prolificacy, the ability of a plant to produce more than one ear, was found to be positively correlated to grain yield, and was improved through selection (Singh *et al.,* 1986). Malhi and Khehra (1987) showed that harvest index, and consequently grain yield, can be improved through selection. The plant characters that impart tolerance to high plant density stress are prolificacy, short plant height, erect leaves, and small tassel.

In the realization of higher grain yield, good standability is an important trait. The relevance of good standability increases in high input intensive mechanised agriculture. Poor standability may be due to root lodging or stem breakage, which are primarily due to weak root system and poor stalk strength, often aided by the incidence of root and stem rots and borers. To have good standability, there should be well-developed root system, strong stem, short plant height, low ear placement, ability to stay green at maturity and resistance to diseases and insect-pests. The 'kick-test' is also used for quick assessment of standability.

Indian maize improvement programme has developed a large number of hybrids and composites (Tables 1 and 2). Of these, hybrids (hyb.) Ganga Safed-2, Ganga-5, Ganga-11, Hi-Starch, Sartaj, Deccan-103 and Deccan-105, and composites (Comp.) Vijay, Kiran, Ageti-76, Navjot and Parbhat merit particular mention.

## 8.2. Stability of Performance

Stability of performance is important to ensure high stable returns to the farmers, particularly so in India where maize is mainly cultivated during monsoon season characterized by erratic rains. In addition to high mean performance, the cultivar should possess an ability to perform well over a range of environments for which resistance/tolerance to stresses is very important. Among various yield components, prolificacy is considered particularly important for imparting stability. Earlier, the focus was on performance over a wide range of target environments, that is, wide adaptation. Now, more attention is being paid to specific adaptation to a given agro-climate, since it is easier to combine high yield with specific adaptation; this also ensures biodiversity at the farm level.

Emphasis should be on the development of management-responsive genotypes for high input irrigated conditions, and on stress-tolerant genotypes for low input, stress-prone environment. Multi-environmental testing, keeping also the target environment in view, is very important to properly assess the genotypes for their stability in performance and adaptation. There were apprehensions among maize breeders that single crosses may not be as stable as double crosses, because the former possess only individual buffering whereas the later have individual as well as population buffering. Experiences, however, clearly showed that it is possible to develop highly stable single crosses.

## 8.3. Maturity

Breeding for appropriate maturity is another important objective. Maize is a short-day plant. The time of flowering is influenced by temperature and photoperiod. Various maturity traits are days to flower, brown husk, kernel moisture at harvest and black layer formation. Days to silk is widely used as an index of maturity even though genetic differences are known for the duration from silking to maturity. Kernel moisture is another commonly used trait for assessing the crop duration. The expression of these traits differs with seasons and locations as these are affected by many environmental factors. Maturity in maize is a quantitatively inherited trait. Selection at inbred and population levels has been used effectively to alter the maturity.

The desirable maturity of cultivars varies depending on the cropping pattern for which the breeding is undertaken. In general, there is a negative correlation between grain yield and early maturity. However, early maturing cultivars are preferred under rainfed conditions, where they escape drought. Multiple cropping patterns or delayed planting also demand cultivars of shorter duration. Long duration cultivars are useful when the cropping systems permit them and management is good.

In India, hybrids and composites developed during the 1960s possessed full season maturity and were later maturing in comparison to the indigenous types. The late maturity of these cultivars was considered to be a limiting factor in their adoption by the farmers. Breeding programmes were, therefore, reoriented with an emphasis on early maturity. Comp. Ageti 76 and Comp. Tarun were the first early maturing cultivars released at the national level, though, some early maturing composites wee released in some states during the 1970s. Indigenous germplasm has been used in the development of early maturing cultivars, such as Comp. Kiran, Comp. Megha and Hyb. Parkash. Among indigenous germplasm, Teenpakhya and Sathi are very early maturing locals.

## 8.4. Biotic and Abiotic Stress Tolerance

In maize, considerable yield losses occur due to diseases and insect pests. Besides drought, cold, water logging, low nitrogen (N), acidity etc. are also important stresses. Most maize breeding is usually done under favourable environment (with the exception of disease resistance breeding), so as to minimise non-genetic variation and enhance response to selection. Further, it is presumed that the cultivars developed under these conditions will perform well in farmers' fields, where the crop is often exposed to different levels of various stresses. But, it must also be appreciated that it may not be possible to exactly simulate the target environment at research stations. Increasing emphasis is now placed on the development of cultivars with resistance to the major stresses prevalent in a given agro-climatic zone.

### 8.4.1. *Disease resistance*

Maize suffers from about 110 diseases on a global basis, caused by fungi, bacteria and viruses. The disease spectrum varies in different agro-climatic zones, but the more serious diseases are leaf blights, downy mildews, stalk rots and rusts. Oligogenes for resistance to some diseases have been reported, though quantitative variation has been reported for most diseases (Smith and White, 1988; Dey *et al.,* 1993). Pedigree and backcross methods, particularly the latter, have been successfully used to incorporate oligogenes into inbred lines. In quantitative inheritance, additive genetic variation has been successfully exploited in inbred lines as well as populations, and selfed progeny (SP) selection has proved very suitable for improving populations. In view of the large number of diseases, emphasis should be laid on multiple disease resistance in cultivars. Dhillon *et al.* (1984) defined the parameters of multiple disease resistance that can be usefully applied to identify desirable genotypes.

In India, about 13.2% of the economic product of maize has been estimated to be lost annually due to diseases. Information has been collected on distribution and appearances of diseases in different maize-growing regions of the country and different protection measures have been worked out (Sharma and Lal, 1998). Methods of creating artificial disease conditions are now available for important diseases such as downy mildew and leaf blights. The most serious diseases in India are turcicum leaf blight (*Drechslera turcica*), maydis leaf blight (*D. maydis*), sorghum downy mildew (*Peronosclerospora sorghi*), post-flowering stalk rot complex (*Macrophomina phaseolina, Fusarium* spp., *Cephalosporium* spp.), and common rust (*Puccinia sorghi*). The improved composites and hybrids developed in India, generally, have a higher level of disease resistance than the indigenous cultivars. Effective selection has been carried out at the level of inbreds and populations. Comp. Partap, Parbhat and Navjot have been identified to possess multiple disease resistance. Inbreds CM104 and CM105 have been reported to possess durable resistance to maydis and turcicum leaf blights (Sharma and Payak, 1990).

### 8.4.2. *Insect-pest resistance*

Insect resistant germplasm is equally important in several production environments. Of the 130 insect-pests that affect maize crop, stem borers, shoot fly, armyworm, jassids, thrips, white ants, pyrilla, grasshoppers, grey weevil, hairy caterpillars, root worms, earworms and leaf miner are more serious, though the spectrum varies in different agro-ecological regions.

Most of the research efforts have gone into breeding for resistance to European corn borer (*Ostrinia nubilalis*), a pest of maize in the USA and Europe. Fall armyworm (*Spodoptera frugiperda*) is another very important pest in tropical and subtropical areas. Quantitative inheritance has been reported for resistance to these and some other pests, though some oligogenes have also been reported. Recurrent selection has been successfully carried out to improve the resistance to European corn borer and fall armyworm (Klenke *et al.,* 1986), and SP selection has been found to be very effective. Populations, such as Multiple Borer Resistant (MBR) and Maize Insect Resistant Tropical (MIRT), developed by the International Maize and Wheat Improvement Center (CIMMYT), Mexico, are being used in many national breeding programmes.

In India, spotted stem borer (*Chilo partellus*) is the most serious pest. Antigua Gr. 1 was identified to have resistance to this borer and was used as the male parent of Hyb. Ganga-5. Antigua Gr. I has also been identified as a multiple borer-resistant source. Recurrent selection was successful to some extent in improving the resistance to spotted stem borer in population J-22 (Sekhon *et al.,* 1992). Incorporation of resistance to insect pests, particularly stem borers, into elite maize germplasm, especially inbred lines, is an important challenge to the Indian maize breeders. The initial breakthrough in developing artificial diets for mass rearing of spotted stem borer and pink stem borer paved the way for developing resistant cultivars. But, progress in breeding for insect resistance has been generally slower in comparison to disease resistance, due to lack of effective insect rearing methods and germplasm screening techniques.

### 8.4.3. *Drought tolerance*

Availability of adequate moisture is an important factor influencing maize production in all tropical and subtropical areas. Drought and low N are encountered practically in all production environments where tropical maize is grown, and breeding programmes to develop tolerant/ resistant lines are receiving emphasis, so as to optimise the use of water and nutrients and maximise the economic product under low-input environments. Effective utilization of drought adaptive traits requires a selection environment and screening procedure that best displays the genetic variation. The timing and level of stress applied should be in consonance with the target environment, but in certain cases, the level of imposed stress may be more severe than that encountered in the target environment.

Genetic differences for drought tolerance have been observed, but breeding for this trait is difficult since its expression is influenced by many factors including the stages at which drought occurs. The damage due to drought, as well as heat, is expressed as top firing, tassel blast and poor seed set, which may be due to failure to produce viable pollen, killing of pollen, drying of the silks or embryo sac abortion. Some morphological traits associated with drought tolerance are: synchronized male and female flowering (reduced anthesis-silking interval), small tassel, small leaf area, prolificacy, adaptation to high plant density, well-developed root system, leaf elongation during drought period, stomatal resistance to water loss, heat tolerance, seed germination and seedling growth at high osmotic pressure created by using mannitol or polyethylene glycol, high abscisic acid and low leaf temperature (Fischer *et al.,* 1983). Recent studies have given more attention to anthesis-silking interval and number of ears per plant under drought (Edmeades *et al.,* 1998). These may be among the most important characters in selecting for drought tolerance in maize. All the traits related to drought tolerance showed continuous variation due to polygenic inheritance and influence of environmental factors. Recurrent selection has been used to develop germplasm suitable to counter stresses, such as drought and low N, at CIMMYT. Studies at CIMMYT have also shown that selection under drought also provides improved tolerance to low N conditions, and that the same regions of the maize genome are involved in rapid ear growth at flowering under stress in both cases.

In India, about 75 per cent of the maize is grown as a rainfed crop. Early maturing indigenous germplasm generally possess a good level of tolerance to drought. Comp. Megha, which has been developed primarily from indigenous germplasm combines drought tolerance with good yield potential.

### 8.4.4. *Cold tolerance*

Cold tolerance is an important breeding objective in temperate maize. The improvement in the ability of the seed to germinate and of the seedling to grow quickly, besides rapid dry-down of kernels under cold conditions, have greatly helped in extending the maize area to higher latitudes, particularly in the northern hemisphere, and in advancing the sowing date and thereby, increasing the crop duration and yield potential. Miedema (1982) has discussed in detail the effects of non-freezing and freezing low temperature stresses on maize, genetic variability for cold tolerance and development of cold tolerant genotypes.

In India, maize is traditionally grown during the hot and humid monsoon season. However, commercial cultivation of maize during winter season started in the 1960s in south India and in Bihar state in north India. Recent studies have opened avenues for extending maize cultivation during winter season in north-west India, where cold tolerance is an important breeding objective (Khehra and Dhillon, 1984). Genetic variability has been observed for leaf yellowing, the most prevalent symptom under non-freezing low temperature stress, but limited variability has been observed for reaction to freezing low temperature stress (Dhillon *et al.,* 1988). Laboratory and field methods have been developed to evaluate germplasm for cold tolerance. Recurrent selection has been effectively employed to improve tolerance to leaf yellowing. Comp. Partap-1 was developed by recurrent selection in Partap for cold tolerance, grain yield and other traits (Dhillon *et al.,* 1984).

## 8.5. Specialty Traits

### 8.5.1. *Nutritional quality*

Maize breeders have been quite successful in developing new cultivars having increased content of starch, oil and protein in the kernel and in some cases, in altering the quality of these constituents. For instance, the genes that modify either the structure or quality of the kernel endosperm have been effectively used to develop specialty corns (Alexander, 1988; Hallauer, 1994). In sweet corn, several genes, such as *sucrose (su), shnmken-2 (sh2), amylose elender (ae), brittle (bt), brittle-2 (bt2), dull (du),* and *waxy (wx),* have been used to enhance the flavour and tenderness. The classical long-term Illinois experiment on the alteration of chemical composition was started by Hopkins in 1896 in variety Burr's White. Through 91 generations of selection, protein content was raised from 10.9 to 32 per cent (Dudley *et al.,* 1992). However, the gain was in zein fraction, which is practically devoid of lysine and tryptophan, two of the essential amino acids. Hybrid cultivars have been developed in the USA and Germany, using the inbreds derived from Illinois High Protein strain, but these did not create any appreciable impact.

A breakthrough was made with the report by Mertz *et al.* (1964) that *opaque-2 (o2)* gene doubled the content of lysine and tryptophan in the endosperm. Opaque maize also proved to be nutritionally superior in feeding experiments. Many such quality-related genes were later reported. Breeding efforts, using *o2,* led to the development of high-lysine cultivars, but these had low grain yield, dull and soft grain, delayed maturity, susceptibility to some diseases and insect-pests, and processing problems due to soft endosperm. Intensive efforts by CIMMYT led to development of several Quality Protein Maize (QPM) populations and heterotic pools, by large-scale backcrossing of improved *o2* donor stocks followed by recurrent selection to accumulate modifiers to improve kernel vitreousness, hardness and other desirable traits while retaining nutritional superiority. Inbreeding was undertaken in these pools and populations with accompanied selection pressure. The resulting inbred lines have yielded hybrids with grain yield and appearance nearly comparable to normal maize, besides better nutritional quality. QPM is gaining popularity in several countries such as China, Argentina, Brazil, Ghana and India.

In India, research on *o2* gene led to the release of three composites (Shakti, Rattan, and Protina) in 1971. However, these composites did not become popular due to various undesirable effects of the o2 gene. Shakti was subjected to intra-population improvement, leading to the development and release of Shakti-1 in 1997. Shakti-1 has high quality protein, vitreous endosperm and high grain yield. Breeding efforts have also led to development of pop corn varieties such as Amber Popcorn, VL Amber Popcorn and Pearl Pop Corn. In recent years, there is an increasing interest for baby corn. VL-42, Him-129 and Parkash have been identified to be suitable for baby corn production.

### 8.5.2. *Apomixis*

The phenomenon of asexual propagation through seed, apomixis, is attracting attention of maize scientists. Apomixis, if transferred successfully in maize, can have revolutionary effects, as it will simplify hybrid seed production and will be a valuable tool to fix hybrid vigour (Hanna *et al.,* 1999). An apomictic hybrid can be grown and multiplied as a single line. Some research teams, notably ORSTOM (France)-CIMMYT group and USDA-ARS, are currently focussing on identification and transfer of genes controlling apomixis from *Tripsacum dactyloides* to maize.

## 9. BREEDING METHODS

Maize is a cross-pollinated crop. Its populations comprise freely interbreeding individuals, heterozygous at most loci, and are heterogeneous. The crop is, therefore, adapted to heterozygosity, which is an essential feature of maize cultivars. Heterozygosity is either maintained during the breeding process or is restored at the end. Inbreeding leads to inbreeding depression resulting in reduction in vigour and size, and appearance of lethals and sub-lethals. The cultivar may be open-pollinated (OP) population or hybrid. The choice of cultivar depends upon resources, stage of breeding programme, seed production and socio-economic factors. Hybrid cultivars have the advantage of higher yield potential and uniformity. They are preferred over OP populations when there is sufficient heterosis. But, their seed production is costlier and complicated.

Major maize breeding methods are germplasm introduction, population improvement and hybrid breeding. All these methods involve selection, which is the most important step in a breeding programme. 'Selection' is discrimination among individuals in the number of off-spring contributed to the next generation. It brings about changes in gene and genotype frequencies and results in improvement of genotypic value of the trait(s) under consideration. Selection acts only on the already existing variability that has its origin in spontaneous mutations and that gets dispersed through natural hybridization, gene segregation and recombination. The naturally occurring variability may be augmented through induced mutations and planned hybridization.

## 9.1. Germplasm Introduction

Introduction of germplasm from one area to another was, and continues to be, an important breeding method, particularly in the developing countries. With the setting up of international agricultural research institutes, the role and contribution of introductions in maize breeding has increased. Introductions have been used directly as commercial cultivars in many countries including India (such as Comp. Laxmi and Suwan-1 released in Bihar state), and as source material to develop cultivars or inbred lines. In the breeding programmes of developed countries, introductions are generally used as sources of superior genes for resistance to diseases and insect-pests and for increasing genetic diversity in the germplasm.

Many workers have suggested that a breeding programme involving the use of exotic germplasm should be started with a small contributing component (<15-20%) of exotic germplasm. Some studies, however, have indicated that a higher proportion of the right exotics may also be beneficial (Hallauer, 1978). Adapting exotics germplasm is, however, a long-term programme. Intermating should be carried out for several generations and selection pressure applied gradually for desirable gene combinations. The immediate use of exotic germplasm may be limited to characters that are controlled by a few genes. The choice of exotic germplasm is often based on geographic origin, pedigree, heterotic patterns and experience of other breeders besides performance of germplasm *per se* and in hybrid combinations with adapted materials. Dudley (1984) developed a method to identify germplasm that contains desirable new alleles.

## 9.2. Population Improvement

Population improvement is carried out through recurrent selection, which involves repeated selection, generation after generation, with recombination among the selects. It aims to gradually increase the frequency of favourable alleles in the population and at the same time maintain genetic variability. The use of mass selection started probably with the domestication of crop plants. In India, prior to 1945, mass selection was the only method adopted to improve local maize types grown by the farmers. Improved types such as KT-41 and Basi, were obtained from local maize types cultivated in Uttar Pradesh and Rajasthan states. Later, varietal hybridization involving indigenous germplasm, accompanied by mass selection resulted in the development of many OP varieties. Six composites were released for general cultivation in 1967 that included Comp. Vikram which was developed from a cross between Indian variety Basi and a Mexican variety, Eto Amarillo (Mukherjee, 1989).

Jenkins (1040) was the first to publish detailed description of a breeding scheme for improving general combining ability (GCA). Hull (1945) described selection for specific combining ability (SCA) and gave the term 'recurrent selection'. Various methods of recurrent selection based on half-sib (HS), full-sib (FS) and selfed (indicated as S with a subscript denoting the generation of seifing) families were described later. Mass selection and its modifications are based on the unreplicated evaluation of the individuals. In family-based methods, HS, FS, *S* or test-cross (TC) families are evaluated in unreplicated or replicated experiments in one or more environments. Family-based selection generally involves three operations: development of families, evaluation of families and recombination of selected families. Some modifications of the standard methods have been suggested wherein these operations have been combined with one or another. The improved populations are being used not only to derive vigorous inbred lines, but also are utilized as commercial cultivars in some developing countries where research programmes and seed industry are not highly developed or organized.

The probability of deriving superior inbred lines is dependent on the proportion of superior genotypes in the base population and the effectiveness of selection during inbreeding. Visual selection during inbreeding is not very effective (as discussed later). An obvious alternative is to increase the sample size of foundation plants for inbreeding. However, experience has shown that the probability of obtaining superior lines does not show a commensurate increase with the increased sample size. A more efficient solution is to conduct recurrent selection to enhance the frequency of favourable alleles in the base population.

Maize populations can be land varieties, synthetics or composites. Synthetics are produced by *inter se* crossing of a number of inbred lines selected for good GCA. The variety is subsequently maintained by open pollination for two to three generations. Composites are produced through population improvement in the germplasm complexes developed by putting together genetically diverse selected germplasm. The choice of germplasm for population formation is a very critical decision, since the population improvement programmes are generally long-term projects. Sub-populations may be developed to meet short-term goals.

The objectives should be clearly defined and materials chosen by giving thorough consideration to performance *per se,* combining ability, plant type, resistance/tolerance to stresses, genetic diversity etc.

There are many methods of recurrent selection for population improvement, which have been discussed by Sprague and Eberhart (1977), Hallauer (1992), Dhillon and Malhi (1996) and others. Depending on the objective of improvement, the various methods of recurrent selection can be classified under two categories, namely intra-population improvement and inter-population improvement.

### 9.2.1. *Intra-population improvement*

Intra-population improvement accumulates genes in such a manner that the mean of reconstituted OP population (mean of the reconstituted selfed population in case of selfed plant/progeny selection) is maximized. Recurrent selection for intra-population improvement may be based on individuals or families. Various methods of intra-population improvement are discussed below.

#### 9.2.1.1. *Mass selection and its modifications*

Mass selection is the oldest, simplest and least expensive procedure. Desirable plants are selected on the basis of their phenotype and their bulked seed is used to produce the next generation completing a cycle of selection in one season. In earlier studies, mass selection was observed to be effective in modifying the less complex characters having high heritability but was generally not effective in improving grain yield. To improve the efficiency of mass selection, Gardner (1961) incorporated some modifications whereby the population was grown under isolation and a sub-plot system for selection was employed to minimize uncontrolled Variation. The modified mass selection proved quite effective and has been extensively used. In selfed-plant mass (SPM) selection, the plants are selfed and modified mass selection is conducted in the resultant $S_1$ population (Dhillon, 1991a).

#### 9.2.1.2. *Half-sib family selection and its modifications*

The HS families are developed' by random mating (RM) in an isolated plot or by pollinating plants with bulk pollen of a large number of plants (TC families are also HSs; TC selection is discussed later). HS families are evaluated and the remnant seed of the selected families is used to reconstitute the population which automatically results in the generation of HS families for evaluation in the next cycle.

Ear-to-row selection, a type of HS selection, was used in the Illinois experiment on the alteration of kernel quality. To improve its efficiency, Lonnquist (1964) suggested modified ear-to-row (MER) selection, in which HS families are planted in different environments for evaluation. The experiment in one environment is sown as an isolated evaluation-cum-recombination block. In this block, ear-to-rows are interplanted with a balanced male (BM) composite developed by mixing an equal number of seeds of all ears under evaluation. The ear-to-rows are detasseled and are, thus, pollinated by the pollen of BM composite. Selection is carried out among and within families; selection among ear-to-rows being based on the performance across environments and that within ear-to-rows being mass selection in isolated block. The MER selection is a unique method of family selection as one cycle of selection is completed in one season; but, it provides no control on pollen parent. It has been used by many maize breeders including those at CIMMYT (Hallauer and Miranda, 1988; Vasal *et al.,* 1997).

9.2.1.3. *Full-sib family selection and its modifications*

Plants are crossed in pairs to produce FS families. The families are evaluated and the population is reconstituted using remnant seed of superior families. FS selection accompanied by intra-family improvement is being used at CIMMYT (Pandey *et al.,* 1991).

In modified FS (MFS) selection, FS families are evaluated, and crosses are made between plants from different selected FS families to recombine the selects and to generate new FS families for evaluation (Lonnquist, see Compton and Lonnquist, 1982). The MFS selection has been extensively used in the Indian maize breeding programme leading to the improvement of many populations and development of a few cultivars such as Diara-3.

9.2.1.4. *Selfed-progeny selection and its modifications*

The selfed-progeny is produced in a population by one ($S_1$), two ($S_2$) or more selfings. The progenies are evaluated and the selected ones are recombined using remnant seed. Mostly, $S_1$ or $S_2$ selection is carried out, but some workers have also conducted $S_3$ selection (Vasal *et al.,* 1995). For some characters, such as disease and insect-pest resistance, SP selection has given higher gain than other methods. However, the gains through SP selection are adversely affected when the contribution of non-additive Variation increases.

In modified $S_1$ ($MS_1$) selection, the evaluation and recombination phases of $S_1$ selection are combined (Dhillon and Khehra, 1989). The experiment in one environment is grown in an isolation as an evaluationcum-recombination block, wherein $S_1$ progenies are interplanted with a BM composite developed by mixing equal number of seeds of all $S_1$ progenies under evaluation. $S_1$ progenies are detasseled and are, thereby, allowed to be pollinated with the pollen of BM composite. Selection is practised among progenies across environments, and within progenies in the isolated block. This method was effectively used in Comp. Kesri (Sekhon *et al.,* 1999).

Many modifications have been suggested by Vasal *et al.* (1997) in evaluation-cum-recombination block-based selection methods (MER, $MS_1$) to enhance their genetic gains. These include: (i) the BM composite should be formed from elite fraction of families; (ii) selection should be conducted in the male rows inter-planted with BM composite for the traits that express before or at flowering; and (iii) the male rows should be planted under high plant density to enable more intense selection.

9.2.1.5. *Test-cross selection*

Plants in an OP population ($S_0$) are selfed and crossed to a tester to produce TC families. On the basis of TC performance, the superior $S_0$ plants are identified and their $S_1$ progenies are recombined to produce the improved population. Alternatively, $S_1$s are produced and crossed with a tester to produce TC families. This adds one season but makes the handling easier and provides an opportunity to select among $S_1$ progenies. The procedure is commonly known as 'recurrent selection for combining ability'. Depending upon the genetic base of the tester, recurrent selection has been classified as (i) recurrent selection for GCA (Jenkins, 1940), in which broad genetic-base tester is used, and (ii) recurrent selection for SCA, in which narrow genetic-base tester is used (Hull, 1945).

9.2.1.6. *Two-stage recurrent selection*

Two-stage (TS) recurrent selection can be based on the evaluation of different types of families and/or individuals. There are many possibilities and the choice depends on many factors including resources and the number of fest sites and off-seasons available. Dhillon (1991b) considered various options and discussed in detail TS recurrent selection involving $S_1$ and HS families. Kaur (1996) carried out two cycles of TS (half-sib and $MS_1$) selection in Comp. Parbhat and reported significant gains.

Dhillon (1998) proposed TS recurrent selection based on the evaluation of crossbred families only (HS families for performance *per se* and TCs for combining ability) and recombination of $S_1$ progenies. Since it involves the evaluation of only cross-bred families, it is expected to be more appropriate for the development of OP cultivars than the TS selection involving SPs. Further, this approach integrates effectively with hybrid breeding as it can evaluate $S_1$s for their combining ability with an unrelated tester.

### 9.2.2. *Inter-population improvement*

Inter-population improvement involves two populations and accumulates genes to maximize the mean of the inter-population cross between their improved versions and the inbred lines derived from them. Inter-population improvement methods are also referred to as 'reciprocal recurrent selection'. However, one population may be similarly improved in which case the TCs of the population with the tester(s) are evaluated; this scheme has been considered earlier in this chapter under intra-population improvement. Various methods of inter-population improvement are discussed below.

#### 9.2.2.1. *Half-sib reciprocal recurrent selection*

The HS reciprocal (HSR) recurrent selection was proposed by Comstock *et al.* (1949) under the term 'reciprocal recurrent selection'. Two genetically diverse populations are taken and plants in each population are selfed and at the same time crossed with several plants taken at random from the other population to produce HS test crosses. TCs are evaluated and $S_1$ progenies of promising $S_0$ plants that had produced superior TCs are recombined within each population to recostitute the improved populations. Khehra *et al.* (1986) reported significant improvement in the performance of an inter-varietal hybrid after two cycles of HSR recurrent selection in $MS_1$-DR and Tuxpeno FBL. Dhillon *et al.* (1986) proposed a modified HSR recurrent selection in which $S_1$ families are developed and crossed with the tester to produce TCs. The merits and demerits of using $S_1$ progenies vs. $S_0$ plants to produce TCs have been discussed earlier.

#### 9.2.2.2. *Full-sib reciprocal recurrent selection*

Hallauer and Eberhart (1970) proposed FS reciprocal (FSR) recurrent selection for use in prolific maize. Two heterotic populations are taken and $S_0$ plants in these populations are simultaneously selfed and crossed in inter-population pairs to produce $S_1$ and FS families, respectively. The FS families are evaluated and $S_1$ seeds of the $S_0$ plants that have produced superior FS families are used to reconstitute the two populations separately. Hallauer (1973) proposed a modified FSR recurrent selection for use in single-eared populations in which $S_0$ plants are selfed to produce $S_1$ line which are crossed to develop FS families.

9.2.2.3. *Modified reciprocal recurrent selection*

Russell and Eberhart (1975) proposed that in a reciprocal recurrent selection, inbred line derived from the opposite population be used as a tester instead of the population; the inbred tester may be replaced with a new elite line after some cycles of selection. The suggestion to use inbred tester was based on the empirical results showing that narrow genetic-base tester was better than broad genetic base tester for improving the population *per se* as well as in cross combinations with related and unrelated tester (Darrah *et al.,* 1972; Russell *et al.,* 1973). Some workers, however, reported that the modified reciprocal recurrent selection was not as effective as expected (Russell *et al.,* 1992; Rademacher *et al.,* 1999). The efficiency of the recurrent selection methods involving inbred tester seems to be highly dependent on the choice of tester.

### 9.2.3. *Comprehensive recurrent selection*

Recurrent selection may have one or more of the following objectives: (i) improvement of random mating (RM) population for the development of OP cultivars, (ii) improvement of selfed generation of the population to develop productive inbred lines, and (iii) improvement of combining ability to develop high performance hybrids. Comprehensive recurrent selection, proposed by Dhillon (1998), provides an opportunity to select for meeting all the three objectives. It is a multi-stage selection based on the evaluation of inbred ($S_1$) and out-bred (HS) families within a population, and TCs with an appropriate tester, and represents a synthesis of intra-population and inter-population improvement. The relative emphasis on different stages of selection is determined by various factors, the most important being the objective. In hybrid breeding, the objective is to improve the population for the derivation of inbred lines having good combing ability, heterotic potential and productivity, whereas in OP cultivar development, the sole objective is to improve the performance of RM generation of the population. Under both situations, TC evaluation (TCs with unrelated tester in hybrid breeding, and TCs with parent-population tester in OP cultivar breeding) should get top emphasis, followed by $S_1$ and HS evaluations in population improvement for hybrid and OP cultivar breeding, respectively.

Sprague and Eberhart (1977), Hallauer and Miranda (1988) and Dhillon and Malhi (1996) may be referred for details on the number of seasons/years required to complete a cycle in each selection method and relative gains from various selection schemes.

## 9.3. Hybrid Breeding

One of the major achievements in plant breeding has been the exploitation of heterosis through commercial cultivation of hybrid maize. Beai (1880) evaluated heterosis and reported up to 52 per cent increase in yield of hybrids over OP parents, and suggested commercial cultivation of $F_1$ varietal hybrids. However, varietal hybrids could occupy only a small acreage. Large-scale exploitation of hybrid vigour can be mainly attributed to the pioneering work by Shull, East and Jones. Shull and East conducted independent experiments on inbreeding and cross-breeding in maize and observed depression due to inbreeding and restoration of vigour on crossing (Shull, 1908; East, 1908, 1909). Shull (1909) on the basis of his experiments initiated in 1905, gave a 'pureline method of corn breeding' which laid the foundation of present-day hybrid breeding. The method involved three steps: (i) large-scale inbreeding to obtain many homozygous or nearly homozygous inbred lines, (ii) testing the selected inbred lines in all possible crosses, and (iii) practical utilization of inbred lines in seed production of single-cross hybrids. Shull recognized that the hybrid produced from inbred lines, which are homozygous and homogenous, would be uniform and true to type. Historical perspectives of hybrid maize development were given by Shull (1952) and Hayes (1963).

There were some problems associated with single crosses due to which maize breeders were slow in adopting the pure-line method. Thèse problems were: (i) good inbred lines capable of producing single crosses appreciably superior to the best OP varieties were not available, (ii) hybrid seed was small and mis-shaped which led to poor germination and planting problems, and (iii) hybrid seed was expensive because of the low yield of the female inbred parent and a substantial proportion of the land devoted to the male inbred parent.

Jones (1918) suggested the use of double-cross hybrids to overcome the practical difficulties associated with single cross hybrids. The first double-cross hybrids, in the 1920s, yielded about 15 per cent higher than the better OP varieties (Duvick, 1999). The adoption of hybrids of maize was initially quite slow. Starting in the mid-1930s, the area planted to hybrids began to increase rapidly and after 15 years, 95 per cent of the maize acreage in the US Corn Belt was under hybrids (Duvick, 1999). Due to concern about the plateauing yield trend for maize in the USA, a few single crosses were put under cultivation by the late 1950s. A rapid shift from the cultivation of double-cross to single-cross hybrids soon occurred. By 1979, 88 per cent of the hybrid maize seed produced in the USA was of single crosses (Zuber and Darrah, 1980). The development of inbred lines having better yield potential and vigour, improved crop production-protection technologies and a well-developed seed industry made the production of seed of single-cross hybrids commercially feasible.

In addition to the work of Shull and Jones, top-cross test for preliminary screening of inbred lines (Davis, 1927), early testing of inbred lines (Jenkins, 1935), prediction of double-cross performance (Jenkins, 1934) and Cockerham's (1961) studies on variability among different types of hybrids greatly facilitated hybrid maize breeding.

### 9.3.1. *Types of hybrids and their merits*

An array of different types of hybrids are being developed and cultivated in maize in contrast to other crops. A single cross is a hybrid between two inbred lines ($I_1 \times I_2$, I denoting an inbred line). A double cross is a hybrid between two single crosses [$(I_1 \times I_2) \times (I_3 \times I_4)$]. A three-way cross is a hybrid between a single-cross parent and an inbred parent [$(I_1 \times I_2) \times I_3$]. Further, there is modified single cross [$(I_1 \times I_2) \times I_2$], double modified single cross [$(I_{1:} \times I'_2) \times (I_2 \times I'_2)$], modified three-way cross [$I_1 \times I_2) \times (I_3 \times I'_3)$], the prime being used to indicate sister lines. Hybrids can also be developed by using non-inbred parent(s). A cross between two varieties is a varietal hybrid ($V_1 \times V_2$, V denoting a variety); between a variety and an inbred line ($V_1 \times I_1$) is a top-cross; and between a single cross and a variety is a double top-cross hybrid [$(I_1 \times I_2) \times V_1$. There are many other types of hybrids involving non-inbred parents (Vasal *et al.*, 1995).

The single, double and three-way cross hybrids have mostly been used commercially. The most striking advantage of single crosses over double and three-way crosses is that single cross breeding is simpler and faster. The probability of identifying two inbred lines that combine well and are vigorous is higher than for three or four lines. The expectation is that the best single cross has the highest yield, followed by the best three-way cross and the best double cross. In the presence of epistasis it may, however, be possible to find a unique double cross or three-way cross as good as the best single cross. This would require evaluation of all possible multi-parent hybrids but it is generally not possible to evaluate all of them even in a small breeding programme. Double and three-way crosses selected on the basis of their predicted performance using single-cross data are developed and evaluated. Thus, complex crosses require two-stage testing, whereas the evaluation of single crosses is a one-stage process. Further, prediction has its limitations and there are chances of missing some good potential hybrids.

Only single-cross hybrids are homogeneous, whereas all other hybrids are heterogeneous. Being uniform, there was some concern about the stability of performance in single crosses as they possess only individual buffering, whereas other hybrids being heterozygous and heterogeneous, possess individual as well as population buffering (Allard and Bradshaw, 1964). But experience showed that stable single-cross hybrids can be identified (Troyer, 1996). The uniformity of single crosses for different agronomic traits has been an important factor in their spread. Seed production in single crosses is also less cumbersome and quicker than complex hybrids, but seed is costlier. The number of seasons and isolation required for seed production of single crosses is less than multi-parent hybrids. The hybrids having non-inbred parents are more variable and are expected to be more stable. Their seed production is easier, but maintenance of genetic purity is difficult. Such hybrids also lack phenotypic appeal. Double top-crosses are under cultivation in India and Pakistan. Double top-crosses and top-crosses are useful as a first step from an OP variety development programme to hybrid breeding. In India, double-crosses and double top-crosses were first released in the early 1960s, whereas the first single-cross hybrid was released in 1995 (Dhillon *et al.,* 1995).

## 9.4. Development and Improvement of Inbred Lines

### 9.4.1. *Inbreeding system*

Inbred lines are generally developed through self-pollination, which is the extreme form of inbreeding and leads to the most rapid fixation of genes. One generation of self-pollination results in the same level of inbreeding as three generations of FS mating and six generations of HS mating (Hailauer and Miranda, 1988). The rate of inbreeding in backcrossing with a homozygous parent is the same as in the selfing. Usually, at least five selfings are needed to obtain nearly homozygous inbred lines.

### 9.4.2. *Methods of inbred line development*

The pedigree method is most widely used to develop inbred lines. Initially pedigree selection was practised in adapted OP landrace cultivars. Later it was observed that repeated sampling of the same landrace cultivar was not productive. This led to the approach of developing planned single crosses of elite lines that complemented each other for different traits, and initiating pedigree selection by sampling their $F_2$ population. Depending on the objectives and availability of inbred lines, complex crosses and backcrosses were also developed, but single crosses are most frequently used by the US maize breeders (Durrah and Zuber, 1986). Recycling of inbreds has been highly effective and there has been concern that the genetic base of germplasm has become restricted. Consequently, many suggestions have been made to broaden the genetic base of the germplasm. It is felt that improved synthetics and populations may gain more emphasis in future. The pedigree method is referred to as the 'Standard method' (Sprague and Eberhart, 1977) when an OP population is sampled.

Seeds of selected plants are planted ear-to-row. Phenotypic selection is carried out both among and within progenies. As selfing progresses, the differences among progenies increase and those within progenies decrease, and the selection pressure is adjusted accordingly. Source populations need to be adequately sampled. However, most breeders prefer to have a smaller sample size and handle a larger number of populations rather than sampling a large number of individuals in a smaller number of populations. Many plant breeders follow the same practice with respect to the number of families and their sample size. Based on a survey of US maize breeders, Bauman (1981) reported that 500 was the most common sample size. Selection and selfing is generally initiated in an $F_2$ population without any genetic recombination. Dhillon *et al.* (1994) proposed sampling of foundation plants for inbreeding as HSs rather than selfs. This approach nearly quadruples the effective population size and has other advantages.

The emphasis given to different traits has also changed over time. An important change is that during earlier years, lines were primarily selected for hybrid performance, but now there is an increased emphasis on vigour and grain yield of lines *per se*. Further, it became known during the late 1940s that heterotic patterns needed to be maintained while deriving lines by recycling inbred lines.

The backcross method is another important method; the importance of source populations developed by backcrossing is next only to single crosses (Darrah and Zuber, 1986). It is an easy and effective method to handle one or two genes and has been widely used to incorporate resistance to disease and insect-pests. For quantitative traits having complex inheritance, the results have been variable. The important factors affecting success are the number of genes controlling the inheritance of a trait and the effect of environment. Normally, three to five backcrosses are made, but the number may vary depending on the recovery of the characters of the recurrent parent, inheritance of the trait under transfer, selection during backcrossing, genetic similarities between recurrent and non-recurrent parent and linkages. When non-recurrent parent is a population, a sufficient number of plants needs to be sampled to represent the population. Richey (1927) gave the concept of 'convergent improvement'. It involves backcrossing to both inbred parents for parallel improvement of both lines by reciprocal transfer of dominant favourable genes present in one lacking in the other.

Several innovative techniques have been proposed for instant development of homozygous inbred lines using maternal and paternal haploidy (Chase, 1952; Sarkar, 1974; Aman and Sarkar, 1978; Kermicle, 1969). Although maternal haploidy was exploited mainly by private sector in derving a number of inbred lines, the technique in general, was not widely utilized due to some constraints (Sprague and Eberhart, 1977; Hallauer *et al.,* 1988). Anther culture was used in China to develop an elite doubled haploid that was used as a parent of a commercial hybrid (Wu, 1986). In spite of their potential, *in vitro* methods such as anther culture were not effectively integrated into breeding programs for inbred line development due to several problems, particularly those associated with plant regeneration and lack of selection pressure during inbreeding. Some modifications may be required for rapid development and screening of doubled haploids for various agronomic traits in breeding programmes.

In India, some inbred lines were introduced during 1950s and '60s from the USA, Latin America and other countries; the most important introduction being CI21E from the USA which was designated as CM202 in the Indian programme. Later on, many inbred lines have been developed and used in hybrid breeding. The commercial hybrids developed by the public sector and their parentage are listed in Table 1. The commercial inbred lines designated as CM (Coordinated Maize) lines are grouped in four categories: yellow, flint (100 series); yellow, dent (200 series); white, flint (300 series); and white, dent (400 series) (parents in 500 and 600 series are yellow and white OP populations, respectively).

### 9.4.3. *Maintenance of inbred lines*

Inbred lines are generally maintained by a system of self-pollination and growing progenies in ear-to-rows so as to observe changes for various traits. One purpose of developing inbred lines is to obtain genotypes whose genetic constitution will be maintained without change. However, significant changes have been reported over successive generations of long-term inbred line maintenance. Russell and Vega (1973) observed random changes in their study on inbred line maintenance by self-pollination. Bogenschutz and Russell (1986) found a definite trend toward reduction in line performance. Further, experience shows that some Indian maize lines are inherently unstable (for example, CM111 and CM123), whereas others are inherently stable.

## 9.5. Combining Ability and Its Evaluation

The value of an inbred line in hybrid breeding ultimately depends on its ability to combine with other lines to produce superior hybrids. Very few productive lines prove to be good combiners. The concept of combining ability has been very useful in hybrid breeding. Sprague and Tatum (1942) partitioned the combining ability in single crosses into GCA and SCA. GCA is the average performance of an inbred line in a series of hybrid combinations, whereas SCA refers to the deviation of the hybrid from the performance expected on the basis of GCA. In the absence of epistasis, GCA and SCA are the measures of additive genetic and dominance variations, respectively. It needs to be appreciated that GCA and SCA effects are not fixed properties of a line but are relative, depending on the particular set of genotypes included in the study. While using a tester, GCA and SCA effects are influenced by the genotypic composition of the tester.

### 9.5.1. *Top-cross test and early testing*

Initially, the lines were selected on the basis of their performance in single crosses produced generally by diallel matings and sometimes by factorial matings. With the development of breeding programmes, the number of test lines increased and it became very difficult to develop and evaluate all possible single crosses. Further, the performance of inbred lines *per se* also did not prove to be a useful guide to select lines for combining ability for grain yield. Davis (1927) suggested the use of the top-cross method for preliminary evaluation of a large number of inbred lines. After Jenkins and Brunson (1932) showed its effectiveness, top-cross test was accepted as a method for preliminary evaluation of new lines for GCA. The lines identified as promising through top-cross test were evaluated in single crosses to identify the most productive specific combinations. Sprague and Tatum (1942) reported that GCA was more important than SCA in unselected lines, whereas the reverse was true in previously selected lines. This supported the preliminary evaluation of a large number of new lines for their GCA.

In the beginning, top-cross evaluation for combining ability was carried out after five or six generations of selfing. However, as breeding programmes expanded, early evaluation for combining ability of inbred lines became important to keep breeding material in manageable limits. In 1935, Jenkins suggested early testing and presented data to show that lines acquired individuality as parents very early during inbreeding and tend to remain fairly stable for combining ability in subsequent generations of inbreeding. Several subsequent workers presented data to support early testing.

Most breeders conduct early testing, but at different levels of inbreeding. Bauman (1981) reported that majority of breeders (78 per cent) conducted test-cross evaluation in $S_2$ to $S_4$ generation, $S_3$ being the most common (33 per cent). Bernardo (1992), based on theoretical considerations, suggested that if heritability is low, as is the case with grain yield, selfing for two or three generations prior to test crossing may be desirable. Early testing enables breeders to discard lines showing poor hybrid performance right at the beginning, thereby, saving resources and helping in better sampling of the base population. Inbreeding can be emphasized in selected lines. Development of many methods of recurrent selection for combining ability, namely recurrent selection for GCA, recurrent selection for SCA and reciprocal recurrent selection enabling selection for both GCA and SCA, is the logical outgrowth of early testing.

### 9.5.2. *Nature of testers*

The correct choice of a tester is very important. In hybrid breeding, on the basis of empirical information, a tester from the opposite heterotic population is used. Hallauer (1975) suggested that a tester should be simple to use, should correctly classify the merit of lines and maximize genetic gain.

For maximum efficiency, choice of a tester depends on the objective of the breeding programme. For example, if the objective is to identify good combiners for a given line or single cross, the appropriate tester is that line or single cross itself, and SCA is of prime importance. The other factors which have bearing on the choice of tester are the stage of development of a breeding programme, availability of the testers, type of germplasm under evaluation and type of hybrids to be developed.

Initially top-cross tests usually involved a broad genetic-base tester. The objective was to have a preliminary evaluation of GCA. In 1948, Green suggested the use of a synthetic tester based on inbred lines in current use. It was believed that the use of narrow genetic-base tester would improve SCA rather than GCA. In some studies, testers with narrow and broad genetic base were compared, and the former was observed to be more effective in improving the population. These results indicated a predominance of additive genetic variability and partial to-complete dominance. An elite inbred tester has the advantage of identifying the lines with good combining ability which can be directly used in a practical breeding programme. Baumart (1981) reported that 80 per cent of the US maize breeders used an inbred tester and 11 per cent a single-cross tester. The use of inbred lines enables breeders to explore SCA, but it seems that efficiency of inbred tester is specific for the tester used some workers also suggested the use of a low performance tester. Though considerable information has been generated on the basis of theoretical considerations and experimental data, the choice of tester is still enigmatic. The tester varies from one breeding programme to another depending upor the objective of the breeder.

## 9.6. Prediction of Hybrid Performance

The number of crosses, particularly multi-parent crosses, increases very rapidly with an increase in the number of parental lines. For $n$ inbred lines, there are $n(n-1)/2$ single crosses, $3n(n-1)(n-2)/6$ three-way crosses and $3n(n-1)(n-2)(n-3)/24$ double crosses. Evidently, it is not possible to develop and evaluate all possible multi-parent crosses among even a small number of lines. Therefore, methods were developed to predict the performance of double crosses. Jenkins (1934) evaluated different prediction methods and reported that the most accurate estimate for a double-cross performance was provided by the mean yield of four non-parental single crosses of the double cross. This method was used widely to predict the performance of double-as well as three-way crosses.

Earlier efforts to predict yield potential of single crosses based on the performance of inbred parents *per se* and molecular marker divergence among the parents have been either unsuccessful in general or of limited utility (Gama and Hallauer, 1977; Melchinger *et al.,* 1992). Animal breeders have been utilizing the Best Linear Unbiased Prediction (BLUP) method for decades for evaluating the genetic merit of animals (Henderson, 1975). Recently, Bernardo (1994, 1996, 1999) paid attention to the prediction of single-cross performance based on BLUP using genetic models involving both GCA and SCA. He took into consideration the known genetic models relationships among parental inbreds, molecular marker data and yield data from related single crosses. The method can be potentially followed for choosing single crosses with high performance and $F_2$ populations for superior inbred line development.

## 9.7. Cytoplasmic Male Sterility

Starting with Rhodes (1931), many workers have reported cytoplasmic male sterility (CMS) in maize. Based on restorer/maintainer reaction patterns Duvick (1965) and Beckett (1971) defined three CMS types: CMS-T (Texas CMS-S (USDA) and CMS-C (Charrua). Laughnan and Gabay-Laughnan (1983) reviewed the variants and genetic properties of CMS System. Before 1970, the use of CMS was thought to be an economical, very satisfactory and practical method of large-scale hybrid seed production in maize. CMS-T was the most satisfactory because it imparted full sterility to most inbred lines and its fertility restoration was relatively easy. CMS-T was used extensively during the 1950s and 1960s. It was estimated that 75 to 80 per cent of the US maize acreage in 1970 had T-cytoplasm (National Academy of Sciences, 1972). In 1970, the maydis leaf blight epidemic severely damaged the crop in the US Corn Belt (Tatum, 1971). The epidemic was identified to be due to a new race (T-race) of *D. maydis,* which was extremely virulent on T-cytoplasm. Thereafter, no CMS was used for seed production in the USA for the next 3 years (1971 to 1973). Since 1974, the use of CMS other than CMS-T started again on a very limited scale and CMS-C was being favoured over CMS-S (Schapaugh, 1987; cf. Wych, 1988).

The maydis leaf blight epidemic was instrumental in influencing the thinking of plant breeders about genetic homogeneity and associated damages of disease and insect-pest epidemics. To overcome the homogeneity associated with CMS, suggestions have been made for using 'multiplasms', a blend of several kinds of male sterile cytoplasm in one hybrid. However, little progress has been made in the discovery or creation of male sterile cytoplasms really different from T, C or S.

## 9.8. Germplasm and Heterotic Patterns

The choice of germplasm may appear to be the easiest, but perhaps, is most critical in plant breeding. In hybrid breeding, germplasm should possess a high level of heterosis, good performance *per se,* inbreeding tolerance and desirable agronomic traits. The probability of identifying superior crosses is greater between populations of known heterotic patterns than within a population.

The heterotic patterns have a strong impact on a breeding programme and, once established, are not easy to change. The most promising germplasm should be evaluated in a series of diallel crosses on the basis of which two (or more) heterotic stocks should be identified for use as tester. These are crossed with diverse germplasm and those showing heterosis with a tester are assigned to the opposite heterotic pool. Unless dealing with very large and diverse germplasm, it would be desirable to work with inbred lines. Further, no germplasm should be put in both pools. The heterotic pools should be broad based, genetically diverse and highly heterotic with acceptable performance *per se* and inbreeding tolerance. Reciprocal recurrent selection accompanied by germplasm introgression should be conducted to enhance heterosis.

It is important that the heterotic pools are made as divergent as possible because heterosis depends on the differences in allele frequencies between two populations. Genes should be concentrated for contrasting traits in two heterotic pools. For example, the seed parent should possess high yield potential, bold kernels, good silk emergence, small tassel and other desirable agronomic features, whereas the pollen parent should provide enough pollen at the level of ear placement or above and should have good pollen spread.

In the Indian maize programme, yellow and white-grained heterotic pools have been synthesized (Sarkar *et al.,* 1995). These include three sets of heterotic pools for different agro-climates, namely Makki Safed × Tuxpeno, Indigenous × Semi-exotic and Ludhiana Lancaster × Ludhiana Stiff Stalk, developed at Punjab Agricultural University (PAU), Ludhiana (Dhillon *et al.,* 1997).

## 9.9. Integration of Recurrent Selection with Cultivar Development

Population improvement programmes may generally be long-term projects on germplasm enhancement, but these need to be integrated with the development of OP and hybrid cultivars to meet immediate needs. Selection methods based on the evaluation of cross-bred families within a population seem to be more appropriate for OP cultivar development as these methods emphasize improvement of RM populations. Base populations for use in hybrid breeding need enhancement in combining ability and the performance of selfed populations. Thus, population improvement methods based on the evaluation of top-crosses involving unrelated tester and SPs integrate better with hybrid breeding. Reciprocal recurrent selection has proved more effective in improving the performance of cross-breds. However, it has not been widely used probably because it is complex, resource consuming and not as efficient at recovering inbred lines as other methods of inbred line development.

Studies carried out at PAU, Ludhiana have shown that recurrent selection accompanied by germplasm introgression has been more effective in cultivar development than selection without introgression of germplasm. For example, MFS selection in Comp. Vijay led to the development of an improved version of Vijay. However, hybridization of Vijay with three other materials followed by population improvement resulted in the development of a better cultivar Comp. Partap. Similarly, MFS selection in Partap did enhance its performance, but varietal hybridization of Partap with Suwan-1 followed by population improvement led to the development of another better cultivar Comp. Parbhat. Similar results may be expected with inter-population improvement.

## 10. CULTIVARS DEVELOPED

Maize breeding in India received great impetus with the establishment of the All India Coordinated Maize Improvement Project (AICMIP) in 1957. Before that, there were some scattered efforts in Punjab, Uttar Pradesh and Delhi on maize breeding. Some improved locals were developed through mass selection. After the second world war, hybrids were introduced from the USA, Australia and other countries, evaluated, and the promising ones identified and released for general cultivation (for example, US13, Texas26, DixielS and NC27). Although these hybrids showed marked superiority over the local types, they did not create any impact because of their unattractive grain type, late maturity, susceptibility to the prevalent diseases, poor inbred lines and above all, lack of seed industry. In 1950, a three-way cross hybrid was developed at Arbhavi and four orange flint, double-cross hybrids were developed in Punjab, including Punjab Hybrid-1, with all parental lines developed from indigenous germplasm. These hybrids, released for cultivation on a limited scale, failed to gain popularity.

In the AICMIP, initially there was emphasis on the development of hybrids using introduced inbred lines. Some indigenous germplasm was also used. A number of double- and double top-cross hybrids were developed and released, starting in 1961. Realising the difficulties associated with seed production and maize cultivation in low-input agriculture, focus was shifted to composite breeding in the mid-1960s and to early maturing composites in the early 1970s. India had probably the largest population improvement programme using MFS selection (though other methods were also used) during the 1970s and early 1980s, leading to the development of improved breeding populations and varieties. Singh *et al.* (1998) provided a brief account of the maize breeding programme in India.

High-yielding hybrids and composites developed and released for general cultivation are listed in Tables 1 and 2. Besides these, there are also a large number of composites and hybrids released at state level and a number of private sector hybrids released at central/state levels. Many of these cultivars, particularly composites Vijay, Kisan, Navjot, Parbhat and Ageti-76, and Hybrids Ganga Safed-2, Hi-starch, Ganga-5, Ganga-11, Deccan-103, Deccan-105 and Sartaj, have become quite popular and have contributed appreciably to increased productivity. Besides high yield, the improved cultivars generally possessed better disease resistance and standability. Indigenous germplasm has been extensively evaluated and some, for example Rudrapur Local and Makki Safed-1, have been used in cultivar development. Early maturing indigenous varieties possess plant type suitable for cultivation under high plant density. Recently, significant progress has been made in breeding single cross hybrids. Full season hybrid Paras and early maturing hybrids Pusa Early Hybrid Makka-1 and 2, Parkash and Vivek Hybrid-4 have been released.

**Table 1:** Public sector maize hybrids released upto 1999 for general cultivation in more than one state in the country since the inception of All India Coordinated Maize Improvement Project.

| ***Hybrid*** | ***Parentage*** | ***Year of release*** | ***Area of recommendation**** |
|---|---|---|---|
| **A.** ***Monsoon season - Full season maturity*** | | | |
| Ganga 1 | (CM101 × CM102) × (CM100 × CM200) | 1961 | |
| Ranjit | (CM103 × CM104) × (CM202 × CM106) | 1961 | |
| Deccan | (CM104 × CM105) × (CM202 × CM201) | 1961 | Gujarat, Madhya Pradesh, Maharashtra, Andhra Pradesh |
| VL54 | (CM107 × CM108) × (CM203 × CM204) | 1962 | |
| Ganga Safed 2 | (CM400 × CM300) × CM600 | 1963 | Across the country |
| Ganga 3 | (CM109 × CM110) × (CM113 × CM112) | 1964 | |
| Him 123 | (CM202 × CM205) × (CM113 × CM112) | 1964 | |
| Ganga 5 | (CM202 × CM205) × CM602 | 1968 | All states except Karnataka |
| Ganga 4 | (CM400 × CM300) × CM602 | 1971 | |
| Deccan 101 | (CM202 × CM206) × (CM115 × CM114) | 1974 | |
| Ganga 9 | (CM202 × CM117) × (CM116 × CM207) | 1979 | Jammu & Kashmir, Himachal Pradesh, Uttar Pradesh, Bihar, West Bengal, Sikkim, North-eastern region, Karnataka |
| Him 128 | (CM301 × CM401) × (CM302 × CM303) | 1979 | Hilly areas of Uttar Pradesh and Himachal Pradesh |

**Table 1:** *(Contd...)*

**Table 1:** *(Contd...)*

| ***Hybrid*** | ***Parentage*** | ***Year of release*** | ***Area of recommendation**** |
|---|---|---|---|
| VL 42 | (CM126 × CM127) × (CM128 × CM129) | 1988 | Jammu & Kashmir, Himachal Pradesh, Uttar Pradesh (hill region), Madhya Pradesh, Maharashtra, Andhra Pradesh, Karnataka |
| Ganga 11 | (CM202 × CM111) × CM501 | 1988 | Across the country |
| Sartaj | (CM122 × CM123) × (CM124 × CM125) | 1988 | Across the country |
| Deccan 109 | (CM119 × CM120) × CM133 | 1994 | Andhra Pradesh, Assam, Bihar Gujarat, Himachal Pradesh, Jammu & Kashmir, Karnataka and Kerala |
| Him 129 | (CM128 × CM129) × CM501 | 1997 | Assam, Gujarat, Himachal Pradesh, Jammu & Kashmir, Madhya Pradesh, Rajasthan, Uttar Pradesh, North-eastern states |
| Parkash** | CM139 × CM140 | 1997 | Across the country under irrigated and rainfed conditions |
| **B. *Monsoon season — Early maturing*** | | | |
| Deccan 107 | (CM119 × CM120) × CM132 | 1992 | Across the country |
| Pusa Early Hybrid Makka-1 | CM135 × CM136 | 1997 | Karnataka, Rajasthan, Madhya Pradesh and Gujarat |
| Pusa Early Hybrid Makka-2 | CM137 × CM138 | 1997 | Karnataka, Rajasthan, Madhya Pradesh and Gujarat |
| Vivek Hybrid 4 | CM212 × CM141 | 1999 | Rajasthan, Gujarat, Madhya Pradesh |
| **C. *Winter season — Full season maturity*** | | | |
| Hi-starch | (CM400 × CM300) × CM601 | 1963 | Bihar, Uttar Pradesh, West Bengal, Orissa, Rajasthan, Gujarat |
| Ganga 5 | (CM202 × CM205) × CM500 | 1968 | Andhra Pradesh, Tamil Nadu, Bihar, Maharashtra, Gujarat, Rajasthan, Uttar Pradesh, Madhya Pradesh, Orissa, West Bengal |
| Ganga 11 | (CM202 × CM111) × CM501 | 1988 | Across the country except hilly areas |
| Deccan 105 | (CM119 × CM120) × (CM211 × CM131) | 1990 | Across the country except hilly areas |
| Trishulata | (CM131 × CM211) × CM120 | 1991 | Across the country except hilly areas |

*Area of recommendation is given only for those cultivars which are presently recommended for cultivation. **Released in Punjab in 1997.

**Table 2:** Maize composites released for general cultivation in more than one state in the country since the inception of All-India Coordinated Maize Improvement Program.

| *Composite* | *Year of release* | *Area of recommendation** |
|---|---|---|
| **A.** ***Monsoon season —*** | | ***Full season maturity*** |
| Amber | 1967 | |
| Jawahar | 1967 | |
| Sona | 1967 | |
| Kisan | 1967 | Across the country except Himachal Pradesh, Madhya Pradesh, Gujarat, Maharashtra, Orissa, Andhra Pradesh, Karnataka and Tamil Nadu |
| Vijay | 1967 | Across the country, except Karnataka. Also released in Nepal and Pakistan |
| Vikram | 1967 | Across the country except Jammu & Kashmir, Himachal Pradesh, Sikkim, West Bengal, North-eastern region, Maharashtra, Andhra Pradesh and Tamil Nadu |
| Partap | 1980 | Punjab and Rajasthan |
| NLD | 1985 | Sikkim, West Bengal and North-eastern region except Assam |
| Parbhat | 1988 | Punjab, Uttar Pradesh, Bihar, Madhya Pradesh, Gujarat, Maharashtra, Karnataka and Tamil Nadu |
| Varun | 1990 | Himachal Pradesh, Andhra Pradesh and Maharashtra |
| Gaurav | 1999 | Rajasthan, Gujarat and Madhya Pradesh |
| **B.** ***Monsoon season —*** | | ***Early maturing*** |
| Ageti 76 | 1982 | Across the country except Karnataka, Rajasthan, Tamil Nadu and Uttar Pradesh (hilly area) |
| Tarun | 1982 | Punjab, Haryana, Uttar Pradesh and Bihar |
| Hunius | 1983 | Jammu and Kashmir, Himachal Pradesh, Uttar Pradesh, Gujarat, Maharashtra, Sikkim, Assam and Mizoram |
| Diara 3 | 1984 | Across the country except Maharashtra |
| D 765 | 1984 | Across the country except Punjab, Haryana, Sikkim and Karnataka |
| Arun | 1987 | Punjab, Haryana, Rajasthan, Uttar Pradesh, Bihar (Diara region) |
| VL88 | 1988 | Hilly areas of Uttar Pradesh and Himachal Pradesh |
| Navjot | 1988 | Across the country |
| Mansar | 1988 | Jammu & Kashmir, Himachal Pradesh, Uttar Pradesh (hill region) |
| Harsha | 1988 | Andhra Pradesh, Karnataka, Madhya Pradesh, Maharashtra |
| Surya | 1988 | Across the country |
| Pusa-1 | 1988 | Punjab, Haryana, Rajasthan, Uttar Pradesh, Madhya Pradesh, Andhra Pradesh, Karnataka, Maharashtra |
| Pusa-2 | 1988 | Punjab, Haryana, Rajasthan, Uttar Pradesh (plains) |
| Madhuri | 1990 | Across the country |
| Mahi Kanchan | 1992 | Punjab, Haryana, Uttar Pradesh (Tarai region), Rajasthan, Madhya Pradesh, Gujarat, Maharashtra, Andhra Pradesh, Karnataka |
| Megha | 1992 | Punjab, Haryana, Rajasthan, Uttar Pradesh, Bihar, West Bengal, Orissa and Madhya Pradesh |

**Table 2:** (*Contd...*)

**Table 2:** (*Contd...*)

| *Composite* | *Year of release* | *Area of recommendation** |
|---|---|---|
| **C. *Winter season — Full season maturity*** | | |
| Partap | 1983 | Punjab and Haryana |
| MCU-508 | 1987 | Bihar and Uttar Pradesh |
| Dhawal | 1988 | Across the country |
| **D. *High quality protein*** | | |
| Protina | 1971 | |
| Rattan | 1971 | |
| Shakti | 1971 | |
| Shakti-1 | 1997 | Across the country; particularly suited for winter season; can also be grown in monsoon season |
| **E. *Pop corn*** | | |
| VL Amber Pop | 1982 | Hilly areas of Uttar Pradesh, Himachal Pradesh and Jammu & Kashmir |
| Amber Pop | 1988 | Peninsular India |
| **F. *Sweet corn*** | | |
| Madhuri | 1990 | Across the country, round the year |

## 11. FUTURE PROSPECTS

Presence of adequate genetic variability and the ability to exploit it are basic requirements of crop breeding. Only a fraction of wide genetic variability available in maize has been exploited so far. Unexploited germplasm, therefore, need to be introduced, evaluated and adapted. In comparison to the use of tropical germplasm materials in temperate regions, exploitation of the temperate germplasm in tropical breeding programmes has received less attention. Therefore, effective and judicious utilization of exotic germplasm, in combination with locally adapted or indigenous germplasm, merits particular emphasis.

Breeding methods and experimental designs will have to be upgraded to enhance Output per unit time and other inputs. Although hybrids have an edge over composites, composite breeding will continue to be relevant in countries such as India. However, with advances in agriculture, hybrids will predominate. Breeding for single crosses and other simple hybrids will be the ultimate goal. To achieve this, the germplasm sources need to be improved for tolerance to inbreeding stress, as the development of vigourous inbred lines is very important for single crosses. In addition to high grain yield and stability of performance, tolerance/resistance to multiple stresses has also become more important with the intensification of agriculture, gradual depletion of natural resources and prevalence of natural vagaries.

Grain quality is gaining considerable significance both nationally and internationally. Due to a perceived increase in demand for specialized products, breeding programmes neeed to be reoriented to tailor varieties to a wide range of specific post-harvest processing requirements designed for developing products for human and livestock health, nutrition and taste. With the betterment of standard of living, the demand for animal products and consequently, animal feed, is bound to increase. Enhanced maize production and productivity is therefore vital for a diversified and sustainable farming system.

Recent developments in molecular marker tools and techniques, particularly marker-assisted selection and DNA fingerprinting, are highly relevant to the breeders. Identification of molecular markers linked to Quantitative Trait Loci for a number of agronomically important traits is an important step towards genotypic evaluation and multi-trait selection. Alien gene transfer, *in vitro* procedures and genetic transformation have also opened up new avenues for exploiting an apparently unlimited gene pool. Transgenic maize is already being cultivated in a sizable area in some countries such as USA. These advances in maize molecular biology and biotechnology, and their integration with conventional breeding, are making maize breeding more precise and cultivar development relatively quicker. The next millenium is likely to be an era of precision breeding with improved germplasm, better experimental designs -and specialized maize cultivars including transgenics.

## REFERENCES


Ahloowalia, B.S. and Dhawan, N.L. (1963). Effect of genetic diversity on combining ability of inbreds of maize. *Indian J. Genet.,* 23: 158–162.

Allard, R.W. and Bradshaw, A.D. (1964). Implications of genotype-environment interaction in applied plant breeding. *Crop Sci.,* 4: 503–508.

Aman, M.A. and Sarkar, K.R. (1978). Selection for haploidy inducing potential in maize. *Indian J. Genet.,* 38: 452–457.

Anderson, E. (1945). Maize in the New World. *In*: Wilson, C.M. (*Ed.*) New Crops for the New World. Macmillan Publishing Co., New York, pp. 27–42.

Anderson, E. and Cutler, H.C. (1942). Races of *Zca mays:* I. Their recognition and classification. *Ann. Mo. Bot. Gard.,* 29: 69–89.

Anonymous (1999). Agricultural statistics at a glance. Department of Agriculture and Cooperation, Ministry of Agriculture, Government of India, New Delhi.

Bauman, L.F. (1981). Review of methods used by breeders to develop superior corn inbreds. *Proc. Annu. Corn Sorghum Res. Conf.,* 36: 199–208.

Beal, J.F. (1880). Report of the Professor of Botany and Horticulture. Michigan Board Agric. Lansing, USA, pp. 287–288.

Beckett, J.B. (1971). Classification of male sterile cytoplasm in maize (*Zea mays* L.). *Crop. Sci.* 11: 724–727.

Bernardo, R. (1992). Retention of genetically superior inbred lines during early generation testcrossing in maize. *Crop Sci.,* 32: 923–927.

Bernardo, R. (1994). Prediction of maize single cross performance using RFLPs and information from related hybrids. *Crop Sci.,* 34: 20–25.

Bernardo, R. (1996). Best linear unbiased prediction of maize single-cross performance. *Crop Sci.,* 36: 50–56.

Bernardo, R. (1999). Best linear unbiased predictor analysis. *In:* Coors, J.G. and Pandey, S. (*Eds.*) Genetics and Exploitation of Heterosis in Crops. Am. Soc. Agron., Madison, Wisconsin, USA. pp. 269–276.

Boggenschutz, T.G. and Russell, W.A. (1986). An evaluation of genetic variation within maize inbred lines maintained by sib-mating and self-pollination. *Euphytica,* 35: 403–412.

Chase, S.S. (1952). Production of homozygous diploids of maize from monoploids. *Agron. J.,* 44: 263–267.

CIMMYT (1994). CIMMYT 1993/94 world maize facts and trends. maize seed industries revisited: Emerging roles of the public and private sectors. CIMMYT, Mexico, D.F. Mexico.

Cockerham, C. (1961). Implications of genetic variance in hybrid breeding programme. *Crop Sci.,* 1: 47–52.

Compton, W.A. and Lonnquist, J.H. (1982). A multiplicative selection index applied to four cycles of full-sibs recurrent selection in maize. *Crop Sci.,* 22: 981–983.

Comstock, R.E., Robinson, H.F. and Harvey, P.H. (1949). A breeding procedure designed to make maximum use of both general and specific combining ability. *Agron. J.,* 41: 360–367.

Crosbie, T.M. and Mock, J.J. (1981). Changes in physiological traits associated with grain yield improvement in three maize programmes. *Crop. Sci.,* 21: 255–259.

Darrah, L.L. and Zuber, M.S. (1986). United States farm maize germplasm base and commercial breeding strategies. *Crop Sci.,* 26: 1109–1113.

Darrah, L.L., Eberhart, S.A. and Penny, L.H. (1972). A maize breeding methods study in Kenya. *Crop Sci.,* 12: 605–608.

Davis, R.L. (1927). Report of the plant breeder. Rep. Puerto Rico Agric. Exp. Stn., Puerto Rico, pp. 14–15.

Dellaporta, S.L. and Calderon-Urrea, A. (1994). The sex determination process in maize. *Science,* 266: 1501–1504.

Dey, S.K., Dhillon, B.S. and Khehra, A.S. (1992). Diseases of maize in Asia — problem and progress. *In*: Sokhi, S.S., Chahal, S.S. and Singh, P.P. (*Eds.*) Progress of Plant Pathological Research. Indian Society of Plant Pathologists, Ludhiana, pp. 83–108.

Dhawan, N.L. (1964). Primitive maize in Sikkim. *Maize Genet. Coop. Newsletter,* 38: 69–70.

Dhawan, N.L. and Singh, J. (1961). Flint x dent maize hybrids give increased yields. *Curr. Sci.,* 30: 233–234.

Dhillon, B.S., Sharma, R.K., Malhotra, V.V. and Khehra, A.S. (1988). Evaluation of maize germplasm for tolerance to low temperature stress under field and laboratory conditions. *J. Agron. Crop. Sci.,* 160: 89–93.

Dhillon, B.S. (1991a). Recurrent mass selection based on selfed-plant evaluation in allogamous species. *Crop Sci.,* 31: 1075–1077.

Dhillon, B.S. (1991b). Alternate recurrent selection of S1 and half-sib families for intrapopulation improvement. *Maydica,* 36: 45–48.

Dhillon, B.S. (1998). Recurrent selection for combining ability and performance *per se* of cross-bred and selfed families. *Maydica,* 43: 155–160.

Dhillon, B.S. and Khehra, A.S. (1989). Modified S, recurrent selection in maize improvement. *Crop Sci.,* 29: 226–228.

Dhillon, B.S. and Malhi, N.S. (1996). Recent advances in recurrent selection for intrapopulation improvement. *Crop Improv.* 23(S): 137–150.

Dhillon, B.S., Kapoor, W.R. and Malhotra, V.V. (1984). 'Partap-1' and 'Partap': Cold tolerant composites of maize. *Progressive Farming,* 21(2): 5–6.

Dhillon, B.S., Khehra, A.S., Dey, S.K., Sharma, S.C. and Saxena, V.K. (1984). Multiple disease resistance in maize. *SABRAO J.*, 16: 69–72.

Dhillon, B.S., Malhi, N.S. and Saxena, V.K. (1997). Development and improvement of heterotic pools in maize. *In*: Proc. Intl. Symp. on Genetics and Exploitation of Heterosis in Crops, CIMMYT, Mexico, pp. 74–75.

Dhillon, B.S., Malhi, N.S., Saxena, V.K. and Khehra, A.S. (1986). Hico breeding in maize. *In:* Napompem, B. and Subhadrabandhu, S. (*Eds.*) New Frontiers in Breeding Researches. Kasetsart Univ., Bangkok, Thailand, pp. 279–285.

Dhillon, B.S., Malhi, N.S., Saxena, V.K., Kapoor, W.R., Pal, S.S., Singh, M. and Khehra, A.S. (1995). Paras – first single cross hybrid of maize in India. *J. Res. Punjab Agric. Univ.,* 32: 238–239.

Dhillon, B.S., Vasal, S.K., Srinivasan, G. and Crossa, J. (1994). Improving the sampling and identification of foundation plants for inbred line development by integrating half-sib family selection with inbreeding. *Cereal Res. Comm.,* 22: 321–325.

Doebley, J. (1990). Molecular evidence for gene flow among *Zea* species. *Bioscience,* 40: 443–448.

Doebley, J. (1992). Mapping the genes that made maize. *Trends Genet.,* 8: 302–307.

Doebley, J. and Stec, A. (1991). Genetic analysis of the morphological differences between maize and teosinte. *Genetics,* 129: 285–295.

Dowswell, C.R., Paliwal, R.L. and Cantrell, R.P. (1996). Maize in the third world. West view Press, Boulder, USA.

Dudley, J.W. (1984). A method for identifying populations containing favourable alleles not present in the elite germplasm. *Crop. Sci.,* 24: 1053–1054.

Duvick, D.N. (1965). Cytoplasmic pollen sterility in corn. *Adv. Genet.* 13: 1–56.

Duvick, D.N. (1992). Genetic contributions to advances in yield of U.S. maize. *Maydica* 37: 69–79.

Duvick, D.N. (1998). Crop improvement: Emerging trends in maize. *In*: Chopra, V.L., Singh, R.B. and Varma, Anupam (*Eds.*,) Crop Productivity and Sustainability - Shaping the Future. Proc. 2nd Int. Crop Sei. Congress. Oxford & IBH Publishing Co., New Delhi, pp. 127–138.

Duvick, D.N. (1999). Heterosis: Feeding people and protecting natural resources. *In*: Coors, J.G. and Pandey, S. (*Eds.*,) Genetics and Exploitation of Heterosis in Crops. Am. Soc. Agron., Madison, Wisconsin, USA. pp. 19–29.

Earle, F.R., Curtis, J.J. and Herllard, J.E. (1946). Composition of the component traits of the corn kernel. *Cereal Chem.,* 23: 504–511.

East, E.M. (1908). Inbreeding in corn. *conm. Agric. Exp. Stn. Rep.,* 1907: 419–428.

East, E.M. (1909). The distinction between development and heredity in inbreeding. *Am. Nat.,* 43: 173–181.

Edmeades, G.O., Bolanos, J., Banziger, M., Ribaut, J.M., White, J.W., Reynolds, M.P., and Lafitte, H.R. (1998). Improving crop yields under water deficits in the tropics. *In*: Chopra, V.L., Singh, R.B. and Varma, Anupam (*Eds.*) Crop Productivity and Sustainability – Shaping the Future. Proc. 2nd Int. Crop. Sci. Congress. Oxford & IBH Publishing Co., New Delhi, pp. 437–451.

Fischer, K.S., Johnson, E.C. and Edmeades, G.O. (1983). Breeding and selection for drought: Resistance in tropical maize. CIMMYT, El Batan, Mexico.

Galinat, W.C. (1971). The origin of maize. *Annu. Rev. Genet.,* 5: 447–478.

Galinat, W.C. (1988). The origin of corn. *In*: Sprague, G.F. and Dudley, J.W. (*Eds.*,) Corn and Corn Improvement. Am. Soc. Agron., Madison, Wisconsin, USA, pp. 1–32.

Galinat, W.C. (1992). Evolution of corn. *Adv. Agron.,* 47: 203–231.

Gama, E.E.C. and Hallauer, A.R. (1977). Relation between inbred and hybrid traits in maize *Crop. Sci.,* 17: 703–706.

Gardner, C.O. (1961). An evaluation of effects of mass selection and seed irradiation with thermal neutrons on yield of corn. *Crop Sci.,* 1: 241–245.

Goodman, M.M. and Brown, W.L. (1988). Races of corn. *In*: Sprague, G.F. and Dudley, J.W. (*Eds*.,) Corn and Corn Improvement. Am. Soc. Agron., Madison, Wisconsin, USA, pp. 33–80.

Green, J.M. (1948). Relative value of two testers for estimating topcross performance in segregating maize populations. *J. Am. Soc. Agron.,* 40: 45–57.

Hallauer, A.R. (1973). Hybrid development and population improvement in reciprocal full-sib selection. *Egyptian J. Genet. Cytol.,* 1: 84–101.

Hallauer, A.R. (1975). Relation of gene action and types of testers in maize breeding procedures. *Proc. Corn Sorghum Res. Conf,,* 30: 150–165.

Hallauer, A.R. (1978). Potential of exotic germplasm for maize improvement. *In* Walder, D.B. (*Ed.*) Maize Breeding and Genetics. John Wiley & Sons, New York, pp. 229–247.

Hallauer, A.R. (1992). Recurrent selection in maize. *Plant Breed. Rev.,* 9: 115–179.

Hallauer, A.R. (1994). Specialty corns. CRC Press, Boca Raton.

Hallauer, A.R. and Eberhart, S.A. (1970). Reciprocal full-sib selection. *Crop Sci.,* 10: 315–316.

Hallauer, A.R. and Miranda, J.B. (1988). Quantitative genetics in maize breeding. Iowa State University Press, Ames, Iowa.

Hallauer, A.R., Russell, W.A. and Lamkey, K.R. (1988). Corn breeding. *In*: Sprague, G.F. and Dudley, J.W. (*Eds.*) Corn and Corn Improvement. Am. Soc. Agron., Madison, Wisconsin, USA

Hanna, W., Ozias-Akins, P. and Röche, D. (1999). Apomixis and heterosis. *In*: Coors, J.G. and Pandey, S. (*Eds.*) Genetics and Exploitation of Heterosis in Crops. Am. Soc. Agron., Madison Wisconsin, USA. pp. 335–342.

Hayes, H.K. (1963). A Professor's Story of Hybrid Corn. Burgess, Minneapolis. USA.

Hull, F.H. (1945). Recurrent selection and specific combining ability in corn. *J. Am. Soc. Agron.,* 37: 134–45.

Jenkins, M.T. (1934). Methods of estimating the performance of double crosses in corn. *J. Am Soc. Agron.,* 26: 199–204.

Jenkins, M.T. (1935). The effect of inbreeding and of selection within inbred lines of maize upon hybrids made after successive generations of selfing. *Iowa State J. Sci.,* 9: 429–450.

Jenkins, M.T. (1940). The segregation of genes affecting yield of grain in maize. *J. Soc. Agron.,* 32: 55—63.

Jenkins, M.T. and Brunson, A.M. (1932). Methods of testing inbred lines of maize in crossbred combination. *J. Am. Soc. Agron.,* 24: 523–530.

Jones, D.F. (1918). The effects of inbreeding and crossbreeding upon development. *Conn Agri: Exp. Stn. Bull.,* 207: 5–100.

Kato, Y.T.A. (1976). Cytological studies of maize and teosinte in relation to their origin and evolution. *Massachusetts Agric Exp. Stn. Bull.* p. 635.

Kato, Y.T.A. (1984). Chromosome morphology and the origin of maize and its races. *In*: Hecht, M.K. (*Ed.*). Evolutionary Biology. Plenum Publishing Co., New York.

Kaur, G. (1996). Recurrent selection based on alternate evaluation of selfed and half-sib families in an open-pollinated population of maize. Ph.D. thesis, Punjab Agricultural University, Ludhiana.

Kermicle, J.L. (1969). Androgenesis conditioned by a mutation in maize. *Science,* 166: 1422–1424.

Khehra, A.S., Dhillon, B.S., Malhi, N.S., Pal, S.S., Saxena, V.K. and Malhotra, V.V. (1986). Reciprocal recurrent selection for multi-trait indices in maize. *Euphytica,* 35: 817–822.

Kienke, T.R., Russell, W.A. and Guthrrie, W.D. (1986). Recurrent selection for resistance to European corn borer in a corn synthetic and correlated effects on agronomic traits. *Crop Sci.,* 26: 864–868.

Kiesselbach, T.A. (1949). The Structure and Reproduction of Corn. Univ. of Nebraska Press, Lincoln.

Laughnan, J.R. and Gabay-Laughnan, S. (1983). Cytoplasmic male sterility in maize. *Annu. Rev.Genet.,* 17: 27–48.
Lonnquist, J.H. (1964). Modification of the ear-to-row procedure for the improvement of maize populations. *Crop Sci.,* 4: 227–228.
Maita, R. and Coors, J.G. (1984). Twenty cycles of biparental mass selection for prolificacy in the open-pollinated maize population Golden Glow. *Crop Sci.,* 36: 1527–1532.
Malhi, N.S. and Khehra, A.S. (1987). Improvement of grain yield through direct selection and selection for harvest index in two maize populations. *Crop Improv.,* 14: 74–78.
McClintock, B. (1950). The origin and behaviour of mutable loci in maize. *Proc. Natl. Acad. Sci. USA,* 36: 344–355.
McClintock, B. (1959). Chromosome constitutions of Mexican and Guatemalan races of maize. *Annu. Rep. Dep. Gen. Carnegie Inst. Washington.* 59: 461–472.
McClintock, B., Kato, Y. and Blumenschein, A. (1981). Chromosome constitution of the races of maize, its significance in the interpretation of the relationships between races and varieties in the Americas. Colegio de Postgraduados, Chapingo, Mexico.
Melchinger, A.E., Boplpemaier, J., Dhillon, B.S., Pollmer, W.G., and Herrmann, R.G. (1992). Genetic diversity for RFLPs in European maize inbreds. II. Relation to the performance of hybrids within versus between heterotic groups for forage trait. *Theor. Appl. Genet.,* 84: 872–681.
Mertz, E.T., Bates, L.S. and Nelson, O.E. (1964). Mutant gene that changes protein composition and increases lysine content of maize endosperm. *Science,* 145: 279–280.
Miedema, P. (1982). The effects of low temperature of *Zea mays. Adv. Agron.,* 35: 93–128.
Mukherjee, B.K. (1989). Maize. *In*: Chopra, V.L. (*Ed.*) Plant Breeding. Oxford & IBH, New Delhi, pp. 199–212.
Mukherjee, B.K. and Dhawan, N.L. (1970). Genetic studies in varieties of maize. I. Genetic analysis of yield and other quantitative characters. *Japanese J. Breed.,* 20: 47–56.
Mukherjee, B.K., Gupta, N.P., Singh, S.B. and Singh, N.N. (1971). Metroglyph analysis of Indian and exotic varieties of maize. *Euphytica,* 20: 113–118.
National Academy of Sciences (1972). Genetic vulnerability of major crops. National Academy of Sciences, Washington., USA.
Newton, K.J. and Courtney, K.M. (1991). Molecular analysis of mitochondria from teosinte-cytoplasm-associated miniature plants. *Maydica,* 36: 153–159.
Pandey, S., Vasal, S.K. and Deutsch, J.A. (1991). Performance of open-pollinated maize cultivars selected from 10 tropical maize populations. *Crop Sci.,* 31: 285–289.
Peterson, P.A. (1987). Mobile elements in plants. CRC *Crit. Rev. Pl. Sci.,* 6: 105–208.
Peterson, P.A. (1999). Mechanisms contributing to genetic diversity in maize populations. *In*: Coors, J.G. and Pandey, S. (*Eds.*) Genetics and Exploitation of Heterosis in Crops, Am. Soc. Agron., Madison, Wisconsin, USA, pp. 149–162.
Prasanna, B.M. and Sarkar, K.R. (1977). Active transposable elements in Indian maize germplasm and assorted genetic testers. *Curr. Sci.,* 73: 464–469.
Radernacher, M.A.M., Hallauer, A.R. and Russell, W.A. (1999). Comparative response of two reciprocal recurrent selection methods in BS21 and BS22 maize populations. *Crop Sci.,* 39: 87–97.
Randolpli, L.F. (1959). The origin of maize. *Indian J. Genet.,* 19: 1–12.
Rawlings, J.C. and Thompson, D.L. (1962). Performance level as criterion for the choice of maize testers. *Crop Sci.,* 2: 217–220.
Rhoades, M.M. (1931). Cytoplasmic inheritance of male sterility in *Zea mays. Science,* 73: 340–341.
Richey, F.D. (1927). The convergent improvement of selfed lines of corn. *Am. Not.,* 61: 430–449.
Rosegrant, M.W., Agcaoili-Sombillam M. and Perez, N.D. (1995). Global food projections to 2020: Implications for investment. Food, Agriculture and Environment Discussion Paper No.5, October 1995. International Food Policy Research Institute, Washington, D.C., USA.

Russell, W.A. (1991). Genetic improvement of maize yield. *Adv. Agron.,* 46: 245–298.
Russell, W.A. and Vega, U.A. (1973). Genetic stability of quantitative characters in successive generations in maize inbred lines. *Euphytica,* 22: 172–180.
Russell, W.A., Blackburn, D.J. and Lamkey, K.R. (1992). Evaluation of a modified reciprocal recurrent selection procedure for maize improvement. *Maydica,* 37: 61–67.
Sarkar, K.R. (1974). Genetic selection technique for production of haploid in higher plants. *In*: Kasha, K.J. (*Ed.*) Haploids in Higher Plants: Advances and Potential. Guelph Univ. Press Canada, pp. 33–41.
Sarkar, K.R., Singh, N.N. and Prasanna, B.M. (1995). Genetic improvement of maize in India. *In*: Deb, D.L. (*Ed.*) Sustaining Crop and Animal Productivity — The Challenge of the Decade Associated Publishing Co., New Delhi, pp. 65–82.
Sekhon, R.S., Dhillon, B.S., Saxena, V.K. and Grewal, M.S. (1999). Modified S1 recurrent selection in a maize composite. *Maydica,* 44: 175–177.
Sekhon, S.S., Dhillon, B.S. and Kanta, Uma (1992). Host plant resistance in maize to insect pests *In*: Dhaliwal, G.S. and Dilawari, V.K. (*Eds.,*) Advances in Host Plant Resistance to Insects. Kalyani Publ., New Delhi, pp. 79–109.
Sharma, R.C. and Lal, S. (1998). Maize diseases and their management. *Indian Farming,* 48: 92–96.
Sharma, R.C. and Payak, M.M. (1990). Durable resistance to two leaf blights in two maize inbred lines. *Theor. Appl. Cenet.,* 80: 542–544.
Shaw, R.H. (1988). Climatic requirement. *In*: Sprague, G.F. and Dudley, J.W. (*Eds.*) Corn and Corn Improvement. Am. Soc. Agron., Madison, Wisconsin, USA. pp. 609-638.
Shepherd, N.S. (1987). Transposable elements and gene tagging. *In*: Shaw, C.H. (*Ed.*) Plan: Molecular biology: A Practical Approach. IRL Press, Washington D.C., pp. 187–220.
Shull, G.H. (1908). The composition of a field of maize. *Am. Breeder's Assoc. Rep.,* 4: 296–301.
Shull, G.H. (1909). A pure-line method of corn breeding. *Am. Breeders's Assoc. Rep.,* 5: 51–59.
Shull, G.H. (1952). Beginnings of the heterosis concept. *In*: Gowen, J.W. (*Ed.*) Heterosis. Iowa State College Press, Ames, USA. pp. 14–48.
Singh, B. (1977). Races of Maize in India. ICAR Publication, New Delhi.
Singh, M., Khehra, A.S. and Dhillon, B.S. (1986). Direct and correlated response to recurrent full sib selection for prolificacy in maize. *Crop Sci.,* 26: 275–278.
Singh, N.N., Gupta, N.P. and Mauria, S. (1996). Maize, *In*: Paroda, R.S. and Chadha, K.L. (*Eds.*) 50 years of Crop Science Research in India. ICAR, New Delhi, pp. 252–264.
Smith, D.R. and White, D.G. (1988). Diseases of corn. *In*: Sprague, G.F. and Dudley, J.W. (*Eds.*) Corn and Corn Improvement. Am. Soc. Agron., Madison, Wisconsin, USA, pp. 687–766.
Sprague, G.F. and Eberhart, S.A. (1977). Corn breeding. *In*: Sprague, G.F. and Dudley, J.W. (*Ed.*) Corn and Corn Improvement. Am. Soc. Agron., Madison, Wisconsin, USA, pp. 305–362.
Sprague, G.F. and Tatum, L.A. (1942). General vs. specific combining ability in single crosses of corn. *J. Am. Soc. Agron.,* 34: 923–932.
Stonor, C.R. and Anderson, E. (1949). Maize among the hill peoples of Assam. *Ann. Mo. Bot. Garden.,* 36: 355–404.
Sturtevant, Von, E.L. (1989). Varieties of corn. USDA Exp. Sta. Bulletin. p. 57.
Sundaresan, V. (1996). Horizontal spread of transposon mutagenesis: New uses for old elements *Trends Plant Sci.,* 1: 184–190.
Suto, T. and Yoshida, Y. (1956). Characteristics of the oriental maize. *In*: Kihara, L (*Ed.*) and anc Crops of Nepal Himalaya, Vol. 2. Fauna and Flora. Res. Soc. Kyoto Univ., Kyoto, Japan, pp. 375–530.
Tanksley, S.W. and Nelson, J.C. (1996). Advanced backcross QTL analysis: A method for the simultaneous discovery and transfer of valuable QTLs from unadapted germplasm into elite lines. *Theor. Appl. Genet.,* 92: 191–203.

Tatum, L.A. (1971). The southern corn leaf blight epidemic. *Science,* 171: 1113–1116.
Troyer, A.F. (1996). Breeding widely adapted, popular maize hybrids. *Euphytica* 92: 163–174.
USDA (1996). Grain: World markets and trade. Circular Series FG 9-96, September 1996.
Vasal, S.K., Dhillon, B.S. and Pandey, S. (1997). Recurrent selection methods based on evaluation cum-recombination block. *Plant Breed. Rev.,* 14: 39–63.
Vasal, S.K., Dhillon, B.S. and Srinivasan, G. (1995). Changing scenario of hybrid maize breeding and research strategies to develop two-parent hybrids. *In*: Rai, M. and Mauria, S. (*Eds.*) Hybrid Research and Development. Indian Soc. Seed Tech., New Delhi, pp. 19–36.
Wellhausen, E.J. (1965). Exotic germplasm for improvement of corn belt maize. *Hybrid Corn Ind. Res. Conf.,* 20: 31–45.
Wellhausen, E.J., Roberts, L.M., Hernandez-Xolocotzi, E. and Mangelsdorf, P.C. (1952). Races of Maize in Mexico. Bussey Inst. Harvard Univ., Cambridge, USA.
Wilkes, H.G. (1981). Maize in India. *Maize Genet. Coop. Newsletter,* 55: 13–15.
Wu, J.L. (1986) Breeding haploid corn by anther culture. *In*: Hu, H. and Yang, H.Y. (*Eds.*). Haploids of higher plants *in vitro.* Springer, Berlin, Germany, p. 149-161.
Wych, R.D. (1988). Production of hybrid seed corn. *In*: Sprague, G.F. and Dudley, J.W. (*Eds.*) Corn and Corn Improvement. Am. Soc. Agron., Maidson, USA, pp. 565–607.
Zuber, M.S. and Darrah, L.L (1980). US corn germplasm base. *Proc. Corn Sorghum Res. Conf.* 35: 234–249.

# 4

# Sorghum

## 1. INTRODUCTION

Sorghum (*Sorghum bicolor* (L.) Moench) has a wide range of adaptation from sea level to an altitude of 3000 metres, a range of rainfall regimes (300-1800 mm), day lengths, soil conditions and varying biotic and abiotic factors depending upon the geographies. Globally, Sorghum is the fifth important food and feed crop. It is largely grown for food under rainfed conditions in the semiarid tropics. In the developed countries, grain Sorghum is a component of animal feeds. The variability in the weather factors, rainfall in particular, during the crop season between regions/locations/years/seasons frequently introduces an uncertainty factor. Rainfall fluctuations, aberrations and catastrophies are not uncommon. Hence, besides adaptation, adaptability and stability of performance assumes importance for successful Sorghum cultivation (Rao *et al.,* 1989).

Efforts in India in facing the problems of yield, adaptation and risks involved in sorghum culture led of a critical evaluation of the temperate and tropical Sorghums and their cross derivatives. The transformation of the tropical Sorghums into widely adapted and stable high yield cultivars resulted in both hybrids and varieties now widely cultivated. The genetical, physiological and adaptational studies published over two decades (1965-1985) gave insights into the process of adaptation, adaptabilility and yield improvement (Rao, 1972, 1981,1982; Rao and Rana, 1982).

ICRISAT's sorghum breeding efforts in West Africa (NGP Rao 1980-83, Annual Reports) largely involved adaptation of India bred tropical-

---

V.L. Chopra (Ed.): Breeding Field Crops I: Practices, Studium Press (LLC), USA.

temperate cross derivatives to West African environments. The introduction and adaptation of such derivatives in Southern African countries by ICRISAT also yielded positive results. The contributions of the conversion programme of tropical Sorghums for temperate adaptation in USA have been well documented.

Various studies in diverse geographic regions have underlined the potential of tropical-temperate crosses for improving yield, adaptation and adaptability across countries and continents.

## 2. ORIGIN, DOMESTICATION AND CLASSIFICATION

The genus sorghum belongs to the tribe andropogoneae of the family Gramineae and includes both wild species and species cultivated for their grain, fodder, syrup and other commercial purposes. All the cultivated Sorghums have a haploid chromosome number of n = 10 and cross readily with each other. All the cultivated forms are grouped under a single species *Sorghum bicolor* (L.) Moench.

### 2.1. Origin

Cytological evidence indicates that the cultivated Sorghums might have evolved from the wild *Arundinacea*. Members of Halepensia (all tetraploids except *S. propinquum*) appear to have a more recent origin and do not seem to have contributed anything to the origin of the cultivated forms. Snowden believed that the wild African *Arundinacea: S. arundinacea, S. verticelliflorum* and S. *sudanese* were the progenitors of the cultivated crop. S. *aethiopicum* has also been regarded as one of the possible progenitors. De Wet *et al.* (1976) suggested that sorghum probably was derived from the wild races, *aethiopicum* or *verticelliflorum* by selection mainly for tough recemes and larger panicles in the Ethiopia-Sudan region of Africa.

Africa is regarded as the place of origin of sorghum since it contains the maximum number of species. Although several wild species of sorghum are collected from India, it does not appear that cultivated sorghum had an independent origin in India, since all the Indian species are found in Africa. In Australia, there are 10 grassy types but these do not appear to be the progenitors of the crop. The evidence, therefore, points to sorghum originating in Africa. To be more specific, the northeastern region of Africa appears to be the most likely place since it contains the maximum diversity of cultivated and wild species as seen from the following (Table 1).

**Table 1:** Sorghum distribution in Africa

| *Region* | *No. of wild species* | *No. of cultivated species* |
|---|---|---|
| North-east Africa (North of latitude 10 S East of longitude 25 E) | 14 species (19 varieties) | 20 species |
| West Africa | 5 species (5 varieties) | 11 species |
| South Africa | 6 species (8 varieties) | 12 species |

It has been argued by some that Ethiopia may not be the centre of origin of cultivated sorghum since primary centres of origin are traditionally linked with the abundance of primitive races (wild and weedy) rather than the highly evolved cultivated types. However, there seems to be no intrinsic reason why a crop plant should not reach its most developed form in its centre of origin, where it has been under selection for the longest time (Doggett, 1970).

## 2.2. Domestication

Cultivated races of sorghum originated by disruptive selection and domestication in Africa by Cushite people who migrated into Ethiopia from the Middle Hast around the fourth millenium before Christ (Doggett, 1970). Diffusion and domestication resulted in response to environmental factors and human needs. The environmental factors included day lengths, altitudes, temperature and rainfall regimes, soil characters etc. The human needs usually selected for bigger panicles, nonshattering habit, large edible grains, crop favorable duration etc. Early domestication of sorghum, therefore, seems to have generated a range of variability for crop duration, a range of plant heights and grain characters to suit the local food needs leading to the development of land races. The *caudatum* race originated in the area of the origin of sorghum. Migration to the high rainfall areas of West Africa resulted in the *guinea* race, *kafir* in east Africa and *durra* in South Asia including India (Harlan and Stemler, 1976) and from there to China, the middle-east and Europe. Sorghum is not native to the westem hemisphere. Temperate Sorghums were derived by temperate adaptation in the United States from the introduction of two *Durra* types from Egypt in 1874, two *kafirs* from South Africa in 1876, Shallu from India by about 1870, and Milo from Columbia in 1879. Even the high lysine Sorghums of Ethiopian origin (IS 11167 and IS 11758) with shrivelled grains which was identified from world collections seem to have evolved during domestication. This migration and domestication generated an amazing range of variability for plant, leaf and kernel characters besides influencing the reproductive System. This process has resulted in divergent polymorphic populations without isolation and resulted in considerable gene flow. Short and early maturing Sorghums, either as a consequence of mutation or introgression, also appeared early and can be seen even today as mixtures in local fields in sudan.

## 2.3. Classification

The amazing variability generated during the process of disruptive selection, introgression, migration and domestication, leading to the occurrence of land races and wild forms across continents led to several types of classification of sorghum.

Among the early attempts at classification of the genus sorghum, the work of Snowden (1936-1955) has been one of the most comprehensive and useful. Since then, several classifications have been proposed, notably, the cytogenetic classification of Garber (1950); the commercial classification of Vinal *et al.* (1936); the numerical classification of de Wet and Huckabay (1967) and Liang and Casady (1967) and the biometrical systems proposed by Murty *et al.* (1967). A general feature about all these systems has been that they take Snowdenian system as the base. None of these systems have become as popt-as that of Snowden. A simpler and practical system of classification of cultivated Sorghums into 5 basic and 10 hybrid races, which can be easily identified from morphological characters of the mature head and spikelet has been suggested by Harlan (1972).

### 2.3.1. *Snowden's classification*

Among the systems proposed, Snowden's (1936) is the most detailed. comprehensive and is much in use. He divided the genus into two sections. *Eusorghum* and *Parasorghum*. *Parasorghums* have bearded nodes, while in *Eusorghums*, the nodes are smooth. *Eusorghum* contains two sub-sections -*Halepensia* and *Arundinacea.*

*Halepensia* has 5 species. *Arundinacea* contains two series - *Sponstanea* are *Sativa.* The series *Spontanea* contains the wild grassy types grouped into 21 species. The series Sativa contains all the cultivated Sorghums falling into 31 species grouped into six subseries - (1) *Drummondii* (2) *Guineensia,* (3) *Nervosa,* (4) *Bicoloria,* (5) *Caffra* and (6) *Durra.*

Snowden's classification points to a relation between wild and cultivated species. The main disadvantage with this system is the extensive spilitting of the cultivated forms into 'species' which in the opinion of many do not merit specific Status.

### 2.3.2. *Commercial groups of sorghum*

Four major groups of Sorghum are generally distinguished - (1) Grain sorghums, (2) Sorgos, (3) Broom corns and (4) Grass Sorghums.

Vinal *et al.* (1936) classified grain Sorghums into *kafir, milo, feterita, durra, shallu* and *kaoling*. These groups, though originally distinct, have become less distinguishable due to extensive hybridization amongst them.

### 2.3.3. *Other attempts*

Garber (1950) attempted a cytotaxonomic classification of the genus into six subgenera - (1) *Eusorghum,* (2) *Chaetosorghum,* (3) *Heterosorghum,* (4) *Sorghastrum,* (5) *Parasorghum* and (6) *Stiposorghum.*

Murty *et al.* (1967) proposed a classification of the Sorghum world collection into 70 working groups and Eusorghums into nine major categories based cr genetic diversity measured by statistical procedures.

In the United States, De wet and Huckabay (1967) numerically analyzed 52 Snowden species. Their analysis pointed to a relation of the wild and cultivated forms. Another numerical taxonomic analysis by Liang and Casady (1966) brought out a distinction between the wild and cultivated forms.

### 2.3.4. *Harlan's classification*

Harlan (1972) distinguished five basic races *S. bicolor* ssp. *bicolor* cultivated races and ten hybrid races. In the *S. bicolor* ssp. *arundanaceum*, he distinguished six races. His system is outlined below:

The 15 races of cultivated sorghum can be identified by mature spikelets alone although head type is sometimes helpful. The classification is based on five fundamental spikelet types as follows:

*Bicolor* (B) : Grain elongate, sometimes slightly obovate, nearly symmetrical dorsoventrally; glumes clasping the grain

***S. bicolor* ssp. *bicolor cultivated races basic races***

| | | | |
|---|---|---|---|
| Race | (1) | *bicolor* | (B) |
| Race | (2) | *guinea* | (G) |
| Race | (3) | *caudatum* | (C) |
| Race | (4) | *kafir* | (K) |
| Race | (5) | *durra* | (D) |

***Hybrid races : all combinations of basic race***

| | | | |
|---|---|---|---|
| Race | (6) | *guinea-bicolor* | (GB) |
| Race | (7) | *caudatum-bicolor* | (CB) |
| Race | (8) | *kafir-bicolor* | (KB) |
| Race | (9) | *durra-bicolor* | (DB) |
| Race | (10) | *guinea-caudatum* | (GC) |
| Race | (11) | *guinea-kafir* | (GK) |
| Race | (12) | *guinea-durra* | (GD) |
| Race | (13) | *kafir-caudatum* | (KC) |
| Race | (14) | *durra-caudatum* | (DC) |
| Race | (15) | *kafir-durra* | (KD) |

***S. bicolor ssp. arundinaceum spontaneous races***

| | | |
|---|---|---|
| Race | (1) | *arundinaceum* |
| Race | (2) | *aethiopicum* |
| Race | (3) | *virgatum* |
| Race | (4) | *verticilliflorum* |
| Race | (5) | *propinquum* |
| Race | (6) | *shatter cane* |

which may be completely covered or exposed as much as V4 of its length at the tip.

*Guinea* (G) : Grain flattened dorsoventrally, sublenticular in outline, twisting at maturity nearly 90 degrees between gaping invoute glumes that are from nearly as long to longer than the grain.

*Caudatum* (C) : Grain markedly asymmetrical, the side next to the lower glume flat or even somewhat concave, the opposite side rounded and bulging; the persistent style often at the tip of a beak pointing toward the lower glume; ½ the length of the grain or less.

*Kafir* (K) : Grain approximately symmetrical, more or less spherical, not twisting, glumes clasping and variable in length.

*Durra* (D) : Grain rounded obovate, bulging and widest above the middle, wedge-shaped at the base; the glumes very wide, the tip of a different texture from the base and often with a transverse crease across the middle.

The International Bureau of Plant Genetic Resources (IBPGR) has recommended this classification to be used in describing Sorghum.

## 2.4. The Sorghum Gene Pool

According to Harlan (1972), all the 42 Snowdenian 'species' (28 cultivated, 11 wild and 3 weedy) constitute the primary Sorghum gene pool. Under this classification, cultivated races (S. *bicolor* ssp. *bicolor*) and their wild and weedy relatives (S. *bicolor* ssp *arundinaceum*) form the primary gene pool. The secondary gene pool includes S. *halepense, miliaceum,* Johnson grass and S. *almum.* The tertiary gene pool includes, *Saccharum, Sorghastrum* and *Miscanthus.*

Botanically, all cultivated races of Sorghum are presently classified under *Sorghum bicolor* (L.) Moench.

## 3. THE LAND RACES AND SPECIFIC ADAPTATION

Originating in Africa, sorghum spread across wide geographic areas. The African continent (North East, East, West and South Africa), South Asia, India, China, USA, Argentina, Venezuela, Central America and Australia covering a wide range of latitudes and longitudes, altitudes, day lengths, rainfall and temperature regimes and a range of biotic and abiotic stresses. Thousands of land races evolved and were cultivated in the respective subregions. This gave rise to the concept that in spite of the wide adaptation of sorghum as a species, the land races are highly specific to certain specific niches. The geographic coverage of sorghum is no doubt large, but it emerged as the main staple food crop in the drought prone semi arid tropics.

There appears a parallelism in the evolution of tropical cultivars across continents. They are tall; late maturing, the growing period being considerably longer than the length of the rainy season; generally photosensitive; and characterized by localized adaptation and low harvest indices. Such tropical cultivars are generally adapted to low population levels and exhibit lower rates of fertilizer response. Under adequate moisture and low population, they do produce large earheads reflecting their individual superiority, but their community performance is poor even when there is no stress. Since flowering generally takes place after the cessation of the rainy season, rainfall fluctuations render them highly vulnerable, and crop losses approach total failure in years of low and erratic rains. Depending on the components of the cropping systems, the degree of damage may vary and one of them might provide some insurance. Yet, sole and mixed crops in traditional systems are low yielding and climate-vulnerable. This is generally so with Sorghum and is applicable with some modifications to other dryland crops and cropping Systems in tropics (Rao, 1982).

Initial crop breeding efforts were also highly localized both in terms of area of adaptation and choice of germplasm. The methods adopted were largely pure line selections in local cultivars and intervarietal hybridization involving an adapted cultivar and a related one for incorporating specific traits. This is largely true for India, Africa, and even USA in the intial stages. Some examples of selection in land races which were cultivated widely in India are: Aispuri, Saoner-1, PJ selections from Parbhani, Maharashtra, Co selections, from Tamilnadu, Vidisha 60-1 of Madhya Pradesh etc. The M35-1, a rabi selection from Karnataka, virtually remains unbeaten even today (Rao, 1972). Dobbs of East Africa and several other selections from African countries still prevail. The Gyp corn, Giant Milo, Red and White *Kafir* are other examples from USA. Yield improvements through selection in land races were marginal. Local preferences like grain appearance, taste of the food preparation, fodder quality etc., prevailed. The marginal increases in yield of the improved cultivars so bred were frequently offset by weather fluctuations and their over all impact on sorghum productivity or production was not conspicuous. Yet the improved cultivars constitute an important source of genes for various adaptation traits depending on conditions under which they evolved.

The assmblage of world collections of Sorghum was first initiated in India under a PL 480 project in cooperation with the Rockefeller Foundation. Their evaluation, classification and cataloguing were also done under this project (Murty *et al.,* 1967). Later this collection was transferred to ICRISAT and provided the initial capital. Further germplasm collections on a global basis were assembled, catalogued and are being maintained at ICRISAT and are available to breeders all over the world.

## 4. PHENOLOGICAL AND PHYSIOLOGICAL ASPECTS OF ADAPTATION OF TROPICAL AND TEMPERATE SORGHUMS

Sorghum is a short day plant. The late forms do not flower under the long day growing conditions in USA. The first sorghums that entered USA were possibly mixtures of varying plant height and maturities. The compulsions of long day growing conditions and mechanical harvesting led US breeders to select short and early maturing forms which over time have been referred to as "temperate sorghums.' The "tropical sorghums." were generally characterized by tallness, long duration, photoperiod sensitivity, low harvest indices and poor community performance. Under increased seed rates, they are grown as forage sorghums also. The timing of the main stages of growth cycles are optimized in relation to mechanisms that are extremely sensitive to day length and temperature. Yet it should be known that 'the temperate type' forms evolved and co-existed with talls in the areas of origin. The design and development of stable agriculture, more particularly in the tropics, required changing the cycles of growth and reproduction in such a way that the emphasis is on the economic product rather man on total dry matter and the more critical phases of growth coincide with favorable periods of climate.

A tropical tall variety, a short variety and hybrids similar to the temperate forms were subjected to growth analysis. (Rao and Venkateswarlu, 1971; Anantharaman *et al.,* 1978). Most traditional kharif sorghums of the Deccan and the central Indian plateaus require 140 days or more to mature, while the duration of a normal rainy season is from the beginning of July to mid or late September. August usually represents the peak rainfall month. Such sorghums usually remain in the vegetative stage till the second week of October, and if rains cease earlier, yield losses are heavy. The total dry matter produced in normal circumstances may be as high as 450 g per plant, and nearly 70% of this is accumulated in the stalk. Kharif sorghums are characterized by a single peak for the rates of growth coinciding with flowering. The behavior of several African sorghums is similar (Goldsworthy, 1970). The temperate sorghums on the other hand produce less dry matter per plant, exhibit two peaks for growth rates coinciding with preflowering and grain-filling stages resulting in a 50:50 dry matter distribution (Anantharaman *et al.,* 1978).

Superior sorghum hybrids and varieties developed from temperate-tropical crosses have reduced maturity duration (100-110 days) and consistently yield well (Table 2). The critical stages of growth-seedling, flower primordia, and grain filling-coincide with periods of assured rainfall or satisfactory moisture profile status. Thus, in breeding for efficient water use for grain production such corrections for duration, dry matter production and differentiation at optimal times of the season are essential and should constitute the first steps in modifying traditional tropical sorghums.

**Table 2:** All India average performance of sorghum hybrids and varieties (kharif)

| | Grain yield (kg/ha) | | | | |
|---|---|---|---|---|---|
| ***Hybrid/ Variety*** | ***1978*** | ***1979*** | ***1980*** | ***Av.*** | ***%CSH-1*** |
| | | ***Hybrids*** | | | |
| CSH-1 | 3682 | 3622 | 3034 | 3370 | 100 |
| CSH-5 | 4307 | 3808 | 3437 | 3851 | 114 |
| CSH-6 | 4265 | 3648 | 3480 | 3798 | 112 |
| CSH-9 | 5036 | 4353 | 3836 | 4408 | 130 |
| | | ***Varieties*** | | | |
| SPV-221 | 3198 | 3303 | 3160 | 3220 | 95 |
| SPV-245 | 3868 | 3564 | 3237 | 3556 | 105 |

Crosses between the "Tropical" and "Temperate" sorghums therefore became an integral part of sorghum breeding in India since mid sixties and this procedure is now followed in all the countries. The genetical and breeding aspects of yield improvement and adaptation are further explored in the following.

## 5. TROPICAL X TEMPERATE CROSSES OF SORGHUM : GENETICAL AND BREEDING ASPECTS OF ADAPTATION AND PERFORMANCE

N.G.P. Rao and colleagues systematically pursued genetical and breeding aspects of Indian (tropical) x Exotic (temperate) crosses and generated valuable data which were published in a series of articles in the Indian Journal of Genetics and Plant Breeding from 1970-1985. This series "Genetic Analysis of Indian x exotic crosses in Sorghum" constituted nearly 40 papers and can be referred to for details.

The primary genetic factors that contributed to both yield and performance are analyzed below.

### 5.1. Significance of Genetics of Plant Height and Maturity

Genetic studies in USA on the genetics of plant height by Quinby and Karper (1954) identified four-height genes designated Dwl, Dw2, Dw3 and Dw4. Genotypes recessive for one, two, three and four genes were designated 1-dwarf, 2-dwarf, 3-dwarf and 4-dwarf respectively. One of them (dw3) was unstable and reverted to tall type frequently. Similarly, the genetics of duration of growth was studied in detail by Quinby (1967). Four loci, Mal, Ma2, Ma3 and Ma4 have been identified and there are many alleles at each locus. Quinby reported 2 dominant and 11 recessive alleles at the Mal locus; 12 dominant and 2 recessive alleles at Ma2 locus; nine dominant and seven recessive alleles at Ma3 locus; and 11 dominant and l recessive allele at Ma4 locus. Combination of dominants and recessives at the four loci result in flowering periods ranging from 40 to over 100 days.

The interrelationships between height and maturity with yield have been studied at the level of described genes and also quantitatively. The genes mal and dw2 are closely linked. The other three major maturity genes appear to be linked to the other three major height genes. The heterozygous condition of the single maturity gene has been reported to result in considerable hybrid vigour. Effects of tall mutations on yield also resulted in higher yields. There is generally a positive regression between yield and maturity. There is evidence that these relationships can be broken and higher yield levels are feasible in the short and early forms also. The understanding and manipulation of height and maturity genes has been a signficant factor in bringing about changes in yield and adaptation (Rao *et al.,* 1973).

### 5.2. Hybrid

The discovery of Stephens and Holland (1954) that the milo cytoplasm interacted with *kafir* nuclear factors resulting in cytoplasmic genetic male sterility led to the advent of commercial hybrid era in the USA. This marked a major step both for elevating yield levels and crossing adaptability barriers. The entire US grows hybrid sorghum.

The first hybrids developed in the USA were based on temperate materials available to them. They soon realized that the hybrid yields were plateauing and their germplasm base needed to be broadened. Since tropical sorghums do not flower in the growing environment of USA, they launched a conversion programme to transfer genes from tropical sorghums to temperate sorghums through a backcross system, known as the conversion programme. They used an experimental Station Mayaguez in Puerto Rico, where both tropical and temperate sorghums flowered and permitted crossing between the two groups. The crosses were grown in Texas where temperate cultivars with tropical traits were selected and the backcross process was continued till the tropical features were captured on dwarf statured plants which flowered and set grain in Texas. The fully converted lines had tropical plant features but lacked yields, panicle size etc. as obtainable in the tropics. Nevertheless they provided valuable sources of breeding material. More than fully converted lines, selections from early stages of the backcross programme were found more useful. This conversion programme enabled US breeders to capitalize on tropical traits and diversify the temperate germplasm base.

Like the temperate cultivars, the initial temperate hybrids developed in USA, were not successful in India and West Africa. It is the line improvement, both males and females, in India that led to the development of superior varieties and hybrids. The first two hybrids released in India, CSH 1 and CSH2, were based on yellow endosperm feterita and hegari male parents derived from African germplasm. But it is the exploitation of African zerazeras that brought about a significant change in the variety-hybrid scenario. The tall zerazeras were directly tested in All India coordinated trials and it was found that they had good yield and grain quality but lodged badly in trials. The derived, short statured male parent of CS 3541 which provided the male parent for three commercial hybrids CSH 5, CSH 6 and CSH 9 has zerazera in its parentage. 296A female parent of CSH 9, has karad local in its parentage. CSH 9, released during 1969-70, is the dominant hybrid today, even after 20 years of efforts made by public, private and international sectors to produce new hybrids. Almost all promising hybrids and lines of India and the rest of the world have Zerazera in their parentage. The contributions of Zerazeras to grain yield, quality and adaptation should be considered phenomenal and the All India coordinated Sorghum programme needs to be recognized for its poineering effort. A large portion of kharif Sorghum area in India is under hybrids. The presently cultivated hybrids in India have wide adaptation during kharif (rainy season).

## 5.3. Varieties

Since line improvement is complementary to hybrid superiority, the Indian Sorghum programme in particular concentrated on this aspect. Swarna, the first variety released, equalled CSH 1 in yield and had yellow endosperm. The recently released varieties, SPV 462 (CO 25), CSV 10 (SB 1066 x CS3541), CSV 11 (SC 108-3 x CS 3541), CSV 13 (IS 12662 x 555 IS 3612 x 2219b x E 35-1) and CSV 15 (SPV 475 x SPV 462) resulted from crosses between derived lines but reveal tropical-temperate parentage in their lineage.

Working at Samaru, Nigeria, N.G.P. Rao concentrated on the long duration types for the Sudanian Zone. His first exercise was to look at the improved lines developed in the Indian and ICRISAT programmes and assess their adaptation. After rigorous screening for the stalk borers Busseola and Sesamia and the prevailing biotic and abiotic environment, about 15 lines were selected for yield testing (1980-83 annual reports). They were simultaneously tested in Cameroon. One of the selections designed Samaru-35 (S-35) performed well in both countries and was further tested extensively in farmer fields in Cameroon and northern Chad. It produced an above average yield of 3.75 tones/hectare across 27 multilocational Station trials in Cameron (1985-86). In West African variety adaptation trials (early group), S-35 produced an average grain yield of 2.37 t/ha during 1987 and 3.23 t/ha during 1988 (Dangi, *et al.* 1998). It has been reported that this variety was widely adapted and acclaimed and ICRISAT undertook a socio-economic study of its impact. S-35 has in its parentage, (SPV 35 x E 35-1) x CS 3541), tropical tall E35-1, the short CS3541 with zerazera in its lineage and SPV 35 an early drought tolerant variety, initially introduced from USA. The case is cited as an example of the potential of temperate x tropical crosses.

In the ICRISAT'S southern African programme located at Bulawaye in Zimbabwe, Rao revealed the suitability and adaptation of derived lines to Southern African environment Zimbabwe, Zambia and some southern African countries. The derived materials bred at the ICRISAT Centre, Hyderabad and the Indian programme performed well, and was the result of critical screening for the prevailing biotic and abiotic factors in the respective regions.

In the breeding nurseries grown at Texas, the promise of the Zera Zera derivatives was conspicuous. Details of the hybrids and varieties released in India are given in Table 6.

## 5.4. Populations

Dogget (1972) and Bholanath (1982) described procedures of population improvement and the results obtained. Population improvement through the use of genetic or cytoplasmic-genetic materials has potential for incorporating diverse alleles from source populations and is useful in broadening the germplasm base and development of sources with multiple resistances and other attributes.

## 5.5. Genotype Alteration and Optimum Plant Type

In a study based on more productive derivatives with a range of heights and maturities obtained from tall, late Indian (tropical) and temperate (short and early) crosses and their parents, a Computer Simulation was done to arrive at an optimum phenotype with respect to yield, maturity and height (Rana *et al.,* 1984). The predicted curve indicated that the present optimum was at about 180 cm height and 68-70 days flowering. There is potential for further improvement upto about 230-240 cm height and about 70-75 days flowering. There is thus considerable scope for further improvement by plant modification. Beyond 75 days flowering, there may not be any yield advantage.

By manipulating biomass, plant height could be increased to 220-240 cms without sacrificing grain yield where fodder is important. Such types, both hybrids and varieties, are becoming available in the Indian programme for fodder production.

This illustrates the potential opportunities offered by tropical x temperate crosses. Studies and experience, however, indicates that recombination potential is low and the recovery of desired types results from some cross combinations only.

## 5.6. The Promise of Biotechnology Homologies Across Species During Evolution

A detailed genetic map of the Sorghum genome has been assembled (Chittenden *et al.,* 1994). This map provides the basis of assessing the magnitude of gene conservation among grass species (Paterson *et al.*, 1995) and for studying genetics of height, maturity and other important traits.

A straight synteny was observed for 2 pairs of linkage groups. In two cases, one Sorghum linkage group corresponded to 2 or 3 sugarcane linkage groups respectively. In other two cases, one sugarcane linkage group corresponded to 2 separate Sorghum linkage groups. No complete correspondance was found in the sugarcane genome. In most cases, loci appeared to be colinear betweeen homoeologous chromosomal segments in sorghum and sugarcane.

The growing amount of evidence that grass species are genetically similar supports the possibility that genes for yield and resistance to biotic and abiotic factors were conserved during the evolutionary divergence of host species. This issue has important implications to improvement of sorghum and raises the possibility that genes in Sorghum may have been derived from wheat, other small grains, or their progenitors.

## 5.7. Marker Assisted Selection for Biotic and Abiotic Factors

For resistance breeding, alien genes are being routinely used. A series of Cry genes are available for incorporation into Sorghum for resistance to different insect phyla. Similarly, transformation for resistance to other biotic factors appears promising. However, traditional methods of determining the genetics of biotic agents, host plants, and their interactions have not been adequate to explain evolutionary relationships, especially formation of biotypes virulent to resistant plant genotypes. Phylogenic analysis of data from comparative DNA sequences offers a methodology to reconstruct evolutionary history and relationships at all taxonomic levels. Molecular methods are providing reliable markers to distinguish between biotypes, races, and cryptic species of economically important insects.

Molecular genetic techniques are also providing exciting opportunities to better understand the genetic relationship between an insect and a resistant plant. This kind of information is needed especially for insects such as shootfly which have overcome several resistance genes in Sorghum. DNA marker technology is currently used to map and identify gene structure conferring resistance traits to plants. Understanding the genetics of the resistance in plants will provide the knowledge to improve resistance deployment strategies. However, it is becoming clear that, with regard to plant resistance to insects, it is equally important to understand the genetics of the insect. Molecular genetic techniques are beginning to provide the opportunity to better understand the relationship of plant genetics to insect genetics.

Molecular markers are specially advantageous for agronomic traits such as resistance to pathogens, insects and nematodes, tolerance to abiotic stress, quality parameters and quantitative traits. Molecular markers that are otherwise difficult to tag, can be handled by using near isogenic lines or recombinant inbred lines. This approach has accelerated the mapping of many genes in crop plants including Sorghum.

Marker assisted selection can be performed in early segregating populations and at early stages of plant development. Marker-assisted selection or identification can be used to pyramid the major genes, including resistance genes, with the ultimate goal of producing varieties with more desirable characters. Thus, with MAS it is now possible for the breeder to conduct many rounds of selection in a year. Molecular marker technology is now integrated into existing plant breeding programmes all over the world in order to allow researchers to access, transfer and combine genes at a rate and with a precision not previously possible. In Sorghum, several linkage maps based on RFLP markers have been established.

Identification of genetic regions affecting morphological traits such as plant height (Pereira and Lee, 1995; Lin *et al.,* 1995), maturity (Lin *et al.,* 1995), and also agronomically important traits such as drought tolerance (Tuinstra *et al.,* 1996) and insect resistance (Tao *et al.,* 1997) have been reported.

## 6. ENVIRONMENTAL RESPONSES AND STABILITY OF PERFORMANCE

### 6.1. Climatic Dimension

The yield stability of sorghum across climates has been dealt with in detail by Rao *et al.* (1989) and Rao (1991). Sorghum has emerged as a major food crop in semiarid tropics and its production is greatly influenced by rainfall fluctuations, aberrations, catastrophies and possible climate change. Both drought and excess rain, particularly late rains, reduce yields and damage the grain. With altered genotypes, hybrids or varieties, rainfall deviations upto 0.5 SD, are manageable and return normal yields, whereas the late locals are likely to fail if the rainfall is low. Excess and late rains over 0.5 SD do not reduce yields but cause grain damage. Efforts are under way to manage such situations. However, such excess rain in vertisols provides for an additional second season crop like safflower or chick pea and provides opportunities for increasing cropping intensity.

## 6.2. Genotype × Environment Interactions and Stability of Performance

Using data from multisite, multi year experiments several studies have been carried out in the All India Sorghum improvement project to understand the performance of genotypes, both improved hybrids and improved varieties of tropical x temperate origin. Only a couple of cases will be cited to illustrate their adaptation and stability. Data on hybrid performance and stability (Table 3) clearly establish superiority of hybrid CSH 1, CSH 2, CSH 6 (early, (CSH 5 and CSH 9 (medium). This superiority is maintained across all environments.

Compared to varieties, hybrids have better buffering abilities against environmental fluctuations as revealed by estimates of components of variance for grain and fodder yields of Sorghum varieties and hybrids during kharif (Table 3). Nevertheless in other studies, there is evidence that improved varieties can yield equal to hybrids if there are no environmental restrictions. Studies by Barah *et al.* (1981) clearly bring out the risk aversion potential of such hybrids.

**Table 3:** Estimates of components of variance for grain and fodder yield of kharif sorghum varieties and hybrids

| *Component* | *Grain yield* | | *Fodder yield* | |
|---|---|---|---|---|
| *of variance* | *Varieties* | *Hybrids* | *Varieties* | *Hybrids* |
| $\sigma^2 g$ | 20.30 | 11.22 | 422.42 | 487.35 |
| $\sigma^2 gl$ | 10.45 | 4.25 | 242.71 | 59.97 |
| $\sigma^2 gy$ | –0.83 | 0.40 | 19.61 | –5.32 |
| $\sigma^2 gly$ | 27.57 | 21.30 | 503.02 | 255.03 |
| $\sigma^2 1$ | 8.36 | 9.57 | 120.24 | 128.74 |

### 6.3. Response to Management and Inputs

The response of improved cultivars, hybrids in this case, are superior to tropical locals in yield, population density and fertilizer N as illustrated in Similar data are also available for improved varieties derived from tropical × temperate crosses.

### 6.4. Insects Pests and Diseases

Almost all the temperate sorghums are susceptible to shoot fly and stemborers, and resistance/tolerance genes are available in tropical cultivars. Thus depending on the area of adaptation, the sources of adaptation for diseases, pests of abiotic stresses, are available in the respective land races where they evolved to suit that environmental complex. It is not our intention to list these sources or give an account of resistance breeding, but suffice it to state that the tropical × temperate crosses provide opportunities to combine yield with genes for diverse traits.

### 6.5. Adaptation to Cropping Systems

Sorghum has been traditionally grown along with inter crops to provide risk aversion. Systematic studies on stability of inter-crop systems (Rao *et al.* 1981) indicated that the Sorghum-pigeonpea system is the most stable (Table 4). Another study on crop competition in intercropping systems indicated green gram (mung) soybean and pigeonpea as least competing in inter crop systems.

**Table 4:** Stability parameters for total yield in intercropping system.

| *Intercrop* | *Sorghum* | | |
|---|---|---|---|
| | *Yield (q/ha)* | *Regression coefficients* | *Deviations* |
| Pigeonpea | 56.85 | 0.92 | NS |
| Castor | 39.57 | 1.00 | NS |
| Groundnut | 50.53 | 0.99 | NS |
| Soybean | 55.53 | 1.03 | NS |
| Mean | 53.58 | – | – |
| SE | 61.9 | – | – |

In tropics, where crop growing periods are the longest, per day production assumes importance and this should be viewed in relation to soil type, rainfall pattern and temperatures. The advent of early maturing hybrids provided a second crop of safflower or chickpea in vertisols of Deccan and Central India. Such opportunities need to be explored in high rainfall situations.

## 7. SORGHUM HYBRIDS AND VARIETIES RELEASED IN INDIA

Although primarily a *Kharif* crop, sorghum is grown in the *Rabi* season also. In fact, there is a sizeable area in Maharashtra which is committed to *Rabi* Sorghum. The Indian breeding programme has been very successful in developing improved varieties and hybrids of Sorghum, as well as the associated production technology, which has made demonstrable impact and greatly enhanced *Kharif* Sorghum productivity. More recently, improved genotypes of *Rabi* Surghum have also become available. The major characteristics of improved hybrids and varieties and the recommended areas for their cultivation have been summarized in Table 6.

## 8. WORLD SORGHUMS TODAY AND TOMORROW

### 8.1. Present Status: Area, Distribution and Uses

Globally, sorghum is cultivated on about 45 million hectares with an annual production of around 64 m.tons. The average yield is still low at 1400 kg/ha. The yields are high in USA, but the tropical yields are low in spite of the demonstrated average yield of at least 2-2.5 tonnes/ha and higher order yields of 4-5 tones. The present global status of Sorghum production is presented in Table 5.

**Table 5.** Changes in area, productivity and production in sorghum in the major countries/ continents

| *Sl. no.* | *Continent/ Country* | *Year* | *Area* | *Yield* | *Production* |
|---|---|---|---|---|---|
| 1 | World | 79-81 | 44,891 | 1,458 | 65,525 |
| | | 97 | 45,323 | 1,414 | 64,071 |
| 2 | USA | 79-81 | 5,273 | 3,618 | 19,157 |
| | | 97 | 3,800 | 4,401 | 16,727 |
| 3 | India | 79-81 | 16,361 | 695 | 11,380 |
| | | 97 | 11,200 | 804 | 9,000 |
| 4 | Africa | 79-81 | 13,597 | 912 | 12,408 |
| | | 97 | 23,564 | 835 | 19,676 |
| 5 | N. C. America | 79-81 | 7,236 | 3,404 | 24,697 |
| | | 97 | 6,125 | 3,843 | 23,540 |
| i, | Asia | 79-81 | 20,759 | 948 | 19,690 |
| | | 97 | 13,606 | 1,114 | 15,163 |
| 7 | Australia | 79-94 | 548 | 2,003 | 1,084 |
| | | 97 | 564 | 1,790 | 1,010 |

*Source :* FAO year between 1998.

**Table 6 :** Characteristics and performance of important sorghum hybrids and varieties released for cultivation in India

| *Hybrid / Variety* | *Grain yield (kg/ha)* | *Fodder yield (kg/ha)* | *Plant height (cm)* | *Duration (days)* | *Major characteristics* | *Area of recommended cultivation* |
|---|---|---|---|---|---|---|
| ***A. Kharif*** | | | | | | |
| | Hybrids | | | | | |
| ***Early duration*** | | | | | | |
| CSH 1 | 3020 | 7500 | 150 | 100 | Dwarf, early, thin stem, long peduncle, long loose panicle, bold seed. | Low rainfall and light soil kharif areas. |
| CSH 6 | 3376 | 8100 | 161 | 98 | Early maturing, thin stem medium bold and hard seed, resistant to grain deterioration, tolerant to leaf spot diseases | Low rainfall tracts to kharif, and late kharif season in AP. Ideally suited for intercropping and ratooning. |
| CSH 14 | 3840 | 8800 | 181 | 103 | Medium tall, early maturings semi loose panicle, bold seed tolerant to grain mold and leaf spot diseases. | All kharif sorghum growing areas in the medium to heavy soils for low rainfall areas. |
| ***Medium duration*** | | | | | | |
| CSH 5 | 3414 | 9300 | 174 | 110 | Medium tall, thick, juicy stem, medium bold seed, large long head, resistant to grain deterioration, resistant to leaf spot diseases. | All kharif areas and late kharif tracts of AP and summer irrigated areas in TN & Karnataka. Well adapted for intercropping and ratooning. |
| CSH 9 | 3865 | 9800 | 182 | 110 | Medium tall, thick, juicy stem, vigorous growth, bold round seed, large semi-compact head, tolerant to grain molds and resistant to leaf diseases. | All kharif sorghum growing areas except in humid areas of Karnataka & TN |
| CSH 13(K&R) | 3924 | 14400 | 261 | 110 | Tall, dual purpose, panicle broad, semi, loose, spindle shape, seed round medium bold, light creamy in colour and free threshing. Tolerance to grain molds, lodging and resistance to leaf spot diseases. | All kharif sorghum growing areas. |

**Table 6:** (*Contd..*).

**Table 6 :** (*Contd...*)

| *Hybrid / Variety* | *Grain yield (kg/ha)* | *Fodder yield (kg/ha)* | *Plant height (cm)* | *Duration (days)* | *Major characteristics* | *Area of recommended cultivation* |
|---|---|---|---|---|---|---|
| | | | | | ***Varieties*** | |
| CSV 10 | 2836 | 10100 | 194 | 112 | Plant 190-200 cm and tan pigmented; stem medium thick and juicy; leaves large, green and semi-erect; earhead oval and compact; glumes short and straw coloured and grain small, round, plump and white pearly. Resistant to stem borer, drought and most of the diseases. | All kharif sorghum areas. Specially suited for Maharashtra, Karnataka, AP and Rajasthan |
| CSV 11 | 3200 | 96500 | 174 | 109 | Medium tall, tan pigmented, medium thick and juicy; leaves medium in size; earhead elliptical and semi-loose; glumes short and straw coloured and grain small, elliptical, light cream coloured and pearly. Tolerant to diseases, pests and drought. | All kharif sorghum growing areas. |
| SPV 462 | 3308 | 9700 | 208 | 111 | Tall, dual purpose, loose, panicle, bold round attractive seed, sweet stalk, tolerant to insect pests grain deterioration. | All kharif sorghum growing areas in TN. |
| CSV 13 | 3525 | 9700 | 181 | 112 | Medium tall, small seed, semi-compact head, thin stem, tolerant to insect pests, grain deterioration and several diseases. | All kharif sorghum growing areas. |
| CSV 15 | 3620 | 12100 | 232 | 110 | Tall, dual purpose, sweet stalk, medium bold round seed, small glume and straw colour, large ear head, oblong shape. compact upto middle and open toward apex, resistant to all leaf spot diseases, tolerant to shootfly and stem borer. | All kharif sorghum growing areas. |

**Table 6:** (*Contd..*).

**Table 6 :** (*Contd...*)

| *Hybrid / Variety* | *Grain yield (kg/ha)* | *Fodder yield (kg/ha)* | *Plant height (cm)* | *Duration (days)* | *Major characteristics* | *Area of recommended cultivation* |
|---|---|---|---|---|---|---|
| **B.** ***Rabi*** | | | | | | |
| | | | | | ***Hybrids*** | |
| CHS 8R | 2173 | 3675 | 102 | 115 | Plants 120-150 cm tall and purple pigmented stem thick and juicy; leaves broad and drooping; ear head conical shaped and semi-compact; glumes blackish purple and grain bold and elliptical flat. Tolerant to shootfly and charcoal rot and non-lodging. | Entire rabi tract of Maharashtra, Karnataka and AP and Gujarat. suitable for early planting |
| CHS 12R | 2564 | 4665 | 201 | 115 | Purple plant type, panicles are semi, compact and conical in shape. Tolerant to charcoal rot. Incidence of shootfly and stemborer is low. | All rabi sorghum growing areas of Maharashtra, Karnataka & AP. |
| CSH 13 (K&R) | 3260 | 5417 | 184 | 113 | Tall, dual purpose, panicle broad, semi loose, spindle shape, seed round medium bold light creamy in colour and free threshing. Tolerance to grain molds, lodging and resistance to leaf spot diseases. | All rabi sorghum growing areas. |
| CSH 15R | 3194 | 5570 | 196 | 110 | Medium tall, early maturing, semi loose panicle, bold seed, tolerant to grain mold and leaf spot diseases. | All kharif sorghum growing areas in the medium to heavy soils for low rainfall areas. |
| | | | | | ***Varieties*** | |
| CSV 8R | 2230 | 4790 | 157 | 120 | Plant 200-230 cm tall and purple pigmented; stem thick and juicy; leaves large and dropping; earhead elliptical and semi-compact; glumes straw coloured with transverse depression near feathery tip and grain bold, round plump and light cream coloured. Tolerant to shootfly but susceptible to charcoal root. | Deccan rabi tract of Maharashtra, Karnataka and AP. Recommended for early planting. |

**Table 6:** (*Contd..*).

**Table 6 :** (*Contd...*)

| *Hybrid / Variety* | *Grain yield (kg/ha)* | *Fodder yield (kg/ha)* | *Plant height (cm)* | *Duration (days)* | *Major characteristics* | *Area of recommended cultivation* |
|---|---|---|---|---|---|---|
| SWATI | 2157 | 5277 | 168 | 117 | Plant 170-190 cm, purple pigmented; stem thick and juicy; leaves large and dropping; earhead elliptical and semi-compact; glumes short and straw coloured and grain bold, round plump and white pearly. Resistant to shootfly and charcoal rot. | All rabi sorghum growing areas of Maharashtra. |
| CSV 14R | 2270 | 5537 | 165 | 117 | Medium tall, purple, white pearly round bold seed, resistance to shootfly and charcoal rot equal to M35-1. | All rabi sorghum growing areas. |
| M 35-1 | 2080 | 6110 | 151 | 119 | Plant 180-200 cm and purple pigmented; stem medium thick and juicy; leaves light, green and dropping; earhead oval shaped and semi-compact; glumes straw coloured and grain bold, round plump and white pearly. Tolerant to shootfly, charcoal rot and drought. | Rabi tract of Deccan, Maharashtra, Karnataka and AP. |

Sorghum is used for preparing different types of food preparations in different parts of the world: unleavened bread (*Bhakri* or *roti* in India), leavened bread (*Kisra* in Ethiopia; *Injera* in Nigeria and Uganda) etc. Sorghum beers of various kinds are produced in Africa. All Sorghums may not be suitable for these preparations and one has to keep in mind the acceptance of grain for the kind of preparation that is to be made.

Besides being a component of feed rations, the industrial uses of Sorghum include starch; energy (alcohol) syrup, straw boards from stalks etc. The feed grain requirement is on the increase for which sorghum has an export potential.

Compared to oilseeds and grain legumes, the realized and potential production of Sorghum, both biomass and grain, are much higher both in drylands and under irrigation. The present production in tropics meets the food needs and if demand is generated, more Sorghum can be produced. The need for diversified uses needs to be explored.

## 8.2. The Decline in Sorghum Area and the Need for Diversified Uses and Demand Generation

Both in Asia and the USA, sorghum area is declining. It is only in Africa that it is on the increase. In India, the loss of acreage is largely due to higher prices offered to oil seeds and grain legumes which are replacing sorghum in spite of their low yields. Besides, wheat and rice are available at subsidized prices in the public distribution system and the use of sorghum as food is declining. Use of sorghum grain in animal feeds is still limited. Alternate uses of grain sorghum are known but are not in vogue on a scale that generates demand.

Diversification of sorghum use and sorghum-based products and demand generation is a must if the productivity of sorghum is to go up and reach its potential. If it is to be used only for food in some developing countries, the increases in the productivity may remain marginal. Presently, the feed grain market seems to be growing. More attention needs to be paid to industrial uses.

## 8.3. Future Research

1. Sorghum represents an amazingly interesting reproductive system. Its reproductive system ranges from total self pollination, outcrossing to often cross pollination; occurrence of genetic and cytoplasmic genetic male sterility systems; self incompatibility

and apomixis. The evolution of these contrasting mechanisms is not understood. They are apparently interrelated and more intensive studies are needed. Development of apomictic hybrids is of importance.

2. In spite of several years of national, international and commercial efforts, only a fraction of globally available germplasm seems to have entered breeding programmes. Once zera zera was identified, zera zera derivatives have become part of most programmes. Attention to original land races is decreasing.

Surprisingly large panicles of considerable grain weight are recorded in Ethiopia, Nigeria and Sudan. We do not seem to have capitalized on their yield genes. We need to took at these tropical genotypes with extremely heavily loaded earheads to bring back that yield potential to desirable backgrounds. The efforts in India were aimed at bringing yield genes from Aispuri, BP 53 and zera zera to early and short statured backgrounds and thus gave the concept of intermediate optimum. More efforts are needed to bring the dominant yield genes from tropical Sorghum to short and early forms. The biotechnology tools should be able to overcome recombination problems confronted in traditional crossing and recombination.

3. Considerable cytoplasmic diversity is known. Of the AI, A2 and A3 cytoplasms reported, only milo (AI) has been exploited. The A2 cytoplasm is receiving some attention. In India, diverse sources of cytoplasmic-genetic steriles and fertility restoration have been reported from tropical Sorghums and detailed characterization of both the sterility and fertility systems have been reported by Rao *et al.* (1984). A temperature sensitive cytoplasmic genetic male sterility system has also been reported. Murty (1995) perfected the two line hybrid development. These are yet to be used commercially. The need for diversification of the cytoplasmic male sterility systems and consequently, the fertility restorer systems is of paramount importance. Cytoplasmic influence on yield also seem to merit attention.
4. Based on the high lysine Sorghums reported from Ethiopia, some attempts were made to upgrade the nutritional quality of grain Sorghum. Apparently this has not fructified. There are opportunities for improving the nutritional and digestive attributes of both grain and fodder. Biotechnology could be of greater help for this.
5. While there is greater success in incorporating disease resistance in cultivars in various regions, incorporation of insect resistance, particularly shootfly, stalk borers, Head bugs etc have met with

only partial success. Insect resistance in sorghum is still a partially exploited field. Similarly, progress on incorporating resistances to abiotic stresses is also slow. Here again, biotechnology tools could result in rapid progress for insect and disease resistance and resistance to abiotic factors.

6. There is need to maximize yield in early duration types, simultaneously tackling the problems of grain spoilage through genetical as well as mechanical means such as harvesting at physiological maturity and grain drying in dryers. If the per day productivity goes up, it will release sorghum land for other crops. This is essential when arable lands are shrinking.
7. Sorghum has opportunities for a wide adaptation base *per se,* across the globe barring special situations like high altitudes, low temperatures, salinity and alkalinity situations. Such niches need special attention. The principles of wide adaptation are well known but dependence should not be restricted to one or a few varieties across the globe. Once high yield and wide adaptation bases at different maturities/heights have been combined through appropriate choice of materials, breeding methods and wide testing, the breeders can use these base materials for incorporation of specific traits suiting local requirements.

Fitting short season sorghum in long duration tracts would add to the productivity of such lands by increasing cropping intensity. If sorghum has to compete with high priced legumes or oilseeds, its productivity should be high and the utility range should generate demand. Otherwise, the research work will remain in the laboratories. It is necessary to promote Sorghum use in cattle feed rations, expand the food product range and promote industrial uses.

In the final analysis, selection for adaptedness involves adaptation and adaptability to a new agricultural system involving changes in management practices and cropping systems, tolerance to both biotic and abiotic stresses and a range of food, feed and industrial uses and products.

## REFERENCES

Anantharaman, P.V., Achuta Rao, K., Kandlikar, S.S. and Rao, N.G.P. (1978). Genetic analysis of some exotic X Indian crosses in Sorghum XIX Patterns of dry matter accumulation. *Indian J. Genet.,* 38: 333–338.

Barah, B.C., Binswanger, H.P., Rana, B.S. and Rao, N.G.P. (1981). The use of risk oversion in plant breeding: concept and application. *Euphytica*, 30: 451–458.

Bholanath, (1982). Population breeding techniques in sorghum. Sorghum in eighties (Ediors; Rao, N.G.P. and House, L.R.) pp 421–434.

Chittenden, L.M., Schertz, K.F., Lin, Y.R., Wing, R.A. and Paterson, A.H. (1994). A detailed RFLP map of Sorghumbico/or x S.propinquum, suitable for high-density mapping, suggesting ancestral duplication of Sorghum chromosomes or chromosomal Segments, *Theor. Appl. Genet.,* 87: 925–933.

Dangi, O.P., Kenpa, R., Rao, N.G.P. and Murty, D.S. (1998). Registration of S-35 Sorghum cultivar, *Crop Science*, 38: 1718.

De Wet, J.M.J. and Huckabay, J.P. (1967). The origin of Sorghum *bicolor.* II. Distribution and domestication. *Evolution*, 21: 787.

De Wet, J.M.J., Harlan, J.R. and Price, E.G. (1976). Variability in Sorghum *bicolor.* In origins of African plant Domestication. pp. 453–463.

Doggett, H. (1970). Sorghum. Longman, Harlow.

Doggett, H. (1972). The improvement of sorghum in East Africa. *In*: Sorghum in seventies (*Eds.,* Rao, N.G.P. and House, L.R.). Oxford University Press, New Delhi, pp. 47–59.

Evans, L.T. (1993). Crop evolution, adaptation and yield. Cambridge University Press.

Garber, E.D. (1950). Cytotaxonomic studies in the genus Sorghum. *Univ. California Pub. Bot.,* 23: 283.

Goldsworthy, P.R. (1970). The growth and yield üf tall and short sorghum in Nigeria. *J. Agric. Science*, Cambridge 75: 109–122.

Harlan, J.R. (1972). Genetic resources in Sorghum. *In*: Sorghum in seventies (*Eds*: Rao, N.G.P. and House, L.R.) Oxford and IBH Publishing Co. New Delhi, pp. 1–38.

Harlan, J.R. and Stemler, A. (1976). The races of sorghum in Africa. In origins of African plant domestication, pp. 465–478.

Liang, G.H.L. and Casady, A.J. (1966). Quantitative presentation on the systematic relationships among twenty-one sorghum species. *Crop Sci.,* 6: 76.

Martin, J.H. (1936). Sorghum improvement, USDA Yearbook of Agriculture. Washington, DC, USA. p. 523.

Murty, B.R., Arunachalam V., Saxena M.B.L. and Govil G.N. (1967). Classification and catalogue of world collection of Sorghum. *Indian J. Genet. Plant Breed.,* 27: ppl (special.no.).

Murty, U.R. (1995). Breeding two line hybrids in *Sorghum bicolor* (L) Moeneh. *Cereal Res. Commn.,* 23: 397–402.

Paterson, A.H., Lin, Y.R., LiZ Schertz, K.F., Doebley, J.F., Pinson, S.R.M., Liu, S.C., Stansel, J.W. and Irvine, J.E. (1995). Convergent domestication of cereal crops by independent mutations at corresponding genetic loci. *Science*, 269: 1714–1718.

Quinby, J.R. (1967). The maturity genes of Sorghum. Academic press. New York. *Advances in Agronomy*, 19: 267–305

Quinby, J.R. and Karper, R.E. (1954). Inheritance of height in Sorghum. *Agronomy J.,* 46: 211–216.

Rana, B.S., Barah, B.C., Binswanger, H.P. and Rao, N.G.P. (1984). Breeding optimum plant types in sorghum. *Indian J. Genet.,* 44: 385–398.

Rao, N.G.P. (1991). Advancing dryland Agriculture: Plant breeding accomplishments and perspective. B.P. Pal memorial lecture *Indian J. Genet.,* 51: 145–173.

Rao, N.G.P. (1972). Sorghum breeding in India: Recent developments. *In*: sorghum in seventies. (*Eds.,* Rao, N.G.P. and House, L.R.) oxford University Press.

Rao, N.G.P. (1981). Genotype alteration: The basis for Agricultural transformation in tropical drylands. Presidential address. *Indian J. Genet.,* 41: 437–449.

Rao, N.G.P. (1982). Transforming traditional Sorghums. *In*: Sorghum in Eighties, ICRISAT, Hyderabad pp 39-59.

Rao, N.G.P. and Rana, B.S. (1982). Selection in temperate-tropical crosses of sorghum. *In*: Sorghum in eighties. ICRISAT pp. 403–419.

Rao, N.G.P. and Venkateswarlu J. (1971). Genetic analysis of some exotic X Indian c1rosses in Sorghum III. Heterosis in relation to dry matter production and nutrient uptake. *Indian J. Genet.,* 31: 156–176.

Rao, N.G.P., Harinarayana, G., Arunchalam, V., Tripathi, D.P. and Balakotaiah, K. (1973). Genetic analysis of some exotic X Indian crosses in Sorghum VI character association under selection. *Indian J. Genet.,* 33: 1–6.

Rao, N.G.P., Rana, B.S. and Tarhalkar, P.R (1981). Stability, productivity profitability of some intercropping systems in dryland agriculture. In Proc. Int. Workshop on intercropping ICRISAT Patancheru, pp. 292–298.

Rao, N.G.P., Tripathi, D.P. and Rana, B.S. (1984). Genetic analysis of cytoplasmic systems in Sorghum. *Indian J. Genet.,* 44: 480–496.

Rao, N.G.R., Rao, G.R.K. and Acharya, H.S. (1989). Yield stability of Sorghum and millet across climate. In Climate and Food Security. IRRI. Manila pp. 165–185.

Stephens J.C. and Holland R.I. (1954). Cytoplasmic male sterility for hybrid sorghum seed production. *J. Agronomy*, 46: 20–23.

Vinall, H.N., Stephens, J.C. and Martin, J.H. (1936). Identification, history and distribution of common Sorghum varieties. U.S. *Dept. Agr. Tech. Bull.,* p. 506.

# 5

# Pearl Millet

## 1. INTRODUCTION

*Pennisetum glaucum* (L) R Br. is commonly known as pearl millet in English and bajra in Hindi. It is the most important and probably has the greatest nutrient potential, of all the millets. It is a robust, quick growing, rainy season cereal grass with large stems, leaves and heads. Being tall and vigorous, with exceptional grain and fodder yielding potential, it is one of the most important dual purpose crop of India.

Pearl millet is grown predominantly in India and Africa. It is generally cultivated in an area with rainfall from 150-600 mm. It can withstand drought to a great extent, but responds well to good management and higher fertility levels (Nirwal and Upadhyaya, 1979; Singh and Maurya, 1969).

Pearl millet grain contains 8.5-15% protein, 5.3-6.0% fat, 1.05-1.7% crude fibre and 65.5-70.0% nitrogen free extract (Popli and Singh, 1972). Upreti and Austin (1972) compared 14 millet hybrids for proximate analysis and found that different hybrids grain were very rich in storage carbohydrates (59-69%) and proteins (11.31 to 19.62%).

It is an excellent forage crop because of its low hydrocynic acid content. The green fodder is rich in protein, calcium, phosphorus and other minerals with oxalic acid in safe limits (Athwal and Gupta, 1966; Gupta, 1975). It is more digestible when fed green to animals rather than chaffed straw.

Production and productivity of pearl millet in India are increasing inspite of reduction in area planted to pearl millet (Table 1). In Africa where the production is more or less stagnent (Table 2).

V.L. Chopra (Ed.): Breeding Field Crops I: Practices, Studium Press (LLC), USA.

In India, from 1996-1998, pearl millet was grown on an average of 9.71 million hectares with an average yield of 7.68 million tonnes. It is the fourth most important food crop, mostly grown in the arid and semi arid regions, particularly in the north western parts of the country in the states of Rajasthan, Maharashtra, Gujarat, Uttar Pradesh and Haryana which account for nearly 95% of the pearl millet area (Table 3).

**Table 1:** Area, production and productivity of pearl millet in India on triennium basis

| *Triennium ending* | *Area (mha)* | *Production (mt)* | *Productivity (kg ha$^{-1}$)* |
|---|---|---|---|
| 1977 | 11.2 | 4.95 | 443 |
| 1980 | 11.02 | 4.75 | 429 |
| 1983 | 11.46 | 5.33 | 465 |
| 1986 | 11.03 | 5.81 | 522 |
| 1989 | 10.67 | 5.19 | 475 |
| 1992 | 10.47 | 6.06 | 577 |
| 1995 | 10.08 | 7.01 | 684 |
| 1998 | 9.71 | 7.68 | 789 |

**Table 2:** Area production and productivity of pearl millet in Africa on triennium basis

| *Triennium ending* | *Area (mha)* | *Production (mt)* | *Productivity (kg ha$^{-1}$)* |
|---|---|---|---|
| 1977 | 16.06 | 9.88 | 614 |
| 1984 | 15.52 | 9.30 | 598 |
| 1991 | 14.92 | 10.53 | 707 |
| 1994 | 16.51 | 10.07 | 598 |

**Table 3.** Average statewise area, production and yield of pearl millet.

| | *Mean of 1995-96 and 1997-98* | | |
|---|---|---|---|
| *State* | *Area (mha)* | *Production (mt)* | *Productivity (kg ha$^{-1}$)* |
| Rajasthan | 4.55 | 1.99 | 432 |
| Maharashtra | 1.76 | 1.30 | 730 |
| Gujarat | 1.08 | 1.28 | 1170 |
| Uttar Pradesh | 0.85 | 1.10 | 1292 |
| Haryana | 0.57 | 0.58 | 1003 |
| Karnataka | 0.37 | 0.22 | 588 |
| Andhra Pradesh | 0.12 | 0.10 | 840 |
| Tamil Nadu | 0.22 | 0.24 | 1128 |
| Madhya Pradesh | 0.14 | 0.13 | 979 |
| Other states | 0.03 | 0.03 | |
| All India | 9.69 | 6.97 | 719 |

## 2. ORIGIN, TAXONOMY AND WILD SPECIES

It is generally agreed that pearl millet is of African origin, though there is some controversy with regard to the specific region of Africa in which it originated. Vavilov (1949-50) placed pearl millet in the Ethiopian center of origin (particularly the region of Abyssinia and Sudan), considering the region of maximum diversity. Considering that the greatest morphological diversity of pearl millet occurs today in West Africa south of the Sahara Desert and north of the forest zone, and that wild progenitor also occurs in this region. Harlan (1971) suggested the centre of origin to be in a belt stretching from western Sudan to Senegal. On the basis of present day distribution also, the Sahel zone of west Africa appears to be the original home of pearl millet (Brunken *et al.,* 1977).

By the early 19$^{th}$ century, pearl millet had nearly as many names as the number of floras. The most common being *Pennisetum typhoideum, Penicillaria spicata, Panicum spicatum* and *Pennisetum alopecuroides* (Chase 1921). Stapf and Hubbard (1933) gave the name *Pennisetum typhoides* (Burm) Stapf *et* Hubb, which was accepted by several modern taxonomist including Bor (1960). Later it was called *Pennisetum americanum* (L.) K. Schum. Currently the prevalent name of pearl millet is *Pennisetum glaucum* (L). R. Br. This topic has been discussed in detail by Jauhar (1981) and Gill (1991).

Rao (1929) from root tip studies, determined the chromosome number of pearl millet as 2n = 14. Later Rangaswamy (1935) studied the chromosomes in dividing cells of the microsporangium and confirmed the chromosome number as 2n = 14. Pantulu (1958) studied the chromosomes at pachytene and grouped them into four classes on the basis of relative length and position of centromere (i) two pairs (Chromosome 1 & 2) which had the greatest length and median centromere (ii) two somewhat shorter pairs (Chromosome 3 & 4) with median to submedian centromeres (iii) two pairs medium sized (Chromosome 5-6 with submedian centromeres; and (iv) the shortest pair (Chromosome 7) with the nucleolus organizer.

Jauhar (1970) suggested that chromosome complement of *P. typhoides* has been derived from a basic set of x = 5 chromosome. He based his suggestion on the cytological studies in haploids, interspecific hybrids and autotetraploids. The conclusion was based on extent of meiotic pairing observed in a haploid complement of *Pennisetum typhoides* where two bivalent per cell (some with two chiasmata each) were observed suggesting duplication of two chromosomes in the species. Jauhar (1968) also considered inter and intra-genomic chromosome pairing in an interspecific hybrid and its bearing of the basic chromosome number in pennisetum. Manga and Pantulu (1971) did not report any bivalent in haploid plants, where as Gill *et al.* (1973) considered that the occurrence of bivalents was the result of segmental homologies among some chromosomes. Powell *et al.* (1975) also reported pairing of chromosomes in haploids and attributed the pairing to the duplicate loci.

*Pennisetum* is a genus with over 140 species (Brunken, 1977) divided the genus into five sections : *Gymnothrix, Eu-Pennisetum, Penicillaria, Heterostachya* and *Brevivalvula* (Stapf and Hubbard, 1934). Pearl millet belongs to the *Penicillaria* section. The *Pennisetum* has species with chromosome numbers in multiples of $x$ = 5, 7, 8 and 9 (Jauhar, 1981). In the $x$ = 5 group in *P. ramosum* (2n = 10). The $x$-7 group includes pearl millet and its wild weedy subspecies (2n = 14), *P. purpureum* (2n = 28), and *P. schweinfurthii* (2n = 14). *Pennisetum massaicum* (2n = 16 and 32) is the only known species in $x$ = 8 group. The rest of the species, in which chromosome numbers have been established belong to the $x$ = 9 group.

A system of primary, secondary and tertiary gene pools has been suggested for dividing the wild germplasm (Harlan and de Wet, 1971). In *Pennisetum,* the primary gene pool includes the wild, grassy and weedy *P. americanum* subspecies (2n = 14) *monodii* and *stenostachyum* that readily cross with pearl millet and produce fertile hybrids (Brunken, 1977). *Monodii* is a rich source of germplasm that can be used to improve pearl millet. Data indicate that it is an excellent source of genetic diversity for new cytoplasm, stable cytoplasmic sterility, pest resistance (disease and insect), fertility restoration, and hybrid vigour (Hanna, 1987). Several wild species have been used in crosses with pearl millet to economic advantage. *Pennisetum purpureum* (2n - 28), commonly known as Napier grass, has been crossed with pearl millet (2n = 14) in India and the U.S.A. and triploids so produced have yielded selections of perennial fodder varieties (Burton, 1944). *P. squamulatum* (2n = 54) is an important drought and cold resistant species which is also a genetic apomict. It has been hybridized with pearl millet to evolve a fodder type, combining forage quality of pearl millet with frost-resistance and perenniality of *P. squamulatum.* Similarly, *P. orientale* (2n - 36) hybrids with pearl millet have a good source for fodder improvement and transfer of apomixis (Dujardin and Hanna, 1983, 1985). Among the intergeneric crosses, buffel grass *Cenchrus ciliaris* (Syn. *Pennisetum ciliare* (L.) Link) (2n = 36) was utilized in crosses with pearl millet (Read and Bashaw, 1974).

## 2.1. Floral Biology

Pearl millet spikelets bear 2 types of florets, one being bisexual and the other staminate. A single pistil with 2 feathery and 3 anthers is enclosed between the lemma and palea. The unisexual staminate florets are sessile and borne below the bisexual flowers. These have 3 anthers and lack the female organs. Pearl millet is a highly protogynous species and thus highly cross pollinated.

The time of panicle exertion from boot leaf varies in inbreds and hybrids. Bhatnagar and Kumar (1960) observed that spike took 6 days to emerge from the sheath with the maximum emergence on the fourth or fifth day. The stylar branches protrude first from the florets at the tip of the head and gradually proceed downwards. Most of the stylar branches on the earheads emerge by the third day. There exists a great variation in the time taken for the complete emergence of the styles in the hybrids than in the inbred lines (Tewari *et al.,* 1971). Anthesis in pearl millet is completed in two phases. The first involves the bisexual florets while the second involves staminate florets. It has been generally observed that the anthers in the sessile male florets emerge 2-3 days after the anthers have emerged in the bisexual florets. Thus most heads continue to shed pollen for 4-6 days. The largest number of anthers emerged between 8 PM and 2 AM. Environmental factors like temperature and humidity have significant role in the anther emergence.

Though protogyny of pearl millet would seem to favour complete cross pollination, several factors may prevent its realization. Since pearl millet bears several tillers that reach anthesis on different dates, it is more likely that self pollination may occur on the late tillers.

For controlled pollination, pearl millet heads are enclosed in a paper bag in order to ensure self pollination. The bagging is done at a stage when most part of the head is still in the boot. Burton and Powell (1968) suggested the use of both butter paper and a brown paper bag for controlled pollination. When most of the stylar branches are exerted, the head is ready to be pollinated. For pollination, the pollen is collected from desirable covered heads in selfing bags. The butter paper bag is removed from the female head which show complete emergence of stigma and covered immediately with pollen containing bag and agitated to pollinate all stigmas.

## 2.2. Genetic Resources

Germplasm collection in pearl millet was initiated in India by the Indian Council of Agricultural Research and Rockefeller foundation. A world collection of germplasm of different millets was assembled and evaluated by the India Agricultural Research Institute, New Delhi. The collection was planted and evaluated at four locations, representing abundant and sparse rainfall, in Northern and Western India. Most lines from

Africa were found to be susceptible to rust, smut and downy mildew. Alleles for early flowering (55 days) were found in East African collection and in some lines from Ghana. Late flowering types (80 days or more) were observed in the West African material particularly from Mali and Senegal. Bold seeded lines were mostly from Kenya, Mali, Sudan and Senegal (Murty *et al.,* 1967; House 1980, 1985; Rockefeller foundation, 1970).

After the establishment of International Crops Research Institute for the Semi Arid Topics (ICRISAT) at Patancheru, germplasm collection and evaluation work– is being carried out there by Genetic Resource Unit. More than 21, 195 accessions from 45 countries have been assembled at ICRISAT upto 1996. Major source of germplasm is from India (7775) and Africa (12531). Among the African countries, Burkina faso (868), Cameroon (988), Mali (1178), Namibia (1126), Niger (1270), Nigeria (1917) and Zimbabwe (1368) contribute considerably to the genetic resources. At present ICRISAT, being a major repository for world pearl millet germplasm collection, maintains about 80% of the variability present in the crop. ICRISAT also maintains 688 accessions from 38 taxa for the wild relatives of pearl millet (Eberhart *et al.,* 1997). Among the wild accessions of pearl millet, the numbers are ssp. *Monodii* (382), *P. pedicellatum* (132), *P. polystachyon* (79), *P. orientale* (20) and *P. purpureum* (16).

Pearl millet germplasm evaluation has identified sources of increased grain yield potential, cytoplasmic male sterile systems (Hanna, 1990, 1993), disease resistance to rust (*Puccinia* sp.) and pyricularia leaf blast (Hanna and Burton, 1987; Singh, 1990; Wilson and Hanna, 1992) and apomixis in several species and wild relatives (Hanna, 1995). Sources of resistance to important diseases such as downy mildew *[Sclerospora graminicola* (Sacc.) Schroet], Smut *[Moeziomyces penicillariae* (Bref) Vanky] and ergot (*Claviceps fusiformis* Lov.) have also been identified (Thakur and King, 1988; Thakur and Singh, 1988; Singh *et al.,* 1993). Through improved screening systems in pearl millet tolerance/resistance to witchweed *[Striga hermonthica* (Del) Benth], head miner (*Hdiocheilus albipunctella* de Joannis), Stern borer (*Coniesta ignefusalis* Hampson), have been identified.

## 2.3. Breeding Objectives

The major objective of breeding pearl millet varieties is to synthesize genotypes that would perform better under poor conditions of cultivation but would respond to better management wherever available. Breeding high yielding cultivars and improvement in stability and adaptability can go a long way in increasing pearl millet yields. Some of the important attributes are high tillering, compactness of the panicle, size of panicle, bold grains (all contributing to yield) and quality characteristics. Fodder yield coupled with non-lodging habit is also very important. Improvement in yielding ability envisages the assembly of the best combination of yield genes into a pearlmillet variety or a hybrid along with the improvement of performance under abiotic and biotic stresses like drought, diseases, lodging and insect pest infestation. Earliness in pearl_millet hybrid and varieties is of paramount importance as the crop is grown in drought prone areas. The plant type should be such as will mature before available moisture is exhausted. Therefore, earliness in maturity is most useful in escaping losses due to drought. Early maturity is also desirable for fitment into different cropping systems.

## 3. BREEDING FOR IMPROVED YIELD

### 3.1. Single Plant Selection

Many varieties of bajra have been developed by single plant selection. The selection criteria were early maturity, synchronous tillering and compact and good ears of desired size. Generally, selections were made from local varieties (Krishnaswamy, 1962). For example, individual plant selection in 'Akola Bajri' led to the development of three improved cultivars Nos. 37,54 and 59 (Pandya *et al.,* 1955). Similarly, CO 2, CO 3 and AKP-1, AKP-2, RSJ, RSK, Punjab Type 55, and A 1/3 (Uthkhede, 1972) were selected from existing varieties. Besides indigenous material, variability introduced from Africa has been helpful in developing varieties. For instance, Babapuri and Jamnagar giant in Gujarat, AF-3 in Maharashtra, improved Ghana, Pusa Moti (Joshi *et al.,* 1961) at IARI, Delhi and S-530 in the Punjab developed from selections made in introduced material were released for commercial cultivation. However, the yield potential of these varieties could not be maintained due to extensive outcrossing with local land races (Athwal and Rachie, 1963).

### 3.2. Mass Selection

In a cross pollinated crop like pearl millet, mass selection is a common method of breeding. Mass selection has been used to maintain the purity and uniformity of varities by the cultivators for a long time. Mass selection is highly effective for characters that have high heritability. The compactness and length of the ear, grain weight, synchrony in flowering of tillers and disease resistance are some of the characters used for screening single plants in mass selection procedure. A number of local types in India have originated in the past by mass selection procedure *e.g.*, T. 55, Co 1 and AKP 1.

### 3.3. Development of Hybrids

Exploitation of hybrid vigour is one of the most efficient means of elevating productivity potential. Pearl millet being a rainfed crop, the hybrids perform better than local cultivars. Work on pearl millet hybrid production was started in India nearly four decades ago but without conspicuous impact on grain yield. A limiting factor was the lack of male sterile lines for convenient hybrid seed production. During fifties hybrids were released for cultivation in Maharashtra and Tamilnadu (Rao *et al.,* 1951; Chavan *et al.,* 1955). The seed of these hybrids was produced by hand pollination utilizing protogyny. Due to the limited seed production the hybrids could not be cultivated on commercial scale.

The discovery of cytoplasmic male sterility by Burton (1958) fulfilled the need for a viable and economic method for producing grain hybrids on a commercial scale. Burton identified cytoplasmic - genetic male sterility in a cross 556 × 23. Two of the four selected plants failed to shed pollen or set seeds when selfed. When these two male sterile plants were pollinated (back crossed) with parent 23, the $F_l$ progeny again failed to shed pollen on seifing. However, when pollen from other lines was used, the seed set was complete. Burton then crossed 41 inbred lines of female sterile plants (556 × 23) × 23. Six of the resulting $F_1$ progeny were male sterile, eight others were partially male sterile, and 27 were male fertile. This observation confirmed the existence of cytoplasmic genetic male sterility in pearl millet. The first male sterile line, Tift 23A, was developed using Tift 23 B as recurrent parent and was released in 1965 (Burton, 1965). Based on Tift 23 A, the first pearl millet hybrid was released in India during 1965 (Athwal, 1965, 1966). Since then more than 50 hybrids have been released (Table 4).

Private sector has also developed equal no of hybrids. Private sector research to develop superior hybrids was initiated by a few seed companies in mid-sixties. Persistent efforts of MAHYCO's pearl millet research team led to the development of MBH 110, the first private sector pearl millet hybrid released by "Central sub-committee on Crop Standards, Notification and Release of Variety" in 1981. The number of companies with private research and development, including multinationals, has steadily increased from about 12 in 1987-88 to over 35 (Govila *et al.,* 1997a).

Thus a large number of genetically diverse hybrids are currently available to farmers. Private companies have also popularized their hybrids in specific areas of adaptation and have contributed to increasing the production of pearl millet.

**Table 4:** Pearl millet hybrids released and notified in India

| *Hybrid* | *Source* | *Year of release* | *Pedigree* | *Remarks* |
|---|---|---|---|---|
| ***Hybrids predominantly bred on Tift 23A*** | | | | |
| HB 1 | Ludhiana | 1965 | Tift 23A x Bil 3B | |
| HB 2 | Jamnagar | 1966 | Tift 23A x J 88 | |
| HB 3 | Jamnagar | 1968 | Tift 23A x J 104 | Highly popular |
| HB 4 | Kanpur (IARI) | 1968 | Tift 23A x K 560 | Highly popular |
| HB 5 | Kanpur (IARI) | 1969 | Tift 23A x K 559 | |
| NHB 3 | Delhi (IARI) | 1975 | 5071A x J 104 | |
| NHB 4 | Delhi (IARI) | 1975 | 5071 A x K 560-230 | |
| NHB 5 | Delhi (IARI) | 1975 | 5071 A x K 559 | |
| PHB 10 | Ludhiana | 1975 | Pb 111A x PIB 155 | |
| PHB 14 | Ludhiana | 1975 | Pb 111A x PIB 228 | |
| GHB 1399 | Jamnagar | 1975 | 126 $D_2$A x J 1399 | |
| ***Hybrids predominantly bred on 5141A*** | | | | |
| BJ 104 | Delhi (IARI | 1977 | 5141A x J 104 | Highly popular |
| BK 560 | Delhi (IARI) | 1977 | 5141A x K 560-230 | Highly popular |
| CJ 104 | Delhi (IARI) | 1977 | 5054 A x J 104 | Moderately popular |
| BD 111 | Delhi (IARI) | 1988 | 5141A x D 111 | |
| GHB 27 | Jamnagar | 1981 | 5141A x J 2002 | |
| BD 763 | Delhi (IARI) | 1982 | 5141A x D 763 | |
| GHB 32 | Jamnagar | 1983 | 5141 A x J 1188 | |
| HHB 45 | Hisar | 1984 | 5141 A x H90/4-5 | |
| COH 2 | Coimbatore | 1984 | 5141 A x PT 1921 | |
| ***Hybrid on genetically diversified male sterile lines*** | | | | |
| CM 46 | Delhi (IARI) | 1981 | 5054 A x M 46 | |
| MBH 110 | MAHYCO | 1981 | MS 2 x PL 2 | Highly popular |
| PHB 47 | Ludhiana | 1983 | PB 111A x PIB 1234 | |
| $X_5$ | Coimbatore | 1984 | PB 111A x PT 1921 | |
| MBH 118 | MAHYCO | 1984 | MS 2 x PL 3 | |
| ICMH 451 | ICRISAT | 1986 | 81 A x ICMP 451 | Highly popular |
| ICMH 501 | ICRISAT | 1986 | 834A x ICMP 501 | |
| MH 182 | Pune | 1986 | PT732A x PNBM83099 | |
| GHB 32 | Jamnagar | 1986 | 5054 A x J 2002 | |
| Pusa 23 | Delhi (IARI) | 1987 | 841A x D 23 | Highly popular |
| HHB 50 | Hisar | 1987 | 841A x H 90/4-5 | |
| MBH 130 | MAHYCO | 1987 | MS 2 x PL 4 | Moderately popular |
| HHB 60 | Hisar | 1988 | 81A x H 77/833-2 | Moderately popular |
| ICMH 423 | ICRISAT | 1988 | 841 A x ICMP 423 | |
| MBH 136 | MAHYCO | 1989 | MS 2 x P 16 | |

**Table 4:** (*Contd..*)

**Table 4:** (*Contd...*)

| *Hybrid* | *Source* | *Year of release* | *Pedigree* | *Remarks* |
|---|---|---|---|---|
| HHB 67 | Hisar | 1990 | 843A × H 77/833-2 | Highly popular |
| VBH 4 | Vijay seeds | 1990 | VBMS 1A × BBR 19 | Moderately popular |
| EKNATH 301 | Nath seeds | 1991 | NBH5 13A × NB 37 | Moderately popular |
| ***Current hybrids*** | | | | |
| MLBH-104 | Mahendra | 1991 | 3A × 13 | Highly popular |
| ICMH 356 | ICRISAT | 1993 | ICMA 88004 × ICMR 356 | Moderately popular |
| Pusa 322 | Delhi (IARI) | 1993 | 841 A × PPMI 301 | Moderately popular |
| HHB 68 | Hisar | 1993 | 842A × H77/833-2 | |
| Pusa 444 | Delhi (IARI) | 1994 | 189A × PPMI-301 | Moderately popular |
| MLBH 267 | Mahendra | 1995 | | Highly popular |
| Pusa 605 | Delhi (IARI) | 1997 | 846A × PPMI-69 | Moderately popular |
| MLBH 44 | Mahendra | 1999 | | Late maturing |
| Nandi 8 | Nandi Seeds | 1999 | | Late maturing |
| Pusa-415* | Delhi (IARI) | 1999 | 576A × PPMI-85 | Moderately popular |

*Indentified by AICPMIP Workshop.

Inspite of its overall success, the pearl millet hybrid programs in India have had occasional setbacks due to downy mildew *[Sclerospora graminicola* (Sacc.) J. Schroet] epidemics and the potential threat posed by smut *[Moesziomyces penicillariae* (Bref.) K. Vanky; syn. *Tolyposporium pencillariae* Bref,] and ergot *[Claviceps fusiformis* (Loveless)] to single cross hybrids. The hybrids HB 3 and HB 4 were very popular during 1968-74. However, when the seed parent of these hybrids (Tift 23 A) became susceptible to downy mildew in 1975, multiplication of hybrids on Tift 23A was discontinued. Two new hybrids BJ 104 and BK 560 (Pokhriyal *et al.,* 1976), produced on seed parent 5141A, became highly popular in pearl millet growing areas of India. The entire hybrid area was occupied by just these two hybrids. BJ 104 was adapted to low rainfall areas but also gave high yields under good management conditions, while BK 560 was adapted to good rainfall areas of the country. Due again to an increase in the downy mildew susceptibility of both parents (5141A and restorer line J 104), hybrid BJ 104 was completely withdrawn from seed multiplication. However, hybrid BK 560 (5141 A × K 560-230) is still cultivated on large areas due to its high grain and fodder yields and farmer demand. Though 5141A is susceptible to downy mildew, its restorer K 560-230 is fairly resistant. Due to the dominant nature of downy mildew resistance, the hybrid does not pose any problems for farmers. During 1981 MAHYCO, a private seed Company, released MBH 110, which was very popular in the state of Maharashtra. Again, due to increased downy mildew susceptibility, this hybrid was withdrawn by the Company after about ten years of successful cultivation.

Since 1986, a large number of hybrids have been released, some of which (ICMH 451, Pusa 23, HHB 67, MLBH 104) are very popular among farmers. Characteristics of some of the hybrids are given in Table 5. Almost all these hybrids were bred from downy mildew-resistant parental lines. Significantly, in all these hybrids, the $A_1$, CMS system has been utilized, but there is no evidence that $A_1$ CMS is associated with downy mildew disease. At this stage, genetically diverse CMS-lines were utilized in the breeding program in India. Characteristics of some of the CMS-lines are given in Table 6. Considerable efforts have gone into the development of these A-lines at the International Crops Research Institute of the Semi-Arid Tropics (ICRISAT), Patancheru; the Indian Agricultural Research Institute (IARI), New Delhi; other institutions in the National Agriculture Research System (NARS) in India; and the Fort Hays Branch Experiment Station of Kansas State University, in the U.S. (Govila *et al.,* 1997a).

Based on the history of hybrid development in India, it is evident that some popular hybrids, most importantly, HB 3, HB 4, BJ 104 and MBH 110 (Dave, 1987; Govila, 1988) had to be withdrawn from farmers fields because of an increase in their susceptibility to downy mildew. A critical appraisal of the situation may now reveal that failure of these hybrids was mainly due to lack of diversity in the parental lines, as all hybrids were first based on Tift 23A and then on 5141A. Out of 20 hybrids available then, 16 were based on three male-sterile lines [5141A (8), Tift 23A (5) and 5054A (3)]; three restorers were male parents of nine commercial hybrids [J 104(4), K 560-230(3) and K 559(2)]. These facts indicate that outbreaks of downy mildew were due to a narrow genetic base among CMS lines and restorers (and thus their hybrids) and their evident lack of durable genetic resistance to downy mildew. Deleterious effects of $A_1$ cytoplasm does not seem to be a major factor.

## 4. DIVERSIFICATION OF CYTOPLASMIC GENIC MALE STERILITY SYSTEM

Predominantly, $A_1$ cytoplasm has been used in pearl millet though several cytoplasmic-genic male sterility system have been found (Kumar and Andrews, 1984; Hanna, 1989). Early in the development of hybrids in pearl millet, four CMS systems were found; all have some disadvantages (Kumar and Andrews, 1984). The first to be found, PT 732A (Madhava Menon, 1959), was not properly described. Burton and

**Table 5:** Characteristics of some of the popular hybrids released in India

| *Hybrid* | *Parentage* | *Average grain yield (kg ha$^{-1}$)* | *Days to 50% flowering* | *Maturity (days)* | *Average plant height (cm)* | *Tller-ing* | *Adapta-tion* | *Remarks* |
|---|---|---|---|---|---|---|---|---|
| HB 3 | Tift 23A × J-104 | 2250 | 45-48 | 75 | 165 | Profuse | All India dry tract | Highly adapted to rainfed conditions |
| HB 4 | Tift 23A × K-560 | 2298 | 50-55 | 85 | 175 | Profuse | All India | Suited to both rainfed and irrigated areas but susceptible to downy mildew |
| BJ 104 | 5141A × J-104 | 2110 | 45-50 | 75-80 | 150 | Profuse | All India | Suited to both rainfed and irrigated areas, fertilizer responsive |
| BK 560 | 5141A × K 560-230 | 2200 | 50-55 | 85-90 | 180 | Profuse | All India | Resistant to downy mildew |
| Pusa 23 | 841A × D 23 | 2312 | 47-52 | 77-82 | 160 | 2-4 | All India | Drought tolerant, downy mildew resistant |
| Pusa 322 | 841A × PPMI-301 | 2463 | 48-52 | 75-80 | 160 | 2-4 | All India | Resistant to downy mildew, lodging |
| ICMH 451 | 81A × ICMP 451 | 2400 | 50-55 | 85-90 | 175 | 2-3 | All India | Resistant to downy mildew and lodging, drought and salinity |
| HHB 67 | 843A × H 77/833-2 | 2135 | 40-42 | 62-68 | 150 | High | Haryana and adjoining drought prone areas | Downy mildew resistant, suited to early and late sowing |
| ICMH 356 | ICMA 88004 × ICMR 356 | 2450 | 45-50 | 75-80 | 160 | 1-4 | All India | Resistant to downy mildew |

Ref. Govila, O.P. *et al.*, 1977a

**Table 6:** Characteristics of some important pearl millet male sterile lines

| *A-line* | *Days to 50 % flowering* | *Plant height (cm)* | *No.of tillers/ plant* | *Panicle width (cm)* | *Panicle length (cm)* | *1000-grain weight (g)* | *Downy mildew reaction* | *Remarks* |
|---|---|---|---|---|---|---|---|---|
| 5141 A | 58 | 155 | 3.4 | 1.49 | 18.9 | 6.0- | Susceptible | Good for high and low input conditions |
| 5054 A | 53 | 150 | 5.1 | 1.30 | 17.5 | 5.3 | Resistant | Good for drought prone areas |
| 81 A | 60 | 75 | 2.3 | 1.40 | 20.0 | 7.6 | Resistant | Good for high input conditions |
| 841 A | 50 | 165 | 2.6 | 1.95 | 15.2 | 6.4 | Resistant | Good for medium maturity hybrids |
| 843 A | 42 | 105 | 4.2 | 2.05 | 16.5 | 10.5 | Susceptible | Good for early hybrids |
| 842 A | 49 | 102 | 2.1 | 1.8 | 16.0 | 11.7 | Susceptible | Good for early hybrids |
| 189 A | 53 | 160 | 2.1 | 2.06 | 18.3 | 6.8 | Highly resistant | Good for medium maturity |
| ICMA 88004 | 45 | 141 | 4.0 | 1.2 | 13.2 | 12.3 | Highly resistant | Good for early hybrids |

Govila, O.P. *et al.*, 1997a

Athwal (1967) described $A_2$ and $A_3$ cytoplasm. Appadurai *et al.* (1982) showed PT 32 A CMS was different from $A_1$, $A_2$ and $A_3$ but did not give complete sterility. Complete and stable male sterility could be obtained with $A_2$ $A_3$. A new $A_4$ system has been found (Hanna, 1989). $A_4$ CMS system in pearl millet offers a high success rate for expression of male sterility and female fertility. However, there is no commercial hybrid which has become popular on cytoplasmic genic male sterility source other than $A_1$ cytoplasm. Large number of male sterile lines in $A_1$ background have been studied for their combining ability (Govila *et al.,* 1997b).

## 4.1. Apomixis

Apomixis has the potential of becoming as important for production of sorghum and millet hybrids as is cytoplasmic-genic male sterility. It has been reported in 1841 and has been studied in a number of species, including tropical grasses (Asker and Jerling, 1992). Of the three basic types of apomixis, apospory is the only type confirmed in millet (Bashaw, 1980). As a result of operation of this type of apomixis, the entire progeny of a plant are derived from somatic cells and are therefore identical to the plant on which the seed is formed. This is true even if the plant on which seed is formed is a hybrid and is therefore, heterozygous. Breeding programme aims to produce apomictic cultivars by crossing the sexual plants by the apomictic plants as males, and selecting apomictic progeny (Bashaw and Hussey, 1992). The discovery of facultative apomixis in sorghum (Rao and Narayana, 1968; Hanna *et al.,* 1970) raised the possibility of exploiting apomixis in grain crops.

Apomixis is not known to occur naturally in pearl millet but it has been induced by mutation studies (Hanna *et al.,* 1992). One mutant, a facultative apomict, produced various levels (average 26%) of maternal progeny.

Apomixis does occur in other species of *Pennisetum.* A number of wild apomictic species were investigated, but the maximum success was obtained with hexaploid (2n = 6x = 64) *P. squamulatum* crossed with tetraploid (2n = 4x = 28) pearl millet (Hanna *et al.,* 1992).

Apomixis would have the greatest impact for producing pearl millet hybrids in India where CMS lines are used. Apomixis reduce the time required to produce hybrids for testing. It will not require CMS and the development and crossing of inbred lines to produce hybrid seed. Instead, hybrid seed could be produced on open-pollinated apomictic hybrids (Schertz *et al.,* 1997).

## 5. FACTORS FOR ADOPTION OF HYBRIDS

The extent of adoption of hybrids and their impact in India continues to be fairly uneven, with a greater impact in areas presenting relatively more favourable climate and soil conditions. The following are among the factors favouring adoption of hybrids.

### 5.1. Stable Fodder and Grain Yield

Pearl millet is a rainfed crop. Highest yield of the hybrids can not be employed as the sole selection criterion. Adoption of hybrid depends on stable grain and fodder yield over years. HB 3, BJ 104 and Pusa 23 are examples of such hybrids.

### 5.2. Desirable Maturity

The most desirable maturity period for hybrids to be widely adopted under Indian conditions is around 70-75 days. Late maturing hybrids may yield more but are likely to experience terminal drought. Hybrid Pusa 23, HHB 67 and MLBH 104 have been adopted by farmers because of their early maturity. Earliness also allows pearl millet to be grown in multiple cropping systems. HHB 67 is preferred-by farmers because it allows convenient double cropping of pearl millet with *Brassica* or chickpea (*Cicer arietinum* L.).

### 5.3. Resistance to Downy Mildew

The main reason for loss of yield of the hybrids HB 3 and HB 4 during 1970 was downy mildew. Later, two more popular hybrids BJ 104 and BK 560 succumbed to downy mildew during 1982-83. A hybrid from private sector, MBH 110, also met the same fate. Thus, breeding of downy mildew resistant male-sterile and restorer lines gained high priority and contributed to the greater adoption of hybrids. Several hybrids with resistance to downy mildew (such as ICMH 451, Pusa 23, HHB 67, ICMH 356, Pusa 322, Pusa 444 and MLBH 267) have been released since 1985 and are under moderate to large scale cultivation.

### 5.4. Economical Seed Production

Public sector seed producing organizations in India are required to produce and sell certified hybrid seed to farmers at a specified rate. Thus certified seed production per unit area becomes very important. One of the main factors for the rapid adoption of hybrid Pusa 23 is the high productivity of female parent 841 A. (Table 7), leading to higher monetary returns to seed producers. A seed producing farmer gets 20% higher profits from multiplying Pusa 23 than from ICMH 451. Good synchronization between male sterile and restorer lines and high fodder and seed yield from the parental line in the certified seed production plot also contributes to higher profits and quick adoption (as was the case with Pusa 23). It is understood that along with economic seed production, the hybrid should give stable yield to the farmers.

**Table 7:** Certified seed production of Pusa 23 and ICMH 451

| *Hybrid* | *A line* | *Area (ha)* | *Seed production (tons)* | *Average seed yield (kg ha$^{-1}$)* |
|---|---|---|---|---|
| ICMH 451 | 81A | 496 | 488 | 983 |
| Pusa 23 | 841A | 467 | 552 | 1183 |

*Source*: Gujarat Cooperative Marketing Federation.

## 6. POPULATION IMPROVEMENT

### 6.1. Composite Varieties

The first successful attempt to develop composite varieties was made by ICRISAT through recurrent selection (Andrews *et al.*, 1985). Changes in gene frequencies in a positive direction for important characters for all the populations studied were achieved. Genetic gains for grain yield ranged from 1.8 per cent (super serere composite) to 5.0 per cent (D 2 composite) per cycle, equalling net gains of 200 to 400 kg/ha per cycle, have been obtained (Table 8). A high degree of downy mildew and smut resistance was also obtained over successive cycles of selection.

**Table 8:** Improvement through recurrent selection in six pearl millet composites

| *Composite* | *No. of cycles* | *Grain yield/cycle* | | *Grain per cycle (%)* | *Downy mildew* | | *Gain per cycle* |
|---|---|---|---|---|---|---|---|
| | | *Co. (tonne ha$^{-1}$)* | *Latest (tonne ha$^{-1}$)* | | *Incidence % Co.* | *Cycle latest* | |
| Super serere | 5 | 1.93 | 2.11 | 1.8 | 2.1 | 1.0 | –0.2 |
| New elite | 3 | 2.36 | 2.57 | 2.6 | 1.4 | 0.0 | –0.5 |
| Inter varietal | 4 | 2.11 | 2.39 | 1.9 | 1.9 | 1.6 | –0.1 |
| Medium | 5 | 1.88 | 2.28 | 3.2 | 4.2 | 3.1 | –0.2 |
| Early | 4 | 1.89 | 2.26 | 4.1 | 5.6 | 4.6 | –0.3 |
| D2 | 2 | 1.97 | 2.27 | 5.0 | 7.5 | 4.9 | –1.3 |

From: Andews *et al.*, 1985

A new variety WC-C75 (ICMV-1) was developed from the 'World Composite' by recurrent selection (Andrews *et al.,* 1985) and was released by the All India Co-ordinated Pearl Millet Improvement Project in 1982. The performance of WC-C75 is shown in Table 9. The world composite random mating population was developed in Nigeria, in 1971, at the Institute for Agricultural Research, Ahmad Bello University. It was constituted from derivatives of numerous crosses between diverse sources of pearl millet germplasm and Nigerian early maturing land races, locally known as 'Gero' millets. Full-sib recurrent selection was conducted on the world composite at ICRISAT. During this selection, 441 full-sib families, derived from selected, heterozygous plants in the previous generation were tested at Coimbatore, Hissar and ICRISAT Centre. Seven superior full-sib families were selected at Coimbatore using supporting data from the other two locations. In the same season, disease free plants from the seven full-sib families were selected from the downy mildew screening nursery at ICRISAT Centre. The resulting $S_1$ bulk was sown in the next season's downy mildew nursery, and bulk pollen was used to enforce intermating. The variety produced by this intermating was named WC-C 75.

**Table 9:** Grain yield, and downy mildew resistance of pearl millet variety WC-C-75 in all India tests from 1977 to 1983

| | ***1977*** | ***1978*** | ***1979*** | ***1980*** | ***1981*** | ***1982*** | ***1983*** | ***Mean*** | ***As percentage of BJ 104*** |
|---|---|---|---|---|---|---|---|---|---|
| Yield | (27) | (33) | (23) | (27) | (30) | (24) | (30) | | |
| (tonnes ha) | | | | | | | | | |
| WC-C-75 | 1.63 | 2.07 | 1.76 | 1.85 | 1.99 | 1.85 | 1.79 | 1.88 | 101 |
| BJ 104 | 1.79 | 1.97 | 1.81 | 1.81 | 2.09 | 1.88 | 1.68 | 1.87 | 100 |
| Local | 1.36 | 1.92 | 1.61 | 1.47 | 1.42 | 1.86 | – | 1.61 | 86 |
| Trial mean | 1.54 | 1.95 | 1.68 | 1.73 | 1.92 | 1.78 | 1.69 | 1.76 | 94 |
| ***Downy mildew incidence (%)*** | | | | | | | | | |
| WC-C-75 | 2.2 | 2.5 | 0.9 | 3.6 | – | 2.2 | 0.0 | 1.6 | 16 |
| BJ-104 | 8.3 | 9.8 | 13.7 | 8.6 | 8.1 | 14.9 | 8.5 | 10.3 | 100 |

From : Andrews *et al.*, 1985

Mass selection within a population for more restricted plant-type and phenology is a common method for developing open pollinated varieties in pearl millet. This approach is exemplified by the development of ICMV 155 through a single cycle of mass selection for grain yield, similar plant-height and maturity in a population after four cycles of progeny based selection (Pheru Singh *et al.,* 1994).

Varieties can be produced by recombining families selected on performance information obtained during the progeny based population improvement programme. Generally a small number (10 to 15) of füll sib or $S_1$, families are selected to produce a variety. The variety ICTP 8203, developed from five $S_2$ progenies from Iniadi land race population from Togo is currently grown on a very large scale in Maharashtra (ICRISAT, 1996).

## 7. BREEDING FOR DISEASE RESISTANCE

Breeding for disease resistance in pearl millet contributes to the stability of grain and fodder yields. Several reviews have been written on breeding for disease resistance where ample information is available on the subject (Louvel 1982; William and Andrews, 1983; Williams, 1984; Andrews *et al.,* 1985; Wilson *et al.,* 1993; Talukdar *et al.,* 1994; Rai and Anand, 1994).

### 7.1. Downy Mildew

The causal organism is *Sclerospora graminicola* (Sacc.) Schroet. It is the most widely spread and destructive disease. This is evident from several epidemics on hybrids in India (Dave, 1987; Govila *et al.,* 1997a). All hybrids released during sixties were based on Tift 23 A, which was bred in the USA where downy mildew is not prevalent. After its introduction to India, neither this line nor the resultant hybrids were tested for disease resistance. The significance of *S. graminicola* was under estimated. With large scale cultivation of hybrids like HB 1, HB 3, BJ 104, the pathogen, whose occurrence had been sporadic, began to multiply leading to accumulation of oosporic inoculum in the soil. Almost all the parental lines showed high susceptibility to downy mildew in such soils. This led to the intensification of research for breeding downy mildew resistant parental lines.

Several downy mildew resistant sources have been identified by ICRISAT (Singh *et al.,* 1990). These have shown very high degree of resistance across sites and years. They include P7 (ICML 12), SDN 503 (ICML 13) 700251 (ICML 14), 700516 (ICML 15) and 700651 (ICML 16).

Genetics of downy mildew resistance has been studied by several authors. However, all studies have been hampered because both the pathogen and host are allogamous and highly variable (Thakur *et al.,* 1991). As a consequence, segregation for resistance in host-plant generally shows continuous variation (Singh *et al.,* 1980; Basavraju *et al.,* 1981; Dass *et al.,* 1984; Shinde *et al.,* 1984). Quantitative inheritance studies of downy mildew resistance have been more successful in identifying parental materials with the ability to transmit high levels of resistance. Many authors (Tyagi and Iqbal Singh, 1989; Deswal and Govila, 1994; Kataria *et al.,* 1994) have generally concluded that non-additive gene action is responsible for much of the heritable variability. The resistance seems to be dominant or partially dominant.

Breeders have utilized the sources for resistance to breed many downy mildew resistant hybrids (*i.e.,* Pusa 23, ICMH 451, HHB 67, MLBH 267, Pusa 444, and Pusa 415.

### 7.2. Smut

*Moesziomyces penicillariae* (Bref.) Vanky Syn *Toliposporium penicillariae* (Bref.) is the causal organism for smut. It is relatively less damaging and more widely spread than downy mildew. At ICRISAT a number of lines have shown high level of resistance across different locations in India over several years (Thakur *et al.,* 1986, 1992; Thakur and King, 1988).

Inheritance for smut resistance indicates that resistance to smut is dominant and simply inherited. (Thakur and Chahal, 1987; Yadav, 1974). Phookan (1987) and Chavan *et al.* (1988) have reported both dominant and additive gene action, additive effects being much larger than dominant effects.

Breeding for smut resistant open pollinated varieties through recurrent selection has shown promise. Two population varieties were derived from smut resistant composite. Population ICMV 82131, ICMV 82132 and two synthetics ICMS 8282 and ICMS 8283 have shown a high level of resistance to smut and downy mildew and have yielded on par with control variety WC-C 75 (Andrews *et al.,* 1985; Thakur and Chahal, 1987).

### 7.3. Ergot

The causal organism for ergot fungus is *Claviceps fusiformis* (Loveless), though more wide spread than smut the disease is of secondary importance. The primary disease cycle begins with airborne ascospores discharged from the germinating sclerotia, which infect pearl millet flowers (Thakur *et al.,* 1984). It contains numerous microconidia that play an important role in secondary spread of the disease. Resistant lines have been developed by intermating less susceptible plants and selecting resistant progenies under high disease pressure for several generations following pedigree and recurrent selection procedure (Gill *et al.,* 1980; Chahal *et al.,* 1981; Thakur *et al.,* 1980, Thakur *et al.,* 1982). A number of lines have shown high levels of resistance across different locations in India and West Africa over several years (Thakur *et al.,* 1985; Thakur and King, 1988).

Inheritance of ergot resistance is more complex and can involve cytoplasmic × nuclear interactions (Thakur *et al.,* 1993; Yadav, 1994). Resistance is recessive and polygenically controlled (Thakur *et al.,* 1983). Ergot resistant hybrids, therefore, can not be bred unless both parents possess the same genes (Virk *et al.,* 1987; Rai and Thakur, 1995).

## 8. BREEDING FOR ABIOTIC STRESS

Drought is the most important factor limiting pearl millet productivity. Studies on drought tolerance/resistance are complicated because of uncertain nature of duration and intensity of dry spells in relation to crop growth stages. There is paucity of reliable information on drought tolerance parameters, and also on the magnitude of genetic variability and heritability of these parameters.

Investigations conducted during the 1980s showed genotypic differences in the ability of the hybrids to accumulate abscisic acid (Hensen *et al.,* 1981) and engineer osmotic adjustment (Hensen *et al.,* 1982) in response to water deficits. Flowering and early grain filling has been demonstrated to be most sensitive to water deficits. Mahalaxmi and Bidinger (1985) and Beiler (1992) showed that terminal drought reduced grain yield by 50% with large variation among genotypes. The grain yield loss is caused by (i) reduction in grain size caused by a reduction in grain filling period (ii) reduction in the grain number affected by grain abortion. Grain yield potential is reduced by more than 50% under terminal drought (Bidinger *et al.,* 1987; Fusell *et al.,* 1991). Both the authors concluded that drought response index (DRI), a measure of drought tolerance was less important than earliness. Threshing percentage (ratio of grain to panicle yield) is a better indicator of terminal drought tolerance (Bidinger and Mahalaxmi, 1993).

## 9. FUTURE OUTLOOK

- Sustained improvement in grain yield of hybrids is one of the most important aspects. With the private sector playing an increasingly greater role in hybrid promotion, cultivated area under hybrid should increase.
- Increasing use of diverse downy mildew resistant sources in downy mildew resistant breeding will ensure sustained yields.

- Incorporation of resistant/tolerance to drought in high yielding cultivar remains a challenge. Concerted efforts will be required to develop and validate effective screening techniques, develop enhanced resistant sources and determine nature of inheritance.
- Diversification of CMS sources and development of restorers would strengthen the hybrid breeding programme.
- In pearl millet, only a fraction of cultivated germplasm has been utilized in breeding programmes. Sources of useful variability in the land races should be studied. International collaboration and cooperation is strongly needed to utilize the unexploited resources of germplasm which in turn would be useful in the development of gene complexes as resources of variability.
- Utilization of wild relatives of pearl millet for novel traits, *e.g.*, disease resistance, fertility restoration, apomixis, may further enhance the ability to breed for high grain yield and stability.
- In Gujarat, summer crop of pearl millet has been reported to give 2.5-3.51 $ha^{-1}$, double the yield than the main kharif season. Search for suitable material for areas in other states would increase the productivity of pearl millet.
- Pearl millet could be a major beneficiary of biotechnological application for enhancements of the hardiness of hybrids in arid environments and establishment of the products of biotechnology as genetically enhanced model grass. The impressive production of biomass on hot and dry lands could justify the choice of pearl millet for engineered products suitable for drought conditions.

## REFERENCES


Andrews, D.J., Gupta, S.C. and Singh, P. (1985). Registration of WC-C-75 pearl millet. *Crop Sci.,* 25L: 199–200.

Andrews, D.J., King, S.B., Witcombe, J.R., Singh, S.D., Rai, K.N., Thakur, R.P., Talukdar, B.S., Chavan, S.B. and Singh, P. (1985). Breeding for disease resistance and yield in pearl millet. *Field Crops Research,* 11: 241–258.

Andrews, D.J., Rai, K.N. and Singh, S.D. (1985). A single dominant gene for rust resistance in pearl millet. *Crop Science,* 25: 565–566.

Appadurai, R., Raveendran, T.S. and Nagarajan, C. (1982). A new male sterility system in pearl millet. *Indien }. Agric. Sci.,* 52: 832–834.

Asker, S.E. and Jerling, L. (1992). Arpmixix in plants. CRC Press, Boca Raton.

Athwal, D.S. (1965). Hybrid bajra - 1 marks a new era. *Indian Farming,* 15(5): 6–7.

Athwal, D.S. (1966). Current plant breeding research with special reference to *Pennisetum. Indian J. Genet.,* 26A: 73–85.

Athwal, D.S. and Gupta, V.P. (1966). Genetic evaluation of grain fodder quality of *Pennisetum.* Annual Research Report. Punjab Agricultural University Ludhiana Punjab, India.

Athwal, D.S., and Rachie, K.O. (1963). Potentialities and future breeding for improvment of bajra. *Indian J. Genet.,* 23: 155–157.

Basavraju, R., Safeeulla, K.M. and Murty, B.R. (1981). Genetic variance and heritability for resistance to downy mildew in pearl millet. *Indian J. Genet.,* 41: 137–143.

Bashaw, E.C. (1980). Apomixis and its application in crop improvement. *In*: W.R. and Hadley, H.H. (*Eds.*) Hybridization of crop plants. American Society of Agronomy and Crop Science Society of America, Madison, W.I.

Bashaw, E.C. and Hussey, M.A. (1992). Apomixis in *Cenchrus. In*: Elgin, J.H. and Miksche, J.P. (*Eds.*) Proceedings of the apomixis workshop, February 11-12, 1992, Atlanta, GA. USDA-ARS, ARS-104. pp. 1–4.

Beiler, P. (1992). Agronomic and physiological aspects of post flowering drought tolerance of pearl millet *(Pennisetum glaucum* (L.) R. Br.) A Dissertation submitted to the Swiss Federal Institute of Technology, Zürich, Switzerland, p. 103.

Bhamagar, M.P. and Kumar, K. (1960). Anthesis studies in Rajasthan bajra *(Pennisetum typhoides). Ind. J. Agric Sci.,* 30: 185–195.

Bidinger, F.R. and Mahalakshmi, V. (1993). Selection for drought tolerance. *In*: cereals program ICRISAT 1993. Annual Report 1992. Patancheru A.P. 502324. India, Cereal Program, International Crops Research Institute for the Semi-Arid Tropics. pp. 57–59

Bidinger, F.R., Mahalakshmi, V. and Rao, G.D.P. (1987). Assessment of drought resistance in pearl millet *[Pennisetum americanum* (L.) Leeke] I. Factor affecting yield under stress. *Australian Journal of Agricultural Research*, 38: 37–48.

Bor N.L. (1960). Grasses of Burma, Ceylon, India and Pakistan (excluding Bambuseae. Pergamon, Press, London.

Brunken, J.N. (1977). A systematic study of penninsetum sect. *Pennisetum* (Graminae). *American Journal of Botany* 64: 161–176.

Burton, G.W. (1944). Hybrids between Napier grass and cat tail millet. *Heredity,* 35: 222–227.

Burton, G.W. (1958). Cytoplasmic male sterility in pearl millet *[Pennisetum glaucum* (L.) P. Br.] *Agron.,* 40: 230.

Burton, G.W. (1965). Pearl millet tift 23A released. *Crops and Soils,* 17(5): 19.

Burton, G.W. and Athwal, D.S. (1967). Two additional sources of cytoplasmic male sterility in pearl millet and their relationship to Tift 23A. *Crop Science,* 7: 209–211.

Burton, G.W. and Powell, J.B. (1968). Pearl millet breeding and cytogenetics. *Adv. Agron.,* 20: 49–89.

Chahal, S.S., Gill, K.S., Phul, P.S. and Singh, N.B. (1981). Effectiveness of recurrent selection for generating ergot resistance in pearl millet. *SABRAO Journal,* 13: 184–186.

Chase, A. (1921). The Linnaen concept of pearl millet. *Amer. J. Bot.,* 8: 41–49.

Chavan, S.B., Thakur, R.D. and Rao, K.P. (1988). Inheritance of smut resistance in pearl millet. *Plant Disease Research,* 3: 192–197.

Chavan, V.M., Patil, J.A. and Chaudhary, B.B. (1955). Hybrid bajri in Bombay State Poona *Agric. College Mag.,* 46: 148–150.

Dass, S., Kapoor, R.L., Paroda, R.S. and Jatasra, D.S. (1984). Gene effects for downy mildew *(Sclerospora graminicola)* resistance in pearl millet. *Indian J. Genet.,* 44: 280–285.

Dave, H.R. (1987). Pearl millet hybrids. In Proc. of the International Pearl Millet workshop ICRISAT, Patancheru, A.P. 502324 India. pp. 139–142.

Deswal, D.P. and Govila, O.P. (1994). Genetics of resistance to downy mildew (*Sclerospora graminicola*) in pearl millet (*Pennisetum glaucum*). *Indian Journal of Agricultural Sciences,* 64: 661–663.

Dujardin, M. and Hanna, W.W. (1983). Meiotic and reproductive behaviour of facultative apomictic BC, offspring derived from *Pennisetum americanum. P. orientale interspecific hybrids. Crop Science,* 23: 156–160.

Dujardin, M. and W.W. Hanna (1985). Cytology and reproduction of reciprocal backcrosses between pearl millet and sexual and apomictic hybrids of pearl millet *(Pennisetum squamulatum). Crop Science,* 25: 659–662.

Eberhart, S.A., Bramel-Cox, P.J. and Prasada Rao, K.E. (1997). Preserving genetic resources. Proceedings of the International Conference on Genetic improvement of Sorghum and pearl millet. at Holiday Inn Plaza, Lubbock Texas No. 97–5: 25–41.

Fussel, L.K., Bidinger, F.R. and Beiler, P. (1991). Crop physiology and breeding for drought tolerance: Research and development. *Field Crops Research,* 27: 183–199.

Gill, B.S., Sharma, H.L. and Dheshi, J.S. (1973). Cytomorphological studies of haploid pearl millet. *Cytologia,* 38: 411–416.

Gill, K.S. (1991). Pearl millet and its improvement ICAR, New Delhi.

Gill, K.S., Chahal, S.S. and Phul, P.S. (1980). Strategy to develop ergot resistance in pearl millet. *In*: Gupta, V.P. and Minocha, J.L. (*Eds.*) Trends in genetical research in Pennisetums. Punjab Agricultural University, Ludhiana, India. pp. 159–161.

Govila, O.P. (1988). Breeding procedures for cross pollinated crops. Pearl millet *In*: Chopra, V.L. (*Ed.*) Plant Breeding. Oxford & IBH Publishing Co. New Delhi. India. p. 213-223

Govila, O.P., Madhusudhana, R. and Unnikrishnan, K.V. (1997b). Diversity in performance per se and heterosis among 4 cytoplasm pearl millet male sterile lines. *International Sorghum and Millet Newsletter,* 38: 116–119.

Govila, O.P., Rai, K.N., Chopra, K.R., Andrews, D.J. and Stegmeier, W.D. (1997a). Breeding pearl millet for developing countries: Indian Experience. Proceedings of the International Conference of Genetic Improvement of Sorghum and Pearl millet. Lubbock, Texas pp. 97–118.

Gupta, V.P. (1975). Fodder improvement in Pennisetums. *Forage Res.,* 1: 54–60.

Hanna, W.W. (1987). Utilization of wild relatives of pearl millet. *In*: Proceedings International Pearl Millet Work Shop. Witcombe, J.R. and Beckerman, S.R. (*Eds.*), ICRISAT, Patancheru, India. pp. 33–42,

Hanna, W.W. (1989). Characteristics and stability of a new nuclear - cytoplasmic male sterility source in pearl millet. *Crop Sci.,* 29: 1457–1459.

Hanna, W.W. (1990). Transfer of germplasm from the secondary to the primary gene pool in *Pennisetum TAG,* 80: 200–204.

Hanna, W.W. (1993), Registration of pearl millet parental lines Tift 8677 and A,/B, Tift 90 D2 E1, *Crop Sci.,* 33: 1119.

Hanna, W.W. (1995). Use of apomixis in cultivar development. *Advanccs in Agronomy,* 54: 333–350.

Hanna, W.W. and Burton, G.W. (1987). Registration of pearl millet inbred parental lines. Tift 85 D2A, and Tift 85D2B. *Crop Sci.,* 27: 1324–1325.

Hanna, W.W., Dujardin, M., Ozias - Akins P. and Arthur, L. (1992). Transfer of apomixis in *Peninsetum In*: Elgin, J.H. and Miksche, J.P. (*Eds.*) Proceedings of apomixis workshop. *Atlanta, G.A. USDA-ARS, ARS,* 104: 30–33.

Hanna, W.W., Schertz, K.F. and Bashaw, E.C. (1970). Apospory in *Sorghum bicolor* (L.). *Moench Science,* 170: 338–339.

Harlan, J.R. (1971). Agricultural origines centres and non centres. *Science,* 174: 468–474.

Harlan, J.R. and de Wet, J.M.J. (1971). Towards a rational classification of cultivated plants. *Taxonomy,* 20: 509–517.

Hensen, I.E., Mahalakshmi, V., Bidinger, F.R. and Alagarsamy, G. (1982). Osmotic adjustment to water stress in pearl millet *[Pennisetum americanum* (L.) Leeke)] under field conditions. *Plant Cell Environment,* 5: 147–154.

Henson, I.E., Mahalakashmi, V., Bidinger, E.R. and Algarswamy, G. (1981). Genotypic variation in pearl millet *[Pennisetum americanum* (L.) Leeke] in the ability to accumulate abscisic acid in response to water stress. *Journal of Experimental Botany,* 32: 899–910.

House, L.R. (1980). A guide to sorghum breeding ICRISAT, Patancheru, India

House, L.R. (1985). A guide to sorghum breeding (2nd edition) ICRISAT, Patancheru, India.

ICRISAT (1996). Improving the unimprovable succeeding with pearl millet. Number 3 in the "Food From Thought" series. International Crops Research Institute for the Semi-Arid Tropics, A.P. 502324, India.

Jauhar, P.P. (1968). Inter and intergenomal chromosome paring in an interspecific hybrid and its bearing on the chromosome number in *Pennisetum. Cenetica,* 39: 360–370.
Jauhar, P.P. (1970). Haploid meiosis and its bearing on the phylogeny of pearl millet *(Pennisetum typhoides). Genetica,* 41: 532–540.
Jauhar, P.P. (1981). Cytogenetics and breeding of pearl millet and related species. New York, U.S.A. Alan R. Liss, Inc. p. 289.
Joshi, A.B., Ahluwalia, M. and Shankar, K. (1961). "Improved Ghana" is better bajra. *Indian Farming,* 11(5): 12.
Kataria, R.P., Yadav, H.P., Beniwal, C.R. and Narwal, M.S. (1994). Genetics of incidence of downy mildevv *(Sclerospora graminicola)* in pearl millet *(Pennisetum glaucum). Indian journal of Agricultural Sciences,* 64: 664–666.
Krishnaswamy, N. (1962). Bajra *Pennisetum typhoides* S&H. *Indian Council of Agric. Res.* New Delhi.
Kumar, A. and Andrews, D.J. (1984). Cytoplasmic mâle sterility in pearl millet *[Pennisetum americanum* (L.) Leeke]. A review. *Adv. Appl. Biol.,* 10: 113–143.
Lounel, D. (1982). Breeding millet (*Pennisetum*) for disease resistance. Centre National de Recherches Agronomiques, Bambey, Senegal.
Madhava Menon, P.M. (1959). Occurrence of cytoplasmic male-sterility in pearl millet *Pennisetum typhoides* stapf & Habb. *Curr. Sci.,* 28: 165–167.
Mahalakashmi, V. and Bidinger, F.R. (1985). Water stress and time of floral initition in pearl millet. *Journal of Agricultural Science,* 105: 437–445.
Manga, V. and Pantulu, J.V. (1971). The meiotic behaviour of a haploid pearl millet. *Genetica,* 42: 319–329.
Murty, B.R., Arunachalam, V. and Saxena, M.B.L. (1967). Classification and catalogue of a world collection of cultivated sorghums and *Pennisetum Indian Journal of Genetics and Plant Breeding,* 27: 1–74.
Nirwal, B.C. and Upadhyaya, U.C. (1979). Growth and yield of hybrid pearl millet HB-1 as influenced by inter and intra row spacings and varying levels of nitrogen. *Indian J. Agronomy,* 24(1): 17–20.
Pandya, P.S., Chavan, V.M. and Shendge, P.Y. (1955). A brief review of the improvement of bajri in Bombay State. Poona, *Agric. Coll. Mag.,* 46: 142–147.
Pantlulu, J.V. (1958). A case of chromosomal interchange in pearl millet. *Curr. Sci.,* 27: 497–498.
Pheru Singh, A., Rai, G.B., Rao, M.N.V. and Witcombe, J.R. (1994). Registration of "ICMV 155" Pearl Millet. *Crop. Sci.,* 34: 1409.
Phookan, A.K. (1987). Studies on pearl millet smut with special reference to pathogenic variability, inheritance of resistance and chemical control. Ph.D. Thesis, Haryana Agricultural University, Hisar, India.
Pokhrial, S.C., Unnikrishnan, K.V., Dass, Ram, Singh Balzor and Patil, R.R. (1976). Combining ability of downy mildew resistent lines in pearl millet. *Indian J. Genet.,* 36: 403–409.
Popli, S. and Singh, R. (1972). Nutrient composition and amino acid pattern of some high yielding varieties of bajra *(Penniselum typhoides)}. Res. HAU,* 2: 213–217.
Powell, J.B., Hanna, W.W. and Burton, G.W. (1975). Origin, cytology and reproductive behaviour of haploids in pearl millet. *Crop Sci.,* 15: 389–392.
Rai, K.N. and Anand Kumar, K. (1994). Pearl millet improvement at ICRISAT - an update. *International Sorghum and Millets Newsletter,* 35: 1–29.
Rai, K.N. and Thakur, R.P. (1995). Ergot reaction of pearl millet hybrids affected by fertility restoration and genetic resistance of parental lines. *Euphytica,* 83: 225–231.
Rangaswamy (1935). On the cytology of *Pennisetum typhoideum* Rich. *Indian Bot. Soc.,* 14: 125–131.
Rao, N.G.P. and Narayana, L.L. (1968). Apomixis in grain sorghum. *Indian Plant Breed,* 28: 121–127.
Rao, N.S. (1929). On the chromosome numbers of some cultivated plants of South India. J. *Indian Bot. Soc.,* 8: 126–128.

Rao, P.K., Nambiar, A.K. and Madhava Menon, P. (1951). Maximization of production by cultivation of hybrid strains with special reference to cumbu (Pearl millet). *Madras Agric. J.,* 38: 95–100.

Read, J.C. and Bashaw, E.C. (1974). Intergeneric hybrid between pearl millet and buffel grass. *Crop. Sci.,* 14: 401–403.

Rockfeller Foundation (1970). Annual Report. New York.

Schertz, K.F. and Ritchey, J.R. (1977). Cytoplasmic genic male sterility system in sorghum. *Crop. Sci.,* 18: 890–893.

Shinde, R.B., Patil, F.B. and Sangave, R.A. (1984). Resistance to downy mildew in pearl millet. *Journal of Maharashtra Agricultural Univ.,* 9: 337–338.

Singh, F., Singh, R.M. Singh, R.B. and Singh, R.K. (1980). Genetic studies of downy mildew resistance in pearl millet. *In*: Gupta, V.P. and Minocha, J.L. (*Eds*.). Trends in genetical research of Peninsetums. Wesley Press, Ludhiana, India. pp. 171–172.

Singh, G. and Maurya, R.A. (1969). Response of hybrid bajra to varying plant populations and levels of nitrogen. *Indian J. Agron.,* 14 (2): 157–158.

Singh, S.D. (1990). Sources of resistance to downy mildew and rust in pearl millet. *Plant Disease,* 74: 871–874.

Singh, S.D., King, S.B. and Malla Reddy, P. (1990). Registration of five pearl millet germplasm sources with stable resistance to downy mildew. *Crop Science*. 30: 1164.

Singh, S.D., King, S.B. and Werder, J. (1993). Downy mildew disease of pearl millet. Information Bulletin No. 37. Patancheru A.P. 502324, India International Crop Research Institute for the Semi Arid Tropics.

Stapf, O. and Hubbard, C.E. (1933). Notes on African grasses XII. Kew Bull. pp. 269–302.

Stapf, O. and Hubbard, C.E. (1934). *Pennisetum*. in Flora of tropical Africa (Prain, D. ed) Vol. 9 Oxford Kent, U.K.: L. Reeve and Co. pp. 954–1070.

Talukdar. B.S., Singh, S.D. and Hash, C.T. (1994). Breeding for resistance to diseases in pearl millet. *In*: Singh, H.G., Mishra, S.N., Singh, T.B., Hari Har Ram and Singh, D.P. (*Eds*.) Crop Breeding in India. International Book distributing Company Lucknow U.P. 226004, India. pp. 176–185.

Tewari, S.N., Singh, D. and Lal, S. (1971). Floral biology of pearl millet *(Pennisetum typhoides S&W. J. Ind. Bot. Soc.,* 50: 45–52.

Thakur, R.P. and Chahal, S.S. (1987). Problems and strategies in control of ergot and smut in pearl millet. *In*: Witcombe, J.R. and Beekerman, S.R. (*Eds*.) Proceedings of the international pearl millet Workshop 7-11 April 1986. ICRISAT Centre, India, International Crop Institute for the Semi Arid Tropcis, Patanchenu A.P. 502324, India. pp. 147–160.

Thakur, R.P. and King, S.B. (1988). Ergot disease of pearlmillet. Information Bulletin No. 24. Patacheru A.P. 502324, India, International Crop Research Institute for Semi Arid Tropics.

Thakur, R.P. and Singh, S.B. (1988). Smut disease of pearl millet. Information Bulletin No. 25. Patancheru A.P. 502324. India, International Crop Research Institute for the Semi-Arid Tropics.

Thakur, R.P., King, S.B., Rai, K.N. and Rao, V.P. (1992). Identification and utilization of smut resistance in pearl millet. Research Bulletin No. ICRISAT. Patancheru, A.P. 502324 India.

Thakur, R.P., Rai, K.M., King, S.B. and Rao, V.P. (1993). Identification and utilization of ergot resistance in pearl millet. Research Bulletin No. 17. International Crop Research Institute for the Semi Arid Tropics Patancheru. A.P. 502324 India.

Thakur, R.P., Rao, V.P. and King, S.B. (1991). Influence of flowering event in cytoplasmic male sterile lines and $F_1$ hybrids on infection by *Claviceps fusiformis* in pearl millet. *Plant Disease,* 75: 1217–1222.

Thakur, R.P., Rao, V.P. and Williams, R.J. (1984). The morphology and disease cycle of ergot caused by *Claviceps fusiformis* in pearl millet. *Phytopathology,* 74: 201–205.

Thakur, R.P., Rao, V.P., Williams, R.J., Chahal, S.S., Mathur, S.B., Pawar, N.B., Nefade, S.D., Shetty, H.S., Singh, Govined and Bangar, S.G. (1985). Identification of stable resistance to ergot in pearl millet. *Plant Disease,* 69: 982–985.

Thakur, R.P., Subba Rao, K.V. and Williams, R.J. (1983). Evaluation of new field screening technique for smut resistance in pearl millet. *Phytopathology*, 73: 1255–58.

Thakur, R.P., Subba Rao, K.V., Williams, R.J., Gupta, S.C., Thakur, D.P., Nafade, S.D., Sundaram, N.V., Frowd, J.A. and Guthrie, E.J. (1986). Identification of stable resistance to smut in pearl millet. *Plant Disease,* 70: 38–41.

Thakur, R.P., Williams, R.J. and Rao, V.P. (1980). Pollination effects on pearl millet ergot. *Phytopathology*, 70: 80–84.

Thakur, R.P., Williams, R.J. and Rao, V.P. (1982): Pollination effects on pearl millet ergot resistance in pearl millet. *Phytopathology,* 72: 406–408.

Tyagi, C.S. and Singh, Iqbal (1989). Genetics of downy mildew resistance in pearl millet. *Bhartiya Krishi Anusandhan Patrika,* 4: 24–30.

Upreti, D.C. and Austin, A. (1972). Varietal differences in the nutrient composition of improved bajra hybrids. *Bull Grain Technol.,* 10: 249–55.

Uthkhede, R.S. (1972). Some breeding procedures used for improvement of pearl millet (*Pennisetum typhoides* (Bum. F.) Staff & C.E. Hubb). *Indian J. Agric. Sei.,* 42: 452–456.

Virk, D.S., Chahal, S.S. and Mangat, B.K. (1987). Factorial analysis of ergot resistance in pearl millet. *Crop Improvement,* 14: 153–156.

William, R.J. and Andrews, D.J. (1983). Breeding for disease and pest resistance in pearl millet. *FAO Plant Protection Bulletin,* 31: 136–158.

Williams, R.J. (1984). Disease resistance in pearl millet. Review of Tropical Plant Pathology, 1: 245–296.

Wilson, J.P. and Hanna, W.W. (1992). Disease resistance in wild *Pennisetum* species. *Plant Disease,* 76: 1171–1175.

Wilson, J.P., Hanna, W.W. and Bondari, K. (1993). Directed use of germplasm resources for breeding rust resistant pearl millet. *Plant Pathol.* (Trends in Agric. Sci.) 1: 67–74.

Yadav, O.P. (1994). Influence of A, cytoplasm in pearl millet. *Plant Breeding Abstracts,* 64: 1375–1379.

Yadav, R.P. (1974). Inheritance of smut resistance in pearl millet. *Agra University Journal of Res. Sci.,* 23: 37–39.

# 6

# Sugarcane

## 1. INTRODUCTION

The importance of sugarcane can be judged from the fact that it is cultivated in nearly 100 countries of the world and meets over 70% of the total sweetener requirement. India has emerged as the largest producer of sugar in the recent years although Brazil has larger area and cane production. In India, the crop is cultivated in almost all states, barring the cold ones, under very diverse conditions. The state of Uttar Pradesh, lying in the subtropics, accounts for half of the sugarcane area in India, which alone is more than that in any other country, except Brazil. Because most operations of cultivation and processing are carried out manually, 35-40 million farmers, 3.5 lakh skilled and unskilled workers are engaged in sugarcane-sugar production chain in India. No wonder, in India it is the second largest agro-based industry after textiles.

Sugarcane, a perennial tropical grass, is grown for the sugar stored in its stem and propagated through stem cuttings. The present day sugarcane cultivar are highly heterozygous, species hybrid, complex polyploids, (designated as *Saccharum.* spp. hybrid). The genus *Saccharum* comprises of three cultivated species, *S. officinarum, S. barberi* and *S. sinense,* while the wild ones are S. *spontaneum* and *S. robustum.* Sugarcane cultivation spans a wide region located between 35°N to 35°S of the equator. The agroclimatic conditions under which sugarcane is grown, affect the duration and the productivity of the crop. The tropical climates permit longer periods of crop growth which result in higher cane yields, but not necessarily the highest sugar content in the cane. The growing season of sugarcane varies from 10 to 12 months in Louisiana to 24 months or more in Hawaii. An integral part of sugarcane cultivation is the practice of taking one or more ratoons (commonly 2-3). A ratoon crop is raised from the underground buds of the previous year's

V.L. Chopra (Ed.): Breeding Field Crops I: Practices, Studium Press (LLC), USA.

stubble. Ratooning ability is thus an important genotypic character determining the adaptability and commercial success of any variety. Under normal agriculture situations, the average cane yield ranges from 60 tonnes $ha^{-1}$ $yr^{-1}$ to 120 tonnes $ha^{-1}$ $yr^{-1}$ (Naidu, 1987). The average sugar recovery (sugar per tonne of sugarcane processed, expressed in percent) may range between 8% to 14%. The climatic conditions of the production environment determine the kind of genetic material which would adapt to such conditions. In turn, the varietal requirements and breeding objectives differ according to the agroclimatic region.

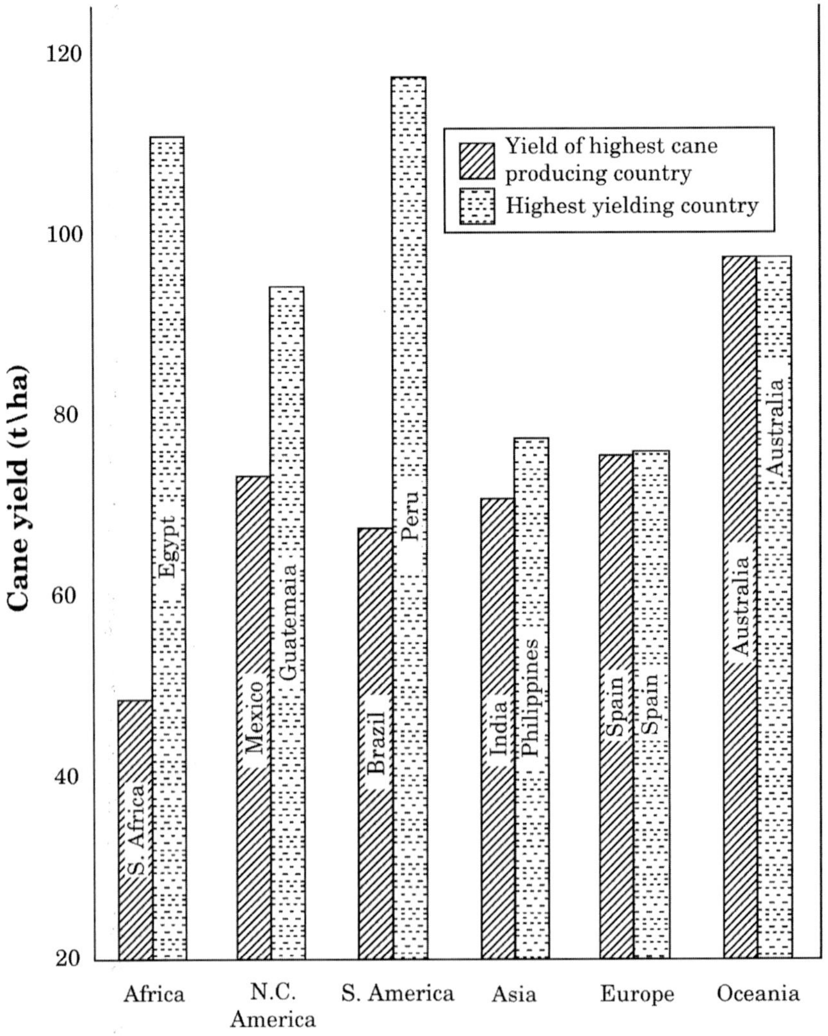


**Fig. 1:** Yield level of country with the highest cane production and that with the highest cane productivity in each continent (Adapted from FAO Production Year Book 1997)

The total world sugar production stands at 126.9 million tonnes, to which sugarcane and sugarbeet contribute nearly 70% and 30%, respectively (F.O. Litch Sugar Statistics 1998). The area and production of sugarcane have increased steadily over the decades and its contribution to the world sugar relative to that of sugarbeet has also increased. Sugarcane is grown on 19.3 million hectares with a respective cane and sugar production of 1214.6 and 85.7 million tonnes (Average of 1995-1997 values, adapted from FAO Production Year Book 1997 and Indian Sugar 1998). The important cane producing countries are Brazil, India, Cuba, China, Thailand, Mexico, Australia and USA. Yield level of countries with the highest sugar production and the highest productivity in each continent is given in Fig. 1.

Sugarcane is grown under diverse conditions in India, nearly comparable to those in the rest of the world. The area under sugarcane in India is divided into five agro-climatic zones, each of which has a separate breeding Programme. Although sugarcane is grown in most of the Indian states, the following states contribute more than 95% of the cane produced in India (Table 1).

**Table 1:** The major sugarcane producing states (1997-98 statistics)

| *Region* | *Area ('000 ha)* | *Cane production ('000 t)* | *Sugar production ('000 t) (%)** | *Cane consump- by factories ('000 t)* |
|---|---|---|---|---|
| ***Tropical*** | | | | |
| Maharashtra | 460 | 34960 | 3847 | 95 |
| Tamil Nadu | 293 | 30470 | 1229 | 74 |
| Karnataka | 241 | 20983 | 959 | 70 |
| Andhra Pradesh | 192 | 14277 | 782 | 71 |
| Gujarat | 155 | 11150 | 889 | 93 |
| Total | 1341 (34.2) | 111640 (42.4) | 7706 (60.0) | |
| ***Sub-tropical*** | | | | |
| Uttar Pradesh | 1956 | 116245 | 3922 | 48 |
| Bihar | 170 | 6320 | 297 | 73 |
| Haryana | 140 | 8400 | 382 | 66 |
| Punjab | 132 | 8700 | 331 | 77 |
| Total | 2398 (61.2) | 139665 (53.8) | 4932 (38.4) | |
| INDIA | 3917 | 260160 | 12852 | 62 |

Value in parenthesis refers to per cent of the national statistic. Ind. Sugar, Dec. 1998.
*Sawhney 1997. *Int. Sug. J.* Vol. 99 (1185E)

It is interesting to note that the tropical region has only one-third of the total area but contributes two-third of the total sugar production. Uttar Pradesh alone has more area and production than all the tropical states put together. It is also important to bear in mind that ratoon crop which constitute nearly half of the sugarcane area contributes only one-third of the total cane production. Enhancing ratoon productivity remains, therefore, an important breeding goal. But since ratoons suffer from neglect and poor management, increasing their productivity will require more than just breeding effort. The variation in the cane and sugar productivity among Indian states is depicted in Fig. 2.

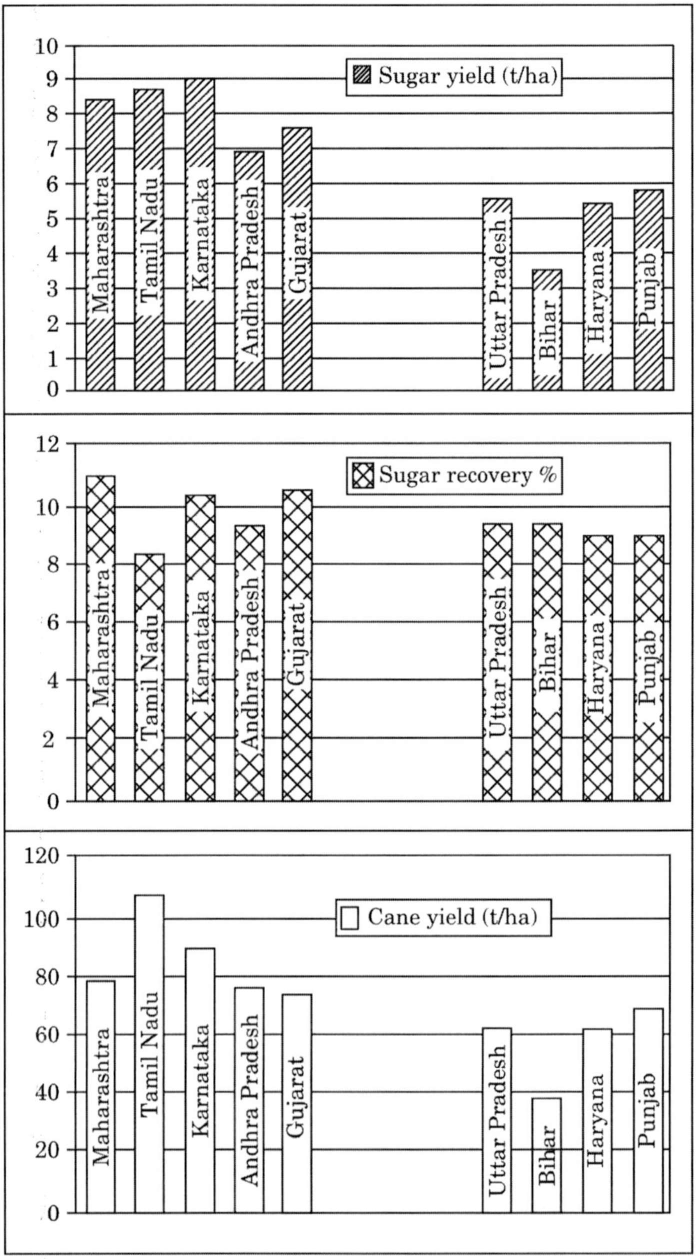


**Fig. 2:** Cane and sugar productivity of important Indian states

It may be mentioned that sugarcane, its products and by-products are put to varied uses. Nearly half of Brazil's cane is used for conversion into alcohol for automobiles, while in India one-third is used for making jaggery and raw sugar. Sugarcane bagasse is used as fuel for the boiler in the sugar mills and for co-generation of electric power. Bagasse is also used in the pulp and paper industry. Sugarcane molasses is used for the production of alcohol in distilleries attached with sugar factories. However, the efficiency of these uses differs considerably (Jadhav, 1997). These diverse end-uses of sugarcane are prone to economy-driven shifts that can call for modification of breeding objectives.

## 2. TAXONOMY

The genus *Saccharum,* established by Linnaeus in 1793, belongs to the family Gramineae, sub-family Panicoideae and tribe Andropogoneae. The classification of Jeswiet (1925) and its modification by Artschwager and Brandes (1958) to include S. *robustum* and *S. edule,* is widely accepted. The key to different species according to these two groups is as follows:

A. Main axis of inflorescence and cluster axis with long hairs. Glumes always 4. Lodicules either ciliate or not. If the spikelets of the same pair do not flower simultaneously, the pedicillate one always blooms first. Culms green, greyish green, greenish bronze, ivory or white.

   1. Lodicules ciliate; long subterranean runners present; growing wild..............................................S. *spontaneum* L.

   2. Lodicules not ciliate, subterranean runners short, sugar producing cultivated plants.

      a. Leaves broad (to 50 mm). Tall cane species, nodes all bobbin shaped, greenish bronze.................................... S. *sinense* Roxb.

      b. Leaves narrow, short inconspicuous cane species. Nodes usually cylindrical, greyish green, white or ivory. Rather limited to India and Pakistan............................... S. *barberi* Jeswiet

B. Main axis of inflorescence never having long hairs, often glabrate; rachis nodes glabrate or with very few hairs. Glumes generally three, sometimes four. Lodicules not ciliate. If the spikelets of the same pair bloom at different times, the sessile one is always the first. Culms pale or dark green to dark yellow, dark red or violet.

   1. Wild plants up to 10 m tall; culms with relatively high fibre and low sucrose content; generally river bank

perennials........................................................ *S. robustum* Brandes et Jeswiet ex Grassl.

2. Cultivated plants
   a. Inflorescence aborted; leaves more or less pubescent ..............................................................S. *edule* Hassk
   b. Inflorescence normal, culms with relatively low fibre and high sucrose.......................................... S. *offcinarum* L.

Systematists differed with Linnaeus on the species included in the genus *Saccharum,* but there has been no consensus as to which others to include. The reason for this confusion has been that sugarcane is vegetatively propagated, many parallel mutations have taken place, the mutants intercross freely and taxonomists have relied on herbarium rather than living material (Alexander, 1973). Mukherjee (1957) coined the term, '*Saccharum* complex' to describe this intermating group. He included *Saccharum, Erianthus* (sect. *Ripidium*), *Sclerostachya* and *Narenga. Miscanthus* sec. *Dianara* was later added to this *Saccharum* complex by Daniels *et al.* (1975).

## 3. *SACCHARUM* SPECIES

The following information is drawn from Stevenson (1965), Sreenivasan *et al.* (1987) and Babu (1990).

### *Saccharum officinarum* L.

This is type species with which sugarcane is identified and is best represented by thick-stemmed colorful canes that flourish in tropical climates (Plate 1). No clone of this species has been found to grow in the wild. These original cultivars are associated with the primitive man in the Malanesian Islands. These were cultivated by the indigenous people of the Pacific Island for chewing. The canes of this species are soft with low fibre, high sugar and low starch. Owing to their majestic appearance, need for good management and incapacity to survive on their own in nature, the Dutch in Java named these 'noble canes'. This species has 80 somatic chromosomes and is considered to be an octaploid with a basic chromosome number of x = 10. Before the hybrid varieties replaced commercial plantations of the cultivated species of sugarcane, the *S. officinarum* cultivars were Yellow Caledonia, Badilla, Lahaina, Black Cheribon, Louisiana Purple, Louisiana Striped, Shamsara, Karun, Kaludai Boothan, etc. In India, Vellai, Poovan and Chittan in Tamil Nadu; Namam, Pattapatti and Rusdali in Karnataka; Telia Cheruka and Patta Cheruku in Andhra Pradesh, Pundia in Maharashtra and

Paunda canes in north India were cultivated for chewing. Many of these names refer to the same variety. For example, the Otaheite was grown as Lahaina in Mauritius and Vellai in India.

The Otaheite was the first of the noble canes to be cultivated worldwide. As a breeding cane, it has not been able to contribute much, but it played a part in the origin of the EK series in Java and is a remote ancestor of POJ 2878. On the other hand, The Cheribon, proved most valuable in hybridization with S. *barbcri* and S. *spontaneum.*

### 3.1. *Saccharum barberi* and *Saccharum sinense*

The famous thin-stalked north Indian canes, mostly used for jaggery *(gur)* making, were studied in detail by Barber (1916a, b). He separated these into five groups, based on morphology of stem, leaf and root. These groups are Sunnabile, Mungo, Nargori, Saretha and Pansahi. Pansahi group was later on placed under *S. sinense* by Jeswiet (1925). Price (1968) classified the Chinese and the north Indian sugarcanes on the basis of chromosome number and gross morphology. He recognized six groups:

| | | |
|---|---|---|
| Mungo 2n=81, 82, 83 | Dhaulu 2n=82 and 83 | Saretha 2n=91, 91+fragments and 92 |
| Nagori 2n=105 to 119 | Pansahi 2n=106 to 120 | Unclassified ca. 2n=104 to 121 |

*S. barberi* and *S. sinense* were in cultivation in India and China before the advent of the man-made hybrids. The notable names being Chunnee, Saretha, Kansar (*S. barberi*) and Uba (*S. sinense*). These have been extensively used in early breeding endeavors, though the success was restricted due to poor flowering and low fertility. This is probably related to their hybrid origin resulting in aneuploid'y and highly irregular meiosis (Sreenivasan *et al.,* 1987). The clones of this species are moderate to good in sugar content and are well adapted to the biotic and abiotic stresses of the subtropical region. These are poor yielders, mainly because the individual cane weight is low.

*S. barberi* and *S. sinense* possess desirable traits like heavy tillering, deep root system and tolerance to drought. The most useful breeding canes of *S. barberi* are found in the Saretha group. Breeders in Java obtained several useful varieties directly from crosses between Chunnee, a Saretha clone, and the noble canes, Black Cheribon and Striped Preanger. Among these POJ 36, POJ 213 and POJ 234 were cultivated extensively and have also been used in breeding. POJ 213 is an ancestor of several POJ, Co and B varieties.

In contrast, Uba, a *S. sinense* cultivar and immune to mosaic, has been used much less in breeding. It is almost sterile and gives few seedlings. Yet some seedlings on crossing have given rise to some useful commercial varieties. The Hawaiian varieties 32-1063 and 49-5, for instance, both have Uba in their ancestry, as have also several of the recent successful Barbados varieties, such as B 45151, B 47258, B 54142 and B 54277.

### 3.2. *Saccharum spontaneum*

*S. spontaneum,* the wild ancesstor of present-day sugarcane, is well known for its large variability and ecological adaptiveness (Panje, 1964). It exists from tropical and subtropical Africa, through the Indian subcontinent, south-east Asia, Malaya, China, Taiwan, Japan, Indonesian Archipelago, Philippines, and New Guinea (Panje and Babu, 1960). It is a polymorphic species in that the clones in the northern submountaneus region of India are small in size and bushy, while those in Assam and peninsular India are vigorous, erect, thick-stalked to tall with long internodes and broad-leaves. These range from annual to perennial, reproduce both sexually and asexually and many forms are highly rhizamatous, with rhizomes growing to several metres. They have pithy stems and often hollow centres. The tillering is profuse, and in general these exhibit marked resistance to moisture stress, low temperature and many of the diseases and pests. The chromosome numbers vary from 2n=40 to 128. Meiosis in *S. spontaneum* is generally normal with bivalent formation, regardless of the chromosome number. The basic chromosome number (x) of this species is considered to be 8.

Panje and Babu (1960) recognized three sectors of geographic distribution based on the chromosomes numbers:

1. *The western sector* (Africa-cum-Mediterranean region) with chromosome numbers ranging from 2n=112 to 128
2. *The eastern sector* (South Asia-cum-Pacific region) with a range of 2n=80-112 chromosomes, and
3. *The central sector* (Indian subcontinent with 2n=40-80 chromosomes.

### 3.3. *Saccharum robustum*

Brandes and Jeswiet were the first to record this species in 1928 and referred to it as *Saccharum robustum* (Stevenson, 1965). Its habitat is mostly along river banks. This species comprises vigorous forms with compact clones up to 10 metres in height. It is similar to *S. spontaneum* in possessing extremely low sugar content. It resembles *S. officinarum* in appearance and susceptibility to mosaic. The stalks are medium in thickness with broad leaves. The clones have a straggling habit with high fibre content. This species is formed of two cytological types 2n=60 and 2n=80; the other variants are to be regarded as aneuploids (Price 1965). The breeding aspect of this species is yet to be studied intensively. *S. robustum* clones have been used in breeding in Barbados, Queensland, Florida and Hawaii. The commercial varieties resulting from the use of this species are members of the 32 MQ series of Queensland, CP 36 series of Florida, and 37-1933 of Hawaii (Babu, 1990).

### 3.4. *Saccharum edule*

This is a species with distribution restricted to New Guinea. It is also similar to *S. robustum* in vegetative characters. It is believed to have arisen from *S. robustum* by mutation and since it bears a swollen and aborted inflorescence, it holds no interest for the breeder. The natives consume it as a vegetable.

The other related genera comprising the *Saccharum* complex are important from the evolutionary and breeding point of view. These possess smaller chromosomal complement as compared to sugarcane. The following table summarizes the characters available for breeding in the *Saccharum* complex:

**Salient characteristics of members of '*Saccharum* complex'**

| | |
|---|---|
| *S. officinarum* | High sugar content, High juice purity, Low non-sugars and starch, High individual stalk weight, Low fibre content, Early maturity, Self-stripping/ detrashing, responsive to management, High tonnage |
| *S. barberi* | Tillering ability, Tolerance to abiotic stresses, Good ratooning ability, Deep root system, Good sucrose, Low in tonnage, Tolerance to major diseases |
| *S. sinense* | Cold tolerance, Immune to mosaic, Poor juice and milling quality |
| *S. spontaneum* | Low nutrient requirement, Resistance to diseases, Resistant to drought, High fibre content, High biomass production, Resistance to stem borer, Highly adapted to varied habitats |
| *S. robustum* | Improved yield, Resistance to water-logging, Resistance to diseases, Responsive to irrigation, Extremely vigorous, Hard, woody and sometimes hollow stem |
| *Erianthus* | Resistance to nematodes and root parasites, good yield and fibre, Lower nutrient requirement, Insect resistance |
| *Narenga and Sclerostachya* | Resistance to almost all diseases, pests and root parasites, Tolerance to drought, Resistance to water-logging |
| *Miscanthus* | Resistance to diseases, high yield, Resistance to cold |

Adapted from Krishnamurthy (1987)

## 4. ORIGIN AND EVOLUTION

The origin of sugarcane and evolution of different species in highly speculative (Stevenson, 1965). Yet, there is consensus of the following conclusions:

| ***Species*** | ***Centre of origin*** | ***Centre of diversity*** |
|---|---|---|
| S. *officinarum* | New Guinea /Indo-Burma-China border | New Guinea |
| *S. barberi* | North India | North India |
| *S. sinense* | China | China |
| *S. spontaneum* | Colder regions of subtropical India | Widely distributed |
| *S. robustum* | New Guinea | New Guinea |

Adapted from Rao (1987)

It may be mentioned here that the three species, S. *barberi, S. spontaneum,* and S. *officinarum* were originally known by the Sanskrit words, Iksu, Kasa and Paundraka, respectively (Deerr, 1949). Two predominant schools of thought exist with regards to origin of sugarcane. One group strongly believes that India is the home of *S. officinarum* (Mukherjee, 1957, Daniels and Daniels, 1975). India is considered the centre of origin with the New Guinea region as the centre of diversity. It is argued that because of the red-rot disease, it could not survive in the centre of origin and migrated to the more favourable climate of New Guinea. All the species included under the *Saccharum* complex exist in India. However, there are few intermediates, particularly with respect of *S. robustum,* which are comparable to the variability for this species found in New Guinea. These intermediate forms are needed to explain the complex introgression necessary for the evolution of *S. officinarum* (Daniels and Roach, 1987).

The region Wallacea (East Indonesia) was proposed as the centre of origin of *S. officinarum* by Deerr (1911). Once *S. robustum* was discovered in a wide range of forms and colours in New Guinea, the area and the species were immediately proclaimed as the originators of *S. officinarum* (Brandes, 1958). *S. robustum* resembled *S. officinarum* morphologically and the typical clone possessed the same chromosome number (2n=80), making this hypothesis the most acceptable (Daniels and Roach, 1987). It is believed that *S. spontaneum* clones in Wallacea are the basic stock which gave rise to *S. officinarum via S. robustum,* following complex introgression with core taxa, *viz, Miscanthus* and *Erianthus,* and with the possible involvement of *Sclerostachya.* These core taxa flower simultaneously in the region, providing a unique opportunity for introgression (Berding and Koike, 1980).

*S. officinarum* is believed to have spread from New Guinea to South Seas, India, and China in prehistoric times. It introgressed with members of the *Saccharum* complex, principally *S. spontaneum,* to produce *S. barberi* in India and *S. sinense* in China. Parthasarathy (1946) put forth that *S. barberi* must have originated by promiscuous hybridization between *S. officinarum* and *S. spontaneum* in the region of Bengal, Bihar and Orissa, the area of maximum diversity in India. There have been disagreements to this hypothesis (Barber, 1915; Venkatraman, 1938; Grassl, 1977 and Rao, 1980). It is suggested that *S. barberi,* particularly the Katha section of the Saretha group, originated in northwest India, independent of *S. officinarum.* Further, it is believed that some forms, especially Saretha of *S. barberi,* arose by mutation and selection. The Mungo group seems to have resulted from hybridization of *S. officinarum* with *Erianthus,* instead of *S. spontaneum.* According to Grassl (1964), *S. sinense* developed in China-Japan area by introgression between *S. officinarum* and tetraploid *Miscanthus.* The possible evolutionary interrelationships are depicted in Fig. 3.

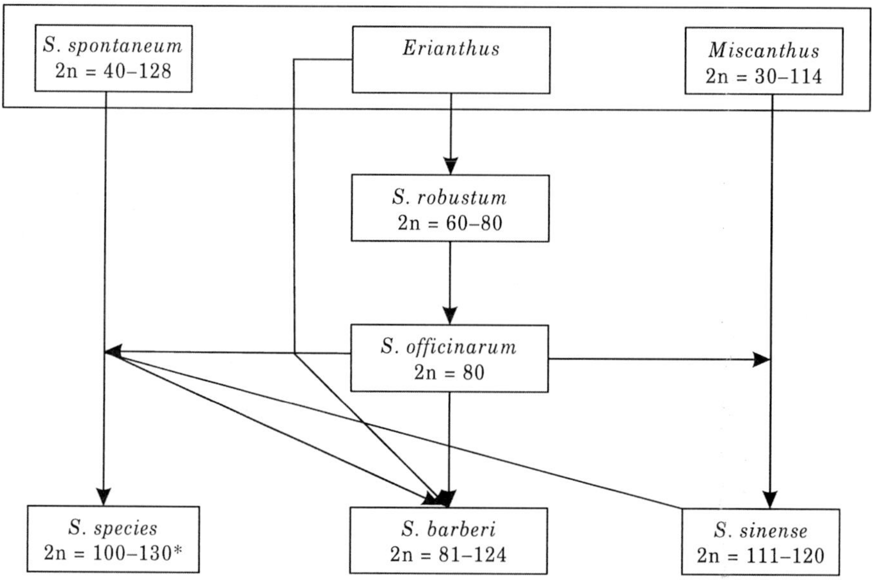


**Fig. 3 :** Speculated evolutionary palhway of *Saccharum* species Adapted from Fauconnier (1993), *Sreenivasan *et al.* (1987)

## 5. GERMPLASM COLLECTION, MAINTENANCE, CHARACTERIZATION AND UTILIZATION

In early times, the movement of germplasm was confined to commercial varieties of *S. officinarum* and were used as introduction to new areas. This is how, noble canes spread to the major cane growing countries through early travelers. In their new habitats, these clones acquired new local names. The expeditions made up to 1921 to the New Guinea region were directed to collect the noble canes for direct introduction to replace the deteriorating varieties under cultivation. It was only when the sugar industry based solely on the noble canes was threatened by disease epidemics, a need was felt to introduce disease resistant sugarcane germplasm adaptable to various ecological conditions. From the expedition of 1928 onwards, emphasis was laid on the collection of wild canes. The origin and movement of canes are well reviewed both by Deerr (1921) and Alexander (1973).

Currently, sugarcane germplasm is held principally in two 'world' collections, one maintained in the USA by the USDA, and the other in India, maintained by the Sugarcane Breeding Institute, Coimbatore, (ICAR). The Status of collection at the two centres is as follows:

| *Germplasm group* | *USA Miami* | *INDIA Coimbatore, Cannanore & Wellington* |
|---|---|---|
| *Saccharum officinarum* | 568 | 762 |
| *S. robustum* | 121 | 144 |
| *S. spontaneum* | 355 | 724 |
| *S. barberi* | 55 | 43 |
| *S. sinense* | 37 | 29 |
| *S. edule* | 29 | – |
| Allied genera | 120 | 386 |
| Man-made hybrids | 219 | 1728 |
| Recent Indian collections | – | 398 |
| New accessions from USA | – | 15 |
| Total | 1504 | 4214 |

(Roach, 1992)

### 5.1. Types of Germplasm Collection

In sugarcane, germplasm conservation in live collections is the most important, although *in vitro* conservation and storage of seed have been attempted too, as a back-up. The difficulty with live collections is that these are vulnerable in the event of natural calamities, besides being prone to diseases and pests. Berding and Roach (1987) reported a loss of 61% of the clones of the US collection between 1957 and 1977. In contrast, the Indian collection is better located and safer. It has been suggested that seed storage under deep-freeze could complement clonal collections (Rao, 1980; Heinz, 1987). But a seed collection can not include accessions that do not flower or produce viable seed. The rationale behind seed collection is to conserve genes and not genotypes, since in sugarcane due to heterozygosity, no genotype is true breeding. The techniques for short and long-term storage of shoot apices under *in vitro* conditions have been developed at SBI in India and IRAT-CIRAD in France, respectively (Sreenivasan and Sreenivasan, 1985; Faulet *et al.,* 1993).

## 5.2. Germplasm Characterization and Documentation

Enthusiasm and support for collection of sugarcane germplasm has not been matched by effort in its conservation, documentation and use (Roach, 1992). It is therefore important that the collections get closely studied and catalogued so as to minimize their repetition and maximize their utilization. An internationally accepted documentation envisages recording of data under four major headings: *viz.* (a) Agricultural, (b) Botanical, (c) Genetical and (d) Disease resistance information. The Indian contribution to documentation has been commendable. The following catalogues have been brought out using the IBPGR descriptors:

*Kanadasami P.A., Sreenivasan T.V., Ramana Rao T.C., Palanachami K. 1987. Sugarcane Genetic Resources. Vol. I. Saccharum spontaneum L. Sugarcane Breeding Institute, Indian Council of Agricultural Research, Coimbatore.*

*Ramano Rao T.C., Sreenivasan T.V., Palanichami K. 1989. Sugarcane Genetic Resources. Vol. II. Saccharum robustum, S. barberi, S. sinense and S. edule. Sugarcane Breeding Institute, Coimbatore.*

*Screenivasan T.V. and Vijayan Nair N. 1991. Sugarcane Genetic Resources. Vol. III. Saccharum officinarum Sugarcane Breeding Institute, Coimbatore.*

*Vijayan Nair N. and Sreenivasan T.V. 1995. Sugarcane database on Co varieties. Sugarcane Breeding Institute, Coimbatore.*

In recent years, biochemical descriptors have overshadowed morphological descriptors. These are highly heritable and considered as single gene products. These are flavonoids, isozymes, RAPD markers and RFLP's (citations in Berding *et al.,* 1997).

## 5.3. Utilization of Germplasm

Utilization of sugarcane germplasm can be discussed under three headings: interspecific, intergenetic and intervarietal hybridization.

Two events serve as landmarks in the genetic development of sugarcane— the discovery of its sexual reproduction, and later, the discovery of the beneficial effects of interspecific hybridization. The two earliest sugarcane research stations in the world were located in Java (Indonesia) and Barbados, both having been established in 1886. It was Soltwedel who observed the occurence of true seed and its germination in Java in 1887. He is also credited with initiating interspecific hybridization (Berding and Roach, 1987).

### 5.4. Interspecific Hybridization

Interspecific hybridization commenced in India a little later than in Java with the establishment of Sugarcane Breeding Institute at Coimbatore in 1912. The first Indian commercial hybrid cane Co 205, was an interspecific hybrid between *S. officinarum,* Vellai and S. *spontaneum* Coimbatore. Subsequently, *S. barberi, S. sinense* and the wild species *S. spontaneum* were utilized, along with *S. officinarum,* for evolving commercial hybrids in India (Venkatraman, 1938). These early species hybrids produced in India formed the basic genetic stock in many other countries. Likewise, the early hybrids produced in Java, like POJ 213, and POJ 2878, etc., were freely utilized by Indian breeders in their breeding programme. As mentioned earlier, forms of *S. robustum* have been used in breeding work in Barbados, Queensland, Florida, and Hawaii.

Roach (1969) provided an excellent review of the cytological consequences of *S. officinarum* × *S. spontaneum* crosses. It was shown that these matings rarely showed n+n progeny. These progenies have a triploid chromosome number relative to that of the parents. The increase in chromosome number in the hybrids has been attributed to the transmission of two haploid chromosome sets of the *S. officinarum* female parent and one by the male parent (2n+n). The increase in the chromosome number of *S. officinarum* in crosses with the wild species *S. spontaneum* has greatly reduced the time taken for *S. spontaneum* nobilisation to the commercial level. But those involving *S. robustum,* due to its n + n transmission, have not figured in the geneology of any of the Indian commercial hybrids. Besides, due to the autosyndetic pairing in interspecific hybrids of *Saccharum,* there is no segmental exchange between species chromosomes. It has been observed that the optimal chromosomal complement of *S. spontaneum* in the genetic make-up of the present-day hybrid commercial clones is only 10-25%.

### 5.5. Intergeneric Hybridization

Although several intergeneric hybrids of *Saccharum* have been reported (Janaki Ammal, 1941; Parthasarathy and Venkatraman, 1942), none of the present day commercial hybrids have any genes from the related genera. Intergeneric hybridization has more academic interest as a biological curiosity than real utility in breeding. It has played a significant role in educidating chromosome transmission. Lately, interest in use of *Erianthus arundinaceus* has expanded (D'Hont *et al.,* 1995). The potential to improve juice quality may arise in *Saccharum* hybrid crosses with *Miscanthus* spp. or *Miscanthidium* (Tai *et al.,* 1991). The following table gives a few examples of the use of basic germplasm in sugarcane improvement:

| ***Parentage*** | ***Progeny*** |
|---|---|
| *S. officinarum* Bandjermasin Hitam open pollinated | POJ 100 |
| *S. officinarum* Vellai × *S. spontaneum* | Co 205 |
| *S. officinarum* × Kassoer BC | POJ 2725 and POJ 2878 |
| Co 6304 × *Erianthus arundinaceum* | Co 87008 |
| IJ 76-501 × Co 285 | 90 Gu 696* |
| (*S. officinarum* Vellai × *S. robustum*) × Co 419 | Co 633 |

*Gu refers to germplasm utilization

### 5.6. Intervarietal Hybridization

Intensive breeding among the varieties developed at different research stations around the world took place with liberal mutual exchanges. Gains were substantial and impressive. The end product of most breeding programs around the world is high-yielding, disease-resistant varieties. However, many breeding programes generate, as an intermediate step, source populations. Such populations are reservoir of some specific character that can contribute to the commercial acceptability of a variety. Source populations can also be developed by screening improved adapted parents for specific traits of interest, and increasing the intensity of those characters through cycles of recurrent selection. Source populations have been developed in several countries for yield components, ratooning ability, erect stalks, cold, drought and salt tolerance, resistance to Fiji disease, borer resistance and sucrose content (Tew, 1987).

The narrow genetic base in sugarcane has been a cause for concern. It appears alarming when one realizes that in the last five decades or so there has not been any enhancement in the sugar content of the cane. Most of the gains in sugar productivity have come through cane yield.

A survey of the number of basic clones utilized in India revealed the following picture (Naidu, 1982 and Sreenivasan, 1987):

| | | | | | |
|---|---|---|---|---|---|
| S. *officinarum* | 23 | *S. barberi* | 3 | S. *sinense* | 3 |
| 5. *Spontaneum* | 2 | *S. robustum* | 1 | Foreign hybrid | 150 |

Similar situation exists in other countries also. Sugarcane breeders all over the world have now recognized this problem and have started utilization of the vast germplasm collection available at their disposal. In all the sugarcane growing countries, wild species have been screened and bred for intraspecific improvement before incorporation in the commercial breeding programmes. In India, emphasis has been laid on nolibizing *S. spontaneum* suited to various requirements. IA (Indo-American) clones have resulted from cultivar × *S. spontaneum* crosses. Similarly, ISH (Inter-Specific Hybrids) have been produced utilizing various accessions from the germplasm collections. These have been extensively evaluated along with accessions of the basic species under various agro-climatic conditions at different stations of S.B.I., Coimbatore. Many of these ISH clones are now available in the National Hybridization Garden at Coimbatore for utilization by the breeders.

## 6. FLORAL BIOLOGY

Flowering in sugarcane is redundant for the commercial crop, but is necessary for breeding. Environments conducive to flowering are available only in tropical region. Yield and quality of the commercial crop show increases to decrease following flowering, depending upon the growing environment, genotype, stresses, etc. For the initial one to two months of flowering. there is no ill effect on yield and quality (Rao, 1968).

The study of floral biology is needed for manipulating natural flowering for making planned crosses. Interspecific hybridization in the earlier phase of breeding efforts and recent attempts at base-broadening by introgressing from members of *Saccharum* complex have required alteration of photoperiod for inducing flowering or pollen storage to effect crosses in India and other places. The specific requirement of photoperiod, moisture and temperature for flowering in sugarcane are naturally met between 10°N and 10°S of the equator. In the northern hemisphere, it takes place during October-November and in the southern hemisphere it occurs in May-June. Between 10-20° N and 10-20°S also, flowering occurs and the seed set is good. *S. spontaneum* clones tend to mature sooner than *S. robustum* clones which are, in turn, earlier than *S. officinarum* clones. Interspecific hybrids and the commercial clones are intermediate (Coleman, 1969). Generally, intensive flowering occurs only in early flowering clones (70-100%), while late flowering clones seldom have more than 30% flowering (citations in Moore and Nuss 1987). Although individual clones have a relatively short flowering season (2-3 weeks), the entire *Saccharum* complex has a long flowering season (5 to 6 weeks). The commercial varieties, which are interspecific hybrids, behave like the *Saccharum* complex.

The inflorescene of sugarcane is an open, branched panicle, termed an 'arrow' because of the shape and appearance. There are about 50,000-80,000 minute flowers in a panicle. The flowers are bisexual and normally fertile (Fig. 4). In most of the varieties fertile pollen is produced, and these varieties are used as male parents. In others, the pollen may be sterile or the anthers are closed and the pollen even if fertile is not released. Such varieties are used as seed parents.

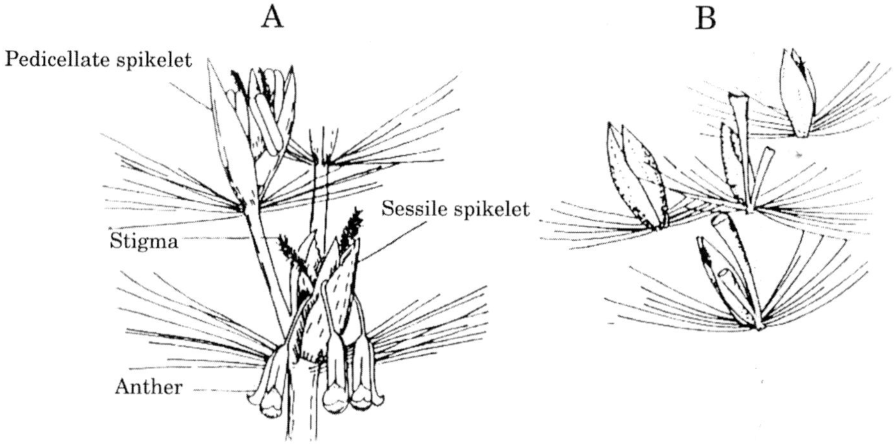


**Fig. 4 :** a) Part of inflorescence of sugarcane plant showing sessile and pedicellate spikelets, the sessile spikelet flowers before the pedicellate spikelet b) Fuzz or true seeds of sugarcane. The stalk of the pedicellate spikelet and a rachis segment ramains attached to the sessile spikelet. The pedicellate spikelet breaks free. The long silky hairs at the base permit the wind to carry the seed for long distances. (From 'Breeding Asian Field Crops', p. 243, Poehlman J.M. and Borthakur D. 1972, *Oxford & IBH Publishing* Co., New Delhi)

Factors determining floral induction and development include age, photoperiod, temperature, moisture and nutrition. The minimum age and the initiation of photoinduction period coincide with the formation of 2-4 mature basal internodes. The flowering stimulus generally occurs in the youngest, most rapidly expanding leaf exposed to the environment, primarily the top visible dewlap (TVD) blade. Generally, the older stalks are more vigorous and more likely to flower. Shortening photoperiods, resulting from a slow decrease in daylength from about

12 h 30 min, induce flowering. Flowering is best in areas where the daylength declines at a rate of 30 to 60 seconds/day from about 12 h 45 min (Berding, 1995). Flower induction requires about 12-½ hours of uninterrupted darkness in each 24 hours. While the timing of flowering is determined by photoperiod, intensity is affected by the temperature (Gosnell 1973). The temperature limits for flowering are 18° and 31°C, the optimum temperature being 23°C during night (Nuss, 1980) and 28°C during day (Clements and Awada, 1967). Low moisture during the initiation period reduces flowering. Adequate moisture is critical for initiation, panicle development, time of panicle emergence, and seed set (Moore and Nuss, 1987). High levels of nitrogen particularly at the time of initiation, may inhibit or delay flowering.

Photoperiod facilities have become an essential tool in several countries. These provide breeders with panicles at the required time and enable the use of parent clones that rarely flower in plots. In Florida, six of the last eight clones produced had at least one parent induced to flower in the photoperiod house. Similarly, in South Africa, clones N 24 to N 26 could not have been bred without such a facility. At Meringa, panicles were obtained in the facility from parent clones that had rarely flowered in Queensland (Nuss and Berding, 1999).

## 7. CROSSING/HYBRIDIZATION TECHNIQUES

### 7.1. Field Crossing

The sugarcane plant flowers when the crop is nearly 8 months old and 2 metres tall. The flowers are thus at an inconvenient height for crossing purpose. Movable ladders have been devised. At Coimbatore, the use of bamboo lanterns with an overhanging almunium cage frame over which cloth bag is put to enclose the arrow has been in vogue (Plate 2). Pollination is effected early in the morning before natural anthesis occurs. The flowering starts at the top of the arrow and proceeds downwards and takes about a week to complete. Flowers open between 5 and 6 A.M. Panicle branches of the parents to be used as males are clipped at this time. These are then induced to open and shed pollen under strong light of electric bulbs, which also provide the necessary warmth. Pollinations are effected on each lantern before the flowers close again. This procedure is repeated for 7 to 10 days till the flowering on each female arrow is complete. Seed matures in 3-4 weeks at which time the arrows are harvested and fluff or fuzz collected.

The availability of male-sterile varieties as female parents is an asset for making controlled crosses in sugarcane. There are innumerable minute spikelets in an inflorescence, making emascualtion very difficult and impractical. Protogyny is also observed in certain genotypes, such as Co 281. In majority of the cases, however, the female parents are chosen on the basis of their poor pollen fertility and it is presumed that on account of sugarcane's preference for foreign pollen, the extent of self-fertilization would be minimal.

## 7.2. Methods Using Detached Flowering Stalk

### 7.2.1. *Stalk preservation during crossing*

As mentioned earlier, sugarcane arrow is at a height that makes pollinations and the associated steps a tedious affair. The sulfurous acid technique for preservation of flowering stalks is in general use by sugarcane breeders. The solution was developed by Verret (1925) to assist in crossing work at the Hawaiin Sugarcane Planters' Association (HSPA) Experiment Station. Keeping arrows in sulfurous acid solution (1 part in 2000) kept inflorescence alive for several weeks. The addition of $H_3PO_4$ improved viability (Mangelsdorf, 1953). The solution used by HSPA consists of 150 ppm $SO_2$, 75 ppm $H_3PO_4$, and 37.5 ppm each of $H_2SO_4$ and $HNO_3$. Although the system is not commonly used, yet it has been successfully applied in West Indies. It was tried at Coimbatore in 1930 but did not give encouraging results. The reason was found to be the accumulation of sulphuric acid at the prevalent temperatures resulting in drying of isolated stalks.

### 7.2.2. *Marcotting*

A technique of isolating canes for subsequent crossing purposes through artificial rooting of standing canes was devised at the Sugarcane Breeding Institute, Coimbatore by Venkatraman and Thomas (1926). Stalks at the short blade or boot stage which are likely to emerge in two weeks time are chosen. Rooting is induced in the bottom-most 1 or 2 nodes by surrounding them with soil, held in place by alkathene which makes it possible to observe root development (Dutt and Hussainy, 1956).

After allowing nearly 3 weeks for rooting, the stalk is severed below the rooted node, and planted in bigger sized pots or in the ground for crossing. Marcotting was first used in India and is now practiced in many countries. In South Africa, (Nuss, 1979), stalks grown in the photoperiod facilities are cut when the inflorescene emerges. A plastic sleeve filled with rooting media is placed near the base of the stalk (marcotting), and then the base of the stalk is immersed in a sulfur dioxide crossing solution.

### 7.2.3. *Potted plants*

For clones and species not amenable to the sulfurous acid technique or marcotting, clones are grown in small containers that can be readily manipulated for crossing. At a newly developed crossing facility at Agali (Kerala), SBI has designed platforms with deep alleys for keeping potted plants such that the arrows are at the platform level to facilitate crossing (Plate 3).

## 7.3. Mating Systems

### 7.3.1. *Proven parent*

It is a parent whose progeny has a high proportion of desirable individuals. This essentially means a parent with high general combining ability. In Australia, a computerized system is in place to pick up parents based on selection rates, *i.e.*, the proportion of seedlings in each cross advanced from the original seedling stage of selection compared to the mean proportion of seedlings advanced for all crosses upto the same stage of selection. A proven parent is decided on multi-year data. Use is made of the polycross progeny to obtain information about breeding merit of different clones. In Hawaii, for identifying proven parents, clones that are promising are placed in a 'melting pot'. Those parents with the best selection record are propagated for further crossing. In India, most of the Co canes have come from this system. Experience shows that a good proven parent very often finds an entry into the list of proven crosses.

### 7.3.2. *Proven cross*

Similarly, a proven cross is one whose progeny consists of a high frequency of desired recombinants or clones of good commercial merit. This may involve parents which themselves may not be proven parents but which exhibit a high magnitude of specific combining ability. In Australia, the selection of proven cross is based on computerized selection rates, *i.e.*, the proportion of individual seedling in each cross advanced from the original seedling stage to the latest stage of selection.

### 7.3.3. *Biparental crosses*

Biparental crosses involve the crossing of two known parental clones and are probably the most widely used by sugarcane workers. The proven cross system is dependent on isolating known parents in pollen-proof enclosures. Pollen-proof enclosures made of cloth provide adequate protection against foreign pollen. In his study, Skinner (1959) used Q 44 as a male-sterile indicator and found that parchment bags and closely woven cloth were completely effective in excluding foreign pollen. Biparental crossing is routine method of mating.

### 7.3.4. *Melting pot / Polycross*

The first melting pot or polycross was set up in Hawaii in 1934. This procedure was first used for evaluating the breeding behaviour of a large number of canes at minimum expense (Warner, 1953). In practice, a group of select genotypes are planted side by side and replicated to ensure random mating. The genotypes included in a polycross are generally adapted and diverse proven parents. The seed is harvested from each genotype so that only the female parent is known with certainty. The method is akin to top cross and provides an estimate of the general combining ability of a parent.

### 7.3.5. *General collection*

General collection refers to harvesting of seed from an arrow that has been open-pollinated by pollen released by clones flowering at the same time in the crossing area. It is the least precise of the crossing techniques and represents one extreme of pollination control, the other being 'selfing'. Thèse two also represent two extremes with regards to the amount of seed set; the general collection being the most productive. Seed set, in general, is not as good when an arrow is enclosed in a bag

### 7.3.6. *Pollen storage*

Because sugarcane pollen is released at the tetrad stage, it is not amenable to storage. The longest period upto which pollen remains viable is 14 days (Sartoris, 1942; Moore, 1976).

## 8. BREEDING OBJECTIVES

Sugarcane is grown for sugar accumulated in its stem. The capacity to produce sugar as dry matter in varying environments is the object of selection for the breeders. The components of sugar yield, which constitute the major breeding objectives, are given below:

| | | | |
|---|---|---|---|
| Sugar yield | Cane yield → ρμα | Number of millable canes → | Germination, tillering ability, growth rate |
| | | Cane weight → | Cane height and girth, cane density, growth rate |
| | ρμ Sucrose % cane → | Juice percent cane → | Fibre content |
| | | Sucrose content in juice → | Sugar accumulation potential |
| | | Purity of juice → | Reducing sugars, Soluble non-sugars |

Further, unlike some other crops where no processing of the natural product is needed for its consumption, there are industrial requirements that affect the economics of sugarcane considerably. The most important of thèse requirements are the sucrose content and the fibre content, because they affect the milling quality and the sugar recovery. Minimal post-harvest deterioration in cane quality, although a desirable character, has not been specifically bred for.

## 8.1. Complementary Characters Affecting Sugar Yield

Biotic and abiotic stresses are important because sugarcane is a full year all season crop and is exposed to a wide range of pests and diseases. The pest and disease problems get aggravated because ratoon crop, which is an integral part of sugarcane cultivation, ensures continued availability of the host. From breeding point of view, red rot, smut, wilt, leaf scald, ratoon stunting disease, and mosaic are the major diseases. Among insect pests, termites, top borer and other borers, scale insects, pyrilla and nematodes are important. With sugarcane area having steadily increased over the years, its cultivation has extended to some poor and marginal soils, afflicted with stresses such as drought, water-logging, salinity, low-fertility soils, etc. Resilient germplasm has been identified for some of thèse stresses, but its efficacy as parental donor stock has not been fully established.

Ratooning ability is vitally important in sugarcane so much so that in some countries selection in the seedling generation is practised in the ratoon crop only. It is the ability of a genotype to produce high ratoon crop yields, which show minimal decline from its plant or younger crop's yield (Milligan *et al.,* 1996). Traits such as high stalk number, bud viability and sprouting under low temperature, vigorous root formation and high biomass accumulation have been suggested as being indicative of better ratooning varieties (Sundra, 1998).

# 9. BREEDING APPROACHIES IN SUGARCANE

## 9.1. Breeding Technique

### 9.1.1. *Inbreeding*

This is an extreme form of gentic assortative mating. The strongest proponent of inbreeding was Stevenson in Barbados. However, there are serious limitations specific to sugarcane which make the selfing technique unattractive as a general breeding approach. Inbreeding depression may limit severely the progeny that can be continually selfed. In the case of *S. officinarum,* selfing leads to loss of vigour. In contrast, *S. spontaneum* has not shown any inbreeding depression. Interspecific hybrids bear inbreeding quite well, without any loss of vigour (Stevenson, 1965; Rao, 1987 and Babu, 1990).

Inbreds have been used with great success as parents of commercial varieties, and also in the development of breeding canes, in several countries. In India Co 314, Co 348, Co 508 were released in 1930's as part of the inbreeding programme for possible commercial cultivation. Ethirajan *et al.* (1977) studied selfs of six hybrid commercial varieties upto $S_3$ generation. It was concluded that elite inbreds may prove good parents for obtaining early maturing, high quality varieties and diesase resistance. Today, selfing is not considered a practical approach for production of commercial varieties but is useful for development of breeding stocks.

### 9.1.2. *Hybridization/Backcrossing (Nobilization)*

The $F_1$ hybrids produced in India from the cross *S. officinarum* × *S. spontaneum* had clear drawbacks, such as high fibre, low sucrose content, high non-sugar fractions and thin stalks, contributed by the wild parent. The earlier varieties, Co 205 and Co 285, did replace the north Indian canes but had similar drawbacks. Backcrossing selected $F_1$'s to the noble parent was considered necessary to improve the commercially desirable attributes. However, the lack of understanding about making crosses at will by inducing and manipuating flowering and absence of facilities forced the use of *S. officinarum* clones other than the original used for backcrossing. This was called 'modified backcrossing'. In later years, adapted commercial hybrids were utilized for backcrossing instead of *S. officinarum* clones, particularly for breeding subtropical canes.

*S. officinarum* × *S. barberi* (Chunnee) crosses were initiated in Java by Kobus in 1897 to produce $F_1$ and backcrossing gernations. Backcross technique adopted by him was specially intended to eliminate undesirable characters of Chunnee. Jesweit adopted this method with *S. officinarum* × *S. spontaneum* crosses for diluting the *Spontaneum* influence in the process of back-crossing with noble canes, to achieve what the Java breeders termed as 'nobilization'. This process is essentially introgressive hybridization to produce an end product with no impairment to the original noble genotype but with the addition of just the favourable complement of non-*officinarum* genotypes.

### 9.1.3. *Recurrent selection*

Recurrent selection methods aim to exploit the general and specific combining ability of parents. Tysdal (1956) was the first to adopt this method in sugarcane. In practice, it involves the crossing of agronomically superior parents with those possessing the desired character, such as high sugar content. Selection is practised in the progenies for high sugar and those with good agronomical characters are intercrossed. A few repeated cycles of intercrossing and screening for high sugar content helps to realize the objective. In Louisiana, recurrent selection has been successfully done to improve sugar content. Improvement in quality of commercial varieties in Australia is attributable to a similar programme.

## 9.2. Supplementary Techniques

### 9.2.1. *Mutation breeding*

Mutation breeding in sugarcane is applied to create chromosomal or genic alterations and rearrangement in a well-bred adapted variety that needs minor genetic readjustment. Due to the complex genetic structure of the sugarcane plant, with a high degree of heterozygosity, polyploidy and cytogenetical pecularities, true breeding material is impossible to obtain. Consequently, the backcross method to eliminate a minor defect, as employed in other genetically well-behaved crops, is impractical in sugarcane. For that reason, mutation breeding has been used sporadically to incorporate resistance to a disease (Rao *et al.*, 1966), improve sugar content (Sankaranarayan and Babu, 1970) and inducing early repening (Jagathesan *et al.*, 1980)

The earlier attempts were made in Hawaii at HSPA, where in 1956, a morphologically distinct variant of H 37-1933, equal in yield to the original clone was obtained. The dose of radiation ranges between 2-10 Kr (citations in Heinz and Tew, 1987; Srivastava *et al.*, 1989). Since mutational changes are random, unintended useful changes may occur. For example, mutation to obtain a red-rot resistant mutant of CoJ 64, a high sugar early maturing red rot susceptible variety, did not succeed in inducing resistance but resulted in a higher yielding mutant which also proved to be better in its flowering behaviour (Shrivastava *et al.*, 1999).

Even though considerable effort has been devoted to mutagenesis in sugarcane, few mutants have occupied large area. Nair (1973) reported a red-rot resistant clone of Co 997, which was similar to the parent clone in yield, sucrose in juice, or commercial cane sugar per hectare. Jagathesan (1982) reported on selection of smut-resistant clones from irradiated susceptible clones. In China, Yuetangfu 83-5, released for commercial cultivation, was bred by repeated radiation method. The mutant showed superior performance for cane yield (7.4% higher) and sucrose content (1.5% higher).

### 9.2.2. *Tissue culture*

Hawaii again was the first to attempt tissue culture of sugarcane (Heinz and Mee, 1969). The chromosomal mosaicism of modern sugarcane hybrids is a built-in source of variants (Evans *et al.*, 1984). Various applications of tissue culture in sugarcane have mostly focussed on obtaining somaclonal variants. A wide range of somaclonal variants have been recovered for yielding ability, sugar quality, insect resistance, flowering, disease resistance, etc. However, not many somaclones have obtained the status of commercial varieties, though mutants and somaclones have enriched the breeding population.

Anther culture is another method of simplifying sugarcane breeding system. Haploids and doubled haploids both have a reduced number of alleles and could potentially substitute for inbred lines which do not exist in sugarcane (Moore *et al.*, 1989). However, success has been achieved in some accessions of *S. spontaneum* only (Fitch and Moore, 1996). Haploids do not flower well, but, in general, dihaploids are not only more vigorous but also flower better (Maretzki, 1987). Haploids have also been used to produce a low-density genomic map of *S. spontaneum,* using RFLPs.

Genetic transformation has been done with embryogenic callus as the recepient system and particle bombardment has been the norm. Stable transformation has been obtained in Australia using gènes for herbicide resistance, but the transformation efficiency is not very high (Birch, 1997). Regeneration from protoplasts has been reported, but there are very few reports of transformation using protoplasts.

Short-and long-term conservation of germplasm has been used in sugarcane in view of the problems of maintaining healthy planting material/propagules. Shoot tip cultures, induced to grow at a very slow rate have been suggested as a means of short-term preservation of germplasm (Sreenivasan and Sreenivasan, 1985; Taylor and Dukic, 1993). Sugarcane apices have been stored at low temperature for long-term storage (Paulet *et al.,* 1993).

### 9.2.3. *Molecular techniques*

Sugarcane has benefited significantly from the emerging molecular techniques. Earlier the genomic identity of the chromosomes with regards to the species was not known. Now specific molecular markers for chromosomes of *S. spontaneum* and *S. officinarum* have allowed knowledge of the proportion of these chromosomes in interspecific commercial hybrids (D'Hont *et al.,* 1996). Phylogenetic relationships are also slowly unfolding. Application of molecular techniques for genomic analysis has yielded results for elucidating cytoplasmic and nuclear polymorphisms, genome mapping, comparative mapping of related species, identification of parental chromosomes in introgression breeding and, marking desired traits for selection (Eksomtramage *et al.,* 1992; citations in Berding *et al.,* 1997).

## 9.3. Genetics of Economie Characters in Sugarcane

### 9.3.1. *Inheritance studies*

Sugarcane is not an ideal plant for genetic studies. Polyploidy, aneuploidy, multivalent formation, multiple species origin, autosyndetic pairing, lack of random mating, partial male fertility, selfing, etc., hamper conduct of genetic studies and interpretation of data. Many mating designs used in quantitative studies can not be attempted because the underlying assumptions are not easily fulfilled. However, Combstock and Robinson's Design II, which is a factorial mating design is suited for sugarcane. Despite the violation of genetic assumptions, the design does give valid information about the non-additive variance from the interaction between the male and female parents (Hogarth, 1987). Mid-parent-offspring regression is yet another useful parameter that provides an estimate of narrow-sense heritability and can be applied on an individual or family basis.

If performance of the seedling can be predicted from the attributes of the parents, most of the genetic effects must be additive, and there will be a high heritability in narrow sense for that character. On the other hand, non-additive genetic control results in low estimates of heritability, as do environmental influences. Inbreeding depression is another indication of the nature of gène control. Cane yield and its components, stalk diameter, stalks per plant and stalk number and stalk length showed inbreeding depression (Hogarth, 1980; Wu *et al.,* 1980). Brix, an indirect indication of sucrose content, has been found to be under additive genetic control and showed no apparent depression. Available evidence suggests that selection of parents for sugar content should be successful, but progeny testing would seem to be necessary for yield of cane. Since sufficient additive genetic variance exists for cane yield, some success shall be achieved in selecting parents for yield.

Unlike other crops, simple inheritance for resistance is not common in sugarcane. A knowledge of the mode of inheritance is probably more important when breeding for disease resistance than any other character. Smut, rust, Fiji disease and the like are relatively simply inherited and predominantly under additive genetic control (Hogarth, 1977; Reimers *et al.,* 1982; Stevenson *et al.,* 1972; Wu *et al.,* 1980). Selection of resistant parents will lead to substantial progress. In comparison, red rot has been responsible for elimination of several varieties. Breeding for resistance to red rot is complicated by the fact that several races of the fungus are involved. Resistant parents produce resistant or moderately resistant progeny. Resistant progeny is also recovered from susceptible × susceptible crosses. In a directed breeding programme for red rot resistance conducted at Sugarcane Breeding Institute from 1976 to 1982, it appeared possible to build up a source population to incorporate genes for resistance. Alexander *et al.* (1979) initiated a programme to develop broad-based resistance against two or more major pathotypes of red rot. However, the use of parents developed for horizontal resistance has not been successful for improving resistance in the progeny. Another reason that has retarded development of suitable varieties is the imprecise screening techniques for red rot.

Unpublished studies in Australia on the mode of inheritance of fibre percent fresh weight show that almost 80 percent of the genetic variance is additive. Hence selection of parents for low or high fibre should be effective in producing the desired level of fibre in the progeny. For characters such as yield, for which about 50% of the genetic variance is non-additive, even less pressure should be put on parent selection.

### 9.3.2. *Character associations/genetic correlations*

Information and understanding of interrelationships among characters are important to aid selection and set limits of each economic character that a breeder can choose without adversely affecting another important character. Invariably, in the well-bred populations, the association between productivity and quality are negatively correlated because both depend on the same photosynthetic process for their substrate. Quality, because it is end result of a highly involved metabolic process, is much more difficult to improve and comes at a much higher energy cost to plant. For yield components, there is lot of mutual compensation, especially in a long duration crop like sugarcane. Nevertheless, selection indices have been made use of in sugarcane (Miller *et al.,* 1972; Pillai and Ethirajan, 1993).

## 9.4. The Breeding Procedure for Varietal Development

The success of sugarcane breeding depends on the choice of parents, making crosses, raising adequate population, and making selection. Every year a breeder attempts 15-20 crosses involving proven parents, varieties or repeats of proven crosses, and makes several scores of experimental crosses. The population size of the proven crosses is large (in the order of $10^3$) to increase chances of getting the desirable recombinants, while those from experimental crosses rarely exceed 500, more commonly around 100 or so. A population size of 75 is considered adequate to assess the worth of a cross. Intervarietal crossing is in vogue. Consideration for selecting a parent are its adaptation in the target area, productivity and quality, ratooning ability, disease resistance, stress tolerance, etc.

Sugarcane seed does not exhibit any dormancy and can be sown immediately. This happens in northern hemisphère in December/ January. In subtropical parts, fluff is not sown before February/March. Since sugarcane seed is very small, gemination is recorded as the number of seedling obtained per gram of seed. The attached hairs harbour pathogens and it is preferable to use defuzzed seed which can then be better treated with a fungicide. Sowing is done in specially prepared seed beds filled with soil and sand mixture. After sowing, seed-beds are covered with polythene sheets to ensure warmth and humidity for good germination.

Seedlings are hardy enough to be transplanted in the field after two to three months. Generally, transplanting is done when the monsoon just sets in so as to maximize survival in the field. Seedlings must be space planted to permit close examination of each seedlings. Most often, seedlings are transplanted individually but one of the methods practised in Hawaii is to transplant seedling in bunches of 3 to 15 per hill.

Selection in the seedling generation ($C_0$) is done either in the plant crop or the ratoon crop of seedling. In any case, it is done after the grand growth period when the drop in atmospheric temperatures promotes sugar accumulation. Although the reliability of selection at this stage is low, it also happens to be the most crucial stage, for a genotype discarded at this stage is permanently lost. Therefore, a liberal selection pressure at this stage is advisable. In some countries, selection does not start before the cane is in clonal stage. Yet, even there, some means of reducing the huge seedling population is employed. In general, when one is breeding a variety, seedlings are selected for growth vigour and this helps reduce the population by 50-60%. Bunch planting is a method to handle very large number of seedlings. In close planted nurseries and bunch plantings, selections are usually represented by single canes in order to minimize errors in establishing parentage.

A general scheme of steps involved in varietal development is presented below (Fig. 5). The number of years involved would vary from place to place depending on the crop duration.

## 9.5. Selection at the Seedling Stage

Selection in original seedling is the least effective of all stages of selection because broad-sense heritabilities are low for most characters. Seedling are influenced considerably by the environment so much so that only 20-30% of the variability is genetic. This renders selection for characters of low heritabilities very unreliable. A perusal of various estimates of broad-sense heritabilities for different characters shows that these are very low on individual basis but much better on family basis. This implies that characters with low heritabilities such as yield, vigour, cane weight, stalk number can be selected for at the level of family. Individual selection for traits of greater heritabilities, such as brix and stalk diameter, may be carried out with greater confidence (Skinner *et al.*, 1987). Letter (1964) considered that, when heritability is in excess of 0.5, individual selection is superior to family selection. The early stages are the most cost effective for screening against diseases.

Marioti (1987) estimated that to guarantee capture of the truely best 10% individuals in a seedling population, a selection rate of 30% is required at the degree of genetic determination (DGD) as high as 0.8%, and of course still higher with lower levels of DGD. Generally, the selection intensity at this stage is 10-30%. The approach in India is also to practice lenient selection pressure on the seedlings in closely spaced nursery, carrying a high proportion forward to the first clonal planting. It takes care of the doubts about the correlation between the growth from cuttings and the original seedling. The practice to select in the ratoon crop of seedling is also a means to improve association between seedling and clonal generation.

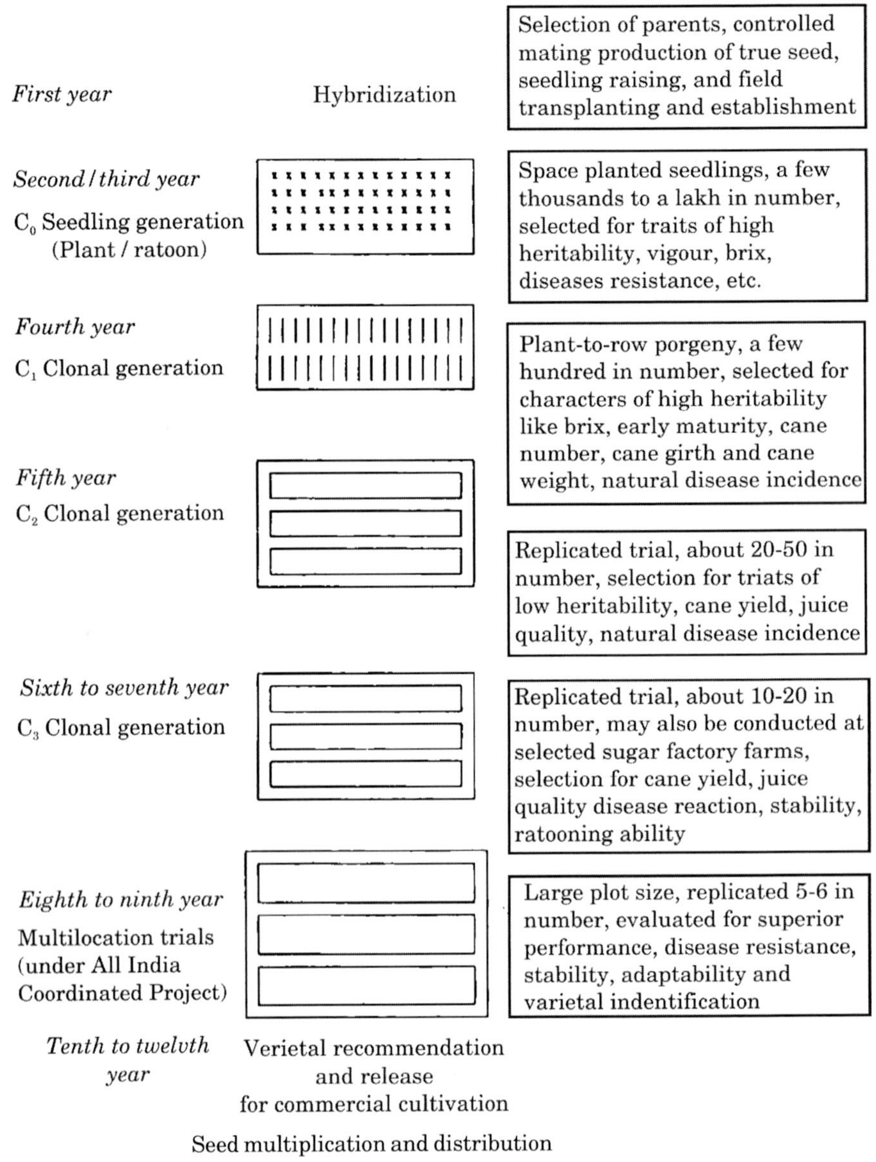


**Fig. 5:** Steps (generalized) in the making of a sugarcane variety.

The adverse effect of intergenotypic competition can be minimized by space planting of seedlings (Kapur and Bhat, 1986). It has been shown that the bunch planting method is inefficient as compared to space planted seedling, unless selection rates are high enough. The elimination of seedling in a bunch is random, pointing to the likehood of losing potential genotypes (Skinner, 1971).

## 9.6. Selection in Clonal Generations

As the quantity of seed from each selection increases, it permits conduct of progressively larger plots with great number of replications within and over years and locations. Lin and Poushinsky (1983) described a modified augumented design originally given by Federer in 1965 which is (Federer, 1965) suitable for early stages of selection in sugarcane. It involves replicated standard varieties and large numbers of unreplicated test lines, the control plots being used to adjust for environmental variation. In order to improve the efficacy of selection, it has been suggested that the mean of a range of standards be used in replicated trials since a single standard is prone to G × E interactions (Simmonds 1979). Skinner (1972) indicated that G × E interactions would have resulted in the rejection of a high proportion of commercial varieties in Australia if only varieties equal or superior to the commercial standard has ben selected. Kapur *et al.* (1998) tried to highlight the error in judgement of the merit of the new varieties in the pipeline stemming from the use of deteriorated standards. It was strongly suggested that the seed of check varieties should be used only after periodic heat treatment.

In India, an All India Coordinated Research Project for sugarcane is in operation since 1966 with the object of testing new technologies developed at various research stations over a wider range of locations. There are five agroclimatic zones, *viz*, North Western, North Central, North Eastern, Peninsular and Coastal zone. Breeders propose promising entries for their particular zone for testing in this system at several participating locations. It comprises of evalution at two stage — a preliminary trial and the final evaluation trial in which the plot size is 6 rows of 8 metres each in a completely randomized block design with four replications. Data are generated for two plant crops and one ratoon crop on all the important economic characters and reaction/natural incidence/infestation to important diseases and pests. A variety is identified on the basis of pooled data from all the locations within a zone. It is then up to the Varietal Release Committe at the national level or the state level to take up each case and recommend the release of a variety for commercial cultivation. This programme has resulted in most of the new varieties coming form regional stations, carrying a suffix next to Co in their names.

## 9.7. Efficiency in Sugarcane Breeding

An advantage with sugarcane breeding is that once a seedling is identified as a potential variety, its genotype is fixed and the maintenance of its genetic potential is a matter of management of its production environment. The most crucial stage is the seedling generation because it represents the entire range of variability present in the population and has the lowest selection efficiency. Each genotype is individually represented. A balance bas to be struck since all measures to enhance its genotypic expression through reducing competition and stressful environment remove it from the actual condition of commercial cultivation. Usually, resources dictate the quality of experimentation. Breeding efficiency in sugarcane may be expressed as follows :

Breeding Efficiency = Transmission Efficiency + Selection Efficiency

(BE) (TE) (SE)

TE and SE are in turn dependent on several characters. Transmission efficiency is dependent on breeding value, meiotic regularity, random mating, seed set and seed quality of a parent. TE is improved with the parent building programme as discussed previously. Selection efficiency is influenced by heritability of a character. Therefore, all those techniques that reduce the influence of environment, G × E, competition etc. shall improve the heritability and thus selection efficiency (Kapur *et al.,* 1998).

## 9.8. Factors Favourably Affecting Selection Efficiency

### 9.8.1. *Cross appraisal for family selection*

Accurate prediction of performance of parental combinations would yield tremendous returns in any crop improvement programme. Despite the fact that computer programmes have been developed, crosses are still decided by breeders' consensus. Chang and Milligan (1992) found that the estimation of the sum of ranks based on family mean values for two individual traits gave accurate prediction of family potential. Family selection is the best means of improving selection efficiency, particularly when low heritability and competition make individual selection unreliable.

### 9.8.2. *Correlated response or use of markers*

Fortunately, sugar content is not influenced by the environment to the same extent as cane yield and is predominantly under the additive gène control. It is indirectly assessed in the field by a hand-held refractometer, which measures total soluble solids (TSS) in the juice on a 0-32 scale. Brix value (in %) has a high correlation with sugar content in cane juice (0.90-0.097). The correlation improves with cane ripening. Refractometer brix has by far been and shall continue to be a very useful correlated character in sugarcane.

Another pair of characters with good association is fibre content and rind hardness. The measurement of rind hardness is non-destructive and conveniently made on intact cane. The correlation between rind hardness and fibre content is high enough to be very useful for screening large number of varieties for fibre percent (Davidson, 1969; Bhat *et al.,* 1985). Walker (1971) found correlations of about 0.6 between fibre content and rind hardness, estimated by resistance to the hand stabber used for extracting juice samples for brix readings. Rind hardness has also been correlated with stem borer tolerance (Rao, 1951). Duttamajumder *et al.* (1999) have, however, held that stabber/piercer is responsible for transmitting mosaic and leaf scald and is a potential source of spread of incipient infection from clone to clone. From a breeder's point of view, this amounts to inadvertent inoculation and screening for resistant genotypes. Recently, Double and Balasundram (1999) have proposed the use of discriminant function in sugarcane for increasing selection efficiency.

### 9.8.3. *Multi-environment testing*

Although time consuming and costly, multi-environment testing helps separate out effects of G × E and identify environments that can best exploit the genetic potential of a genotype. Ratoon performance is like multi-year testing, but for the fact that the effects due to ratooning ability and year get confounded. Therefore, in sugarcane, as soon as facilities permit and the number of selections has been reduced to a manageable level, sugar mills or other research stations are involved in location testing within the zone.

### 9.8.4. *Technological advances*

Biochemical markers have been around for quite some time but have not become a routine. Thèse have been used to establish distinctness of various clones. Biotechnology offeres selection procedures, which are inherently different from traditional procedures. Lee (1995) described four major applications of DNA markers: (i) assessment of genetic diversity and merit (ii) characterization of plant genomes (iii) analysis of complex traits and processes and (iv) marker-assisted selection. The apparent slow application of molecular markers to sugarcane (Moore, 1996) is due to complex polyploidy and difficulty of identifying traits coded by major genes. Marker-assisted sugarcane breeding has been used to select out hybrids from the progeny and to pinpoint selfs in a hybrid progeny between *S. spontaneum* and commercial hybrids (Pan and Legendre, 1999).

The most promising application is *bulk segregant analysis* as an alternative to marker analysis. This technique has been used to detect polymorphisms in bulked DNA from individuals of extreme fibre values within a family (Msomi and Botha, 1994). Molecular markers have been used to detect DNA of a foreign genome (smut) in sugarcane. This has great potential in diagonstics and quarantine. Technological advances in computers, mechanization of cane cultivation, and near infra-red spectroscopy for analysis of sugarcane quality are finding increasing application in sugarcane.

## 10. BREEDING ACHIEVEMENTS

Sugarcane yields are among the highest for any crop. Being a C4 plant, it is an efficient converter of solar energy. Nevertheless, record yields are only approximately 65% of the theoretical maximum (Moore *et al.*, 1997). If all the factors are favourable, the physiological yield potential of 12 months' sugarcane crop is worked out to be 340 t/ha. The highest cane yield of 214 metric tonnes per hectare is in Hawaii having tropical conditions and 24 months of age at harvest. Many farmers in tropical region of India achieve yield levels of around 250 t/ha. In national competitions, Maharashtra farmers have obtained 338 t/ha cane yield (Hapse, 1999). However, annualized average cane yields for different countries vary between 40 to 95 t/ha (Fry, 1999, Fig. 6). With regards to sugar content and sugar yield, while Columbia has the highest sugar yield. Australia has the highest sugar content in cane (Fig. 7).

With regards to sugar accumulation, which is the single most important character, efforts have been made to hasten maturity mostly at the cost of cane yield since it reduces the time span for active growth. This line of breeding has been an industrial requirement since the mills must start as early and for as long as permitted by the biology of the crop. As a result, development of early maturing varieties is viewed not only as a necessity but also as the evolution of a more efficient plant type. A matching replacement of the high sugar early commercial wonder CoJ 64 has not been found in more than three decades. This is not because of failure to get high sugar genotypes but inability to combine this trait with the other required attributes of commercial variety. Disease resistance has been the biggest bottleneck in this effort. The difficulty arises because gènes for sugar content are derived from *S. officinarum* and those for resistances corne from *S. spontaneum,* and the two types

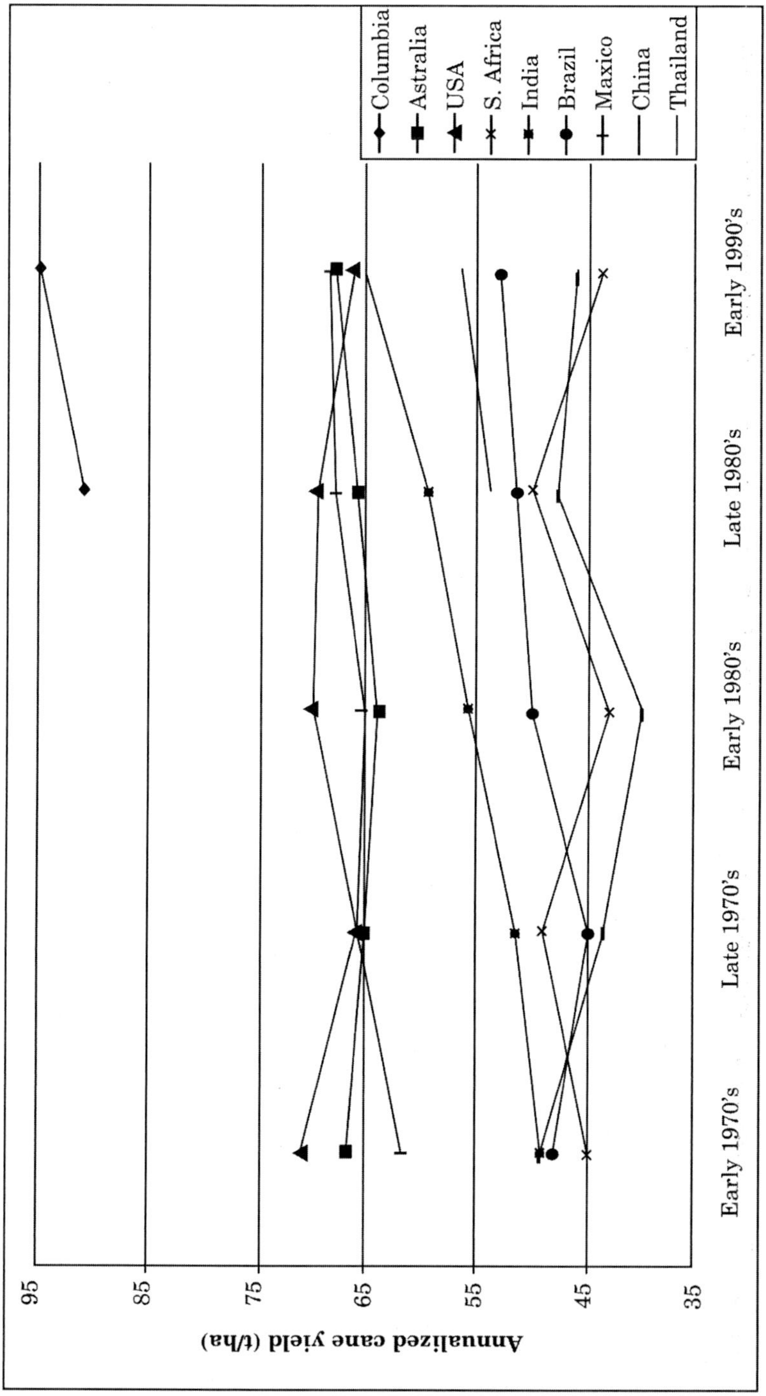


**Fig. 6:** Annualized cane yield of principal sugarcane growing countries (Adapted from Fry (1999)).

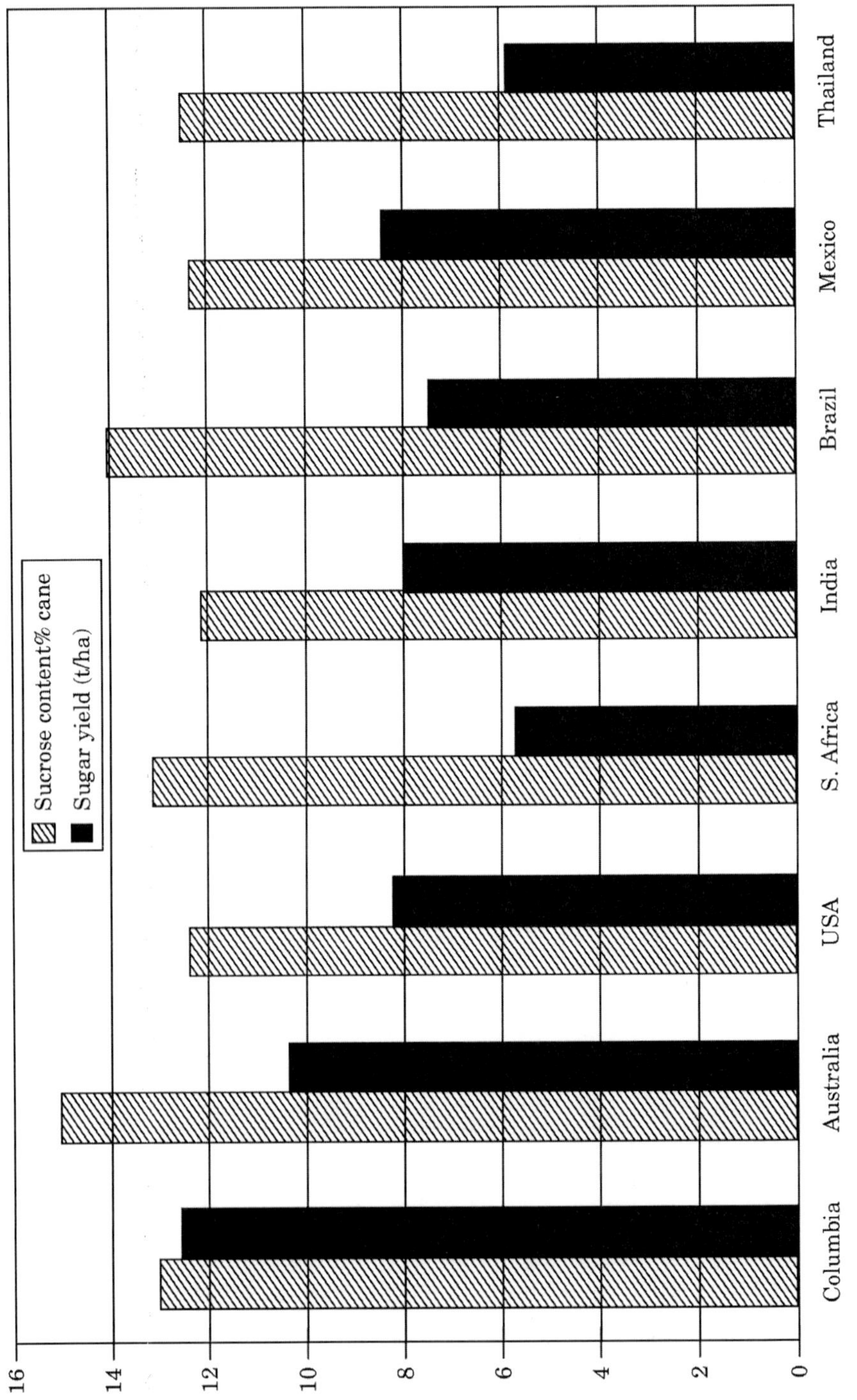


**Fig. 7:** Sugar content and productivity of principal sugarcane growing countries (Adapted from Fry, 1999)

are hard to recombine because of a very limited segmental exchange between chromosomes of the two genomes.

There was a steady improvement in cane yield and sugar content in the early years of breeding and selection programme. This was achieved through intercrossing of the derivatives of original hybrids and selection from large populations in different environments. However, starting from mid-fifties through sixties all major countries were concerned about slow genetic gains. Sugarcane Research Stations of Hawaii and Lousiana were the first to change their strategies (Sreenivasan and Bhagyalakshmi, 1997). Most of the countries have made genetic gains in sugar yields since then, but many have achieved it through improved cane yields (such as Hawaii, India, Barbados). On the other hand, Australia, Louisiana and Taiwan have been successful in improving sugar content of cane, along with the cane yield. Improvements in early sucrose in Taiwan between 1959 and 1994, reviewed by Lo and Chen (1995) showed 4% units improvement in early season and 2% units increase at peak maturity. In 1950's, Louisiana adopted recurrent selection programme to improve cane yield and sucrose. The elegant use of recurrent selection spanning over a period of over 60 years involving five selection cycles in Louisiana is an exemplary breeding effort. There was a 31-39% increase over five breeding cycles, with progress lessening with each successive cycle. Sucrose % cane increased from a mean of 10.8 to 14.1 (Legendre, 1995).

Starting from 1950's, the Hawaiian Sugar Planters' Association (HSPA) introduced the polycross system with emphasis on continued introduction of new germplasm and a planned programe of recurrent selection for yield (as sugar per hectare). In Hawaii, sucrose yield, showed a long term uptrend from 1912 to 1994, with a peak of 13.6 t/ha in 1988 to 12.0 t/ha/yr in 1994 (Berding *et al.,* 1997). In Australia, the cane yields increased by 1.9% per annum from 1948 to 1975, of which 50% may be due to genetic improvement. According to Berding and Skinner (1987), the varietal change from Pindar to Q 90 in Northern Queensland resulted in an improvement of 31% in sugar yield.

In India, the dramatic success of the earlier hardy Co varieties in totally replacing the indigenous cultivars of sub-tropical India is well-known. The following decade wise appraisal spanning over half a century, provides testimony to the sugarcane/sugar revolution that was ushered into the country as early as the 40's. Between 1930 to 1956 area under sugarcane increased by 143.3%, cane production by 290%, sugar production by 525%, yield by 100% and sugar recovery by 17.5%. There has, however, been little improvement in sugar recovery all these years (Fig. 8).

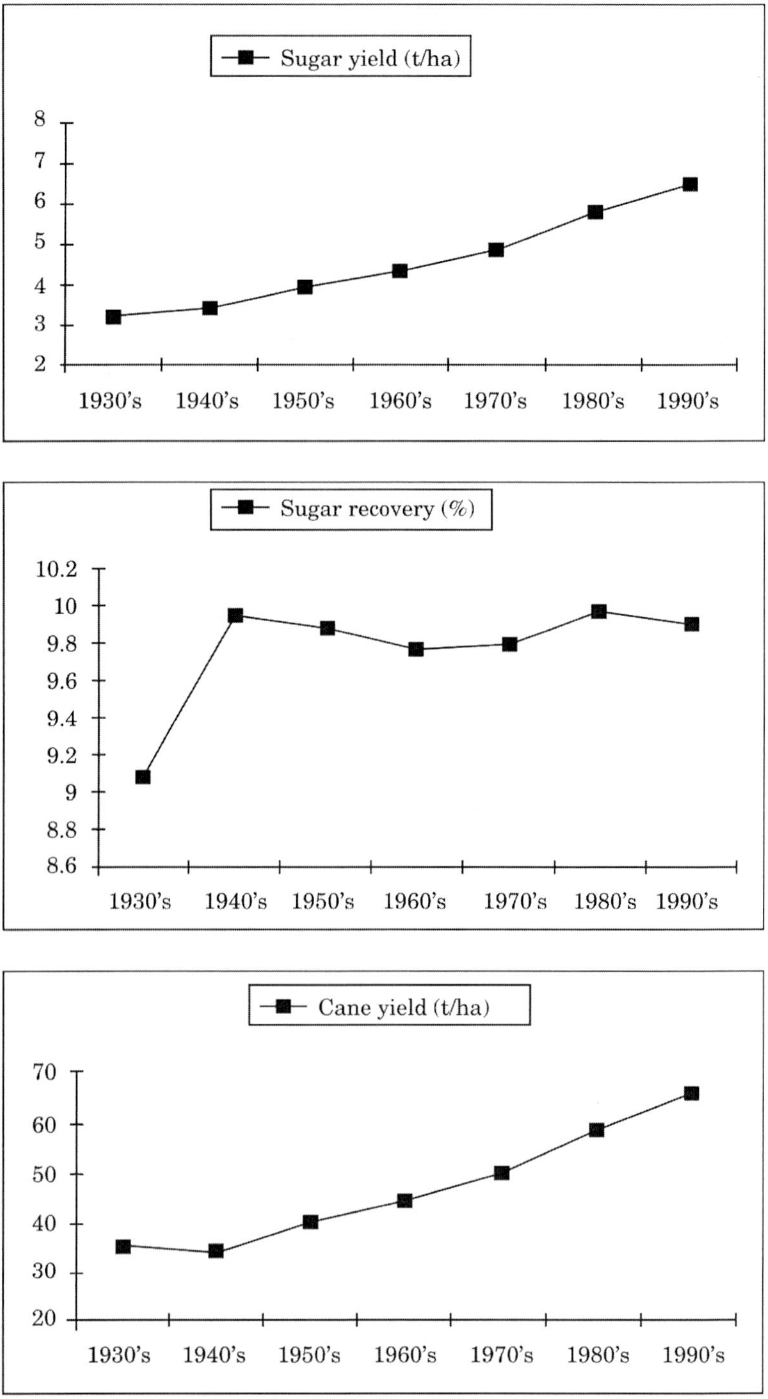


**Fig. 8.** Sugarcane improvement in India over the decades (Adapted from Indian Sugar, 1998)

## 11. VARIETIES

It is well recognized that sugarcane varieties have played a substantial role in the increase in productivity. Coupled with good cultivation conditions, genetic improvement has been responsible for 50-75% of the increase. Interestingly, all the commercial varieties world over, can be traced back to Co (Coimbatore, India and POJ (Proefstation Oost Java) canes. The most common is perhaps POJ 2878. A closer look at the pedigrees of varieties in different countries highlights the small number of accessions of the basic species that make-up the genetic base of the present day varieties. This also reveals the vast reservoir of genetic variability afforded by polyploidy and heterozygosity in the original clones to have sustained the steady genetic advances made till date.

Another feature that can be noticed is that a variety bred in one environment may adapt better in other areas. NCo 310 is one such variety, which is being grown in several countries. The same is true for Coimbatore and Barbados varieties. Interestingly, the leading varieties in mainland China (F 134), Indonesia (F 154) and Thailand (F 140) are from Taiwan. All three are major sugar producers with much larger area than Taiwan, providing evidence that the benefits of a breeding effort can be far reaching even when this may not have been anticipated (Tew, 1987). Most sugarcane growing countries now desist depending heavily on a single variety for fear of disease epidemics.

### 11.1. Indian Varietal Scenario

The first variety bred at Coimbatore, Co 205, due to its inherent superiority, was accepted by the farmers of old Punjab and replaced the local Katha. In 1928, Co 312 was released which reigned for nearly three decades. Co 285 was taken to Cuba and Florida for commercial cultivation. Co 356, highly resistant to borers and moderately resistant to red rot wilt, and smut was released and occupied a prominent position in the terai areas of Eastern Uttar Pradesh. Currently, varieties bearing the suffix of the research station, such as CoC, CoJ, CoLk, CoPant, CoS, etc. are among the commercially released varieties in different states. Among those that have left a mark are Co 312, Co 419, Co 740, Co 975, Co 1148, CoC 671, CoJ 64, CoS 767, and BO 91.

### 11.2. Naming of Sugarcane Varieties

An alphanumeric system of designating clones has been adopted since early 1900's wherein the first one to three capitalized letters refer to the place of origin, a two digit year designation, and a selection number.

Another system involves a call number and a series number, *e.g.*, Q 107. Two organizations continue to prefer giving names to released varieties, Colonial Sugar Refiners Ltd. *e.g.*, Trojan, and Fiji Sugar Corportion Ltd. Fijian islands, *e.g.*, Mana.

**Call sign of hybrid varieties**

| *Call sign* | *Example* | *Origin of Fuzz Suffix : site of selection* | *Organi -zation* | *Country* |
|---|---|---|---|---|
| B | B 37172 | Barbados | BSSCVTS | Barbados |
| BO | BO91 | Pusa, Bihar | | India |
| C | C87-51 | Cuba, Central Jaranu | INICA | Cuba |
| CB | CB49-260 | Brazil, Campes, Rio de Janeiro | EECRJ | Republic of Brazil |
| Cl | Cl 59-1052 | Clewiston, Florida | USDA | USA |
| CO | Co 1148 | Coimbatore | ICAR | India |
| | CoA 7601 | Anakapalle, Andhra Pradesh | | |
| | CoC 671 | Cuddlore, Tamil Nadu | | |
| | CoJ 64 | Jalandhar, Punjab | | |
| | CoLk 8001 | Lucknow, U.P. | | |
| | CoH 70 | Haryana | | |
| | Co Pl | Pusa, Bihar | | |
| | CoPant 84211 | Pantnagar, U.P. | | |
| | CoS 767 | Shahjahanpur, U.P. | | |
| | CoSe 92423 | Seorahi, Uttar Pradesh | | |
| | CoSi 86071 | Sirugamani, Tamil Nadu | | |
| | CoT 8201 | Tirupati, Andhra Pradesh | | |
| CP | CP 70-1133 | Canal Point, USA | USDA | USA |
| F | F 160 | Formosa, Taiwan | TSRI | ROC |
| G | G68-88 | Egypt, Giza | SCR1 | Egypt |
| H | H 1462-4621 | Hawaii | HSPA | USA |
| M | M2173/63 | Mauritius | MSIRI | Mauritius |
| Mex | Mex57-473 | Mexico | 1MPA | Mexico |
| N | N14 | South Africa | SASA | South Africa |
| NCo | NCo 310 | India, Coimbatore | SASA | South Africa |
| POJ | POJ 2878 | East Java | POJ | Indonesia |
| Q | Q63 | Queensland | BSES | Australia |
| ROC | ROC5 | Taiwan | TSRI | Republic of China |
| Tue | Tuc68-19 | Argentina, Tucuman | EEAOC | Argentina |

Adapted from Tew (1987)

## 11.3. Varietal Description and Pedigree

Excellent manuals have been brought out by SBI, Coimbatore describing varieties developed till recently. An example is reproduced hère for giving an idea of the descriptors used and the involved pedigree of sugarcane varieties (Fig. 9a,b). With the advent of the era of intellectual property rights, there is an attempt now to prepare DNA finger prints of new varieties (Chang and Fu, 1999). This would have another useful spin-off benefit in establishing whether or not varietal decline in sugarcane is attributable to genetic changes as well.

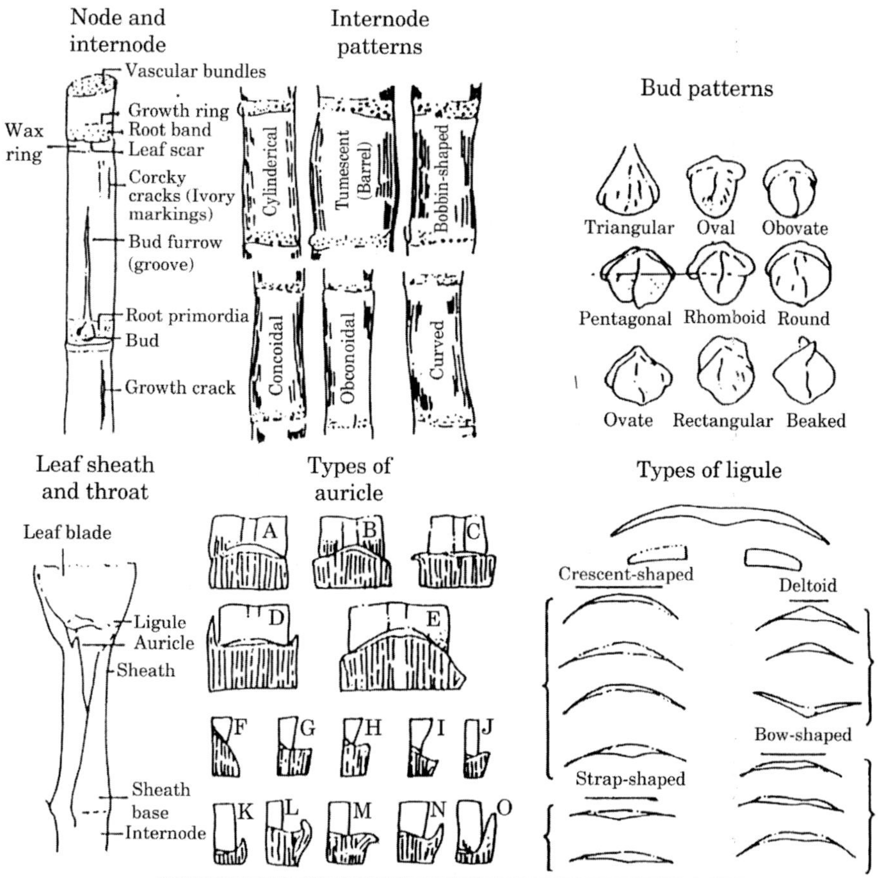


(a) Auricle absent, (b) Auricle transitional (c) Inner auricle calcarate, (d) Both auricles lanceolate (e) Both auricles transitional but inner one with small deltoid hood inserted low, (f) Sloping transitional, (g) Straight transitional, (h) Ascending transitional, (i) Dentoid (j) Dentoid, (k) Short lanceolate, (l) Uniciform, (m) Calcarate, (n) Falcate (o) Long lanceolate

(After Artschwager and Brandes 1958)

**Fig. 9a:** Morphological descriptors used in sugarcane

## 11.4. Variety Maintenance and Seed Increase

Seed multiplication rate in sugarcane is 1:8-10 by conventional methods of planting a three-budded stem cutting called sett. This introduces a long gestation period (generally about 3-5 years) between the release of a variety and its cultivation on a commercial scale. The process is land, money and time consuming. Options which ensure a seed multiplication rate of 1:30-40 are now available to hasten process. Thèse techniques, such as spaced transplanting technique (STP), polybag method, bud chip, etc., make use of the single budded sett. In contrast, *in vitro* seed multiplication under aseptic conditions called 'micropropagation' is now a well-established technology in sugarcane. This employs the apical meristem or the shoot-tip as the starting material and has a potential of giving in a year planting material for six hectares from one shoot-tip. A greater advantage is that the resulting planting material is free from diseases and pests.

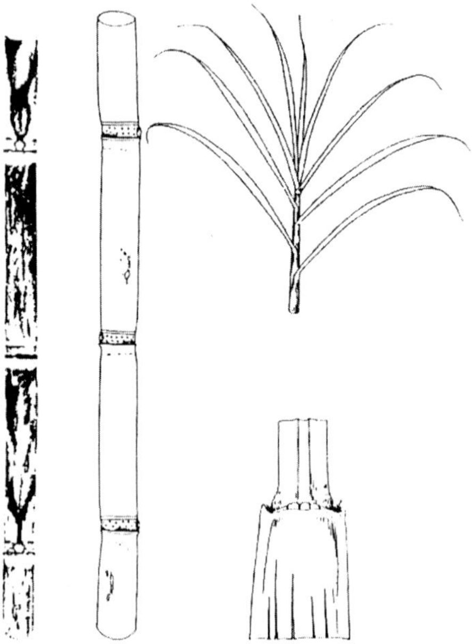

**Fig. 9b:** (*Contd...*)

Seed quality in sugarcane is very important. Being vegetatively propagated, a variety is generally maintained live in the field, where it is prone to attacks by diseases and pests. These cryptic infections along with several other known and unknown factors keep a genotype from performing to its true potential and lead to a phenomenon called 'varietal decline'. Varieties differ in their rate of decline. The less hardy ones requiring high management decline much faster. This implies that seed programme must be much stronger and strictly followed. This unfortunately is wanting. Consequently, potential of a new variety is rarely realized. A moist hot air treatment (MHAT) of seed canes is recommended for the nucleus seed. This helps to control ratoon stunting disease, smut, GSD, leaf scald, etc. The fact that the potential of a variety

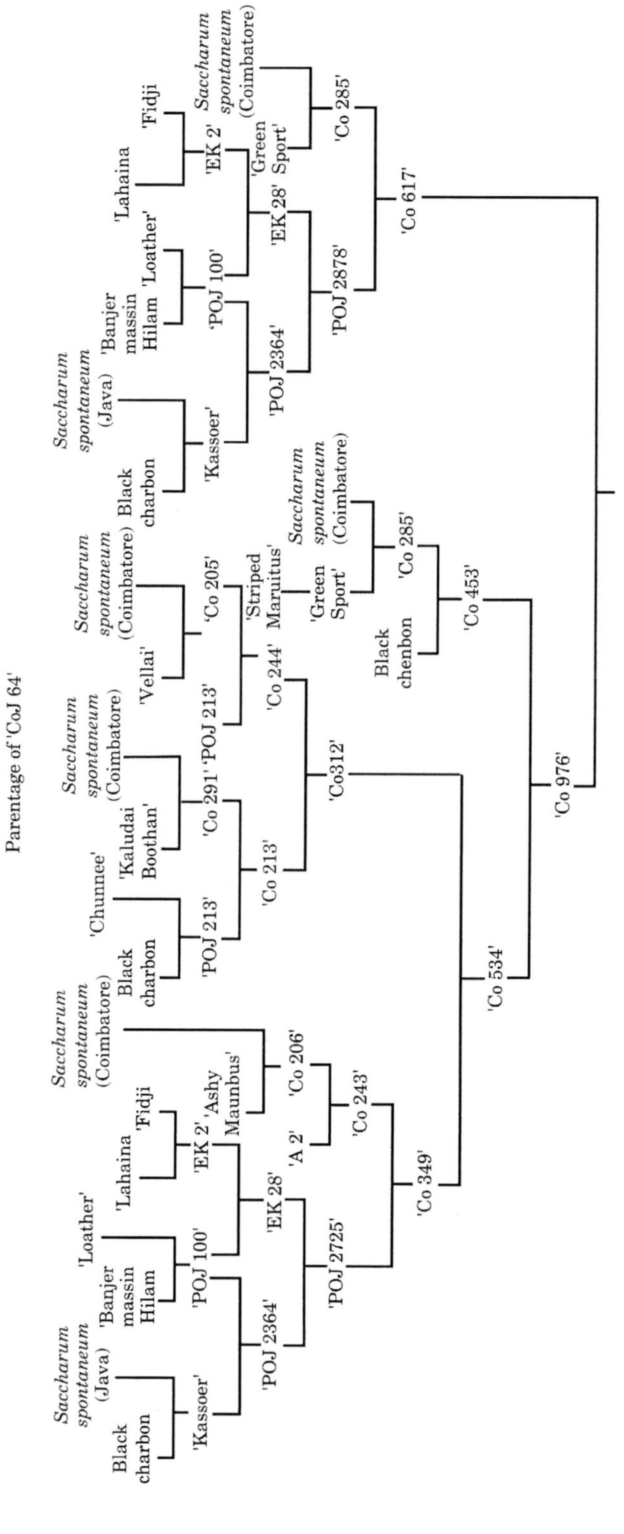


**Fig. 9b:** Pedigree of a popular north Indian sugarcane variety (From : Sugarcane Varieties under Cultivation in India, by P. Sankaranarayan, B.V. Natarajan and S. Marimuthammal, ICAR, New Delhi, 1986, pp. 53)

can be largely restored by seed treatment (MHAT or micropropagation) and crop sanitation, suggests that the reason for varietal deterioration are largely not genetic. A generalized scheme is given for the efficient production of sugarcane seed.

**Quality seed production in sugarcane**

| *Year* | *Type of seed* | *Area* | *Particulars* |
|---|---|---|---|
| First | Breeder's | 1 ha | Crop raised from micropropagated plantlets, Moist hot-air/aerated steam treated source material |
| Second | Foundation | 0-40 ha | STP/polybag/bud-chip nursery raised, settling transplanted seed crop |
| Third | Certified | 1000 ha | Seed for commercial crop |

Kapur and Lai (1999)

## 12. FUTURE RESEARCH DIRECTIONS

The Indian sugar scenario is projected in the 'Vision 2020: HSR Perspective Plan', ICAR (1997), keeping in view the population growth, per capita consumption and export obligations. It is projected that the total sweetener requirement (sugar and gur) of the country would be about 48 million tonnes of which 27.29 million tonnes would be sugar. To meet this requirement, 415 million tonnes of sugarcane will have to be produced, with a 60% drawl of cane for sugar production. This would imply that cane yield will have to be raised to 100 t/ha and the sugar recovery to 11.0%.

This sets the goals for sugarcane scientists not only in effecting desired genetic improvement but also in optimizing sugarcane production to ensure that India is globally competitive in sugar trade. The contribution of breeders in developing varieties with enhanced potential for sugar productivity in the diverse agro-climatic conditions shall have to involve work along the following lines.

### 12.1. Genetic Base Broadening and Parent Building

This involves continuing efforts to collect, conserve and evaluate sugarcane germplasm in as many target environment as possible; ascertaining the worth of promising accessions as parents, their improvement and, the development of gene pool and breeding stocks for specific traits for incorporation in the active breeding pool. Enhancing cytoplasmic diversity.

## 12.2. Artificial Control of Flowering to Make Planned Crosses

There is an urgent need to develop infra-structure for induction and manipulation of flowering at most of the crossing stations, and to have facilities for pollen and true seed (fuzz) stroage.

## 12.3. Gaining Better Genetic Understanding of the Crop

We need to understand the optimal chromosomal balance of the component species of a variety for desired agronomic performance, quality, disease resistance, tolerance to abiotic stresses, etc. Techniques to promote interspecific segmental exchange between chromosomes, inheritance studies for economic characters with appropriate material, etc. need to be undertaken.

## 12.4. Combining Sugar Productivity with Field Tolerance to Biotic and Abiotic Stresses

Breeding for enhanced sugar productivity under stress environments. Developing varieties with broad-based tolerances rather than absolute resistance to contain pathogens and pests, etc.

## 12.5. Genetic Enhancement of Ratoon Productivity

Ratooning ability is dependent on disease resistance, tolerance to biotic and abiotic stresses, particularly low temperature, efficient root development, etc. Studies to identify plant characters leading to better ratooning ability must be strengthened.

## 12.6. Strengthening of Seed Programme and Ensuring Use of Quality Seed

This is one area which is perhaps the most important, next only to a variety. Researchable issues include further refinement of seed health norms, exploring the scope for non-conventional propagules for cultivation, germplasm storage and exchange, etc.

## 12.7. Imparting Precision to the Breeding Process

Better ability to genetically manipulate the crop may be gained by the use of molecular techniques such as tracing chromosomal inheritance, establishing hybridity, genetic transformation, sourcing useful gènes for sucrose accumulation, disease resistance; marker-assisted selection, characterization of germplasm and varieties by DNA fingerprinting, *in vitro* germplasm conservation, haploid production, somatic hybridization to exploit cytoplasmic diversity and anti-sense RNA technology to minimize post-harvest inversion of sucrose. There is considerable scope for refining the selection process so as to enhance breeding efficiency.

## REFERENCES


Alexander A.G. (1973). Sugarcane physiology. Elsevier, Amsterdam, p. 752.

Alexander K.C., Kandasami P.A., Ramana Rao, T.C., Mohan Raj, D. and Rao, W.M. 1979. A new approach to genetic defence against red rot disease of sugarcane. Indian Sug,, 28: 659–696.

Artschwager, E. and Brandes, E.W. 1958. Sugarcane *(Saccharum officinarum* L): Origin, classification, charactersistics, and descriptions of representative clones. U.S *Dep. Agric. Agric. Handb.,* 122: 307.

Babu C.N. (1990). Sugarcane. Allied Publisher Pvt. Ltd. New Delhi, p. 252.

Barbar C.A. (1916b). Studies in Indian sugarcanes, No. 2. Mem. *Dept. Agric. India, Bot. Ser.,* 8: 103–199.

Barber C.A. (1916a). The classification of indigenous Indian canes. *Agric. J. India*, 11(4): 371–376.

Barber, C.A. (1915). Studies in Indian sugarcanes. No. 1. Punjab canes. *Mem. Dept. Agric. Ind. Bot. Ser.,* 7(1): 3–106.

Berding N. and Roach, B.T. (1987). Germplasm collection, maintenance, and use. *In*: Heinz, D.J. (*Ed.*), Sugarcane Improvement Through Breeding, Elsevier, Amsterdam, pp. 143–210.

Berding, N. (1995). Improving flowering of sugarcane for breeding: Progress and prospects. *Proceedings Australien Society Sugar Cane Technologists*, 18: 87–176.

Berding, N. and Skinner J.C. (1987). Traditional breeding methods, *In*: Anonymous (*Ed.*), Copersucar International Sugarcane Breeding Workshop. Copersucar, Brazil, pp. 269–320.

Berding, N., Moore, P.H. and Smith, G.R. 1997. Advances in breeding technology for sugarcane. *In*: Keating, B.A. and Wison, F.R. (*Eds.*) Intensive Sugarcane Production: Meeting the Challenges Beyond 2000. CAB International, Wallingford, UK, pp. 189–220.

Bhat, S.R., Kapur, R. and Tripathi, B.K. (1985). Association analysis of rind hardnesss and fibre content in sugarcane. *Ind. Genet.,* 45: 130–135.

Birch, R.G. (1997). Transgenic sugarcane: Opportunities and limitations. *In*: Keating, B.A. and Wilson, J.R. (*Eds.*) Intensive Sugarcane Production: Meeting the Challenges Beyond 2000. CAB International Wallingford, UK: pp. 125–140.

Brandes, E.W. (1958). Origin, classification and characterization. *In*: Artschwager, E. and Brandes, E.W. Sugarcane (*Saccharum officinarum* L), *U.S. Dept. Agric Handb.,* 122: 1–35, 260–262.

Breaux, R.D. (1987). Some breeding strategies with biparental and polycrosses. Proc. Copersucar Int. Sug. Br. Workshop, Sao Paulo, Brazil, pp. 71–85

Chang Y.S. and Milligan, S.B. (1992). Estimating the potential of sugarcane families to produce elite genotypes using bivariate prediction methods. *Theoretical and Applied Genetics*, 84: 633–639.

Chang, Y.S. and Fu, Y.M. (1999). Protection of sugarcane variety intellectual property rights using DNA amplified fingerprinting. Paper presented in XXIII Cong. ISSCT, held at New Delhi.

Clements, H.F. and Awada, M. (1967). Experiments on the artificial induction of flowering in sugarcane. *Proc. Int. Soc. Sugar Cane Technol.,* 12: 795–812.

Coleman, R.E. (1969). Physiology of flowering in sugarcane. *Proc. Int. Soc. Sugar Cane Technol.,* 13: 992–1000.

D'Hont, A., Girvet, L., Lu, Y.H., Roques, D., Feldman, P., Rao, P.S., Daugrois, J.H., Dufor, P., Berding, N., Walker, D.I.T., Harmon, P. and Glazsmann, J.C. (1996). The genome of modern sugarcane varieties. *Proc. Int. Soc. Sugar Cane Technol.,* 22: 363–367.

D'Hont, A., Rao, P.S., Feldmann, P., Grivet, L., Islam–Faridi, N., Taylor, P. and Glaszmann, J.C. (1995). Identification and characterization of sugarcane intergenotypic hybrids, *Saccharum officinarum* x *Eiranthus arundinaceus,* with molecular markers and DNA *in situ* hybridization. *Theoretical and Applied Genetics*, 91: 320–326.

Daniels, J. and Daniels, C.A. (1975). Geographical, historical and cultural aspects of the origin of Indian and Chinese sugarcanes S. *barberi* and S. *sinense. Sugarcane Breed. Newsl.,* 36: 42–44.

Daniels, J. and Roach, B.T. (1987). Taxonomy and evolution. *In*: Heinz, D.J. (*Ed.*) Sugarcane improvement through breeding. Elsevier, Amsterdam, The Netherlands, pp. 7–83.

Davidson (1968). Correlation of rind hardness and fibre in sugarcane. *Proc. Int. Cong. Sug. Cane Technol.,* 13: 1723–1728.

Deerr, N. (1911). Cane sugar: A textbook on the agriculture of the sugar cane, the manufacture of cane sugar and the analysis of sugar–house products together with a chapter on the fermentation of molasses. Norman Rodger, Manchester, p. 592.

Deerr, N. (1921). Cane sugar: A Textbook on the agriculture of the sugar cane, the manufacture of cane sugar and analysis of sugar–house product. 2"d ed. Norman Rodger, London, p. 644.

Deerr, N. (1949). The history of sugar. Chapman & Hall, London, p. 636.

Doule, R. and Balasundaram, N. (1999). Discriminant function — an efficient technique for selection in sugarcane. Paper presented in XXIII Cong. ISSCT, held at New Delhi from 22–26, Feb. 1999.

Dutt, N.L. and Hussainy, S.A. (1956). Some recent features of cane breeding Technique at Coimbatore, *Proc. ISSCT*, 9: 607–617.

Duttamajumder, S.K., Srivastava, B.L. and Kapur, R. (1999). Wilt disease of sugarcane: A major deterrent in breeding for high sugar in subtropical India. Paper presented in Symposium on Microbs, environment and Plant Diseases, at Lucknow, Indian Phytopathology Society.

Eksomtramage, T., Paulet, F, Noyer, J.L., Feldmann, P. and Glaszmann, J.C. (1992). Utility *of* isozymes in sugarcane breeding. *Sugarcane,* pp. 14–21.

Ethirajan, A.S., Santhakumariamma, P.N. and Velayudham, N. (1977). Studies in successive inbred generations of selected sugarcane cultivars. *Proc. 1SSCT*, 16: 269–273.

Evans, D.A., Sharp, W.R. and Medina Filho, H.P. (1984). Somaclonal and gametoclonal variation. *Am. J. Bot.,* 71: 759–774.

Fauconnier, R. (1993). Sugar Cane. The Macmillan Press Ltd., London, p. 140.

Fitch, M.M.M. and Moore, P.H. (1996). Haploids in sugarcane. *In*: In vitro Haploid Production in Higher Plants, Jain, S.M., Sopory, S.K. and Veilleux, R.E. (*Eds.*), Kluwer Academic Publishers, Netherlands

Fry, J. (1999). International productivity comparisons. Cooperative Sugar 30(9): 861–876

Gosnell, J.M. (1973). Some factors affecting flowering in sugarcane. *Proc. South Afr. Technol. Assn.,* 47: 144–147.

Grassl, C.O. (1964). *Saccharum robustum* and other wild relatives of noble sugarcanes. *J. Arnold Arbor. Harv. Univ.,* 27: 234–252.

Grassl, C.O. (1977). The origin of sugar producing cultivars of *Saccharum. Sugarcane Breed. Newsl.,* 39: 8–33.

Heinz, D.J. (1987). Sugarcane improvement through breeding. Elsevier, Amsterdam, The Netherlands, p. 603.

Heinz, D.J. and Mee, G.W.P. (1969). Plant differentiation from callus tissue of *Saccharum* species. *Crop. Sci.,* 9: 346–348

Heinz, D.J. and Tew, T.L. (1987). Hybridization procedures. *In*: Heinz, D.J. (*Ed.*). Sugarcane improvement through breeding. Elsevier, Amsterdam, The Netherlands, pp. 313–342.

Hogarh, D.M. (1980). The effect of accidental selfing on the analysis of a diallel cross with sugarcane. *Euphytica*, 29: 737–746.

Hogarth, D.M. (1977). Quantitative inheritance studies in sugarcane III. The effect of competition and violation of genetic assumption on estimation of genetic variance components. *Aust. J. Agric Res.*, 28: 257–268.

Hogarth, D.M. (1987). Genetics of sugarcane. *In*: Heinz. D.J. (*Ed.*). Sugarcane improvement through breeding. Elsevier, Amsterdam, The Netherlands, pp. 255–271.

Jadhav, M.G. (1997). Benchmarks in sugar industry at world level. *Coop. Sug.*, 28(12): 895–898.

Jagathesan, D., Alexander, K.C., Sreenivasan, T.V., Williams, A. and Devayani, K.R. (1980). Mutation breeding. Paper presented at the 4'" Co–ordination Meeting on Improvement of Vegetatively Propagated Crops and Tree Crops through Induced Mutations, held during February. FAO/IAEA, Sugarcane Breeding Institute, Coimbatore.

Janaki Ammal, E.K. (1941). Intergeneric hybrids of *Saccharum. Genet.*, 41: 217–253.

Jeswiet, J. (1925). Beschrijving der soorten van het suikerriet. II De Bijdrage. Bijdrage tôt de systematiek van het geslacht *Saccharum. Arch. Suik. Ned. Indie*, 33(3): 391–404.

Kapur, R. and Bhat, S.R. (1989). The nature of intergenotypic interactions in sugarcane. *Sugar Cane No*, 3: 11–16.

Kapur, R. and Lal, J. (1999). Seed multiplication through micropropagation. *In*: Shahi, H.N. and Solomn, S.S. (*Eds.*) Research Perspectives for the Indian Sugar Industry beyond 2000. Technical bulletin No. 40, Indian Institute of Sugarcane Research, Lucknow, pp. 46–50.

Kapur, R., Srivastava, B.L. and Duttamajumder, S.K. (1998). Efficiency in sugarcane breeding. Discussion paper in the ISSCT 4'h Breeding and Germ Plasm Workshop, Selection Efficiency in Breeding, Mauritius

Krishnamurthy, M. (1987). Sugarcane gentic resources and their utilization through conventional and unconventional approaches. *In*: Naidu, K.M., Sreenivasan, T.V. and Premchandran, M.N. (*Eds.*) Sugarcane Varietal Improvement. Sugarcane Breeding Institute, Coimbatore, India, pp. 163–176.

Latter, B.D.H. (1964). Selection methods in the breeding of cross–fertilized pasture species. *In*: Barnard, C. (*Ed.*) Grasses and Grasslands. Macmillan, London, pp. 168–181.

Lee, D.J. (1995). DNA markers and plant breeding programs. *In*: Spark, D.L. (*Ed.*), Advances in Agronomy. Academic Press, San Diego, USA, pp. 265–344.

Legendre, B.L. (1995). Potential for increasing sucrose content of sugarcane. An assessment of recurrent selection in Louisiana. *Sugarcane*, 3: 4–8.

Lin, C.S. and Poushinsky, G. (1983). A modified augumented design for an early stage of plant selection involving a large number of test lines without replication. *Biometrics*, 39: 553–561.

Lo C.C. and Chen, Y.H. (1995). Breeding for sucrose content improvement in sugarcane varieties. *Taiwan Sugar*, 42: 10–16.

Mangelsdorf, A.J. (1953). Sugarcane breeding in Hawaii. Part II. Hawaiian Planters' Rec. 54: No. 3

Mariotii, J.A. (1987). Selection for stability and adaptability. Proc. Copersucar Int. Sugarcane Br. Workshop, Sao Paulo, Brazil, pp. 249–258.

Meretzki, M. (1987). Tissue culture: Its prospects and problems. *In*: Heinz, D.J. (*Ed.*) Sugarcane Improvement through Breeding. Elsevier, Amsterdam, pp. 343–384.

Miller, J.D., James, N.I. and Lyrne, P.M. (1978). Selection indices in sugarcane. *Crop Sci.*, 17: 369–372.

Milligan, S.B., Gravois, K.A. and Martin, F.A. (1996). Inheritance of sugarcane ratooning ability and the relationship of younger crop traits to older crop traits. *Crop Sci.*, 36: 45–50.

Moore, P.H. (1976). Studies on sugarcane pollen. II. Pollen storage. *Phyton.*, 34:71–80

Moore, P.H. (1996). Progress in sugarcane molecular biology. *Proc. Int. Soc. Sugar Cane Technol.,* 22: 353–362

Moore, P.H. and Nuss, K.J. (1987). Flowering and flower synchronization. *In*: Heinz, D.J. (*Ed.*), Sugarcane Improvement through Breeding. Elsevier, Amsterdam, the Netherlands, pp. 273–311.

Moore, P.H., Botha, F.C., Furbank, R.T. and Grof, C.P.L. (1997). Potential for overcoming physio–biochemical limits to sucrose accumulation. *In*: Keating, B.A. and Wison, F.R. (*Eds.*) Intensive Sugarcane Production: Meeting the Challenges Beyond 2000. CAB International, Wallingford, UK, pp. 141–155.

Msomi, N. and Botha, F.C. (1994). Identification of molecular markers linked to fibre using bulk segregant analysis. Proc. South African Sugar Technologists' *Assoc.*, 68: 41–45.

Mukherjee, S.K. (1957). Origin and distribution of *Saccharum. Bot. Gaz.,* 119: 55–61.

Naidu, K.M. (1982). Germplasm of sugarcane: Its utilization by sugarcane breeders in India. *In*: Singh, R.B. and Chomchalow, N. (*Eds.*). Genetic Resources and the Plant Breeder, pp. 89–94.

Naidu, K.M. (1987). Potential yield in sugarcane and its realization through varietal improvement. *In*: Naidu, K.M., Sreenivasan, T.V. and Premchandran, M.N. (*Eds.*) Sugarcane Varietal Improvement. Sugarcane Breeding Institute, Coimbatore, India, pp. 1–18.

Nair, M.M. (1973). Note on an induced red–rot resistant mutant of Co 997 variety of sugarcane. *Indian J. Agric. Sci.,* 43(3): 323–324.

Nuss, K.J. (1979). Factors influencing the numbers of seedling obtained from sugarcane crosses. *Proc. South Afr. Sugar Technol.,* 53: 167–169.

Nuss, K.J. (1980). Effects of photoperiod and temperature on initiation and development of flowers in sugarcane. *Proc. Int. Soc. Sugar Cane Technol.,* 17: 486–493.

Nuss. K.J. and Berding, N. 1999. Planned recombination in sugarcane breeding: Artificial initiation of flowering in sugarcane in subtropical and tropical conditions. Paper presented in XXIII ISSCT Congr. Held at New Delhi from 22–26 Feb., 1999

Pan, Y.B. and Legendre, B.L. (1999). Marker–assisted sugarcane breeding. Sugar Azucar, June issue, p. 27.

Panje R.R. (1954). Studies in *Saccharum spontaneum* and allied grasses. III. Recent exploration for *Saccharum spontaneum* and related grasses in India. *Proc. Int. Soc. Sugar Cane Technol.,* 8: 491–503.

Panje, R.R. and Babu, C.N. (1960). Studies on *Saccharum spontaneum* Distribution and geographical association of chromosome numbers. *Cytolgia,* 25: 152–172.

Parthasarthy, N. (1946). The probable origin of North Indian Sugarcane. *J. Ind. Bot. Soc.,* (lyenger Commem. Vol.): 133–150.

Parthasarthy, N. and Venkataraman, T.S. (1942). Yet more parents for sugarcane breeding. *Curr. Sci.,* 11: 150.

Paulet, F., Engelmann, F. and Glaszmann. J.C. (1993). Cryopreservation of apices of *in vitro* plantlets of sugarcane (*Saccharum* spp. hybrids) using encapsulation/dehydration. *Plant Cell Reports*, 12: 525–529.

Pillai, S.V. and Ethirajan, A.S. (1993). Selection indices for sugarcane improvement at three stages of selection. *Euphytica*, 71(2): 155–159.

Price, S. (1965). Cytology of *Saccharum robustum* and related sympatric species and natural hybrids. U.S.D.A., *Agric. Res. Serv., Tech. Bull*, 13: 37–47.

Price, S. (1968). Cytology of Chinese and North Indian sugarcane. *Econ. Bot.,* 22: 155–164.

Rao, J.T. (1951). Anatomical characters of stem in relation to rind hardness and borer attack in sugarcane. Proc. First Biennial Cong. Sugarcane Workers in the Indian Union, Part II (Botany section) pp. 41–47.

Rao, J.T. (1968). Flowering in sugarcane not harmful if harvested within three months. *Sug. News* (India) 1(l): l–2.

Rao, J.T. (1980). Botanical researches on sugarcane (*Saccharum* L.) germplasm with reference to the origin of species. *In*: Current Trends in Botanical Research, Nagraj M. and Malik C.P. (*Eds.*), Kalyani, New Delhi, pp. 173–181.

Rao, J.T. (1987). Sugarcane origin taxonomy, breeding and variety. *In*: Naidu, K.M., Sreenivasam, T.V. and Premchandran, M.N. (*Eds.*) Sugarcane Varietal Improvement. Sugarcane Breeding Institute, Coimbatore, India, pp. 83–113.

Rao, J.T., Shrinivasan, K.V. and Alexander, K.C. (1966). Red rot resistant mutant of sugarcane induced by gamma irradiation. *Proc. Indian Acad. of Sci.,* 640: 224–230.

Rao, P.S. (1980). Fertility, seed storage and seed viability in sugarcane. *Proc. Int. Soc. Sugar Cane Technol.,* 17: 1236–1240.

Reimers, J.F., Hall, P. and Hogath, D.M. (1982). The relationship between Fiji disease susceptibility and yield. *Proc. Aust. Sugar Cane Technol.,* pp. 103–110.

Roach, B.T. (1969). Quantitative effects of hybridization in *Saccharum officinarum* x *Saccharum spontaneum* crosses. Proc. 13'" Cong. ISSCT, pp. 939–954.

Roach, B.T. (1992). Case for a core collection of sugarcane germplasm. Proc. XXI Congress of ISSCT. Pp. 339–352.

Sankaranarayan, P. and Babu, C.N. (1970). Effect of chronic gamma irradiation in sugarcane varieties. *Ind. J. Hered.,* 2(2): 9–102.

Sartoris, G.B. (1942). Longevity of sugarcane and corn pollen—a method for long–distance shipment of sugarcane pollen by airplane. *Am. J. Bot.,* 29: 395–400.

Sawhney, D.M. (1997). The Indian sugar industry. Venue of the XXIII ISSCT *Congress. Int. Sugar Jnl.,* 99(118): 426–430.

Shrivastava, A.K., Shahi, H.N., Solomon, S., Lai, J. and Kulshreshtha, N. (1999). Sugar production in 21st century: Exploring potential of high sugar—early ripening varieties. Technical Bulletin No. 38, HSR, Lucknow

Simmonds, N.W. (1979). The importance of plant breeding on sugarcane yields in Barbados. *Trop. Agric.,* 56: 4.

Skinner, J.C. (1959). Controlled pollinations in sugarcane. *Ind. J. Agric Sci.,* 51: 562–567.

Skinner, J.C. (1971). Selection is sugarcane. A review. *Proc. Int. Soc. Cane Technol.,* 14: 149–162.

Skinner, J.C. (1972). Description of sugarcane III. Botanical descriptions. *Proc. ISSCT,* 14: 124–127.

Skinner, J.C., Hogarth, D.M. and Wu, K.K. (1987). Selection methods, criteria and indices. *In*: Heinz, D.J. (*Ed.*) Sugarcane Improvement through Breeding. Elsevier, Amserdam, pp. 409–453.

Sreenivasan, T.V, Ahloowalia, B.S. and Heinz, D.J. (1987). Cytogenetics. *In*: Heinz, D.J. (*Ed.*) Sugarcane improvement through Breeding. Elsevier, Amsterdam, pp. 211–253.

Sreenivasan, T.V. and Bhagyalakshmi, K.V. (1997). Genetic improvement of sugarcane. Indian *J. Sugarcane Technol.,* 12(2): 1–10.

Sreenivasan, T.V. and Sreenivasan, Jalaja (1985). *In vitro* sugar cane germplasm storage. *Sugar Cane,* (l): 1–2.

Srivastava, B.L., Bhat, S.R. and Tripathi, B.K. (1989). Variability induced through vegetative mutagenesis in sugarcane. *Phytomorphology,* 39(4): 291–297.

Stevenson, G.C. (1965). Genetics and breeding of sugarcane. Longman, London, p. 284.

Stevenson, N.D., Brown, A.H.D. and Latter, B.D.H. (1972). Quantitative genetics of sugarcane IV. Genetics of Fiji disease resistance. *Theor. Appl. Genet.,* 42: 262–266.

Sundra, B. (1998). Sugarcane, Vikas Publishing House Pvt. Ltd., New Delhi, p. 292.

Tai, P.Y.D., Gan, H., He, H. and Miller, J.D. (1991). Phenotypic characteristics of F2 and BC, progenies from sugarcane intergeneric crosses. *J. Am. Soc. Sugar Cane Technol.,* 11: 38–47.

Taylor, P.W.J. and Dukic, S. (1993). Development of an *in vitro* culture technique for conservation of *Saccharum* spp. hybrid germplasm. *Plant Cell, Tissue and Organ Culture,* 34: 217–222.

Tew, T.L. (1987). New varieties. *In*: Heinz, D.J. (*Ed.*) Sugarcane Improvement through Breeding Elsevier, Amsterdam. pp. 559–594.

Tysdal, H.M. (1956). Promising new procedures in sugarcane breeding. *Proc. ISSCT*, 9: 618–631.

Venkarraman, T.S. (1938). Hybridization in and with the genus *Saccharum*. *Proc. Ind. Sci. Congr.,* 25(Part 2 section 9): 267–284.

Venkatraman, T.S. and Thomas, R. (1926). Sugarcane breeding techniques. Isolation of live arrows from undesired pollen through artificial rooting of canes. *Agric. J. India*, 21: 203–209.

Verret, J.A. (1925). A method for handling cane tassel for breeding work. *Hawaii Plant Rec.,* 29: 84–94.

Walker, D.I.T. (1971). Cane hardness and fibre content. *ISSCT Sugarcane Breeders Newsletter*, 28: 10.

Warner, J.N. (1953). The evolution of a philosophy on sugarcane breeding in Hawaii. *Haw. Plant. Rec.,* 54: 3.

Wu, K.K., Heinz, D.J., Meyer, H.K. and Ladd, S.L. (1980). Combining ability and parental evalution in five selected clones of sugarcane (*Saccharum* sp. Hybrids). *Theor. Appl. Genet.,* 56: 241–244.

# 7

# Pigeonpea

## 1. INTRODUCTION

Pigeonpea is one of the most important pulse crops of India and ranks second to chickpea in area and production. As *'dal'*, it is an important constituent of the Indian meal. It contains 20-21% protein. It supplements well with the cereals, as the proteins from the two sources together provide all the essential amino acids required for human nutrition. Pigeonpea has a deep root system which helps the plant to grow under limited moisture condition. It also improves the soil characteristics and fertility status. Being a legume it fixes nitrogen which is not only sufficient for its own growth but also leaves the residual nitrogen to the extent of approximately 40kg/ha (Kumar Rao *et al.*, 1981). It provides organic matter to the soil through leaf fall. In some parts of the country, specially Gujarat and Maharashtra, its tender green pods are used as vegetable. The outer integuments of seed together with part of kernel are good feed for cattle. The stalks of the plants are used for fuel, basket making and roofing etc.

Traditional land races and cultivars of pigeonpea mature in 180-280 days. The long duration types are sown as mixed crop or inter-crop in June-July and harvested in March-April. With the advent of early maturing varieties (100-160 days), the crop can be harvested in November to December, which allows another crop like wheat to be taken. Early duration cultivars are usually grown as a pure crop.

## 2. AREA, PRODUCTION AND PRODUCTIVITY TRENDS

During 1996-97 the area under pigeonpea was 3.61 m. ha, the production

V.L. Chopra (Ed.): Breeding Field Crops I: Practices, Studium Press (LLC), USA.

was 2.70 m. tonnes and the productivity 747kg/ha. However, during 1997-98 the corresponding figures were reduced to 3.5, 2.04 and 583 due to adverse weather conditions. Trends in area, production and productivity of pigeonpea have been presented in Table 1 on all India basis and in Table 2 for major pulse growing states. It may be seen that the area and production has increased, while productivity in the country has been stagnating over the years. Considering the state-wise trends, the area and production of pigeonpea have significantly increased in the states of Maharashtra, Gujarat, A.P., Orissa and Tamilnadu, while there is decreasing trend in Bihar, U.P. and M.P. Mixed trend was observed in production in Karnataka. Increasing trend in productivity was observed in Orissa, while other states showed fluctuating trends.

**Table 1:** All India area (million hects), production (million tonnes) and yield (kg/ha) of pigeonpea.

| *Year* | *Area* | *Production* | *Yield* |
|---|---|---|---|
| 1964-65 | 2.58 | 1.89 | 733 |
| 1965-66 | 2.56 | 1.73 | 678 |
| 1966-67 | 2.52 | 1.13 | 448 |
| 1967-68 | 2.67 | 1.74 | 653 |
| 1968-69 | 2.53 | 1.82 | 718 |
| 1969-70 | 2.67 | 1.84 | 690 |
| 1970-71 | 2.66 | 1.88 | 709 |
| 1971-72 | 2.35 | 1.68 | 718 |
| 1972-73 | 2.42 | 1.93 | 795 |
| 1973-74 | 2.65 | 1.41 | 532 |
| 1974-75 | 2.53 | 1.83 | 725 |
| 1975-76 | 2.67 | 2.10 | 786 |
| 1976-77 | 2.57 | 1.73 | 672 |
| 1977-78 | 2.63 | 1.93 | 735 |
| 1978-79 | 2.64 | 1.89 | 716 |
| 1979-80 | 2.73 | 1.76 | 643 |
| 1980-81 | 2.84 | 1.96 | 689 |
| 1981-82 | 3.00 | 2.24 | 745 |
| 1982-83 | 2.93 | 1.99 | 680 |
| 1983-84 | 3.22 | 2.58 | 801 |
| 1984-85 | 3.16 | 2.58 | 819 |
| 1985-86 | 3.18 | 2.44 | 767 |
| 1986-87 | 3.15 | 2.27 | 722 |
| 1987-88 | 3.33 | 2.28 | 685 |
| 1988-89 | 3.49 | 2.72 | 779 |
| 1989-90 | 3.60 | 2.75 | 763 |
| 1990-91 | 3.59 | 2.41 | 673 |
| 1991-92 | 3.63 | 2.13 | 588 |
| 1992-93 | 3.58 | 2.33 | 652 |
| 1993-94 | 3.53 | 2.69 | 762 |
| 1994-95 | 3.31 | 2.14 | 644 |
| 1995-96 | 3.45 | 2.31 | 670 |
| 1996-97 | 3.61 | 2.70 | 747 |
| 1997-98 | 3.50 | 2.04 | 583 |

**Table 2:** Trends in area ('000 ha), production ('000 tonnes) and yield (kg/ha) of pigeonpea in different states.

| *State* | | *71-75* | *76-80* | *81-85* | *86-90* | *91-95* | *96-98* |
|---|---|---|---|---|---|---|---|
| A.P. | A | 194.85 | 199.26 | 245.62 | 311.84 | 320.18 | 333.33 |
| | P | 45.4 | 38.2 | 55.86 | 71.72 | 94.88 | 99.23 |
| | Y | 233 | 192 | 227 | 230 | 296 | 298 |
| Bihar | A | 120.98 | 94.86 | 86.6 | 75.48 | 68.88 | 67.86 |
| | P | 97.06 | 67.4 | 93.26 | 88.44 | 80.8 | 71.76 |
| | Y | 802 | 707 | 1077 | 1172 | 1173 | 1058 |
| Gujarat | A | 89.58 | 121.06 | 261.18 | 333.04 | 398.78 | 398.6 |
| | P | 39.66 | 63.16 | 194.64 | 209.94 | 308.64 | 321.36 |
| | Y | 443 | 522 | 745 | 630 | 774 | 806 |
| Karnataka | A | 280.58 | 319.88 | 352.46 | 461.34 | 414.98 | 430.1 |
| | P | 136.86 | 197.48 | 166.32 | 183.38 | 142.52 | 175.13 |
| | Y | 488 | 617 | 471 | 397 | 343 | 407 |
| M.P. | A | 518.9 | 517.3 | 513.98 | 447.4 | 415.9 | 385.83 |
| | P | 403.86 | 322.16 | 407.92 | 451.26 | 370.22 | 285.1 |
| | y | 778 | 623 | 794 | 1009 | 890 | 739 |
| Maharashtra | A | 569.88 | 657.74 | 716.24 | 828.86 | 1026.1 | 1037.3 |
| | P | 298.02 | 371.66 | 431.6 | 533.46 | 529.96 | 583.86 |
| | Y | 523 | 565 | 603 | 644 | 516 | 563 |
| Orissa | A | 52.36 | 60.56 | 123.2 | 144.3 | 166.3 | 148.26 |
| | P | 27.68 | 28.98 | 77.28 | 111.48 | 128.04 | 91.4 |
| | Y | 529 | 478 | 627 | 773 | 770 | 617 |
| Rajasthan | A | 30.12 | 38.92 | 31.74 | 22.38 | 24.42 | 33.03 |
| | P | 13.36 | 14.14 | 13.62 | 10.86 | 12.0 | 22.8 |
| | Y | 444 | 429 | 429 | 485 | 491 | 690 |
| Tamil Nadu | A | 84.04 | 77.52 | 105.34 | 124.66 | 111.58 | 92.47 |
| | P | 31.74 | 43.3 | 67.04 | 92.7 | 70.14 | 72.36 |
| | Y | 378 | 559 | 636 | 744 | 629 | 783 |
| U.P. | A | 536.3 | 524.68 | 512.96 | 506.74 | 513.04 | 488.76 |
| | P | 614.9 | 692.48 | 697.68 | 655.38 | 548.32 | 514.6 |
| | Y | 1147 | 1319 | 1360 | 1293 | 1069 | 1053 |
| West Bengal | A | 26.2 | 24.66 | 23.06 | 8.04 | 4.94 | 3.6 |
| | P | 21.92 | 23.7 | 20.5 | 8.0 | 3.44 | 2.53 |
| | Y | 832 | 961 | 889 | 889 | 686 | 704 |

## 3. ORIGIN, TAXONOMY AND FLORAL BIOLOGY

### 3.1. Origin

According to van der Maesen (1990), pigeonpea originated in India and spread to other countries quite early. A secondary centre of diversity is reported to be eastern Africa. The range of diversity of the crop in India is much larger and this made Vavilov (1951) to list the pigeonpea as of Indian origin.

## 3.2. Taxonomy

Pigeonpea, *Cajanns cajan* (L) Millspaugh, is the only cultivated food crop of the Cajaninae subtribe of the leguminous tribe Phaseoleae. The subtribe Cajaninae is well distinguished by the presence of vesicular glands on the leaves (usually more on undersurface), calyx and pods (van der Maesen, 1990). The cultivated pigeonpea stands alone as a crop species in the subtribe. The taxonomy of *Cajanus* has been revised by van der Maesen (1986). Its wild relatives earlier commonly classified in *Atylosia* do not differ significantly from *Cajanus* to warrant generic status. According to van der Maesen (1990) the morphological, cytological, chemical and hybridization data support this merger, even if the needed taxonomic changes are inconvenient. He further indicates that the pigeonpea originated from *Cajanus cajanifolius.* Several other *Atylosia* ancestors, now considered cogeneric with *Cajanus,* may have contributed by introgression. The plant is perennial in habit but is grown as an annual. The profuse vegetative growth and poor ability to convert the dry matter into grain may be attributed to its perennial nature. This reflects the self-preservation tendency of the plant which is also associated with shedding of flowers, partially filled pods and leaves under stress conditions. Numerous types of pigeonpea are known that differ in height, time of maturity, colour, size and shape of pods and seeds (Pathak, 1970). The chromosome number of all *Cajanus* species is n=11. (Akinola *et al.*, 1972; van der Maesen, 1986) with notable exception of African species C. *kertsingii* which has n = 16 (Gill and Hussaini, 1986).

## 3.3. Floral Biology

The flowers are borne in short terminal or axillary racemes. They are clustered on peduncles which may be 1-8 cm. long. Flower colour may be yellow or yellow with purple veins or diffuse red. Flowers are papilionaceous, bracteate bracteolate; calyx five, gamosepalous; corolla five, free; stamens, diadelphous; ovary unicarpellary, unilocular, superior, sub-sessile with 2-9 ovules; style long, filiform, much upcurved; stigma capitate and glandular-papillate.

Pigeonpea flowers can be self-pollinated or cross-pollinated. Self-pollination occurs in bud before the flower opens. Although the stigma is completely covered with the pollen of its own flower, considerable outcrossing occurs in pigeonpea. Reddy and Mishra (1981) reported that the percentage of 'self' was negligible when flower buds were pollinated with foreign pollen without emasculation. This indicates that foreign pollen has an advantage over native pollen in affecting fertilization. Some of the reasons attributed to it are delayed germination and slow pollen tube growth of the native pollen. Such mechanism provides sufficient gap for foreign pollen to be introduced into the stigma and thus it favours out-crossing. Among the insects involved in cross-pollination are *Apis florea, Apis dorseta* and *Megachile* spp. (Williams, 1977; Pathak 1970). Mehta and Dave (1931) found that the smaller bees transfer pollen when their heads and legs are thrust forcefully through the keel petal. On the other hand, with its weight, the heavy bee, *Megachile lanata* depresses the keel and releases the stamen from which it deliberately collects pollen. Anthesis normally occurs between 8.00 and 17.00 h and flowers may remain open for 6 to 48 h. Flowering period appears to be influenced by weather conditions (Datta and Deb, 1970). The natural cross-pollination varied from 3.79 to 26.66 percent depending upon the variety and site (Prasad *et al.*, 1972). Majority of workers have reported the range of cross-pollination from 5-40%.

## 4. MATURITY GROUPS AND AREAS OF ADAPTATION

Pigeonpea is grown in highly diverse agroecological environments and in varied crop production and management systems. There is a range of maturity duration (100 to 300 days) and plant types (determinate to indeterminate) which fulfil the requirements of different production niches and management systems. Broadly, there are three important maturity groups *i.e.*, early (upto 150 days), medium (between 150-200 days) and late (above 200 days). Within these maturity groups are clear-cut plant types such as indeterminate, semideterminate and determinate on the one hand and compact, semicompact and spreading etc. on the other. Crop improvement work needs to be done strictly in relation to agroecological environment and cropping systems. This becomes all the more important because of complex influence of temperature and photo-period on crop phenology, plant height and harvest index in different production environments. This justifies the emphasis on evolving cultivars with lower sensitivity to photo-period and temperature. These traits may be incorporated into plant types with efficient partitioning and lower competition. This approach is likely to enhance production efficiency. The next step would be to stabilize the efficiency so achieved through alleviating biotic and abiotic constraints.

### 4.1. Early Duration

This group has three subgroups: extra early (Prabhat group; 100-120 days maturity), early (UPAS 120 group; 130-140 days maturity) and medium early (Type 21 group; 140 -160 days maturity). These maturity periods may be further reduced as we move from north to south of the country.

Extra early types can be managed without irrigation in rainfed areas and allow double cropping.

Early types are suitable for (i) irrigated areas of U.P., Haryana, Punjab and parts of Gujarat and Rajasthan where double cropping is possible and pigeonpea-wheat rotation can be a dominant rotation, (ii) rice fallows of Andhra Pradesh, Orissa, Karnataka and Tamilnadu (iii) dry farming regions of Gujarat, Rajasthan and Maharashtra, where monsoon rains cease early.

Medium-early types are suitable for rainfed farming systems in western M.P. and for intercropping with cotton, groundnut and sorghum in certain areas of U.P., Gujarat and Maharashtra. They can also be grown on sub-mountain regions upto an altitude of 3000 feet.

It may be mentioned here that development of early maturing varieties is a recent phenomenon (after 1970) and such varieties have a narrow genetic base. Resistances to various biotic and abiotic stresses have to be incorporated although they may escape frost, terminal drought and pod borer (*Helicoverpa armigera*) damage due to early maturity. They are relatively stable in phenology and agronomic performance over a range of environments and can be grown as safe crop in multiple cropping systems. They are also amenble to ratooning in South India where winters are moderate.

### 4.2. Medium Duration

There are two sub-groups in this maturity group: Medium maturity (BDN-2 group; 150-170 days) and medium-late maturity (C11 group; 180-190 days).

Medium maturing varieties are suitable for (i) rainfed farming systems of Maharashtra, parts of M.P., south Bihar, northern Karnataka, central Gujarat, A.P., parts of W.B. and Orissa and (ii) mixed cropping systems of Mirzapur, Sidhi and Shahdol districts of U.P. and M.P. as replacement of late varieties and (iii) regions of Tamilnadu, Rajasthan, Bundelkhand and A.P. Medium late maturing varieties are suitable for (i) intercropping with cotton and groundnut (ii) regions of Tamilnadu, A.P. Rajasthan, Bundelkhand and M.P. (iii) upland rice areas of south Bihar.

### 4.3. Late Duration

Late duration varieties can be grouped into two sub-groups: medium -late (Bahar group; 220-240 days) and late (T.7 group; 260-280 days) Medium-late types suffer less damage from pod borer (*Helicoverpa armigera*) compared to late types as the peak infestation occurs in late March and early April by the time varieties of Bahar maturity are harvested. Medium late and late types are suitable for mixed or intercropping. They are suitable (i) for rainfed areas of U.P., part of M.P, Bihar, Rajasthan, Orissa and some parts of Assam and Tripura. (ii) for post-raining season in eastern U.P. and Bihar. (iii) Late types can also be grown as perennial in *jhum* areas of N.E. Hills region to rejuvenate the soil, (iv) for growing on rice bunds in south-east and north east regions of the country and (v) for alley cropping in agroforestry systems

## 5. OBJECTIVES AND CHALLENGES

### 5.1. Breeding Objectives

1. Increasing yield with acceptable grain quality and stability.
2. Incorporating resistance to diseases *viz.* sterility mosaic, wilt and Phytophthora blight.
3. Incorporating resistance to pests (pod borer and pod fly).
4. Incorporating resistance to abiotic stresses *viz.*, waterlogging, drought, extremes of temperature and salinity and incorporating photo-thermal insensitivity.
5. Developing varieties for specific areas of adaptation and for existing and new cropping systems.

### 5.2. Challenges

The major challenges arise from the following characteristics of pigeonpea.

1. Highly sensitive to changes in photoperiod and temperature.
2. Highly sensitive to water-logging.
3. High genotype × environment interaction and high inter-plant competition.
4. High biomass but poor harvest index due to poor partitioning.
5. Indeterminate growth habit and perennial nature.
6. Determinate types more susceptible to pests and have greater tendency for flower drop.

7. About 10-40% cross pollination makes the crop difficult to handle.
8. Many agro-ecological niches and cropping systems put a heavy demand on breeder to develop variety for each situation.
9. Sources of resistance to Phytophthora blight, water logging, frost and pod borer not available in primary gene pool.
10. Resistance to multiple adversities is necessary which requires massive effort including the development of quick screening techniques.
11. Lack of international effort and interest in pigeonpea.

### 5.3. Plant Types for the Future

Ariyanayagam *et al.* (1977) have proposed incorporation of characters such as those quoted below for developing desirable plant types.

- Genetic dwarf in relatively less photoperiod and temperature-sensitive background, having open canopies, fewer branches, less foliage than the existing types and long flowering branches.
- Indeterminate plant types, in relatively less photoperiods and temperature sensitive backgrounds of about 100 cm. height, with a few secondary branches, short internodes, large number of nodes, small leaves, small pods, fewer seeds per pod, seed size between 8 and 10 g/100 grains and with deep rooting.
- *Cajanus sericeus* architecture if recaptured in a pigeonpea background may enhance partitioning. Fruiting is on the main stem and branches and pods are sessile. It has shallow roots and few tertiary branches.
- Determinate plant types of less than 100 cm. height having open canopy of few branches, small leaves, small pods, fewer seeds per pod, seed size not exceeding 10 g/100 grains, open inflorescence and deep roots.
- Gene-cytoplasmic male sterile pigeonpea (Ariyanayagam *et al.*, 1993): This should facilitate efficient exploration of pigeonpea germplasm for high heterosis. Hybrids of determinate and indeterminate habits of high herterosis combining characters that avoid competition but have efficient partitioning may be developed.

In order to develop efficient plant types of reduced sensitivity to both photoperiod and temperature, a three pronged approach has been proposed by Ariyanayagam *et al.* (1993). It consists intially of identification from the primary and secondary gene pools, low sensitivity to photoperiod and temperature for different crop growth stages and recombining them appropriately. Following this, the incorporation of characteristics conducive to better partitioning of biomass than the traditional types is proposed. These two stages are likely to enhance the productive potential of the crop. In order to stabilize and sustain the gains from these efforts, alleviation of constraints to productivity caused by abiotic and biotic factors is advocated by them.

## 6. GENETIC RESOURCES RELEVANT TO BREEDING OBJECTIVES

The crop's evolution through natural hybridization, selection for adaptation to a wide range of agro-ecosystems, and selection by man has resulted in numerous locally adapted land races with a wide genetic base. During the process of evolution, the plant has developed several adaptive features such as ability to produce a high biomass, prolonged flowering and over production of flowers. These are primitive traits and lead to low harvest index. However, there is tremendous variability for specifie traits in the world collection of germplasm at ICRISAT as reported by Remanandan (1990) (Table 3).

**Table 3:** Range of variability in the Pigeonpea germplasm (Remanadan, 1990)

| *Character* | *Maximum* | *Minimum* |
|---|---|---|
| 50% flowering (days) | 55.0 | 237.0 |
| 75% maturity (days) | 97.0 | 299.0 |
| Plant height (cm.) | 39.0 | 385.0 |
| Primary branches (number) | 2.0 | 66.0 |
| Secondary branches (number) | 0.3 | 145.3 |
| Racemes (number) | 6.0 | 915.0 |
| Seeds per pod (number) | 1.6 | 7.6 |
| 100-seed mass (g) | 2.8 | 25.8 |
| Harvest index (%) | 0.6 | 62.7 |
| Shelling ratio (%) | 5.3 | 87.5 |
| Seed protein (5) | 12.4 | 29.5 |

The use of germplasm lines in crop improvement can be made in two ways: direct use as a released variety or as a source for specifie characters such as yield component, resistance to diseases/pests or abiotic stresses, quality characters, adaptive characters etc. The utilization of germplasm resources of pigeonpea in India has been reviewed (Asthana, 1988; Lao *et al.*, 1989; Asthana and Chandra, 1997; Singh and Rana, 1977). Asthana and Chandra (1997) have listed 28 varieties of pigeonpea which are direct selections from land races and have been released for different parts of India. The promising among them are UPAS 120 in the early group; BDN 2 (wilt resistant), C 11 (wilt resistant), Maruthi (wilt resistant), Hy 3-C (exotic, bold seed), LRG 30, T 15-15, No. 148, Co 2, Co 4 in the medium maturity group and T 7, Bahar (SMD resistant)

Khargone 2, Gwalior 3, NP WR 15 (wilt resistant) in the late maturity group.

The sources of resistance to diseases and pests and of other useful traits in pigeonpea are reported in Table 4.

**Table 4:** Sources of resistance to diseases and pests and of other useful traits in pigeonpea.

| *Sl. no.* | *Resistance/Trait* | *Centre* | *Sources* |
|---|---|---|---|
| 1. | Sterility mosaic, wilt and Phytophthora resistance | Patancharu (ICRISAT) | Banda Paiera, ICP 1348, ICP 7336, ICP 8862, Purple 1, ICP 74360, ICPL 83024, ICP 7273 |
| 2. | Sterility mosaic and wilt resistance | Badnapur | BSMR 540 BSMR 294 BSMR 736 |
| | | Pantnagar | Pant A 8508 |
| | | Patancharu (ICRISAT) | ICP 227, ICP 366, ICP 11289, Bhavainsagar, ICPL 83027, ICPL 83024, IPL 87119, ICP 10958, ICPL 85047, ICP 8860, PR 5449, ICPL 84023, PS 397430 Sel; ICPL 7867. |
| | | N. Delhi, IARI | HY 3C, NPWR 15 |
| | | Dholi | DA 11, DA 15 |
| | | Kanpur (IIPR) | PDA 85-1, DPA 85-14 DPPA 85-7 DPPA 85-12 DPPA 85-15 |
| 3. | Wilt and Phytophthora resistance | Patancharu (ICRISAT) | ICP 138, ICP 7273 |
| 4. | Sterility mosaic resistance | Patancharu (ICRISAT) | Bahar, DA 3L |
| | | Badnapur | BSMR numbers 1,2,65,294,544, 175 and 203, BON 543 |
| | | Pantnagar | Plant A-3, Plant A 8505 |
| | | Faizabad | MDA 88-2 |
| | | Kanpur (IIPR) | E 83-2, E 83-5 |
| | | Lam | LRG 30 |
| | | Rahuri | PT 8205, PT 8206, 8710, PT 9208 |
| | | Patancheru | Purple, ICP 211, ICPL 269, ICP 8309, ICP 8607, ICPI 10979, ICPL 11049, ICP 11206, ICP 11206, ICP 86105, ICP 88047 etc. |
| 5. | Wilt resistance | Kanpur (CSAU) | KWR 1 |
| | | N. Delhi, IARI | NP (WR) 15, Pusa 17. |
| | | Badanpur | BWR 370, BDNI, BDN 2, BSMR 270, BSMR 540, BWR 254, KWR 24. C 11, AWR 74115 |
| | | Akola | DPPA 85-1, PDA 89-1, |
| | | Kanpur (IIPR) | DPA 92-1. |
| | | Gulbarga | GPS 30 |
| | | Sehore | SPMA 1, DPMA8 |
| | | Rahuri | PT 8707, PT 8710 |
| | | Patancheru (ICRISAT) | ICPL 270, ICP 8867, ICP 9177, ICP 11289, ICP 12748, ICP 84008, ICPL 84036, ICPL 8804, ICP 87104, ICPL 89044. |
| 6. | Phytophthora resistance/tolerance | S.K. Nagar | GAUT 82-53, GAUT 82-55, GAUT 82-104 ICP 4135, ICP 8564, ICP 8610, ICP 8692 |
| | | Patancheru (ICRISAT) | ICP 7200, ICPL 304 |
| | | Ludhiana | AL 595 |

**Table 4:** *(Contd...)*

| *Sl. no.* | *Resistance/Trait* | *Centre* | *Sources* |
|---|---|---|---|
| | | Kanpur (IIPR) | KPBR 80-1-4, KPBR 80-2-1, KPBR 80-2-2 |
| 7. | Alternaria blight resistance | Dholi | DA 11 |
| | | N. Delhi, IARI | Pusa 18, Pusa 4, Pusa 14 |
| | | Patancheru (ICRISAT) | ICPL 366 |
| 8. | Pod borer resistance | Ludhiana | AL592, AL593, AL594, *Rhynchosia bractest, R. sericea* |
| | | Patancheru (ICRISAT) | ICP332, ICP1903, ICPL84060, ICPL 84660, ICPL 87088 |
| | | Coimbatore | MMP 78-49 |
| 9. | Podfly resistance | Kanpur (IIPR) | PDA 89-E, MA2/3 |
| | | Patancheru (ICRISAT) | ICP 1503 E, ICP 8102 |
| 10. | Reniform nematode resistance | Dholi | Basant |
| 11. | Bold seed (>10g/100 seed weight) | N. Delhi, IARI | HY3C |
| | | Barahampore | BSR1 |
| | | Hisar | 83 H 8-21 |
| | | Sehore | Shahganj bold |
| | | Ludhiana | AL 230, TC 1048-10, TC 899-9, AL 1235, AL 1239, Al 1240, AL 1245, AL 1250. ICPL 289, ICP 7942, ICPL 270, ICPL 312, |
| | | Patancheru (ICRISAT) | ICPL 84058 |
| | | Rahuri | PT 221 |
| 12. | Long fruiting branches | S.K. Nagar | T 15-15 |
| | | Badnapur | BSMR 544 |
| 13. | Cluster flowering | Kanpur (IIPR) | PDA 3, PDA 81-1, PDA 86-3 |
| 14. | Higher no. of seeds per pod, | Patancheru (ICRISAT) | ICP 9154, ICPL 312 |
| 15. | Compact plant type | Kanpur (IIPR) | E 83-1, Bahar |
| 16. | Early maturity <120 days | Pantnagar | UPAS 120, Pant A 3 |
| | | Kanpur (CSAU&T) | Prabhat |
| | | Patancheru (ICRISAT) | ICPL 84035, ICPL 85024 |
| 17. | Dwarf | Patancheru (ICRISAT) | D 2, D 6 |
| 18. | Dwarf and early | Patancheru (ICRISAT) | ICPL 83015, ICPL 84023, ICPL 8509 |
| 19. | Drought tolerance | Patancheru (ICRISAT) | BDN 5, ICPL 8340, ICP 3233, PBN/A33, ICP 4865 |

***Other less important diseases***

| | | |
|---|---|---|
| Cercospora leaf spot | Patancheru (ICRISAT) | UC 2568/1, UC 796/1 UC2113/1 |
| Powdery mildew | -do- | ICP 9150, ICP 9177 |
| Dry root rot | -do- | ICPL 86005, ICPL 91028 |
| Phoma stem canker | -do- | AL 133, AL 136, ICPL 84018, 1COL 148. |
| Phyllody | -do- | BDN 5, ICPL 83057, MRG 66 |
| Halo blight | -do- | GW 3, ICPL 362 |
| Root knot | -do- | ICP 11289, ICP 11299 |

Some of the lines listed in Table 4 have already been used in the breeding programmes. It may be mentioned here that the traditional types belong to late maturity groups in northern region and to medium maturity group in southern region of the country. Many varieties have been developed from land races in these groups. But in early maturity group which is of recent origin (1970 onwards), not many land races are available and most of the present day varieties have been developed through hybridization using the disease resistant sources available in the germplasm collection. In the late group, land races are still holding the ground because of their tolerance to diseases, water logging and other stress factors. These traits have accumulated from centuries of cultivation and natural selection.

Germplasm collections are being maintained at ICAR and ICRISAT Patancheru, NBPGR, New Delhi. Working collections are being maintained at IIPR, Kanpur, and centres of All India Pigeonpea Improvement Project. ICRISAT has published a catalogue on pigeonpea germplasm (Remanandan *et al.,* 1988).

### 6.1. Breeding Methods Employed and Progress Achieved

Selection, hybridization and mutation breeding have been used in the development of varieties.

#### 6.1.1. *Direct selection from land races germplasm.*

Pigeonpea has been grown in India for a long time and a lot of natural variability has resulted from natural selection under various agro-ecological situations. Several good varieties were developed in the past through simple selection from these land races. Since they were time tested, many of them are still holding the ground *e.g.*, T.7, UPAS 120, Bihar, BDN 2, C11, No. 148, T15-15, LRG 30, HY 3C etc. and are not easy to replace. They are well suited to the cropping systems in respective regions, have built in tolerances to prevailing adverse situations, yield well under favourable situations and have good market value. There is scope to make further selections. Some of the above mentioned varieties have also found acceptance in other states and are being used as national checks in All India Coordinated varietal trials *e.g.*, Bahar (Late), BDN 2 (Medium) and UPAS 120 (Early) in the respective maturity groups.

#### 6.1.2. *Hybridization*

Systematic breeding work started after independence in some states but there was not much interaction between the states in exchanging the seed material and they mostly worked in isolation. However, with the advent of All India Pulse Improvement Project in 1967 with centres in major pulse growing states, the work on pigeonpea breeding got a fillip with good support from other disciplines especially plant pathology and agronomy. Disease screening nurseries were developed, five maturity groups were demarcated, varietal trials across locations were set up in each maturity group, techniques of screening against various biotic and abiotic stresses were developed in some cases, germplasm lines were exchanged, donors were identified and crossing programmes were developed at state as well as at national levels. This Coordinated approach yielded very good results. The establishment of ICRISAT in 1972 at Patancheru Hyderabad also helped the process of crop improvement. The hybridization programmes led to the development of several improved varieties in early, medium early and medium maturity groups with resistance to one or more diseases. The development of varieties through hybridization (Asthana and Chandra, 1995) are briefly discussed below.

An early maturing variety, Type 21, derived from cross Tl × T190 was among the varieties developed in early years of hybridization programmes. Later, another extra early variety Prabhat was developed from the same cross. Early maturing genotype T1 involved in the cross, was selected in 1953 from Gorakhpur (U.P.) for pigeonpea-sugarcane rotation. Cultivars T 21 and Prabhat have been used frequently in hybridization programmes to develop early maturing varieties. Another early maturing variety UPAS 120, selected from germplasm line P 4758, has been used extensively in hybridization. An exotic variety Brazil 1-1 in combination with NPWR 15, NP 41 and NP 69 led to the development of early maturing varieties Mukta, Sharda and Pusa Ageti, respectively. Prabhat in combination with ICP 6997 led to the development of ICPL 151. In West Bengal, variety W.B. 20 (105), suitable for pre-rabi sowing was developed from cross Prabhat × B 517. Pusa Ageti in combination with Khargone 2 and T 21 led to the development of two good varieties Pusa 74 and Pusa 84 respectively. Variety ICPL 87 was developed from a cross between Type 21 and JA 277. Type 21 in combination with UPAS 120 led to the development of two remarkable varieties, Manak and Sagar. UPAS 120 was used for the development of two varieties Pusa 33 and Pusa 85 in combination with C 11 and No. 148, respectively. Among the medium and late maturing groups, varieties JA 3 and AS 71-31 are the product of cross C 11 × No. 148.

It is apparent that a limited number of genotypes (Type 1, UPAS 120, Prabhat and Brazil 1-1) has been used as source of earliness in most of the breeding programmes. There is need to utilize new sources with different genetic backgrounds to bring about genetic diversity in breeding programmes.

Handling of segregating generations requires lot of care because of considerable amount of outcrossing and high G × E interaction. Selection based on single plant yield in early segregating generations has not been very effective. Bulk hybrid advance by single pod descent appears to be a better procedure for breeding high yielding lines (Green *et al.*, 1979). Early generation testing ($F_3$) and selection in intercropping with sorghum was suggested for improving yield in that system (Nerker, 1981). Saxena and Sharma (1983) concluded, from a study involving eight crosses, that low yielding crosses can be rejected on their $F_1$ performance and that the $F_2$ performance was consistently related to cross performance in succeeding generations. Another approach could be to select bulk populations (Composites), which may retain genetic heterogeneity but look homogeneous phenotypically, to exploit the breeding/pollination behaviour of pigeonpea.

### 6.2. Mutation Breeding

Five varieties of pigeonpea developed through mutation breeding have so far been released in the country. These are TT 5; TT 6 and Pusa 855 developed from Type 21; Co2 and Co4 developed from Col. TT5 and TT6 varieties developed at BARC, Bombay by irradiating seeds with gamma rays, have bolder seeds and higher yield compared to Type 21 (Pawar *et al.*, 1984). Pusa 855 was developed at IARI with higher yield and bolder seed. Cultivar Co2 developed at Coimbatore from Co1 was found suitable for both rainfed and irrigated conditions.

A review of spontaneous and induced mutations in pigeonpea has been done by Singh (1991).

## 7. HYBRID PIGEONPEA

The exploitation of heterosis through development of hybrids in pigeonpea is a recent approach to increase productivity. The identification of genetic male sterility (Reddy *et al.*, 1978) and outcrossing to the extent of 20-40% in the crop paved the way. This source of male sterility ($ms_1$ gene) is characterized by translucent anthers resulting from the non-separation of tetrads. A little later, another source of genetic male sterility ($ms_2$) was discovered which was characterized by brown, shriveled, arrow-head shaped anthers devoid of pollen (Wallis *et al.*, 1981; Dundas *et al.*, 1982). The allelic relationship between the two sources of male-sterility was studied and Saxena *et al.* (1983)

reported non-allelic monogenic recessive control. Massive conversion programmes were taken up both at ICRISAT and Indian National Programme. Initially, the male sterile lines ms Prabhat DT, Ms Prabhat NDT and ms 3783 were used in the hybrid synthesis. Later on about two dozen male sterile lines were developed through conversion using important varieties. Large number of experimental hybrids were produced and tested in multilocation trials in the country. The first pigeons hybrid ICPH 8 developed by ICRISAT was released in 1991 for central zone (Saxena *et al.*, 1997). It is short duration and indeterminate. Its parents are ms Prabhat (determinate) and ICPL 161 (indeterminate). It was one week late in maturity than UPAS 120. Later on two more hybrids *viz* PPH 4 from PAU Ludhiana in 1994 for Punjab and COH 1 in 1994 and COH 2 in 1997 from TNAU, Coimbatore were released for Tamilnadu. Two more hybrids AKPH 4101 and AKPH 2022 from PDKV, Akola have been released in 1998. They mature in 135 and 190 days respectively in central zone.

Seed production in genetic male sterility based hybrids is tedious and labour and cost intensive as 50% of male fertile sibs need elimination with the onset of flowering in the seed parent. To get rid of this problem, efforts were made to isolate cytoplasmic genetic sources of male sterility at various centres. CMS sources were isolated from different backgrounds. CMS 288A using *Cajanus scarabaeoides* was isolated at GAU, S.K. Nagar and CMS 1024 was isolated as spontaneous mutant having pin type flowers at NDUAT, Faizabad. The CMS sources using *C. sericeus* are also under development at ICRISAT, Patancheru and BARC, Trombay. Identification of suitable restorers and maintainers is on the anvil and will pave the way for production of CMS based hybrids. The work at S.K. Nagar is in advanced stage.

### 7.1. Population Improvement

Population improvement programmes involving genetic male sterility are in progress at some centres. This approach is used to increase recombination by intermating large number of genotypes with desired traits. Such populations, after one or two cycles of intermating, may serve as source material for drawing desirable lines for use in breeding programmes.

## 8. BREEDING FOR BIOTIC STRESSES

### 8.1. Breeding for Disease Resistance

Pigeonpea suffers from three important diseases *viz.* wilt, sterility mosaic and phytophthora. According to Dhar and Reddy (1999) the incidence of these diseases in different zones of the country and the estimated damages are as follows:

| ***Disease*** | ***Zone/state*** | ***Extent of damage (%) estimated in the zone*** |
|---|---|---|
| Wilt | NWPZ (UP, Bihar, WB) | 20-25 |
| Phytophthora blight | NEPZ (UP, WB) NWPZ (West UP, Delhi, Punjab) | 5-10 (upto 25% in early crop) |
| Sterility mosaic | NEPZ (UP, Bihar) CZ (Maharashtra) SZ (TN, Karnataka) | 10-15 |

### 8.1.1. *Wilt*

It is caused by *Fusarium udum.* Baldev and Amin (1974) pointed out the existence of different races of the pathogen for the first time. Subsequently, other workers have reported the occurrence of pathogenic variability. Two strains have been reported by Reddy and Raju (1993). Wilt resistant varieties are ICP 8863, ICPL 87119 (Asha), Maruthi (ICP 8863), BDN 1, BDN 2, C 11, NP (WR) 15, Narendra Arhar 1, DA 11, ICPL 87 (Pragati), Jawahar (KM 7), TTC, BSMR 736 and ICPL 87051.

Pal (1934) reported wilt resistance to be governed by multiple genes, while Shaw (1936) and Pathak (1970) suggested that it was governed by two complementary genes. Pawar and Mayee (1986) attributed resistance to single dominant gene.

### 8.1.2. *Sterility mosaic*

The causal organism is still not known. It spreads through mite vector, *Aceria cajani.* Five strains have been reported by Reddy *et al.* (1993). Singh *et al.* (1983) reported resistance to be controlled by four independent non-allelic genes. Sharma *et al.* (1984) implicated two genes and more than two alleles at each locus and reported that susceptibility was dominant over resistance and tolerance and that the tolerant reaction was dominant over the resistance of certain lines.

The varieties resistant to sterility mosaic are Bahar, DA 11 (Sharad) and Narendra Arhar-1 for north east plain zone; Hy 3c, ICPL 8705 and ICPL 87119 (Asha) for south zone and BSMR 736 and ICPL 87119 (Asha) for central zone.

### 8.1.3. *Phytophthora blight*

The disease is caused by *Phytophthora drechsleri* f.sp. *cajani.* The pathogen is highly variable. Sharma *et al.* (1982) reported the resistance to be governed by a single dominant gene, which was common in all the seven disease resistant parents used by them. None of the released varieties is resistant. However, some breeding lines are reported to be tolerant *viz.*, GAUT 82-55, KPBR 80-1-4, GAUT 82-104, KPBR 80-2 and ICP 8103. Some accessions of *Cajanus platycarpus* are reported to be resistant to *Phytophthora* blight. Short duration varieties are more susceptible compared to late maturing types.

Another disease, *Alternaria* blight occurs in Bihar and Eastern UP in the crop sown in pre-rabi season. This fungus is also variable and is known as *Alternaria alternata.* Resistance to this disease is governed by a recessive gene (Sharma *et al.,* 1987 and Singh *et al.*, 1988). Resistant varieties are DA 11 (Sharad, Pusa 9, ICPL 366, 20 (105) and MA 128-1.

Efforts are now being made to develop varieties with multiple disease resistance. Varieties such as Asha, BGMR 736, Narendra Arhar 1, ICPL 87051, DA 11, Pusa 9 have exhibited resistance to at least two diseases each as indicated above.

## 9. BREEDING FOR INSECT PEST RESISTANCE

Pod borer *(Helicoverpa armigera)* and pod fly *(Melanagronyza obtusa)* are the most important pests of pigeonpea besides Maruca etc. But no variety resistant to these pests could so far be released inspite of lot of efforts. Lai *et al.* (1986) observed that by reducing the maturity period of long duration cultivars in northern plains and selecting for shorter reproductive duration, podfly damage can be escaped. Similarly, late maturing varieties could escape damage of pod borer if crop matured before 10th standard week as the pest inflicts the maximum damage between 10th & 16th standard week (Yadav *et al.*, 1989). Single plant progenies through selfing need to be advanced for 5-6 years to fix the resistant character (Dias *et al.*, 1980). Based on 6-11 years of screening, over a dozen pigeonpea lines have been identified as resistant to both pod borer and podfly (Lai and Sachan, 1992). Some of the podfly resistant sources are PDA 89-2E (JA *17),* PDA 88-2E (GNG local), PDA 88-IE (JNAM 240) and ICP 7946 and some of the pod borer resistant sources are ICPL 332, ICP 1903, ICPL 84060 and ICPL 84660.

## 10. BREEDING FOR ABIOTIC STRESSES

The major abiotic stresses are drought, waterlogging, extremes of temperature, frost injury and salinity. Effective screening techniques have yet to be perfected for these traits. In short and medium duration varieties, effect of terminal drought can be minimized by reducing the crop duration. Late maturing cultivars are generally more tolerant to water logging than medium duration ones, while short duration cultivars are quite susceptible. Hybrid ICPH 8 appeared more tolerant than both the parents. Indeterminate types are relatively tolerant to drought compared to determinate types. Genetic variation in salinity tolerance has been reported (ICRISAT, 1986) and ICPL 227 appeared more tolerant.

Pigeonpea is extremely sensitive to extremes of temperature. Low sensitivity to temperature at different growth stages needs to be established. Temperature accounts for 60 per cent of total variation influencing the number of days from emergence to floral initiation. Photoperiod's share of the variation was no more than 10 per cent (Turnbull *et al.*, 1981). Field screening may be done at selected sites representing varied photoperiod and temperature environments. Dwarfing genes may also be used to help modulate phenology, to improve partitioning and to reduce the foliage (Ariyanayagam *et al.*, 1997).

## 11. BREEDING FOR PRODUCTION SYSTEMS

As discussed earlier, different phenological groups and plant types are required for different agro-ecological niches and cropping systems. The requirements could be for mono-cropping, double cropping, multiple cropping on the one hand and for sole, intercropping or mixed cropping on the other. Perennial crop may be useful for alley cropping in agro-forestry or for rejuvenating *Jhum* (shifting cultivation) areas. Short duration cultivars may be ratooned in south India where winter is mild. It is desirable that, as far as possible, selection should be done in the actual growing situations. However, it may not always be possible or practical due to difficulty in operation. The other alternative is crop modeling, but it requires large amount of precise data collection for selected environments and their interpretation.

## 12. BREEDING FOR QUALITY TRAITS

Grain quality refers to nutritive value, antinutritional factors, dehulling quality, cooking quality and consumer acceptance. Seed size, shape and colour are important traits for market acceptability. These may vary from region to region *e.g.*, white seed coat is preferred in Gujarat and some areas of Maharashtra. High protein content is desirable. Saxena *et al.* (1987) used wild pigeonpea species to develop high protein lines and suggested that protein content is a dominant character in pigeonpea and is not correlated with seed size. Methionine and cystine are the two sulphur containing amino acids which are limiting in pulses, and high protein genotypes may not have high protein quality. The range of methionine content of 636 pigeonpea germplasm accessions varied from 0.82 to 1.45 g/100 g protein (Singh, 1997). The protein content in grain varies from 23.1 to 26.2% with a mean of 23% (Jambunathan and Singh, 1981). However, one line HPL 40 was reported to have 31.1% protein. Among the antinutritional factors, trypsin inhibitor ranged from 8.1-12.1, amylase inhibitor from 22.5 to 34.2 while phenols ranged from 3.0 to 18.3 in pigeonpea (Singh, 1988). This variability could be used for reducing antinutritional factors. By improving the hulling quality, the recovery of *dal* may be improved by 20%. The cooking time of pigeonpea *dal* may vary from 20–68 minutes. It is understood that bolder seeds take more time to cook. Not much work has been done towards genetic enhancement of quality traits, although looking at the variability there is enough scope for improvement.

## 13. BREEDING FOR SPECIAL TRAITS

Fresh green pea from green pods are used as vegetable in some parts of Gujarat and Maharashtra. There is need to develop such types in early and medium maturity groups (Jain *et al.,* 1981).

Self-pollinating genotypes with cleistogamous flowers may be developed so that maintenance of genotypes and breeding cultivars through selection and hybridization becomes easier and less cumbersome.

Breeding for higher photosynthetic efficiency with reduced respiration losses and reduced foliage may be considered for improving harvest index.

Interspecific hybridization especially with *C. scarabaeoides, C. sericeus* and *C. platycarpus* may be resorted to for improving the plant types, incorporating resistance to various stresses and to improve some of the quality traits.

## 14. SUCCESSFUL VARIETIES AND HYBRIDS DEVELOPED

During the last two decades a number of promising varieties have been developed and are listed in Table 5.

**Table 5:** Pigeonpea varieties

| ***Zone*** | ***Variety*** | ***Year of identifica-tion/release*** | ***Area of adoption*** |
|---|---|---|---|
| North Hill Zone | Pusa Ageti (SD) | 1974 | Whole zone |
| (H.P., J&K and U.P. Hills) | T 21(DS) | 1974 | Whole zone |
| | UPAS 120 (SD) | 1976 | Jammu region |
| | ICPL 151 (Jagriti (SD) | 1989 | Whole zone |
| | ICPL 85010 | 1994 | Plains of H. P. |
| North West Plain Zone | T 21 (SD) | 1974 | Whole zone |
| (Delhi, Punjab, Western | UPAS 120 (SD) | 1976 | Whole zone |
| U.P., Haryana, North | AL 15(SD) (DPT) | 1982 | Punjab |
| Rajasthan) | Manak (SD) | 1981 | Whole zone |
| | Pusa 33 (SD) | 1987 | Whole zone |
| | ICPL 151 Oagriti (SD) | 1989 | Whole zone |
| | Pusa 855 (SD) | 1993 | Whole zone |
| | H 82-1 (Paras) (SD) | 1993 | Whole zone |
| | PPH 4 (Hybrid) (SD) | 1994 | Punjab |
| | AL 201 (SD) | 1993 | Punjab |
| Northern East Plain Zone | T 21 | 1974 | Whole zone |
| (Central & Eastern U.P., | UPAS 120 (SD) | 1976 | Whole zone |
| Bihar, WB & Assam) | T17 (LD) | 1978 | U.P. |
| | B517 (Chuni) (LD) | 1982 | W.B. |
| | B7(Sweta) (LD) | 1982 | W.B. |
| | 20 (105)/Rabi (LD) | 1984 | Whole zone |
| | Bahar (SMR) (LD) (PR) | 1986 | Whole zone |
| | T 7 (LD) | 1988 | U.P. |
| | Pus7a 9(LD) (PR) (AR) | 1993 | Whole zone |
| | DA 11 (Sharad)(AR) (PR) | 1986 | Bihar |
| | Birsa Arhar 1 (MD) (WR) | 1992 | Plateau region of Bihar |
| Central Zone (M.P., | T 21 (SD) | 1974 | Whole zone |
| Rajasthan, Maharashtra | BND 1 (WR) (MD) | 1976 | Maharashtra |
| and Gujarat) | BDN 2 (WR) (MD) | 1976 | Maharashtra |
| | JA3 | 1982 | M.P. |
| | Pusa 4 (SD) | 1982 | Whole zone |
| | No. 148 (MD) | 1982 | Whole zone |
| | PT 301 (MD) | 1982 | Whole zone |
| | C 11 (WR) (MD) | 1982 | Whole zone |
| | PT 221 (MD) | 1982 | Whole zone |
| | Hyderabad 185 (MD) | 1982 | Whole zone |
| | TT 6(Vishakha) (WR) (MD) | 1983 | Whole zone |
| | T 15-15 (MD) | 1985 | Gujarat |
| | TAT 10 (SD) | 1985 | Maharashtra |
| | ICPL 8863 (Maruthi) (WR) | 1985 | Maharashtra |
| | AKPH 4101 (Hyb) | 1997 | Whole zone |
| | ICPL 87 (Pragati) (SD) | 1986 | Whole zone |
| | Pusa 33 (SD) | 1988 | Whole zone |
| | ICPL 151 (Jagriti) (SD) | 1989 | Whole zone |
| | ICPH 8 (Hybrid) (SD) | 1991 | Whole zone |
| | JA 4 (MD) | 1991 | M.P. |

**Table 5:** (*Contd...*)

**Table 5:** (*Contd...*)

| *Zone* | *Variety* | *Year of identification/ release* | *Area of adoption* |
|---|---|---|---|
| | Gujarat Tur 100 (MD) | 1992 | Gujarat |
| | ICPL 87119 (Asha) (WR & SMR) | 1994 | Whole zone |
| | KM 7 (MD) | 1995 | Maharashtra |
| | BSMR 736 (MD) | 1978 | M.P. |
| | BSMR 175 (MD) | 1991 | Maharashtra |
| South Zone (Orissa, Karnataka, Tamilnadu & A.P.) | HY 3A (MD) | 1982 | Whole zone |
| | HY 3C (SMR) (MD) | 1982 | Whole zone |
| | LRG 30 (Palandu) (MD) | 1982 | Whole zone |
| | GS 1 (LD) | 1982 | Karnataka |
| | PT 221 (MD) | 1982 | Karnataka |
| | TT 6 (Vishakha) (WR) (SD) | 1993 | Whole zone |
| | SA 1 (LD) | 1985 | Whole zone |
| | ICPL 87 (Pragati) (SD) | 1986 | Whole zone |
| | Maruthi (ICPL 8863) (WR) | 1986 | A.P., Karnataka |
| | ICPL 87119 (Asha) (MD) | 1993 | Whole zone |
| | Vamban 1 (LD) | 1992 | Tamil Nadu |
| | KM 7 (MD) | 1994 | Whole zone |
| | CoH 1 (Hybrid) (SD) | 1994 | T.N. |
| | ICPL 332 (Abhaya) | 1989 | A.P. |
| | Co6 | 1991 | T.N. |
| | ICPL 84031 (Durga) | 1997 | A.P. |
| | CoH 2 (Hybrid) | 1997 | T.N. |
| | TTB 7 (MD) | 1988 | Karnataka |
| | ICPH 8 (Hybrid) | 1991 | Orissa |
| | BDN 2 (WR) (MD) | 1976 | A.P. |
| | C 11 (WR) (MD) | 1982 | A.P. |
| | ICPL 85010 (SD) | 1997 | A.P. |

WR-Wilt résistant, SMR-Sterility mosaic résistant, AR-Alternaria résistant, SD-Short duration, MD-Medium duration, LD-Long duration, PR-Pre-rabi, DPT-Determinate plant type

Among the varieties developed are (i) Early maturing varieties for rotation with wheat (ii) Wilt and sterility mosaic resistant varieties, (iii) Post-rainy season varieties resistant to *Alternaria* blight, (iv) Medium-late maturing, sterility mosaic resistant, pod borer escaping and compact plant type *viz.* Bahar for closer planting and (v) Pod fly tolerant varieties.

## 15. SEED PRODUCTION

The projections for the requirement of Certified, Foundation, Breeder and Nucleus seed of pigeonpea at 15% replacement rate with 10%, 20%, 50% and 100% buffer stock for each category of seed (C/s, F/s, B/s and

N/s) respectively by different states of the country for the year 2002 are as follows:

| *State* | *Certified seed (Th.q.)* | *Foundation seed (q.)* | *Breeder seed (q.)* | *Nucleus seed (kg)* |
|---|---|---|---|---|
| Andhra Pradesh | 12.3 | 264 | 7.10 | 14.1 |
| Assam | 0.3 | 6 | 0.10 | 0.3 |
| Bihar | 3.0 | 64 | 1.74 | 3.4 |
| Gujarat | 15.4 | 331 | 9.00 | 17.7 |
| Haryana | 1.2 | 26 | 0.70 | 1.4 |
| Karnataka | 14.4 | 309 | 8.30 | 16.5 |
| Madhya Pradesh | 15.4 | 331 | 9.00 | 17.7 |
| Maharashtra | 41.0 | 880 | 24.0 | 47.0 |
| Orissa | 6.5 | 140 | 3.75 | 7.5 |
| Punjab | 0.4 | 9 | 0.21 | 0.5 |
| Rajasthan | 0.7 | 15 | 0.40 | 0.8 |
| Tamil Nadu | 4.9 | 105 | 2.80 | 5.6 |
| Uttar Pradesh | 20.3 | 436 | 11.80 | 23.3 |
| West Bengal | 0.2 | 4 | 0.10 | 0.2 |
| **All India** | **136.0** | **2920** | **79.00** | **156.0** |

The present position of total Breeder Seed Production of pigeonpea is satisfactory though there are several loopholes. The varietal mismatch in terms of specific requirement is to be avoided. Seed production must be monitored to ensure that there is no break in seed chain. All Breeder Seed should be used for the production of Foundation seed and all the Foundation seed should be used for the production of Certified seed. It is also necessary that the best varieties for the region are indented.

## 16. FUTURE STRATEGIES

Pigeonpea plant is characterized by high biomass and low harvest index. It is also highly sensitive to environmental changes especially temperature, moisture and photo period. High G × E interaction, high coefficient of variability, often cross pollinated nature and susceptibility to diseases and insect pests are major constraints in effecting genetic enhancement for yield. Thus very systematic efforts for evaluating the germplasm, selection of parents, employing appropriate breeding methods, characterization and selection of testing sites etc. are required. Knowledge of basic physiology of the plants concerned with better partitioning and better adaptability to fluctuating environments needs to be generated.

Development of suitable plant types for different production systems with higher genetic yield potential is possible when concerted efforts are made towards this activity without distraction from maintenance breeding such as incorporation of resistances to biotic and abiotic factors. While doing so, either the resistant parents have to be chosen or the breeding material is to be protected from such harsh environments. Breeding material is to be sown in such a way that every plant gets equal opportunity to express itself.

It will be better if wider spacing is used in the early stages. Short duration plant types with reduced vegetative growth, higher harvest index, reduced sensitivity to temperature and photo-period variations with long fruiting branches appear to hold much promise for the future.

A large number of breeding lines preferably in $F_4$ generation selected for higher yield potential may be exposed to the desired environmental situations and production system for making appropriate selections. If necessary, crosses may be made with resistant sources to incorporate desired resistances in the higher yielding genetic backgrounds.

Besides exploiting variability in the primary gene pool, it is desirable to make crosses with allied species like *C. scarabaeoides, C. sericeus* and *C. platycarpus* to create more variability for morphological and physiological traits and also to incorporate resistance to various stresses.

Priority should be assigned to exploitation of heterosis using the CMS system especially in early and medium duration groups.

Resistance to wilt, sterility mosaic and phytophthora has to be combined. Integrated pest management approach towards pod borer and podfly has to be adopted along with incorporation of genetic resistance as far as possible. Suitable high yielding cultivars for *pre-rabi* (September) sowing in north east plain zone and for pre-monsoon sowing (May) with pre-sowing irrigation for north west plain zone need to be developed besides developing cultivars of the normal *kharif* season.

Supply of certified seeds of all recommended varieties of pigeonpea should be ensured each year with the replacement rate of 15%.

Efforts should be made for improving the grain quality, protein percentage and sulphur containing amino acids and reducing anti-nutritional factors.

Developments in biotechnology should also be exploited in pigeonpea for developing transgenic plants *e.g.,* incorporating *Bt.* gene for pod borer resistance and gene transfer across the allied species. Marker assisted selection would go a long way in speeding up the breeding process for developing improved genotypes with desired traits.

## REFERENCES


Akinola, J.O., Pritchar, A.J. and Whiteman, P.C. (1972). Chromosome number in pigeonpea (*Cajanus cajan* (L.) Mill sp. *Journal of Australian Institutc of Agricultural Science,* 38: 305–306.

Ariyanayagam, R.P., Nageshwar Rao, A. and Zaveri, P.P. (1993). Gene cytoplasmic male sterile pigeonpea. *International Pigeonpea Newsletter,* p. 18.

Ariyanaygam, R.P., Singh, N.B., Jain, K.C. and Asthana, A.N. (1997). Plant types for higher productivity of pigeonpea. In: *Recent Advanccs in Pulses Research* 1997 *Eds.* Asthana, A.N. and Massod, Ali, ISPRD, IIPR, Kanpur. pp. 89–108.

Asthana, A.N. (1988). Collection and utilization of genetic diversity in pulse crops. *In: Plant Genetic Resources: India perspective. Eds.* Paroda, R.S., Arora, R.K. and Chandel, K.P.S. NBPGR, New Delhi, pp. 243–260.

Asthana, A.N. and Chandra, S. (1995). Varietal improvement in pulse crops—current trends and future prospects. *In: Genetic Research and Education: Current trends and the next fifty years.* (Sharma, B. *et al., Eds.*) Indian Society of Genetics of Plant Breeding, New Delhi. pp. 925–959.

Asthana, A.N. and Chandra, S. (1997). Utilization of pulse germplasm in India. *In: Recent Advances in Pulses Research. Eds.*, Asthana, A.N. and Massod, Ali. ISPRD, IIPR Kanpur, pp. 757–784.

Baldev, B. and Amin, K.S. (1974). Studies on the existence of races in *Fusarium udum* causing wilt of *Cajanus cajan. SABRAO Journal,* 6: 201–205.

Datta, P.C. and Deb, A. (1970). Floral biology of *Cajanus cajan* (L.) Mill sp. Var. Bicolor, D.B. (Papi). *Bull. Bot. Soc. Bengal,* 24: 135–145.

Dhar, Vishwa and Reddy, M.V. (1999). Disease management strategies for increasing pulses production. Paper presented in the Brain Storming Meeting on Pulses production held at NBPGR, New Delhi.

Dias, C.A.R., Lai, S.S. and Yadava, C.P. (1980). Relative susceptibility of pigeonpea cultivars against the pod fly, *Melanagromyza obtusa* under field conditions. *In: Proceedings of the International Workshop on Pigeonpea,* Vol.2, 1CRISAT Centre, Patancheru, India pp. 33–40.

Dundas, I.S., Saxena, K.B. and Byth, D.E. (1982). Pollen mother cell and anther wall development in a photoperiod insensitive male sterile mutant of pigeonpea *(Cajanus cajan* (L.) Mill sp.) *Euphytica,* 31: 371–375.

Gill, L.S. and Husaini, S.W.H. (1986). Cytological observations in Legnminosae from Southern Nigeria. *Willdenowia,* 15: 521–527.

Green J.M., Sharma, D., Saxena, K.B., Reddy, L.J. and Gupta, S.C. (1979). Pigeonpea Breeding at 1CRISAT. Paper presented at the Regional Workshop on Tropical Grain Legumes, 18–22 June 1979, University of West Indies, St. Augustine, Trinidad.

ICRISAT, (1986). Annual report 1985. Patancheru, A.P. India : ICRISAT p. 182.

Jain, K.C., Sharma, D., Gupta, S.C., Reddy, L.J. and Singh, U. (1981). Breeding for vegetable type pigeonpea. In: *Proceedings of International Workshop on Pigeonpea* ICRISAT, Hyderabad, India, 1: 165–177.

Jambunathan, R. and Singh, U. (1981). Grain quality of pigeonpea *In*: *Proc. International Workshop on pigeonpea, ICRISAT*, Hyderabad, India, I: 351–356.

Kumar Rao, J.V.D.K., Dart, P.J. Matsumoto, T. and Day, J.M. (1981). Nitrogen fixation by pigoenepa. In *proceedings of the international workshop on pigeonpea,* ICRISAT Centre, India, Patancheru, A.P. India. *ICRISAT*, 1: 190–199.

Lal, S., Asthana, A.N. and Gowda, C.L. (1989). Use of chickpea and pigeonpea germplasm and their impact on crop improvement in India. *In*: *Collaboration on Genetic Resources:* Summary proceedings of a joint ICRISAT/NBPGR (ICAR) workshop on germplasm exploraiton and evaluation in India, 14–15 November 1988, ICRISAT Centre, India Patancheru, A.P. India. ICRISAT pp. 101–103.

Lal, S.S. and Sachan, J.N. (1992). Host plant resistance in integrated pest management of chickpea and pigeonpea. Sachan, J.N. (Eds.) *New Fronticrs in Pulses Research and Development:* Proceedings of National Symposium, 10–12 Nov. 1989. DPR., Kanpur pp. 166–177.

Lal, S.S., Yadava, C.P. and Chandra, S. (1986). Suppression of pod fly damage through varietal selection. *International Pigeonpea Newsletter,* 5: 42–43.

Mehta, D.N. and Dave, B.B. (1931). Studies in *Cajanus indicus. Ment. Dep. Agric. India. Bot. Ser.,* 19: 1–25.

Nerkar Y.S. (1981). Performance of early generation lines under different cropping systems and its bearing on the selection procedures in pigeonpea breeding. *In*: *Proceedings of the International Workshop on Pigeonpea,* vol. 2, 15–19, December 1980, ICRISAT Centre, India Patancheru, Vol. 2, 15–19, December 1980, ICRISAT Centre, India Patancheru, A.P. India: ICRISAT pp. 159–163.

Pal, B.P. (1934). Recent progress in plant breeding at Pusa. *Agriculture and Live stock in India,* 4: 505–515.

Pathak, G.N. (1970). Red gram *Cajanus cajan* (L.) Millsp. *In*: *Pulse crops of India* (*Ed.* Kachroo, P.). ICAR, New Delhi, pp. 14–53.

Pawar, N.B. and Mayee, C.D. (1986). Reaction of pigeonpea genotypes and their crosses to Fusarium wilt. *Indian Phytopathology,* 39: 70–74.

Pawar, S.E., Thakare, R.G., Mitra, R., Krishna, T.G. and Bhatia, C.R. (1984). Induced mutations for the genetic improvement of pulse corps. *In*: Srivastava, H.C. *et al.* (*Eds.*), *Pulse production – Constraints and opportunites.* Oxford and 1BH Publishing Co. New Delhi, India pp. 361–367.

Prasad, S., Prakash, R. and Hassan, M.A. (1972). Natural crossing in pigeonpea *(Cajanus cajan* (L.) Mill sp.). *Mysore J. Agric. Sci.,* 6: 426–429.

Reddy, B.V.S., Green, J.M. and Bisen, S.S. (1978). Genetic male sterility in pigeonpea. *Crop Science,* 18: 362–364.

Reddy, L.J. and Mishra, A.K. (1981). Is emasculation necessary for pigeonpea hybridization. *International Pigeonpea Newsletter* 1: 12–13.

Reddy, M.V. and Raju, T.N. (1993). Pathogenic variability in pigeonpea wilt pathogen *Fusarium udum*. *In*: *Plant disease problems in central India.* Proceedings of symposium 28–29 Nov. 1991. Directorate of Rice Research Hyderabad, India. Central Zone, Indian Phytopathological Society pp. 32–34.

Reddy, M.V., Raju, T.N., Nene, Y.L., Amin, K.S., Arjunan, G., Astaputre, J.V., Sinha, B.K., Muniyappa, V., Reddy, S.V., Ghanekar, A.M., Gupta, R.P. and Gangadharan, K. (1993). Variability in sterility mosaic pathogen of pigeonpea in India. *Indian Phytopathology,* 46(3): 206–212.

Remanandan, P. (1990). Genetic resources. *In*: *Pigeonpea* (Nene, Y.L. Susan Hall, D. and Shukla, V.K. (*Eds.*) CAB International U.K. pp. 89–105

Remanandan, P., Sastry, D.V.S.S.R. and Mangesha, M.H. (1988). *1CRISAT Pigeonpea Germplnsm Catalog:* Evaluation and Analysis. Patancheru, A.P. India. 1CRISAT, p. 90.

Saxena, K.B. and Sharma, D. (1983). Early generation testing in pigeonpea *(Cajanus cajan* (L.) Mill sp.). *Tropical Plant Science Research,* 1(4): 309–313.

Saxena, K.B., Chauhan, Y.S., Kumar, R.V., Ariyanayagam, R.P., Srivastava, O.P., Johansen, C. and Asthana, A.N. (1997). Heterosis breeding for higher yield in pigeonpea. In: *Recent Advances in Pulses Research,* Asthana, A.N. and Masood, Ali *Eds*., Indian Society of Pulses Research and Development, IIPR, Kanpur, India pp. 109–125.

Saxena, K.B., Paris, D.G., Singh, U. and Kumar, R.V. (1987). Relationship between seed size and protein content in newly developed high protein lines of pigeonpea. *Plant Foods for Human Nutrition,* 36: 335–340.

Saxena, K.B., Wallis, E.S. and Byth, D.E. (1983). A new gene for male sterility in pigeonpea (*Cajanus cajan* (L.) Mill sp.) *Hcrcdity,* 51: 419–421.

Sharma D., Kannaiyan, J. and Reddy, L.J. (1982). Inheritance of resistance to blight in pigeonpea. *Plant Disease,* 66: 22–25.

Sharma, D., Gupta, S.C., Rai, G.S. and Reddy, M.V. (1984). Inheritance of resistance to sterility mosaic disease in pigeonpea. *Indian Journal of Genetics and Plant Breeding,* 44: 84–90.

Sharma, D., Kannaiyan, J. and Saxena, K.B. (1987). Sources and inheritance of resistance of alternaria blight in pigeonpea. SABRAO *journal,* 19: 109–114.

Shaw, F.J.F. (1936). Studies in indian pulses: The inheritance of morphological characters and wilt resistance in *arhar* (*Cajanus indiens* spreng). Indian *Journal of Agricultural Sciences,* 6: 139–187.

Singh, B.V., Pandya, B.P., Gautam, P.L., Beniwal, S.P.S. and Pandey, M.P. (1983). Inheritance of resistance to sterility mosaic virus in pigeonpea. *Indian Journal of Genetics and Plant Breeding*, 43: 487–493.

Singh, Bhag and Rana, R.S. (1997). Pulse germplasm collection and enhancement at NBPGR. Present accomplishments and future prospects. *In Recent Advances in Pulses Research.* A.N. and Massod, A.H. (*Eds*.). ISPRD, IIPR, Kanpur, pp. 743–755.

Singh, D.P. (1991). Pigeonpea. *In*: *Genetics and breeding of pulse crops.* Kalyani Publishers, New Delhi, pp. 62–115.

Singh, U. (1988). Antinutritional factors of chickpea and pigeonpea and their removal by processing. *Plant Foods for Human Nutrition,* 38: 251–261.

Singh, U. (1997). Grain quality improvement in pulses: Current status and future research needs. *In*: *Recent Advances in Pulses Resenrch,* Asthana, A.N. and Massod, Ali *Eds*. 1SPRD, Kanpur, India pp. 677–693.

Singh, U.P., Singh, P. and Singh, R.M. (1988). Inheritance of field resistance to alternaria blight of pigeonpea. *International Pigeonpea Newslettcr,* 7: 4–5.

Turnbull, L.V., Whiteman, P.C. and Byth, D.E. (1981). The influence of temperature and photoperiod on floral development of early flowering pigeonpea. *In*: *Proceedings of the International Workshop on Pigeonpea,* vol. 2, 15–19 Dec.1980, ICRISAT Centre, India, Patancheru, A.P. India : ICRISAT. pp. 217–222.

Van–der Maesen L.J.G. (1990). *Pigeonpea:* Origin, history, isolation and taxonomy. *In*: *The Pigeonpea:* Nene, Y.L. Hall, S.D. and Sheila, V.K. (*Eds*.) CAB International. ICRISAT pp. 15–46.

Van–der Maesen L.J.G. Cajanus, D.C. and Atylosia W.A. (1986). Agricultural University Wageningen papers 85–4. Agri. Univ. Wageningen, the Netherlands, p. 225.

Vavilov, N.I. (1951). The origin variation, immunity and breeding of cultivated plants, *Chronica Botanica,* 13 (1/6): 1–366.

Wallis, E.S., Saxena, K.B. and Byth, D.E. (1981). A new source of genetic male sterility in pigeonpea. *In*: *Proceedings of the International Workshop on Pigeonpea* Vol. 2, 15–19 December 1980, ICRISAT Centre, India. Patancheru, A.P, India ICRISAT, pp. 105–108.

Wiliams, I.H. (1977). Behaviour of insects foraging on pigeonpea (*Cajanus cajan*) (L.) Mill sp. in India. *Tropical Agriculture* (Trinidad) 54: 353–363.

Yadava, C.P., Lai, S.S., Dias, C.A.R. and Nigam, R. (1989). Host evasion–a prospectiveapproach for suppressing *Heliothis armigera. International Pigeonpea Newsletter,* (2): 62–64.

# 8

# Chickpea

## 1. INTRODUCTION

Chickpea (*Cicer arietinum* L.) is the third most important grain legume in the world which is grown in almost all continents except Antarctica. However, its cultivation is more extensive in the semi-arid tropics particularly in the rainfed ecology of the Indian subcontinent, the Mediterranean region, the West Asian and North African region, Eastern Africa and Latin America. Expansion of this crop to new niches, such as Australia in recent years, has been remarkable. This crop is of immense importance in Asia which grows more than 90% of chickpea, mainly in the fragile and rainfed ecosystem, where successful cultivation of cereal crops is uncertain and risky.

Chickpea has been well recognized as a valuable source of dietary protein particularly in the developing countries where supplementation of cereal-based diets with legumes is the best solution to widespread protein energy malnutrition (PEM). According to one estimate, more than half of the world's PEM problem is in South Asia. About 53% of the malnourished (338 million children below 15 years of age are underweight and under-nourished) live in India. The per capita available 17.3 g/day chickpea is a source of approximately 3.1% (69.5 Kcal) energy and 6.3% (3.4g) protein to Indian diet besides being a major source of calcium and iron (12%) (Tables 1 and 2).

In addition to being an important item of human food and animal feed, chickpea also plays an important role in sustaining soil productivity by fixing atmospheric nitrogen in association with *Rhizobia*. Chickpea is estimated to fix upto 141 kg N per ha (Rupela, 1987). Crop management

V.L. Chopra (Ed.): Breeding Field Crops I: Practices, Studium Press (LLC), USA.

practices such as planting time, nutrient use and water management significantly influence biological nitrogen fixation (Ali *et al.*, 1998). Benefit from chickpea to succeeding cereal crop (*e.g.*, maize) is estimated equivalent to 60-70 kg N/ha (Ahlawat *et al.*, 1981). Thus growing chickpea helps in sustaining cereal-based cropping systems in a country like India, where rice-wheat (9.7 m ha) and rice-rice (2.1 m ha) cropping systems are lifeline for food security. Chickpea has comparative advantage in contributing to crop diversification, rotation and mixed cropping. Short duration varieties developed for multiple cropping systems can help raise cropping intensity, which is low (130%) in India.

**Table 1:** Importance of chickpea in nutrient supply in India

| *Nutrient* | *Per 100 g seed of chickpea*[1] | *Daily per capita nutrient supply in India* | *Share of chickpea in daily per capita nutrient supply** |
|---|---|---|---|
| Energy (Kcal) | 396.0 | 2197.0 | 68.51 (3.12%) |
| Protein (g) | 19.4 | 53.2 | 3.36 (6.31%) |
| Fat (g) | 5.5 | 38.9 | 0.95 (2.45%) |
| Calcium (mg) | 280.0 | 417.0 | 48.44 (11.62%) |
| Iron (mg) | 12.3 | 14.9 | 2.13 (14.28%) |
| Phosphorus (mg) | 301.0 | - | - |

*Based on the per capita availability of chickpea @ 17.3 g/day 970 m population
[1]M.R. Reddy. Status of pulse production: An overview. *J. Rural Development* 8: 645-655.

**Table 2.** Per capita availability of food grains and pulses in India

| *Year* | *Food grains (g/day)* | *Cereals (g/day)* | *Pulses (g/day)* | *Chickpea (g/day)* |
|---|---|---|---|---|
| 1970 | 455.0 | 403.1 | 51.9 | 20.0 |
| 1980 | 410.4 | 379.5 | 30.9 | 10.7 |
| 1990 | 472.6 | 431.5 | 41.1 | 10.7 |
| 1996 | 498.0 | 464.0 | 34.0 | – |
| 1998 | 565.0 | – | 36.9 | 17.3 |

## 2. AREA, PRODUCTION AND PRODUCTIVITY

Chickpea is cultivated globally on about 11.3 million hectares adding 8.8 million tonnes of grains annually to the global food basket with an average productivity of 777 kg/ha. The major chickpea-growing countries in order of their significance are India, Turkey, Pakistan, Iran, Australia, Mexico, Ethiopia, Myanmar, Spain and Bangladesh. Together they contribute 96% to the global production (Table 3). India has the distinction of being the largest chickpea producer and accounts for over 64% and 68% of the total area and production in the world. It grows chickpea on about 7.5 million hectares producing 6.1 million tonnes of grains, which represents 33% and 47% of the national pulse acreage and production, respectively (Table 4). Inspite of sizeable reduction of area (-0.70% annually), it has maintained its share of 47% to the total

**Table 3:** Global area, production and yield of chickpea (FAO, 1997)

| *Continent/ Country* | *Area (m ha)* | *Production (mt)* | *Yield (kg/ha)* |
|---|---|---|---|
| World | 11.33 | 8.81 | 777 |
| Asia | 10.35 | 8.02 | 774 |
| Africa | 0.45 | 0.26 | 585 |
| Australia | 0.24 | 0.21 | 882 |
| Europe | 0.14 | 0.09 | 594 |
| India | 7.30 | 6.00 | 822 |
| Turkey | 0.78 | 0.72 | 925 |
| Pakistan | 1.10 | 0.59 | 540 |
| Iran | 0.73 | 0.36 | 497 |
| Myanmar | 0.19 | 0.14 | 730 |
| Bangladesh | 0.08 | 0.06 | 728 |
| Syria | 0.09 | 0.06 | 624 |
| Spain | 0.12 | 0.07 | 601 |
| Ethiopia | 0.19 | 0.13 | 686 |
| Mexico | 0.14 | 0.22 | 1613 |

**Table 4.** Area (m ha), production (mt) and productivity (kg/ha) trends in chickpea as compared to total pulses in India

| *Year* | *Chickpea* | | | *Pulses* | | | *Contribution (%) of chickpea in total pulse* | |
|---|---|---|---|---|---|---|---|---|
| | *Area* | *Prod* | *Yield* | *Area* | *Prod* | *Yield* | *Area* | *Production* |
| 1959-60 | 10.33 | 5.62 | 544 | 24.83 | 11.80 | 475 | 41.60 | 47.63 |
| 1964-65 | 8.87 | 5.78 | 651 | 23.88 | 12.42 | 520 | 37.15 | 46.54 |
| 1969-70 | 7.75 | 5.55 | 715 | 22.02 | 11.69 | 531 | 35.20 | 47.48 |
| 1974-75 | 7.04 | 4.02 | 570 | 22.03 | 10.02 | 455 | 31.63 | 40.12 |
| 1979-80 | 6.99 | 3.36 | 481 | 22.26 | 8.57 | 385 | 31.40 | 39.21 |
| 1984-85 | 6.91 | 4.56 | 661 | 22.74 | 11.96 | 526 | 30.39 | 38.13 |
| 1989-90 | 6.47 | 4.22 | 652 | 23.41 | 12.86 | 549 | 27.64 | 32.82 |
| 1994-95 | 7.54 | 6.44 | 853 | 23.17 | 14.12 | 609 | 32.54 | 45.61 |
| 1997-98 | 7.54 | 6.13 | 812 | 22.85 | 13.07 | 572 | 33.00 | 46.90 |
| ***Annual growth rate (%)*** | | | | | | | | |
| 1960-70 | –2.50 | –0.12 | | 3.14 | –1.13 | | –0.09 | 1.18 |
| 1970-80 | –0.97 | –3.95 | | –3.27 | 0.11 | | –2.67 | –2.75 |
| 1980-90 | –0.70 | 2.56 | | 3.56 | 0.52 | | 5.01 | 4.26 |
| 1990-98 | 2.10 | 5.66 | | 3.07 | –0.30 | | 0.20 | 0.52 |
| 1960-98 | –0.70 | 0.21 | | 1.30 | –0.21 | | 0.28 | 1.30 |

pulse production. Chickpea production has gone up marginally from 5.62 to 6.13 million tonnes between 1959-60 and 1997-98, thus registering a positive annual growth of 0.21%. This suggests yield improvement (1.3% annually) as the key component of the production advance made in the crop.While chickpea has witnessed a positive growth in area, production and productivity during the past eight years (1990-98), pulses as a group could not achieve similar growth. However, the productivity of chickpea in the country is still far below that in Egypt, Mexico, Sudan, China, Israel, Lebanon, Yemen, Greece and Italy.

Notwithstanding its distribution throughout the country, six states *viz.,* Madhya Pradesh, Rajasthan, Uttar Pradesh, Haryana, Maharashtra and Karnataka, together contribute 90% of total production (Table 5). Over the years, Punjab, Haryana, Uttar Pradesh, Rajasthan and Bihar have witnessed negative growth in area and production whereas Madhya Pradesh, Gujarat, Maharashtra, Andhra Pradesh and Karnataka have shown positive growth. A perusal of chickpea production statistics in different states indicates considerable disparity in the realized yields between northern and southern states (Table 6). While states such as Madhya Pradesh, Rajasthan, Uttar Pradesh, Haryana and Punjab have recorded an average yield of 890 kg/ha, states such as Karnataka, Maharashtra and Assam recorded less than 400 kg/ ha. The major factors contributing to low yields in southern states are the shorter period available for the crop growth and incidence of terminal drought.

**Table 5:** Area, production and yield of chickpea in different states in India (1997-98)

| *State* | *Area (000'ha)* | | *Production (000't)* | | *Yield (kg/ha)* | |
|---|---|---|---|---|---|---|
| Madhya Pradesh | 2593.2 | (34.4%) | 2419.9 | (39.6%) | 933 | (114.9%) |
| Rajasthan | 2213.9 | (29.4%) | 1924.6 | (31.5%) | 869 | (107.0%) |
| Uttar Pradesh | 869.8 | (11.5%) | 720.0 | (11.8%) | 835 | (102.8%) |
| Maharashtra | 715.1 | (9.5%) | 290.9 | (4.8%) | 407 | (50.1%) |
| Haryana | 355.0 | (4.7%) | 310.0 | (5.1%) | 873 | (107.5%) |
| Karnataka | 336.9 | (4.5%) | 115.5 | (1.9%) | 343 | (42.2%) |
| Bihar | 127.1 | (1.7%) | 91.9 | (1.5%) | 723 | (89.0%) |
| Gujarat | 123.3 | (1.6%) | 98.8 | (1.6%) | 801 | (98.6%) |
| Andhra Pradesh | 119.7 | (1.6%) | 89.9 | (1.5%) | 751 | (92.5%) |
| Orissa | 35.0 | | 22.0 | | 629 | (77.5%) |
| West Bengal | 25.5 | | 17.0 | | 667 | (82.1%) |
| Punjab | 13.2 | | 10.9 | | 826 | (101.7%) |
| Others (Assam & TN) | 8.9 | | 5.5 | | 618 | (76.1%) |
| **(All India)** | **7536.6** | | **6116.9** | | **812** | **(100%)** |

Values in parentheses represent the share (%) to the national average.

**Table 6:** Distribution of chickpea producing states by yield levels

| *Productivity level (kg/ha)* | *No. of states* | *Average yield (kg/ha)* | *Chickpea area (000 ha)* | *Share of area (%)* | *Production (000 qtls)* | *Share of production (%)* |
|---|---|---|---|---|---|---|
| Below<500 | 3 Karnataka, Maharashtra, Assam | 386.6 | 1055.0 | 14 | 407.9 | 6 |
| >500 to 750 | 5 Andhra Pradesh, Bihar, Orissa, West Bengal Tamil Nadu | 741.4 | 303.2 | 4 | 224.8 | 4 |
| >750 | 6 Gujarat, Haryana, Madhya Pradesh, Punjab, Rajasthan, Uttar Pradesh | 889.1 | 6168.4 | 82 | 5484.2 | 90 |
| Total | 14 | 812.7 | 7526.6 | 100 | 6116.9 | 100 |

# 3. ORIGIN AND BREEDING SYSTEMS

## 3.1. Taxonomy

Chickpea belongs to the genus *Cicer, tribe Cicereae,* subfamily *Papilionoideae* of the family *Leguminosae.* Originally, *Cicer* was classified in the tribe *Vicieae Alef.* Subsequently accumulated information on morphological, cytogenetic and molecular aspects made its position sufficiently distinct to be considered a tribe of its own, the *Cicereae* (Kupicha, 1977; Nozzolillo, 1985). Apart from many original features from morphological point of view, the basic chromosome number of *Cicer* (x=8) differs from that of *Pisum* and *Lens* (x=7), the other genera of the *tribe Vicieae* (Ramanujam, 1976). On the basis of interphase nuclear structure in *Leguminosae*, Patankar and Ranjekar (1984) observed less condensed chromatin (12%) in *Cicer* chromosomes as compared to 38-62% in other genera of *Vicieae.* Evidence from scanning electron microscopy also favoured its transfer from *Vicieae* to the monogenic *Cicereae.* Synteny among the three genera further confirms *Pisum* and *Lens* as the closest genomes followed by *Pisum* and *Cicer,* and Lens and *Cicer,* thus confirming the evolutionary distances among these genera with *Cicer* being separated first from the other two genera on the index of genetic similarity.

In addition to the cultivated species *Cicer arietinum,* there are about 42 recognized wild species in the genus *Cicer* (Table 7). Of them, nine are annual and the remaining perennial in nature. Geographical distribution of the wild species is confined to areas around the Mediterranean Sea, Russia, Ethiopia and Sudan and in the Himalayan Mountains of India. There is hardly any reference of the cultivated species found in the wild state.

**Table 7:** *Cicer* species and their distribution

| *Sl. no.* | *Species* | *Distribution* |
|---|---|---|
| ***Annual*** | | |
| 1. | *C. arietinum* | Mediterranean region to Burma, Ethiopia, Mexico, Chile |
| 2. | *C. chorassanicum* | N&C Afghanistan, N & NE Iran |
| 3. | *C. bijugum* | SE Turkey, N Syria, N Iraq |
| 4. | *C. cuneatum* | Ethiopia, SE Egypt, NE Sudan, Saudi Arabia |
| 5. | *C. echinospermum* | Turkey, E Anatolia, N Iraq |
| 6. | *C. judaicum* | Palestine, Lebanon |
| 7. | *C. pinnatifidum* | Cyprus, N Iraq, Syria, Turkey, USSR |
| 8. | *C. reticulatum* | E Turkey |
| 9. | *C. yamashitae* | Afghanistan |
| ***Perennial*** | | |
| 10. | *C. acanthophyllum* | Afghanistan, Pakistan, USSR |
| 11. | *C. anatolicum* | Turkey, Iran, Iraq, Armenia |
| 12. | *C. atlanticum* | Morocco |
| 13. | *C. balcaricum* | Caucasus (USSR) |
| 14. | *C. baldshuanicum* | USSR |
| 15. | *C. canariense* | Canary islands, Tenerife and La Palma |
| 16. | *C. fedtschenkoi* | USSR, N & NE Afghanistan |
| 17. | *C. flexuosum* | USSR |
| 18. | *C. floribundum* | Turkey |
| 19. | *C. graecum* | Greece |
| 20. | *C. grande* | USSR |
| 21. | *C. heterophyllum* | Turkey |
| 22. | *C. incanum* | USSR |
| 23. | *C. incisum* | Greece, Turkey, Iran, Lebanon, USSR |
| 24. | *C. isauricum* | Turkey |
| 25. | *C. kermanense* | SE Iran |
| 26. | *C. korshinskyi* | USSR |
| 27. | *C. laetum* | USSR |
| 28. | *C. macrocanthum* | Afghanistan, India, Pakistan, USSR |
| 29. | *C. microphyllum* | E Afghanistan, Tibet, India, Pakistan, USSR |
| 30. | *C. mogoltavicum* | USSR |
| 31. | *C. montbrettii* | Albania, Bulgaria, Turkey |
| 32. | *C. multijugum* | Afghanistan |
| 33. | *C. nuristanicum* | Afghanistan, India, Pakistan |
| 34. | *C. oxyodon* | Iran, Afghanistan, N Iraq |
| 35. | *C. paucijugum* | USSR |
| 36. | *C. pungens* | Afghanistan, USSR |
| 37. | *C, rassuloviae* | USSR |
| 38. | *C. rechingeri* | Afghanistan |
| 39. | *C. songaricum* | USSR |
| 40. | *C. spiroceras* | Iran |
| 41. | *C. stapfianum* | Iran |
| 42. | *C. subaphyllum* | Iran |
| 43. | *C. tragacanthoides* | Iran, USSR |

Eco-geographical diversity often used to discriminate between *desi* and *kabuli* as separate groups within the cultivated species is the result of selection by man for desired quality and adaptation to new niches in nature. Small-seeded *desi,* usually with brown seed coat, and large-seeded *kabuli,* usually with white seed coat, are also classified as microsperma and macrosperma. *Kabuli* cultivars do not contain anthocyanin pigment on the foliage, have larger leaves and more basal branches than *desi* types. *Desi* cultivars are better adapted to East Asian regions including the Indian subcontinent whereas *kabuli* types are preferred and adapted in the middle East and the Mediterranean region.

## 3.2. Origin

de Candolle (1883) traced the origin of chickpea to an area south of the Caucasus and northern Persia. Vavilov (1926) designated southwest Asia and the Mediterranean as primary and Ethiopia as secondary centres of diversity. However, the most probable centre of origin seems to be southeastern Turkey and adjoining Syria (Ladizinsky, 1975) since the most closely related wild species of *C. arietinum* namely, *C. bijugum, C. echinospermum* and *C. reticulatum* have been widely distributed in this Fertile Crescent. From its place of origin in western Asia, it subsequently spread to the Indian subcontinent and Europe (Singh and Auckland, 1975). Based on the crossability relationship with the cultivated species and geographical distribution of various wild species, the most probable wild progenitor of the cultivated chickpea seems to be *C. reticulatum.* It is also possible that both had originated from a common ancestor.

It is generally considered that the *kabuli* type owes its origin to selection from the most primitive *desi.* The divergence probably occurred in comparatively recent time and almost certainly in the Near East or Mediterranean region (Hawtin and Singh, 1980). The basis of selection was white flowered plant and its correlated colourless seed, which appeared as a mutant in the local microsperma population. In view of the narrow genetic pool of macrosperma as compared to microsperma, it is highly probable that *kabuli* was evolved through natural mutation and selection from *desi* type. Sustained preference and contingent selection led to the present diversification of forms.

It is believed that chickpea was domesticated at least 8000 years back as evidenced from various archaeological findings. The most significant one was from Hacilar near Burdur in Turkey when its 6250 BC remains were unearthed (Helbaek, 1970). Subsequently, the crop must have spread and domesticated in other countries with arid/semi-arid and subtropical environments. It is believed that the Hellenes took the crop from Turkey westward to the Mediterranean and eastward to India. Excavations from Atranjikhera in Uttar Pradesh yielded fossil grains probably dating back to 2000 BC (Chowdury *et al.,* 1971). The frequent use of the word *'chanaka'* for chickpea in the *'Sanskrit'* literature shows its ancient history of cultivation.

## 3.3. Botanical Characteristics

Chickpea is an indeterminate annual herbaceous shrub with yellowish green to bluish green or purple foliage. Plants are erect, semi-erect or prostrate. The main stem is round and the branches quadrangular and ribbed. Branches originate from the first node in the axils of simple scale-like leaves. Basal primary branches on the main stem are more vigorous than those that arise at the upper nodes. Plants are profusely branched with secondary and tertiary branches at various levels. Chickpea possesses a deep tap root system with three to four well-defined rows of lateral roots. The primary and secondary roots may develop large lobbed nodules that contain *Rhizobia* which fix atmospheric nitrogen symbiotically. The first two nodes on the main stem have simple scale-like leaves fused with two lateral scale-like stipulae. Leaves are borne singly at each node from the third node onwards. They are compound, arranged in an alternate phyllotaxy and generally imparipinnate having 11 to 13 leaflets. Types with a highly dissected compound leaf or with simple leaf laminae or multipinnate also occur (Singh and Singh, 1995). The leaf structure is bifacial with stomata in equal abundance on both the upper and lower leaf surfaces. The normal floral botany of chickpea is fairly consistent with a single monocarpellary flower on each peduncle with five sepals, five (2+2+1) petals, and ten stamens in diadelphous (9+1) condition. Occasionally, twin polycarpellary flowers per peduncle are also reported (Kaul and Solanki, 1950; Pundir *et al.,* 1988). The flowers are borne axillary on short jointed peduncles arising from the leaf axil and are situated opposite the leaves. They are white, pink, purple or blue in colour. Yellow deformed buds, which desiccate without opening, and termed pseudo-flowers, appear on the first few flowering buds. The pods are typically inflated ending in a mucro, which sometimes looks like a thorn containing seed(s) attached to the ventral suture. The basal pods have generally two seeds and occasionally three seeds. The foliage as well as the pod wall is covered with abundant glandular hairs, which have been described as trichome hydathodes. They secrete highly acidic exudates predominantly containing malic acid (94.2%) and small amount of oxalic (5.6%) and acetic (0.2%) acids. Seeds are characteristically 'beaked' sometimes angular and very frequently 'ram head' with a ridged or smooth seed coat. Seed colour varies from chalky white, burgundy and brown to black and is determined by colour and thickness of seed coat and colour of cotyledons. Germination is hypogeal and cotyledons have axillary buds. Indeterminate nature of the crop makes its vegetative structures such as roots, nodules, stems and leaves to grow ceaselessly even after the initiation of flowering. Photosynthesis in chickpea, as in other grain legumes, is by the C3 carboxylic acid pathway. Since it is a quantitative long day plant, air temperature, photoperiod and their interaction markedly affect the time of initiation of flower buds and their subsequent expansion into open flowers. Small-seeded cultivars usually flower over a longer period than the large-seeded cultivars. Only 20 to 50% of the perfect flowers set pods. Number of pods per plant may very from 30 to 150 depending on genotypes and growing conditions.

### 3.4. Genomic Evolution

Chickpea genome has eight pairs of somatic chromosome (lyengar, 1939; Ramanujam and Joshi, 1941; Ladizinsky and Adler, 1976b) and as it responds very well to polyploidization (Ramanujam and Joshi, 1941; Sohoo *et al.,* 1970; Phadnis and Narkhede, 1972; Pundir *et al.,* 1983), it does not appear to be a primary or a secondary polyploid. Cytological studies reveal that all species, both cultivated and wild, of the genus *Cicer* are diploid with 2n chromosome number of 16. However, very rarely in some plants the somatic chromosome number is found to be 2n=14 (Rao, 1929; Dixit, 1932; van der Maesen, 1972) and survival of such plants in nature remains doubtful. Based on the findings of secondary association, constant attachment of four chromosomes to the nucleolus and the presence of four satellites, lyengar (1939) considered *C. arietinum* to be an allotetraploid where duplication of chromosomes had taken place during evolution. From karyotypic studies on seven cultivars, Phadnis (1970) found chickpea to be diploid and ruled out the possibility of this species being tetraploid. The occurence of 2n=14 in some studies further supports genomic status of *C. arietinum* as diploid. On the basis of crossability and cytogenetic relationships among seven *Cicer* species, Ladizinsky and Adler (1976a, 1976b) placed *C. reticulatum,* and *C. echinospermum* in one group (primary gene pool) and *C. judaicum, C. pinnatifidum* and *C. bijugum* in another group (tertiary gene pool). *C. cumeatum* showed strong cross incompatibility with either of the two groups. Ocampo *et al.* (1992) classified nine annual species into two groups using karyotype symmetry indices. The first group included *C. arietinum, C. reticulatum,* and *C. echinospermum,* while the second group comprised the remaining species. Labdi *et al.*

(1996) also studied the phylogenetic relationships using isozyme polymorphism and confirmed the above grouping with the second group resulting in three clusters. The conventional approaches used for assigning new genome(s) are based on morphological, physiological and biochemical differences, crossing relationships, chromosome number and chromosome pairing behaviour of $F_1$ hybrids between species with known and unknown genomic constitutions. Inadequacy of world collections of annual and perennial species of *Cicer,* difficulty in making inter-specific crosses due to small size and cleistogamous nature of the flowers, and failure to obtain $F_1$ hybrids between cultivated and distantly related species mainly due to strong hybridization barriers are, in fact, the major reasons for not assigning genome(s) to various species of the *Cicer.* In the last two decades, a number of studies have demonstrated the utility and potential of molecular tools to solve many of the problems and controversies of evolution and biosystematics that have remained unsolved inspite of best efforts made through conventional approaches (Avise, 1994).

### 3.5. Floral Biology

Chickpea is predominantly a self-pollinated crop, perhaps, obligatory since pollination takes place at the hooded bud stage. Pollen is most viable when the flower is half opened, and pollination occurs 12 to 24 h before the flower is fully expanded (Eshel, 1968). During the early stages of green bud development and enlargement, the style elongates and the stamens remain clustered at the base of the ovary. At the so called white bud stage, when white petals have emerged from the calyx but are still enfolded, filaments elongate so that anthers are positioned close to the stigma. At this stage, pollen is shed and most of it lands on the stigmatic surface. It adheres to papillate cells in a small localized area at the most distal region of the stigma. Full bloom occurs approximately 24 h after pollen is shed. The white bud stage is the stage of floral development that has been empirically suggested as most appropriate for hybridization in chickpea because at this stage, stigma is most receptive and pollen viability is high. Crossing attempts involving either emasculation or no emasculation have given erratic results (23 to 98% hybrid seeds) and this compounded by the low rate of natural seed set (18 to 52%) due to flower drops has hampered works on genetic and breeding research. The low rate of success may be attributed not only to the stage of bud development but also to the small number of papillate cells on the stigmatic surface that are receptive to pollen. Thus flowers for cross-pollination should be selected carefully so that pollen with the highest viability is available.

## 4. GENETIC RESOURCES RELEVANT TO BREEDING OBJECTIVES

Conservation of plant genetic resources is as old as agriculture itself. However, systematic work on genetic resources related to crops of agricultural importance in general and for breeding objective in particular has been taken up after the classical work of Vavilov (1926) on centres of genetic diversity and the realization by the breeders of its importance in plant improvement.

Chickpea is one of the six pulse crops with rich genetic resources. About 67,500 accessions conserved in various gene banks (Table 8) worldwide are potential gene sources for desired improvement. A very large number of native varieties, land races, genetic stocks, improved breeding lines and released varieties along with the wild species constitute the genetic resources in chickpea (Table 9).

**Table 8:** The six largest *Ex situ* germplasm collections of chickpea

| *S.no.* | *Organization/country* | *No. of accessions maintained* | *Share (%) in the total collection* |
|---|---|---|---|
| 1. | ICRISAT, Patancheru, India | 17550 | 26% |
| 2. | ICARDA, Aleppo, Syria | 10125 | 15% |
| 3. | PARC, Islamabad, Pakistan | 6075 | 9% |
| 4. | USDA, RPIS, Pullman, USA | 6075 | 9% |
| 5. | SPII, Karaj, Iran | 5400 | 8% |
| 6. | V1R, Laningrad, Russia | 2700 | 4% |
| | Others | 19575 | 29% |
| | **Total** | **67500** | |

*Source*: FAO, 1996. Report on the state of the world's plant genetic resources for food and agriculture, pp. 75.

**Table 9:** Composition of chickpea germplasm maintained Worldwide

| | |
|---|---|
| Land races/old cultivars | 39% |
| Advanced cultivars/breeding lines | 7% |
| Wild species | 1% |
| Other (mixed and unknown) | 53% |

*Source*: FAO, 1996. Report on the state of the world's plant genetic resources for food and agriculture, pp. 75.

### 4.1. Collection

Systematic collection of chickpea germplasm since the beginning of the $20^{th}$ century has helped assemble a large number of accessions in national and international centres. Regional pulse improvement project of USDA assembled 7064 accessions from India and Iran in early seventies. Some notable expeditions for collecting chickpea germplasm were those made in the USSR (Vavilov, 1926; Broue *et al.*, 1975), Mexico (Campos *et al.*, 1961), Peru (Budin and Shmaraev, 1971), Afghanistan (Gubanov *et al.*, 1975), Ethiopia (Bezuneh, 1975; Toll, 1980; Pundir and Mengesha, 1983), Bangladesh (Anonymous, 1979), India (Anonymous, 1980; Pundir, 1982; Govil, 1983; Pundir *et al.*, 1989), Pakistan (Ahmad *et al.*, 1982), Morocco (Pundir *et al.*, 1989) and Myanmar (Pundir *et al.*, 1991). With the establishment of the All India Coordinated Pulses Improvement Project (AICPIP) in 1966 and International Crops Research Institute for the Semi-Arid Tropics (ICRISAT) at Patancheru in 1972, a new era of chickpea research began wherein systematic collection, evaluation and documentation of traditional and elite germplasm have been taken up. Further impetus was given to exploration, collection and conservation of chickpea genetic resources with the establishment of National Bureau of Plant Genetic Resources (NBPGR) in 1976 and International Centre for Agriculture Research in the Dry Areas in 1977. A total of 9,580 accessions comprising of 8,648 indigenous and 932 exotic are maintained as base collection at NBPGR. About 13,452 accessions maintained as working collections by various research centres under AICPIP are, however, repetitive in nature and include a great number of duplicates.

In addition to the diversity available within the cultivated species, a lot of interest is generated recently in the wild species of *Cicer* with the realization that they form wealth of genetic resources not only for resistance against biotic and abiotic stresses but also for yield traits (van der Maesen and Pundir, 1984). A systematic screening of the available accessions of wild species at ICRISAT and ICARDA has resulted in the identification of valuable sources of resistance (Table 10). For example, *C., judaicum, C. montbretii* and C. *pinnatifidum* possess genes for resistance to *Ascochyta* blight (Singh *et al.*, 1981); C. *bijugum* to *Heterodera ciceri* (Singh *et al.*, 1980); and *C. bijugum, C. echinospermum* and *C. reticulatum* to cold (Singh *et al.*, 1990). Several crosses have been attempted between cultigens and the wild species, but so far only cross between *C. arietinum* × *C. reticulatum* has given fertile hybrids (Landizinsky and Adler, 1976b; Pundir and van der Maesen, 1983). *Cicer echinospermum* is crossable to the cultivated species but hybrids are completely self sterile due to presence of a reciprocal translocation. Seeds can, however, be obtained by back crossing to *C. arietinum.* Once the crossing barriers between cultigens and the wild species are broken, potential variability hidden in the wild species would be accessible to breeders for desired improvement.

**Table 10:** Annual wild species of chickpea and their importance

| *Species* | *Somatic chromosome no.* | *Sources of resistance to* |
|---|---|---|
| *C. arietinum* | 14, 16, 24, 32, 33 | *Ascochyta* blight, *Fusarium* wilt Leaf miner, Cold, Drought |
| *C. chorassanicum* | 16 | Leaf miner |
| *C. cuneatum* | 16 | Leaf miner, Seed beetle, *Ascochyta* blight |
| *C. judaicum* | 16 | Leaf miner, Seed beetle, *Ascochyta* blight, Cold |
| *C. pinnatifidum* | 16 | Leaf miner, Seed beetle, *Ascochyta* blight, Cold |
| *C. reticulatum* | 16 | *Fusarium* wilt, Seed beetle, Cold, *Ascochyta* blight |
| *C. yamashitae* | 16 | - |
| *C. bijugum* | 16 | *Ascochyta* blight, Cyst nematode, Seed beetle, Cold |
| *C. echinospermum* | 16 | Leaf miner, Seed beetle, Cold |

## 4.2. Evaluation

Evaluation of chickpea germplasm bas been restricted to a small subset of accessions, which appeared promising and/or potential sources of valuable genes for resistance against biotic and abiotic stresses. Bulk of the accessions stored in different gene banks still awaits systematic and comprehensive characterization and evaluation for further utilization in breeding programmes. There are several reports in the literature regarding evaluation and utilization of chickpea germplasm for specific characters. However, the first systematic evaluation was attempted at ICRISAT wherein about 12,000 accessions, evaluated for yield and yield attributes, have revealed great genetic variability (Table 11). Screening of the germplasm for key stresses resulted in the identification of a

**Table 11:** Range of variability for quantitative traits in chickpea germplasm

| | *Range* | | | |
|---|---|---|---|---|
| *Trait* | *Minimum* | *Maximum* | *Mean* | *Variance* |
| Days to 50% flowering | 33 | 107 | 64.2 | 138.6 |
| Flowering duration (days) | 13 | 75 | 35.9 | 49.6 |
| Plant height (cm) | 14.2 | 96.3 | 38.3 | 77.0 |
| Days to maturity | 84 | 169 | 117.5 | 203.4 |
| Pods per plant | 3 | 238 | 38.9 | 564.7 |
| Seeds per pod | 1 | 3.2 | 1.2 | - |
| 100-seed mass (g) | 3.8 | 59.1 | 16.1 | 40.4 |
| Harvest index (%) | 21.9 | 64.8 | - | - |
| Seed protein (%) | 12.1 | 29.6 | 19.8 | 6.0 |
| Seed yield (kg/ha) | 70 | 5130 | 1286.0 | 422571.5 |

*Source*: R.P.S. Pundir, K.N. Reddy and M.H. Mengesha. 1988. ICRISAT Chickpea germplasm catalogue: Evaluation and analysis Patancheru, India. p. 94.

number of donor sources for broadening the genetic base of released varieties (Table 12). However, what is lacking is a systematic multi-location screening of chickpea germplasm under controlled conditions as well as in hot spots under different agro-climatic zones.

**Table 12:** Sources of tolerance against major stresses in chickpea

| *Stress* | *Total accessions screened* | *Accessions showing tolerance (1-4 scale)* |
|---|---|---|
| *Ascochyta* blight | 19370 | 32 |
| *Fusarium* wilt | 2636 | 28 |
| | 2150 (IIPR) | 23 |
| Leaf miner | 5474 | 8 |
| Seed beetle | 5153 | - |
| Cyst nematode | 9257 | - |
| Cold | 9095 | 13 |
| Drought | 1000 | 3 |

*Source*: K.B. Saxena and O. Singh. 1997. Prospects of creating higher yield potential in chickpea. *In* : Recent advances in Pulses Research. A.N. Asthana and M. Ali (*Eds*). ISPRD, IIPR, Kanpur, India, pp. 66-88.

## 4.3. Utilization

Among the major chickpea-growing countries, India has made better use of indigenous as well as exotic germplasm for improving yield potential and stability by incorporating relevant genes and insulating varieties against key pests and diseases. Prior to sixties, local germplasm was directly processed for the development of varieties to meet the immediate requirement. As a result, a total of 20 varieties were released till 1960 of which 80% were pure line selection (Table 13). Afterwards, variability created through hybridization/ recombination between genotype having desired traits and the widely adapted cultivars has been utilized for further improvement. Many donors have been identified for a range of traits of economic importance. However, only a small number have so far been utilized in the breeding programme (Table 14) resulting in the release of about 110 high yielding varieties suitable for various agro-ecological zones to combat the prevailing stress.

**Table 13:** Pattern in the use of different breeding methodologies for chickpea improvement during various time periods

| *Period* | *Total* | *Selection* | *Mutation* | *Hybridization* |
|---|---|---|---|---|
| Before 1960 | 20 | 16 (80%) | 0 | 4 (20%) |
| 1960-69 | 6 | 2 (33%) | 1 (17%) | 3 (50%) |
| 1970-79 | 20 | 6 (30%) | 0 | 14 (70%) |
| 1980-89 | 29 | 3 (10%) | 4 (14%) | 22 (76%) |
| 1990-99 | 36 | 7 (19%) | 1 (3%) | 28 (78%) |
| **Total** | **111** | **34 (31%)** | **6 (5%)** | **71 (64%)** |

Values in parentheses represent percentage of the developed varieties.

**Table 14:** Donors identified and used in chickpea breeding programmes

| ***Characteristics*** | ***Donors identified*** | ***Donors used*** |
|---|---|---|
| Bold seeds | 82 | K850, KTP1, L144, BGG8, RSG216, Ofera, N31, Cyprus local, Bhim, H85-69, E100Y(M), BG256, Phule G5, Vishwas, Gaurav, RSG143-1, ICCC42, Annegiri, Bheema, BDNG342, KW118, RSG540, IPC92-39, IPC94-131, DCP92-1, GLK88016, H86-18, BG391, BDNG342, ILC116, BG364 |
| Double podded | 18 | JG62, DCP92-1, M109, JG1265, ICC4928, 1CCC30, KTP1, Annegiri mutant, Sel436, RSG44, RSG538, F5, K850, Anupam |
| Multi-seeded | 12 | RSG540, IPC94-19, ICC12118, ICC1052, PDG85-13, HMS6, JG201, HUG211, H86-48, HUG237 |
| Tall (>60 cm) | 15 | DGM727, 2D-287, ICC810198, BG276, RSG236, RSG536, RSG668, RSG155 |
| Erect | 12 | K850, L409, L410, BG274, BG273, Chaffa, RSG46, IPC92-39, ICC4958 |
| Basal/profuse branching | 3 | ICC7002, IPC71, Bushy mutant |
| Long fruiting branch | 1 | T3 |
| Secondary branches | 3 | JM 2106, C. *reticulatum* |
| Profuse podding | 2 | ICCC42, CO2 |
| Short internode | 2 | E 100Y(M), JGM1 |
| Wide adaptability | 3 | Pusa256, C235, GPF7035 |
| Early/extra early | 28 | PDG84-16, ICCV2, IPC92-39, RSG44, JG74, Anupam, Radhey, Chaffa, BDNG259-1, LD153, GNG146, BGM683, RSG46, 1CCV 89244, 1CCV 92332 |
| ***Biotic stresses*** | | |
| *Fusaricum Wilt* | 123 | WR315, CPS1, WR375, JC74, JC315, JG1265, K315, K850, Avrodhi, GW6, BDN9-3, BCP4, Annegiril, PKK2, GL8834, GL87079, Phule G5, Phule G81-1-1, Phule G12, Phule 87207, ICCV10, ICCV2, ICCC32, ICCC37, ICCC42, KPG59, H86-72, IPC92-37, DCP92-3, SAKI8516, BGM443, Dohad yellow, PDG83-84, GNG426, JCP13, JCP27, BDNG88, CL83119, CL84038, H82-2, GNG663, K315, KPG259-4, GL86123, KPG143-1, H86-72, H86-18, GPF2 |
| *Ascochyta* blight | 47 | EIOOY(M), E100Y, PG82-1, EC26446, BRG8, PDG1, ICC7002, GL84038, GL84099, BG276, H82-5, H86-18, H75-35, Guarav, GLK88016, 1LC1069, BG267, DG257, GNG469, BG362, GL90169 |
| *Botrytis* grey mold | 10 | BG276,1CC1069,1CC12483, Dhanush, (CCW92, ICCV41 |
| Root rots | 6 | H208, 1CC596, CoG6, ICCV10 |
| Stunt | 6 | - |
| Pod borer | 27 | PDE2, BDNG, H1R236,1CC12483, PDE2-3, P202,1CC506, BG362, GL1014, PDG90-2E |

**Table 14:** (*Contd...*)

**Table 14:** (*Contd...*)

| *Characteristics* | *Donors identified* | *Donors used* |
|---|---|---|
| Root knot nematode | 4 | - |
| Bruchid tolerance | 1 | DCP92-2 |
| ***Abiotic stresses*** | | |
| Drought tolerance | 9 | ICC4958, Phule G5, Annegiri, Plule G81-1-1, Bheema, K850, ICCV10 |
| Heat tolerance | 1 | ICC92944 |
| Cold tolerance | 4 | ICC88501, ICC92329, ICC92504 |
| Salt tolerance | 7 | CSG8962, CSG8893, CSG88101 |
| Non-lodging | 4 | DCP92-3, L411, L410 |

## 5. BREEDING METHODS EMPLOYED

Genetic improvement of chickpea has continued since domestication of the crop. However, the major advances through breeding process appear to be confined to recent times as systematic research works started only in 1966, when the All India Coordinated Pulses Improvement Project (AICPIP) was initiated. Before its coming into being, efforts were directed more towards selection of pure lines from the heterogeneous land races/ local germplasm and identification of varieties for specific adaptation. These varieties were well adapted to the climatic conditions prevailing in that specific domain but performed poorly outside the area of recommendation, thus resulting in wide fluctuation in yield and production. With AICPIP in place, opportunities were created to infuse new variability in breeding programmes through hybridization and exchange, which started giving rich dividend in terms of new varieties of wider adaptability coupled with resistance to key stresses.

The breeding method to be employed for achieving improvement depends on the breeding objectives and the feasibility with which the character under consideration is amenable besides, of course, the resources at breeder's disposal and the advances already made. Breeding strategy for chickpea improvement has gone through a sea change over years. If it was pure line selection as the most preferred method upto sixties, then the pedigree method of selection following hybridization has been most extensively employed after-wards. Though many variants of pedigree method such as bulk-pedigree, single-seed descent, single-pod descent, etc., were suggested and applied but the classical pedigree method remains the most widely applied method for selecting better recombinants. Besides back cross method for improving a specific trait in otherwise already improved variety, mutation breeding has also been employed occasionally (Kharkwal, 1983; Dahiya *et al.,* 1984) for creating new variability or breaking unfavourable linkages that limit improvement in chickpea. Prominent varieties developed through different breeding methods are as follows :

| | |
|---|---|
| **Pure line selection** | Dohad yellow, Chaffa, BDN9-3, Annegiri, JG1, JG62, JG74, JG221, JG315, Ujjain 21, Ujjain 24, BR77, BR78, Gwalior2, G24, 536, K468, K4, RS10, D8, Jyoti, Warangal, COI, CO2 |
| **Hybridization** | H355, Hara Chhole, GNG16, C214, C235, H203, BC209, Gaurav, Pant G114, GG588, BG212, BG329, BG362, BG240, ICC4, BG256, RSG44, Type3, Radhey, KPG59, K850, Phule G5, JG5, Phule G12, ICCV2, L144, L550, ICCC32, ICCV2 |
| **Mutation** | Pusa408, Pusa413, Pusa417, RSG2, RS11, WGG2 |

## 5.1. Breeding Objectives

Since chickpea is grown mainly in rainfed areas by marginal farmers, the breeding objectives were oriented more towards developing high yielding and stable varieties in addition to the following:

- Incorporation of resistance/tolerance to major biotic and abiotic stresses
- Development of high yielding, short duration varieties for nontraditional areas and cropping systems
- Incorporation of bold seededness in high yielding background
- Simultaneous improvement of biomass and harvest index
- Development of varieties responsive to high inputs
- Introgression of genes in accessible to conventional breeding through wide hybridization to broaden the genetic base of cultigens.

## 6. PROGRESS ACHIEVED

A significant contribution to chickpea improvement has been made in minimizing the adverse impact of biotic and abiotic stresses through incorporation of resistance/tolerance. This has helped stabilize chickpea production in the country despite its cultivation being relegated to marginal environments and reduction in the area under its cultivation. In fact, the past decade has witnessed improvement in the productivity touching 812 kg/ha. The salient progress made for different ecologies is discussed below:

### 6.1. Rainfed Ecology

More than 80% area under chickpea cultivation is rainfed. Therefore, most of the improvement programmes have centred on stabilizing yield through alleviation of the stresses prevalent in this ecology.

### 6.2. Breeding for High and Stable Yield

The primary objective of chickpea improvement programmes has been to raise the genetic yield threshold and stability across environments. Efforts were made to fulfill this objective by evaluating advanced breeding lines generated by different research centres at AICPIP locations spread across the country over the years. This has resulted in identification of more than 90 varieties since the inception of AICPIP. Some of them are C235, L550, Gaurav, PBG1, JG74, H208, Pusa209, Pusa256, Radhey, Avrodhi, Udai, Pusa372, Chaffa, Pant G114, K850, Annegiri, BDN9-3 and ICCV10. These genotypes are not only high yielding under different situations but also form a good agronomic base for further improvement.

### 6.3. Breeding for Resistance to Biotic Stresses

Replacement of a large number of land races with a few improved cultivars has made disease-pest syndrome increasingly more complex and unmanageable, necessitating shift in research emphasis towards resistance breeding. Systematic collection, screening and utilization of germplasm from the primary gene pool for finding alternate/additional resistant sources against major pests and their races have led to the release of several high yielding pest resistant varieties. The major diseases and insect pests affecting chickpea crop are *Fusarium wilt, Ascochyta* blight, dry root rot, *Botrytis* grey mold, *Helicoverpa* pod borer and root knot nematode.

#### 6.3.1. *Fusarium wilt*

*Fusarium* wilt (*Fusarium oxysporum* spp. *ciceri*) is a major disease particularly in dry areas of all the zones. The pathogen exists in as many as five races. Screening of more than 12,000 accessions by a simple and reliable screening technique has resulted in the identification of stable resistant sources by national and international programmes (Nene and Haware, 1980). Genetics of resistance against race 1 (Kumar and Haware, 1982; Sidhu *et al.,* 1983; Smithson *et al.,* 1983; Upadhyaya *et al.,* 1983a, 1983b) and race 2 (Pathak *et al.,* 1975; Gumber *et al.,* 1995; Kumar, 1998) have been worked out. This has helped systematic incorporation of the resistance from stable donors such as WR315, CPS1, P436-2, GW3-1 and KW17 into high yielding background to develop resistant varieties like Pusa212, JG315, ICCC32, Avrodhi, BG244, Phule G5, ICCV10 and H355. Advance lines (GL87078 and GL87079) possessing resistance to all the four races have been identified (Singh *et al.,* 1994).

### 6.3.2. *Ascochyta blight*

*Ascochyta* blight caused by *Ascochyta rabiei* poses a severe obstacle to realizing the potential yield of high yielding chickpea varieties particularly in the cool and humid climate of the northwest plain zone (NWPZ). Racial differences have been reported from India and the Mediterranean region, and as many as six races of the pathogen are in existence. Inheritance studies on blight resistance reveal dominant as well as recessive gene controlling the trait but the genetic control seems to be much more complex than what it appears to be in literature. Development of a simple and reliable field screening technique has been instrumental in screening more than 20,000 accessions in national and international programmes. Several reliable resistant sources such as E100Y, EIOOY(M), BRG8, NEC206, ILC202 and others are identified and prominent varieties such as Gaurav, BG261, C235, GNG146, PBG1 and GNG469 combining resistance to the disease have been developed and grown on large areas.

### 6.3.3. *Other diseases*

There are several other diseases such as *Botrytis* grey mold (*Botrytis cinerea*) in the northern plain zone and dry root rot (*Rhizoctonia bataticola*) in all the zones that can seriously damage chickpea crop when environment is favourable for disease development. Resistant sources to dry root rot have been identified (C104 and H208). Since a single dominant gene controls resistance, it is not difficult to incorporate resistance into the high yielding background. Improved lines such as H86-84, H86-18, ICC8383 and ICC10466 having resistance to root rot along with wilt have been identified, and H355 and ICCVIO are released as resistant varieties. Resistant varieties such as BG276 and Dhanush against *Botrytis* grey mold have also been developed besides identification of resistant sources such as ILC202, ICC1069, ICC11321, P1528 and 235-38 (Singh *et al.,* 1982).

### 6.3.4. *Nematodes*

Among numerous nematodes attacking chickpea, two nematodes, cyst (*Heterodera ciceri*) and root rot (*Meloidogyne* spp.), are most widespread. Some of the lines such as Bheema, N31, N59, ICC92, ICC5875 and ICC6371 have shown tolerance against *Meloidogyne*. However, stable and usable resistance against the root rot within the cultivated species is still elusive. Evaluation of the wild species has led to the identification of C. *bijugum, C. pinnatifidum* and C. *reticulatum* as a potential source of resistance against *Heterodera ciceri.*

### 6.3.5. *Helicoverpa Pod Borer*

Pod borer *(H. armigera)* attacks chickpea from the seedling stage to near maturity and can cause severe damage. Screening of more than 14,800 germplasm accessions against the pest at ICRISAT has resulted in identification of one accession, ICC506, with fairly good tolerance. Later, the national programmes could identify several lines (PDE2, P202, GL645, PDG84-10) possessing tolerance to this dreaded insect pest. These are being utilized in the crossing programmes for combining resistance with high yield. The most effective breeding approach to combine tolerance to *Helicoverpa* is suggested to be one using non-preference/antibiosis through recurrent selection.

## 6.4. Breeding for Tolerance to Abiotic Stresses

Among abiotic stresses, terminal drought, high temperature during the reproductive stage, cold sensitivity during the vegetative and flowering stages, and salinity/alkalinity throughout the crop period are the major constraints causing low yield and instability in the rainfed ecology. Breeding efforts have been directed towards alleviation of these constraints to help stabilize chickpea yield.

### 6.4.1. *Drought tolerance*

Drought is one of the major abiotic stresses as chickpea is mostly grown on residual moisture. Two major breeding strategies are followed to alleviate the moisture stress: one by breeding for traits that enable the plants to escape drought and another by breeding drought tolerant lines. Early plant vigour, fast ground cover and large seed size besides high root biomass, long and deep root system, high leaf water potential and small leaflets are some of the attributes showing significant association with drought tolerance. High harvest index, large number of pods per unit area and high grain mass along with early maturity are associated with drought escape. Regulation of cellular turgor pressure and hydration through osmotic adjustment have been shown to increase the yield potential of chickpea upto 20% under high water-deficit environments. C235 is found to be a good osmoregulator. However, lack of a simple repeatable screening technique applicable on a large-scale has been the major hindrance in breeding for drought tolerance. Screening of germplasm accessions under irrigated and non-irrigated conditions has resulted in the identification of two drought resistant lines, ICC4958 and ICC10488 giving significantly higher yield than the best check, Annegiri (Saxena, 1987). Other genotypes showing consistent tolerance to drought are ICCV10, Phule G5, K850, Vijay, RSG44, RSG143-1 and RSG936 (Ali, 1999).

A diversified bulk population breeding method is suggested that used drought tolerant line as one of the parents for improving the adaptation of high yielding lines.

Breeding for early maturity has been directed towards the development of extra short duration materials for environments where the growing season is short and the characteristic of drought escape is essential for raising a successful crop. Since genetic analysis of different components of crop duration in chickpea reveals earliness to be governed by recessive genes with predominance of additive gene action (Kumar *et al.,* 1999), recurrent selection would be effective in accumulating alleles for earliness in the high yielding background. Donors identified for earliness have been used for the development of varieties such as ICCV2, BG372 and KPG59, which are gaining acceptance among the farmers of rainfed ecology because of their early maturity combined with other desirable traits.

### 6.4.2 *Tolerance to low temperature*

Chickpea being a cool-season food legume, faces low temperature to the tune of 0-5°C for about 15-20 days in the north plain zone. Prevalence of such a low temperature at the early flowering stage causes flower abortion, leading to 15-30% yield loss. Search for germplasm accessions which can retain flowers and set pods under these conditions has led to the identification of M450, ICCV88501, ICCV88502, ICCV88503, ICCV88506 and ILC8262. Several introductions from Russia and wild species have shown fairly good level of cold tolerance. Their utilization in the breeding programme is expected to make a breakthrough in chickpea production in the north plain zone by bringing a part of wheat area under chickpea after rice harvest.

### 6.4.3. *Other abiotic stresses*

Prevalence of temperatures above 30°C especially during the reproductive stage and soil salinity throughout the life cycle mainly because of improper water management can cause severe stress to chickpea crop. Continuous efforts in screening genotypes have led to the identification of tolerant sources for high temperature (ICCV92944 and ICCX 830107) and salinity (CSG8893, E100Y, CSG8894, H893-84, H81-69 and H85-10). Karnal Chana-1 (CSG 8962), the first salt tolerant variety released for NWPZ, is the result of a successful breeding programme in the direction of identifying salt tolerant lines with high yield potential.

## 6.5. Irrigated Ecology

Chickpea is grown not only in the rainfed ecology but also under irrigated conditions (about 20%) that cause excessive vegetative growth and lodging. Efforts to breed for adaptation to such conditions have yielded some success in the identification of improved materials and released varieties such as Pusa256, Phule G5, DCP92-3, BGD107 and GNG1178. These lines, to some extent, respond to high inputs. A large area under cereal-based cropping systems particularly rice-wheat offers a good scope for expansion of chickpea area in irrigated ecology if the varieties suitable for late-sown conditions are developed. Varieties suitable for late-sown conditions are BG372, KPG59, PBG1 and Pusa256.

## 6.6. Improvement of Quality Traits

Physical, nutritional and cooking qualities of chickpea grains are important on account of the variety of uses to which it is put. *Desi* type is normally dehusked and split to *dal* or used as flour *(besan)*. *Kabuli* type is cooked as whole seeds after overnight soaking *(Chhola)* whereas greeen seeded *desi* is utilized mainly for table purposes. Because of the varied usage and local preferences, the following quality parameters are very important:

| | |
|---|---|
| Physical parameters | Seed size, shape and colour |
| Cooking parameters | Short cooking time, Water absorbption capacity |
| Nutritional parameters | Protein content,<br>Protein quality (digestibility, amino acid balance) |

Inspite of wide genetic variability for protein content (Williams and Singh, 1987) and other quality parameters within the primary gene pool, the protein content has not been the basis of selection in the breeding programmes except as a criterion to reject those lines which have less protein than the check variety in the advanced variety trials.

A great amount of genetic variability exists for seed size within *desi* and *kabuli* types, some *desi* types being as large as *kabuli* and some *kabuli* types as small as *desi* (Kumar and Singh, 1995). Predominance of additive gene effects coupled with high heritability has made bold-seeded character the most amenable through breeding process. In recent years, many bold seeded varieties of *desi* types such as Pusa 256, Phule G5, Vishal, GNG496, etc., have been developed to meet consumer preference.

### 6.7. *Kabuli-desi* Introgression

Introgression of genes between divergent subgroups within a species has yielded spectacular successes in the past. Such examples exist in wheat, rice, maize and several other crops. With the availability of divergent and complementary gene pools in the form of *desi* and *kabuli* types in chickpea, similar breeding efforts have been directed to combine primary branches, seed weight and upright compact growth habit of *kabuli* types in *desi* background, and seeds per pod, pods per plant and drought tolerance of *desi* types in *kabuli* background. Several high yielding and widely adapted varieties such as L104, L144, L550 and Pusa267 among *kabuli* types and Pusa244, Pusa256 and Pusa261 among *desi* types have emanated from such *kabuli x desi* crosses. However, the success fell short of expectation mainly because of narrow genetic divergence between the two types, genetic drift towards *desi* type and non-recovery of desired types. This could, however, be overcome by growing larger (three to four times that of within type $F_2$s) population in $F_2$. Alternate back crossing has also been suggested to recover desired type.

## 7. SEED PRODUCTION REQUIREMENT

Availability of quality seed of improved varieties is vital for translating potential yield into reality. However, non-availability of quality seed remains one of the greatest impediments in bridging the wide gap between potential and harvested yields. It is assessed that the availability of quality seeds in time can increase at least 20% production in chickpea even with the available varieties and production technologies. Generally four classes of pure seeds namely, nucleus, breeder, foundation and certified are produced. Since the nucleus and breeder seeds are produced by the concerned breeder(s) and/or by the institution, they are true to their types and form the basis for foundation and certified seeds. The present status of seed production in chickpea indicates that indents for breeder seed is low. Planned requirement at 15% replacement with 10%, 20%, 50% and 100% buffer stock for certified, foundation, breeder and nucleus seeds, respectively is worked out for chickpea (Table 15). At present, 41 varieties are in the seed production chain. Among them, breeder seed requirement of ICC VIO, Pusa256, GNG496, Phule G5, JG315, JG74, Pusa372, C235 and Vijay exceeds 28 tonnes.

**Table 15:** Planned requirement of certified, foundation, breeder and nucleus seed in different states

| ***State*** | | ***Seed requirement*** | | | |
|---|---|---|---|---|---|
| | ***Year*** | ***Certified (000 qtls)*** | ***Foundation (000 qtls)*** | ***Breeder (qtls)*** | ***Nucleus (kg)*** |
| Andhra Pradesh | 1999 | 15.2 | 1.21 | 119 | 866 |
| | 2000 | 15.3 | 1.22 | 120 | 874 |
| | 2001 | 15.5 | 1.23 | 121 | 881 |
| | 2002 | 15.6 | 1.23 | 122 | 886 |
| Bihar | 1999 | 16.8 | 1.33 | 132 | 958 |
| | 2000 | 17.0 | 1.34 | 133 | 965 |
| | 2001 | 17.1 | 1.35 | 134 | 972 |
| | 2002 | 17.2 | 1.36 | 135 | 978 |
| Gujarat | 1999 | 14.1 | 1.12 | 111 | 803 |
| | 2000 | 14.2 | 1.13 | 112 | 810 |
| | 2001 | 14.4 | 1.14 | 113 | 817 |
| | 2002 | 14.5 | 1.15 | 113 | 823 |
| Haryana | 1999 | 50.0 | 3.96 | 392 | 2846 |
| | 2000 | 50.2 | 3.98 | 394 | 2860 |
| | 2001 | 50.5 | 4.00 | 396 | 2874 |
| | 2002 | 50.7 | 4.02 | 398 | 2886 |
| Karnataka | 1999 | 43.1 | 3.41 | 338 | 2451 |
| | 2000 | 43.3 | 3.43 | 340 | 2466 |
| | 2001 | 43.6 | 3.45 | 342 | 2480 |
| | 2002 | 43.8 | 3.47 | 343 | 2491 |
| Madhya Pradesh | 1999 | 325.0 | 25.73 | 2548 | 18500 |
| | 2000 | 326.3 | 25.84 | 2559 | 18576 |
| | 2001 | 327.7 | 26.95 | 2569 | 18653 |
| | 2002 | 329.1 | 27.04 | 2578 | 18718 |
| Maharashtra | 1999 | 91.1 | 7.21 | 714 | 5185 |
| | 2000 | 91.6 | 725 | 718 | 5213 |
| | 2001 | 92.1 | 7.29 | 722 | 5241 |
| | 2002 | 92.6 | 7.32 | 725 | 5264 |
| Rajasthan | 1999 | 185.6 | 14.70 | 1455 | 10567 |
| | 2000 | 186.4 | 14.76 | 1461 | 10608 |
| | 2001 | 187.1 | 14.82 | 1467 | 10661 |
| | 2002 | 187.9 | 14.87 | 1472 | 10686 |

**Table 15:** (*Contd...*)

**Table 15:** (*Contd...*)

| ***State*** | ***Year*** | ***Seed requirement*** | | | |
|---|---|---|---|---|---|
| | | ***Certified (000 qtls)*** | ***Foundation (000 qtls)*** | ***Breeder (qtls)*** | ***Nucleus (kg)*** |
| Uttar Pradesh | 1999 | 133.4 | 10.60 | 1046 | 7594 |
| | 2000 | 134.1 | 10.60 | 1052 | 7636 |
| | 2001 | 134.9 | 10.70 | 1058 | 7678 |
| | 2002 | 135.6 | 10.70 | 1062 | 7714 |
| Other | 1999 | 8.1 | 0.65 | 63.9 | 464 |
| | 2000 | 8.1 | 0.65 | 63.9 | 464 |
| | 2001 | 8.1 | 0.65 | 63.9 | 464 |
| | 2002 | 8.1 | 0.65 | 63.9 | 464 |
| Ail India | 1999 | 887.7 | 70.30 | 6960 | 50529 |
| | 2000 | 892.1 | 70.65 | 6993 | 50776 |
| | 2001 | 896.3 | 71.10 | 7028 | 51022 |
| | 2002 | 900.7 | 71.30 | 7056 | 51228 |

## 8. FUTURE STRATEGIES

Despite the development of high-yielding disease resistant varieties coupled with improved production technology, a major breakthrough in yield parallel to major cereals is still elusive in chickpea. The problem of instability still persists because of newly emerging races/ biotypes of the pathogens/pests for which stable sources of resistance are either limited or are yet to be found. Therefore, intensive multi-disciplinary research efforts are warranted using the following technological options:

### 8.1. Consolidation of Yield Gains through Multiple Resistance

A wide choice of resistant varieties for specific pest/disease has helped greatly to minimize yield losses. Since the incidence of diseases and insect pests is often not predictable, varieties having resistance to more than one stress provide greater insurance against crop failures. This requires immediate steps to simultaneously screen the chickpea germplasm against the major stresses of the region and pool the diverse genes in high yielding background through bulk pedigree method. By growing multiple resistant varieties, the productivity of chickpea can be substantially consolidated by managing the stresses efficiently and production can be increased further by adoption of location specific high yielding varieties. Some of the advance lines having multiple resistance developed at various centres are as follows:

| | |
|---|---|
| Wilt + Dry root rot | H86-84, H86-18, JCC8383, ICC10466 |
| Wilt + *Helicoverpa* pod borer | ICCL 86102, ICC18611, ICCX730020 |
| Wilt + *Ascochyta* blight | GL83119, GL84038, GL84096, CL84107, H83-84, H83-60, Flip83-7-C, Flip82-74-C, ILC171, GL91058, CL91060, GL88341, Flip96-41,1CCV89445,ICC1272, ICC3137, IC4074, 1PC 97-1 |
| Wilt + *Ascochyta* blight + Grey mold | GL84135, GL88395, GL88356, GL84107, GL88366 |

## 8.2. Breeding for New Ideotype

Chickpea is as efficient as any C3 plant in utilizing solar energy for dry matter production. However, it lags behind in efficient partitioning of dry matter because of its indeterminate growth habit. This, coupled with mono-carpic senescence (once flowering takes place, most of the leaves start falling) causes serious constraint in pod filling. Efforts are needed to design varieties with determinate growth habit and efficient source-sink kinetics through early seedling vigour, fast leaf development (high LAI), synchronous flowering, slow senescence, and increased rate of dry matter production and partitioning.

Besides these physiological considerations, the plant type has to be re-structured as per the environmental requirement and prevailing cropping systems. For example, characteristics such as dense and long root system, small leaf size, early vigour, relatively few branches and early maturity along with efficient dry matter accumulation in seeds should be incorporated in breeding materials for drought-prone environments (Saxena and Johansen, 1990; Calcagno and Gallo, 1993; Singh, 1997). Under conditions of wet and cool winter followed by rapid warming in spring and terminal drought such as those prevalent in the Mediterranean environments and NWPZ in India, the new plant type needs to combine early flowering and tolerance to high temperature so as to avoid drought stress during pod set (Sedgley *et al.,* 1990). Under high input conditions, a plant of erect habit with few branches sown at high density should lead to slow moisture depletion in winter and result in higher biological yield and harvest index.

Ideotype for late sown rainfed conditions in north India should possess early vigour, 50-60 cm height, 60-70 pods/plant, 2-3 primary branches, 9-10 secondary branches, double poddedness and 20-35g/100-seed weight (Singh, 1997).

## 8.3. Broadening the Genetic Base through Wide Hybridization

For diversification and broadening the genetic base of cultivated germplasm, introgression of as yet unexplored genes from the wild relatives will minimize the risk of epidemics. Wild species of chickpea are rich reservoir of not only resistant genes against various biotic and abiotic stresses but also of genes responsible for high yield, more seeds per pod, hybrid vigour, etc. (Jaiswal and Singh, 1989; Singh and Ocampo, 1997). Conventional crossing has been successful in producing inter-specific hybrids between *C. arietinum* and *C. reticulatum*. Recent success in inter-specific hybrid between *C. arietinum* and *C. echinospermum* and availability of new biotechnology tools for circumventing crossing barriers have further brightened the prospects of transferring useful traits from primary and tertiary gene pools in chickpea.

## 8.4. Biotechnological Options

Use of molecular markers and genomics have emerged as an applied research option during the past one and a half decade, and promise to assist breeders in finding solution to many agricultural problems unsolved hitherto. A detailed genome map for chickpea is being developed using molecular (RFLP, RAPD, AFLP, microsatellites), isozyme and morphological markers. This will help in identifying and locating genes of interest and their precise transfer through marker aided selection. Genes imparting resistance against *Fusarium* wilt have already been tagged using RAPD markers (Mayer *et al.*, 1997). Ongoing work on the identification of markers for the genes imparting resistance to key diseases such as *Ascochyta blight* and insect pests such as *Helicoverpa* pod borer will enable the selection of resistant types and pyramiding of resistant genes from diverse genetic backgrounds. However, the use of marker technology in chickpea is restricted because of the limited number of markers identified and genes of interest tagged. A more saturated and well-distributed genome map is required for its actual application. Transformation of chickpea by introduction of *'Bt'* gene and other toxin coding gene(s) has been shown to protect crop against *Helicoverpa* pod borer. Similar efforts are being made to develop transgenics by transferring *'Basta'* and *'PGIP'* genes. Although several biotechnological options are open for chickpea crop, their use may continue to be restricted because of the nature of crop and resources available.

**Annexure 1**

Successful varieties developed and their salient features

| *Name of varieties* | *Pedigree* | *Year or release* | *Developing institute* | *Release domain* | *Special features* |
|---|---|---|---|---|---|
| ***Kabuli*** | | | | | |
| L550 | P 67 × Rabat | 1978 | PAU, Ludhiana | NWPZ, CZ, NHZ, NEPZ | Bushy, bold seeds, Creamy white round, 20-25 q/ha, 135-140 days to maturity |
| ICCV 32 | L550 × L2 | 1984 | ICRISAT, Patancheru | CZ | Resistant to wilt, tolerant to root rot & pod borer, 16-19 q/ha yield |
| Pusa 267 | (US613 × BEG482) × P 9623 | 1988 | IARI, New Delhi | NWPZ | |
| ICCV 2 | F3(K850/GW5/7/ P458) x F3 (L550/ Guamuchil) | 1993 | ICRISAT, Patancheru | SZ | Resistant to wilt, tolerant to salinity, short duration, medium large seed, 15-18 q/ha yield |
| ***Desi*** | | | | | |
| C 235 | IP58 × Cl 234 | 1973 | HAU, Hisar | NWPZ Rainfed Areas | Medium tall, semi erect, medium bold seed, tolerant to *Ascochyta* blight, wide adaptation, 20 q/ha yield |
| Radhey | 197 × 76 | 1982 | CSAU&T, Kanpur | NEPZ | Tall, bold seed, late maturity, 20-25 q/ha yield |
| K 850 | Banda local x Etah bold | 1982 | CSAU&T, Kanpur | NPZ | Medium tall, upright, large foliage, round smooth bold seeds, 145-150 days duration 25-30 q/ha yield |
| JG 315 | PLS | 1984 | JNKVV, Jabalpur | CZ | Erect, 40-45 cm tall, medium seed size, Resistant to wilt, 20 q/ha yield, 145-150 days duration. |
| Pusa 256 | (JG62 x 850-3/27) × (L550 × H208) | 1985 | IARI, New Delhi | NWPZ, NEPZ | Semi-spreading to erect, broad leaves, bold and light brown seeds, tolerant to *Ascochyta* blight and wilt, 25-30 q/ha yield |
| Phule G5 | B110 × N31 | 1986 | MPKV, Rahuri | CZ | Erect, tall, bold and smooth seeds, tolerant to wilt and pod borer, 20-25 q/ha yield |
| Avrodhi | T3 × K315 | 1987 | CSAU&T, Kanpur | NEPZ | Resistant to wilt |
| PBG-1 | CG578 × NEC206 | 1988 | PAU, Ludhiana | NWPZ | Resistant to *Ascochyta* blight |
| Haryana | F61 × L550 | 1990 | HAU, Hisar | NWPZ | |

**Table** (*Contd...*)

**Table** (*Contd...*)

| ***Name of varieties*** | ***Pedigree*** | ***Year or release*** | ***Developing institute*** | ***Release domain*** | ***Special features*** |
|---|---|---|---|---|---|
| Chana no. 1 | | | | | |
| JG74 | PLS | 1991 | JNKVV, Jabalpur | NEHZ, WB, MP | Early maturing, medium seed size, coarse seed coat, 15-20 q/ha yield |
| RSG44 | JG62 × F496 | 1992 | RAU, Durgapura | Rajasthan | Semi-erect, medium tall (40-65cm), synchronous maturity (135-150 days), double podded, drought tolerant, 23 q/ha yield |
| KPG59 | Radhey × K 468 | 1992 | CSAU&T, Kanpur | NWPZ, NEPZ | Resistant to wilt, suitable for late planting, 130-145 days to maturity, 20-22 q/ha yield |
| ICCV10 | P 1231 × 1265 | 1992 | ICRISAT, Patancheru | CZ & SZ | Resistant to wilt and dry root rot |
| Pusa372 | P 1231 × P 1265 | 1993 | IARI, New Delhi | NWPZ, NEPZ | |
| Vijay | P127 × Annegiri | 1993 | MPKV, Rahuri | CZ | |
| GNG663 | GNG16 × GNG146 | 1994 | RAU, Ganganagar | NWPZ | Resistant to wilt and root rot |
| KWR108 | PLS | 1995 | CSAU&T, Kanpur | NWPZ | Rasistant to *Ascochyta* blight with, root rot, tolerant to pod borer. |
| Pusa 391 | ICC3935 × Pusa256 | 1996 | IARI, New Delhi | CZ | Moderate resistant to wilt, |
| GNG469 | Annegiri × H75-35 | 1996 | RAU, Ganganagar | NWPZ | Resistant to wilt and root rot |
| CSG8962 | PLS | 1997 | CSSRI, Karnal | NWPZ | Suitable for salt affected areas |
| DCP92-3 | PLS | 1997 | IIPR, Kanpur | NWPZ | Suitable for high input conditions |

## REFERENCES


Ahlawat, I.P.S., Singh, A. and Saraf, C.S. (1981). Effects of winter legumes on the nitrogen economy and productivity of succeeding cereals. *Experimental Agriculture,* 17: 57–62.

Ahmad, Z., Mohamed, A.S., Hagani, A.M., Hashmi, N.l. and Malik, B.A. (1982). Collecting chickpea and lentil in Pakistan. *Plant Genetic Resources Ncu'sl,* 52: 1–4.

Ali, M. (1999). Annual Progress Report 1998–99. All India Coordinated Research Project on Chickpea (1CAR), I1PR, Kanpur, India, pp. 84–85.

Ali, M., Mishra, J.P., Ahlawat, I.P.S., Kumar, R. and Chauhan, Y.S. (1998). Effective management of legumes for maximizing biological nitrogen fixation and other benefits. *In: Procecdings, residual effect of legumes in rice and wheat cropping Systems of thc Indo–Gangetic Plains Ed.* by Kumar Rao, J.V.D.K., Johansen, C. and Rajo, J.J. ICRISAT, Patanchem, India, pp. 107–128.

Anonymous. (1979). Pulses in Bangladesh. *Plant Genetic Resources Newsl,* 39: 26.

Anonymous. (1980). Notes from genetic resources centres. *Plant Genetic Resources Newsl,* 44: 34–35.

Avise, J.C. (1994). Molecular markers, natural history and evolution. Chapman & Hall, N.Y., USA, p. 511.

Bezuneh, T. (1975). Status of chickpea production and research in Ethiopia. *In: Proceedings of the International Workshop on Grain Legumes,* ICRISAT, 13–16 Jan 1975, Patancheru, Hyderabad, India. pp. 95–101.

Broue, P., Cornish, P.S., Kaehne, I.D. and Mathison, M.J. (1975). Plant collecting in central Asia and the Caucasus Region of USSR. *Australian Plant Introduction Review,* 10: 11–26.

Budin, K.Z. and Shmaraev, G.E. (1971). The centres of origin and specifie diversity of cultivated plants. *Trudy po prikladnoi Botanike, Genetike i sclektsii,* 45: 238–270.

Calcagno, F. and Gallo, G. (1993). Physiological and morphological basis of abiotic stress resistance in chickpea. In: *Breeding for stress tolerance in cool season food legumes.* John Wiley & Sons Ltd. Chichester, U.K. pp. 293–309.

Campos, T.A., Borloug, N.E., Garcia, S.A. and Vazquez. (1961). Selection of chickpea cultivars in three regions of Mexico. *Agricultura Tecnica in Mexico,* 11: 16–18.

Chowdury, K.A., Saraswat, K.S., Hasan, S.N. and Gaur, R.G. (1971). 4000–3500 year–old barley, rice and pulses from Atranjikhera. *Science and Culture,* 37: 531–533.

Dahiya, B.S., Lather, V.S., Solanki, I.S. and Kumar, R. (1984). Useful spontaneous mutants in chickpea. *Int. Chickpea Neuvl,* 11: 4–6.

de Candolle, A. (1883). Origine des plantes cultivees. Paris pp. 258–260.

Dixit, P.D. (1932). Studies in Indian Pulses: A note on the cytology of kabuli and desi types. *Indian J. Agric. Sci., 2:* 385–390.

Eshel, V. (1968). Flower development and pollen viability of chickpea *(Cicer arietinum* L.). *Israel J. Agric Res.,* 18: 31–33.

Govil, J.N. (1983). Field collection of chickpea germplasm. *Indian J. Agric. Res.,* 17: 109–113.

Gubanov, I.A., Pavlov, V.M. and Yunus, M.K. (1975). Notes on rare species of Afghanistan. Byulleten Moskovskogo obshchestva i spytatelei Priordy. *Otdel Biologiclieskii,* 80: 82–91.

Gumber, R.K., Kumar, J. and Haware, M.P. (1995). Inheritance of resistance to *Fusarium* wilt in Chickpea 329 chickpea. *Plant Breeding,* 114: 277–279.

Hawtin, G.C. and Singh, K.B. 1980. Kabuli–desi introgression: Problems and prospects. *In: Proceedings of International Workshop on Chickpea Improvement.* ICRISAT, Hyderabad, India. pp. 51–60.

Helbaek, H. (1970). The plant husbandry at Hacillar. In: *Excavation al Hacilar* (J. Mellaart ed.). Edinburgh Univ. Press. U.K. pp. 189–244.

Jaiswal, H.K. and Singh, B.D. (1989). Analysis of gene effects for yield traits in crosses between *C. arietinum* and *C. reticulatum* L. *Indian* /. *Genêt.,* 49: 9–17.

Kaul, K.N. and Solanki, M.S. (1950). Polycarpy in *Cicer arietinum. Curr. Sci.*, 19: 61–62.

Kharkwal, M.C. (1983). Mutation breeding for chickpea improvement. *Int. Chickpea Newsl.,* 9: 4–5.

Kumar, J. and Haware, M.P. (1982). Inheritance of resistance to *Fusarium* wilt in chickpea. *Phytopathology*, 72: 1035–1036.

Kumar, S. (1998). Inheritance of resistance to *Fusarium* wilt (race 2) in chickpea. *Plant Breeding,* 117: 139–142.

Kumar, S. and Singh, O. (1995). Inheritance of seed size in chickpea. *J. Genet. and Breed.,* 49: 99–104.

Kumar, S., van Rheenen, H.A. and Singh, O. (1999). Genetic analysis of different components of crop duration in chickpea *J. Genet, B Breed.,* 53: 189–200.

Kupicha, F.K. (1977). The delimitation of the tribe *Vicieae* and the relationships of *Cicer* L. *Botanical J. Linnean Society,* 74: 131–162.

Labdi, M., Robertson, L.D., Singh, K.B. and Charrier, A. 1996. Genetic diversity and phylogenetic reiationships among the annual *Cicer* species as revealed by isozyme polymorphism. *Euphytica,* 88: 181–188.

Ladizinsky, G. (1975). A new *Cicer* from Turkey. *Notes from the Royal Botanical Garden Edinburgh,* 34: 201–202.

Ladizinsky, G. and Adler, A. (1975). The origin of chickpea as indicated by seed protein electrophoresis. *Israel J. Bot.*, 24: 211–217.

Ladizinsky, G. and Adler, A. (1976a). The origin of chickpea (*Cicer arietinum* L.). *Euphytica,* 25: 211–217.

Ladizinsky, G. and Aider, A. (1976b). Genetic reiationships among the annual species of *Cicer* L. *Theor Appl Genet.,* 48: 197–203.

lyengar, N.K. (1939). Cytological investigations on the genus *Cicer. Ami. Bot.* (London), 3: 271–305.

Mayer, M.S., Tullu, A., Simon, C.J., Kumar, J., Kraft, J.M., Kaiser, W.J. and Muehlbauer, F.J. (1997). Development of a DNA marker for fusarium wilt resistance in chickpea. *Crop Sci.*, 37: 1625–1629.

Nene, Y.L. and Haware, M.P. (1980). Screening chickpea for resistance to wilt. *Plant Dis.,* 64: 379–380.

Nozzolillo, C. (1985). Seedling morphology and anatomy of eight *Cicer* species and their taxonomic value. *Canadian J. Bot.,* 63: 1–6.

Ocampo, B., Venora, G., Errico, A., Singh, K.B. and Saccardo, F. (1992). Karyotype analysis in the genus *Cicer. J. Genet. and Breed.,* 46: 229–240.

Patankar, S. and Ranjekar, P.K. (1984). Condensed chromatin and its under–replication during root differentiation in leguminosae. *Plant Cell Reports,* 3: 250–253.

Pathak, M.M., Singh, K.P. and Lal, S.B. (1975). Inheritance of resistance to wilt (*F. oxysporum* sp. *ciceri*) in gram. *Indian J. Farm Sci.*, 3: 10–11.

Phadnis, B.A. (1970). Karyotypic studies in varieteis of *Cicer arietinum L.J. Cytology and Genet.,* 5: 80–88.

Phadnis, B.A. and Narkhede, M.N. (1972). Chromosome behaviour in colchicine–induced autotetraploids of *Cicer arietinum* L. *Cytologia,* 37: 415–421.

Pundir, R.P.S. (1982). Collection of chickpea germplasm in the Jammu region of India. *Int. Chickpea Newsl,* 7: 3.

Pundir, R.P.S. and Mengesha, M.H. (1983). Collection of chickpea germplasm in Ethiopia. *Int. Chickpea Newsl.,* 8: 6–7.

Pundir, R.P.S. and van der Maesen, L.J.G. (1983). Interspecific hybridization in *Cicer. Int. Chickpea Newl.,* 8: 4–5.

Pundir, R.P.S., Holly, L. and Tahiri, A. (1989). Collection of chickpea germplasm in Morocco. *Int. Chickpea Netvsl.* 20: 9–11.

Pundir, R.P.S., Mengesha, M.H. and Reddy, K.N. (1988). Occurrence and genetics of a natural mutant of chickpea having twin–flower peduncles and polycarpy. *J. Heredity,* 79: 479–481.

Pundir, R.P.S., Rao, N.K. and van der Maesen, L.J.G. (1983). Induced autotetraploidy in chickpea *(Cicer arietinum* L.) *Theor Appl Genet.*, 65: 119–122.

Pundir, R.P.S., Shwe, A. and Aung, K. (1991). Collection of chickpea germplasm in Myanmar. *Int. Chickpea Newsl.,* 25:17–18.

Pundir, R.P.S., Telang, S.W., Singh, J. and Singh, B. (1989). Collection of germplasm of chickpea landraces in Madhya Pradesh, India. *Int. Chickpea Neiisl,* 20: 11–13.

Ramanujam, S. (1976). Chickpea. *In*: Evolution of crop plants ed. by N.W. Simmonds. Longman, London and New York, USA. pp. 157–159.

Ramanujam, S. and Joshi, A.B. (1941). Colchicine–induced polyploidy in crop plants. 1. gram (*Cicer. arietinum* L.) *Indian J. Agric. Sci.,* 9: 835–849.

Rao, N.S. (1929). Further contributions to the cytology of some crop plants of South India. J. *Indian Bot. Soc.,* 18: 222–229.

Rupela, O.P. (1987). Modulation and nitrogen fixation in chickpea *In*: The Chickpea, *Eds.* by Saxena, M.C. and Singh, K.B. CAB International/lCARDA, Wallingford, U.K. pp. 191–206.

Saxena, N.P. (1987). Screening for adaptation to drought: case study with chickpea and pigeonpea. *In: Adaptation of chickpea and pigeonpea to abiotic stresses.* Proceeding of the Consultants Workshop, 19–21 Dec 1984. ICRISAT, Patencheru, India. pp. 63–76.

Saxena, N.P. and Johansen, C. (1990). Chickpea ideotypes for genetic enhancement of yield and yield stability in South Asia. In: *Chickpea in the Nineties.* Proceedings of the second International Workshop on Chickpea Improvement, ICRISAT, Patancheru, India. pp. 81–85.

Sedgley, R.H., Siddique, K.H.M. and Walton, G.M. (1990). Chickpea ideotype for Mediterranean environments. *In*: *Chickpea in the Nineties,* Proceedings of the second International Workshop on Chickpea Improvement, ICRISAT, Patancheru, India pp. 87–91.

Sidhu, J.S., Singh, K.P. and Slinkard, A.E. (1983). Inheritance of resistance to *Fusarium* wilt in chickpeas. *J. Hered.,* 74: 68.

Singh, B.B. and Singh, D.R (1995). Inheritance of multipinnate leaf type in chickpea *(Cicer arietinum). Indian J. Genet.,* 55: 214–215.

Singh, D.P. (1997). Tailoring the plant type in pulse crops. *Plant Breeding Abstracts*, 67: 1213–1220.

Singh, G., Kapoor, S. and Singh, K. (1982). Screening chickpea for gray mold resistance. *Int. Chickpea Neuvl,* 7: 13–14.

Singh, K.B. and Auckland, A.K. (1975). Chickpea Breeding at ICRISAT. *In*: Proceedings *of the Workshop on Grain Legumes,* ICRISAT, Patancheru, India. pp. 3–13.

Singh, K.B. and Ocampo, B. (1997). Exploitation of wild species for yield improvement in chickpea. *Theor Appl Genet,* 95: 418–423.

Singh, K.B. Malhotra, R.S. and Saxena, M.C. (1990). Sources for tolerance to cold in *Cicer* species. *Crop* Sci., 30: 1136–1138.

Singh, K.B., Divito, M., Greco, N. and Saxena, M.C. (1980). Reaction of wild *Cicer* spp. lines to *Heterodera ciceri. Nematologia Mediterranean*, 17: 113–114.

Singh, K.B., Hawtin, G.C., Nene, Y.L. and Reddy, M.V. (1981). Resistance in chickpea to *Ascochyta rabiei. Plant Dis.,* 65: 586–587.

Singh, K.B., Malhotra, R.S., Halila, M.H. Knights, E.J. and Verma, M.M. (1994). Current status and future strategy in breeding chickpea for resistance to biotic and abiotic stresses *Euphytica,* 73: 137–149.

Smithson, J.B., Kumar, J., Haware, M.P., and Singh, H. (1983). Complementation between genes for late wilting of race 1 of *Fusarium oxysporium t.* sp. *ciceri* in chickpea. Proc. Int. Genet. Cong. 1ARI, New Delhi.

Sohoo, M.S., Athwal, D.S. and Chandra, S. (1970). Colchicine–induced polyploidy in chickpea *(Cicer arietinum* L). *Theor Appl Genet,,* 40: 163–168.

Toll, J. (1980). Collecting in Ethiopia. *Plant Genetic Resources Nausl.,* 43: 36–39.

Upadhyaya, H.D., Haware, M.P., Kumar, J. and Smithson, J.B. (1983a). Resistance to wilt in chickpea, I. Inheritance for late wilting in response to race 1. *Euphytica,* 32: 447–452.

Upadhyaya, H.D., Smithson, J.B. Haware, M.P. and Kumar, J. (1983b). Resistance to wilt in chickpea, II. Further evidence of two gènes for resistance to race 1. *Euphytica*, 32: 749–755.

van der Maesen, L.J.G. (1972). *Cicier L.,* a monograph of the genus with special reference to the chickpea (*Cicer arietinum* L.), its ecology and cultivation. Veenman and Zonen, Wageningen, The Netherlands. p. 342.

van der Maesen, L.J.G. and Pundir, R.P.S. (1984). Availability and use of wild *Cicer* germplasm. *Plant Genet Resources Neivsl.,* 57: 19–24.

Vavilov, N.I. (1926). Studies on the origin of cultivated plants. Leningrad, pp 129–238.

William, P.C. and Singh, U. (1987). Nutritional quality and the evaluation of quality in breeding programmes. *In*: The chickpea ed. by Saxena, M.C. and Singh, K.B. CAB International/ICARDA, Wallingford, U.K. pp. 329–356.

# 9

# Mungbean

## 1. INTRODUCTION

Mungbean (*Vigna radiata* (L.) Wilczek) is an important food legume which is extensively grown from humid to arid and semi arid regions. The annual global mungbean production is around 2.5 to 3.0 million metric tonnes from an area of about 5.0 million hectares (Poehlman, 1991). India accounts for about 45% of the total world production. Mungbean is cultivated in Thailand, China, Philippines, Srilanka, India, Myanmar, Bangladesh, Indonesia, Pakistan, Nepal, Australia, East Africa, United States of America, Western South America and Caribbean region and Bhutan. In India, mungbean is mainly cultivated in Rajasthan, Maharashtra, Andhra Pradesh, Orissa, Karnataka, Bihar, Madhya Pradesh and Uttar Pradesh. It is a short duration crop and is grown as a sole crop as well as in inter and multiple cropping systems and has remained favoured choice of the farmers as a *kharif* crop in rainfed conditions of India. With increased irrigation facilities through new irrigation projects and remunerative prices, this crop occupies considerable area during spring, summer and *rabi* seasons in several states of India.

## 2. IMPORTANCE

Mungbean is a source of easily digestible protein (20.0 to 28.4 per cent). It also contains 3.3 per cent fat, 5.9 per cent fibre, 51.2 per cent carbohydrates, 3.4 per cent minerals, 0.3 per cent vitamins and 10.2 percent moisture. It enriches the soil through atmospheric nitrogen fixation and adds humus (dry leaves and green manure) to soil. It also

V.L. Chopra (Ed.): Breeding Field Crops I: Practices, Studium Press (LLC), USA.

acts as cover crop and protects soil from erosion through winds (as summer crop) and rains (as *kharif* crop). Mungbean can be used as dehulled grain, hulled (Dahl) husked and dehusked dahl: Soaked and sprouted grains are used as *salad* and breakfast. It is also used for preparing a variety of savoury and sweet dishes. Mungbean is also useful for animals as it is a palatable fodder and concentrates for milch cattles. Mungbean is a rich source of amino acids : cystine (55 mg), isolucine (264 mg), leucine (484 mg) lysine (436 mg), metheonine (75 mg) phenylalanine (378 mg), threonine (205 mg) tryptophan (68 mg), tyrosine (187 mg) and valine (324 mg) expressed in milligram per gram of nitrogen (data adopted from Haytowitz and Mathew, 1986). Mineral composition of mungbean seeds per 100 g reflects calcium (132 mg), iron (6.7 mg), magnesium (189 mg), phosphorus (367 mg), potassium (1246 mg), sodium (15 mg), zinc (2.6 mg), copper (0.941 mg) and manganese (1.03 mg) (Haytowitz and Mathew, 1986). Vitamin content of 100 gm mungbean seeds is ascorbic acid (4.8 mg), thiamin (0.621 mg), riboflavin (0.233 mg) niacin (2.25 mg), pantothenic acid (1.9 mg), $B_6$ (0.382 mg), folacin (625 mg) and vitamin A (114). Considering its chemical composition and varied uses, mungbean emerged as very important food legume.

## 3. AREA, PRODUCTION AND PRODUCTIVITY

India ranks first in the world in area as well as production of mungbean followed by China, Thailand, Indonesia, Myanmar and Pakistan (Table 1).

**Table 1:** Area, production and productivity in Mungbean growing countries

| *Country* | *Year* | *Area 1000 ha* | *Production 1000 million tonnes* | *Productivity kg/ha* | *Source of Information* |
|---|---|---|---|---|---|
| India | 1984-85 | 2725.0 | 1115.0 | 409.0 | Sandhu *et al.*, 1988 |
| China | 1987 | 500 | 337.5 | 675.0 | Ling *et al.*, 1988 |
| Thailand | 1986 | 434.3 | 262.0 | 606.0 | Chainuvati *et al.*, 1988 |
| Indonesia | 1985 | 280.0 | 192.0 | 800.0 | Brotonegoro *et al.*, 1988 |
| Myanmar | 1984-86 (avg.) | 240.0 | 160.0 | 667.0 | R.B. Singh *et al.*, 1988 |
| Pakistan | 1986 | 115.0 | 58.0 | 504.0 | Bashir *et al.*, 1988 |

In India, Rajasthan ranks first in area, Maharashtra in production and Bihar in productivity. Area, production and productivity of important mungbean growing states during year 1997-98 are given in Table 2. Statistical information on all India basis regarding area, production and productivity in Table 3:

**Table 2:** Area, production and productivity of mungbean in different states of India

| ***States*** | ***Area (million hactare)*** | ***Production (million tonnes)*** | ***Productivity (kgs/ha)*** |
|---|---|---|---|
| Rajasthan | 0.631 | 0.164 | 260 |
| Maharashtra | 0.624 | 0.195 | 313 |
| Andhara Pradesh | 0.436 | 0.122 | 281 |
| Orissa | 0.249 | 0.052 | 208 |
| Karnataka | 0.247 | 0.046 | 187 |
| Bihar | 0.189 | 0.105 | 560 |
| Madhya Pradesh | 0.121 | 0.041 | 337 |
| Uttar Pradesh | 0.112 | 0.042 | 374 |

*Source* : Project coordinator report *kharif* pulse MULLaRP Group Mcet 1999.

**Table 3:** Yearwise All India area (million hactares), production (million tonnes) and yield (kg/ha) of Mungbean

| ***Year*** | ***Area*** | ***Production*** | ***Yield*** |
|---|---|---|---|
| 1965-66 | 1.83 | 0.53 | 288 |
| 1966-67 | 1.87 | 0.50 | 269 |
| 1967-68 | 1.98 | 0.59 | 297 |
| 1968-69 | 1.98 | 0.52 | 264 |
| 1969-70 | 1.67 | 0.40 | 237 |
| 1970-71 | 2.03 | 0.61 | 299 |
| 1971-72 | 2.03 | 0.62 | 308 |
| 1972-73 | 2.10 | 0.55 | 266 |
| 1973-74 | 2.48 | 0.82 | 329 |
| 1974-75 | 2.32 | 0.77 | 333 |
| 1975-76 | 2.52 | 0.80 | 316 |
| 1976-77 | 2.41 | 0.76 | 317 |
| 1977-78 | 2.34 | 0.80 | 336 |
| 1978-79 | 2.76 | 0.91 | 330 |
| 1979-80 | 2.46 | 0.66 | 269 |
| 1980-81 | 2.84 | 0.88 | 311 |
| 1981-82 | 2.85 | 1.06 | 376 |
| 1982-83 | 2.63 | 1.06 | 400 |
| 1983-84 | 3.02 | 1.35 | 447 |
| 1984-85 | 2.97 | 1.20 | 403 |
| 1985-86 | 2.86 | 1.05 | 367 |
| 1986-87 | 3.13 | 1.09 | 349 |
| 1987-88 | 2.98 | 1.29 | 426 |
| 1988-89 | 3.42 | 1.42 | 415 |
| 1989-90 | 3.35 | 1.32 | 393 |
| 1990-91 | 3.44 | 1.37 | 399 |
| 1991-92 | 3.47 | 1.35 | 389 |
| 1992-93 | 2.99 | 1.41 | 471 |
| 1993-94 | 2.94 | 1.23 | 419 |
| 1994-95 | 2.90 | 1.07 | 369 |
| 1995-96 | 2.71 | 0.82 | 303 |
| 1996-97 | 3.08 | 1.31 | 425 |
| 1997-98 | 3.04 | 0.88 | 291 |

*Source* : Directorate of Eco. and Stat., New Delhi

### 3.1. Productivity Trend

Since the start of All India Coordinated Pulse Improvement Project in 1965-66, statistics regarding pulses production and productivity has been systematically recorded. There was progressive, though slight, increase in production and productivity upto 1983-84. Productivity was maximum in 1992-93 (471 kg/ha) and decreased to 291 kg/ha in 1997-98. The drastic decrease in production (0.88 mt) and productivity (291 kg/ha) in 1997-98 was caused by adverse climatic conditions (cloudy weather and continuous rains at maturity) and incidence of insect pests and diseases. Productivity trend from the year 1965-66 to 1997-98 is tabulated below:

| *Year* | *Yield* |
|---|---|
| 1965-66 | 288 |
| 1966-67 | 269 |
| 1967-68 | 297 |
| 1968-69 | 264 |
| 1969-70 | 237 |
| 1970-71 | 299 |
| 1971-72 | 308 |
| 1972-73 | 266 |
| 1973-74 | 329 |
| 1974-75 | 333 |
| 1975-76 | 316 |
| 1976-77 | 317 |
| 1977-78 | 336 |
| 1978-79 | 330 |
| 1979-80 | 269 |
| 1980-81 | 311 |
| 1981-82 | 376 |
| 1982-83 | 400 |
| 1983-84 | 447 |
| 1984-85 | 403 |
| 1985-86 | 367 |
| 1986-87 | 349 |
| 1987-88 | 426 |
| 1988-89 | 415 |
| 1989-90 | 393 |
| 1990-91 | 399 |
| 1991-92 | 389 |
| 1992-93 | 471 |
| 1993-94 | 419 |
| 1994-95 | 369 |
| 1995-96 | 303 |
| 1996-97 | 425 |
| 1997-98 | 291 |

## 4. ORIGIN AND BREEDING SYSTEM

### 4.1. Origin

Mungbean originated in Indo-Burma region of South East Asia. Vavilov (1951) included mungbean and urdbean (*V. mungo*) in the Hindustani centre of origin of cultivated plants which includes erstwhile Burma and excludes north west India. Vavilov identified Central Asiatic Centre, which includes north west India, Afghanistan and several adjoining Soviet Republics as primary centre of origin of mungbean. Zeven and Zhukovsky (1975) included mungbean in their Indochinese/Indonesian centre of diversity which is comprised of part of Myanmar, South China, Indochina, Indonesia and Philippines. Mungbean has been grown in India since very early time and carbonized grains of this crop are found in Chalcolithic site, Navdatoli-Maheshwar, in Madhya Pradesh (India). The site was dated *circa* 1660 to 1440 BC (Vishnu-Mittre, 1974). Carbonized grains of mungbean have also been identified from Daimabad, a Chalcolithic site in western Maharashtra that was dated *circa* 2200 to 1000 BC (Kajale, 1977). Mung is the Sanskrit name of mungbean, which reflects its ancient cultivation in India. Presence of wild proginator of mungbean *Vigna radiata* var. *sublobata* also confirms India and Indo Burma region as place of origin of Mungbean.

### 4.2. Taxonomy

Mungbean belongs to the order leguminosae and family Papilionoideae. Botanically recognized as *Vigna radiata* (L.) Wilczek, the taxonomic status of mungbean is given below:

| | |
|---|---|
| Kingdom | Plantae |
| Division | Spermatophyta |
| Sub division | Angiospermae |
| Class | Dicotyledoneae |
| Order | Leguminosae |
| Family | Popilionoideae |
| Tribe | Phaseoleae |
| Genus | Vigna |
| Subgenus | Ceratotopis; |
| Species | Radiata |
| Variety | Radiata |

(Rachie and Roberts, 1974; Jain and Mehra, 1980)

Mungbean has the diploid chromosome number 2n=2x=22 which was established by Karpechenko (1925) and confirmed by Kumar and

Abraham (1942 a and b). Autotetraploid can be induced by treating apical bud of seedling plant with Colchicine (Kumar and Abraham, 1942 a and b). Autotetraploid plant of mungbean is characterised by very slow growth, small size, fewer branches and late flowering compared to the diploid plant (Kabi and Bhaduri, 1978). So far no natural amphidiploid has been identified with genome homologous to *Vigna radiata* L. Wilczek.

### 4.3. Floral Biology

Mungbean is predominantly a self pollinated crop. The flower is light yellowish olive to yellow in colour with 5 sapals and 5 petals. The outer most petal is known as standard and covers 2 free petals known as wings. The innermost, 2 fused petals are known as keels. The 10 anthers are present in diadelphus condition (9+1). The gynoecium is one with marginal placentation.

## 5. BREEDING OBJECTIVES AND CHALLENGES

### 5.1. Objectives

The objective of any crop breeding effort is to elevate genetic production potential and to sustain the expression of this potential by creating combinations which are insulated against losses caused by perturbances of diseases, pests and unfavourable environments. For mungbean, breading objectives can be summarized as follows:

#### 5.1.1. *Yield and duration*

(i) Development of high yielding (more than 20.0 q/ha) varieties with bold seeds (5.0-7.0 g/100 seed wt) and YMV resistance for *kharif* season.

(ii) Development of 70-80 days synchronous varieties with grain yield potential of 20.0 to 25.0 q/ha and bold seed for spring season.

(iii) Development of extra early (50-60 days) synchronous and yellow mosaic virus resistant varieties for summer season for the states of Haryana and Punjab for planting after harvest of wheat.

#### 5.1.2. *Stresses*

*A. Biotic stresses (Diseases and Pests)*

(i) Development of resistant varieties and identification of new sources of resistance to yellow mosaic virus, *Cercospora* leaf spots and powdery mildew.

(ii) Development of genotypes resistant to major pests like Thrips, Jassids and Bihar hairy cater pillar, red beetles and storage pest bruchid.

*B. Abiotic stresses*

(i) Development of genotypes for tolerance to high temperature during summer season.

(ii) Development of genotypes for tolerance to pre harvest sprouting due to rains at maturity in *kharif* season.

(iii) Development of genotypes for tolerance to moisture stress.

(iv) Development of genotypes for cold tolerance for expanding mungbean cultivation in hilly regions.

### 5.1.3. *Quality traits*

Development of varieties with high protein content and balanced amino acid profile.

### 5.1.4. *Plant type*

Developing conceptual ideo types for high and stable yield and testing these concepts

### 5.1.5. *Input and management*

Development of genotypes responsive to better management and high dozes of fertilizers etc.

## 5.2. Challenges

Mungbean improvement faces many challenges which include :

(i) Competition with very high yielding and well established cereal crops, like paddy and maize in *kharif* season (North India) and paddy, groundnut etc in South India.

(ii) Limited availability of yellow mosaic virus resistant varieties for *kharif* and summer season and powdery mildew resistant varieties for *rabi* season for coastal states (States of Tamil Nadu, Andhra Pradesh, Orissa) of the country.

(iii) Non availability of quality seed in adequate quantity.

(iv) Non availability of right insecticides and fungicides in adequate quantity at proper time.

(v) Inadequate supply of canal water and erratic supply of electricity resulting in heavy yield losses in spring and summer crops.
(vi) Grazing of spring/summer mung crop by stray and wild animals *i.e.,* blue bulls.
(vii) Limitation of demonstrations of improved varieties and production technologies for spring summer and *kharif* seasons.
(viii) Lack of timely publicity on production technology
(ix) Lack of remunerative price

## 6. BREEDING FOR RESISTANCE TO STRESSES

Two major stresses confront mungbean *i.e.*, biotic and abiotic. Biotic stresses comprise the incidence to insect pest and diseases whereas abiotic stresses include drought, cold, water logging and high temperature. The ability of plants to avert or resist the establishment and activities of insect pests and diseases comes under resistance to biotic stresses. The ability of plants to thrive well under drought, cold water logging and high temperature conditions represents resistance to abiotic stresses. The development of genotypes which can thrive under biotic and abiotic stresses is dealt with in the following.

### 6.1. Biotic

#### *A. Pest resistance*

The important points to be considered in breeding for pests resistance are as under:

*Nature of damage*

(i) Chewing (ii) Sucking of sap and Juice (iii) Cutting of plant parts (iv) Secretion of poisonous substances harmful for plant health (v) damage to plant roots.

*Nature of resistance*

1. *Preference*: Choice of insect pests for host plant.
2. *Antibiosis*: Protoplasm of host plants act as antibiosis and restricts the activities of pests.
3. *Tolerance*: Capacity of host plant to withstand pest attack.
4. *Resistance*: Ability of host plant to prevent or oppose the activities of pests.

*Factors influencing Pest resistance*

(a) *Natural conditions*: (i) Extremely high or low temperature (ii) Low humidity.

(b) *Protoplamic*: Presence of poisionous substances in protoplasm which distroy the insect pests.

(c) *Acquired or induced immunity*: Plant that recovers from attack of a pest may remain immune from infection from the same pest.

(d) *Inherited resistance*: Resistance is due to heridity.

(e) Physiological compatibility

*Types of resistance*

1. *Immune*: 100 percent resistant
2. *Escape*: Healthy plants avoid the pest's attack
3. *Endurance*: Ability of plants to survive inspite of pest attack.

*Resistant donors identified for pest resistance*

| | | |
|---|---|---|
| Resistant to whitefly | : | ML 682, ML 881 |
| Resistant to Jassids | : | ML 803 |
| Resistant to thrips | : | ML 194 |
| Resistant bruchids | : | V 2817 (AVRDC) |

***B. Disease resistance***

The following points should be considered for breeding disease resistant genotypes.

*Source of disease resistance*:

(i) Diversity of germplasm

(ii) Intervarietal, interspecific and intergeneric hybridization

(iii) Search in wild and other cultivated species

(iv) Creation of mutations

*Basis of freedom from disease*

1. Special qualities like earliness.
2. Structural characteristics like thick cuticle on stem and leaves.
3. Production of toxic substances by host plants which are poisonous to the pathogens.
4. Resistance governed by genes.

*Nature of damage*

(i) Infection of foliage causes leaf spots, necrosis, chlorosis and mosaic.

(ii) Wilting of plants parts.

(iii) Rotting of plants parts like root rot, stem rot.

(iv) Dropping of leaves, flowers and fruits.

(v) Atrophy, hypertrophy and malformation

*Pre-requisits*

(a) Identification of disease resistant material.

(b) Time of onset and spread of disease.

(c) Lines selected as resistant in green houses should also be tested in field over the years.

(d) Selected lines should be graded as immune, resistant, tolerant and susceptible.

*Types of disease resistance*

1. *Morphogical*: Thickness of stem and leaves.
2. *Physiological*:
   (a) *Functional*: Stomata remain closed and prevent the entry of germ tube of fungus.
   (b) *Protoplasmic*: Protoplasm composed of many acid protein and enzymes which prevent growth of fungus.

*Mechanism of disease development*

(i) Contact

(ii) Penetrance

(iii) Establishment

(iv) Development

List of resistant donors for diseases resistance to major diseases.

*Yellow mosaic virus*

Samrat (PDM 84-139), Basanti (PDM 84-143), Kanchan (PDM 116), ML 267, NDM 88-14, PDM 88-219, Pantmung 4 etc.

*Cercospora leaf spots*

ML 682, ML 131, ML 936, ML 938, *Vigina glabrascens* etc.

*Powdery mildew*

JRUM l, TARM l, TARM 18.

Methods of breeding

1. Introduction
2. Selection

*(a) Selection in natural populations*

(i) Only immune types should be selected.
(ii) Selected types must be homozygous otherwise they will segregate.
(iii) Protoplasmic resistance is more suitable.
(iv) Selected types should be rigourously tested in green houses and field conditions.
(v) Artificial epiphytotic testing is necessary before selection.

*(b) Selection in hybrid population*

(i) There should be sufficient collection of wild and resistant gene pool.
(ii) Hybridization between superior agronomic varieties and resistant types.
(iii) Testing of lines for gca before crossing.
(iv) Testing for resistance in advance generation.
(v) Final selection of resistant varieties is made.

3. *Mutation breeding*: When resistant genes are not available

## 6.2. Abiotic Stress

Among the abiotic stresses drought, cold, waterlogging, high temperature (summer mungbean), grain deterioration due to rains at maturity are major stresses.

### *Drought resistance*

Ability of plants to thrive in moisture stress conditions is known as drought resistance.

### *Characteristics that lead to drought tolerance*

*(a) Morphological*

(i) Well developed root system (ii) Reduced leaf surface (iii) Thick cuticle (iv) Poor inter cellular space

*(b) Physiological*

(i) Development of hydrophyllic colloids (ii) Earliness (iii) Leaf fall during dry season (iv) High viscocity and elasticity of protoplasm (v) High osmatic pressure (vi) Low respiration rate (vii) High adenine content (viii) High level of bound water (ix) High proline accumulation (x) High ascorbic acid content.

***Methods of breeding***

Breeding methods are same as given in pest resistance

*Donars*

Moti (PDM 54), PDM 84-199, PDM 84-139 and other extra early maturing lines. For other abiotic stresses, methods of breeding are same as for drought resistance *i.e.,* resistant varieties for cold and waterlogging can also be developed by screening and evaluation of early generation breeding material under these stresses conditions.

***Genetic resources relevant to breeding objectives***

1. *Wild relatives with useful genes*

Species contributing useful genes are given below

- *Vigna radiata* var. *sublobata (Roxb) vcrde*: It contains genes for resistance against mungbean yellow mosaic virus, storage insect pest bruchid and water logging.
- *Vigna umbellata (Thunb) Ohwi & Ohashi*: In this species genes for resistance to beanfly are present.
- *Vigna glabrescens:* This species contains genes for resistance to *Cercospora* leaf spot disease,
- *Vigna khandalensis:* It contains genes for resistance to drought (moisture stress) and calcarious soil.

2. *Genetically enhanced germplasm: Identification and development*

A major requirement of mungbean breeding programme is insulating the crop against losses caused by yellow mosaic virus (YMV). Although some yellow mosaic virus resistant varieties have been developed and released in India during last two decades, the resistance of many of them is breaking down due to presence of different strains of yellow mosaic virus. A few varieties which have maintained stable resistance to YMV over locations, years and seasons are Samrat (PDM 84-139),

Basanti (PDM 84-143), PDM 88-219, Kanchan (PDM 116), ML 267 and Narendra Mung 1 (NOM 88-14). Other diseases of mungbean which cause severe losses are powdery mildew (PM) (particularly in South India) and Cercospora leaf spot disease (Cls). Indian variety TARM 18 (PDM 54 × RUM 5) shows resistance to PM and moderate resistance to Cls. Thailand variety KPS#1, Korean varieties Nampyeong nokdu, kuemseong nokdu and Kyeongseon nokdu and Chinesel variety Elu # 2 are resistant to both PM & Cls diseases. An Australian variety Emerald (VC 3528 A Sel) is resistant to 3 diseases: PM, Cls and BB (Bacterial blight). Other genetic resources which contribute to yield attributes and desirable physiological traits are given in Table 4.

**Table 4:** Mungbean genetic resources relevant to specific attributes

| ***Characters*** | ***Genotypes*** |
|---|---|
| Pod length | PDM 84-155, PDM 84-164, KFS#1, PDM 97-279 |
| No. of seeds per pod | PDM 11 |
| Bold seed | PDM 84-164, KPS#1, PDM 97-279 |
| (> 5.0 g/100 seeds wt.) | Pusa bold 2 |
| No. of clusters per plant | Samrat (PDM 84-139) |
| Podding from the lower nodes | Samrat (PDM 84-139} |
| No. of pods per plant | PDM 11, Samrat, Kanchan (PDM 116), PDM 90-233, PDM 90-237, PDM 91-259, ML 337, Hyb 12-4, |
| Extra early maturity {55-60 days) | PDM 85-199, 12/333, SML 32 |
| Drought tolerance | Moti (PDM 54) |
| Tolerance to pre harvest sprouting | Samrat, Basanti, PDM 91-243 |
| Bruchid resistance Resistant to both *C. chinensis* CL.) & *C. analis* (F) | V2817(AVRDC) |
| Tolerance to waterlogging | PSU-1 (Variety of Thialand) |
| Tolerance to calcarious soils | Chai Nat 60 (released variety of Thailand) |

## 7. GENETICAL STUDIES

An understanding of the mode of inheritance of the targeted trait greatly helps in devising the appropriate breeding strategy and realization of results. Information on inheritance of relevant traits is reviewed in the following:

### 7.1. Genetics of qualitative characters

#### 7.1.1. *Seed colour*

Bose (1939) crossed dark green seeded mungbean with pale lemon yellow seeded type and obtained 4 phenotypes in $F_2$- dark green, green, greenish yellow and lemon yellow. He postulated two gene pairs AA and BB with independent segregation. Dwivedi and Singh (1986) crossed cultivar LH 293 that had dark green and black marbling seed colour with T44 that had greenish yellow seed colour. Four seed coat colours were obtained in $F_2$: nine dark green with black marbling, three green with sparse black marbling, three matte green and one greenish dull yellow. They proposed two genes for conditioning seed coat colour in the cross with symbol Dsgm and Dsgm 2. The parent LH 293 was homozygous dominant at both loci.

### 7.1.2. *Flower colour*

An allelic series of three genes were reported to control pale green yellow, bryta yellow an naphthalene yellow flower colours respectively in that order of dominance.

### 7.1.3. *Pod colour*

The genes for flower colour also affect the premature pod colour (Bose, 1939). Purple pigmentation in the vertical suture of premature pod is due to a single dominant gene. Two independent recessive genes control light popcorn and almond biscuit colour, while two dominant alleles produce black pod colour. Pathak and Singh (1963) pointed out that Black pods are probably due to single gene dominant over light brown pod.

### 7.1.4. *Photoperiod response*

Photoperiod insensitivity is dominant over photoperiod sensitivity (Verma, 1971; Tewari and Ramanujam, 1976 b). Early flowering and early maturity is either dominant or partially dominant and probably controlled by two genes (Tewari and Ramanujam, 1976 b).

### 7.1.5. *Sterility*

Male and female sterile mutants obtained through various methods have been reported. In all cases sterility appears to be monogenic recessive (Ganguli, 1972; 1973).

### 7.1.6. *Seed shattering*

Seed shattering at maturity is due to a single dominant gene (Verma and Krishi, 1969).

#### 7.1.7. *Seed size*

Small seed size is dominant over bold seed (Sen and Murthy, 1960).

### 7.2. Genetics of Disease Resistance

#### 7.2.1. *Yellow mosaic virus resistance*

Inheritance of resistance to yellow mosaic virus was reported to be governed by two recessive genes (Shukla *et al.,* 1978), monogenic dominant in crosses with resistant mungbean cultivar 15229, and digenic recessive in crosses with resistant cultivar L 24-2 (Sandhu *et al.,* 1985). Mishra (1989) reported that inheritance of resistance to yellow mosaic virus in mungbean is governed by three recessive genes without any reciprocal differences. He also reported the non additive gene action as a mode of inheritance to YMV resistance. Incidence of yellow mosaic virus in mungbean varies from year to year, location to location and variety to variety. Differences in the incidence of yellow mosaic virus observed in a given variety at different locations indicate the possibilities of occurence of different strain of yellow mosaic virus at different locations (Mishra and Asthana, 1996).

#### 7.2.2. *Cercospora leaf spot resistance*

Resistance in mungbean cultivars EC 27807-2, EC 27261-3 and ML1 to *Cercospora canescens* Ellis and Martin is inherited as due to a single dominant gene according to Thakur *et al.* (1977 b), and a single recessive gene accordingly to Mishra *et al.* (1988). Gene action for resistance to *Cercospora* leaf spot pathogen was reported to be additive (Leabwon and Oupadissakoon, 1984).

#### 7.2.3. *Powdery mildew resistance*

Resistance to powdery mildew is controlled by single dominant gene (AVRDC, 1979) although it has also been reported to be governed by genes with additive gene action (Yohe and Pochlman, 1975) and recessive polygenes (AVRDC, 1981a and b). RFLP study also showed that quantitative genes are controlling powdery mildew resistance.

## 8. GENETICS OF QUANTITATIVE CHARACTERS

### 8.1. Genetic Variability

Genetic variability was studied in large collection by several workers

(Singh and Malhortra, 1970a; Paroda and Thomas, 1988 and Sandhu *et al.*, 1988).

### *Heritability, combining ability and gene action for yield and major yield contributing characters*

In mungbean, as in other crops, grain yield is a complex character which is influenced by both genetic and environmental factors. The phenotypic variance of yield is made up of genetic and environmental interactions. The proportion of phenotypic variance of a trait due to genetic component determines the heritability for the trait. If calculated from the total genetic component, it is called broad sense and when calculated on the basis of only additive portion as genetic component, it is referred to as narrow sense heritability. Heritability values in narrow sense were moderate to high for grain yield and 100 seed weight in mungbean (Mishra, 1989).

Inheritance of yield and yield attributes has been studied for combining ability and type of gene action through diallel crosses (Yohe and Pochlman, 1975; Reddy and Sreeramlu, 1982). Preponderance of additive gene effect was indicated for yield and yield attributes from their studies. The results of the studies by Mishra (1989) showed the preponderance of additive genetic variance for pod length and seed size and non-additive genetic variance for grain yield and rest of the characters.

## 8.2. Heterosis

Heterosis for grain yield and yield components was reported by Bhatnagar and Singh (1964), Mishra *et al.* (1970) and Swindell and Pochlman (1976). Mishra (1989), reported significant and positive heterosis over superior parents in 23 crosses for grain yield. Reddy *et al.* (1994) reported heterosis of 75.9% and 50.3% over the mid parent and the better parent respectively for grain yield.

## 8.3. Correlations and Path Coefficients

Correlations and path coefficient of various yield contributing traits, *viz.,* pods/ plant, pod length, seed per pod and seed weight, to yield were studied by several workers. The results of Thandapani and Rao (1984) showed that number of clusters per plant had direct effect on yield and pod length. Seed weight was also directly associated with yield. Kumari and George (1985) recommended selection for pods per plant and 100 seeds weight for increasing yield. Mishra (1989) found higher magnitude of correlation coefficients at genotypic level than at phenotypic level revealing that significant correlation between the traits were primarily due to genetic causes. Among the important negative correlations, were those for days to maturity with pod length, grain yield, seeds per pod, plant height and 100 seed weight. Pod length was positively correlated with seeds per pod and pods per plant with grain yield per plant. Pods per plant and pod length had direct positive effects while yellow mosaic virus reaction, days to maturity and 100 seed weight had direct negative effects on grain yield.

## 8.4. Breeding Methods Employed for Variety Development

Mungbean is a self pollinated crop. All the breeding methods prescribed for self pollinated crops can be employed for improving this crop also. Various methods of mungbean improvement are summarized below.

### 8.4.1. *Introduction*

Introduction is the quickest method of getting a variety into commercial agriculture. The variety can be introduced, acclimatized and released for general cultivation within a short time.

***Types of Introduction***

(i) *Inter continental*: When a variety/genotype is introduced from one continent to another.

(ii) *Intracontinental*: When a variety is introduced from one country to another within the same continent, for example Chinamung.

(iii) *Inter-state*: When variety is introduced from one state to another within the same country, for example K 851

### 8.4.2. *Selection*

Selection in plant breeding is used both as a "Verb" to signify the action of sorting out individual plants from heterogenous mass and as "noun" to identify the lines that have been isolated from the mixture. Pure line selection is a rapid and efficient selection procedure to obtain a new variety. Here, single plants are selected from mixed native collections/populations. Individual plant progenies of each plant are grown and evaluated in an augmented design and superior progenies are selected for multilocation trials. The most superior progeny is multiplied and released.

*Examples*: PDM 11, PDM 54, BM 4 etc.

### 8.4.3. *Hybridization*

Hybridization refers to crossing of two or more parents with different genetic make up. It is used to combine the desirable characters of two or more lines into one line. For successful hybridization programme, right choice of parents and knowledge of their general combining ability is necessary. Parent selection will be facilitated if there is a clear concept of the objectives of the breeding programme. The segregating hybrid population can be handled by the following methods.

(a) *Pedigree method*: Here record of individual plant and plant progenies is maintained in each generation and genetic gain is calculated. The method is most effective when selection is practised for characters accurately identified by phenotypes and less effective for quantitative characters such as grain yield which are influenced by environment. Successful examples: PDM 84-139, PDM 84-143, PDM 85-178.

(b) *Bulk method*: In this method desirable single plants are selected from $F_2$ bulk population. Seed of different selected plants is bulked to grow $F_3$ bulk population. Repeat the cycle in $F_4$ generation. In $F_5$ generation, progenies of selected plants are grown in progeny rows and promising progenies are selected. In $F_6$ - $F_8$ generation, 20 row blocks from 2-3 selected progenies are grown. In $F_9$ and $F_{10}$ replicated trials and yield trials are conducted. Seed of superior most line is multiplied and released for general cultivation.

(c) *Back cross method*: In this method $F_1$ is back crossed to recurrent parent and the process is repeated upto $BC_5$. $BC_6$ is selfed. In $F_8$ ($BC_7$), different lines are inter-crossed to restore the hybrid vigour. In $10^{th}$ year, the variety is released for general cultivation.

(d) *Single seed descent method*: In this method single plants are selected from $F_2$ onwards. A single seed is picked from each selected plant and bulked to grow next generation. This process is repeated upto $F_5$. Further processing is done as for pedigree method.

(e) *Selective intermating*: It is modified form of recurrent selection with two cycles of intermating. The method is particularly effective for quantitatively inherited traits.

(f) *Multiple crossing*: This method is used to combine genes from three or more parents through a series of crosses.

  (1) *Three way crosses:* Here first we cross two parents *viz* (A×B) then $F_1$ is crossed with parent C *i.e.*, (A×B) × C

  (2) *Four way crosses:* Here, first we make single crosses then

$F_1$'s of both single crossed are combined in the following fashions

(A×B) × (C×D)

(g) *Mutation breeding:* Creation of genetic change by chemical mutagens or irradiation and its utilization in crop improvement is called mutation breeding. In this method seeds are treated either with physical or chemical mutagens and sown immediately in field to raise $M_1$ generation. In $M_1$ generation every plant is kept separately for further investigation. In $M_2$ to $M_5$ generations, progeny rows are grown and true mutants are selected. In $M_6$, agronomic trials are conducted and in $M_7$, mutants which outperform the check are finally selected, named and released. Example: Pant $M_2$ and MUM 2.

## 8.5. Progress Achieved in Relation to Productivity Enhancement

(1) *Under irrigated ecology*: With increased availability of irrigation, area under mungbean has increased in spring and summer season in northern India and *rabi* season in South India. Productivity in these situations is high because of better weather parameters and less incidence of diseases and insects pests. Productivity of mungbean variety Samrat (PDM 84-139) in a farmer field demonstration at village Kurmi Khera in Kanpur Dehat district of U.P., was 1473 kg/ha during 1996. Similarly, this variety has given the productivity of 1205 kg/ha (average yield of 16 field demonstrations) against national productivity 291 kg/ha during spring/summer 1997-98 under UNDP programme in Etah district of U.P. Hence we can see that there is tremendous enhancement in productivity potential of newly developed mungbean varieties like PDM 11 and PDM 84-139 as revealed by Table 5.

**Table 5:** Productivity (yield kg/ha) of mungbean during 1997-98 of field demonstration laid out under UNDP programme in district Etah.

| *Sl. no.* | *Crop/Variety* | *No. of demonstrations* | *Area (Hactare)* | *Yield (kg/ha)* | | |
|---|---|---|---|---|---|---|
| | | | | *Max.* | *Min.* | *Average* |
| 1. | Mung PDM 11 | 19 | 5.8 | 1150 | 850 | 1027.6 |
| 2. | Mung PDM 54 | 20 | 5.8 | 1100 | 750 | 858.7 |
| 3. | Mung (PDM 84-139) | 16 | 4.0 | 1375 | 950 | 1205.5 |

*Source*: Programme Coordinator UNDP, IIPR, Kanpur

Productivity and total production can also be increased by inter cropping of mungbean with spring sown sugarcane crop. Intercropping also increases the productivity of companion sugarcane crop.

(2) *Productivity enhancement under rainfed ecology:* There is considerable and continuous enhancement in productivity of mungbean since 1965-66 the start of All India Coordinated Pulses Improvement Project. In the year 1965-66, the productivity was 288 kg/ha which increased to 471 kg/ha during 1992-93 but reduced drasticaly to 291 kg/ha during 1997-98. This drastic reduction was due to adverse weather parameters and severe attack of insect pests and diseases.

*Improvement in quality traits*

The major quality traits in mungbean is protein content which varies from 21.0 (PDM 84-143) to 28.4 (PDM 73) percent (Yadav, 1988) and is governed by both additive and non-additive gene action for the inheritance (Singh and Singh, 1973; Singh, 1974). Tewari and Ramanujam (1976a) observed predominantly additive gene action for this trait. The mungbean protein is high in lysine and deficient in methionin. Variations among mungbean germplasm for protein (lysine and methionin) content were reported by Yohe *et al.* (1971) and others indicating that there may be potential for genetic improvement of this trait. Other quality traits are seed size, colour, attractiveness, antinutritional factors such as flatulence and trypsin inhibitor. The variability in protein content is given in Table 6.

**Table 6:** Variability in protein content in different genotypes of mungbean.

| *Genotypes* | *Protein content* | *Genotypes* | *Protein content* |
|---|---|---|---|
| PDM-1 | 23.44 | PDM-43 | 24.57 |
| PDM-2 | 24.57 | PDM-44 | 22.41 |
| PDM-3 | 24.60 | PDM-45 | 26.18 |
| PDM-4 | 24.23 | PDM-53 | 24.28 |
| PDM-5 | 24.63 | PDM-54 | 25.89 |
| PDM-6 | 24.43 | PDM-62 | 25.45 |
| PDM-7 | 24.78 | PDM-73 | 28.42 |
| PDM-9 | 23.31 | PDM-75 | 26.18 |
| PDM-10 | 24.50 | PDM-87 | 24.79 |
| PDM-11 | 28.05 | PDM-109 | 27.47 |
| PDM-12 | 24.25 | PDM-116 | 28.44 |
| PDM-13 | 26.18 | PDM-123 | 24.79 |
| PDM-14 | 25.53 | PDM-124 | 27.06 |
| PDM-15 | 27.06 | PDM-128 | 25.53 |
| PDM-19 | 25.75 | PDM-139 | 25.23 |
| PDM-20 | 26.32 | PDM-143 | 21.03 |
| PDM-21 | 27.28 | PDM-145 | 26.69 |
| PDM-22 | 25.07 | PDM-146 | 26.98 |
| PDM-23 | 26.54 | PDM-177 | 22.36 |
| PDM-24 | 25.53 | PDM-182 | 27.06 |
| PDM-27 | 23.32 | PDM-185 | 27.06 |
| PDM-32 | 23.32 | PDM-188 | 24.57 |
| PDM-40 | 24.65 | PDM-192 | 21.08 |
| PDM-41 | 24.50 | K-851 Check | 22.87 |
| PDM-42 | 25.09 | ML-131 Check | 23.43 |

## Seed production requirement

The seed production requirement for different categories of seed *i.e.*, breeder foundation and certified seed by 2020 AD is given below.

***Requirement of seed based on seed-yield of 6.0 q/ha; multiplication ratio of 1 : 30 and seeding rate of 0.20 q/ha.***

| | | | |
|---|---|---|---|
| 1999 AD | Breeder seed produced | : | 180.0 q |
| 2000 AD | Breeder | : | 246.0 q |
| | Foundation | : | 5300.0 q |
| | Certified | : | 132000.0 q |
| 2010 AD | (projected) | | |
| | Breeder | : | 290.0 q |
| | Foundation | : | 5900.0 q |
| | Certified | : | 148000.0 q |
| 2020 AD | (projected) | | |
| | Breeder | : | 330.0 q |
| | Foundation | : | 6600.0 q |
| | Certified | : | 165000.0 q |

*Source*: Vision-2020 IIPR perspective plan.

*Future strategies for greater impact*

For enhancement of grain yield and yield contributing components of mungbean, which had shown significance of both additive as well as non-additive genetic variance, simultaneous exploitation of both addtive and dominance should be made. For effective utilization of additive genetic variance, population improvement with some modification could be effective. Yield and yield components can be improved following recurrent selection in biparental progenies derived by intermating of selected plants in segregating generations. This would also help in accumulating favourable genes and breaking undesirable linkages. The presence of non additive gene action would necessitate the maintenance of heterozygosity in the population. Heterosis breeding will be more rewarding for improvement of characters showing non-additive genetic variance. Selective intermating of the derivatives of hybrids may prove more useful for development of high yielding genotypes and combining desirable genes of many segregants from different parents. Future strategies should be directed towards sustaining high yield on farmers field. In India development of extra early and synchronous varieties of mungbean with yellow mosaic virus resistance would lead to the expansion of area under summer crop (after the harvest of wheat) in north Indian states *viz.* Punjab, Haryana, Delhi and Western, U.P. which will lead to increased mungbean production. Similarly, incorporation of cold tolerance will help the extension of mungbean cultivation in hilly regions. Development of high yielding powdery mildew resistant genotypes will help in increasing area and production during *rabi* season in south Indian and coastal states. Inter-cropping of mungbean (varieties PDM 11 PDM 84-139) with spring sown sugarcane will not only increase the mungbean area and production but will also increase the productivity of companion sugarcane crop. Development of mungbean varieties suitable to high input conditions will boost the production of mungbean. To feed the expanding population, we have to launch the hybrids development programme for which development of cytoplasmic and cytoplasmic genetic male sterile lines are prerequisite. Integrated diseases and pests management for major diseases and pests of mungbean will also help in stablizing the mungbean production. Availability of quality seed to farmers would insure good production. Development of donor for multiple disease resistance and multi-diversity resistance (YMV and sucking insect in summer mungbean) will also stablize mungbean production. Use of bio-technological tools in breeding programme will also help in overcoming intractable bottle necks.

## REFERENCES

AVRDC, (1981a). Progress Report 1979 Asian Vegetable Research and Development Centre Shanhua, Tainan, Taiwan, ROC. pp. 71–79.

AVRDC, (1981b). Progress Report 1980 AVRDC Shanhua, Tainan, Taiwan ROC, pp. 40–50.

Bhatnagar, P.S. and Singh, B. (1964). Heterosis in mungbean. *Indian J. Genet.,* 24: 89–91.

Bose, R.D. (1939). Studies in Indian Pulses IX Contributions to genetics of mung (*Phaseolus radiatus* Linn).

Brotnegoro, S.B.S. Radjit and Laumans, Q.J. (1988). Mungbean research and development in east java Indonesia. Mungbean. Proc. Second International Symposium AVRDC. Shanhua Taiwan.

Chainuvati, C, Potan, N. and Worasan, T. (1988). Mungbean and blackgram production in Thailand. Mungbean. Proc. Second International Symposium AVRDC. Shanhua Taiwan.

Dwivedi, S. and Singh, D.P. (1986). Inheritance of purple pigmentation and seed colour in greengram. *Crop Improvement,* 13: 63–66.

Ganguli, P.K. (1972). Cytogenetic study of an induced flower colour mutation in greengram (*Phaseolus aureus* Roxb). *Indian Sci. Congr. Assoc. Proc.* 59: 553.

Ganguli, P.K. (1973). Radiation induced sterile mutant in green gram. (*Phaseolus aureus* Roxb). *Indian Sei. Congr. Assoc. Proc.,* 60: 640–614.

Haytowitz. D.B. and Mathew, R.H. (1986). Composition of foods. Legumes and legume products United States Deptt. of Agriculture Hand Book No. pp. 8–16.

Jain, H.K. and Mehra, K.L. (1980). Evolution adaptation, relationship and uses of species of Vigna cultivated in India *In*: Summer, R.J. field and Bunting, A.H. (*Eds*.). Advance in Legume Science Royal Botanical Gardens, Kew, England pp. 459–468.

Kabi, M.C. and Bhaduri, P.N. (1978). Nodulating behaviour of colchicine induced polyploids in *Phaseolus aureus* Roxb. *Madras Agric. J.,* 60: 1331–1334.

Karpenchnko, G.D. (1925). Chromosomes of phaseolinae Bull. *Appl Bot.* Leningrad 14: 143–148.

Kajale, M.D. (1977). On the botanical findings from excavations at Daimabad a chalcolithic site in Western Maharastra. *India Curr. Sci.* 46: 818–819.

Kumar, L.S.S. and Abraham, A. (1942a). Induction of polyploidy in crop plants. *Curr. Sci.,* 11: 112–113.

Kumar, L.S.S. and Abraham, A. (1942b). A study of colchicine induced polyploidy in *Phaseolus radiatus* L. *Univ. Bombay,* 11: 30–37.

Kumari, K.T.P. and George, M.K. (1985). Correlation and path analysis in green gram *Agric. Res.,* Kerala, 20: 82–85.

Leabwon, U and Oupadissakoon (1984). Inheritance of resistance to *Cercospora* leaf spot resistance in mungbean. *The Kassetsart Journal* (National Science) 18: 14–19.

Ling, Y., Gu, H., Liu, C. and Sun, L. (1988). Mungbean production in China and AVRDC;s varieties performance in Jiangsu province Mungbean Proc. Second International Symposium. AVRDC Shanhua Taiwan.

Mishra, R.C. Sahu, R.C. and Tripathi, D. (1970). A note on heterosis in green gram (*Phaseolus aureus* Roxb) *Curr. Sci.,* 39: 190–191.

Mishra, S.P., Asthana, A.N. and Yadav, L. (1988). Inheritance of *Cercospora* leaf spot resistance in mungbean (*Vigna radiata* (L) Wilezek). *Zeitschriff fiir Pflaiizenzuchtung* 100: 228–229.

Mishra, S.P. (1989). Studies on yellow mosaic virus resistance in mungbean *Vigna radinta* (L) Wilczek. Thesis submitted for the degree of Doctor of Science in Agriculture Botany to Kanpur University, Kanpur.

Mishra, S.P. and Asthana, A.N. (1996). Inheritance of yellow mosaic virus resistance in mungbean (*Vigna radiatas* (L) Wilezek) in Recent Advance in Mungbean Research (Asthana, A.N. Kim, D.H. (*Ed.*) Indian Society of Pulses Research IIPR, pp. 214–219.

Paroda, R.S. and Thomas, T.A. (1988). Genetic resource of mungbean (*Vigna radiata* (L.) Wilczek) in India Mungbean Proc. Second Internat. Symp. AVRDC. Shanhua Taiwan ROC pp. 19–28.

Pochlman, J.M. (1991). The mungbean. Oxford & IBH Co. Pvt. Ltd. New Delhi.

Pathak, G.N. and Singh, B. (1963). Inheritance studies in green gram. *Indian. Genet.,* 23: 215–218.

Rachie, K.O. and Roberrts, L.M. (1974). Grain legumes of lowland tropic. *Adv. Agron.,* 26: 1–132.

Reddy, P.R. and Sreeramlu, C. (1982). Heterosis and combining ability for yield and its components in green gram (*Vigna radiata* (L.) Wilczek) *Genetica Agraia,* 36: 297–308.

Reddy Shekhar, M., Raja Reddy, K. and Raja Reddy, C. (1994). Heterosis for yield and yield components in mungbean (*Vigna radiata* (L.) Wilczek) *Ind. Genet.,* 54: 1–5.

Sandhu, T.S., Brar, J.S., Sandhu, S.S. and Verma, M.M. (1985). Inheritance of resistance to mungbean yellow mosaic virus in green gram. *J. Res. Punjab Agril. Univ.*, 22: 607–611.

Sandhu, T.S., Singh, K. and Singh, B. (1988). Mungbean germplasm resources evaluation and utilization. Mungbean, Mungbean. Proc. Second International Symposium AVRDC. Shanhua Taiwan.

Sen, N.K. and Murty, ASN (1960). Inheritance of seed weight in green gram (*Phaseolus aureus* Roxb). *Bull. Bot. Soc. Bengal,* 14: 80–81.

Singh, K.B. and Malhotra, R.S. (1970a). Estimates of genetic and environmental variability in mungbean *Phaseolus aureus. Madras Agr. J.,* 57: 155–159.

Singh, T.P. and Singh, K.B. (1973b). Combining ability for protein content in mungbean *Indian J. Genet. Pl. Breed.,* 33: 430–435.

Singh, T.P. (1974). Epistatic bias and gene action for protein content in green gram (*Phaseolus aureus* Roxb). *Euphytica,* 23: 459–465.

Singh, V.P. and Chaturvedi, S.N. (1981). Gamma–ray induced sterile mutant in mungbean. *Pulse crops Newsletter,* 1: 41–42.

Singh, R.B. (1988). Trends and prospects of mungbean production in South and South East Asia. Mungbean. Proc. Second International Symposium AVRDC. Shanhua Taiwan.

Shukla, G.P., Pandya, B.P. and Singh, D.P. (1978). Yellow mosaic virus in mungbean *Indian J. Genet.,* 38: 357–360.

Swindell. R.E. and Pohlman, J.M. (1976). Heterois in mungbean (*Vigna radiata* (L.) Wilczek). *Trop. Agri.,* 53: 25–30.

Thandapani, V. and Rao, J.S. (1984). Yield parameters and their significance in green gram. (*Vigna radiata* (L.) Wilczek) genotypes in relation to yield. *Madras Agric. J.,* 711: 232–234.

Thakur, R.P., Patel, P.N. and Verma, J.P. (1977b). Genetic relationship between reaction to bacterial leaf spot, yellow mosaic and Cercospora leaf spot diseases in mungbean *Vigna radiata. Euphytica,* 26: 765–774.

Tewari, A.S. and Ramanujam, S. (1976a). Combining ability and heterosis for protein content in mungbean. *Indian J. Genet.,* 36: 353–357.

Tewari, A.S. and Ramanujam, S. (1976b). Flowering response in mungbean. *Indian J. Genet.,* 36: 418–419.

Vavilov, N.1. (1951). The origin, variation immunity and breeding of cultivated plants (Translation by Chester, K.S.). *Chron. Bot.,* 13: 1–364.

Verma, S.N.P. and Krishi, J.N. (1969). Inheritance of some qualitative characters in green gram. (*Phaseolus aureus* Roxb). *Indian J. Hered.* 1: 105–106.

Verma, S.N.P. (1971). Inheritance of photosensitivity in mungbean (*Phaseolus aureus* Roxb) *Mysore J. Agric. Sci.,* 5: 477–480.

Vishnu mettre (1974). The beginning of agriculture paleo–botanical evidence in India *In*: Hutchinson, Joseph (*Ed.*) Evolutionary studies in world crops. Cambridge University Press Cambridge England. pp. 3–30.

Vision (1997). IIPR Publication Kanpur.

Yadav, L. (1988). Studies on selection parameters in mungbean M.Sc. thesis submitted for M.Sc. (Ag.) degree to CSAUAT Kanpur.

Yohe, J.M., Watt, E.E., Bashandi, M.M.H., Sechler, D.T. and Poehlman, J.M. (1971). Evaluation of mungbean (*Phaseolus aureus* Roxb) strains at Columbia, Missouri in 1970, University Miscellaneous Publication pp. 71–4.

Yohe, J.M. and Poehlman, J.M. (1975). Regression correlations and combining ability in mungbean (*Vigna radiata* (L.) Wilczek). *Trop. Agric.* (Trinidad), 52: 343–352.

Zeven, A.C. and Zhukovsky, P.M. (1975). Discovery of cultivated plants and their centres of diversity, Centre for Agricultural Publishing and Documentation, Wageningen the Netherlands p. 219.

**Successful Indan varieties of mungbean**

| *Name of variety* | *Developing Institutions* | *Pedigree* | *Year of release (R) Identification (I) for seasons* | *Distinguishing characters* | *Release domains* |
|---|---|---|---|---|---|
| PDM-11 | Directorate of Pulses Research, Kanpur | Sel. from LM-595 | 1987 (R) spring/ summer | Matures in 70-75 in spring, 60-65 days in summer, tall (40-50 cm), erect, green, medium size trifoliate leaves, long brownish black pods, shining green medium size seed, resistant to YMV and tolerant to high temp. yield potential 15-20 q/ha in spring and 10-15 q/ha in summer no problem of pod shatering and pod dropping. | Gujarat, M.P., Maharashtra, South Eastern Rajasthan and U.P. for spring. East Bihar, West Bengal & Assam for summer. |
| Moti (PDM-54) | Directorate of Pulses Research, Kanpur | Sel. from germplasm of Bahraich Distt. of U.P. | 1987 (R) *kharif* & summer | Matures in 60-65 days, erect, dwarf (20-30 cm), small light green foliage, profuse podding, pods short and thick blackish brown, shining green bold seed (4.0-4.5 g/100 seed wt.) multiple disease resistant to yellow mosaic virus Macrophomina blight and mosaic mottle, yield potential 10-15 q/ha in Kharif and 10-12 q/ha in summer. | U.P. and Bihar for summer. U.R, Bihar A.F., Tamilnadu. Karnataka, Kerala & NEH states for *kharif* |
| Basanti (PDM-143) | Directorate of Pulses Research, Kanpur | ML 20/19 × G 65 | 1990 (I) *kharif* & spring | Matures in 65-70 days, erect medium hight (30-40 cm) small green trifoliate leaves, brownish black pods, green medium size seed, multiple disease resistant to yellow mosaic virus anthracnose and Macrophomina blight, tolerance to preharvest sprouting, yield potential 12-15 q/ha. | East Bihar, West Bengal & Assam for spring & kharif both. Orissa, north part A.P. and Eastern part of M.P. for *kharif*. |

**Table** *(Contd...)*

| *Name of variety* | *Developing Institutions* | *Pedigree* | *Year of release (R) Identification (I) for seasons* | *Distinguishing characters* | *Release domains* |
|---|---|---|---|---|---|
| Samrat (PDM-139) | Directorate of Pulses Research, Kanpur | ML 20/19 × ML 5 | 1992 (I) Summer | Matures in 60-65 days erect dwarf (20-30 cm), small green trifoliate leaves podding from the lower hodes ($2^{nd}$) high no. of clusters/ plant and profuse podding, long pods, shining green bold seed. Multiple disease resistant to yellow mosaic virus, powdery mildew and anthrocnose tolerance to bruchid, root knot and cyst nematodes. Yield potential 12-18 q/ha/ | U.P., Bihar, West Bengal and Assam |
| PDM-85-78 | Indian Institute of Pulses Research, Kanpur | Type 44 × Hyb 12 - 14 | 1995 (R) spring | Matures in 70-80 days, erect, tall good podding, shining green medium size seed, resistance to yellow mosaic virus yield potential 10-15 q/ha. | Karnataka state |
| BM 4 | MKVV Reg. Res. Stn., Badnapur | Sel. From M2 | 1992 (R) *Kharif* | Semi spreding, profuse podding green medium size seed. Yield potential 10-12 q/ha. | Gujarat, M.P., Maharashtra and Bundelkhand region of U.P. |
| MUM 2 | Meerut University, Meerut | Mutant of K 851 | 1992 (R) | Late erect tall, profuse branching, shining green medium size seed, tolerant to YMV yield potential 10-12 q/ha. | Punjab, Haryana Delhi and Western U.P. |
| TARM 1 | BARC & PKV Akola | RUM 5 × TPM 1 | 1996 (R) (Rabi) | Late spreading habit, small green seed, colour resistance to powdery mildew and tolerance to YMV and root rot, yield potential 8-10 q/ha. | Maharashtra, Gujarat, M.P, A.P., Karnataka, Tamilnadu and Kerala. |

**Table** (*Contd...*)

| Name of variety | Developing Institutions | Pedigree | Year of release (R) Identification (I) for seasons | Distinguishing characters | Release domains |
|---|---|---|---|---|---|
| Basant (MH 85-111) | HAU, Hisar | K851 x L 24-2 | 1993 (I) | Early, erect, good podding, shining green resistance to YMV. | Punjab, Haryana, Delhi, Western U.P. |
| Pusa 9072 | IARI, New Delhi | Pusa 106 × 10-215 | 1995 (R) (Rabi) | Late, semi erect, large size green trifoliate leaves, resistance to powdery mildew, yield potential 8-10 q/ha. | A.P, Tamilnadu, Kerala and Karnataka |
| TARM 18 | BARG & PKV, Akola | PDM 54 x RUM 5 | 1996 (R) (Rabi) | Early, erect, small green seed, resistance to PM, MYMV and root rot, yield potential 8-10 q/ha. | A.P, Tamilnadu, Kerala and Karnataka |
| Pant M4 (UPM 92-1) | GBPUAT, Pantnagar | Type 44 x UPU 2 | 1997 (I) | Late, erect, tall, large dark green trifoliate leaves, resistance to YMV, yield potential 10-12 | U.P., Bihar, West Bengal, Assam |
| Pusa 9531 | IARI, New Delhi | NM 9473 selection | 1998 (I) Spring & Summer | Early, erect, good podding, resistant to YMV, yield potential 10-12. | Punjab, Haryana, Delhi, Western U.P. for spring Maharashtra, Gujarat, M.P., Bundelkhand for summer |
| HUM1 | BHU, Varanasi | BHM x Pant U30 | 1999 (R) spring | Early, erect, good podding, resistance to YMV, yield potential 10-12 q/ha. | Gujarat, Maharashtra, M.P., A.P., Tamilnadu, Kerala & Karnataka |
| Nampyeong nokdu | Kyeong Ju choi Jeonnam, Korea | V 298/VC 1089 B | 1993 (R) | Erect, dull green medium size seed. Resistant to cercospora leaf spots, PM & YMV, yield potential 12-15 q/ha. | Korea |

**Table** *(Contd...)*

| *Name of variety* | *Developing Institutions* | *Pedigree* | *Year of release (R) Identification (I) for seasons* | *Distinguishing characters* | *Release domains* |
|---|---|---|---|---|---|
| NIBA Mung | Institute of Agriculure & Biology, Faisalabad, Pakistan | VC 1973 × 6601 (F1 Gamma ray treated) | 1990 | Early, dark green large trifoliate leaves, erect, shining green bold seed (6.1 g/100 seed wt.) tolerant CLS, resistant to YMV, yield potential 15-20 q/ha. | Pakistan |
| Emerlad | CSIRO, Australia | VC 3528 Sel. | 1994 | Late (80-90 days) erect shining green bold seed (6.5 g) resistant to CLS, PM & BB, yield potential 30 q/ha. | Australia |
| Zhoong Lu # 9 | Beijing, China | VC 1973 A | 1986 | Medium maturity (60-70 days) shining green bold seed (6.0-6.5 g) yield potential 11-47 q/ha. | China |
| PSB MG 2 | AVRDC PPO BPI LBNCRDCR Matias FA Javilla | V 2768 B × NH 36 | 1996 (R) | Early, erect shining dull bold (6.0 - 6.5 g) seed, moderately resistant to CLS, yield potetial 12-13 q/ha. | Philippines |
| Harsha | HP Ariya/Miratne FCRDI | CES-55 x MI-3-133F | 1990 (R) | Early (55-60 days), semi erect, resistant to YMC & root rot yield potential 20 q/ha. | Sri-Lanka |
| PSU 1 | Prince of Songkla University | Sel. from VC 2768 A | | Erect, green very bold (7.2 g) seed size, resistant to PM, yield potential 22 q/ha. | Thiland |
| KPS# 1 | AVRDC/TOP | VC 1973 A (CESID-21/EG-MG 16) | 1986 (R) | Medium maturity (65-75 days), green large trifoliate leaves, resistant to Cls & PM but highly susceptible to YMV. Very bold (7.2 g) seed, yield potential 12.5-31.3 q/ha in Thailand | Thiland |
| HL 89-E3 | IAS | IPBM 79-9-82 | 1991 (R) | Early (56-62 days), erect green white bold (5.0-5.3 g) seed resistant to CLS & YMV. Yield potential 10-18 q/ha | Vietnam |

(R) = Released, (I) = Identified, YMV = Yellow Mosaic Virus, CLS = Cercospora leaf spot, PM = Powdery mildew, BB = Bacterial blight, MMV = Mosaic mottle virus.

# 10

# Soybean

## 1. INTRODUCTION

Indian agriculture is studded with several land-marks. The "Yellow revolution", which doubled oilseed production from 10.8 million tonnes in 1985-86 to 21.5 million tonnes in 1993-94, is one of them. Rapeseed/mustard, soybean and sunflower have significant contribution in this spurt of growth. Soybean ranks first among the oilseeds in the world and has now found a prominent place in India. It is the third major oilseed crop of the country next only to groundnut and rapeseed-mustard. India ranks fifth in the world in area and production of soybean (Table 1).

**Table 1:** Global coverage of soybean (1997-98)

| *Sl. no.* | *Country* | *Area (million ha)* | *Yield (t/ha)* | *Production (million t)* |
|---|---|---|---|---|
| 1. | United States | 27.97 | 2.62 | 73.18 |
| 2. | Brazil | 13.00 | 2.42 | 31.50 |
| 3. | China | 8.35 | 1.76 | 14.73 |
| 4. | Argentina | 6.95 | 2.76 | 19.20 |
| 5. | India | 5.86 | 1.15 | 6.72 |
| 6. | European Union | 0.46 | 3.44 | 1.57 |
| 7. | Paraguay | 1.20 | 2.49 | 2.99 |
| 8. | Others | 5.22 | 1.31 | 6.84 |
| | Total | 69.01 | 2.27 | 156.73 |

*Source*: Oilseeds: World Markets and Trade, USDA, May, 1999, and Agricultural Statistics at a Glance, Dir. Economics and Statistics, Min. of Agriculture, GOI.

Soybean has seen phenomenal growth in area and production in India (Paroda, 1999). Area under soybean cultivation has steadily increased over the years from the level of 3000 ha in 1969. Soybean production almost doubled from 2.49 million tonnes in 1991-92 to about

V.L. Chopra (Ed.): Breeding Field Crops I: Practices, Studium Press (LLC), USA.

5 million tonnes in 1995-96. This corresponds to a growth rate of 15-20% per annum during the period which obviously is one of the highest for any crop in the recent past. Present area coverage by soybean is around 6 million ha. The predominant soybean-growing states are M.P. (74% area), Maharashtra (15% area) and Rajasthan (9% area). The crop could be extended to non-traditional regions. It has already been demonstrated to be a successful crop in north-eastern and southern regions for which suitable varieties and production practices have been identified (Tiwari *et al.,* 1994).

An analysis of growth shows that during the decade 1984 to 1994, the increase in area and production of soybean has been 4.6 and 5.7 times respectively (Table 2). The increase in yield was, however, only 1.17 times during the period. The contribution of area and productivity towards production enhancement was 82% and 18% respectively.

**Table 2:** Growth and source of growth in soybean production in India

| *Period* | *Area ('000 ha)* | *Production ('000 tonnes)* | *Yield in kg/ha* |
|---|---|---|---|
| Triennium average (upto 1984) | 743 | 524 | 708 |
| Triennium average (upto 1994) | 4176 | 3503 | 827 |
| Absolute increase | 3433 | 2979 | 119 |
| Increase (%) | 462 | 569 | 17 |
| Increase due to yield : 18% | | | |
| Increase due to area : 82% | | | |

The growth in area of soybean is continuing. The estimated area coverage is 8 m ha by 2000 AD and 10 m ha by 2010 AD. It is expected that productivity enhancement to 1.25 t/ha by 2000 AD and 1.5 t/ha 2010 AD will be achieved so that a production of 15 million tonnes by 2010 in India can be expected (Holt *et al.,* 1997).

## 2. EARLY FEASIBILITY TRIALS AND EVENTUAL RENAISSANCE OF SOYBEAN IN INDIA

Early feasibility trials of soybean were undertaken at Nagpur in 1885, at Madras in 1888, Lahore in 1894, Bombay Presidency during 1901, and Pune and Surat in 1904. Although these earlier attempts were not encouraging, sustained work carried out in several states paved the way for successful cultivation of soybean in India (Kaltenbach and Legros, 1936; Kale, 1936).

Soybean was introduced into the Malwa plateau of Madhya Pradesh, the present niche of the crop, long back when it was the erstwhile Holker State of the Central India. The records and annual reports of the Institute of Plant Industry (IPI), Indore reveal that soybean was introduced and taken up for varietal evaluation in 1932. By the year 1936, feasibility of soybean cultivation in the Central India was established. Varieties "Ototan" (black-seeded) and "Easy Cook" were promoted from 1935 to 1952 in addition to "Punjab White", a promising 'desi' (country) type. The farmers cultivated the crop in a limited scale, mostly in areas prone to water-logging, for green manuring and as a soil cover. The seeds were used as animal feed and as adulterant with the pigeonpea seeds.

Of special interest is the detailed account of soybean and its cultivation practices given by Father of the Nation, Mahatma Gandhi, which was published in the Journal "Harijan" in November, 1935. He referred to black, yellow and other colours of soybean grain. He recommended that soybean flour can be mixed with wheat flour in the proportion of 1:5 for making "chapaties".

In recent times, the feasibility of successful soybean cultivation was demonstrated starting in 1963-64 using yellow-seeded soybean lines like Bragg, Clark 63 and Lee, introduced from the USA. These trials were carried out at the Jawaharlal Nehru Krishi Vishwa Vidyalaya (JNKVV), Jabalpur, Madhya Pradesh and the Govind Ballabh Pant University of Agriculture and Technology (GBPUA&T), Pantnagar, Uttar Pradesh under a major collaboration with the University of Ilinois/ USAID, USA. Subsequently, cultivation practices suitable for Indian conditions (Saxena *et al.,* 1971) and several promising soybean varieties were identified (Saxena and Pandey, 1971; Lal and Mehta, 1972; Lal *et al.,* 1974; Singh and Saxena, 1975). An economic assessment carried out during those days by Williams *et al.* (1974) estimated about two million hectares of area was potentially available for soybean cultivation in place of soybean in Madhya Pradesh and Uttar Pradesh utilising mainly the wet season fallow land.

It was only in the mid-seventies and later that the area and production has picked up after the export of deoiled cake (DOC) of soybean, became an important commodity. The farmers had a strong incentive to plant '*kharif* (rainy-season) fallows with a black-seeded soybean variety, 'Kalitur', known to Indians since ages in one form or the other. Other varieties which were popular, but grown to lesser extent than 'Kalitur', during the period were 'Punjab 1', a yellow-seeded selection from 'Nanking' variety of China, and 'T-49', a yellow-seeded indigenous variety with small seeds and high germinability.

Thus, soybean area saw a phenomenal growth starting with mid-seventies owing to confluence of all essentials *viz.* the export potential for soymeal, establishment of soybean extraction plants, availability of large tracts of wet-land/'*kharif* fallows, support price and other conducive policy environment and the ingenuity and risk-taking capacity of Indian farmers and enterpreneurs. Its cultivation has brought about positive socio-economic changes in the life of farmers particularly in Central India. The saga, as to how a marginal crop became a major cash/oilseed crop, has been told by Tiwari *et al.* (1999).

Although it was the traditional black soybean variety which started the establishment process of soybean, the exotic yellow-seeded varieties came handy for consolidation of early gains.

## 3. CONSOLIDATION OF INITIAL GAINS AND MAINTAINING THE GROWTH

The wide acceptability of the crop placed heavy demand for newer plant varieties and general technical back-stopping, agro-inputs, grain procurement, processing and refining, export facilitation etc. To meet the requirements, several organisations came into being notable among which are the co-operatives in the state of Madhya Pradesh, the National Research Centre for Soybean and several others which collectively led to the consolidation of early gains.

The R & D set up for soybean was always ahead of its time in India. The ICAR started the All India Coordinated Research Project on Soybean (AICRPS) in 1967 when hardly any area of significance was under the crop. The National Research Centre for Soybean (NRCS) at Indore in central India was opened in 1987 when soybean covered only about 1.5 million hectares. The AICRPS, now working as an integral part of NRCS, has a country wide outreach network of 28 centres comprising 7 main centres, 13 sub-centres and 8 voluntary centres to carry out location-specific research for varietal development and refinement/standardisation of production technology for soybean through multilocation trials all over the country. Comprehensive reviews of soybean production technology have been made (Bhatnagar and Tiwari, 1990a; Prabhakar *et al.,* 1992; Bhatnagar and Tiwari, 1997a). The contribution of the JNKVV, Jabalpur and GBPUA&T, Pantnagar was significant in promoting the crop through effective and efficient back-stopping.

Commercial success of soybean owes much to the concurrent development of the soy-industry which provided remunerative market to the growers. The growth of soybean industry has been phenomenal resulting in an installed capacity of 15.6 million tonnes against the present production of about 6 million tonnes. Presently, there are 166 soybean processing plants spread over 10 states across the country. The maximum number *i.e.*, 76 is in Madhya Pradesh followed by 40 in Maharashtra.

Favourable policy interventions such as support price, market Intervention etc. were responsible for the spread of soybean. The role of co-operatives such as NDDB and MPOILFED has also been significant. The collective efforts of ICAR, State Agricultural Universities, the State Department of Agriculture of Madhya Pradesh, Technology Mission on Oilseeds (TMO), co-operatives etc. have led to the strengthenig of R & D activity culminating in remarkable enhancement in area and production of soybean.

## 4. PROCESSING, DOMESTIC UTILISATION AND EXPORT

The world produces about 150 million metric tonnes of soybean, of which less than 10% is used directly as human food. Much of the soymeal is used for animal feed. The efficiency of converting soy-protein to animal protein is only 25%.

India presently produces about 6 million tonnes of soybean per annum. Out of this, 5% is used for food and feed, 10% for seed and 85% for oil extraction (Nawab Ali, 1996). Recovery of oil is about 17.65% and that of soymeal is about 82.35%.

Out of 6 million tonnes, the quantity available for crushing is 5 million metric tonnes which gives 4 million metric tonnes of soymeal. The domestic consumption of soymeal is steadily increasing and is currently placed at l million metric tonnes. This provides an exportable surplus of around 3 million metric tonnes (Jain, 1999). This huge quantity of precious protein is exported as deoiled cake.

The Soybean Processing and Utilisation project has developed 13 soy-products, 19 soybean processing equipments and pilot scale production facilities for full-fat soy flour, partially de-fatted soy-flour, soy-milk, soy-paneer and soy-fortified biscuits (Nawab Ali, 1996). There are several cottage level manufactures who market soy-paneer and the needed machinery. Soy-fortified biscuits technology has been commercialised as SOYBIX. Manufactures have been promoted for soybean dehuller and flaker at Bhopal. A number of upcoming entrepreneurs have been trained in soy-milk and soy-paneer production. At present, there are 90 soy-food manufacturers in India.

Soybean has attained important status in agriculture and oil economy of the country. Exports of soymeal rose from Rs. 2990 million in 1988-89 to over Rs. 24000 million in 1996-97. The export earnings are now experiencing recession especially in value. The edible oil sector in India is now self-reliant. During last couple of years the earnings from export have exceeded the expenditure on import bill for edible oil.

## 5. ORIGIN AND CYTO-TAXONOMY OF SOYBEANS

### 5.1. Origin and Introduction

Soybean originated in China. Its origin probably dates back to 2800 B.C. Its first domestication occurred in eastern half of North China around $11^{th}$ Century B.C. (Hymowitz, 1970). The eastern half of North China was believed to be the primary centre and Manchuria, the secondary centre of origin of soybean. Recently, Chang Ruzhen (1989) discussed different hypotheses on centre of origin. It is now largely accepted that lower and middle Yellow River valley is the main centre of origin of soybean.

Introduction of soybean to India dates back to 1000 A.D. The crop entered in northern part of Indian sub-continent from central China through the silk-route running across the Tibetan plateau (Hymowitz and Kaizuma, 1981). Around the same time, distincly different germplasm was grown in Central India, which is supposed to have been introduced from Japan, south China and south-east Asia (Hymowitz and Kaizuma, 1981). William (1932) had mentioned the cultivation of "Moluccus (old name of Indonesia) soybean" in India in 1798.

Soybean was known to Indians since ages. Black-seeded soybean was sporadically grown under the names like Bhatt, Bhatmash or Kalitur in north-Indian Kumaon and Garhwal hills of Uttrakhand and scattered pockets of the central India (now Madhya Pradesh). Soybean was being utilised as a source of food in the Kumaon hills and also in the Naga hills. Earlier documents established that the plant was known to the Angami Nagas as *Tsu Dza*, a name resembling *Soja*. The fact that this cultivated plant possesses, even among the aboriginal tribes, names which are original and in no way modem derivatives, points to an ancient cultivation (Watt, 1890).

### 5.2. Cyto-taxonomy

The cultivated soybean, *Glycine max* (I) Merrill, is a self-pollinated crop belonging to the family 'Leguminosae' and sub-family 'Papilionoidae'. The genus *Glycine* consists of two sub-genera *Glycine* and *Soja* (Moench) F.J. Herm. The sub-genus *Soja* comprises the cultivated soybean *G. max* (L.) Merrill and its annual wild progenitor *Glycine soja* Sieb and Zucc. The latter hybridises readily with the cultigen. The diploid chromosome number of these two species is 2n = 40. The other sub-genus *Glycine* is composed of more than 15 wild perennial species. Out of these, two species namely *G. tabacina* (2n = 40, 80) and *G. tomentella*

(2n = 38, 40, 78, 80) have polyploid forms whereas the other species are diploid (2n = 40).

Singh *et al.* (1988) and Hymowitz and Singh (1992) have comprehensively assigned genome symbols to several species of both the sub-genera. The cultivated soybean, *G. max* (L.) Merrill, and the progenitor *G. soja* Sieb and Zucc. are the two species which have been given the genome symbol 'GG'.

## 6. SOYBEAN BREEDING METHODS

Soybean improvement has been carried out through conventional breeding methods and recently by using new tools such as biotechnology. Results of pedigree analysis and diversity analysis in major soybean growing countries like USA (Delannay *et al.,* 1983; Manjarrez-Sandoval *et al.,* 1997; Kisha *et al.,* 1998; Thompson and Nelson, 1998), India (Karmakar and Bhatnagar, 1996) and China (Gai, 1999) have indicated that so far breeders have used only a small part of available genetic resources and soybean varieties have a very narrow genetic base. Genetics of many characters in soybean has been worked out and several reviews are available (Palmer and Kilen, 1987; Halwankar *et al.,* 1990; Prabhakar and Tiwari, 1996).

Most released cultivars from public institutions have resulted from single crosses or pure line selections (Bernard *et al.,* 1988) or from long back cross programmes with its wild relative *Glycine soja* (Fehr *et al.,* 1990). Induced mutagenesis has limitations in creating variability (Borojevic, 1990). Biotechnology overcomes these handicaps (Specht and Graef, 1996). Several breeding methods have been employed for attaining different breeding objectives and cultivar development in soybean as briefly presented below.

### 6.1. Introduction and Selection

In India, the earlier soybean varieties cultivated were largely introductions from the U.S.A. The exotic soybean varieties released in India are 'Bragg', 'Clark 63', 'Davis', 'Hardee', 'Improved Pelican', 'KM 1' (Introduced from AVRDC, Taiwan) and 'Monetta' (EC 2587).

### 6.2. Pedigree Method

The pedigree method is the most commonly used method for selection from segregating generations from crosses in self-pollinated crops like soybean. In this method, individual plants are selected till the progenies become homozygous (Fehr, 1978). Pedigree selection is effective for those characters where the trait(s) under selection are easily discerned.

Boerma and Cooper (1975[a]) reported that pedigree selection procedure in soybean retained more yield variability than either early generation testing or single seed descent method. Byron and Orf (1991) found that pedigree selection procedure was the costliest because it used phenotypic evaluation of plants in the $F_2$ and phenotypic evaluation of progeny rows in the $F_3$ $F_4$, and $F_5$ generations. It required more time, land-area and labour than single-seed-descent method.

Most of the Indian varieties *viz.* JS 76-205, JS 75-46, JS 335, PK 262, PK 327, PK 308, PK 416, PK 472, PK 564, SL 96, MACS 13, MACS 58, KHSb 2, Pusa 16, Pusa 20 and Pusa 24 have been developed using pedigree method.

### 6.3. Single Seed-descent Method

The single seed-descent method was originally proposed as a modified pedigree method of selection in soybean by Brim (1966) and has been quite popular among soybean breeders especially in USA. Varieties such as 'Century' and Telia' were selected from populations advanced by single seed descent method. This method requires the least handling and results in rapid advance of early generations. In this method, a single seed from each $F_2$ plant is bulked to raise the $F_3$ generation and the same procedure is followed for subsequent generations also till $F_5$ or $F_6$ when the plants would have become nearly homozygous. Several varieties such as 'Century' (Wilcox *et al.,* 1980) have resulted from the use of this method. Empig and Fehr (1971) reported maximum genetic gain per unit time with the use of single seed descent method without loss in efficiency by growing multiple generations utilising post-rainy or winter crops or artificial environments. Byron and Orf (1991) compared the efficiency of three different selection procedures where single seed descent with early maturity selection emerged as the most cost-effective procedure which required the least resources.

### 6.4. Mass Selection

Mass selection has been practised in soybean especially in association with either the bulk or single seed descent method (Fehr, 1987). Indirect mass selection for specific gravity was used to change the frequency of segregants for protein and oil content and composition (Smith and Weber, 1968; Fehr and Weber, 1968). Cianzio *et al.* (1982) also used indirect mass selection for seed size by harvesting one or a few seeds from plants with appropriate pod width.

## 6.5. Bulk Method

Bulk method of breeding depends primarily on natural selection to increase the frequency of superior genotypes. In soybean, bulk method of breeding has not been found superior or feasible except in cases where effect of natural selection in bulk populations was effective for improving quantitative characters. Torrie (1958) and Raeber and Weber (1953) compared bulk method of breeding with other methods of advancing generations. They found slight differences in seed yield after following bulk method in soybean but no impact was realised for either plant height or lodging index.

Leudders *et al.* (1973) compared bulk pedigree and early generation testing in soybean. They reported that lines selected from populations advanced by the three methods showed no difference in seed yield. Empig and Fehr (1971) evaluated four methods of generation advance and found that the mean values for different methods including bulk method did not differ significantly and differences in genotypic variance among methods were not consistent in all crosses. They concluded that single-seed-descent method was the most efficient. Degago and Caviness (1987) studied seed yield of soybean bulk population grown for 10 to 18 years in two environments. Their results indicated that bulk method of breeding for soybean is more effective where there is a consistent year to year selection pressure from a disease or other stress factors.

## 6.6. Early Generation Testing

Experiments evaluating early generation yield testing in soybean have been reported (Weiss *et al.,* 1947; Voigt and Weber, 1960; Boerma and Cooper, 1975a, b). The testing could aim at selection among population and selection within populations.

For selection among populations, heterosis of $F_1$ in soybean could not serve as a means of identifying superior populations (Weiss *et al.,* 1947). Similar results were obtained in India also (Singh, 1987). In the space-planted and bulk populations, it was not feasible to have rigorous selection among crosses although the inferior or less promising $F_2$ populations, especially for characters like high degree of lodging, could be rejected.

Early generation testing for yield within a population has been used to a limited scale in soybean. For this, the bulk family procedure is the simplest and most widely adopted. Cultivars developed by early generation testing of heterogeneous lines include 'Elf and related determinate cultivars of maturity groups II and III (Cooper, 1981).

Boerma and Cooper (1972) used a modified early generation testing procedure where selection was based on combined generation means. They found the method partially effective for identifying superior yielding $F_2$-derived soybean lines from which higher yielding lines could be subsequently selected. Cooper (1990) used a modified early generation testing procedure for yield selection in soybean which resulted in the release of 8 high yielding soybean cultivars. This could probably be owing to the reason that a large proportion of genetic variance for yield in soybean is additive (Brim and Cockerham, 1961; Gates *et al.*, 1960), whereby $F_2$ plants which receive a superior complement of yield genes, should produce high yielding $F_2$-derived progeny. Further, the yield of $F_2$-derived lines should be indicative of yield potential of pure lines, that could be derived from them.

## 6.7. Recurrent Selection/Population Improvement

Recurrent selection has been successfully used in soybean improvement for incorporating resistance to iron-deficiency chlorosis in calcareous soils (Prohaska and Fehr, 1981) and manipulation of the proportion of various fatty acids in soybean oil (Carter *et al.*, 1986).

Kenworthy and Brim (1979) studied the response to several cycles of recurrent selection for increased seed yield in soybean. They observed an average seed yield increase of 134 kgs per hectare per cycle of selection and concluded that recurrent selection may be used to develop populations of greater diversity and productivity in soybean. Brim and Burton (1979) and Burton and Brim (1981) reported similar significant progress from recurrent selection for increased seed protein and oil in soybeans. Miller and Fehr (1979) obtained increase in seed protein by practising direct recurrent selection in soybean.

Sumarno and Fehr (1982) observed a significant linear increase in yield per cycle for the mean of early maturing as well as late maturing parents, but observed no significant change in yield for the mean of medium-maturing parents. Piper and Fehr (1987) compared genetic response to five alternative strategies of recurrent selection for seed yield in soybean. Their result indicated that multiple generations of intermating did not enhance genetic gain and that the two stage yield test was superior to one stage test for improvement of seed yield.

The difficulty of obtaining large number of crossed seeds was observed by Brim (1973) as a limitation in the use of recurrent selection programmes in soybean. Brim and Stuber (1973) described a procedure which used application of genetic male sterility in recurrent selection schemes in soybean that eliminates hand pollination. Tinius *et al.* (1991) used an intermating population which segregated for genetic male sterility. Desired generations of random mating were completed by harvesting only male-sterile plants from natural crossing blocks. They could increase seed size and seed yield through such recurrent mass selection faciliated by genetic male-sterility. Wilcox (1998) also used male sterility in recurrent selection in soybean and obtained increased seed protein with eight cycles of recurrent selection.

## 6.8. Backcross Method

In soybean, varieties like 'Chippewa 64', 'Ames 71', 'Cutler 71' and 'Hood 75' have been developed by backcross method for transfer of genes controlling specific resistance to diseases and pests like phytophthora rot, cyst nematode and root-knot nematode to susceptible cultivars (Fehr, 1987). Limited back-crossing has also been useful in soybean improvement. In India, PK 515', a line resistant to yellow mosaic virus and moderately resistant to Bihar hairy caterpillar was developed by effecting back cross *i.e.*, (G. *formosana (soja)* × Bragg) × Bragg and then the resultant progeny were routed through pedigree method (Ram *et al.*, 1984)

## 6.9. Varietal Blends, Composites and Multilines

Mixtures or blends of certain soybean cultivars have been reported to perform better than their components grown separately in pure stands. However, the increases are often small, difficult to detect or non-significant (Probst, 1957; Walker and Fehr, 1978; Sumarno and Fehr, 1980; Sutton and Weaver, 1989). Improved yield performance of certain mixtures is believed to be due to greater yield stability resulting from increased resilience to environmental aberrations, when compared with performance of components in pure stands (Smith *et al.*, 1967; Schutz and Brim, 1971). Bhatnagar *et al.* (1994) evaluated 15 varietal blends resulting from combination of 6 Indian pure varieties. The differences in yield among blends and varieties were highly significant but none of the blends proved significantly higher in yield than the highest yielding component.

Beneficial homeostatic effects of heterogeneity could have contradictory implications in breeding procedure as the increased stability across environments may also result in lower yield under a favourable individual environment where some components could have given far superior performance (Byth and Weber, 1968).

## 6.10. Mutation Breeding

Induced mutations in Indian soybeans have been reported for several attributes such as quantitative traits, seed coat colour, enhanced seed germinability and storability, shattering habit, leaf and floral modifications and male sterility. Disrupting the negative association between oil and protein content in soybean through mutagenesis has also been reported (Bhatnagar *et al.*, 1992). Mutation breeding has been successfully used to improve the indigenous varieties *viz.* Bhat and Kalitur of India (Bhatnagar and Tiwari, 1991). Varieties directly released through mutation breeding in the country include 'Birsa Soybean 1' (parent 'Sepaya Black'), 'VL Soya 1' (parent 'Bragg') and 'NRC 2' (parent 'Bragg'). Most of the work has concentrated on defect-rectification of Indian soybean varieties for characters such as seed coat colour, seed longevity etc. (Bhatnagar and Tiwari, 1997[b]).

## 6.11. Hybrid Soybean Development

Despite the numerous reports of significant heterosis for seed yield in soybean (Nelson and Bernard, 1984) the future of commercial hybrid soybean cultivars is yet uncertain because it is dependent not only on exploitable heterosis but also on economies, of producing large quantity of hybrid seed.

It was reported by Weiss (1949) that when a dominant trait in the male parent is available to differentiate hybrids from selfs, emasculation may be omitted and hand pollination may be carried out directly. There is little likelihood of self-pollination in such non-emasculated flowers onto which viable pollen from a different male parent has been used. This is because pollen of the non-emasculated flower would not be viable until 5 to 10 hours after hybridisation was attempted. Walker *et al.* (1979) confirmed that emasculation of soybean flower prior to pollination is not needed. The non-emasculation was found to be more efficient than the emasculation procedure due to the time and labour saved and the resultant more hybrid seed set per pollination. This behaviour of soybean pollination and fertilization could be utilized for hybrid seed production using hand pollination and omitting emasculation when a dominant marker is there in the male parent.

Reports are available on male sterility and cytoplasmic male sterility systems in soybean. At least seven nuclear male-sterile mutants have been documented in soybean (Jin *et al.*, 1998). Carter *et al.* (1983) proposed a method for transferring genetic male sterility to soybean line by accomplishing backcrosses with recurrent parent throught insect vectors in natural crossing blocks. A method for production of experimental quantities of hybrid soybean seed was proposed by Burton and Carter (1983). The method makes use of two traits, genetic male sterility ($ms_1$ $ms_1$ or $ms_2$ $ms_2$) and green seed embryo ($d_1d_1$, $d_2d_2$). The green seed embryo shows itself through a yellow seed coat to give the soybean seed a green phenotype that can be easily recognised. Male sterile maintainer lines marked with green seed embryos would be used as female parents. The male parent could be any cultivar (or strain) which has a yellow seed embryo ($D_1$ $D_2$ or both), and which flowers synchronously with the female parent. Cross pollination should be effected by insect vectors in blocks where the male and female lines are inter-planted. Yellow seeds harvested from green seeded male sterile plants would mark $F_1$ hybrid seeds.

The first report of cytoplasmic male sterility in soybean came through a USA patent taken by Davis (1985). He used 'Elf', 'Bedford' and 'Braxton' as parents to create a cytoplasmic-nuclear male-sterile line. Later, several sources of nuclear-cytoplasmic male sterile lines and their maintainers and restorers were reported in China by Sun *et al.* (1997) and Sun (1999) such as 035×167, NJCMS1A, NJCMS1B, W931A and W931B, and FuCMS series. The former one was developed from an interspecific cross, and the latter three were developed from crosses between cultivated parents. In addition, a photoperiod-sensitive male sterile line was also reported to have potential for hybrid seed production. Vectors such as bees and thrips have also been tried for pollination by some researchers.

Identification of desirable cross combinations giving significantly higher seed yield combined with the use of male sterile lines and methods of producing large quantifies of hybrid soybean seed have not yet reached the level of commercial acceptability.

## 6.12. Methods Employing New Tools of Crop Improvement

### 6.12.1. *Transformation using biotechnology*

Biotechnology has converted all living organisms to a single gene pool. It is an effective tool to the plant breeder for improving yield and quality wherein incorporation of genetic variability is not limited by sexual compatibility considerations.

Several transgenics have been developed in soybean globally and some even transferred to developing countries using *Bt* (Krattiger, 1997) and other genes. However, biotechnology as a tool is yet to be utilised for soybean improvement in India. Owing largely to the efforts of the Department of Biotechnology, in collaboration with the ICAR, a regulatory mechanism for testing/evaluation of Genetically Modified

Organisms (GMOs) is in place in the country. This area also requires collaboration between public and private sector. The development of transgenics needs to be carefully assessed keeping in view the preferences of some soymeal-importing countries which insist on non- genetically modified organism (non-GMOs).

### 6.12.2. *DNA markers/Molecular breeding in soybean*

Molecular breeding using marker assisted selection and quantitative trait loci (QTLs) offers immense scope for soybean improvement. Varietal characterisation using biochemical and molecular markers as well as DNA-finger printing is also required to be taken up in view of the proposed plant variety protection legislation.

The first DNA-marker based linkage maps of soybean were constructed using restriction fragment length polymorphism (RFLP) markers. Subsequent maps have included simple sequence repeat (SSR), random amplified polymorphic DNA (RAPD), and amplified fragment length polymorphism (AFLP) markers. These new PCR-based methods like AFLP developed by Vos *et al.* (1995) have already been used in soybean (Maughan *et al.*, 1996). The most recent version of the soybean linkage map is based upon a framework of 600 + SSR markers and contains 20 consensus linkage groups with a total of about 1400 DNA markers. These include RFLP, SSR, RAPD, and AFLP markers along with a number of isozyme and classical loci (Cregan, 1999). The adoption of single nucleotide polymorphisms (SNPs), a third generation of genetic markers, is a likely course to follow in soybean (Grimm *et al.*, 1999).

The approach of expressed sequence tags (ESTs) has also been resorted to in soybean (Shoemaker *et al.*, 1999). Progress has also been made to use QTLs for yield improvement in soybean. Molecular markers linked to increased yield have been detected mainly in Minnesota, lowa and Illinois in USA and also in Chile (Keim *et al.*, 1990 and 1997; Mansur *et al.*, 1996; Njiti *et al.*, 1997). Mostly recombinant inbred lines have been used. Several moderate to high density genetic maps of soybean have become available.

## 7. SOYBEAN BREEDING IN INDIA - PRESENT STATUS AND FUTURE PRIORITIES

### 7.1. Germplasm and Varieties in India

About 2500 germplasm accessions are being maintained and evaluated at the National Research Centre for Soybean (ICAR), Indore for facilitating their utilisation in soybean improvement. A germplasm catalogue with 17 descriptors of about 2000 accessions have been published by the NRCS (ICAR). In India, 65 improved varieties of soybean have been bred and released for cultivation since the mid-sixties. The first set of soybean varieties, recommended and notified in the year 1969, consisted mostly of exotic varieties *viz.* Bragg, Clark-63, Davis and Improved Pelican. 'Kalitur', our indigenous variety, is among them (Table 3).

**Table 3:** Soybean Varieties released/notified for cultivation in India

| ***Year*** | ***Varieties notified*** |
|---|---|
| 1969 | Bragg*, Clark-63*, Davis*, Improved Pelican*, Kalitur, Lee* |
| 1974 | Ankur |
| 1975 | Punjab-1 |
| 1976 | Hardee* |
| 1977 | Alanka |
| 1978 | Type 49 |
| 1979 | KHSb 2, Shilajeet |
| 1980 | CO-1, Gaurav, KM-1 |
| 1981 | Birsa Soy, Durga, Pusa 40 |
| 1982 | JS 2, PK262, PK 327, VL Soya 1 |
| 1983 | Guj. Soy 1, Guj. Soya 2, Pusa 22 |
| 1984 | JS 75-46, JS 76-205, MACS 13, PK 308, SL 4 |
| 1985 | Monetta*, Pusa 37 |
| 1986 | PK 416, SL 96, PK 472 |
| 1987 | Pusa 16, Pusa 24, Shivalik |
| 1988 | PK 471, Pusa 20 |
| 1989 | MACS 58, VL Soya 2, |
| 1990 | Shivalik, ADT-1, JS 80-21 |
| 1991 | JS 80-21, JS 71-05, PK 564 |
| 1992 | MACS 124, MACS 57 |
| 1993 | |
| 1994 | JS 335, PK 1024, JS 79-81 |
| 1995 | PK 1029, MAUS 1, MAUS 2, CO 2, KB 79, VLS 21 |
| 1996 | NRC 2, NRC 7, NRC 12, PK 1042 |
| 1998 | MACS 450 |
| 1999 | JS 90-41 |

*Exotic varieties

*Note*: Some varieties although identified for release by the A1CRPS Workshop *viz.* Pusa-22 (in 1983), Pusa 37 (in 1985), Pusa 40 (in 1981) and PK 471 (in 1988) were subsequently not released/notified. In 1999, variety VLS 47 bas been identified for release.

It is to be noted that the Indian varieties of today represent different groups based on their breeding history. There are soybean varieties which are land races or selection from them and have been known since long. These are (a) a pool of black-seeded indigenous varieties such as 'Bhat'/ 'Bhatmash' which represent the habitat of northern region but are also cultivated in scattered pockets of central India under names such as 'Kalitur' and 'Kala Hulga', (b) yellow-seeded pool of northern/Tehri-

Garhwal region presently represented by 'JS *2*', and (c) a pool of indigenous varieties with yellow-coloured small seeds such as those represented by 'Type 49'. These varieties, in their original form, have been cultivated in small pockets since long. Plant breeders have either identified them through trials or practised simple selection on them. The variety 'Punjab 1', although representing a selection from the exotic 'Nanking' variety, is also known to have been adopted quite early by the farmers.

Soybean is highly photo-sensitive and is generally latitude-specific in its suitability for cultivation. The areawise suitability of Indian varieties is presented in Table 4. Out of these, 29 varieties are presently in the seed production chain. These are JS 335, JS 80-21, JS 71-05, NRC 2, NRC 7, NRC 12, MACS 13, MACS 58, MACS 124, Punjab 1, PK 262, PK 416, PK 472, PK 564, PK 1029, PK 1024, PK 1042 and Pusa 16. The average production of breeder seed during last three years was around 4500 q per year.

**Table 4:** Soybean varieties of India

| *Sl. no.* | *Variety* | *Area of adaptablity* | *Maturity duration (days)* | *Yield (q/ha)* |
|---|---|---|---|---|
| 1. | ADT1 | Rice fallows of Tamil Nadu | 85-90 | 20-22 |
| 2 | Alankar (PK 71-21) | Northern plains | 115-120 | 20-25 |
| 3. | Ankur (UPSM-38) | Northern plains | 115-120 | 20-25 |
| 4. | Ahilya-1 (NRC 2) | Madhya Pradesh | 103-106 | 25-30 |
| 5. | Ahilya-2 (NRC 12) | Madhya Pradesh | 96-99 | 25-30 |
| 6. | Ahilya-3 (NRC 7) | Madhya Pradesh | 90-99 | 25-30 |
| 7 | Birsa Soy 1 | Bihar plateau | 106-110 | 20-25 |
| 8. | Bragg | Throughout India | 112-115 | 15-20 |
| 9. | Clark 63 | Northern & Central zone | 80-85 | 15-20 |
| 10. | Co 1 | Tamil Nadu | 85-90 | 17-20 |
| 11. | Co 2 | Tamil Nadu | 75-90 | 13-14 |
| 12. | Davis | Southern zone | 110-115 | 15-20 |
| 13. | Durga (JS 72-280) | Central zone | 102-105 | 20-22 |
| 14. | Gaurav (JS 72-44) | Central zone | 104-106 | 20-25 |
| 15. | Guj Soy 1 | Low rainfall areas of Gujarat | 90-95 | 15-20 |
| 16. | Guj Soy 2 | Medium to high rainfall areas of Gujarat | 105-110 | 22-25 |
| 17. | Hardee | Karnataka | 105-110 | 22-25 |
| 18. | Improved Pelican | Southern zone | 112-115 | 15-20 |
| 19. | JS 2 | Central zone | 90-95 | 18-20 |
| 20. | JS 75-46 | Central zone | 100-106 | 25-30 |
| 21. | JS 76-205 | Central zone | 105-110 | 20-25 |
| 22. | JS 80-21 | Central zone | 90-109 | 25-30 |
| 23. | JS 71-05 | Malwa plateau of MP | 90-95 | 25-30 |
| 24. | JS 335 | Central zone | 95-100 | 20-24 |
| 25. | JS 79-81 | Madhya Pradesh | 102-105 | 25-32 |
| 26. | JS 90-41 | Madhya Pradesh | 90-95 | 20-24 |
| 27. | Kalitur | MP & Bundelkhand region | 120-130 | 18-20 |

**Table 4:** (*Contd...*)

**Table 4:** *(Contd...)*

| *Sl. no.* | *Variety* | *Area of adaptablity* | *Maturity duration (days)* | *Yield (q/ha)* |
|---|---|---|---|---|
| 28. | KB 79 (Sneha) | Karnataka | 85-93 | 17-18 |
| 29. | KHSb 2 | Karnataka | 115-120 | 20-25 |
| 30. | KM 1 | Tamil Nadu | 95-100 | 12-15 |
| 31. | Lee | Northern hill zone | 105-115 | 21-25 |
| 32. | MACS 13 | Central zone | 90-100 | 25-30 |
| 33. | MACS 57 | Maharashtra during rabi/ summer | 85-100 | 25-30 |
| 34. | MACS 58 | Central zone | 90-100 | 25-30 |
| 35. | MACS 124 | Southern zone | 95-105 | 25-30 |
| 36. | MACS 450 | Southern zone | 95-100 | 30-35 |
| 37. | MAUS 1 | Maharashtra | 90-95 | 25-30 |
| 38. | MAUS 2 (Pooja) | Maharashtra and Southern zone | 105-110 | 25-30 |
| 39. | Monetta | Central & southern zone | 80-85 | 20-23 |
| 40. | Pant Soya 564 | Northern plain zone | 94-102 | 30-35 |
| 41. | PK 262 | Northern hill northern plain zones | 120-125 | 25-30 |
| 42. | PK 308 | Northern hill & northern plain zones | 110-115 | 20-25 |
| 43. | PK 327 | Northern hill & northern plain zones | 100-105 | 20-25 |
| 44. | PK 416 | Northern hill & northern plain zones | 115-120 | 30-35 |
| 45. | PK 472 | Northern plain & central zones | 100-105 | 30-35 |
| 46. | PK 471 | Southern zone & northern hill zones | 90-95 | 25-30 |
| 47. | PK 1024 | Northern plain zone | 115-118 | 25-30 |
| 48. | Pk 1029 | Southern zone | 90-95 | 25-30 |
| 49. | PK 1042 | Northern plain zone | 110-119 | 30-35 |
| 50. | Punjab 1 | Central, northern plain & northern hill zones | 95-100 | 25-30 |
| 51. | Pusa 16 (DS 73-16) | Northern plain & northern hill zones | 105-115 | 25-30 |
| 52. | Pusa 24 (DS 74-24-2) | Northern plain & northern hill zones | 110-115 | 25-30 |
| 53. | Pusa 20 | Northern hill zone | 105-120 | 25-30 |
| 54. | Pusa 22 | Northern plain zone | 105-110 | 25-30 |
| 55. | Pusa 37 (DS 76-1-37-1) | Northern plain zone | 105-115 | 25-30 |
| 56. | Pusa 40 | Southern zone | 110-115 | 25-30 |
| 57. | Shilajeet (UPSM 19) | Northern hill zone & northern plain zone | 100-105 | 20-25 |
| 58. | Shivalik (Himso 333) | Himachal Pradesh (upto 990 m above m.s.l.) | 120-125 | 25-32 |
| 59. | SL 4 | Northern plain zone | 100-106 | 16-20 |
| 60. | SL 96 | Punjab | 110-112 | 18-20 |
| 61. | Type 49 | Central zone | 125-130 | 20-25 |
| 62. | VL Soya 1 | U.P. | 110-113 | 20-25 |
| 63. | VL Soya 2 | Northern hill zone | 104-116 | 25-30 |
| 64. | VL Soya 21 | Northern Uttar Pradesh | 120-122 | 20-25 |
| 65. | VL Soya 47 | Northern hill zone | 115-120 | 30-35 |

*Source*: Updated from Bhatnagar, P.S. and Tiwari, S.P. 1990b. Soybean varieties of India. NRCS Technical Bulletin No. 2, pp. 1-11.

The exploitable yield potential of varieties is 3 to 3.5 tonnes per ha. It has been estimated that between 1969 to 1993, the annual genetic gain in seed yield of soybean varieties has been about 22 kg/ha (Karmakar and Bhatnagar, 1996). Earlier, the emphasis was on breeding varieties with high yield and to some extent, resistance to diseases. Now equal importance is being given to resistance to insects, suitability for food uses, long juvenility and also resistance to rust.

The achievement of productivity enhancement is, however, small. This is mainly due to the fact that soybean is grown primarily under rainfed conditions. Only about 25% of area under oilseeds is irrigated. Moreover, the area under the crop is rapidly increasing and every year a sizeable number of new farmers are added. It will take time for full realisation of high yields which are being reaped by experienced farmers of Malwa plateau.

### 7.2. Enhancing Genetic Potential for Yield

There is a need to enhance the genetic potential for yield in soybean varieties of India. This is different from checking the yield erosion due to insect-pests and diseases, shattering loss etc. Long juvenility *i.e.*, delayed flowering under short day conditions, is important for accumulating high biomass and high yield in Indian conditions where the growing period is about 100 days compared to 130 to 140 days in USA. Yield comparison across countries and latitude should be based on productivity per day rather than on absolute yield realised.

Most soybean varieties are highly sensitive to changes in latitude or planting date because of their responses to variations in photoperiod. The short photoperiod of the tropics causes most soybean germplasm to flower and mature too rapidly to attain adequate growth and partition it into high yield. The use of the long juvenility trait was the solution found by soybean breeders (Hartwig and Kiihl, 1979; Hinson, 1989; Kiihl and Garcia, 1989) to this problem. During the juvenile period, soybean does not flower even though appropriate photoperiodic conditions exist and the extended period permits greater vegetative growth. Initial sources of this character were Santa Maria, PI 1559925 and PI 2400664. It is controlled by one, two or more recessive genes, but is also influenced by the genetic background of the material (Hartwig and Kiihl, 1979; Hinson, 1989; Kiihl and Garcia, 1989). Since long juvenility trait causes a delay in flowering and maturity, it is necessary to identify lines that show rapid seed fill so that the maturity of the line is not delayed beyond acceptable level.

Incorporation of long-juvenile trait to delay flowering under short-day conditions has been demonstrated to impart yielding ability, less genotypes × sowing date and genotype × location interaction resulting in superior photoperiodic adaptation to different sowing dates (Tomikins and Shipe, 1997). Germplasm lines possessing long juvenile trait *viz.* PI 159925, PI 260664, Santa Maria, Ocepar 8, Ocepar 9 and Paragonia were introduced from Brazil and USA. These lines were evaluated and suitable ones are being utilised at the NRCS (ICAR) for yield enhancement. Yield potential in Indian varieties could be further increased by combining long-juvenility trait (using sources *viz.*, PI 159925', PI 240664', 'Santa Maria', 'Ocepar 8', 'Ocepar 9' and Paragonia' introduced from Brazil and (USA) and genes for high total biomass and high harvest-index.

Pods per plant is a significant component to increase yields (Prabhakar and Tiwari, 1993). Characters such as high pod-fill duration/high rate of seed-fill, super nodulation and promiscuity, high pod number per unit area, and more seeds per pod are also important and breeding programmes have taken these into account. A number of soybean lines having four-seeded pods have been developed (Tiwari and Bhatnagar, 1994). There is also a need to enhance the resilience of a genotype to environment changes over seasons and locations. Procedure for achieving this objective including polygon breeding (van Rheenen *et al.*, 1991) have been recommended.

For selection, a range of procedures from visual (Dao and Ram, 1992) to complex criteria such as index selection (Singh and Dalal, 1979) have been recommended and practised in India. It is also important to employ newly identified physiological parameters like specifie leaf weight (Bhatia *et al.*, 1996a), dry matter yield (Singh and Ram, 1983, Pushpendra and Ram, 1990), efficient and high nodulation and better translocation and partitioning. It is worth mentioning that variety 'Hardee' was identified to possess most of these requirements (Bhatia *et al.*, 1996a). 'Hardee' is an often-used donor for high yield and has contributed towards development of a number of high yielding soybean cultivars of India *viz.* 'PK 472'. 'PK 308', 'PK 471' and 'PK 262'.

### 7.3. High Seed Longevity

Soybean is classified under the least storable group. Its seed is highly sensitive to mechanical and temperature injury. Bold seeds are more prone to lose longevity fast (Paschall and Ellis, 1978; Tiwari and Joshi, 1989). Efforts are being made at the NRCS to combine longevity with yield and bold-seededness (Karmakar *et al.,* 1999). Availability of quality seeds is being ensured through breeder seed production by the NRCS and AICRPS (ICAR).

Besides deterioration in seed germinability/longevity during storage, there may be reduction in seed viability due to field weathering (Bhatia *et al.,* 1996[b]). Small-seeded genotypes are generally resistant to field weathering (Dassou and Kueneman, 1984; Bhatia *et al.*, 1993).

Soybean seed is sensitive to damage in threshing and other post-harvest operations. The seed should be well-dried after threshing with specific soybean threshers which run at low cylinder speed. Seeds should be stored in moisture proof bags.

### 7.4. Pod-shattering

Pod-shattering is common under Indian conditions. Extent of yield loss due to pod-shatterng may range from negligible to significant depending upon time of harvesting, environmental conditions and genetic constitution of the variety. Use of shattering resistant/tolerant varieties (Tiwari and Bhatnagar, 1988, 1993), and measures such as timely harvesting of the crop are recommended (Tiwari and Bhatnagar, 1989).

Very early harvesting may result in shrivelled and green seeds whereas delayed harvesting leads to deterioration in seed viability (Wilcox *et al.*, 1974). Physiological maturity of seed is indicated when pods lose their green colour and turn golden, black or gray (Gbikpi and Crookston, 1981). A few days after this stage, the crop is ready for harvest. Cultivation of 3 or 4 varieties of different maturity will enable staggering of harvesting to allow for easy management and minimising shattering losses. Care should be taken to harvest the plants from as close to the ground as possible. Good reapers and combines are now available and are being used in India to manage the large area under soybean.

### 7.5. Resistance to Insect Pests and Diseases

Among the insect-pests, girdle beetle (*Obereopsis brevis*), stem fly (*Melanagromyza sojae*), green semiloopers (*Chrysodeixis acuta* and *Thysanoplusia orichalcea*), hairy caterpillar *(Spilarctia obliqua)*, pod borer (*Helicoverpa armigera*), leaf miner (*Aproaerema modicella*) and white fly (*Bemisia tabaci*) are of economic importance in different regions (Singh *et al.*, 1990). Economic threshold levels are also being used in decision making for pesticide application. A large number of nematodes *viz.*, *Pratylenchus, Tylenchus, Helycotylenchus* and *Heterodera* from rhizosphere, and *Rhabditis* from aerial parts, have also been observed to be associated with soybean.

Important soybean diseases occuring in India include rust, sclerotium rot, rhizoctonia root rot, bacterial pustules, myrothecium leaf spot, soybean mosaic, yellow mosaic, alternaria leaf spot and bud blight.

Development of varieties resistant to yellow mosaic virus has played important role in sustaining and spreading soybean cultivation especially in Tarai region of northern India. Immunity to yellow mosaic virus existing in a germplasm line, PI 171443 (UPSM 534), which was introduced from China has been exploited to breed varieties resistant to the disease (Singh *et al.,* 1974[a] and 1974[b]; Ram *et al.,* 1981).

The rust caused by *Phakopsora pachyrhizi* which was earlier confined to pockets of the northern hills, has now assumed serious proportion in parts of Madhya Pradesh, Maharashtra and Karnataka. A renewed thrust has been laid on breeding varieties with resistance to rust. Studies on survival and carryover of pathogen, initiation of disease and the factors associated etc. are being undertaken vigorously. Resistant/tolerant varieties *viz*, PK 1024, PK 1029, JS 80-21 and their selection, and Ankur have been developed. Resistant germplasm lines *viz.* EC 389160, EC 389170 and EC 389178 have been identified, seed-multiplied and distributed to different centres.

It has been demonstrated that about 30 per cent additional yield can be realised, if proper and timely plant protection measures are taken (Sharma and Shukla, 1997). The IPM paradigm for soybean in India is in its infancy but individual components of IPM have been validated (Sharma, 1999). A sound IPM package has been developed for adoption by the farmers (TMOP, 1998). *Bacillus thuringiensis* and *Beauveria bassiana* based biopesticides have great potential in the management of defoliating caterpillars. Likewise, seed treatment with *Trichoderma viride* gives good control of charcoal rot and collar rot.

Breeding of varieties resistant/tolerant to insect pests and diseases has gained momentum in India. Large scale screening through appropriate techniques has led to identification of promising donors. Two insect-resistant strains *viz.* UPIR-1 and UPIR-2 were found to be promising at Pantnagar in north India. IR-2 in particular has been used in breeding programmes. Resistant donors *viz.* NRC 7, PI 171444, PI 171451, PI 227987, PI 229358 (for multiple resistance to insects), L-592 (for girdle beetle), MACS 6613 and MACS 74 are also being utilised for incorporating insect resistance. Ram *et al.* (1989) reported *Glycine soja* to be resistant to Bihar hairy caterpillar. Using this source, varieties resistant to this insect have been developed.

Educating the farmers on field scouting, identification of insect pests and natural enemies, agro-eco-system analysis (AESA) and economic threshold level (ETL) is gradually changing their perception of plant protection technology.

A computer based-system, SOYPEST, has been developed for identification and management of major insect pests (Saini *et al.,* 1997). The system facilitates identification of insects on the basis of damage symptoms and morphology of adults and larvae. It subsequently suggests suitable control measures. With extensive, country-wide information technology (IT) net-working, being undertaken by Agricultural Research Information System (ARIS) of ICAR, the SOYPEST will be extremely useful for researchers, extension personnel and farmers belonging to new, non-traditional soybean areas.

Of late, soybean cultivation is hampered by the incidence of no-podding syndrome or bud-proliferation in Central India and a fungal complex causing rot in Terai region of northern India. The plant affected with no-podding syndrome exhibit typical symptoms of bud-proliferation, phyllody, witches' broom or machismo diseases (Sinclair and Backman, 1989). Presence of phytoplasms confirmed by using the Diene's test, along with nematodes has been associated with the affected plants (Bhatia *et al.*, 1999). A management strategy to contain the syndrome has been developed and recommended to the farmers.

## 7.6. Tailoring Varieties for Feed and Food Uses

The recent increase home-utilisation of soymeal to the tune of 1.0 million tonnes in India is highly encouraging (Jain, 1999). Recession in the global price of soymeal has also prompted several private agencies and solvent extraction plant owners to initiate diversified use of soymeal in the country. In near future the use of soybean as an animal feed will be much more than as human food.

Soybean seed has an ideal chemical constitution (Wilson, 1999) as given in Table 5. It has about 40% protein and 20% oil in seeds. Soybean reduces the risk of cancer and is good for heart. It lowers blood cholesterol. Saturated fatty acids in soybean oil are only 15%. The recent studies have shown that soybean alleviates pains of women-physiology. Soybean isoflavones, resembling human sex hormone estrogen but being much weak, can greatly help alleviate menopause symptoms *viz.*, hot flashes and night sweats that often interfere with vitality. Several such new products are practically/potentially available.

**Table 5:** Chemical composition of soybean seeds

| *Sl. no.* | *Constituent* | *% content* |
|---|---|---|
| 1. | Protein | 30-40% |
| 2. | Lipid | 16-20% |
| 3. | Moisture | 13% |
| 4. | Ash | 4 - 5% |
| 5. | Carbohyd rates | 31% |
| 6. | Sugars | 2.5 - 8.2% |
| 6.1. | Oligosaccharides | 0.15 - 5% |
| 6.2. | Raffinose | 1 - 2% |
| 6.3. | Stachyose | 1.4-4.1% |
| 6.4. | Starch and fibre | Less than 1% |
| 7. | Other constituents<br>Phospholipids, trypsin inhibitors, phytatic acid, isoflavones, vitamins, saponins, other trace compounds | Negligible % |

Despite its virtues, there are constraints associated with food uses of soybean (Liu, 1999). These are beany flavour, oxidative instability of soy-oil, nutritional quality of soy proteins (sulphur containing amino-acids such as methionine, cystein, cystine are less), flatulence due to raffinose and stachyose and low consumer acceptance. Recent reports show that certain anti-nutritional factors such as raffinose and stachyose are favourable to increase bifido-bacteria in the colon giving protection against pathogenic microbes.

Soybean has a beany flavour which is not liked in India. This is due to the presence of lipoxygenases ($Ix_1$, $Ix_2$, and $Ix_3$,) which catalyse the hydroperoxidation of some unsaturated fatty acids and lipids. The oxidation products further decompose to middle chain aldehydes and alcohols which are responsible for the undesirable grassy-beany flavour and bitter taste in soybean products. Mutants lacking $lx_1$ (PI 408251), $Ix_2$ (PI 86023) $Ix_3$ ('Wase Natsu' *i.e.*, PI 417458, and 'I-Higo-Wase' *i.e.*, P.I. 205085) bave been reported (Hildebrand and Hymowitz, 1982; Kitamura *et al.*, 1983, 1985).

Varieties which bave low proportion of unsaturated fatty acids may also be desirable for reducing beany flavour. On an average, the current soybean varieties contain 60% polyunsaturated fatty acids in seed oil (Table 6).

**Table 6.** Fatty acid composition of soybean oil

| *Fatty acid* | *Type* | *Mean/range* |
|---|---|---|
| Palmitic (C16) | Saturated | 11% ± 1% |
| Stearic (C18) | Saturated | 4% ± 1% |
| Oleic (C18:1) | Monounsaturated | 25% ± 3% |
| Linoleic (C18:2) | Polyunsaturated | 50% ± 3% |
| Linolenic (C18:3) | Polyunsaturated | 9% ± 3% |

Trypsin inhibitor proteins, especially the Kunitz trypsin inhibitor (SBTI-$A_2$), are considered the major anti-nutritional factors in raw mature soybeans. Mutants lacking in trypsin inhibitor are available (Hymowitz and Hadley, 1972; Orf and Hymowitz, 1977 and 1979) and can be employed for extending the use of soybean in raw form and as flour without the need of heat-inactivation of the protein inhibitor. These lines are yet to be obtained and used for breeding in India.

Varieties with high protein and oil namely, 'Punjab 1' (41% protein) and 'NRC 7' (up to 22% oil) are available in India. Varieties like Punjab 1', 'Hardee' and PK 472' have been found suitable for food uses and 'tofu'-making. 'Tofu' (soy-paneer), prepared from these varieties has organoleptic acceptance in India (Bhatnagar and Tiwari, 1991). MACS-124 has been identified to possess relatively less lipoxygenase. Recently a green soybean variety, 'Hara-Soya (Himso 1563)', has been developed which is suitable for use as a vegetable at green pod stage. Further efforts are being made for breeding varieties for diversified uses.

Presently there are 90 soy-food manufactures in India. The products presently being offered include soy milk, full-fat soyflour, defatted soy-flour, nuggets, soy grits, tofu, soy-protein concentrates, lecithin (powder and fluid) as an emulsifying agent, soy sterol etc. Some of the soy-products, *viz.* soyflour, treated *soydal,* tofu, texturized soyproteins, soy-beverages and soybased snack-foods have great market potential. Available recipes and guidelines to use soybean in daily diet (Vaidehi, 1981) need to be popularised among house-wives. The challenge is to develop technologies that are simple and require only modest capital investment so that they become attractive to small-scale and cottage industry.

## 7.7. Varieties Suitable for Mechanised Farming

Although soybean received early attention for developing farm implements and machines such as soybean thresher specific to the crop (Singh *et al.,* 1977), farm mechanisation is only partial. The present status indicates that the tillage, planting and threshing operations are mechanized to only about 50% (Holt *et al.,* 1997). The trend towards mechanisation is, however, quite clear. For example, harvesting which was being carried out by and large manually, is now being done by reapers and combines. The combines are gradually reaching the fields of even medium to small farmers who engage the machines on custom-hire basis. A gradual but steady change is taking place from manual to mechanised cultivation on account of acute labour shortage, very limited time available for planting in black cotton soils and pod-shattering nature of crop.

Varieties suitable for mechanical harvesting are needed. These varieties must possess high insertion point of the first pod so that reapers and combines do not leave behind unreaped pods. Varieties *viz.* MACS-58, Durga, Punjab 1, Shivalik, Kalitur and Pusa 40 possess such suitability for mechanical harvesting. Two varieties *viz.* Pusa 40 and PK 262 have been identified to possess a desirable combination of high insertion point of the lowest pod, facilitating mechanical harvesting, and long seed filling duration, a desirable character associated with high yield (Karmakar *et al.*, 1994).

## 7.8. Extending Soybean to Non-traditional Areas

There is a substantial scope to increase both area and productivity of soybean in India. The crop, which is presently confined to central India, could be extended to many non-traditional regions especially in north-eastern and southern regions for which suitable varieties and production practices have been identified (Bhatnagar and Tiwari, 1993; Tiwari *et al.*, 1994). It has been found that the variety 'JS 80-21' is particularly suited for areas in and around Shillong. Very high yields have been recorded in Gangtok and Tadong (Sikkim) with soybean varieties *viz.*, 'NRC 2' (4767 kg/ha), 'PK 472' (4392 kg/ha) and 'PK 262' (4350 kg/ha).

A large number of multilocation varietal trials are being conducted by the NRCS (ICAR). A set of 16 varieties was evaluated in new non-traditional soybean growing regions. The top-ranking varieties were JS 75-46, JS 335, Pusa 16, PK 472 and JS 80-21. Regionwise recommendations have been made for 35 locations.

## 7.9. Increasing Role of the Private Sector

Soybean is a much sought after crop by multi-national companies dealing with seed. Using biotechnological tools, several multi-national companies have developed transgenics in soybean. These include "Round Up Ready" soybean, a variety resistant to "Round Up" herbicide. This variety covers sizeable area in USA and is estimated to cover about 30% area in Brazil. Similarly, "Liberty Link Soybean" has come out which is resistant to Liberty herbicide.

Use of transgenics may be useful for insulating the crops against biotic and abiotic stresses. The adoption of the technology, however, needs to be looked in a context of the national perspective and global trade, particularly the reservations shown by some countries in accepting the products such as soymeal from GMOs.

## 8. GLOBAL COMPETITIVENESS OF INDIAN SOYBEAN

The present demand of soybean in the country is around 15 million tonnes whereas the domestic production is about 6 million tonnes. Under the provisions of GATT, quantitative restrictions on import are to be lifted if our balance of payment position is comfortable. This could lead to an increase in import and may even pose a threat of dumping of soybean grain. Domestic prices of soybean grain and soymeal are presently very close to global prices (about US $ 240 per tonne for grain and about US $ 195 per tonne for soymeal). However, the domestic price of soyoil is higher *i.e.*, about US $ 820 per tonne against global price of about US $ 600 per tonne (reference year 1998). The current large global supplies and below-normal growth in usage is boosting stocks and hurting prices.

Indian soymeal export scenario presents several advantages. The country is near the importing Asia-Pacific markets. This helps in transportation, market-sensing etc. Small contingents are also undertaken for export. Moreover, the Indian soymeal has a relatively higher protein content (Jain, 1996).

Our capabilities have to be improved in credit dealing, shipment facilities including port development, sanitation and phyto-sanitation etc. Recently, futures' exchange is being established by SOPA to provide a resilience, stability and continuum for enabling export over a long period.

It is opined by some that removal of quantitative restrictions would facilitate regular supply of soybean to the Indian solvent extraction plants which will bring revenue in the form of foreign exchange through export of soymeal. However, a better alternative is to enhance the production and productivity of Indian soybean. It is imperative that soybean produced in India is globally competitive. Sanitation and phytosanitation (SPS) as provided for in the SPS. Agreement under the WTO has also to be observed. Indian SPS System is presently under review and is being strengthened/revamped. Productivity growth is also essential to protect domestic producers. This is to be supplemented with suitable tariffication and other anti-dumping measures.

Soybean is a global crop with myriad facets of improvement, production and uses (Wilcox, 1987; PAO, 1994). Indian soybeans have to be globally competitive in the present era of opening-up of world trade and liberalized economy. It needs to be borne in mind that comparative advantage is not always natural; in most cases it has to be earned.

**The Success Story**

| | | |
|---|---|---|
| Nature | : | A marginal and traditional food plant |
| Period | : | Since ages |
| Vehicle | : | Black/indigenous land race (s) |
| Location | : | Foothills of Himalayas |

↓ Introduction and trials

| | | |
|---|---|---|
| Nature | : | An experimental crop - feasibility trials |
| Period | : | Early part of the century - Alull 1962-63 onwards |
| Vehicle | : | Yellow soybeans from USA |
| Location | : | Mostly in central and northern India |

↓ The renaissance

| | | |
|---|---|---|
| Nature | : | A cash crop |
| Period | : | Mid seventies |
| Vehicle | : | Traditional black variety |
| Location | : | Malwa Plateau of central India |

↓ Consolidation of gains Phenomenal growth

| | | |
|---|---|---|
| Nature | : | A major cash-cum-feed/food crop |
| Period | : | 1985 onwards |
| Vehicle | : | Improved yellow seeded varieties |
| Location | : | Central India - mostly states of Madhya Pradesh, Maharashtra and Rajasthan |

## 9. ACKNOWLEDGEMENTS

I express my sincere gratitude to all the past and present constituents of the NRCS and AICRPS (ICAR) whose contributions and work has been freely referred to in this article.

## REFERENCES

Bernard, R.L., Juvik, G.A., Hartwig, E.E. and Edwards Jr., C.J. (1988). Origins and pedigrees of public soybean varieties in the United States and Canada. *USDA Technology Bulletin,* 1: 746.

Bhatia, V.S., Bhatnagar, P.S. and Joshi, O.P. (1996[1]). Screening of Indian soybean genotypes for seed longevity as affected by field weathering. *Soybean Genetics Newsletter,* 23 : 102–104.

Bhatia, V.S., Rani, Anita, Gupta, G.K., Sharma, A.N. and Joshi, O.P. (1999). Occurrence of a new MLOs–nematodes associated disease of soybean in India. *In: "Proceedings of the World Soybean Research Conference VI",* held at Chicago, USA, August 4–7, 1999. *Ed.* Kauffman, H.E. The Univ. of Illinois, USA. p. 615.

Bhatia, V.S., Tiwari, S.P. and Joshi, O.P. (1996°). Inter–relationship of leaf photosynthesis specific leaf weight and leaf anatomical characters in soybean. *Indian J. Plant Physiol, New Series,* 1(1): 6–9.

Bhatia, V.S., Tiwari, S.P., Joshi, O.P. and Sharma, A.N. (1993). Field weathering in soybean. *Seed Research,* 21: 92–93.

Bhatnagar, P.S. and Tiwari, S.P. (1990a). Technology for increasing soybean production in India. *NRCS Technical Bulletin No.,* 1: 29–45.

Bhatnagar, P.S. and Tiwari, S.P. (1990b). Soybean varieties of India. NRCS *Technical Bulletin No.,* 2: 1–11.

Bhatnagar, P.S. and Tiwari, S.P. (1991). Genotypic differences for organoleptic acceptance of soyapaneer (tofu). *Biovigyanam,* p. 17.

Bhatnagar, P.S. and Tiwari, S.P. (1991). Soybean improvement through mutation breeding in India. *In*: "Plant Mutation Breeding for Crop Improvement Vol. 1 – Proceedings of an International Symposium, Vienna, Austria (18–22 June, 1990)." *IAEA Publi. SM-3U/44.* pp. 381–384.

Bhatnagar, P.S. and Tiwari, S.P. (1993). Extending soybean to non–traditional regions and seasons. *In*: *"Sustainability in oilseeds". Ed.* Prasad, M.V.R. ISOR, Hyderabad. pp. 574–579.

Bhatnagar, P.S. and Tiwari, S.P. (1997b). Defect rectification of India soybean varieties through mutagenesis. *In*: "Proceeding of the World Soybean Res. Conf V" held at Chiang Mai, Thailand. Ed. Banpot Napompeth. Kasetsart University Press, Bangkok, pp. 21–23.

Bhatnagar, P.S. and Tiwari. S.P. (1997a). Soybean *In*: "Efficient management of dryland crops in India – Oilseeds". Ed.: Singh, R.P., Reddy, P.S. and Kiresur, V. Indian Society of Oilseeds Research Publi., DOR, Rajendranagar, Hyderabad. pp. 113–139.

Bhatnagar, P.S., Tiwari, S.P. and Singh, C. (1992). Disrupting the negative association between oil and protein content in soybean seeds through mutagenesis. *Mutation Breeding Newsletter,* 39: 7.

Bhatnagar, PS., Karmakar, P.G. Prabhakar and Kumar, Vipin (1994). Genotypic compatability for yield in variety blends of soybean. *Soybeans Genetics Newsleter,* 21: 101–103.

Boerma, H.R. and Cooper, R.L. (1972). Effectiveness of early generation yield selection in soybeans using combined generation means. *Agron. Abstr.* p. 23.

Boerma, H.R. and Cooper, R.L. (1975a). Comparison of three selection procedures for yield in soybean. *Crop Sci.,* 15: 225–229.

Boerma, H.R. and Cooper, R.L. (1975b). Effectiveness of early generation yield selection of heterogeneous lines in soybean. *Crop Sci.,* 15: 313–315.

Borojevic, S. (1990). Principals and methods of plant breeding. Elsevier Science Publishers, BG, Amsterdam.

Brim, C.A. (1966). A modified pedigree method of selection in soybean. *Crop Sci.,* 6: 220.

Brim, C.A. (1973). *In*: 'Soybeans improvement production and uses' (Caldwell, B.E. *Ed.*), pp. 155–185.

Brim, C.A. and Burton, J.W. (1979). Recurrent selection in soybeans: II. Selection for increased percent protein in seeds. *Crop Sci.,* 19: 494–498.

Brim, C.A. and Cockerham, C.C. (1961). Inheritance of quantitative characters in soybeans. *Crop Sci.,* 1: 187–190.

Brim, C.A. and Stuber (1973). Application of genetic male sterility to recurrent selection schemes in soybeans. *Crop Sci.,* 13: 528–530.

Burton, J.W. and Brim, C.A. (1981). Recurrent selection in soybeans, III. Selection for increased percent oil in seeds. *Crop Sci.,* 21: 31–34.

Burton, J.W. and Carter Jr., T.E. (1983). A method for production of experimental quantifies of hybrid soybean seed. *Crop Sci.,* 23: 388–390.

Byron, D.F. and Orf, J.H. (1991). Comparison of three procedures for development of early maturmg soybean lines. *Crop Sci.,* 31: 656–660.

Byth, D.E. and Weber, C.R. (1968). Effects of genetic heterogeneity within two soybean populations. I : Variability within environments and stability across environments. *Crop Sci.,* 8: 44–47.

Carter, B.F., Burton, J.W., Wilson, R.F. and Carter Jr., J.E. (1986). Cumulative response to various recurrent selection schemes in soybean: Oil quantity and correlated agronomic traits. *Crop Sci.,* 26: 853–858.

Carter, T.E. Jr., Burton, J.W. and Young, M.F. (1983). An efficient method for transferring genetic male sterility to soybean lines. *Crop Sci.,* 23: 387–388.

Chang Ruzhen. (1989). Studies on the origin of cultivated soybean (*Glycine max* (L.) Mer.). *Oil Crops of China,* 1: 1–6.

Cianzio, S.R., Frank, S.J. and Fehr, W.R. (1982). Seed width to pod width ratio for identification of green soybean pods that have attained maximum length and width. *Crop Sci.,* 22: 443– 466.

Cooper, R.L. (1981). Breeding semi–dwarf soybeans. *In*: *'Plant Breeding Reviews'.* Janick (ed.) *Avi. Publ–co. West port, CT*. 3: 289– 311.

Cooper, R.L. (1990). Modified early generation testing procedure for yield selection in soybean. *Crop Sci.,* 30: 417–419.

Cregan, P.B. (1999). DNA markers, maps and technologies. *In*: "Proceedings of the World Soybean Research Conference VI", held at Chicago, USA, August 4–7, 1999. *Ed.* Kauffman, E.H. The Univ., of Illinois, USA. pp. 46–58.

Dao, P.T. and Ram, H.H. (1992). Visual selection for seed yield in standard plots in soybean. *Soybean Genet. Newsl.,* 19: 57–60.

Dassou, S. and Kueneman, E.A. (1984). Screening methodology for resistance to field weathering of soybean seed. *Crop Sci.,* 24: 774–779.

Davis, W.H. (1985). Route to hybrid soybean production. *United States Patent,* 4:545–46.

Deagago, Y. and Caviness, C.E. (1987). Seed yield of soybean bulk populations grown for 10 to 18 years in two environments. *Crop Sci.,* 27: 207–210.

Delannay, X., Rodgers, D.M. and Palmer, R.G. (1983). Relative genetic contributions among ancestral lines to North American soybean cultivars. *Crop. Sci.,* 23: 944–949.

Empig, I.T. and Fehr, W.R. (1971). Evaluation of methods for generation advance in bulk hybrid soybean population. *Crop Sci.,* 11: 51–54.

FAO (1994). Tropical soybean: Improvement and production. *FAO Plant Production and Protection Series, No.* 27: 1–254.

Fehr, W.R. (1978). In: *"Soybean Physiology, Agronomy and Utilisation"* Ed. N.G. Norman. A.P. Inc. pp. 1–249.

Fehr, W.R. (1987). Breeding methods for cultivar development. *In: "Soybeans: Improvement, production and uses". Ed.* Wilcox, J.R. *Agronomy Ser. No.* 16, 249–293.

Fehr, W.R. and Weber, C.R. (1968). Mass selection by seed size and specific gravity in soybean population. *Crop Sci.,* 8: 551–554.

Fehr, W.R., Cianzio, S.R. and Welke, G.A. (1990). Registration of "SS 202". *Soybean Crop Science,* 30: 1361.

Gai, Junyi. (1999) Strategies and approaches for future breeding towards high yields in China. *In*: *"Proceedings of the World Soybean Research Conference VI",* held at Chicago, USA, August 4–7, 1999, *Ed.*, Kauffman, H.E. The Univ. of Illinois, USA. pp. 126–130.

Gandhi, M.K. (Mahatma Gandhi). (1935). *"Soyabean ki kheti".* Harijan, Novermber 9,1935 Issue. (Reproduced in *'Kheti',* October, 1995 Issue, ICAR Publication). (In Hindi).

Gates, C.E., Weber, C.R. and Horner, T.W. (1960). A linkage study of quantitative characters in a soybean cross. *Agron. J.,* 52: 45–49.

Gbikpi, P.J. and Crookston, R.K. (1981). A whole plant indicator of soybean physiology maturity. *Crop Science,* 21: 469–473.

Grimin, D.R., Denesh, D., Mudge, J., Young, N.D. and Gregan, P.B. (1999). Asessment of single nucleotide polymorphisms (SNPs) in soybean. *Plant Animal Genome* VII, p. 140.

Halwankar, G.B., Raut, V.M. and Patil, V.P. (1990). Genetic constituents of morphological characters of soybean – a review. *Biovigyanam,* 16: 38–50.

Hartwig, E.E. and Kiihl, R.À.S. (1979). Identification and utilization of a delayed flowering character in soybeans for short day conditions. *Field Crops Res.,* 2: 145–151.

Hildebrand, D.F. and Hymowitz, T. (1982). Inheritance of lipoxygenase–1 activity in soybean seeds. *Crop Sci.,* 22: 851–853.

Hinson, K. (1989). The use of a long juvenile trait in cultivar development. *In*: Pascale, A.J. *Ed.* Actas IV Conf. Mundial de Investigacion en soja, Buenos Aires, 5–9 Mar. Buenos Aires, Argentica, Association Argentina de la Soja (AASOJA). pp. 983–987.

Holt, D.A., Kauffman, H.E., Bellaso, C., Bhatnagar, P.S., Galerani, P., Huan, S. and Roessing, A. (1997). *Procecdings of the Conference:* Meeting the Demand for Food in the 21st Century : Challenges and Opportunites for Illinois Agriculture. May 28, 1997 (In Press).

Hymowitz, T. (1970). On the domestication of the soybean. *Econ. Bot.,* 24(4): 408–421.

Hymowitz, T. and Hadley, H.H. (1972). Inheritance of a trypsin inhibitor variant in seed protein of soybean. *Crop Sci.,* 12: 107–108.

Hymowitz, T. and Kaizuma, N. (1981). Soybean seed protein electrophoresis profiles from 15 Asian countries of regions; hypothesis on paths of dissemination of soybean from China. *Economie Botany,* 35(1): 10–23.

Hymowitz, T. and Singh, R.J. (1992). Biosystematics of the genus *Glycine. Soybean Genet. Newsl.,* 19: 184–185.

Jain, Davish. (1996). The scenario for a "yellow revolution". *SOPA Digest* Special Issue on "AH India Conference on Soybean Development (May 24–25, 1996)". Soybean Processors Association of India Publications, pp. 1–3.

Jain, Davish. (1999). Soya–industry scenario. SOPA *Digcst.* Soybean Processors Association of India Publication, May, 1999 Issue, pp. 27–30.

Jin, W., Palmer, R.G., Horner, H.T. and Shoemaker, R.C. (1998). Molecular mapping of a male–sterile gene in soybean. *Crop Sci.,* 38: 1681–1685.

Kale, F.S. (1936). *Soybean, its value in dietetics, cultivation and uses.* Baroda State Press, Baroda. pp. 1–479.

Kaltenbach, D. and Legros, J. (1936). Soya: Selection, classification of varieties, varieties cultivated in various countries. Institute of Agriculture (Rome). *Monthly Bulletin of Science and Practical Agriculture.* 27(8): 284.

Karmakar, P.G. and Bhatnagar, P.S. (1996). Genetic improvement of soybean varieties released in India from 1969 to 1993. *Euphytica,* 90: 95–103.

Karmakar, P.G., Tara Satyavathi, C., Husain, S.M. and Bharadwaj, Ch. (1999). Screening for identification of bold seeded lines having good seed longevity under ambient storage in advanced generation of soybean crosses. *In*: "Proceedings of the World Soybean Research Conference VI", held at Chicago, USA, August 4–7, 1999. *Ed.* Kauffman, H.E. The Univ. of Illinois, USA. pp. 459.

Karmakar, P.G., Tiwari, S.P. and Kumar, V. (1994). Seed–filling duration and height insertion of the lowest pod in Indian soybean varieties. *Soybean Genetics Newsletter (Lowa U.S.A.)*, 21: 104–107.

Keim, P., Diers, B.W., Oison, T.C. and Shoemaker, R.C. (1990). RFLP mapping in soybean: Association between marker loci and variation in qualitative traits. *Genetics,* 126: 735–742.

Keim, P., Schupp, J.M., Travis, S.E., Clayton, K., Tong, Zhu, Liang, Shi, Ferreira, A. and Webb, D.M. (1997). A high–density soybean genetic map based on AFLP markers. *Crop Sci.,* 37(2): 537–543.

Kenworthy, W.J. and Brim, C.A. (1979). Recurrent selection is soybeans, I: Seed yield, *Crop Sci.,* 19: 315–318.

Kiihl, R.A.S. and Garcia, A. (1989). The use of a long juvenile trait in breeding soybean cultivar. *In* A.J. Pascale, ed. Actas IV Conf. Mundial de Investigacion en Soja. Buenos Aires, 5–9 Mar. Buenos Aires, Argentin», Association Argentin» de la Soja (AASOJA). pp. 994–1000.

Kisha, T.J., Diers, B.W., Hoyt, J.M. and Sneller, C.H. (1998). Genetic diversity among soybean plant introductions and north American germplasm. *Crop Sci.,* 38: 1669–1680.

Kitamura, K., Davies, C.AS., Kaizuma, N. and Nielson, N.C. (1983). Genetic analysis of a null– allele for lipoxygenase–3 in soybean seeds. *Crop Sci.,* 23: 924–927.

Kitamura, K., Kumagai, T. and Kikuchi, A. (1985). Inheritance of lipoxygenase–2 and genetic relationship among for lipoxygenase–1, –2, and –3 isozymes in soybean seeds. *Japon J. Breed.,* 35: 413–420.

Krattiger, A.F. (1997). Insect resistance in crops: A case study of *Bacillus thuringiensis (Bt)* and its transfer to developing countries. *ISAAA Brie l s No. 2. 1SAAA, Ithaca, NY.* pp. 1–42.

Lal, M.S. and Mehta, S.K. (1972). Performance of soybean varieties from the USA. *Indian Journal of Agricultural Sciences,* 42: 461–463.

Lal, M.S., Mehta, S.K. and Pandya, S.C. (1974). Stability of performance of soybean varieties in Madhya Pradesh. *Indian Journal Agricultural Sciences,* 44: 217–220.

Leudders, V.D., Duclos, L.A. and Watson, A.L. (1973). Bulk pedigree and early generation testing breeding methods compared in soybean. *Crop Sci.,* 13: 363–364.

Liu, Keshun. (1999). Current constraints in soybean food utilization and efforts to overcome them. *In "Proceedings of the World Soybean Research Conference VI",* held at Chicago, USA, August 4–7, 1999. *Ed.* Kauffman, H.E. The Univ. of Illinois, USA pp. 409–418.

Manjarrez–Sandoval, P., Carter, T.E. Jr, Webb, D.M and Burton, J.W. (1997). RFLP genetic similarity and coefficient of parentage as genetic variance predictors for soybean yield. *Crop Sci.,* 30: 1033–1040.

Mansur, L.M., Orf, J.M., Chase, K., Jarvick, T., . Cregan P.B. and Lark, K.G. (1996). Genetic mapping of agronomic traits using recombinant inbred lines of soybean. *Crop Sci.,* 36: 1327–1336.

Maughan, P.J., Saghai Maroof, M.A. Buss. G.R. and Huestis, G.M. (1996). Amplified fragment length polymorphism (AFLP) in soybean: Species diversity, inheritance, and near–isogenic line analysis. *Theor. Appl. Genet.* 93: 392–401.

Miller, J.E. and Fehr, W.R. (1979). Direct and indirect recurrent selection for protein in soybean. *Crop Sci.,* 19: 101–106.

Nawab Ali, (1996). Processing and utilization of soybean with special reference to soybean meal. *SOFA Digest:* Special Issue. May 24–25, 1996, pp. 65–75.

Nelson, R.L. and Bernard, R.L. (1984). Production and performance of hybrid soybeans. *Crop Sci.,* 24: 549–553.

Njiti, V.N., Schidt, C.A., Schmidt, M.E. and Lightfoot, D.A. (1997). Mapping loci underlying yield in Illinois. *Soybean Genetics Neivsletter,* 24: 136–138.

Orf, J.H. and Hymowitz, T. (1977). Inheritance of a second trypsin inhibitor variant in seed protein of soybeans. *Crop Sci.,* 17: 811–813.

Orf. J.H. and Hymowitz, T. (1979). Inheritance of the absence of the Kunitz trypsin inhibitor in seed protein of soybeans. *Crop Sci.,* 19: 107–109.

Palmer, R.G. and Kilen, T.C. (1987). Qualitative genetics and cytogenetics. In 'Soybean : Improvement, production and uses'. *Ed.* Wilcox, J.R. *Agronomy,* 16: 135–209.

Paroda, R.S. (1999). Status of soybean research and development in India. *In: "Proceedings of the World Soybean Research Conference VI",* held at Chicago, USA, August 4–7, 1999. *Ed.* Kauffman, H.E. The Univ. of Illinois, USA. pp. 13–23.

Paschall, E.H. and Ellis, M.A. (1978). Variation in seed quality characteristics of tropically grown soybeans. *Crop Science,* 18: 837–840.

Piper, T.E. and Fehr, W.R. (1987). Yield improvement in a soybean population by utilising alternative strategies of recurrent selection. *Crop Sci.,* 27: 172–178.

Prabhakar and Tiwari, S.P. (1996). Genetic improvement of soybean. *In*: *'Genetic improvement of oilseed crops'. Eds.* Nizam, Jafar, Farook, S.A. and Khan, LA. Ukaaz Publi., Hyderabad, India pp. 43–60.

Prabhakar and Tiwari. S.P. (1993). Multiple regression analysis for seed yield in soybean. *Soybean Genetics Newsletter* (lowa, USA). 20: 70–72.

Prabhakar, S.P. Tiwari and Bhatnagar, P.S. (1992). Production technology for augmenting soybean productivity in India. *Journal of Oilseeds Research,* 9: 1–13.

Probst, A.H. (1957). Performance of variety blends in soybeans. *Agron. J.,* 49: 148–150.

Prohaska, K.R. and Fehr, W.R. (1981). Recurrent selection for resistance to iron deficiency chlorosis in soybean. *Crop Sci.,* 21: 524–526.

Pushpendra and Ram, H.H. (1990). Dry matter yield as an effective selection criterion in soybean. *Tropical Agriculture,* 67: 57–60.

Raeber, J.G. and Weber, C.R. (1953). Effectiveness of selection for yield on soybean crosses by bulk and pedigree system of breeding. *Agron J.,* 45: 363–366.

Ram, H.H., Pushpendra, K. Singh and Ranjit (1989). *Glycine soja*: A source of resistance for Bihar hairy Caterpillar, *Spiiosoma (=Diacrisia) obliqua* Wallace in soybean. *Soybean Genet. Newsl.,* 16: 52–53.

Ram, H.H., Pushpendra, K. Singh and Verma, V.D. (1981). Breeding soybean varieties for the northern India. *Soybean Genetics Newsletter,* 8: 74–78.

Ram, H.H., Pushpendra, K. Singh and Verma, V.D. (1984). Performance of new breeding lines of soybean having resistance gene from *Glycine soja. Indian J. Agric.. Sci.,* 54: 1027–1029.

Saini, H.S., Sharma, A.N. and Kamal, Raj (1997). Graphical user interface for a Fuzzy Expert System : *SOYPEST.* Vivek, 10: 2–10.

Saxena, M.C. (1975). Soybean in Indian Agriculture. *Seed Technology News,* 5: 1–2.

Saxena, M.C. and Pandey, R.K. (1971). Characteristics and performance of some promising varieties of soybean at Pantnagar. *Indian Journal of Agricultural Sciences,* 41: 355–360.

Saxena, M.C., Pandey, R.K. and Hymowitz, T. (1971). Agronomic requirements of soybean [*Glycine max* (L.) Merr.]. *Ind. J. Agril. Sci.,* 41: 339–344.

Schutz, W.M. and Brim, C.A. (1971). Intergenotypic competition in soybean. III : An evaluation of stability in multiline mixtures. *Crop Sci.,* 11: 684–689.

Sharma, A.N. (1999), Insect pest management in soybean. *In*: *IPM Systems in Agriculture Volume 5– Oilsecds.* (*Eds.* Upadhyay, R.K., Mukerji, K.G. and Rajak, R.L.), Aditya Books Pvt. Ltd. New Delhi, India pp. 137–169.

Sharma, A.N. and Shukla, A.K. (1997). Effect of insect and disease control measures on soybean (*Glycine max* (L.) Merrill) yield in Madhya Pradesh. *Journal of Oilsecds Research,* 14: 324–326.

Shoemaker, R.C., Graham, M. and Laura Marek, D. (1999). *In*: *"Proceedings of the World Soybean Research Conference VI",* held at Chicago, USA, August 4–7, 1999. Ed. H.E. Kauffman, The Univ. of Illunois, USA. pp. 59–61.

Sinclair, J.B. and Backman, P.A. (1989). Compendium of soybean diseases, 3nd ed. Phytopathological Society Press, *Minnesota, USA,* pp. 1–106.

Singh, B.B. and Saxena, M.C. (1975). Soybean varieties for different agro–climatic zones in India. *Seed Technology News,* 5: 5–7.

Singh, B.B., Gupta, S.C. and Singh, B.D. (1974a). Sources of field resistance to rust and yellow mosaic diseases of soybean. *Indian Journal of Genetics,* 34: 400–404.

Singh, B.B., Singh, B.D. and Gupta, S.C. (1974b). P.1.171443 and *G. formosana* resistant sources for yellow mosaic. *Soybean Genetic Newsletter,* 1: 17–18.

Singh, B.S., Kulshrestha, S.P. and Krishna, Ram (1977). Development and performance of soybean thresher. *GBPUA&T Publication No. AER–9,* Pantnagar (Nainital.) pp. 1–49.

Singh, K. (1987). Selecting parental cultivars and crosses, and visual selection for seed yield in early generation in soybean. Ph. D. *Thesis, GBPUAT,* Pantnagar, India.

Singh, K. and Ram, H.H. (1983). Dry matter yield and branching ability as selection parameters in soybean. *Soybean Genet. Newsletter.* 10: 13–15.

Singh, O.P., Verma, S.N. and Nema, K.K. (1990). *Insect pest of soybean in India.* International Book Distributors, Dehra Dun. India.

Singh, R.J., Kollipara, K.P. and Hymowitiz, T. (1988), Further data on the genomic relationships among wild perennial species (2n = 40) of the genus *Glycine* Wild, *Genome,* 30: 166–176.

Singh. C.B. and Dalal, M.A. (1979). Index selection in soybean. *Indian J. Genet. PI. Breed.* 39(2): 234–236.

Smith, R.R. and Weber, C.R. (1968). Mass selection by specifie gravity for protein and oil in soybean populations. *Crop. Sci.,* 8: 373–377.

Smith, R.R., Byth, D.E., Caldwell, B.E. and Weber, C.R. (1967). Phenotypic stability in soybean populations. *Crop. Sci.,* 7: 590–592.

Specht, J.E. and Graef, G.L. (1996). Limitations and potential of genetic manipulation of soybean. *In*: Soybean Genetics, Molecular Biology and Biotechnology (*Eds*. Verma, D.P.S. and Shoemaker, R.C.)., *CAS International, U.K.* pp. 91–106.

Sumarno and Fehr, W.R. (1980). Response to recurrent selection for yield in soybean. *Crop Sci.,* 22: 251–254.

Sumarno and Fehr, W.R. (1982). Response to recurrent selection for yield in soybean. *Crop Sci.,* 22: 295–299.

Sun, H., Linmei, Z. and Mei, H. (1997). Cytoplasmic–nuclear male sterile soybean line from interspecific crosses between *G. max* and *G. soja. In*: *"Proc. World Soybean Research Conference V, Chiang Mai, Thailand (Feb. 21–27, 1994)".* Kasetsart Univ. Press, Thailand. pp. 99–102.

Sun, H., Zhao, L.M., Li, J.P. and Wang, Y.Q. (1999). The investigation of heterosis and pollen transfer in soybean. *In: "Proceedings of the World Soybean Research Conference VI",* held at Chicago, USA, August 4–7, 1999. *Ed.* Kauffman, H.E. The Univ. of Illnois, USA. pp. 489–490.

Sutton, J.D. and Weaver, D.B. (1989). Intergenotypic competition between late planted determinate and indeterminate soybean. *Crop Sci.,* 29: 1506–1510.

Thompson. J.A. and Nelson, R.L. (1998). Utilisation of diverse germplasm for soybean yield improvement. *Crop Sci.,* 38: 1362–1368.

Tinius, C.N., Burton, J.W. and Carter Jr. T.E. (1991). Recurrent selection for seed size in soybean. I: Response to selection m replicate populations. *Crop. Sci,,* 31: 1137–1141.

Tiwari, S.P. and Bhatnagar, P.S. (1988). Pod–shattering of soybean in India. *Journal of Oilseeds Research,* 5: 92–93.

Tiwari, S.P. and Bhatnagar, P.S. (1989). Minimising pod–shattering in soybean. *Indian Farming,.* 39: 23–24.

Tiwari, S.P. and Bhatnagar, P.S. (1993). Consistent resistance for pod–shattering in soybean *(Glycine max)* varieties. *Indian Journal of Agricultural Sciences,* 63: 33–34.

Tiwari, S.P. and Bhatnagar, P.S. (1994). Transgressive segregants with four–seeded pods in soybean. *Soybean Genetics Newsletter,* 21: 135–136.

Tiwari, S.P. and Joshi, H.J. (1989). Correlation and path–analysis for seed quality characters in soybean. *Journal of Oilseeds Research,* 6: 51–57.

Tiwari, S.P., Bhatnagar, P.S. and Prabhakar. (1994). Identification of suitable soybean *(Glycine max)* varieties for non–traditional regions of India. *Ind. J. Agril. Sci.,* 64: 872–874.

Tiwari, S.P., Joshi, O.P. and Sharma, A.N. (1999). The advent and renaissance of soybean in India – *The saga of success.* NRC for Soybean (ICAR) Publi. pp. 1–58.

TMOP. (1998). Integrated pest management package for soybean, Technology Mission on Oilseeds and Pulses, DAC, Govt. of India, Krishi Bhawan, New Delhi, pp. 1–14.

Tomkins, J.P. and Shipe, E.R. (1997). Environmental adaptation of long–juvenile soybean cultivars and elite strains. *Agrononiy J.,* 89(2): 257–262.

Torrie, J.H. (1958). A comparison of pedigree and bulk methods of breeding soybean crosses. *Agron. J.,* 50: 198–200.

Vaidehi, M.P. (1981). *Soya uses in daily diet.* UAS, Bangalore, pp. 1–38.

Van Rheenen, H.A., Rangasamy, P., Shinde, V.K., Reddy, L.R.P. and Gomathinayagam, P. (1991). Polygon breeding: Old hat or new trick. *International Chickpea Newsletter, ICRISAT,* No. 25: 6–7.

Voigt, R.L. and Weber, C.R. (1960). Effectiveness of selection methods for yield in soybean crosses, *Agron. J.,* 52: 527–530.

Vos. P., Hogers, R., Bleeker, M., Reijans, M., van de Lee, T., Homes, M., Frijters, A., Pot, J., Peleman, J., Kuiper, M. and Zabeau, M. (1995). AFLP™: A new technique for DNA fingerprinting. *Nucleic Acids Research,* 23(21): 4407–4414.

Walker, A.K. and Fehr, W.R. (1978). Yield stability of soybean mixtures and multiple pure stands. *Crops Sci.,* 18: 719–723.

Walker, A.K., Cianzio, S.R., Bravo, J.A. and Fehr, W.R. (1979). Comparison of emasculation and non–emasculation for hybridisation of soybean. *Crop. Sci.,* 19: 285–286.

Watt, G. (1890). *A Dictionary of the Economie Products of India.* Volume III Cosmo Publications, Delhi, India, pp. 509–511. (Second reprint 1972).

Weiss, M.G. (1949). *Soybeans. Adv. Agron.* 1: 77–157.

Weiss, M.G., Weber, C.R. and Kahon, R.R. (1947). Early generation testing in soybean. *J. Am. Soc. Agron.,* 39: 791–811.

Wilcox, J.R. (1987). Soybeans: Improvement, production and uses. Second edition. ASA Inc., CSSA Inc. and SSSA Inc., Madison, Wisconsin, USA. pp. 1–888.

Wilcox, J.R. (1998). Increasing seed protein in soybean with eight cycles of recurrent selection. *Crop Sci.* 38: 1536–1540.

Wilcox, J.R., Abney, T.S., Laviolette, F.A. and Athow, K.L. (1974). Deterioration of soybean seed quality associated with delayed harvest. *Plant Disease Reporter,* 58: 130–133.

Wilcox, J.R., Athow, K.L., Abney, T.S., Laviolette, F.A. and Richards, T.L. (1980). Registration of Century soybean. *Crop. Sci.,* 20: 415.

William, R, (1932). *Flora India; or description of Indian plants.* Ed. William Carey, edition 2, vol. II. pp. 314–315.

Williams, S.W., Hendrix, W.E. and Von open, M.L. (1974). Potential production of soybean in north Central India, Univ. Illinois, Urbana. *INTSOY Ser.* p. 5.

Wilson, L.A. (1999). Current developments in soyfood processing in North America. In: *"Proceedings of the World Soybean Research Conference VI",* held at Chicago, USA, August 4–7, 1999. Ed. H.E. Kauffman, The Univ. of Illinois USA. pp. 394–402.

# 11

# Oilseed *Brassicas*

## 1. INTRODUCTION

The cultivation of *Brassica* crops go back to Harappan times. They were in use in Vedic civilization. Much before the Christian era, they were used in India for manifold purposes, *viz.*, edible oils, vegetables, fodder, preparation and seasoning of food articles. They have been used in medicine, condiments, pickles and in several religious ceremonies. *Brassica* oils, in addition, served as an important raw material for industrial products like soaps, lubricants, paints, plasticizers, etc. (Prakash and Hinata, 1980).

The small round seed contains on an average 37 per cent oil and the seed meal contains more than 40 per cent protein. In the Indian sub continent, the meal is utilized as high quality protein feed supplement for livestock. The last two decades have transformed the usage of *Brassica* oils and seed meal at global level. This is primarily due to modifications made in the composition of fatty acids and glucosinolates and the new products that have been developed. The modified products have expanded the world market and increased the value of oil and high protein meal.

## 2. AREA, PRODUCTION AND PRODUCTIVITY

### 2.1. World Scenario

Rapeseed-mustard is the world's second most important oilseed. A perusal of Table 1 indicates world production of rapeseed-mustard has doubled in the last decade. This is the only crop commodity where such a significant increase in production has been witnessed. The year 1985-

V.L. Chopra (Ed.): Breeding Field Crops I: Practices, Studium Press (LLC), USA.

86, assumes special significance in oilseed history of India. Realizing the urgent need for reducing imports of edible oils and oilseeds, the Govt. of India launched Technology Mission on Oilseed (TMOP). The mission was a success. In a short span of 7 years, the production of oilseeds doubled and import drastically reduced. The increase in production affected the world edible oil economy, when a comparison of the figures of 1986 with latest statistics is made. The estimates for 1999-2000 indicate that the total oilseed production is likely to exceed 300 million tons (mt), with rapeseed-mustard exceeding 40 mt. It indicates that the crop commodity continues to be the fastest growing world source of edible oils and is one of the few species with potential to meet the growing edible oil needs of many countries in Asia, Africa and America. China, India and Canada are the major rapeseed-mustard growing countries of the world. They contribute 72.4 per cent of the total rapeseed-mustard production of the world with India as the largest producer contributing 27.5 per cent (Table 2). A comparison of the status of the crop during 1986 and 1997 indicates that a country like Australia to be heading as a major rapeseed-mustard producer of the world with 1.2 mt production in 1999.

**Table 1:** Area, production and yield of oilseeds in the world (1986 and 1997)

| *Crop* | *Area ('000' ha)* | | *Production ('000 mt')* | | *Yield (kg/ha)* | |
|---|---|---|---|---|---|---|
| | *1986* | *1997* | *1986* | *1997* | *1986* | *1997* |
| Groundnut | 18812 | 23700 | 21012 | 30169 | 1117 | 1273 |
| Rapeseed-Mustard | 14921 | 24198 | 19640 | 35103 | 1316 | 1451 |
| Soybean | 51905 | 67619 | 94355 | 147029 | 1818 | 2174 |
| Sesame | 6672 | 7347 | 2286 | 2688 | 343 | 366 |
| Sunflower | 15192 | 20244 | 20930 | 24670 | 1378 | 1219 |
| Safflower | 1300 | 1039 | 672 | 933 | 517 | 898 |
| Linseed | 4896 | 3419 | 2924 | 2463 | 597 | 720 |
| Castor | 1708 | 1374 | 1032 | 1294 | 604 | 942 |
| Total | 122078 | 148940 | 165137 | 244349 | 1353 | 1641 |

*Source*: Oil World, 1999.

**Table 2:** Area, production and yield of rapeseed-mustard in major countries of the world (1986 and 1997)

| *Country* | *Area ('000' ha)* | | *Production ('000 mt')* | | *Yield (kg/ha)* | |
|---|---|---|---|---|---|---|
| | *1986* | *1997* | *1986* | *1997* | *1986* | *1997* |
| India | 3979 | 6813 | 2681 | 9660 | 674 | 1022 |
| China | 4917 | 6791 | 5882 | 9540 | 1196 | 1405 |
| Canada | 2640 | 4813 | 3787 | 6198 | 1434 | 1288 |
| Poland | 515 | 317 | 1298 | 595 | 2520 | 1877 |
| United Germany | 459 | 918 | 1415 | 2843 | 3083 | 3097 |
| France | 392 | 988 | 1048 | 3486 | 2673 | 2528 |
| Australia | 66 | 655 | 76 | 769 | 1152 | 1174 |
| Pakistan | 351 | 354 | 250 | 286 | 712 | 808 |
| United Kingdom | 299 | 467 | 951 | 1509 | 3181 | 3231 |

## 2.2. Indian Scenario

Rapeseed-Mustard is the second most important edible oilseed of India after groundnut in terms of the acreage. The cultivation of rapeseed-mustard which was earlier confined to the northern belt has now spread to non-traditional areas in western and southern region of the country. Rajasthan followed by Uttar Pradesh, Madhya Pradesh and Haryana altogether contribute 81 per cent in acreage and 82.9 per cent in total rapeseed-mustard production (Table 3). Rajasthan alone contributes 39.3 and 38.2 per cent to acreage and production in the country, respectively.

**Table 3:** Area, production and yield of rapeseed-mustard in different states in India (1986 and 1998)

| *State* | *Area ('000' ha)* | | *Production ('000 mt')* | | *Yield (kg/ha)* | |
|---|---|---|---|---|---|---|
| | *1986* | *1998* | *1986* | *1998* | *1986* | *1998* |
| Andhra Pradesh | 1.1 | 2.8 | 0.1 | 0.7 | - | - |
| Arunachal Pradesh | 14.6 | 20.5 | 12.1 | 19.1 | - | 932 |
| Assam | 291.0 | 279.3 | 137.7 | 154.6 | 473 | 554 |
| Bihar | 85.8 | 100.7 | 62.4 | 89.3 | 727 | 887 |
| Delhi | - | 5.6 | - | 0.8 | - | - |
| Gujarat | 192.4 | 345.6 | 208.9 | 350.0 | 1086 | 1013 |
| Haryana | 342.0 | 555.0 | 274.0 | 370.0 | 801 | 667 |
| Himachal Pradesh | 6.9 | 10.0 | 2.0 | 5.7 | - | - |
| Jammu & Kashmir | 61.7 | 62.6 | 63.8 | 45.1 | 1034 | 720 |
| Karnataka | 4.7 | 4.8 | 1.1 | 1.2 | - | - |
| Madhya Pradesh | 338.2 | 736.8 | 182.0 | 423.1 | 538 | 574 |
| Maharashtra | 4.8 | 11.1 | 1.4 | 2.3 | - | - |
| Manipur | 4.0 | 1.9 | 2.7 | 0.9 | - | - |
| Meghalya | 6.7 | 6.9 | 4.5 | 4.4 | - | - |
| Mizoram | - | 3.5 | - | 6.3 | - | - |
| Nagaland | 5.8 | 10.0 | 4.7 | 8.0 | - | - |
| Orissa | 146.5 | 19.8 | 80.6 | 3.2 | 550 | 162 |
| Punjab | 146.0 | 70.0 | 148.0 | 61.0 | 1014 | 871 |
| Rajasthan | 1014.8 | 3275.7 | 664.9 | 2193.3 | 655 | 670 |
| Sikkim | 6.6 | 5.6 | 4.7 | 4.3 | - | - |
| Tamilnadu | 0.8 | 0.8 | 0.2 | 0.1 | - | - |
| Tripura | 3.1 | 5.7 | 2.2 | 4.9 | - | - |
| Uttar Pradesh | 1069.3 | 1203.0 | 658.3 | 713.6 | 616 | 593 |
| West Bengal | 231.6 | 327.1 | 163.4 | 251.0 | 706 | 767 |

# 3. ORIGIN

## 3.1. Origin of *Brassica*

The world *Brassica* originated from the *Bresic* or *Bresych,* the Celtic name for cabbage and a contraction of *praesecare* (to cut off early) since the leaves were removed for fodder (Hegi, 1919).

### 3.1.1. *Brassica juncea*

Middle East seems to be the place of origin because wild forms of *B. campestris* and *B. nigra* occur together (Olsson, 1960; Mizushima and Tsunoda, 1967; Prakash and Hinata, 1980). The regions of south-western China and north-western India constitute two secondary centres where there is enormous diversity. Biochemical studies support this finding (Vaughan *et al.,* 1963) and further provide evidence for the existence of two geographical races, Chinese and Indian (Vaughan and Gordon, 1973). This evidence is supported by Song *et al.* (1988) through RFLP studies and suggests two centres of origin (i) Middle East and (ii) China.

### 3.1.2. *Brassica campestris*

Oilseed forms appear to have evolved from European-Mediterranean area, with a secondary centre of origin in Asia (Downey, 1983). Of the *Brassica* crops, *B. campestris* has the widest distribution with secondary centres of diversity in Europe, Western USSR, Central Asia and the Near East (Sinskaia, 1928; Vavilov, 1949; Mizushima and Tsunoda, 1967). The Asian types comprising three ecotypes *viz.*, brown sarson, yellow sarson and toria, are distinct from the European oleiferous types, not only in general morphology but also in chemical composition of the seed. Protein analysis also supports separate origin of Asian and European types, although it is clear from the chemotaxonomy that Indian sub-continent forms of sarson and toria are area conspecific with European turnip rape as well as wild turnips (Vaughan *et al.,* 1966). Brown sarson which includes both *lotni* (self-incompatible) and *tora* (self-compatible) types, is the oldest. Of these two, *lotni* is older and tora is a derivative from hybridization between yellow sarson and *lotni* brown sarson. The ecotypes yellow sarson and toria are again derived from brown sarson; the former being the mutant for quality and latter being the result of selection (Hinata and Prakash, 1984).

### 3.1.3. *Eruca sativa*

It is a recent introduction to India. South Europe and North Africa are believed to be the native place of *Eruca sativa.*

### 3.1.4. *Brassica napus*

Mediterranean region is the place of its origin where its two parents, *viz., B. oleracea and B. campestris* grow together (Sinskaia, 1928).

### 3.1.5. *Brassica carinala*

East African plateau is regarded as the place of its origin.

### 3.1.6. *Brassica nigra*

According to Sinskaia (1928), there are two major geographic forms, western and eastern. The western form is grown in Europe, Africa, Asia Minor and over Afghanistan. The eastern form is grown in India, Far west, Palestine and Syria.

## 4. CLASSIFICATION

The genus *Brassica,* belonging to the family *Cruciferae (Brassicaceae),* tribe *Brassiceae* and sub-tribe *Brassicinae,* includes the largest number of economic plants. They are cultivated in a wide range of environments. They have the ability to survive and grow at relatively low temperatures. In view of this, they are regarded as one of the few edible sources that are successfully cultivated in extremes of the temperate regions. These characteristics make them adaptable for cultivation at high elevations and as winter crops in the sub tropics.

The *Brassica* oilseed in India, is collectively referred to as rapeseed-mustard. The word 'rape', has arisen from the Latin word *rapum,* meaning turnip while the word 'mustard' has been derived from European practice of mixing the sweet "must" of old wine with crushed seeds of *Brassica nigra* (L.) Koch to form a hot paste (Hemingway, 1976). Toxopeus and Oost (1985) strongly advocated that the name *B. campestris* be changed to *B. rapa* since floral parts of the two are indistinguishable, both have the same chromosome number (2n = 20) and are fully interfertile. They practically developed a scientifically sound intraspecific classification of *B. rapa* L. in which cultivars are grouped on the basis of certain shared few and easily observable characters which may be morphological, physiological or agronomical. The botanical and common names of commonly grown species of rapeseed-mustard are classified in Table 4. Of the species cultivated in India, *Brassica juncea* is the most predominant accounting for more than 80 per cent followed by *Brassica rapa* L. ssp. *toria* covering nearly 14 percent. *Eruca sativa, B rapa* L. ssp. *brown sarson* and others occupy nearly 6 per cent of the total area. While most of the species of the crop commodity are grown both in sandy and heavy soils and under both irrigated and rainfed conditions, *Eruca sativa* and *Brassica carinata* are grown in very poor sandy soils in low rainfall areas. Rapeseed-mustard crop commodity is grown on marginal and sub-marginal lands, either as a pure crop or as mixed inter-cropped with wheat, sugarcane, lentil, gram, pea, etc.

**Table 4:** Botanical name, genome, chromosome number and English name of cultivated rapeseed-mustard species

| ***Botanical name*** | ***Genome*** | ***Chromosome number (2n)*** | ***Common English name*** |
|---|---|---|---|
| *Brassica juncea* (L.) Czern. & Coss. | AABB | 36 | Indian mustard/ Brown mustard |
| *Brassica rapa* L. ssp. *toria* (syn. B. *campestris* L. var. *toria*) | AA | 20 | Indian rape/Rapeseed/ Toria |
| *Brassica rapa* L. ssp. *brown sarson* (syn. *B. campestris* L. var. *brown sarson*) | AA | 20 | Brown sarson/ Rapeseed |
| *Brassica rapa* L. ssp. *yellow sarson* (syn. *B. campestris* L. var. *yellow sarson*) | AA | 20 | Colza/Yellow sarson/ Rapeseed |
| *Brassica nigra* (L.) Koch | BB | 16 | Black mustard |
| *Brassica napus* L. | AACC | 38 | Rapeseed / Rutabagas |
| *Brassica carinata* A Br. | BBCC | 34 | Abyssinian mustard/ Ethiopian mustard |
| *Eruca sativa* Mill. | EE | 22 | Rocket/Salad |

## 5. NOMENCLATURE

*Brassica,* is of much interest to taxonomists as it includes a large number of species. There is much confusion about the proper nomenclature of the group in general, and *sarson* and *toria* in particular. The confusions in *sarson* and *toria* have aggravated by the fact that plants are predominantly cross pollinated and uniform population of any variety is difficult to come across.

The Indian *Brassica,* as already mentioned belongs to two genera *Brassica* and *Eruca.* While the genus *Brassica* includes the three distinct species, *viz.*, *B. campestris* (syn. *B. rapa*) (brown sarson, yellow sarson and toria), *B. juncea* and *B. nigra,* the genus *Eruca* is represented by *Eruca sativa* (taramira or Duan). From the long list of names used for yellow sarson, brown sarson and toria, it is evident that there is still lack of unanimity among the workers regarding the Latin names to be used for the different forms. The classification of the different forms into species will, however, depend upon the way in which the species concept is defined. Stebbins (1950) said, "all agree that species must consist of system of populations that are separated from each other by complete or atleast sharp discontinuities in the variation patterns and these discontinuities must have genetic basis, *i.e.*, they must reflect the existance of isolating mechanisms which greatly hinder or completely prevent the transfer of genes from one system of population to another."

The difference observed among yellow sarson, brown sarson, yellow toria and brown toria are not enough to warrant separate species designation (Alam, 1945). Therefore, they were placed together into one species. A critical examination of the morphological traits of yellow sarson, brown sarson and toria would reveal that these three are morphologically different and have distinct mating systems. While toria is self-incompatible and highly cross pollinated, yellow sarson is highly self pollinated. On the other hand, brown sarson, *tora* types are self compatible while brown sarson *lotni* types are self-incompatible and highly cross-pollinated. They are also cultivated under distinct eco-geographical areas. In view of such dissimilarity within the species, these three types are considered as distinct sub-species of *B. rapa* L. (syn. *B. campestris* L.).

Besides, there is another oilseed crop, taramira (*Eruca sativa*) belonging to the tribe *Brassiceae.* Initially it was placed in the genus *Brassica* and named as *Brassica eruca* L. Later, it was referred by Roxburgh (1832) as *Brassica erucoides.* Subsequently, it was placed under a separate genus *Eruca* as *Eruca sativa* Lam. This is known as Rocket in Europe.

Polymorphism in leaf shape of *B. juncea* led to its classification under various specific and varietal names. A large number of workers (Bailey, 1922; Vaughan and Gordon, 1973; Prakash and Hinata, 1980) reviewed the nomenclature of *B. juncea.* Based upon the views of different workers, the grouping on the basis of the variation in volatile oil and seed protein in B. *juncea* made by Voughan *et al.* (1963) appears reasonable. The well defined groups are :

| | | |
|---|---|---|
| *B. juncea var. sarepenta* | : | Lyrate lobed basal leaves |
| *B. juncea var. integrifolia* | : | Entire or lobed basal leaves |
| B. *juncea var. japonica* | : | Dissected basal leaves |
| *B. juncea var. crispifolia* | : | Dissected crisp leaves. |

## 6. FLORAL BIOLOGY

The inflorescene is of *corymbose raceme* type. The flowering is indeterminate beginning at the lowest end on the main shoot. The buds flower within two hours after sun rise. The stigma becomes receptive even two to three days before the flower opens and thus facilitates selfing by bud pollination. The dehiscing side of the anther sacs face the stigma, but as the time of dehiscence approaches, the inner whorls of the four anthers undergo a twist of 60° to 180° and result in extrorse dehiscence in the case of the self-incompatible types. The outer whorl of the two anthers do not show this twist and dehisce introrsely. The dehiscence of all the anthers in self-compatible types is introrse. Pollination is carried out in nature both by insects and wind but mainly bees, which visit the flowers for nectar. The positioning of the nectaries is such that in self-incompatible types, the bodies of bees get smeared with pollen and in the self-compatible types, the bees affect self-pollination by pressing the inner whorl of introrsely dehisced anthers while extracting the nectar and bringing them in contact with the stigmatic surface.

### 6.1. Techniques

In *Brassica,* controlled pollination is relatively easy. For purpose of controlled hybridization, it is necessary to carry out emasculation. When the plant just commences its peak-bloom period, a lateral shoot without any fruit of the first or second order is chosen. About six to eight buds, likely to open on the following day or a day after that, are left for emasculation. The emasculation can be done with the help of fine forceps or with a pair of scissors. After removal of stamens, the opened buds are closed gently by rubbing the forceps along the sepals in an upward direction. A thin muslin cloth bag or perchment paper bag then protects the emasculated buds. For generating precise scientific information/ material, the branch of the plant which is to function as the male parent is bagged. No emasculation is obviously necessary here. Both these operations are to be done in the afternoon. On the following day, petri-dish pairs are taken one for each male parent. Fresh flowers are collected early in the morning around 7 am in these petri-dishes. At this time, the anthers would not have dehisced. These petri-dishes are placed in a tray and carried to the female parents that have been emasculated on the previous afternoon. The anthers in the petri-dishes by this time are dehisced inside the petri-dish due to the warmth of the sun. One anther is taken by its filament and used for pollinating the emasculated flowers. If the anthers are dehisced well, just a tender touch of the stigma would suffice. One anther can be used to pollinate upto eight flowers. Thereafter, the pollinated portion of the twig is covered with muslin cloth bag or perchment paper bag and tied at the bottom. A second dusting may be given on the following day when there is doubt about the success of the first pollination, *e.g.*, cloudy day or frosty night after pollination. In large scale pollination, it is possible to pollinate immediately after emasculation with nearly 100 per cent success. Fertilization is effected 20-24 hours after pollination. Emasculation is omitted when self pollination is desired. In self-incompatible types, the pollinations are done at the bud stage, preferably using freshly opened flowers. For better or healthy development of fruits, leaves and branches are removed when there is reasonable development of fruits. After pollination, sometimes siliquae are seen to be either shrivelled or empty. Such a condition is referred to as pseudogamy. On the other hand, well formed seeds, can give rise only to metromorphic progenies. This is indicative of formation of seeds through parthenogenesis. The true hybridity of the seeds can be confirmed only after a study of the $F_1$ generation.

## 7. GENETIC RESOURCES

### 7.1. Improvement of Cultivated Species

Collection, maintenance and evaluation of genetically diverse genotypes of species are pre-requisites for well planned varietal improvement programmes. In rapeseed-mustard, breeders have been working with limited germplasm. This has been one of the major bottlenecks in *Brassica* improvement. The sizeable collection of germplasm available in the country does not represent the entire variability available in the indigenous material. With the establishment of the Germplasm Management Unit in the Project Coordinating Unit (Rapeseed-Mustard) by the Indian Council of Agricultural Research at the CCS-Haryana Agricultural University, Hisar in 1981 and its subsequent shifting into the National Research Centre on Rapeseed-Mustard at Bharatpur in 1993, efforts were made to collect the indigenous as well as to introduce exotic germplasm of *Brassica* and its wild allies. These collections have been maintained and studied in detail in accordance with prepared descriptor (Kumar *et al.,* 1999). Systematic, planned and coordinated efforts have resulted in collection/assembly of 17439 accessions of cultivated, wild and allied species. Nearly 9500 working collections are being maintained in the country. In recent years, 4000 accessions have been evaluated and characterized at the National Research Centre on Rapeseed-Mustard for various agro-morphological traits and biotic stresses. Information collected on germplasm of rapeseed-mustard in the country demonstrates the availability of valuable genetic reservoir which could be exploited for improving the existing cultivars. Genetic stocks were subsequently classified into different maturity groups, *viz.*, early, medium and late types. The sources for resistance to pests, diseases, salinity, frost and drought were identified and utilized in resistance breeding programmes. Improved or local varieties which were otherwise very promising were improved. Interspecific hybridization was also used for the transfer of economic characters. The systematic evaluation for various morpho-agronomic, quality traits, biotic and abiotic stresses, resulted in the identification of donors for use in the varietal improvement programme (Table 5). Amongst the exotic collections, Midas and Tower of *B. napus;* Candle, Span, Torch and Tobin varieties of *B. rapa* have been found to be promising. The Span variety, possessing low erucic acid has also been found to be tolerant to frost injury. The sources for frost resistance, namely RW 175 and DBS 1 identified in *B. juncea* and *B. rapa,* respectively, are being used in hybridization programme. Likewise, the sources for resistance/tolerance to *Alternaria* blight and white rust diseases (RC 781 and YRT 3) and aphid resistance (T 6342 and Cream white flower and glossy stem identified from the genetic stock of *B. juncea*) have extensively been used in hybridization programme and several varieties/strains were developed. *B. carinata,* by and large, has been found to be free from white rust and downy mildew infection.

### 7.2. Search for New Oilseed Crops

The possibility of exploiting genetic resources as new oilseed crops for edible and non-edible purposes was explored (Kumar and Tsunoda, 1976, 1978, 1980; Kumar and Singh, 1979). In an extensive study of 54 species of wild Cruciferae, large variation in oil content and fatty acid composition was observed (Kumar and Tsunoda, 1980). A wild crucifer, *Conringia orientalis* (L.) Dumort belonging to tribe *Brassiceae,* collected from natural population from Algeria, was found to possess nutritionally favourable proportions of unsaturated fatty acids, *i.e.*, 24.8 and 3.7 per cent of linoleic and linolenic acids, respectively, and 28.8 per cent erucic acid. The potential of this species is being examined as a new oilseed crop.

## 8. BREEDING OBJECTIVES

The major objectives are the development of varieties for yield, plant type, maturity, resistance to various stresses like disease, insect-pest, frost, salinity, drought, shattering resistance and quality.

**Table 5:** Promising donors identified for different agro-morphological and quality traits

| ***Stress/Condition*** | ***Germplasm/Lines/Genotypes/ Varieties*** |
|---|---|
| ***Biotic stress*** | |
| *Alternaria* blight | *B. juncea* : RC 781, PYSR 8, PYSR 13, PR 10<br>*B. rapa* ssp *yellow sarson* : PYS 16<br>*B. rapa* ssp *toria* : PT 77, Bhabhari<br>*B. juncea* : RC 781, KRV Tall, SR 142-2, PHR 1, Jatai Sarson, 38-39, KYM 95-5 |
| White rust | PWR 17, PWR 9541, JMMWR 93-37, JMMWR 94-1-2<br>Newton, Blaze, Metapolka, Purbiraya, NDYS 2, Ca YS 76, GSB 7027 |
| White rust, downy mildew and *Alternaria* blight | *B. juncea* :<br>Exotic lines : EC 126743, EC 126745, EC 126746<br>Zem 1, Zem 2, Lethbridge 22 and Domo Cutlass, Span, *B. carinata, B. alba, B. napus* (Tower) are resistant to white rust and downy mildew. |
| Orobanche | *B. juncea* : Durgamani |
| Mustard aphid | *B. rapa* : IB 787, Chamba 1,2<br>*B. juncea* : T6342, B 85 (Glossy), PR 52, B 85 (white flower)<br>*B. napus* : GSL 1, Karab, Gulivar, PI 171538<br>*B. hirta* : PI 751516 |
| ***Abiotic stress*** | |
| Drought | *B. juncea* : RH 781, RH 785, RH 819, RH 7361, RH 7513, Vardan, Durgamani, Pusa Barani, *B. tournefortii* |
| Frost | *B. rapa* : Bele, Candle, Span, FR 80 (KBS - 3)<br>*B. juncea* : RH 781, RW 32-2, PR 52, PR 2030, RH 851, DIRA 343, NDR 8604 |
| ***Quality traits*** | |
| High oil content | *B. juncea* : PR 36, EC 126743-1, EC 126743, Donskaja, NDYR 10, NDRY8<br>*B. rapa* : KT 101, TK 8503, PT 5, PT 25, PT 48 |
| Low erucic acid | *B. juncea* : Zem 1, Zem 2, EC 287711, TERI (OE) M-21, TERI (OE) M08, PBCM 1150-6 |
| Low glucosinolate | *B. rapa* : Tobin, Candle,<br>*B. juncea* : BJ 1058, RC 247, RC 270, RS 79, RS 81, EC 287711 |
| Yellow seed coat | *B. rapa* : Tobin, Bele, Torch<br>*B. juncea* : TM 2, TM 4, TM 17, TM 21, YRT 1, RIK 1-1, Domo, UU 22 |
| ***Other agronomic attributes of B. juncea*** | |
| Earliness | IB 1755, IB 1886, Seeta, BR 40, BR 46 |
| Non shattering | RH 30, RIK 8, P 26-31, PR 10, Pusa Bold, Rajat |
| Bold seeds | RH 30, Pusa Bold, R 74-3, Pusa 1002, NDR 8501 |
| Intercropping | PR 43, RH 30, RH 781, RH 785, Laha 101, Vardan, Sanjucta Asech |

## 8.1. Increased Seed Yield

The average yield in India is 900 kg/ha which is far below the world average. Poor management particularly inadequate use of even critical inputs like improved varieties, fertilizers and timely plant protection are the major causes of low yields. Yield, is the most important and complex trait. To improve this trait, the first and the foremost requirement is broadening the genetic base so that the breeders can utilize variability. For this purpose, as already stated, the germplasm is to be collected, evaluated and utilized. This should be followed by interspecific and intergeneric crosses and large scale artificial synthesis of *B. juncea* and *B. carinata*. Larger seed size and increased oil content are the most important consideration in breeding for higher economic gains. Number of pods on the main raceme, number of pods/plants, number of seeds/pod and seed weight are positively correlated (Thompson, 1983; Shabana *et al.,* 1990). Physiological basis of increased seed yield demonstrates highly positive correlation between yield and total dry matter (Thurling, 1974). Based upon series of experiments, Thurling (1991) concluded that early flowering and maximum light penetration of the crop canopy are required to get increased seed yield. This calls upon the development of apetalous genotype where 30 per cent higher solar radiation is transmitted (Mendham *et al.,* 1991).

### 8.2. Plant Types

The available recommended varieties are mostly of open branching habit which normally fall down and make harvesting difficult. Further, tertiary and subsequent branching does not contribute much towards the yield. When inter-cropped with wheat or gram, rapeseed-mustard lowers the yield of companion crop because of shading effect. Development of plant types for specifie situation, therefore, assumes significance for different cropping systems like rainfed, irrigated, water logged or wet soils, *paira* cropping etc., to get enhanced productivity.

### 8.3. Early Maturity

Considering the need for increasing the production and productivity *per se* of agricultural crops to meet the food requirements of the ever growing population of the country, it is necessary to increase the intensity of cropping. For multiple cropping sequence, early maturing toria, brown sarson, yellow sarson and mustard varieties are required depending upon the agro-ecology and the crop to follow. For example, in Jammu, H.P., Punjab, Haryana, and western U.P., an early maturing toria or brown sarson variety is required while for eastern India early maturing yellow sarson or toria is required so that the farmers may take up a succeeding crop wheat or jute or sugarcane. Since early maturing varieties are normally lower yielders, efforts are required develop varieties which are early maturing and have higher per day productivity.

### 8.4. Resistance Breeding

Inspite of serious research efforts over the last three decades, the high yielding varieties of rapeseed-mustard developed are not stable. This is because of their vulnerability to biotic stresses like *Alternaria* leaf spot/ blight *(Alternaria brassicae / brassicicola);* white rust (*Albugo candida / cruciferarum);* downy mildew *(Peronospora parasitica);* powdery mildew *(Erysiphe cruciferarum);* wilt *(Fusarium oxysporum);* white stem rot *(Sclerotinia sclerotiorum),* collar rot *(Rhizoctonia bataticola)* diseases and mustard aphid *(Lipaphis erysimi);* saw fly *(Athalia proxima);* painted bug *(Bagrada cruciferarum);* leaf miner *(Phytotomiza horticola);* Bihar hairy caterpiller *(Diacrisia obliqua)* pests. Such a big pest complex and abiotic stresses like drought, salinity and frost, take heavy toll to the rapeseed-mustard crops. Development of high yielding cultivars possessing resistance/tolerance to such stresses assumes significance for bringing about stability in production.

### 8.5. Shattering Resistance

It is observed that siliquae have the tendency to dehisce resulting in seed shattering. This holds true of all cultivated rapeseed-mustard cultivars and more particularly *B. napus.* It leads to heavy loss in the yield before and during harvest. It is, therefore, necessary to breed varieties in which siliquae hold the seed for sufficient time after maturity to permit harvesting with minimal loss. Though, *B. juncea* is relatively tolerant to shattering, in view of its wide adaptation, it is desirable to further improve this trait.

### 8.6. Breeding for Seed Quality

#### 8.6.1. *Oil quality*

Rapeseed-mustard crop commodity has oil content ranging from 35 (*B. sativa / B. carinata*) to 46 per cent (*Brassica rapa* ssp. *yellow sarson*). Extensive investigations on nutritional effect of consumption of rapeseed-mustard oil high in erucic acid have not shown any adverse effect on human beings. Nevertheless, the elimination or reduction of erucic acid is desirable since it improves the fatty acid balance and the nutritional status of the oil. For further improving oil quality, elevated level of oleic acid and better ratio of linoleic acid linolenic acid (2:1) are desirable.

### 8.6.2. *Seed meal*

*Brassica* seed meal is a good source of protein. It is a better source of lysine, methoinine, cysteine, calcium, iron, manganese, selenium, phosphorus and magnesium than soybean meal (Clandinin *et al.,* 1978). Inspite of nutritionally superior characteristics of the meal, its utilization in feed industries is limited and rare in food industries. This is mainly because of the presence of toxic glucosinolates in the meal which cause enlargement of thyroid glands in humans and animals and results in poor growth performance. Another factor affecting the utilization of meal is the higher content of fibre in the seed coat. It is, therefore, necessary to eliminate or reduce glucosinolates and fibres from rapeseed and mustard. It has been observed that yellow seeded types have low fibre content and relatively more oil content.

## 9. GENETICS OF ECONOMICALLY IMPORTANT TRAITS

Before undertaking a breeding programme, it is necessary that genetics of the trait to be improved is known. Genetical studies for many quantitative and qualitative characters have been carried out. The large number of reports on the inheritance of economically important traits are summarized in Table 6.

## 10. BREEDING METHODS EMPLOYED

The breeding methodologies depend upon the mating systems. As already stated *B. juncea, B. napus* and *B. carinata* are essentially self-pollinated. On the other hand, *B. rapa* ssp *brown sarson (lotni* type) and *B. rapa* ssp *tora* are highly cross-pollinated while *B. rapa* ssp. *brown sarson (tora* type) and *yellow sarson* are predominantly self-pollinated. Consequently, breeding methods used are different.

### 10.1. Hybridization

Hybridization is used to combine the superior characteristics of two or more genotypes. Rapeseed-mustard plants exhibit high degree of crossability with related as well as with distantly related forms, varieties or even genera. At the inter-specific level, hybrids are obtained with relative ease with *B. rapa.* The elementary species can be crossed with each other and the hybrids obtained from these crosses are totally sterile. But, this sterility can be overcome by chromosome doubling through colchicine treatment. The hybrids resemble the three amphidiploid

**Table 6:** Genetics of economically important traits

| ***Crop*** | ***Inheritance/Gene action*** | ***Character (s)*** | ***Reference (s)*** |
|---|---|---|---|
| Indian Mustard *(Brassica juncea)* | Additive and dominance | Plant height | Singh and Singh (1972), Tiwari and Singh (1973), Singh *et al.* (1985), Singh *et al.* (1989) |
| | | Number of primary branches | Singh and Singh (1972), Paul *et al.* (1976) |
| | | Number of secondary branches | Singh and Singh (1972), Paul *et al.* (1976) |
| | | Length of main axis | Chaudhary and Sharma (1982), Singh (1973), Singh *et al.* (1986), Singh and Singh (1991) |
| | | Length of siliqua | Singh and Singh (1972) |
| | | Number of seeds per siliqua | Singh and Singh (1972), Paul *et al.* (1976), Kumar *et al.* (1998) |
| | | 1000-seed weight | Yadava and Gupta (1975), Dixit *et al.* (1983), Singh *et al.* (1989), Yadav *et al.* (1992) |
| | | Oil content | Singh *et al.* (1986), Pahuja *et al.* (1996) |
| | Non-additive | Plant height | Jain *et al.* (1988) |
| | | Days to maturity | Yadava *et al.* (1981) |
| | | Numer of secondary branches | Anand and Rawat (1978), Singh *et al.* (1982), Badwal and Labana (1987), Singh and Mittal (1993), Chauhan (1987). |
| | | Length of main axis | Singh *et al.* (1989) |
| | | Length of siliqua | Chaudhary and Sharma (1982), Chauhan (1987), Gupta *et al.* (1987) |
| | | Number of seeds per siliqua | Chauhan (1987), Singh (1973), Anand and Rawat (1978), Yadava *et al.* (1981), Jain *et al.* (1988) |
| | | Seed yield per plant | Chauhan (1987), Anand and Rawat (1978), Govil *et al.* (1981), Yadava *et al.* (1981), Singh *et al.* (1982), Reddy (1983) |
| | | Yield and yield components | Anand and Rawat (1973) |
| | | 1000-seed weight | Chauhan and Singh (1980), Singh *et al.* (1987), Yadava *et al.* (1981), Singh *et al.* (1986), Jain *et al.* (1988) |

**Table 6:** *Contd...*

**Table 6:** *Contd...*

| *Crop* | *Inheri tance/Gene action* | *Character (s)* | *Reference (s)* |
|---|---|---|---|
| | | Oil content | Kumar *et al.* (1982), Gupta *et al.* (1985), Govil *et al.* (1981), Badwai and Labana (1987) |
| Additive and non-additive | | Length of main axis | Singh *et al.* (1981), Kumar *et al.* (1998), Singh and Mitta l (1993) |
| | | Number of siliquae on main axis | Badwal and Labana (1987), Singh (1991), Rawat (1992), Singh and Mittal (1993), Singh *et al.* (1981), Verma *et al.* (1991) |
| | | Length of siliqua | Badwal and Labana (1987), Pradhan *et al.* (1993) |
| | | Seed yield/plant | Yadava *et al.* (1974), Jindal and Labana (1986), Singh *et al.* (1985), Singh *et al.* (1987), Labana (1987), Singh and Mittal (1993), Ram *et al.* (1976), Badwal and Labana (1987) |
| | | 1000-seed weight | Ram *et al.* (1976), Badwal and Labana (1987), Singh *et al.* (1987), Dixit *et al.* (1983), Kashi *et al.* (1976), Sharma and Singh (1994), Rishipal *et al.* (1993) |
| | | Oil content | Govil *et al.* (1983), Yadava *et al.* (1981) |
| *B. rapa* ssp *toria sarson* | Yield and its components | | Singh and Singh (1989) |
| *B. rapa* ssp. *brown* | | Yield and its components | Swamy (1971) |
| Indian Mustard *(Brassica juncea)* | Additive and non-additive | Plant height | Labana *et al.* (1975), Asthana and Pandey (1977), Jindal and Labana (1986), Badwal and Labana (1987), Kumar *et al.* (1994), Kashi *et al.* (1976), Ram *et al.* (1976), Singh *et al.* (1989), Diwakar and Singh (1993), Singh and Mittal (1993), Singh *et al.* (1981) |
| | | Days to 50% flowering | Pradhan *et al.* (1993) |
| | | Days to maturity | Yadava *et al.* (1976) |
| | | Number of primary branches | Singh *et al.* (1973), Labana *et al.* (1975), Singh *et al.* (1982), Singh *et al.* (1985), Jindal and Labana (1986), Badwal and Labana (1987), Yadav (1992), Singh *et al.* (1981), Yadav (1983), Kumar *et al.* (1998) |

**Table 6:** *Contd...*

**Table 6:** (*Contd...*)

| ***Crop*** | ***Inheri tance/Gene action*** | ***Character (s)*** | ***Reference (s)*** |
|---|---|---|---|
| | | Number of secondary branches | Yadav *et al.* (1974), Singh *et al.* (1985), Jindal and Labana (1986), Kumar *et al.* (1994) |
| | Dominance | Plant height<br>Length of siliqua | Sachan and Singh (1988), Kumar *et al.* (1994) |
| | Dominance gene effect | Leaf diffusive conductance | Chaudhary *et al.* (1989) |
| | | Transpirational cooling | Chaudhary *et al.* (1989) |
| | Additive | Plant height | Singh (1973), Singh *et al.* (1982), Pradhan *et al.* (1993), Chauhan (1987) |
| | | Number of primary branches | Anand and Rawat (1978), Chauhan (1987), Singh and Mittal (1993) |
| | | Number of secondary branches | Singh (1973), Rawat (1975), Singh *et al.* (1986) |
| | | Length of main axis | Chauhan (1987) |
| | | Number of seeds per siliqua | Singh *et al.* (1986) |
| | | 1000-seed weight | Paul *et al.* (1976), Yadav (1992), Singh *et al.* (1996) |
| | Predominantly/Mainly additive | Plant height | Yadav *et al.* (1974), Rawat (1975), Gupta *et al.* (1987), Singh *et al.* (1996), Bhadouria *et al.* (1991), Yadav (1992) |
| | | Number of secondary branches | Asthana and Pandey (1977) |
| | | Length of siliqua | Bhadouria *et al.* (1990), Yadav (1992), Singh *et al.* (1996), Kumar *et al.* (1998) |
| | | Number of seeds per siliqua | Rawat (1975), Bhadouria *et al.* (1991) |
| | | Seed yield per plant | Singh and Singh (1972), Rawat (1975), Tiwari and Singh (1973), Asthana and Pandey (1977), Bhadouria *et al.* (1991) |
| | | 1000-seed weight | Kumar and Singh (1987), Pradhan *et al.* (1993), Malkhandale (1993) |
| | | Oil content | Rawat (1975) |
| | Mainly/Predominantly non-additive | Plant height | Yadav (1983) |
| | | Days of 50% flowering | Yadav (1992) |
| | | Number of primary branches | Gupta *et al.* (1987) |

**Table 6:** (*Contd...*)

**Table 6:** (*Contd...*)

| *Crop* | *Inheri tance/Gene action* | *Character (s)* | *Reference (s)* |
|---|---|---|---|
| | | Number of seeds per siliqua | Gupta *et al.* (1987), Yadav (1992), Pradhan *et al.* (1993) |
| | | Seed yield per plant | Labana *et al.* (1975), Anand and Reddy (1987), Gupta et al. (1987), Prakash *et al.* (1987), Kumar *et al.* (1994), Yadav (1992), Pradhan *et al.* (1993) |
| | | Oil content | Labana *et al.* (1987), Prakash *et al.* (1987), Yashpal (1991) |
| *Brassica rapa* ssp. *toria* | | Yield and its components | Singh *et al.* (1977) |
| Indian-Mustard (*Brassica juncea*) | Dominance and Epistasis | Plant height | Chaudhary and Sharma (1982), Kumar *et al.* (1998) |
| | | Number of primary branches | Chaudhary and Sharma (1982) |
| | | Number of secondary branches | Singh *et al.* (1981), Kumar *et al.* (1998) |
| | | Number of siliquae on main axis | Kumar *et al.* (1998) |
| | | Seed yield per plant | Singh *et al.* (1981), Yadav *et al.* (1990) |
| | Dominant and additive x additive | Harvest index | Yadava *et al.* (1990) |
| | | Seed yield | Yadava *et al.* (1990) |
| | Predominantly/Mainly dominance | Number of siliquae on main axis | Singh *et al.* (1996) |
| | | Number of seeds per siliqua | Prakash *et al.* (1987) |
| | Partial dominance | Plant height | Labana *et al.* (1984) |
| | | Days to 50% flowering | Kumar *et al.* (1994) |
| | | Seed yield per plant | Kumar *et al.* (1994) |
| | Additive x additive | Number of primary branches | Singh *et al.* (1986) |
| | | Number of seeds per siliqua | Kumar *et al.* (1998) |
| Indian Mustard (*Brassica juncea*) | Double recessive | Yellow/brown seeds | Chauhan (1987), Dhillon *et al.* (1990) |
| | Duplicate recessive, maternal inheri tance | Yellow/brown seeds | Rawat (1987) |

**Table 6:** (*Contd...*)

**Table 6:** (*Contd...*)

| ***Crop*** | ***Inheri tance/Gene action*** | ***Character (s)*** | ***Reference (s)*** |
|---|---|---|---|
| *Brassica rapa* ssp *brown sarson* | Monogenic dominant | Glossy/hairy stem | Sengupta and Mukhopadhya (1981) |
| | | Appressed siliqua/spreading | Pokhriyal *et al.* (1964) |
| | Monogenic recessive | Yellow/brown seeds | Singh and Srivastava (1974) |
| | | Eliptical/round | Pal and Singh (1990) |
| | | Small/bold seeds | Pal and Singh (1990) |
| | Two supplementary genes | Purple/Yellow seeds | Sun (1945) |
| | | Appressed siliqua/spreading | Brar *et al.* (1991) |
| | Digenic recessive incomplete dominance & Dominant epistasis | Yellow/black seeds | Pal and Singh (1990) |
| | | Hairy/glabrous | Dixit and Singh (1973) |
| | Digenic | Branching basal/top | Yadava (1988) |
| | Digenic interaction | Relative water potential and osmotic potential | Chaudhary *et al.* (1989) |
| *Brassica rapa* ssp. *toria* | Monogenic recessive | Yellow/brown seeds | Ahmed and Zuberi (1971) |
| | Digenic epistatic | | |
| | | Bloomed /bloomless | Singh (1955) |
| | | Single two valued/multivalued | Mohammad *et al.* (1943) |
| | | Complex/simple | Pathak and Singh (1949) |
| | | Curved/straight siliqua | Dixit (1972) |
| *Brassica rapa ssp brown sarson* | Digenic epistatic | Yellow/brown seeds | Mohammad *et al.* (1943) |

species, *viz.*, *B. juncea*, *B. carinata* and *B. napus* (Chopra *et al.*, 1995). From these crosses the breeders can synthesize new amphidiploids from chosen elementary species. Crossability at the inter-varietal level is more relevant to plant breeders than the inter-generic and inter-specific hybrids. It is often assumed that intervarietal crosses always result in successful hybrids and that free recombination of characters would result in the desired introgression. This, however, is not usually the case.

Some inter-varietal hybrids, particularly involving *B. rapa,* are markedly sterile. In some cases, sterility is manifested in the later generations. In toria x yellow sarson cross, success is achieved only when the self-compatible material is used as the female parent. The reciprocal cross does not succeed. A cytological analysis of the hybrids can be very rewarding from the breeders' point of view (Rajan, 1966). It is possible to predict from the cytological data whether in a given hybrid, recombination is likely to be high or low. This assumes significance when it is realized that the success of any hybrid programme depends on the extent of recombination taking place. Since there is a considerable metromorphic seed formation in Brassicas, the aforesaid facts about crossability provide reliable criterion of whether or not efforts should be expanded on a particular inter-specific and inter-generic cross. Attention should be confined to true hybrids only. At the inter-varietal level, metromorphs are more likely to be mistaken for hybrids particularly when the parental varieties do not differ markedly. The breeder should take proper precaution against this source of error.

## 10.2. Selection

Different methods of selection, *viz.*, mass selection, pure line selection, bulk selection and pedigree selection are being followed for crop improvement in rapeseed-mustard. Mass selection with some modifications is followed both in self-pollinating types like *B. juncea.*, *B. napus, B. carinata* as well as in cross pollinating ecotypes of B. *campestris.* A large number of mustard varieties in India *viz.*, Durgamani, Seeta, Shekhar, Krishna and Kranti have been developed through mass selection. *Brassica napus* variety GSL 1 is also a product of mass selection. For the predominantly self-pollinating *B. juncea* and *B. napus* species, the most commonly used breeding procedure for cultivar development is pedigree selection. The breeding objectives must be clearly defined and suitable parents identified. Potential parents should be intensively evaluated over a wide range of environments so that their good attributes and limitations are clearly known before crosses are made and the selection programme begins.

Once the parents have been selected, artificial hybridization is performed. Fifteen to twenty $F_1$ plants from each cross are grown and the plants within each cross are either open-pollinated or selfed. $F_2$ seeds from $F_1$ plants of each cross are harvested in bulk and sown. Depending upon the objective of the cross, 1000 to 3000 open-pollinated $F_2$ plants are individually harvested. The $F_3$ progenies from seeds of each plant are grown in a single row for agronomic evaluation. Depending on the amount of available seed, the single row nursery may have one, two or three replicates. The rows are evaluated visually. Five to ten single $F_3$ plants are harvested from each row. In $F_4$ generation, selection is practised first between families of progeny rows ($F_3$ derived lines) that were obtained from plants harvested from the same $F_3$ row and then among rows within selected families.

In cross-pollinating types like *B. rapa,* mass selection aims at developing an open-pollinating population. Pedigree method of selection used in *Brassica* improvement differs from that being used in cereals. Since these crops have a high multiplication ratio (1000 : 1) and the plant to plant outcrossing rate is much higher, the replicated progeny testing can begin as early as in $F_3$ and a certain level of heterosis from the initial cross can be captured and retained in subsequent generations (Downey and Rimmer, 1993).

## 10.3. Recurrent Selection

This method is useful for improving quantitatively inherited characters in cross-pollinating species. In *B. rapa,* where self-incompatibility ensures a high degree of heterogeneity, recurrent selection is the most effective method for increasing seed yield as well as oil content. In population improvement, plant breeders aim at increasing the frequency of desirable alleles through selection of superior recombinants. Recurrent selection typically starts with harvesting of individual open pollinated plants from the source population. A portion of the seed from each plant is sown in a single progeny row and the remaining seed of these plants is saved as reserve. The agronomic characters of progeny rows are evaluated visually and superior rows are identified. The selected rows are harvested separately and seeds are analysed for characters like oil content, glucosinolates, seed colour, seed size, protein and fibre. Equal quantities of reserve seed from selected single plants, based on the progeny performance, is composited. The first recurrent selection cycle is started when the new composite is grown in an isolated plot where random mating occurs among the plants within the composite. Harvesting of single plants is done from this composite. A bulk seed sample is harvested from the remaining plants of each composite for use in replicated yield trails to determine response to selection in each recurrent selection cycle for the characteristics under improvement. Recurrent selection is continued till reasonable response to selection is achieved. Each cycle of recurrent selection produces a new population that may be a potential cultivar. The improved population with increased frequency of desirable alleles can be used as a cultivar *per se* or as a source of identifying individuals that can be used for developing inbred lines, pureline cultivars or parents of a hybrid. Bhawani is an example of toria variety developed through recurrent selection. In white mustard *(Sinapis alba),* long-term experiments (12 years) on recurrent selection have led to improvement in the number of seeds/pod, oil content, fatty acid composition and nematode resistance (Olsson and Persson, 1986). In the final round of selection, the number of seeds/pod had increased by 67 per cent and oil content by up to 37.4 per cent in the positive selection against 30.3 per cent of the check. The total difference between positive and negative selection for all characters was 14.78 ± 0.63 per cent. Simultaneous selection for seed yield and oil content was also effective.

## 10.4. Development of Synthetics and Composites

In *B. rapa,* the level of heterosis for yield is significant. Because of high degree of natural outcrossing and the absence of an efficient system of pollination control, composites and synthetics are used to capture part of the available heterosis. This is the most practical and effective breeding method. In the development of a synthetic variety, inbred lines with superior combining ability are used in cross-pollinated types. In composites, combining ability test of lines is not taken into consideration. Only the selfed seeds or open-pollinated seeds of selected lines are grown in isolation. In synthetics, polycross technique is generally used. In this method, selfing is done for 2-3 generations before the polycross test is conducted. At this stage, a small quantity of seed is saved from each of the selfed plants. In India, composites and synthetics of toria, brown sarson and taramira have been developed and released for commercial cultivation. The most popular synthetic varieties developed are Pusa Kalyani of brown sarson and Sangam of toria. The most popular composite variety of toria is TLC 1 (Toria Ludhinana Composite 1).

## 10.5. Backcrossing

The backcrossing approach has been successfully used to transfer simply inherited traits such as disease resistance, low erucic acid and glucosinolate content into agronomically superior genotypes (Harvey and Downey, 1964; Lein, 1970; Morice, 1974; Kirk and Hurlstone, 1983).

The erucic acid content of seed is controlled by the genotype of the embryo. This means that individual $F_2$ seeds, borne on $F_1$ plants, have different erucic acid levels.The half seed method makes it possible to select individual seeds on the basis of their erucic content. Selected seeds are grown and backcrossed. The heterozygous $F_1$ plant ($E_1 e_1 E_2 e_2$ ) is backcrossed to the recurrent high erucic acid parent ($P_1$). Heterozygous $BCF_2$ seeds ($E_1 e_1 E_2 e_2$ are selected and plant obtained from the seeds are backcrossed. This permits a backcross to be made in every generation, thus speeding up the breeding programme. After the last backcross, selfing is done to identify the low erucic acid ($e_1 e_1 e_2 e_2$) genotype. Backcross method is also employed for diversifying the nuclear background of various cytoplasmic male sterility system and the restorers in heterosis breeding programme.

## 10.6. Gamete Selection

This is an efficient method used for selecting salinity tolerant genotypes through screening of pollen grains at different NaCl concentrations. Tyagi and Rangaswami (1993) observed close correlation between pollen and whole plant tolerance to salinity. The level of response of the pollen grains to *Alternaria* blight toxin was in agreement with the degree of susceptibility or resistance to the disease under field conditions (Shivanna and Sawhney, 1993).

## 10.7. Mutation Breeding

Using ionizing radiations (X-rays and Cobalt-60 gamma rays) and chemicals such as Ethyl Methane Sulphonate (EMS), efforts have been made to improve *Brassica* oilseed crops (Das and Kumar, 1969; Kumar, 1972; Kumar and Das, 1971,1974, 1977). The promising strains developed possessed economic traits like very bold seed, dwarfness, long siliquae (Anonymous, 1975). Mutant lines with 3 per cent linolenic acid have been identified using EMS and X-ray in *B. napus* (Rakaw, 1973; Robbelen and Nitsch, 1975).

## 10.8. Development of Altered Plant Types

In India, there are two categories of areas for cropping system of rapeseed-mustard, *viz.*, areas of marginal productivity and areas of advance agronomy. In areas of marginal productivity, farmers prefer rapeseed-mustard varieties suitable for mixed cropping or intercropping because crops are raised under various kinds of stresses. In areas of advanced agronomy, on the other hand, fertilizer responsive varieties suitable for pure cropping are utilized. The crops which are raised under irrigated conditions demand plant types that are suitable for either of the conditions. Further, for rice-fallows where *paira* cropping is followed, a short duration, compact and dwarf plant type is required. Therefore, in breeding varieties suitable for mixed or intercroping, plants with semi-compact branching habit and medium height which can cope with various kinds of stresses should be selected. In brown sarson, promising strains, *viz.*, BS 34-43, BS 34-47, BS 34-55, and B 47-4 were developed for areas of marginal productivity. In a preliminary yield trial conducted under low fertility conditions (25 N + 12.5 P kg/ha), the aforesaid strains gave significantly higher yield than the check variety BSH 1 (Anonymous, 1975).

For areas of advanced agronomy, fertilizer responsive varieties with erect plant type would be ideal. This will increase the per unit plant population which in turn substantially increased the seed yield. In brown sarson, a plant type of this pattern has been reconstructed from a cross between BSH 1 × DS 17 M. The spreading and bushy growth of BSH 1 could be reduced. The resultant compact and erect plants could grow at higher plant densities. This particular strain (BS 34-65) has given significantly higher yield (19 q/ha) than the local BSH 1 (15.5 q/ha) under irrigated conditions (Anonymous, 1975).

## 10.9. Shattering Resistance

In order to develop shattering resistant varieties, it is desirable to introduce genes for shattering resistance into the high yielding, well adapted varieties. Realizing the importance of *B. juncea,* work on improvement of shattering resistance was taken up (Kumar, 1984). Two genotypes RH 8130 (2164 kg/ha) and RH 8131 (2145 kg/ha) yielded higher than the standard check (shattering resistant donor) RH 30 (1865 kg/ha). In order to introduce shattering resistance in *B. napus,* Prakash and Chopra (1988) were able to introgress shattering resistance from *B. juncea* variety RH 30.

## 10.10. Heterosis Breeding

Hybrids offer an opportunity for mobilising greater genetic variation and heterotic response. Success in developing hybrids in any crop depends on 3 factors: (a) availability of heterotic response for economic yield, (b) effective mechanism for abolishing the male fertility of female lines and fertility restoration and (c) economic feasibility in terms of cost involved in seed production. Rapeseed-mustard are well suited for hybrid breeding because of their natural biological characteristics which promote outcrossing and demonstrated yield advantage over pure line cultivars.

A wide range of heterosis has been reported in rapeseed-mustard by researchers. However, reports about heterosis over standard check cultivars (s) are meagre. Most of the reports are based upon higher mid parental value or better parent, recorded on single plant basis. In *B. juncea,* significant heterosis of more than 100 per cent has been reported (Pradhan *et al.,* 1993). There are five ways which can be employed for hybrid yield advantage in *Brassica, i.e.,* cytoplasmic male sterility (CMS), self-incompatibility, genetic male sterility, chemical hybridizing agents and genetically engineered male sterility. Notable among the available CMS system are *polima, ogura, tournefortii, oxyrrhina, siifolia, trachystoma, moricandia* and *lyratus* (Prakash *et al.,* 1998a). Cytoplasmic male sterility (CMS)-nuclear male fertility restorer system has been perfected for developing hybrids in *B. napus* and *B. juncea.* Hybrids in *B. napus* have been released for commercial cultivation in many parts of the world including India, where CMS based hybrid, PGSH 51 giving more than 15 per cent higher yield, was released in 1994. The most successful *B. napus* hybrid to date is the Chinese variety Qinyou No. 2 giving more than 43 per cent higher yield than the check variety. Success has been achieved in transferring the cytoplasm of *ogura, oxyrrhina, tournefortii, siifolia, moricandia, trachystoma* and *enarthrocarpus* into *B. juncea.* However, the success in developing the hybrid could not be achieved due to non-availability of fertility restorer genes and developmental constraints such as chlorosis. Two recently developed CMS-fertility restoration systems *viz., mori* and *trachy* appear to be very promising for hybrid development (Prakash *et al.,* 1998b). Chlorosis associated with *mori* CMS system, has now been rectified and diversified into improved background of identified heterotic combination for developing commercial hybrids. Preliminary hybrids based on *mori* system are under evaluation at PAU, Ludhiana mainly to judge the extent and stability of fertility restoration. Prospects of hybrids based upon barnase/barstar system of pollination control also appear to be promising. Molecular constructs containing barnase/barstar genes are being deployed in *B. juncea* to develop male sterile and fertility restorer lines. In *B. rapa* ssp *brown sarson* and *toria,* self incompatibility which is an effective mechanism for out crossing, may be used for hybrid development. However, its use has proved impracticable since the inbreds obtained through continuous selfing exhibit high level of inbreeding depression and are very difficult to maintain by continuous selfing.

Thus, the difficulties and costs associated with production of parental seed stock, would severely limit the potential of this through crosses with *B. rapa* carrying S alleles. To avoid the potential problem of poor seed set in commercial hybrid fields, due to poor pollen dispersal among the self-incompatible plants, Thompson (1983) proposed the use of a three-way hybrid using a dominant self-compatible line as the third parent. Self-incompatibility is dominant over self compatibility. The production of hybrid cultivar using genetic male sterility system is also possible. Genic male sterility in *B. rapa, B. napus* and *B. juncea* has been reported long back (Chowdhury and Das, 1966, 1967; Das and Pandey, 1961; Badwal and Labana, 1983). However, its large scale exploitation has not been possible because of problems associated with identification of markers. Nevertheless, in regions where adequate and inexpensive labours are available, this system is likely to work efficiently by removing male fertile segregants from female lines before flowering. In yellow sarson, using genic male sterility, an experimental hybrid, BCH 16 giving 19 per cent yield advantage has been developed (Anonymous, 2000).

## 10.11. Improvement of Quality Traits

### 10.11.1. *The oil*

*Brassica* oilseeds provide nutritionally desirable oil with excellent keeping qualities for both the edible oil market and the manufacturer of margarines and shortenings. In addition, they give higher seed yield with low inputs and have adaptability to a wide range of environments. The seed contains 40 - 44 per cent oil and 45-50 per cent long chain monounsaturated fatty acid *viz.*, erucic acid (C 22:1). Nutritional studies on the consumption of rapeseed-mustard oil having high erucic acid in the diet have demonstrated the retarding effect on mice, rats, ducklings and turkeys. It is poorly utilised by the body. The prolonged feeding of high erucic acid oil to rats and monkeys produced myocardial lipidosis and myocardial fibrosis. Although comparable results are not available for humans, elimination of long chain monoenoic fatty acids (C 20:1, C 22:1) improves the fatty acid balance. Further, low erucic acid (< 2 per cent) results in simultaneous reduction in eicosenoic acid with corresponding increase in oleic acid. It suggests that precursor of eicosenoic acid and erucic acid is oleic acid and that some extra amount which is desaturated in biosynthetic pathways, has resulted in increasing the levels of linoleic (C 18:2) and linolenic acid (C 18:3). The new product, *i.e.*, high oleic acid (C 18:1) has found wide acceptance as a liquid oil in the international market.

### 10.11.2. *The seed meal*

In the Indian sub-continent, traditionally, there has been strong regional preference for pungency. While in Eastern parts of the country, high pungency is preferred, in the North and Western parts, oil with little or no pungency is acceptable. For the crop to be competitive, the highest possible value needs to be obtained from meal which remains after oil extraction. The meal contains about 40-42 per cent high quality protein, fat (10-14 per cent), minerals (6-9 per cent) and fibre (6-8 per cent). It is nutritionally comparable to soya protein. The value of the meal as high quality protein source is lowered due to the presence in the seed of sulphur-based compounds, called glucosinolates. The intact glucosinolates are harmless. However, the myrosinase enzyme present in the seed, chemically splits the glucosinolate into glucose and nutritionally undesirable toxic isothiocynates, oxazolidinethione or nitriles. Higher consumption of meal of such seeds in the diet causes enlargement of thyroids, palatability problems, etc. This is particularly true for non ruminants like pigs and poultry. Reducing the level of glucosinolates would permit the utilization of high value proteins in feed and food industries.

### 10.11.3. *Genetic studies*

Genetic studies have shown that erucic acid content in *B. napus* is controlled by multiple alleles. Homozygosity levels of 5-10,10-35 and above 35 per cent erucic acid were reported (Jonsson, 1977). These were controlled by alleles in one, one or two, and two loci, respectively. Anand and Downey (1981) identified five genes in *B. napus* and designated them as e, Ea, Eb, Ec, and Ed. They act in additive manner and result in erucic acid levels of <1, 10, 15, 30 and 35 per cent, respectively. In *B. campestris,* occurence of a single major gene exhibiting no dominance determine the erucic acid content (Dorrell and Downey, 1964; Kumar, 1978). Two genes showing no dominance and acting in an additive manner, each with two alleles, control the erucic acid content in *B. juncea* (Kirk and Hurlstone, 1983). Similar genetic control was suggested in *B. carinata* (Fernanadez Escobar *et al.,* 1988).

### 10.11.4. *Canola*

The term 'Canola' refers to the nutritionally improved cultivars of oilseed Brassicas possessing less than 2 per cent erucic acid in seed oil and less than 30μ moles glucosinolates per gram defatted meal. The cultivars possessing such a level of erucic acid and glucosinolate are also called '00' (Double Zero) types.

### 10.11.5. *Quality cultivar development*

One of the major objective in quality improvement is the development of canola quality rapeseed-mustard. The methodology being followed at the National Research Centre on Rapeseed-Mustard, Bharatpur to breed for "00" types is presented in Fig. 1. For developing canola quality *B. juncea* possessing additional trait like yellow seed colour or white rust resistance, a three-way crossing programme is suggested.

## 10.12. Breeding for Resistance/Tolerance

This would include development of varieties possessing tolerance or resistance to major diseases and aphid pest; salinity, frost and drought which cause heavy damage to the crop.

1. *Biotic stresses*: *Alternaria* blight, white rust and aphid and other pests.
2. *Abiotic stresses*: Salt, frost and drought.

### 10.12.1. *Biotic stresses*

#### 10.12.1.1. *Diseases*

Major diseases of rapeseed-mustard are Altenaria blight *(Alternaria brassicae)*, white rust *(Albugo candida)*, downy mildew *(Peronospora parasitica)*, powdery mildew *(Erysiphae cruciferarum)* and *Sclerotinia* stem rot *(Sclerotinia sclerotiorum)*. These diseases cause substantial yield reduction. In case of *Alternaria* blight the damage to the crop ranges from 10-75 per cent and in case of white rust, it is as high as 90 per cent.

(a) *Alternaria blight:* For *Alternaria* blight disease sources for resistance such as RC 781 and YRT 3 were utilised as donor parent in back cross breeding programme. Two strains RH 8113 and RH 8114, moderately resistant to this disease, were developed. These strains gave appreciably higher seed yield than the local variety. The variety RH 8113 (Saurabh) has been released for general cultivation in 1990.

(b) *White rust:* Utilising the resource genes for white rust resistance, R 908, L 4, obtained from Canada, a number of white rust resistant

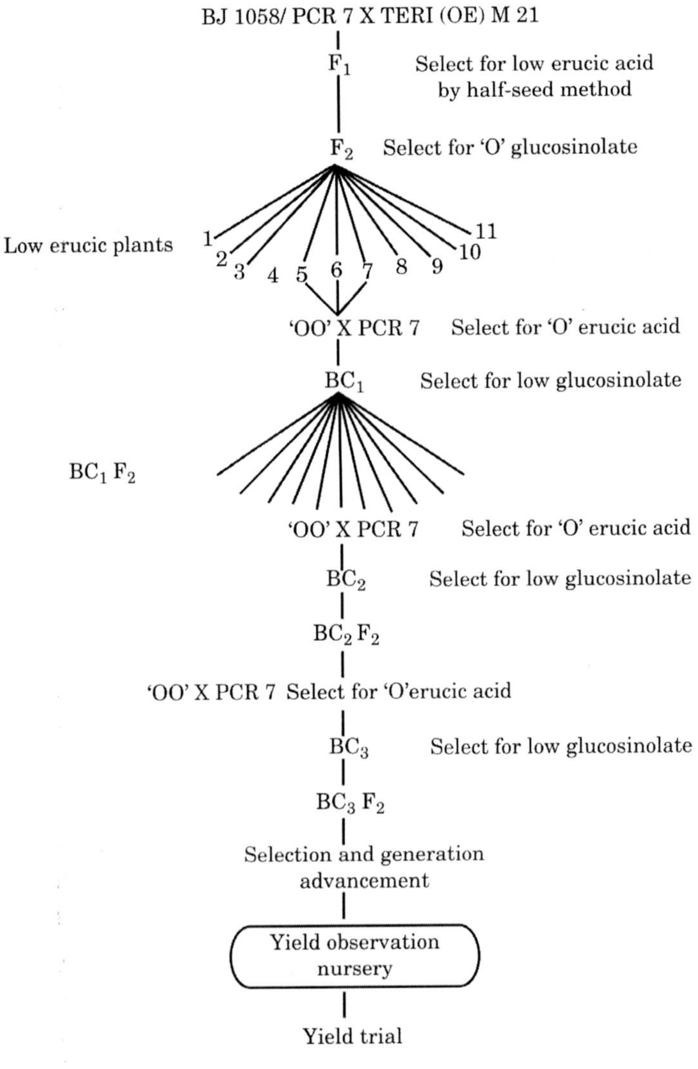


**Fig. 1:** Development of 'OO' *B. juncea*

lines have been developed in background of Varuna, Pusa Bold and Rohini varieties through back cross method. Important amongst them are JMMWR 93-7, JMMWR 93-19 and JMMWR 93-38. These strains have consistently shown resistance for white rust disease in the National Disease Nurseries for five years (1993-97). The strains JMMWR 93-7, JMMWR 93-39 have also been found resistant to downy mildew. The variety JMMWR 93-39 (Jawahar Mustard 1) has been released as white rust resistant variety in 1999 for general cultivation.

10.12.1.2. *Aphid pest*

Major insect-pest damaging rapeseed and mustard crops are mustard aphid (*Lipaphis erysimi*), mustard sawfly (*Althalia proxima*) and painted bug (*Bagrada cruciferarum*). In heavy infestation, the yield losses could be as high as 97 per cent due to aphid and 15 per cent due to sawfly. Painted bug causes loss to the tune of 30 per cent in yield and 3-4 per cent in oil content. Breeding for resistant varieties to aphid has been in progress but is hampered by lack of true resistant sources.

(a) *Aphid:* To develop aphid resistant mustard, a line T 6342 has been commonly used as donor parent. Using the back cross method, strains RH 7846, RH 7847 RH 7848 and CSR 1017 developed by hybridization, have been found to be high yielding and aphid tolerant. Two mutant lines, one having cream-white flower color and the other having glossy stem character have been identified. When evaluated, it was observed that the glossy stem population was less prone to the attack of aphid compared to the cream white flowered population. Abraham and Bhatia (1994) developed a new detached leaf method for screening against aphid tolerance. Using *in vitro* seedling screening coupled with mass selection for tolerant types, promising lines of mustard from a cross between RLM 514 × T 6342 have been developed.

Among the species evaluated for aphid resistance, *Brassica alba* was found to support the lowest aphid population. Genetical studies revealed the presence of both additive as well as non-additive genes in the inheritance of aphid resistance.

### 10.12.2. *Abiotic stress*

(a) *Salt tolerance:* Soil salinity as well as irrigation with brackish water affect large area under rapeseed-mustard especially in the states of Rajasthan, Haryana, Punjab and Uttar Pradesh. The yield reduction due to salinity/sodicity has been reported to be upto 33 per cent. At high ESP (42), the reduction in seed yield could be 50 per cent. The salt stress also reduced oil content and altered the fatty acid composition of oil. A large number of improved germplasm lines are available (CS 416, RH 8816, RH 8701, RK 9807 and RK 9703) which can be used as donors for resistant cultivar development. Sustained breeding efforts have resulted in release of resistant varieties CS 52 and NDR 8501 which give 10-20 per cent higher yield than the checks like Varuna under saline soil conditions (Ece 8-10 dS/m). CS 52 also tolerates irrigation water upto Ece 12 dS/m. It has tolerance to alkalinity also.

(b) *Frost tolerance:* Rapeseed-mustard is a frost susceptible crop. In northern states of the country frost is common in the second half of January and this concides with flowering and pod formation. Yield losses upto 70 per cent have been reported due to a single exposure to frost. Freezing injury reduces the rate of photosynthesis but slightly enhances the transpiration rate. Promising donors being used in breeding programme of *B. juncea* are RH 8814, RH 8602, RH 8824 and RH 781. The variety RH 781 is a frost tolerant variety. Dhawan *et al.* (1983) categorised mustard varieties Prakash and RH 7846 as less susceptible; RH 30 and RH 779 as moderately susceptible and RH 765, PR 15, PR 1003 and Pusa Bold as highly susceptible. In brown sarson *(B. campestris),* crosses were made between Pusa Kalyani and Yukina in Japan with a view to transfer frost tolerance into brown sarson. Subsequently, the promising progenies were grown in India during 1977-81. One of the selected lines, FR 80, was found to be very promising in frost prone areas of Himachal Pradesh and recommended for release for general cultivation as KBS 3. This variety has also given, on an average, 10 q/ha seed yield even under Ist week of December planting conditions in Himachal Pradesh.

(c) *Drought tolerance:* Rapeseed and mustard is grown as a rainfed crop on conserved moisture received from monsoon rains in 37 per cent of the total area under the crop. Substantial area in Bihar, West Bengal, Assam, Rajasthan, U.P., M.P. and Orissa is rainfed. Depending on planting time and winter rains, the crop is exposed to water stress at one or more phenological stages. Genetic variation in osmo regulation exists in *Brassicas*. Transpirational cooling and water loss from excised leaves were better correlated with yield than osmo regulation. The genotypes which could extract moisture from deep soil profiles during the reproductive phase would yield higher. Osmotic adjustment and transpirational coolings have been reported to be controlled by single gene. It is suggested that recurrent selection should be practiced for incorporating drought tolerance. Several high yielding varieties like Vardan, RH 781, RH 819 and Pusa Barani have been released for cultivation for drought prone areas.

## 11. UTILISATION OF PLANT BIOTECHNOLOGY TOOLS IN CULTIVAR DEVELOPMENT

Plant biotechnology can be defined as the application of tissue culture and molecular genetics to develop or produce a commodity from plants. Tissue culture refers to the maintenance and propagation of plant parts (as small as a single cell) in biologically pure (axenic) and controlled environments Molecular genetics includes techniques for isolating, characterising, recombining, multiplying and transferring discrete fragments of DNA that contain genes coding for specific traits. The fact that a whole plant can be regenerated from a single cell makes tissue culture a valuable tool for proliferating genetically identical material and selecting promising variants.

To be effective, plant biotechnology must be well integrated into established plant breeding and crop production practices. The average amount of time that is required to develop, test and release a new variety, normally takes 8-10 years. The procedure has many stages including germplasm management, selection of suitable parents, genetic stabilisation, multilocation testing of newly developed strains, agro-production and protection technologies, quality testing, seed multiplication, etc., (Fig. 2) indicates that biotechnology can contribute signficantly to crop improvement programme and reduce the period by 2-3 years. For details, readers may refer to Chopra and Prakash (1997).

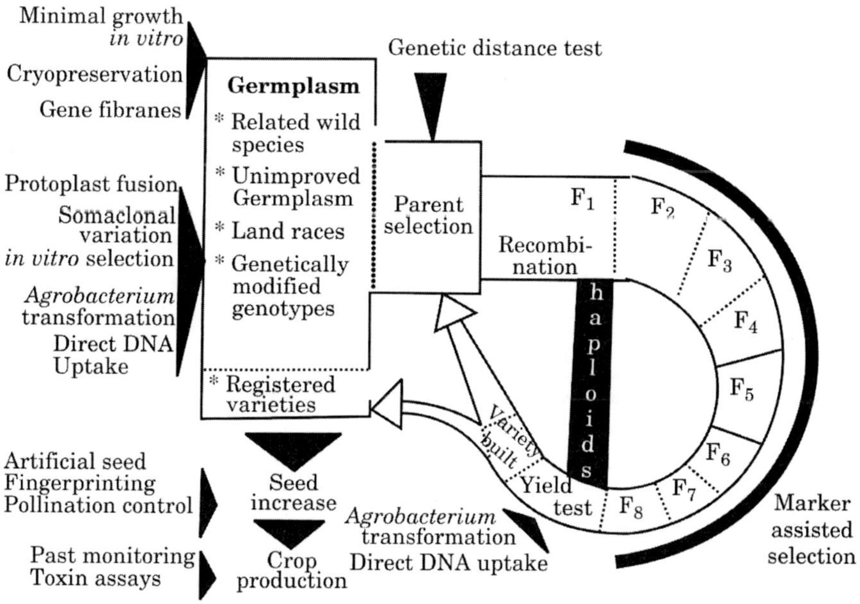


**Fig. 2:** Inputs from biotechnology into the plant improvement cycle (After Pauls, 1995)

Utilizing the biotechnological tools (somaclonal variation), the National Research Centre on Plant Biotechnology, IARI, New Delhi has evolved a high yielding, bold seeded and shattering resistant variety,

Pusa Jaikisan (Bio 902) of *B. juncea.* This variety gives on an average 19 per cent higher yield than the standard check variety, Varuna. The Government of India notified this variety for general cultivation in Rajasthan, Gujarat and Maharashtra in 1994. The procedure followed for the development of Pusa Jaikisan is presented in Fig. 3.

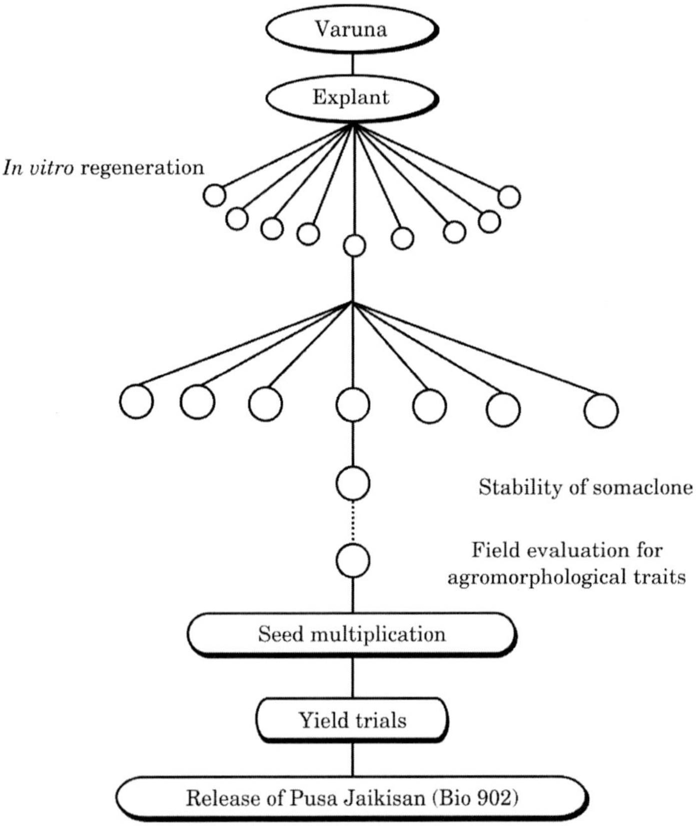


**Fig. 3:** Development of Pusa Jaikisan (BIO 902)

## 12. QUALITY SEED PRODUCTION

One of the major bottlenecks in enhancing the production and productivity of this crop commodity is the lack of availability of quality seeds. Production of adequate quantity of quality seed is, therefore, of vital importance. The breeder who has developed a variety has to ensure that the breeder seed produced by him is derived from the population which has been grown in a plot where recommended isolation distance has been maintained. Further, almost all the plants have the diagnostic traits for that particular variety. Any lapse at this stage, would affect the quality of the seed. The breeders seed is amplified in stages to produce certified seed.

The recommendations made on isolation distance for production of foundation and certified seed of *B. juncea* are :

(*i*) Foundation seed 200 m

(*ii*) Certified seed 50 m

The seed certification standards for notified varieties of rapeseed-mustard crop commodity have been fixed by the Government of India as the minimum limits of germination and purity for labelling (Table 7).

**Table 7.** Seed certification standards for rapeseed-mustard (in per cent)

| ***Pure seed*** (Min.) | | ***Inert matter*** (Max.) | | ***Other crop seeds*** (Max.) | | ***Total weed seeds*** (Max.) | | ***Objectionable weed seeds*** (Max.) | |
|---|---|---|---|---|---|---|---|---|---|
| F | C | F | C | F | C | F | C | F | C |
| 97.0 | 97.0 | 3.0 | 3.0 | 10/kg | 20/kg | 10/kg | 20/kg | 5/kg | 10/kg |

| ***Germination*** (Min.) | | ***Moisture (Maximum)*** ***Oridinary container*** | | ***Vapour proof container*** | | ***Other distinguishable varieties*** | |
|---|---|---|---|---|---|---|---|
| F | C | F | C | F | C | F | C |
| 85 | 85 | 08.0 | 08.0 | 05.0 | 05.0 | 0.1-0.5 | By No. |

F: Foundation seed, C: Certified seed

## 13. RAPESEED-MUSTARD VARIETIES

A list of varieties recommended for different regions of the country for general cultivation is given in Table 8.

## 14. CHALLENGES AND SUGGESTED APPROACH

It is estimated that the country would need to produce 24 million tonnes of rape seed-mustard oilseed by 2020 AD to meet the domestic requirement. To achieve the target envisaged, it is necessary that constraints/challenges limiting the productivity of rapeseed-mustard crop commodity are removed.

**Table 8:** Rapeseed-Mustard varieties of India

| *Sl. no.* | *Variety* | *Year of recommendation* | *Area of adaptation* |
|---|---|---|---|
| ***Toria (Brassica rapa* L. ssp. *toria)*** | | | |
| 1 | Agrani (B 54) | 1980 | West Bengal |
| 2 | Bhawani (TK 8401) | 1985 | Uttar Pradesh |
| 3 | BR 23 | Prior to 1951 | Bihar |
| 4 | DK 1 | 1970 | Himachal Pradesh |
| 5 | ITSA | 1961 | Haryana & Punjab |
| 6 | Jawahar Toria | 1996 | Madhya Pradesh |
| 7 | M 27 | 1956 | Assam, Orissa & All NEH States |
| 8 | Panchali (TWC 3) | 1986 | West Bengal |
| 9 | PBT 37 | 1993 | Punjab |
| 10 | PT 30 | 1985 | Uttar Pradesh |
| 11 | PT 303 | 1985 | Assam, Haryana, Punjab, Orissa, Uttar Pradesh & West Bengal |
| 12 | PT 507 B | 1990 | Eastern states of the country |
| 13 | RAUTS 17 | 1986 | Bihar |
| 14 | Sangam | 1974 | Haryana |
| 15 | Suman (TH 68) | 1990 | Haryana |
| 16 | T 9 | 1961 | Arunachal Pradesh, Madhya Pradesh, Manipur, Meghalaya, Rajasthan, Tripura & Uttar Pradesh |
| 17 | T 36 | 1963 | Uttar Pradesh |
| 18 | TL 15 | 1978 | Himachal Pradesh & Punjab |
| 19 | TLC 1 | 1983 | Punjab |
| 20 | TS 29 | 1980 | Assam |
| 21 | TS 36 | 1994 | Assam |
| 22 | TS 38 | 1994 | Assam |
| ***Yellow sarson (B. rapa* L. ssp. *yellow sarson)*** | | | |
| 1 | 66-197-3 | 1980 | Bihar, Central & Western India |
| 2 | Benoy (B 9) | 1980 | West Bengal |
| 3 | Indira (PYS 6) | 1984 | Eastern India |
| 4 | Jhumka (NC 1) | 1992 | West Bengal |
| 5 | K 88 | 1973 | Central & Western Uttar Pradesh |
| 6 | Narendra Sarson 2 (NDYS 2) | 1996 | Madhya Pradesh & Uttar Pradesh |
| 7 | Patan Sarson 66 | 1966 | Northern Gujarat |
| 8 | Pusa Gold | 1997 | Delhi |
| 9 | Rajendra Sarson 1 (RAUDYS 89-115) | 1998 | Bihar |
| 10 | Subinoy (YSB 19-7-C) | 1982 | West Bengal |
| 11 | Swarna (RAUDY 89-07) | 1998 | Bihar |
| 12 | T151 | 1957 | Uttar Pradesh |
| 13 | YSPb24 | 1966 | Haryana, Punjab, Rajasthan and Himachal Pradesh |

**Table 8:** (*Contd...*)

**Table 8:** (*Contd...*)

| *Sl. no.* | *Variety* | *Year of recommendation* | *Area of adaptation* |
|---|---|---|---|
| ***Brown sarson (B. rapa* L ssp. *brown sarson)*** | | | |
| 1 | BS 2 | 1966 | South Western Uttar Pradesh |
| 2 | BS 70 | 1966 | Eastern Uttar Pradesh |
| 3 | BSH 1 | 1966 | Himachal Pradesh, Haryana, Punjab, Rajasthan & Uttar Pradesh |
| 4 | KS 101 | 1997 | Kashmir Valley |
| 5 | KBS 3 | 1996 | Himachal Pradesh |
| 6 | KOS 1 | 1978 | Kashmir Valley |
| 7 | Pusa Kalyani (PN 15-5/19) | 1973 | Assam, Bihar, Haryana, Punjab, Rajasthan, Uttar Pradesh & West Bengal |
| ***Taramira (Eruca sativa* Mill.*)*** | | | |
| 1 | ITSA | 1961 | Haryana, Punjab, Rajasthan & parts of Uttar Pradesh |
| 2 | RTM 314 | 1995 | Haryana, Punjab, Rajasthan & Uttar Pradesh |
| 3 | T 27 | 1974 | Haryana |
| 4 | TMC 1 | 1980 | Punjab |
| 5 | TMLC 2 | 1990 | Punjab |
| ***Gobhi sarson (B. napus* L.*)*** | | | |
| 1 | GSL 1 | 1985 | Punjab |
| 2 | GSL 2 | 1994 | Punjab |
| 3 | Hyola 401 | 1996 | Haryana, Himachal Pradesh & Punjab |
| 4 | Neelam (HPN 3) | 1998 | Himachal Pradesh |
| 5 | PGSH 51 | 1994 | Punjab |
| 6 | Sheetal 1 (HPN 1) | 1994 | Low & mid Hills of Himachal Pradesh |
| ***Indian Mustard (B. juncea* (L.) Czern. & Coss.*)*** | | | |
| 1 | Aravali (RN 393) | 1998 | Haryana, Punjab & Rajasthan |
| 2 | Bhagirathi (RW 351) | 1984 | West Bengal |
| 3 | BR 40 | 1960 | Gangetic alluvial soils of south Bihar |
| 4 | CS 52 | 1997 | Sodic & Saline soils of Haryana, Rajasthan, Uttar Pradesh |
| 5 | Durgamani | 1968 | Rajasthan |
| 6 | GM 1 | 1989 | Dry sandy to medium black soil of Gujarat |
| 7 | GM 2 | 1996 | Gujarat |
| 8 | Jagannath (VSL 5) | 1998 | Madhya Pradesh, Uttar Pradesh and parts of Rajasthan (Bharatpur, Kota) |
| 9 | Jawahar Mustard 1 (JMMWR 93-39) | 1999 | Madhya Pradesh |
| 10 | Kranti | 1982 | Bihar, Delhi, Haryana, Madhya Pradesh, Orissa, Punjab, Rajasthan, Uttar Pradesh & West Bengal |
| 11 | Krishna | 1983 | Bihar, Delhi, Haryana, Madhya Pradesh, Orissa, Punjab, Rajasthan & Uttar Pradesh |
| 12 | KRV 74 | 1984 | Madhya Pradesh & Uttar Pradesh |
| 13 | Laha 101 | 1947 | Uttar Pradesh |
| 14 | Laxmi | 1996 | Haryana |

**Table 8:** (*Contd...*)

| *Sl. no.* | *Variety* | *Year of recommendation* | *Area of adaptation* |
|---|---|---|---|
| 15 | Mustard Karishma (PR 8988) | 1995 | Western Uttar Pradesh |
| 16 | Narendra Rai (NDR 8501) | 1990 | Madhya Pradesh & Uttar Pradesh |
| 17 | Patan Mustard 67 (PM 67) | 1967 | Mehsana & Banskantha districts of Gujarat |
| 18 | PBR 91 | 1994 | Punjab |
| 19 | PBR 97 | 1996 | Haryana, Himachal Pradesh, Jammu, Punjab & Rajasthan |
| 20 | Parkash | 1974 | Haryana |
| 21 | Pusa Agrani (SEJ 2) | 1997 | Delhi, Haryana, Punjab & Rajasthan |
| 22 | Pusa Bihar (DIRA 247) | 1989 | Assam, Bihar, Orissa & West Bengal |
| 23 | Pusa Basant (DIRA 367) | 1989 | Assam, Bihar, Orissa & West Bengal |
| 24 | Pusa Bold (PR 45) | 1984 | Uttar Pradesh, Rajasthan, Madhya Pradesh & Delhi |
| 25 | Pusa Jaikisan (Bio 902) | 1993 | Gujarat, Maharashtra & Western Rajasthan |
| 26 | Rajat (PCR 7) | 1993 | Gujarat, Maharashtra & Western Rajasthan |
| 27 | RCC 4 | 1996 | Himachal Pradesh |
| 28 | RH 30 | 1983 | Haryana, Jammu, Punjab, Northern Rajasthan & Western Uttar Pradesh |
| 29 | RH 781 | 1990 | Haryana |
| 30 | RH 785 | 1983 | Orissa & West Bengal |
| 31 | RH 819 | 1990 | Haryana |
| 32 | RH 7361 | 1984 | Haryana |
| 33 | RK 9 | 1985 | Madhya Pradesh & Uttar Pradesh |
| 34 | RK 14 | 1984 | Madhya Pradesh & Uttar Pradesh |
| 35 | RL 18 | 1937 | Haryana, Punjab & Rajasthan |
| 36 | RL 1359 | 1987 | Punjab |
| 37 | RLM 185 | 1983 | Madhya Pradesh & Uttar Pradesh |
| 38 | RLM 198 | 1981 | Punjab |
| 39 | RLM 514 | 1980 | Punjab |
| 40 | RLM 619 | 1985 | Punjab |
| 41 | Rohini | 1995 | Madhya Pradesh & Uttar Pradesh |
| 42 | Sanjucta Asech (4C-6-3/II) | 1988 | West Bengal |
| 43 | Sarama | 1984 | West Bengal |
| 44 | Saurabh (RH 8113) | 1985 | Haryana |
| 45 | Seeta (B 85) | 1980 | West Bengal |
| 46 | TM 2 | 1987 | Assam |
| 47 | TM 4 | 1987 | Assam |
| 48 | Vaibhav (RK 1418) | 1985 | Madhya Pradesh & Uttar Pradesh |
| 49 | Vardan (RK 1467) | 1985 | Madhya Pradesh & Uttar Pradesh |
| 50 | Varuna (T 59) | 1975 | Entire mustard growing areas of the country |
| ***Karan Rai (B. carinata* A Br.)** | | | |
| 1 | Kiran (PBC 9221) | 1997 | Uttar Pradesh |
| 2 | PC 5 | 1994 | Punjab |
| 3 | Pusa Gaurav (DLSC 1) | 1995 | Delhi |

| ***Constraints/Challenges*** | ***Suggested strateg(y)ies*** |
|---|---|
| * Instability in yield and production because of absence of appropriate donor sources for major biotic stresses like *Alternaria* blight, white rust, *Sclerotinia* disease and aphid pest; and abiotic stresses like drought, frost and salinity. Identified sources possess low level of tolerance/ resistance. Knowledge about their mechanism of resistance is limited. | * Collection of germplasm from newer areas, breeding for increased level of resistance or tolerance either through the use of biotechnological tools or conventional breeding may be followed. |
| * Species, in general, are having low productivity because of their inherent physiological nature (C3) and diverse mating behaviour. Further, sizeable area is under poor yielding species of rapeseed-mustard, cultivated in marginal and sub-marginal lands. | * Efforts need to be made to develop plants with high harvest index, responsive to low inputs like fertilizer and water. |
| * Non-availability of varieties for specific cropping system, and non traditional areas, *viz*., after cotton and bajra harvest in northern India and rice-fallow including *paira* cropping in eastern and central India, after sugarcane in Maharashtra and for different cropping situations. | * Development of plant types for specific situations. |
| * In *B. juncea,* hybrid development programme, a perfect three-line breeding system is lacking though one of the cytoplasmic male sterility-restorer system, *mori* has been perfected. The other available CMS systems are behaving as a cytoplasmic male sterility system and not as cytoplasmic genetic MS system. | * With the availability of *mori* CMS and restoration system, it is now necessary to diversify the nuclear background of *mori* CMS and restorer for use in commercial mustard hybrids production. In other CMS system, improvement to get stable CMS-restorer, system can be achieved either through protoplast fusion or through genetic manipulation. In *B. rapa* ssp *yellow sarson,* identification of genetic markers like long siliqua, narrow serrated leaves, spreading bud bunch (pendent type) at early stage of growth and development of 3-line breeding system may be pursued. |
| * Non-availability of short duration high yielding toria (less than 85 days) varieties because of undesirable linkage between maturity and seed yield. | * Very early maturity lines (< 80 days) of toria but very poor yielders are available in Bastar region of Madhya Pradesh. Use of such germplasm and population improvement to enhance the productivity per day should be the approach. |
| * Indigenous sources with rich quality of oil and seed meal are available but are poor yielders. Exotic quality materials are late maturing and poor yielders. They are susceptible to pests and diseases | * To develop cultivars possessing nutritionally superior oil and seed meal quality in the indigenous material, conventional breeding methods would overcome the problem of poor yield. For development of very high oleic and erucic acid and low saturated fatty acids (below 3 per cent), available germplam is to be looked into. In the absence of such trait in the gene-bank, biotechnological tools are to be used to transfer alien gene. |

## REFERENCES


Abraham, U. and Bhatia, C.R. (1994). Testing for tolerance to aphid in Indian mustard, *Brassica juncea* (L.) Czern and Coss. *Plant Breed,* 112: 260–263.

Ahmed, S. U. and Zuberi, M.I. (1971). Inheritance of seed coat colour in *Brassica campestris* L. var. *toria. Crop Sci.*, 11: 309–310.

Alam, Z. (1945). Nomenclature of oleiferous *Brassicas* cultivated in Punjab. *Indian J. Agri.* Sci., 15: 173–181.

Anand, I.J. and Downey, R.K. (1981). A study of erucic acid alleles in digenomic rapeseed *(Brassica napus* L.). *Can. I. Plant. Sci.,* 613: 199–203.

Anand, I.J. and Rawat, D.S. (1978). Combining ability studies on Indian mustard. Z. *Pflanzenzucht,* 81: 241–247.

Anand, I.J. and Reddy, W.R. (1987). Estimates of gene effects for seed yield and its components in Indian x exotic mustard. *J. Oilseeds Res.,* 4: 1–8.

Anonymous, (1975). Annual Report AICORRO in Haryana; Haryana Agricultural University, Hissar, pp. 1–221.

Anoymous. (2000). Progress Report, 1990–99. Promotion of Research and Development efforts on Hybrids in selected crops: *Brassica*. N.D. University of Agriculture and Technology, Faizabad, pp. 1–10.

Asthana, A.N. and Pandey, V.K. (1977). Combining ability and rank correlation in a diallel cross of Indian mustard *(Brassica juncea). Expt. Agric.,* 13: 71–79

Badwal, S.S. and Labana, K.S. (1983). Male sterility in Indian mustard [*Brassica juncea* (L.) Czern. & Coss.] Proc. 15th Int. Congress of Genet, 12–21. 193 (Abstract).

Badwal, S.S. and Labana, K.S. (1987). Combining ability for seed size, oil and protein content in Indian mustard. *Crop Improv.,* 14: 10–13.

Bailey, L.H. (1922). The cultivated *Brassicas* I. *Gentes Herb.,* 1: 53–108.

Bhadouria, S.S., Jain, G. and Tiwari, A.S. (1991). Combining ability analysis in Indian mustard [*Brassica juncea* (L.) Czern. & Coss]. Golden Jubilee Symposium on Genetic Research and Education: Current Trends and Next Fifty Years. Feb. 12–15: 1991, New Delhi. Abst. Vol. II, 443.

Brar, B.K., Dhillon, S.S., Singh, K. and Labana, K.S. 1991. Genetics of qualitative traits in Indian mustard *(Brassica juncea). Cruciferae Newsletter,* 14–15: 54–55.

Burkill, I.H. (1930). The Chinese mustards is the Malay Peninsula. *Gad's Bull.* 5: 99–117.

Chaudhary, B.D., Singh, D.P., Singh, P. and Kumar, A. (1989). Inheritance studies of plant water relations in *Brassica juncea. Biologia Plant,* 31: 203–206.

Chaudhary, B.K. and Sharma, S.K. (1982). Note on the inheritance of some quantitative characters in a cross of Indian mustard. *Indian J. Agric. Sci.,* 52: 23–25.

Chauhan, Y.S. (1987). Genetic analysis for yield and its components in Indian mustard. *Indian J. Agric. Res.,* 21: 77–82.

Chauhan, Y.S. and Singh, D.P. (1980). Inheritance of seed weight in Indian mustard. *Indian J. Genet.,* 40: 597–599.

Chopra, V.L. and Prakash, S. (1997). Oil seed and Vegetable Brassicas: Indian Perspective. Oxford & IBH Publishing Co. Pvt. Ltd., New Delhi, pp. 1–294.

Chopra, V.L., Kirti, P.B. and Prakash, S. 1995. Accessing and exploiting genes of breeding value of distant relatives of Crop *Brassicas*. *Genetica,* 97: 305–312

Chowdhury, J.B. and Das, K. (1966). Male sterility in yellow sarson. *Ind. ]. Genet.* 26: 374–380.

Chowdhury, J.B. and Das, K. (1967). Male sterility genes in brown sarson. *Ind. J. Genet.,* 27: 284–288.

Clandinin, D.R., Ichikawa, S., Robblee, A.R. and Thomas, D. (1978). The use of glucosinolate type rapeseed meal in rations for layers and broilers. Proceedings 5th International. Rapeseed Congress, Malmo, Sweden, 2: 284–286.

Das, K. and Kumar, P.R. (1969). Induction of polymeric variation in brown sarson. *Indian Agriculturist,* 13: 19–26.

Das, K. and Pandey, B.D. (1961). Male sterility in brown sarson. *Ind. J. Genet.,* 21: 185–190.

Dhawan, A.K., Chhabra, M.L. and Yadava, T.P. (1983). Freezing injury in oilseed *Brassica* species. *Ann. Bot.,* 51: 673–677.

Dhillon, S.S., Labana, K.S. and Banga, S.K. (1990). Studies on heterosis and combining ability in Indian mustard [*Brassica juncea* (L.) Czern and Coss.] *J. Res. PAU,* 27: 1–8.

Diwakar, M.C. and Singh, A.K. (1993). Combining ability for oil and yield attributes in yellow seeded Indian mustard [*Brassica juncea* (L.) Czern. and Coss.]. *Ann. Agric. Res.*, 14: 194–198.

Dixit, R.K. (1972). Note on inheritance of a new siliqua mutant in Indian colza *(Brassica campestris* L. var. Sarson Prain). *Indian J. Agric. Sci.,* 42: 648.

Dixit, R.K. and Singh, H.G. (1973). Genetics of leaf hairiness in *Brassica juncea* Coss. *Madras Agric. J.,* 60: 1872.

Dixit, R.K., Prasad, K. and Srivastava, A.N. (1983). Combining ability for quality characters in Indian mustard. *Indian J. Agric. Sci.,* 53: 776–778.

Dorrell, D.C. and Downey, R.K. (1964). The inheritance of erucic acid content in rapeseed (*Brassica campestris*). *Can. J. Plant Sci.,* 44: 499–504.

Downey, R.K. (1983). The origin and description of Brassica oilseed crops. *In*: High and low erucic acid Rapeseed oils: Production, Usage, Chemistry and Taxicological Evaluation. *Eds*: J.K., Kramar, G., Sauer, F.D.R. and Pigden, W.J. Academic Press, New York, pp 1–20.

Downey, R.K., and Rimmer, S.R. (1993). Agronomic improvement in oilseed *Brassicas. Adv. Agron.,* 50: 1–66.

Fernanadez–Escobar, J., Domingguez, J., Martin, A. and Fernandez Martinez, J.M. (1988). Genetics of erucic acid content in inter specifie hybrids of Ethiopian mustard (*Brassica carinata* Braun) and rapeseed (*B. napus* L.). *Plant Breed,* 100: 310–315.

Govil, S.K., Chuabey, C.N. and Chauhan, Y.S. (1981). Combining ability studies in Indian mustard. *Indian J. Agric. Sci.,* 51: 623–626.

Govil, S.K., Srivastava, A.N. and Chauhan, Y.S. (1983). Gene action for oil content in Indian mustard. *Indian J. Argic Sci.,* 53: 404–406.

Gupta, M.L., Labana, K.S. and Badwal, S.S. (1987). Combinging ability analysis of yield and its components in Indian mustard. In 7th Intern. Rapeseed Cong. Poznan, Poland, pp. 348–353.

Gupta, S.K., Thakral, S.K., Yadava, T.P. and Kumar, P. (1985). Combining ability and genetic architecture of oil content in Indian mustard. *Haryana Agric. Univ. J. Res.,* 15: 467–470.

Harvey, B.L. and Downey, R.K. (1964). The inheritance of erucic acid content in rapeseed (*Brassica napus). Can. J. Plant Sci.*, 44: 104–111.

Hegi, G. (1919). *Illustrierte Flora von Mittel–Europe.* 4. Munchen.

Hemingway, J.S. (1976). Mustard : *Brassica* ssp. and *Sinapis alba* (*Cruciferae*). *In*: Evolution of Crop Plants. Ed. N.W. Simmonds. Longmans, Green, New York, pp. 55–59.

Hinata, K. and Prakash, S. (1984). Enthnobotany and evolutionary origin of Indian oleiferous *Brassicae. Indian J. Genet.,* 44: 102–112.

Jain, A.K., Tiwari, A.S., Kushwah, V.S. and Hirve, C.D. (1988). Genetics of quantitative trait in Indian mustard. *Indian. J. Genet.,* 48: 117–119.

Jindal, S.K. and Labana, K.S. (1986). Combining ability in a complete diallel cross of Indian mustard. *Indian J. Agric Sci.,* 56: 75–79.

Jonsson, R. (1977). Erucic acid heredity in rapeseed *(Brassica napus* L.) and *Brassica campestris, Hereditas,* 87: 159–170.

Kashi, R., Singh, D., Verma, V.S. and Katiyar, R.P. (1976). Inter relationship between some metric traits in segregating population of Indian mustard *(Brassica juncea* (L.) Czern. & Coss.). *J. Maharashtra Agric. Univ.,* 1: 21–22.

Kirk, J.T.O. and Hurlstone, C.G. (1983). Variation and inheritance of erucic acid content in *Brassica juncea. Z. Pflanzenzucht,* 90: 331–338.

Kumar, P. and Singh, M.M. (1987). Inheritance of seed weight in Indian mustard. *J. Oilseeds Res.,* 4: 297–299.

Kumar, P., Thakral, N.K., Yadav, T.P., Lekhraj and Chandra, N. (1998). Inheritance of yield attributing traits in Indian mustard (*Brassica juncea* L.) *Cruciferae Newsletter.,* 20: 73–74.

Kumar, P., Yadava, T.P. and Dhawan, K. (1982). Combining ability analysis for oil content in Indian mustard, *Indian J. Agric Sci.,* 52: 219–221.

Kumar, P.R. (1972). Radiation induced variability in improvement of brown sarson. *Rad. Bot.,* 12: 309–313.

Kumar, P.R. (1978). Quality breeding in brown sarson. In : *Proc. V. Int. Rapeseed Congress, Malmo, Sweden,* 2 : 131–135.

Kumar, P.R. and Das, K. (1977). Induced quantitative variation in self–compatible and self–incompatible forms in *Brassica. Ind. J. Gen. and PI. Breed.,* 37: 5–11.

Kumar, P.R. and Das. K. (1974). Genetic studies in irradiated *Brassica.* SABRAO Proc. *Ind. J. Gen.* and *Pl. Breed.,* 34A: 696–702.

Kumar, P.R. and Tsunoda, S. (1976). Isolation of zero erucic acid species in wild *Cruciferae. SABRAOJ.,* 8: 177–179.

Kumar, P.R. and Tsunoda, S. (1978). Fatty acid spectrum of Mediterranean wild *Cruciferae. Journal American Oil Chemists' Society,* 55: 320–323.

Kumar, P.R. and Tsunoda, S. (1980). Variation in oil content and fatty acids composition among seeds from the *Cruciferae. In*: *Brassica* Crops and Wild Allies: Biology and Breeding, *Eds.,* Tsunoda, S., Hinata, K. and Gomez–Campo, C. Japan Scientific Societies Press, Tokyo, pp. 235–252.

Kumar, V., Singh, D., Pundir, S.R., Kamboj, M.C. and Chandra, N. (1994). Genetics of yield and its components in Indian mustard [*Brassica juncea* (L.) Czern & Coss.]. *Crop Res.,* 7: 243–246.

Labana, K.S., Badwal, S.S. and Chaurasia, B.D. (1975). Heterosis and combining ability analysis in [*Brassica juncea* (L.) Czern & Coss.]. *Crop Improv.,* 2: 46–51.

Labana, K.S., Chaurasia, B.D. and Sangha, A.S. (1984). Inheritance studies for some yield components in Indian mustard. *Crop Improv.,* 11: 58–60.

Labana, K.S., Chaurasia, B.D. and Sangha, A.S. (1987). Inheritance of oil content in Indian mustard. *Indian J. Agric. Sci.,* 57: 539–543.

Lein, K.A. (1970). Quantitative Best immungs method en fur samen glucosinolate in *Brassica* Arten and ihre Anwendung in der Zuchtung von Glucosinolataramen Raps. *Z. Pflazenucht,* 63: 137–154.

Malkhandale, J.D. (1993). Diallel analysis for some metric traits in Indian mustard. *Ann. Plant Physiol.,* 7: 247–250

Mansfeld, R. (1959). *Prodr. Enum. Spec. Plant. Agr. Hort,* 2: 90

Mendham, N.J., Ruo, M.S.S. and Buzza. G.C. 1991. The apetalous flower character as a component of a high yielding ideotype. Proc. 8th Int. Rapeseed Conf., Cambridge, pp. 596–600.

Mizushima, U. and Tsunda, S. (1967). A plant exploration in *Brassica* and allied genera. *Tohoku J. Agri. Res.,* 17: 249–277.

Mohammad, A., Singh, R. and Zafar, A. (1943). Inheritance of seed colour in some oleiferous *Brassicae, Indian J. Genet.,* 2: 112–127.

Morice, J. (1974). Selection d'ybe varuete de colza sans acids erucique et sans glucosinolates. *In*: Proc. *4th Intl. Rapeseed Conf.* Giessen, West Germany, pp. 31–47.

Olsson, G. (1960). Species crosses *within* the genus *Brassica*. I. Artificial *Brassica juncea* Coss. *Hereditas*, 46: 171–222.

Olsson, G. and Persson, C. (1986). Recurrent selection in white mustard *(Sinapis alba* L.) *In*: *Svalof 1886–1986 : Research and Results, in Plant Breeding,* Ed. G. Olsson, pp. 53–55.

Pahuja, S.K., Sangwan, R.S., Arora, R.N. and Jindal, Y. (1996). Gene effects for oil content in Indian mustard [*Brassica juncea* (L.) Czern and Coss.]. H.A.U.J. *Res.,* 26: 163–167.

Pal, Y., and Singh, H. (1990). A note on inheritance of seed colour, size and seed shape in Indian mustard. *J. Oilseeds Res.,* 7: 69–72.

Pathak, G.N. and Singh, B.B. (1949). Mutation in *Brassica campestirs* Linn var. sarson Prain. *Curr. Sci.,* 18: 253–254.

Paul, N.K., Joarder, O.I. and Eunus, A.M. (1976). Analysis of yield and some of its components in mustard, *Indian J. Agric Sci.,* 46: 517–524.

Pauls, K.P. (1995). Plant biotechnology for crop improvement. *In*: Biotechnology Advances, Elsevier Science Inc. 13: 673–693.

Pokhriyal, S.C., Kumar, V. and Mangat, K.S. (1964). Inheritance studies in *Brassica juncea* Coss. *Indian Oilseeds J.*, 8: 293–296.

Pradhan, A.K., Sodhi, Y.S., Mukhopadhayay, A. and Pental, D. (1993). Heterosis breeding in Indian mustard [*Brassica juncea* (L.) Czern. & Coss.]. Analysis of component characters contributing to heterosis for yield. *Euphytica,* 69: 219–229.

Prakash, S. and Hinata, K. (1980). Taxonomy, cytogenetics and origin of *Brassica,* a review. *Oper. Bot.,* 55: 1–57.

Prakash, S., and Chopra, V.L. (1988). Introgression of resistance to shattering in *Brassica napus* from *Brassica juncea* through non–homologous recombination. *Plant Breed,* 101 : 167–168.

Prakash, S., Kirti, P.B. and Chopra, V.L. (1998a). Development of cytoplasmic male sterility–fertility restoration systems of variable origin in mustard – *Brassica juncea. Acta Horticulture,* 459: 299–304.

Prakash, S., Kirti, P.B., Bhat, S.R., Gaikwad, K., Dinesh Kumar, V. and Chopra, V.L. (1998b). A *Moriandia arvensis* based cytoplasmic male sterlity and fertility restoration system in *Brassica juncea. Theor. Appl. Genet.,* 97: 488–492.

Rajan, S.S. (1966). Brassica Breeding Procedures. Indian Council of Agricultural Research., pp. 1–29.

Rakaw, G. (1973). Selection for content of linoleic and linolenic acids in rapeseed for mutagenic treatment. *Z. Pfanzenzitcht,* 69: 62–82.

Ram, K., Chauhan, Y.S. and Katiyar, R.P. (1976). Partial diallel analysis in F2 generation in Indian mustard. *Indian J. Agric. Sci.,* 46: 229–232.

Rawat, D.S. (1975). Genetical studies on yield, oil content and characters related to yield in *Brassica juncea* L. Czern & Coss. Ph. D. Thesis, IARI, New Delhi.

Rawat, D.S. (1987). Line x tester analysis and rank index in Indian mustard. *Ann. Agric. Res.,* 8: 173–182.

Rawat, D.S. (1992). Analysis of reciprocal differences in Indian mustard. *Acta Agron. Hung.,* 41: 227–233.

Reddy, W.R. (1983). Genetics of seed coat colour and quantitative characters related to yield in Indian mustard [*Brassica juncea* (L.) Czern. & Coss.] M.Se. Thesis, IARI, New Delhi.

Rishipal, Prakash, Kumar and Kumar, R (1993). Generation mean analysis of yield and its attributes in Indian mustard *(Brassica juncea). Indian J. Agric Sci.,* 63: 807–813.

Robbelen, G. and Nitsch, A. (1975). Genetical and physiological investigation on mutants for polyenoic fatty acids in rapeseed, *Brassica napus* L. I. Selection and description of new mutants. *Z. Pflanzenzucht,* 75: 93–195.

Roxburgh, W. (1832). *Flora Indica* Ed. W. Carrey. Serampore, Vol III: 117–124.

Sachan, J.N. and Singh, B. (1988). Genetic analysis of quantitative characters in a cross of Indian mustard *(Brassica juncea ssp. juncea). Indian J. Agric. Sci.,* 58: 41–42.

Schiemann, E. (1932). Entsehung der Kulturpflanzen Handb. Verbwis. Lfg., p. 15.

Schulz, O.E. (1919). *Crudferae–Brassiceae,* Part I. *Brassicinae* and *Raphaninae.* In: *Ed.* Engler, A. *Das Planzenreich,* Leipzig, Vol IV: 1–290.

Sengupta, K. and Mukhpaodhyay, S. (1981). Inheritance of glossy stem character in *Brassica juncea (L.)* Czern. & Coss. *Cwr, Sci.,* 50: 32–33.

Shabana, R., Shrief, S.A., Ibrahim. A.F. and Geisler, G. (1990). Correlation and path coefficient analysis for some new released (00) spring rapeseed cultivars grown tmder different competitive Systems. *J. Agron. Crop. Sci.,* 165: 138–143.

Sharma, J.K. and Singh, H.B. (1994). Combining ability studies of seed and seedling traits in Indian mustard [*Brassica juncea (L.)* Czern. & Coss.]. *J. Seed Res.,* 22: 119–123.

Sharma, J.K., Singh, H.B. and Thakur, H.L. (1992). Genetics of seedling traits in Indian mustard, *Crop Improv.,* 19: 113–115.

Shivana, K.R. and Sawhney, V.K. (1993). Pollen selection for *Alternaria* resistance in oilseed *Brassica* response of pollen grain and leaves to toxin of *A. brassicae. Theor. Appl. Genet.,* 86: 339–344.

Singh Hari and Yashpal, (1991). Genetic components and combining ability analysis of oil content in Indian mustard. *J. Oilseeds Res.*, 8: 117–120.

Singh, A. B., Chauhan, Y. S. and Singh, P. (1981). Genetics of yield in Indian mustard. *Indian J. Genet.,* 41: 130–136.

Singh, A.B., Chauhan, Y.S. and Singh, P. (1982). Components of genetic variation in Indian mustard. *Indian J. Agric.* Sci., 52: 634–638.

Singh, D. (1955). Inheritance of a new leaf type in rape. *Curr, Sci.,* 24: 237–238.

Singh, D. and Singh, H. (1989). Inheritance studies on white rust *(Albugo candida)* resistance. In *XV Int. Cong. Genetics,* Toronto, Canada, Abstract 32, p. 566.

Singh, D., Sachan, J.N., Ram, B., Singh, B. and Singh, S.P. (1986). Combining ability in Indian mustard. *J. Oilseeds* Res., 3: 1–7.

Singh, D.N. and Singh, B. (1991). Comparative study on diallel, partial diallel and line x tester analysis in Indian mustard *(Brassica juncea). Indian J. Genet.,* 51: 400–404.

Singh, G.P. and Mittal, R.K. (1993). Combining ability analysis for yield and yield contributing traits in Indian mustard [*Brassica juncea* (L.) Czern & Coss]. *Ann. Agric. Res.,* 14: 205–210.

Singh, H., Lather, V.S. and Singh, D. (1985). Extent of heterosis in relation to genotype diversity in Indian x exotic crosses of Indian mustard [*Brassica juncea* (L.) Czern. & Coss.]. *Genet. Iber.,* 37: 97–105.

Singh, I.S., Singh, H., Singh, S.P. and Singh, A.B. (1977). Diallel analysis in yellow seeded rai (*Brassica campestris L.* var. sarson Prain). *Indian J. Agric Sci.*, 41: 315–323.

Singh, J.N., Yadav, M.C. and Sheik, I.A. (1996). Geneticai studies for yield and oil content in *Brassica juncea* (L.) Czern. & Coss. *Indian J. Genet.,* 56: 299–304.

Singh, R.M., Singh, H.G., Talukdar, B.S., Chauhan, Y.S. and Singh, A.K. (1973). Heterosis in Indian mustard *(Brassica juncea). Indian J. Farm Sci.*, 1: 15–20.

Singh, R.N., and Srivastava, A.N. (1974). Note on the breeding behaviour of a yellow seeded rai [*Brassica juncea* (L.) Coss.]. *Sci. and Cutt.,* 40: 407.

Singh, R.P., Singh, D.P., Singh, P. and Choudhary, B.D. (1987). Character association and inter dependence of morphophysiological variables in Indian mustard. *Res. Dev. Rep.,* 4: 177–183.

Singh, S.P. (1973). Heterosis and combining ability estimates in Indian mustard. *Crop Sci.,* 13: 497–499.

Singh, S.P. and Singh D.P. (1972). Inheritance of yield and other agronomic characters in Indian mustard. *Canad. J. Genet. Cytol.,* 14: 227–233.

Singh, V.S., Srivastava, A.N. and Ahmad, Z. (1989). Combining ability in F1 and F2 generation of a diallel cross in Indian mustard. *Crop Improve.*, 16: 164–167.

Sinskaia, E.N. (1928). The oleiferous plants and root crops of the family cruciferae. Bull. *Appl. Bot. Genet. PI. Breed.*, 175: 3–166.

Song, K.M., Osbom, T.C. and Williams, P.H. (1988). *Brassica* taxonomy based on nuclear restriction fragment length polymorphism (RFLPs). 1. Genome evolution of diploid and amphidiploid species. *Theor. Appl. Genet.*, 75: 784–795.

Stebbins, G.L. (1950). Variation and Evolution in Higher Plants. Columbia Univ. Press, New York.

Sun, P.C. (1945). The evolution of taxonomic characters of cultivated *Brassica* with a key to species and varieties. I. The characters. *Bull. Torr. Bot. Club,* 73: 181–244.

Swamy, R.T. (1971). Combining ability in some varieties of brown sarson. *Agric. Res. J. Kerala,* 9: 63–67.

Thompson, K.F. (1983). Breeding Winter Oilseed Rapeseed *Brassica napus. Adv. Appl. Biol.*, 7: 1–104.

Thurling, N. (1974). Morphological determination of yield in rapeseed (*Brassica campestris* and *B. napus*). I. Growth the morphological characters. *Aust. J. Agric. Res.*, 25: 697–710.

Thurling, N. (1991). Application of the ideotype concept in breeding for higher yield in the oilseed *Brassicas. Field Crop Res.*, 26: 201–221.

Tiwari, L.P. and Singh, A.B. (1973). Diallel cross analysis of quantitative traits in Indian mustard. *Indian J. Agric Sci.*, 43: 1055–1059.

Tiwari, L.P. and Singh, A.B. (1975). Combining ability studies in Indian mustard. [*Brassica juncea* (L.) Czern. & Coss.]. *Indian J. Agric. Sci.*, 9: 171–176.

Toxopeus. H., and Oost, E.H. (1985). A cultivar classification of *Brassica rapa* L. *Cruciferae Newsletter,* 10: 6–7.

Tyagi, R.K. and Rangaswamy, N.S. (1993). Screening of pollen grains *vis–a–vis* whole plants of oilseed *Brassicas* for tolerance to salt. *Theor. Appl. Genet,,* 87: 343–346.

Vaughan, J.G., Hemingway, J.S. and Schofield, H.J. (1963). Contribution to a study of variations in *Brassica juncea* Czern. & Coss. *J. Linn. Soc. (Bot.),* 58: 435–447.

Vaughan, J.G., Waite, A., Boulter, D. and Waiters, S. (1966). Comparative studies of the seed proteins of *Brassica campestris, B. oleracea,* and *B. nigra. J. Exp. Bot.*, 17: 332–343.

Vaughan., J.G. and Gordon, E.I. (1973). A taxonomic study of *Brassica juncea* using the techniques of electrophoresis, gas liquid chromatography and serology. *Ann. Bot.,* 37: 167–184.

Vavilov, N.I. (1949). The origin, variation, immunity and breeding of cultivated plants. *Chron. Bot.,* 13: 1–364.

Verma, O.P., Singh, R.K., Singh, Karan, Singh, P.V. and Singh, K. (1992). Gene effects for six metric trait in Indian mustard *(Brassica juncea). Indian J. Agric. Sci.,* 62: 827–829.

Yadav, A.K., Singh, H. and Yadav, I.S. (1990). Geneticai analysis of harvest index, biological yield and seed yield in Indian mustard [*Brassica juncea* (L.) Czern & Coss.]. *J. Oilseeds Res.,* 7: 16–20.

Yadav, C.K. (1983). Studies on genetics of yield and its components in Indian mustard. *Thesis Abst., H.A.U.,* 9: 186–187.

Yadav, D.S. (1988). Genetics of basal branching, adaxial hairy leaves and clump flowering in mustard. *Crudferae Newsletter,* 13: 27.

Yadav, M.C. (1992). Genetics of seed yield and oil content in *Brassica juncea* (L.) Czern. & Coss. M. Se. Thesis, IARI, New Delhi.

Yadav, O.P., Yadava, T.P. and Kumar, P. (1992). Combining ability studies for seed yield, its component characters and oil content in Indian mustard [*Brassica juncea* (L.) Czern. & Coss.]. *J. Oilseeds Res.,* 9: 14–20.

Yadava, T. P. and Gupta, V.P. (1975). Heterosis and Genetic architecture for oil content in mustard. *Indian J. Genet.,* 35: 152–155.

Yadava, T. P., Singh, H., Gupta, V.P. and Rana, R.K. (1974). Heterosis and combining ability in raya for yield and its components. *Indian J. Genet.,* 34: 684–695.

Yadava, T.P., Gupta, V.P. and Singh, H. (1976). Inheritance of the days to flowering and maturity in mustard. *SABRAO J.,* 8: 81–83.

Yadava, T.P., Kumar, P. and Yadav, A.K. (1981). Genetic architecture for yield and its components traits in Indian mustard. *Indian J. Agric. Sci.,* 51: 374–378.

Yadava, T.P., Yadav, A.K. and Kumar, P. (1981). Genetic analysis for oil content in Indian mustard. *Indian J. Agric.* Sri., 51: 371–373.

# 12

# Sunflower

## 1. INTRODUCTION

Among the oilseed crops, sunflower (*Helianthus annuus* L.) occupies fourth position in area and production in the world after soybean, rapeseed- mustard and groundnut. World harvest of sunflower was 24.41 mt (average of 1994-96) from 20.38 mha (FAO Production Year book, 1996). World sunflower production has remained almost stable over the last decade. Argentina, Russian Federation, Ukraine, France and the USA are the top five countries in the world with respect to production (Table 1). Europe alone accounts for about 50 per cent of world area

**Table 1:** Area, production and productivity in important sunflower growing countries of the world (1996).

| *Country* | *Area ('000 ha)* | | *Production ('000 t)* | | *Seed yield (kg/ha)* | |
|---|---|---|---|---|---|---|
| Argentina | 3228 | (15.4)* | 5300 | (21.1) | 1960 | (163.7) |
| Russian Federation | 3943 | (18.8) | 3000 | (11.9) | 761 | (63.6) |
| India | 2200 | (10.5) | 1450 | (5.8) | 659 | (55.0) |
| Ukraine | 2021 | (9.6) | 2123 | (8.4) | 1050 | (87.7) |
| Spain | 1094 | (5.2) | 1200 | (4.8) | 1105 | (92.3) |
| USA | 1011 | (4.8) | 1627 | (6.5) | 1609 | (134.4) |
| Romania | 915 | (4.4) | 1090 | (4.3) | 1105 | (92.3) |
| France | 891 | (4.2) | 1997 | (7.9) | 2241 | (187.2) |
| China | 820 | (3.9) | 1360 | (5.4) | 1659 | (138.6) |
| S.Africa | 576 | (2.7) | 720 | (2.9) | 1250 | (104.4) |
| Turkey | 575 | (2.7) | 780 | (3.1) | 1357 | (113.4) |
| Bulgaria | 500 | (2.4) | 530 | (2.1) | 1060 | (88.5) |
| Italy | 225 | (1.1) | 515 | (2.0) | 2289 | (191.2) |
| Others | 2964 | (14.1) | 3409 | (13.6) | 1150 | (96.1) |
| World | 20963 | | 25101 | | 1197 | |

*Source*: FAO Production Year book, 1996 p. 111,
*Figures in parenthesis indicate per cent of world figure.

V.L. Chopra (Ed.): Breeding Field Crops I: Practices, Studium Press (LLC), USA.

and total production. Asia and Africa share about 21 and 6 per cent of the total sunflower area in the world respectively. India is among the top three countries in area after Argentine and Russian Federation. Notwithstanding spectacular spurt in area, the productivity is only 55 per cent of world average (1197 kg/ha).

In India, groundnut, rapeseed-mustard and soybean are major oilseed crops contributing 87 per cent to total oilseed production (22.01 mt). The total area under sunflower rose steadily from a mere 2.87 lakh ha in 1981-83 to 22.43 lakh ha in 1993-95 (Table 2). A substantial increase in area (164.31%) and production (124.19%) was observed in the triennium 1984-86. The per cent change in area declined in subsequent trienniums. A similar trend was observed for production also except for a slight recovery in the triennium 1990-92. However, the productivity ranged between 5 to 6 q/ha in the last two decades with exceptional decline during 1987-89 due to severe incidence of *Alternaria* blight. Decomposition Analysis indicated that in most of the trienniums, the increase in production was mainly contributed by increase in area rather than yield and their interaction effects. Nevertheless, during 1987-89 to 1990-92 triennium period, the yield contribution showed positive bearing on production.

**Table 2:** Triennium averages for area, production and yield of sunflower in India from 1981-83 to 1996-98.

| | *1981-83* | *1984-86* | *1987-89* | *1990-92* | *1993-95* | *1996-98* |
|---|---|---|---|---|---|---|
| Area | 287.8 | 760.7 | 1259.2 | 1646.3 | 2243.5 | 1919.6 |
| ('000 ha) | | (164.31)* | (65.53) | (30.74) | (36.27) | (-14.44) |
| Production | 151.7 | 340.1 | 475.1 | 899.5 | 1245.7 | 1147.9 |
| ('000 t) | | (124.19) | (39.69) | (89.33) | (38.49) | (-7.85) |
| Yield (kg/ha) | 539 | 444 | 377 | 543 | 561 | 596.0 |
| | | (-17.63) | (-15.09) | (44.03) | (3.31) | (6.24) |

*Source*: (1) DOR 1995. Oilseeds Situation in India. A statistical overview. Directorate of Oilseeds Research, Hyderabad. (2) Directorate of Oilseeds Development, Hyderabad.
* Figures in parenthesis indicate per cent change over previous triennium.

Karnataka, Maharashtra and Andhra Pradesh are the major producers of sunflower in India and together contribute 87 per cent in area and 70 per cent in production (Fig. 1). Other important sunflower growing states are Punjab, Haryana, Tamil Nadu and Uttar Pradesh. In Punjab and Haryana, sunflower cultivation started in the year 1989-90 with 20,000 and 8,000 ha respectively.

Over the years, Punjab and Haryana have established as a potential sunflower growing states with productivity more than 14 q/ha which is

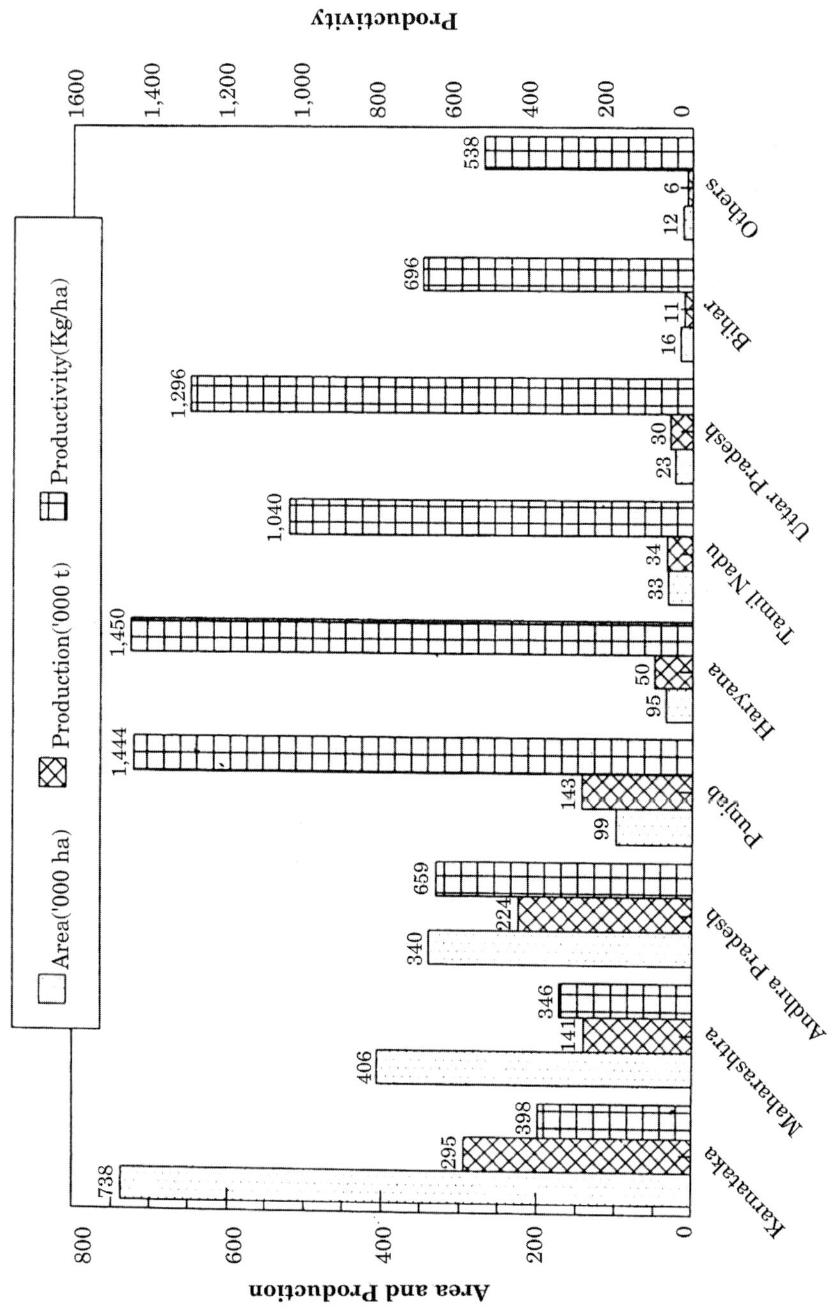


**Fig. 1:** Area, production and productivity in sunflower growing states of India (1997-98)

above world average and comparable to productivity levels in some European countries. The decline in total production and productivity in the country has been compensated to some extent by increased production in these two states.

Despite phenomenal growth rate in area expansion, the productivity of sunflower crop in India has remained low. Karnataka, in South India, is called the "Sunflower State" as it alone accounts for more than 43 per cent of the total sunflower area in the country. However, the productivity is only 4 q/ha. In general, productivity is low as sunflower moves from North India to South India. Rainfed cultivation, biotic and abiotic stresses and poor quality seed are some of the important factors responsible for low productivity. The decline in acreage and production during 1996-98, has been also due to the incidence of a new viral disease (necrosis) in Southern and Central peninsula comprising Karnataka, Andhra Pradesh, Maharashtra and Tamil Nadu. Of late, soybean has emerged as a remunerative crop because of higher productivity and as a consequence, a part of sunflower area was diverted to soybean planting in rainy season.

Sunflower is cultivated in three distinct seasons *viz.*; rainy (June-July), post rainy (September-October) and summer irrigated (December-January). However it is sown round the year in India. About 40 per cent of total sunflower area is planted in rainy season, the productivity of which is less than the crop planted in post rainy season. Presently, high yielding open pollinated varieties and hybrids identified for cultivation are gown irrespective of seasons resulting in erratic performance of the varieties. Photoperiod insensitivity in sunflower is a strength but seems to be a threat also as it favours outbreaks of diseases due to continuous cropping.

Wide variation exists in flowering and maturity periods of sunflower across environments. On an average, crop matures in about 95 days in the south to about 120 days in the north. High productivity in north can be attributed to longer duration of the crop and high applied inputs. Sunflower cultivation and hybrid seed production has gained new dimension after the launch of New Seed Policy in 1988. It resulted in the import of exotic hybrids and germplasm lines, which subsequently helped to diversify genetic base of sunflower cultivars grown in India. In coming years, major emphasis is to be placed on increasing productivity and yield stability across environments. This necessitates development of high seed yield cultivars with inbuilt resistance to biotic and abiotic stresses. Besides, efforts are needed to promote value added agricultural products of sunflower.

## 2. ORIGIN

Cultivated sunflower (*Helianthus annuus* L.) derives its generic name *Helianthus* from the Greek word *helios* meaning sun and *anthos* meaning flower. *Helianthus* is placed in the tribe Heliantheae of the family Asteraceae. The genus *Helianthus* comprises 49 species and 19 sub species with 12 annual and 37 perennial species (Heiser *et al.,* 1969; Schilling and Heiser, 1981). All species are native to North America and are believed to have originated in the Southwest to Central United States. This hypothesis is supported by archaeological evidence (Heiser, 1951). The diverse species are adapted to variable habitats and possess variability for most economic and agronomic characteristics which include insect and disease resistance and seed quality traits (Thompson *et al.,* 1981; Rogers *et al.,* 1982). The genus has a basic chromosome number of x = 17 and comprises of diploid (2n=34), tetraploid (2n=68) and hexaploid (2n=102) species. Two domesticated species, *H. annuus* (diploid) and *H.tuberosus* (hexaploid) are cultivated, the former as an edible oil crop and the latter as a food and fodder. *H. annuus,* one of the most variable and widespread species, includes wild, weedy and cultivated forms. Wild *Helianthus* species constitute the basic genetic stock from which the cultivated sunflower originated (Seiler, 1992) The wild species have contributed specific characteristics for sunflower improvement (Thompson *et al.,* 1981; Seiler, 1988). Sunflower was introduced into Europe during the $16^{th}$ century through Spain, gradually spreading to other parts of Europe including erstwhile USSR where it was transformed as an edible oilseed crop. Although the USA is credited as centre of origin of sunflower, it attracted attention only when high oil Russian cultivars were reintroduced in the 1960s.

### 2.1. Morphology and Floral Biology

The cultivated sunflower for oil purpose is an annual having a single unbranched stem terminating in a large capitulum. It exhibits wide range of variation for morphological characteristics. Plant height varies from 50 to over 500 cm with stem diameter ranging from 1 to 10 cm. Plant height depends on number and length of internodes. Sparse hairs are seen all along the stem. The elongation of stem ceases after ray floret opening in the inflorescence. Wild species and majority of the restorer lines are branching types, each branch originating from the leaf axil and terminating with a small-sized inflorescence. Hockett and Knowles (1970) recognised four different branching forms. The plant has a strong central root called tap-root which penetrates soil to a depth of 150 to 300 cm. The lateral roots spread widely from 60 to 150 cm. In cultivated sunflower, generally 20 to 25 leaves are borne on the stem.

Leaves are produced in opposite-alternate pairs and exhibit wide differences for colour, size, shape, margin, surface, hairiness, apex and petiole length.

The inflorescence is a capitulum or head which varies in size and shape. Most of the cultivated varieties in India show a range of 15 to 25 cm for head diameter. The shape of head may be either concave, convex or flat attached to main stem at varying angles. Involucral bracts (phyllaries) which vary in size and shape surround the head. Sunflower head consists of two types of flowers. The outer flowers, which are usually yellow, are ray florets. These flowers are sterile but do attract insect pollinators. The inner disc florets, which are hermaphrodite and fertile, are arranged in arcs radiating from the centre of the head.

Each disc floret consists of inferior ovary, two pappus scales (modified sepals) and a tubular corolla formed by the fusion of five petals, except at the tip. Five anthers are united to form a tube with separate filaments attached to the base of corolla tube. Inside the anther tube is the style, terminating in a divided stigma. When the flower is fully developed, the style is elongated and the bifid stigma curls outward.

The flowering process begins with unfloding of outer ray florets. The outer whorl of disc flowers open first proceeding gradually towards the centre of the head. In general, 2 to 4 whorls open daily and complete flowering occurs within a head in 5-8 days. The flowering period will be longer if heads are large or weather is cool and cloudy. Anthesis takes place in the morning hours between 06.00-08.00 hrs on warm sunny days. Anthesis is delayed if weather is cool, cloudy or wet. The sunflower is protandrous. Pollen is dehisced within the anther tube. As the style elongates and pushes up through the anther tube, the pollen is mechanically forced out. The style continues to elongate untile the stigmas emerge from the anther tube and the lobes separate, exposing their pollen receptive surfaces. Pollination and fertilization occurs when the spiny viable pollen is transferred to stigmatic surface. Putt (1940) observed limited role of wind in pollen transfer. Cross pollination is favoured by insects, in particular, honey bees.

Sunflower seed (achene) comprise pericarp (seed coat or hull) derived from the ovary wall and the kernel which is mostly embryo. The pericarp comprises between 20 per cent (oil types) and 40 per cent (confectionery types) of seed weight. Seed exhibits a wide range of variation for seed weight, seed coat colour and size (Fig. 2). Total seed yield in a head is the product of total number of seeds and seed weight.

**Fig. 2 :** Variation in sunflower seed size and colour.

## 3. GERMPLASM RESOURCES

Varietal improvement in sunflower though successful all these years, is based on narrow genetic base (Skoric, 1992; Korell *et al.,* 1996a). Increased breeding efforts are required to broaden the genetic variability of cultivated sunflower. Many wild species of *Helianthus* have been identified as sources of resistence to pathogens causing major diseases of cultivated sunflower (Table 3). Both intra and interspecific cross derivatives were used to incorporate disease resistant genes into domestic cultivars. The wild species also serve as a source of cytoplasmic male sterility (Leclercq, 1969) and fertility restoration genes (Kinman, 1970). Wild sunflower species exhibit a wide range of variation for oil content and fatty acid composition (Fick *et al.,* 1976; Fernandez-Martinez and Knowles, 1976; Dorell and Whelan, 1978; Thompson *et al.,* 1978, 1981; Seiler 1982, 1983, 1984, 1985a,b, 1994). *H. niveus, H. salicifolius, H. petiolaris H. porteri, H. exilis, H. debilis* have been identified as potential sources for high oil content and for alteration of fatty acid composition. H. *paradoxus, H. debilis* and *H. annuus*, native to salty desert areas, possess genes for salt tolerance (Chandler and Jan, 1984). *H. argophyllus* is a well established source of tolerance to drought (Skoric, 1992, Baldini *et al.,* 1993). Recently comprehensive literature on interspecific hybridization has been compiled and discussed by Jan (1997). Based on the information generated hitherto, it is possible to form primary gene pool using potential wild species for specific objectives in breeding programmes. Secondary gene pool populations involving incompatible wild species have to be attempted using the embryo culture system (Chandler and Beard, 1983; Espinasse *el al.*, 1991; Krauter *et al.*, 1991). The utility of wild species of *Helianthus* as a reservoir of genes for disease and insect resistance was recognised early by Pustovoit *et al.* (1976). Exploration of germplasm has resulted in collection and distribution of wild species at the National Plant Germplasm System, Plant Introduction at Ames, lowa (Seiler and Rieseberg, 1997).

**Table 3:** Potential species of Helianthus used in disease resistance breeding

| ***Alternaria*** | ***Rust*** | ***Downy mildew*** | ***Sclerotinia wilt*** |
|---|---|---|---|
| H. *praecox* (A)* | *H. praecox* ssp *hirtus* (A) | *H. annuus* (A) | *H. giganteus* (P) |
| *H. debilis* (A) | *H. agrophyllus* (A) | *H. deserticola* (A) | *H. laevigatus* (P) |
| *H. tuberosus* (P)* | *H. annuus* (A) | *H. praecox* ssp *hirtus* (A) | *H. mollis* (P) |
| *H. hirsutus* (P) | *H. hirsutus* (P) | *H. argophyllus* (A) | *H. resinosus* (P) |
| *H. mollis* (P) | *H. petiolaris* (P) | *H. paradoxus* (A) | *H. salicifolius* (P) |
| *H. decapetalus* (P) | *H. tuberosus* (P) | *H. grosseserratus* (P) | |
| *H. pauciflorus* (P) | | *H. tuberosus* (P) | |
| | | *H. maximiliani* (P) | |
| | | *H. nuttallii* (P) | |
| | | *H. pauciflorus* (P) | |
| | ***References*** | | |
| Morris *et al.*, 1983; | Putt and Sackston 1963; | Pustovoit *et al.*, 1976; | Thompson *et al.*, 1978; |
| Lipps and Herr (1986); | Thompson *et al.*, 1978; | Miller and Gulya, 1988 | Serieys, 1987; |
| Block (1992); | Quresh *et al.*, 1989; | Seiler, 1991a,b; | Skoric, 1987; |
| Sujata *et al.*, 1997 | Seiler, 1992; | Fick *et al.*, 1974; | |
| | Mc Carter, 1993; | Thompson et *al.*, 1978; | Pustovoit and Gubin, |
| | Jan, 1997. | Miller and Gulya, 1991 | 1974. |

(A)*-Annual & (P)* - Perennial

In India, the National Bureau of Plant Genetic Resources (NBPGR), New Delhi, supports the national crop improvement programme by augmenting germplasm sources of cultivated and wild species through introduction and exploration. A total of 657 accessions of sunflower germplasm lines, mostly introductions, are maintained at the Project Coordinating Unit (Sunflower), Bangalore (Virupakshappa and Sindagi, 1988). Recently, at the Directorate of Oilseeds Research, Hyderabad, a total of 22 wild species (diploid, tetraploid and hexaploid groups) are maintained in the species garden (Sujata and Prabhakaran, 1997). However, the potential of wild species has not been fully exploited to benefit the ongoing sunflower crop improvement programmes in India.

## 4. GENETICS

### 4.1. Qualitative Characters

Miller and Fick (1997) have recently summarised results of genetic analysis relating to stem, leaf and petiole characteristics in sunflower. A few studies on floral (ray floret colour and shape) and morphological variations of leaf (leaf tip, mid-rib colour, margin and petiole pigmentation) indicated that most of these qualitative characters are governed by 1 to 2 pairs of genes (Leclercq, 1968; Fick, 1976; Deokar and Patil, 1975; Luckiewicz, 1975; Skaloud and Kovacik, 1974; Hiremath and Giriraj, 1984). Stigma colour was found to be controlled by 4 pairs of alleles (Joshi *et al.,* 1994) in contrast to a single allele reported earlier by Luckiewicz (1975). A pleiotropic gene, designated as $Ptl_a$, acts as a complementary gene for the expression of pigmentation in leaf and floral parts (Joshi *et al.,* 1994). Inheritance of chlorophyll deficient variants has been studied by several workers (Joshi and Giriraj, 1995; Fambrini and Pugliesi, 1996; Rodriguez *et al.,* 1998) and reported a recessive gene control for the character.

### 4.2. Genetic Male Sterility

Genetic male sterility in sunflower was first identified by Kuptsov in the year 1934 (Fick, 1978). Putt and Heiser (1966) observed variation in the degree of male sterility. The studies of Vranceanu (1970), Burlov (1974) and Jambhulkar (1994) support the view that genetic male sterility involves a recessive gene. Vranceanu and Stoenescu (1972) observed that male sterility gene was linked to purple pigmentation at the seedling stage. Spirova (1978), reported independent segregation of male sterility and anthocyanin colour.

### 4.3. Quantitative Characters

The nature of gene action for important economic characters has been briefly summarised in Table 4. In general, these results indicate predominance of non-additive gene action for seed yield, test weight, plant height, head diameter, per cent seed filling and stem diameter. More reports are in favour of additive gene action for days to flowering, oil content and hull content. A few reports suggest both additive, non-additive and dominance for days to flowering, test weight, plant height, oil content and seed yield. Dominant and epistatic effects were suggested for oil content (Russell, 1953; Gupta and Khanna, 1982). The conflicting results on the inheritance of quantitive characters arise due to differences in the base material, size of the population, genotype × environment interactions and mating design adopted for the study. Hence, the results can not be generalised for the entire variability present in the crop.

**Table 4:** Nature of gene action for various characters in sunflower

| *Character* | *Gene action* | *References* |
|---|---|---|
| | Additive | Dua and Yadava, 1985; Manjunath and Goud, 1983; Kadkol *et al.,* 1984; Berretta and Miller, 1985; Giriraj *et al.,* 1987. |
| Days to flowering | Additive and Non-additive | Putt, 1966; Gangappa *et al.,* 1997 |
| | Non additive | Setty and Singh, 1977; Manjunath, 1978; Rao *et al.,* 1992; Kandhola *et al.,* 1995. |
| | Additive | Rao and Singh, 1977; Setty and Singh, 1977; Sheriff and Appadurai, 1985; Miller and Hammond, 1991. |
| Plant height | Additive and Non-additive | Berretta and Miller, 1985; Sheriff *et al.,* 1985; Gangappa *et al.,* 1997. |
| | Non additive | Dua and Yadava, 1983; Pathak *et al.,* 1985; Sheriff *et al.,* 1985; Giriraj *et al.,* 1987; Naik *et al.,* 1988; Toms and Pooni, 1995. |
| Head diameter | Additive | Rao and Singh, 1977; Shinde *et al.,* 1983. |
| | Non-additive | Manjunath, 1978; Dua and Yadava, 1983; Kadkol *et al.,* 1984; Sudhakar *et al.,* 1984; Rao *et al.,* 1992; Javed and Aslam, 1995. |
| Leaf area | Additive | Sudhakar *et al.,* 1984; Sheriff and Appadurai, 1985. |
| | Non-additive | Berretta and Miller, 1985; Sheriff *et al.,* 1985 |
| | Additive | Srivastava and Mishra, 1976; Sindagi *et al.,* 1979; Shinde *et al.,* 1983; Toms and Pooni, 1995. |
| Seed yield | Additive and Non-additive | Gupta and Khanna (1982). |
| | Non-additive | Kovacik and Skaloud, 1972; Kadkol *et al.,* 1984; Alba *et al.,* 1985; Pathak *et al.,* 1985; Giriraj *et al.,*1987; Marinkovic, 1993. |
| Test weight | Additive | Putt, 1966; Rao and Singh, 1977; Naik *et al.,* 1988. |
| | Non-additive | Dua and Yadava, 1983; Kadkol *et al.,* 1984; Sudhakar *et al.,* 1984; Pathak *et al.,* 1985; Giriraj *et al.,* 1987; Javed and Aslam, 1995. |
| Oil content | Additive | Fick, 1975; Sindagi *et al.,* 1979; Leon *et al.,* 1995. |
| | Additive and Non-additive | Putt, 1966, Gupta and Khanna, 1982. |
| | Non-additive | Tuberosa *et al.,* 1982; Dua and Yadava, 1983; Pathak *et al.,* 1985; Giriraj *et al.,* 1987; Naik *et al.,* 1988. |

## 4.4. Heritability

The magnitude of heritable variation is of utmost importance since it has relevance to selection response. Most of the studies on heritability in sunflower are based on broad-sense heritability estimates. Stem diameter is reported to be moderate (Reddy and Reddy, 1979) to highly hertiable (Pathak, 1974; Srivastava and Mishra, 1976). High heritability has been reported for test weight (Singh *et al.,* 1977; Kshirsagar *et al.,* 1995). Heritability for oil content has been studied by several workers but the results reported differ considerably. Most of the reports indicate that oil content is a highly heritable character (Varshney and Singh, 1977; Fick, 1975). Marinkovic (1993), however, reported low heritability for this character. Venkateswaralu *et al.* (1980) reported high heritability for leaf number and low heritability for leaf area index.

## 4.5. Character Association

Grafius (1964) opined that it would be meaningful if the structure of yield is probed through its component characters. Studies on correlation help to identify the characters associated with yield. A brief review on the association of characters in sunflower with seed yield is presented in Table 5. Seed yield has been shown to be apparently correlated with stem girth, head diameter, plant height, test weight, oil content, days to maturity and number of leaves. Burns (1970) opined that yield estimates based on head size would be more accurate than actual seed weight. However, Khanna (1972) and Jain *et al.*(1978) reported negative association between number of filled seeds and head diameter. It is the density of filled seeds within the head which determines the final seed yield in sunflower. Oil content was negatively correlated with hull per centage and protein content (Dedio, 1982; Mandai and Singh, 1993) and positively correlated with test weight (Fick *et al.,* 1974). Strong positive correlation between oil content and kernel per cent has been found (Putt, 1943; Russell, 1953). Significant correlation between $F_0$ (hybrid) and $F_1$ generation seeds for seed characteristics suggested the possibility of prior prediction of $F_1$ performance based upon $F_0$ values (Kini and Seetharam, 1994).

While studying path coefficient analysis among the characters, Shabana (1974), Anand and Chandra (1979), Giriraj *et al.* (1979), Pathak *et al.* (1983), Dhaduk *et al.* (1985), Mishra *et al.* (1985), Singh and Labana (1990) and Punia and Gill (1994) highlighted the direct influence of plant height, head diameter, total number of filled seeds and test weight on seed yield in sunflower. Laxmanrao *et al.* (1985) reported that harvest index had maximum direct effect on seed yield through kernel oil content and husk content.

**Table 5:** Association of seed yield with its component characters in sunflower

| ***Seed yield with*** | ***Positive association*** | ***Negative association*** |
|---|---|---|
| Head diameter | Putt, 1943; Russell, 1953; Burns, 1970; Skoric, 1974; Singh *et al.*, 1972; Varshney and Singh *et al.*, 1977, Alba and Greco, 1979; Giriraj *et al.,* 1979; Ghanavati and Nahavandi, 1981; Pathak and Dixit, 1984; Rao, 1987; Tanimu and Ado, 1988; Vanishree *et al.,* 1988; Niranjanmurthy and Shambulingappa, 1989; Punia and Gill, 1994; | Khanna, 1972; Alba *et al.,* 1979 |
| Plant height | Putt, 1943; Schuster, 1964; Shabana, 1974; Pathak, 1974; Anand and Chandra, 1979; Giriraj *et al.,* 1979, Chaudhary and Anand, 1985; 1993. | Lakshmanaiah, 1980 |
| Days to maturity | Putt, 1943; Russell, 1953; Kovacik and Skaloud,1972; Varshney and Singh, 1977; Tanimu and Ado, 1988; Singh and Labana, 1990. | – |
| Test weight | Giriraj *et al.,* 1979; Vanishree *et al.,* 1988; Chaudhary and Anand, 1993; Punia and Gill, 1994. | – |
| Number of seeds | Shabana, 1974; Pathak *et al.,* 1983. | – |
| Leaf area | Shabana, 1974; Giriraj *et al.,* 1987. | – |
| Stem diameter | Putt, 1943; Russell, 1953; Pathak, 1974 | Khanna, 1972 |
| Total dry matter | Pathak, 1974; Giriraj *et al.,* 1987. | – |
| Havest index | Giriraj *et al.,* 1987. | |
| Oil content | Schuster, 1964; Ghanavathi and Nahavandi, 1981. | Shabana, 1974; Zali *et al.,* 1977 |

## 5. INBREEDING AND HETEROSIS

### 5.1. Inbreeding

The value of inbreeding in sunflower was recognized as early as 1920s to improve uniformity and derive different inbred lines (Cardon, 1922; Hamilton 1926). Putt (1941) indicated that self-fertility was affected by inbreeding. Unrau and White (1944) noticed 35 per cent decline in seed yield after one generation of selfing in an open pollinated variety.

Kovacik and Skaloud (1980) suggested sib-crossing to alleviate the ill effects of inbreeding process. Schuster (1970a, 1970b, 1980) and Giriraj *et al.* (1985a) observed most striking inbreeding depression for seed yield, plant height, and head diameter. Inbreeding depression was of lower magnitude for oil content and test weight (Giriraj *et al.,* 1986).

### 5.2. Heterosis

The studies on heterosis in sunflower prior to 1970 relate to breeding material involving inter-line, inter-varietal and top cross hybrids. The results of these studies indicated superior performance of hybrids over parental lines for seed yield, oil content, head diameter and plant height (Unrau and White, 1944; Schuster, 1964; Putt, 1966). The discovery of cytoplasmic male sterility in sunflower (Leclereq, 1969) and subsequent identification of fertility restoration (Enns *et al.,* 1970; Kinman, 1970; Vranceanu and Stoenescu, 1970; Leclereq, 1971) prompted a large number of workers to measure magnitude of heterosis in hybrid combinations involving cytoplasmic male sterile lines and fertility restorer lines. Such studies in many sunflower growing countries, subsequently helped to identify promising hybrids for large scale cultivation. The literature on heterosis in sunflower after 1970 is extensive. A very high degree of heterosis has been observed for seed yield, head diameter, test weight and plant height (Seetharam *et al.,* 1977; Sheriff *et al.,* 1985; Madrap and Makne, 1993). Heterosis for seed yield has been attributed to higher magnitude of heterotic effect for number of filled seeds, leaf area, head diameter and test weight (Giriraj *et al.,* 1986). Moderate to high heterotic effect has been reported for oil content (Fick and Zimmer, 1974; Setharam *et al.,* 1977; Gangappa *et al.,* 1997) while Kovacik and Skaloud (1978) and Giriraj *et al.* (1986) did not observe appreciable heterosis for this character. Negative heterosis for days to flowering implied early flowering over parental lines (Chaudhary and Anand, 1984; Giriraj *et al.,* 1986). Gill and Punia (1996) compared heterotic effect in single, three-way and double cross sunflower hybrids. The results showed that single-cross hybrids were more suitable for exploiting heterosis for seed yield and component characters over three-way and double-cross hybrids. Joshi *et al.* (1997) state that magnitude of heterosis was not related to genetic divergence of parents involved in the cross combination.

## 6. FATTY ACID COMPOSITION IN SUNFLOWER OIL

The oil of sunflower seed contains approximately 10 per cent saturated, mostly palmitic and stearic, and 90 per cent unsaturated (mostly oleic and linoleic) fatty acids (Lakshminarayana *et al.,* 1984). The proportion of oleic and linoleic acids is influenced by environment, mostly temperature. Accumulation of linoleic acid is favoured in rainy season (Lakshminarayana *et al.,* 1984). Inverse relationship between oleic and linoleic acid has been established (Kinman and Earle, 1964; Canvin, 1965; Baldini *et al.,* 1991, Badwal *et al.,* 1993; Rather *et al.,* 1998). Higher oleic is reported to have negative association with germination and self-compatibility and positive association with earliness. (Fernandez-Martinez *et al.,* 1993). Such studies are required in tropical countries to assess relationship of oleic acid with self compatibility and earliness.

A high oleic mutant has been identified by Soldatov (1976) in VNIIMK-8931 following chemical mutagenesis (0.5 per cent dimethyl sulfonate). After inter-crossing high oleic progenies from the original mutant plant, a new cultivar *viz.*; Pervenets was developed with 75 per cent oleic acid. Soon after, studies on the inheritance of oleic acid have been carried out in lines derived from Pervenets (Fick, 1984; Urie, 1985; Miller *et al.,* 1987; Fernandez-Martinez *et al.,* 1989). These studies suggested involvement of one or more major dominant OL genes in conjunction with modifier genes in the control of the character.

## 7. CHLOROGENIC ACID AND TOCOPHEROL COMPOSITION IN SUNFLOWER SEED

Chlorogenic acid (CA) constitutes more than 70 per cent of the total phenolics in sunflower seeds. It darkens upon oxidation to a green or brown colour and adversely affects meal quality. Processing methods have been developed to inactivate or extract CA. However, it is desirable to screen genotypes with reduced levels of CA. Dorrell (1976) studied variation in CA content in three populations of sunflower. Seed had overall mean of 2.8 per cent CA against 2.1 per cent mean value of wild sunflower lines. Significant correlation existed between CA and oil content.

Tocopherols (Vitamin E) are the powerful natural fat-soluble antioxidants, which impart stability during storage and use. They exist in four forms *viz.*, alpha, beta, gamma and delta of which alpha-form account for 96 per cent of the tocopherol-complex with low antioxidant properties. For increasing "shelf-life", higher content of gamma form of tocopherol is desirable. Screening of large number of germplasm lines led to the identification of a high gamma-tocopherol (95 per cent) sunflower line. Tocopherol composition in sunflower seeds is reported to be controlled by two non-allelic genes designated as tph 1 and tph 2 (Demurin, 1993).

## 8. SELF-INCOMPATIBILITY AND SEED-FILLING

Cross pollination in sunflower is primarily attributed to self-incompatibility mechanism operating in the crop. Miller and Fick (1997) state that the degree of self incompatibility and self-fertility depends on three factors *viz.*; genetic control, environment and morphology of floral structures. Self incompatibility was first reported in sunflower by Habura (1957) and later confirmed by Luciano *et al.* (1965) and Asthana (1973). The genetic and physiological nature of self-incompatibility in sunflower is not fully understood. The self-incompatibility is sporophytic in nature and determined by two pairs of dominant alleles (S), one of them controlling the pollen traits and the other pistil characteristics (Habura, 1957; Ivanov, 1975). The genetic control of self-incompatibility is complex and highly influenced by the environment (Vranceanu *et al.,* 1978).

Seed set or seed filling in sunflower is also a complex phenomenon and different workers ascribed it to genotype, nutrition, self or cross incompatibility, pollination, moisture stress, translocation of photosynthates, temperature, relative humidity location or other environmental effects (Khanna, 1972; Udayakumar *et al.,* 1976; Vranceanu *et al.,* 1978; Chaudhary and Anand, 1981; Roath and Miller, 1982; Seetharam, 1982; Shivaraju *et al.,* 1987). Seed filling problem assumes serious dimension in monsoon season if the peak flowering phase coincides with rains resulting in pollen wash out or low pollinator activity (George and Shein, 1980; Swamygowda and Giriraj, 1989). Under such situations, self-fertile populations or hybrids assume great importance (Koath and Miller, 1982). High self-fertile inbreds in hybrid combinations produce high self-fertile hybrids (Fick and Zimmer, 1976; Skaloud and Kovacik, 1994).

## 9. CYTOPLASMIC MALE STERILITY AND FERTILITY RESTORATION

Cytoplasmic male sterility was first discovered by Leclercq (1969) in a cross of *H. petiolaris* × *H. annuus* (variety Armaviriskiy 9345) which has been subsequently coded as PET 1 cytoplasm. Globally this cytoplasmic source is used for commercial hybrid seed production. Many new sources of cytosteriles have been obtained by crossing wild species (Whelan, 1980; 1981; Heiser, 1982; Vranceanu *et al.,* 1986; Serieys and Vincourt, 1987; Miller and Wolf, 1991). A total of 41 additional new cytoplasmic male sterility sources other than PET 1 cytoplasm have been compiled by Miller and Fick (1997). Newly developed molecular techniques employed for differentiating PET 1 cytoplasm and cytoplasmic sources derived from interspecific crosses have been critically examined by Korell *et al.* (1996b).

Kinman (1990) identified fertility-restoring gene for Leclercq's PET 1 cytoplasm. Subsequently, Enns *et al.* (1970), Leclercq, (1971); Fick *et al.* (1974); Vranceanu and Stoenescu (1978) reported genes for fertility restoration in wild species. The frequency of restorer genes has been found to be much higher in the annual species than in the perennial species (Seiler, 1992). Kinman (1970) reported a single dominant gene, $Rf_1$ for fertility restoration. Later reports indicated involvement of two independent complementary genes for fertility restoration (Fick and Zimmer, 1974; Dominguez Gimenez and Fick, 1975; Reddy and Thammiraju, 1977; Miller, 1996).

Stability of two new sources of cytoplasm over environments has been reported (Virupakshappa *et al.,* 1991; Rajanna *et al.,* 1998). Increased breeding efforts are required to identify restorers with desirable agronomic characters to these new cytoplasm sources. The newly developed cytosteriles have not been successfully used in the production of hybrid seeds for commercial cultivation.

## 10. SUNFLOWER IMPROVEMENT

Sunflower has a long history of development. The presently cultivated sunflower has passed through three distinct periods of improvement. The early period of 1900-1940 has been associated with Academician Pustovoit and his group in erstwhile USSR who transformed branching wild species of sunflower into mono-stem and recognized its potentiality as a source of edible oil. By 1940, cultivars with 33 per cent oil content were available for cultivation. The second phase of sunflower development (1940-1960) was devoted to basic studies on floral biology, association of characters, disease resistance, self incompatibility, inbreeding and heterosis. These studies were mostly carried out in North American and European countries.

Significant developments in sunflower improvement took place in third phase after 1960. This era witnessed identification of stable cytoplasmic source in France and fertility restoring source in the USA. Commercial cultivation of hybrid cultivars became a reality in early seventies throughtout the world. Besides, during this period, major emphasis was laid on disease resistance breeding, diversification of cytoplasmic sterilty and fertility restoration sources, manipulation of fatty acid composition, conservation, characterization and exploitation of wild species for desirable agronomic attributes. The history of sunflower development in the current millennium, in brief, relates to sunflower improvement for both seed yield and oil content coupled with inbuilt tolerance to pathogens of major diseases and also spread of the crop to all the continents.

## 11. BREEDING METHODS

Sunflower belongs to cross-pollinated group of crop plants. Pollination occurs primarily by insects. The typical flower morphology is amenable to both population breeding and heterosis breeding.

### 11.1. Population Breeding

***Mass selection*:** In this method, desirable plants in a population under open pollination are selected based on phenotypic characters. Selected plants are harvested and bulked to raise next generation either as an elite culture or as a source population. A good number of open pollinated varieties were developed in the past by mass selection in the erstwhile Soviet Union. Mass selection is of particular value in eliminating plants with undesirable characteristics and maintaining the varietal population.

### 11.2. Pustovoit's Method of Reserves

Mass selection as a method of breeding for developing a variety had little impact until Pustovoit developed an effective and successful method for improving sunflower cultivars during 1920s. The method popularly known as varietal renovation or Pustovoit's method of reserves is a form of recurrent selection based on selection of individual plants with desirable attributes, progeny evaluation and subsequent cross pollination in the best progenies. The resultant product of this method may be related to intra-varietal hybrid population which exploits additive genetic variance for economie characters. In India, Pustovoit's method of breeding has been successfully adopted in commercially grown open pollinated varieties. The original method has been slightly modified to suit local condition in that the second year progeny testing for diseases is not followed (Fig. 3). The method comprises the following steps.

1. A total of 5,000 to 8,000 individual plants are selected in the base population raised under isolation. Selection is based on uniform plant height, maturity, size and shape of head.
2. Selected plants are evaluated for seed yield, oil content, test weight and hull content. On the basis of these analyses 20 to 25 per cent of the best plants are advanced for progeny testing. A single row of selected progenies is raised and for every 10 to 20 progenies a check is included which is the best cultivar most similar to the progenies being evaluated. After harvest of progeny trial, laboratory evaluation is done again for seed yield, oil content and

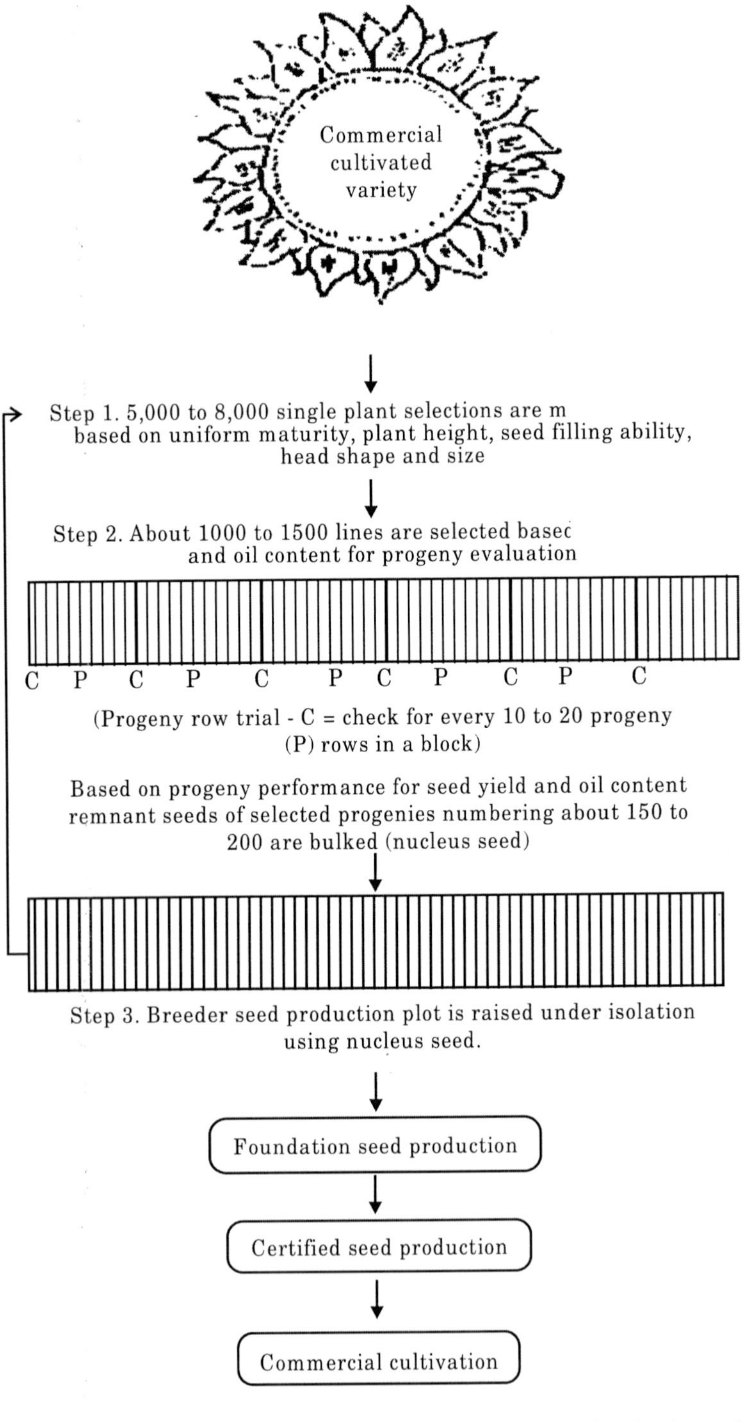


**Fig. 3:** Pustovoit scheme of varietal renovation and seed production in sunflower as followed in India

other agronomic attributes. Finally, 150 to 200 progenies showing superiority over check are selected.

3. The remnant (reserve) seeds of selected progenies from the original plants are identified and bulked. Part of this seed is grown for repeating cyclic selection as detailed above and the other part is channeled into seed production chain (breeder-foundation-certified seed production).

In the Soviet Union, Pustovoit's breeding method gave spectacular results in increasing oil content. The mean oil content of 33 per cent in 1940 was increased to over 50 per cent in 1973. Besides, the method has been useful in developing cultivars with early maturity and resistance to diseases (Gundaev, 1971). Giriraj *et al.* (1985b) assessed the response to selection for oil content in EC 68415 (Armaviriski-3497) by following Pustovoit's method of reserves. At the end of fifth cyclic selection, the mean seed oil content was increased to 46.9 per cent from 41.4 per cent in the base population. In India, varietal renovation initiated in commercially grown varieties based on Pustovoit's scheme was not only helpful in stabilising seed yield and oil content across locations but it also ensured quality seed supply for planting. This had great impact in sustaining sunflower cultivation in eighties.

## 11.3. Heterosis Breeding

As early as 1940, Eric D. Putt in Canada carried out studies on exploitation of heterosis in sunflower taking advantage of natural outcrossing which was up to 78 per cent in some inbred lines. In some European countries attempts were made to develop a hybrid system based on the self-incompatibility of lines and genetic male sterility. However, these methods failed to realise full yield potential of hybrids because of higher proportion of selfs in hybrid seed.

A landmark in production of hybrid seeds based on cytoplasmic-restorer system (Leclercq, 1969; Kinman, 1970) resulted in wide spread cultivation of hybrid cultivars in mid seventies. Since then, major emphasis has been laid on heterosis breeding. Hybrid cultivars have distinct advantages over open pollinated varieties. These advantages include production stability, response to high-input, high self fertility, uniformity in growth and maturity (Seetharam, 1982).

Success in heterosis breeding is dependent on the choice of inbred lines with desirable attributes for producing superior crosses. Procedures adopted for the development of inbreds, cytoplasmic male sterile lines, and fertility restorer lines are briefly presented in the following paragraphs.

***Development of inbred lines***: The base material used for developing inbred lines include open pollinated varieties, inter-varietal hybrids, hybrids based on inbred lines, interspecific hybrids and different gene pools (Skoric, 1992). Most of the inbred lines have been derived from open pollinated varieties. The plants with desirable characteristics are covered with cloth bag soon after unfolding of one or two ray floret in the capitulum. Because of low self-fertility, it is some times necessary to assist pollination by gently rubbing the covered cloth bag against the capitulum in order to obtain sufficient number crops of seeds. The selfed seeds are sown next season and the process of selfing the best plants is continued for five to six generations. Alternate self-and-sib-pollination was suggested to maintain inbred lines (Vranceanu *et al.,* 1974). Inbred lines are tested for combining ability, generally after reaching the desired level of uniformity. Chemical induction of male sterility by gibberellic acid (GA) has been found to be effective to produce crossed seeds for combining ability test (Piquemal, 1970; Seetharam and Kusuma Kumari, 1975). The ill effects of GA treated plants include stem elongation, incomplete male sterility, reduced female fertility and low seed set.

***Development of cytoplasmic male sterile lines***: It is necessary to have a stable cytoplasmic male sterile line as donor parent to convert inbreds into cytoplasmic male sterile lines. An inbred line with desirable attributes is crossed with the donor. In the next generation, the sterile $F_1$ is crossed with the inbred line to produce the first backcross generation. After six generations of backcrossing, the inbred line is converted to the cytoplasmic male sterile form. The original inbred line serves as the maintainer (B line) for the newly developed cytoplasmic sterile line.

***Development of fertility restorer line***: Incorporation of fertility restorer genes into an inbred line involves crossing of the inbred line to a restorer line of proven performance and test crossing with a cytoplasmic male sterile line to as certain which plants possess fertility restorer genes in subsequent generations. Restorer lines can also be derived by selfing cytoplasmic-based male fertile hybrids and isolating fertile lines carrying restorer genes in subsequent generations (Fick and Swallers, 1972). Combining ability of the newly derived cytoplasmic and restorer lines is assessed either by top cross test, line x tester analysis or diallel analysis. Lines with good combining ability are used to produce single cross hybrids for evaluation across locations to identify high yielding hybrids.

In recent years, emphasis is laid on developing three-way hybrids because of their genetic heterogeneity and wider adaptability. Three-way hybrids were more stable than single-cross hybrids in the studies reported by Fick and Zimmer (1976), Giriraj *et al.* (1988), Schuster and

Friedt (1988). However, while synthesising a three-way hybrid, the additional line involved in the combination should possess desirable characteristics which are lacking in parental lines of single-cross hybrids.

## 12. BREEDING FOR DISEASE RESISTANCE

Sunflower is plagued by more than 30 diseases. Of these, in India, only three diseases are of economic importance. These include *Alternaria* leaf spot/blight, rust and downy mildew. Disease severity has increased many folds in the last decade due to intensive cropping all throughout the year (Seetharam and Ravikumar, 1996). Comprehensive information on sunflower diseases has been published by Kolte (1985).

### 12.1. *Alternaria* Leaf Spot/blight

*Alternaria* leaf spot/blight caused by *Alternaria helianthi,* is one of the major diseases on sunflower seen in the entire sunflower growing states in India. Yield loss up to 80 per cent has been reported (Reddy and Gupta, 1977; Agrawal *et al.,* 1979; Balasubrahmanyam and Kolte, 1980). The disease intensity is more in rainy season. In India, its occurrence has been reported by Anil kumar *et al.* (1974). The disease results in the reduction of seed number and test weight (Srinivas *et al.,* 1998). All diploid wild species and their hybrids have been reported to be highly susceptible to *Alternaria* disease (Sujatha *et al.,* 1997). *H. tuberosus* is good source of resistance to *A. helianthi* (Lipps and Herr, 1986). However, Ravikumar *et al.* (1995) did not observe tolerance to *Alternaria* in lines derived from *H. tuberosus.* New inoculation techniques have been suggested for screening sunflower genotypes resistance to Alternaria disease (Reddy *et al.,* 1990; Ravikumar, 1997; Sujatha *et al.,* 1997; Ravikumar and Chikkodi, 1998). Identifying field resistance to this disease in cultivars and potential donors is attached high priority.

### 12.2. Rust

Sunflower rust, caused by *Puccinia helianthi* is a major fungal disease in all the sunflower growing countries of the world. Sackston (1962) for the first time identified four races on three inbred lines (rust differentials) and cultivated sunflower in North America. This group of four races is called North American (NA) Races, 1,2,3 and 4. Hoes and Put (1962) described nine races of *P. helianthi* on 14 inbred lines. Inheritance of resistance to rust in sunflower was first reported by Putt and Sackston (1963) and genes for resistance designated as $R_1$ and $R_2$. Many wild species contain rust resistance genes which have been successfully incorporated into domestic cultivars (Hennessy and Sackston, 1972; Zimmer and Rehdar, 1976; Thompson *et al.,* 1978).

Most of the hybrid cultivars under cultivation in India are tolerant to rust. The severity of the disease is more in monsoon season. In post-rainy and summer season crop, rust is generally observed after flowering and as a result, its effect on seed yield is not much. In India, race 1,3 and 4 are prevalent of which race 3 is the most predominant (Patil and Anahosur, 1997).

### 12.3. Downy Mildew

Downy mildew of sunflower caused by *Plasmopara halstedii* is the most destructive disease of global importance. In India, its incidence was first observed in Maharashtra in 1984 (Mayee and Patil, 1986). Pathogenic variability in *P. halstedii* was recognised soon after the release of downy mildew resistant cultivars. The first genetic resistance source for Race-1 found in Europe was identified in the Romanian inbred line AD 66. Resistance was controlled by a dominant gene designated as $Pl_1$ (Vranceanu, 1970). Zimmer and Kinman (1972) identified resistance to Race 2 commonly referred to as Red River race prevalent in North America to be conditioned by a single dominant gene. This gene was designated as $Pl_2$. Subsequently, $Pl_3$ and $Pl_4$ genes were found to confer resistance to Race 1 and 2 and $P1_5$ gene was effective against Race 3. Vear, 1974; Vranceanu *et al.,* 1981 a; Miller and Gulya, 1987).

Sackston *et al.* (1990) have reported involvement of nine genes ($PI_1$ to $P1_9$) for conferring downy mildew resistance. In erstwhile USSR, cultivars resistant to downy mildew have been derived from interspecific crosses of *H. annuus* and *H. tuberosus.* Additional sources of resistance have been identified recently (Miller and Gulya, 1991). In India, Race 1 is predominant (Patil and Mayee, 1990). At Oilseeds Research Station, Latur (Maharashtra) downy mildew sick plot has been developed for screening sunflower genotypes for resistance to downy mildew. Prevalent race pattern varies with locations and cultivars grown. In India, presently more than 30 sunflower cultivars are spread over in different states. Hence, continuous monitoring for new races of *P. halstedii* and breeding for resistance to the identified races are required to develop hybrids with inbuilt resistance to downy mildew disease.

## 13. BREEDING FOR DROUGHT AND SALT TOLERANCE

In many parts of the world, sunflower is grown as a rainfed crop in drought-prone areas. Breeding for drought tolerance in sunflower is most relevant to tropical countries of arid and semi-arid regions. Sunflower is considered as a fairly drought tolerant crop due to its inherent ability to extract moisture from lower soil depth. Drought tolerance in sunflower is a complex trait as it is affected by morphological and physiological characteristics (Miller and Fick, 1997). Based on the evaluation of 25 sunflower cultivars, Fereres *et al.* (1983) concluded that the ratio of drought stress yield to irrigated yield and soil moisture extraction capability indicates relative drought tolerance of a cultivar. Giminez and Fereres (1986) and Ravishankar *et al.* (1991) favoured late maturing sunflower genotypes for drought situations because of their better soil moisture extraction capacity and higher leaf area recovery after alleviation of stress.

*H. argophyllus* has been recognised as a potential source of tolerance to drought (Skoric, 1992). Baldini *et al.* (1993); Korell *et al.* (1996 a,b) and several others have related drought tolerance mechanism of *H. argophyllus* to less reduction in dry matter production, increased root: shoot ratio, denser root system, better water use efficiency, higher photosynthetic rate and osmotic adjustment.

Considering the variability in germplasm and research information already generated, Connor and Hall (1997) have indicated the possibility of developing drought tolerant cultivars of sunflower without much loss of seed yield potential.

Sunflower is also grown on saline soils, particulary under irrigated conditions in arid climates. It is moderately tolerant to soil salinity (Francois, 1996). Bhatt and Indirakutty (1973) considered sunflower as a reclaimer of salt affected soils. *H. paradoxus, H. debilis* and a wild population of *H. annuus* which are confined to salty desert areas have been identified to possess high degree of tolerance to salt concentration (Korell *et al.,* 1996b). Hussain and Rehman (1993) identified two promising salt tolerant sunflower genotypes based on high $K^+/N^+$ ratio. One major dominant gene and a recessive modifier gene appear to be involved in the control of seedling tolerance to salinity in the crosses involving *H. paradoxus* (Miller, 1995).

## 14. BREEDING FOR CONFECTIONERY SUNFLOWER

In India, sunflower is grown for oil purpose and breeding efforts are concentrated on oil type sunflower to maximize productivity per unit area. In temperate countries, non-oilseed or confectionery cultivars are available for consumption in the form of raw or roasted and salted snack. Non-oilseed sunflower genotypes are prized if they have large seed;

loose hull with bright stripes; low oil; high oleic acid; free from insect; fungi; and extraneous sunflower plant parts (Lofgren, 1997). Recently, emphasis is laid on the promotion of value-added agricultural products for export and domestic market. One of the oil type hybrids (MSFH 17) has been identified as a confectionery sunflower for export of raw kernels after dehulling. Research efforts are now in progress to identify suitable confectionery sunflower genotypes. Preliminary effort initiated at Dharwad (Karnataka), led to the identification of a few genotypes with typical non-oilseed characteristics (Manjula, 1997). In India, the work on the development of hybrid varieties in non-oilseed sunflower has received meagre attention in the past. However, research effort devoted in the last two to three years indicate the possibility of developing suitable cultivars in the near future.

## 15. MUTATION BREEDING

Mutagenesis is a potential tool to broaden variability and to isolate desirable economic traits in a shorter period compared to conventional breeding procedures. A wide range of variability for oil content, fatty acid composition, morphological characteristics, test weight, hull content and flowering has been reported in mutants derived through chemical and physical mutagens (Gundaev, 1971; Soldatov, 1976; Ilyas Ahmad and Goud, 1978; Vranceanu and Stoenescu, 1982; Giriraj *et al.,* 1990; Deshpande and Giriraj, 1997). Genetic male sterile lines have been also derived through mutation breeding (Vranceanu, 1970). Induced mutagenesis in wild species of sunflower may be attempted to generate new variability.

## 16. BIOTECHNOLOGY IN SUNFLOWER IMPROVEMENT

Interspecific hybridization in sunflower has contributed significantly to disease resistance breeding and development of new sources of cytoplasmic male sterility. However, barriers to interspecific gene transfer exist between cultivated sunflower and wild species limiting free flow of useful genes. Biotechnological aproaches have been successful in overcoming the problems associated with conventional breeding process. Friedt (1992) and Bidney and Scelonge (1997) have reviewed and discussed the scope of new methods of biotechnology relevant to sunflower improvement.

Although sunflower is considered to be a "recalcitrant" species to tissue culture procedures (Freyssinet and Freyssinet, 1988), new techniques are now available for culture initiation and plant regeneration. Chandler and Beard (1983) proposed a two step embryo culture process. A total of

53 interspecific *Helianthus* combinations were successfully produced of which 21 combinations were not successful earlier by conventional methods. Subsequently, several workers employed embryo rescue techniques to obtain many wide hybrids in the genus *Helianthus* (Espinasse *et al.,* 1991; Krauter *et al.,* 1991). Embryo rescue techniques avoid dormancy barrier and are also useful in speeding up the turn over of generations (Chandler and Beard, 1983; Gopalkrishna *et al.,* 1993; Jambhulkar, 1995). In one year, a given inbred line can be converted into a cytoplasmic male sterile line by adopting this technique.

There are several reports of regeneration of entire plants from cultured hypocotyls, cotyledons, stem segments, leaf pieces, shoot tips and anthers (Hendrickson, 1954; Paterson and Everett, 1985; Krauter and Friedt, 1991; Nemeth and Frank, 1992; Patil *et al.,* 1993; Badigannavar and Kuruvinshetti, 1996, Graciela *et al.,* 1996). Screening *in vitro* for disease resistance from cultured somatic tissue *via* callus was suggested by Friedt (1992). Protoplast fusion by somatic hybridization is yet another potent tool to overcome sexual incompatibility between related species (Chandler and Beard, 1978).

The use of modern techniques is necessary for the efficient exploitation of wild species in breeding programme (Korell *et al.,* 1996 a; 1996 b). Molecular marker based techniques like RFLP (Restriction Fragment Length Polymorphism) and RAPD (Random Amplified Polymorphic DNA) are being used to provide finer information at DNA level about the traits under study. A composite map using seven $F_2$ populations has been arranged in 17 major linkage groups including 238 loci and four small segments with 2-5 marker loci covering 1573 cM at an overall average marker interval of 7 cM (Gentzbittel *et al.,* 1999). Three linkage maps of cultivated sunflower have been published earlier by Berry *et al.* (1995), Gentzbittel *et al.* (1995), Jan *et al.* (1998). The availability of more saturated linkage maps will increase the efficiency of sunflower breeding programmes.

Following are some of the important genes mapped using molecular marker techniques in sunflower.

(i) Sources of cytoplasmic male sterility in sunflower (Horn *et al.,* 1991; Kohler *et al.,* 1991).

(ii) Fertility restoration and apical branching (Berry *et al.,* 1994; Gentzbittel *et al.,* 1994).

(iii) Quantitative Trait Loci (QTL) affecting seed characteristics (Leon *et al.,* 1995).

(iv) Downy mildew resistance loci (Mouzeyar *et al.,* 1995; Roeckel-Drevet *et al.,* 1996; Vear *et al.,* 1997).

(v) QTLs for *Sclerotinia sclerotiorum* resistance (Mestries *et al.,* 1998).

(vi) Candidate genes for both downy mildew and *Sclerotinia sclerotiorum* (Gentzbittel *et al.,* 1998).

Apart from this, genetic diversity through DNA finger printing has been assessed using 24 inbred lines by utilizing six AFLP (Amplified Fragment Length Polymorphism) primer combinations (Hongtrakul *et al.,* 1997).

## 17. VARIETAL IMPROVEMENT IN INDIA

Four varietal populations *viz*; VNIIMK 8931 (EC 68413), Peredovik (EC 68414), Amaviriski 3497 (EC 68415) and Armaverts (EC 69874) introduced from erstwhile USSR and Sunrise from Canada were evaluated across the country during the early 1970s. Two varieties, *viz.*, EC 68414 and EC 68415 were recognised for large scale cultivation in the country. Poor seed set, poor market outlet, low price, and bird damage were some of the serious impediments to successful sunflower cultivation. With a view to sustain sunflower cultivation in the country, sunflower breeding work was started under the All India Coordinated Research Project on Oilseeds in 1972 at five centres, *viz.,*; Akola, Bangalore, Coimbatore, Digraj and Kota. Both basic and applied research on sunflower was carried out on a variety of problems including poor seed set in varietal populations. The importance of maintaining stability for seed and oil yield across locations was soon recognised and five seed production centres were established in the year 1977 exclusively for varietal renovation of cultivated open pollinated varieties and production of quality seeds for planting. Release of early maturing variety *viz.*, Morden (Seetharam *et al.,* 1978) and the development and release of the first sunflower hybrid-BSH 1 in 1980 (Seetharam *et al.,* 1980; Seetharam, 1981) helped to renew and revive interest in sunflower crop. In the last two decades, a number of varieties and hybrids have been released for cultivation (Table 6). At Akola (Maharashtra), a high yielding variety 'Surya' (PKV-SUF-72-37) was developed by mass selection in Latur bulk. It recorded 15 per cent more seed yield over EC 68414. An early maturing variety SS 56 from Solapur and CO 1 from Coimbatore were evolved for cultivation in Maharashtra and Tamil Nadu respectively. During 1996, two more open pollinated varieties *viz.*; GAUSF 15 for Gujarat and TNAUSF 7(CO 4) for Tamil Nadu were identified for cultivation.

**Table 6:** List of released varieties/hybrids of sunflower in India

| *Variety/ hybrid* | *Year of release* | *Adaptation zone* | *Special feature, if any* |
|---|---|---|---|
| ***Varieties*** | | | |
| EC 68414 | 1972 | Andhra Pradesh, Tamil Nadu, Maharashtra, Uttar Pradesh. | Tall growing, high yield potential of USSR origin. |
| EC 68415 | 1972 | Karnataka | Tall growing, high yield potential of USSR origin. |
| Morden | 1979 | All states | Early maturity, dwarf stature, suitable for mixed and multiple cropping. |
| Surya | 1983 | Maharashtra | Striped seed coat, low oil yield. |
| CO 1 | 1983 | Tamil Nadu | Early maturity. |
| CO 2 | 1986 | Tamil Nadu | Medium height, normal duration, tolerant to rust. |
| SS 56 | 1987 | Maharashtra | Early maturity, dwarf. |
| CO 3 | 1995 | Tamil Nadu | Tall growing, normal duration |
| GAUSF 15 | 1996 | Gujarat | _ |
| CO 4 | 1996 | All states | Normal duration, high oil content |
| ***Hybrids*** | | | |
| BSH 1 | 1980 | All states | Medium height, tolerant to rust. |
| APSH 11 | 1987 | Andhra Pradesh | – |
| MSFH 1 | 1986 | All states | – |
| MSFH 8 | 1986 | All states | – |
| MSFH 17 | 1988 | All states | Wide adaptability, tolerant to *Alternaria* |
| LDMRSH 3 | 1988 | Maharashtra | Resistant to downy mildew |
| KBSH 1 | 1990 | All states | High oil yielding, wide adaptability. |
| PAC 36 | 1995 | All states | - |
| Jwalamukhi | 1996 | All states | - |
| Sungene 85 | 1996 | AH states | Early maturity. |
| PSH 36 | 1996 | Punjab | - |
| DSH 1 | 1997 | Northern parts of Karnataka | Resistant to downy mildew, high oleic acid content. |

After the release of first ever sunflower hybird BSH-1 in the year 1980, cultivation of open pollinated varieties was gradually replaced by hybrid cultivars in the mid eighties. According to Virupakshappa (1995), the acreage under hybrids and open pollinated varieties is in the ratio of 60:40. In 1990s, hybrid varieties developed in both public and corporate sector dominated sunflower cultivation. A few hybrid cultivars are location specific. LDMRSH 3 possess high degree of resistance to downy mildew. It is recommended for cultivation in Maharashtra, where the disease is endemic. Like-wise, cultivation of APSH 11 and PSH 36 is confined to Andhra Pradesh and Punjab respectively. Recently, DSH 1, an early maturing hybrid with high oleic acid and resistance to downy mildew disease has been released for cultivation in northern parts of Karnataka.

## 18. HYBRID SEED PRODUCTION REQUIREMENTS

Virupakshappa *et al.* (1998) have compiled and published literature relating to hybrid seed production in sunflower. Release of a potential hybrid for commercial cultivation and the package for its hybrid seed production should go together. Information on synchronization of flowering of parental lines, optimum row ratio, nutritional requirements etc. is required to get higher hybrid seed yield in seed production programme. A row ratio of 1:3 of pollen parent and seed parent was suggested for hybrid seed production of BSH-1 (Satyanarayana and Seetharam, 1983; Seetharam and Satyanarayana, 1983). Block planting is most convenient when parental lines of a hybrid differ in flowering. In temperate countries, 8 to 12 rows of seed parent are alternated with 2 to 3 rows of pollen parent. Domesticated honey bee *(Apis mellifera)* is abundant to pollinate in seed production field and 10 to 12 q of hybrid seed per hectare is harvested (Skoric, 1992). In India, in hybrid seed production plots, natural pollination is to be supplemented by hand pollination and about 6 to 8 q hybrid seed is obtained. Activity of honey bees (*A. dorsata, A. cerana indica* and *A. florea*) is desirable to promote seed set and seed yield in commercial sunflower fields. However, in hybrid seed production fields, honey bees carry away dehisced pollen and the frequency of their visit to seed parent is less. Inadequate quantity of pollen for effective hand pollination owing to "pollen theft" by natural pollinators is one of the limiting factors for low hybrid seed yield (Giriraj, 1996).

Prescribed isolation standards are followed for certification of hybrid seed. In the USA and some European countries, isolation distance vary between 0.5 to 2.4 km for hybrid seed and 1.6 to 5.0 km for foundation seed production of parental lines (Anfinrud, 1997). In India, an isolation distance of 400 m for hybrid seed and 600 m for foundation seed production is followed (Tunwar and Singh, 1988). The prescribed isolation based on experience may not be sufficient to prevent outcrossing from other pollen sources. Isolation standard for different seed categories in sunflower is a topic of debate.

A single-cross hybrid is a three-line hybrid involving production and maintenance of A,B and R lines through paired crossing at regular intervals. Maintenance breeding of parental lines assumes importance to check deterioration in the performance of hybrids over years (Seetharam and Virupakshappa, 1993; Giriraj, 1996).

## 19. PROBLEMS AND FUTURE STRATEGIES

Sunflower is a typical example of introduction and domestication in India. However, in the last two decades it has witnessed boom and bust. Of late, decline in area has been noticed from its peak of over 2 mha for the triennium ending 1993-95. This declining trend in the sunflower area and its lower productivity over the years are causes of concern for the sustainable growth of the crop in the next millennium. The problems of sunflower cultivation and suggested future approaches have been presented under the following four heads.

1. Net productivity increase
2. Abiotic and biotic stresses
3. Quality aspects and special purposes and
4. Biotechnological approaches

**1. *Net productivity increase*:** The possibility of realising 20 q oil yield per hectare by increasing seed number (>1500 per plant), seed weight (>80 g per 1000 seeds), and oil content (>50 per cent) has been indicated by Skoric (1992). Temperate countries provide ideal conditions for realizing such potential. However, in tropical countries there is need to orient breeding efforts to obtain at least 6 to 8 q oil yield per hectare by identifying hybrid combinations consistently producing 15 to 20 q/ha of seed yield and having more than 40 per cent oil content. Diversification of germplasm resources by exploiting wild relatives deserves emphasis. Besides, there is need to broaden genetic base of CMS and fertility restorers for enhancing hybrid performance. Improving flexibility of sunflower through breeding for different cropping systems will promote sunflower area as has happened with soybean.

**2. *Abiotic and biotic stresses*:** Sunflower in India is mostly cultivated in rainfed environment which is basically unfavourable for realizing high seed yield potential of released cultivars. Soil moisture stress coupled with disease pressure further aggravates the situation. Present sunflower scenario is also threatened by outbreak of a viral disease called sunflower necrosis. Its incidence is particularly worrying in South India, which was hitherto considered as a "yellow belt" of India. Hence, following areas of research have greater opportunities in sunflower improvement.

(a) Development of drought tolerant cultivars.

(b) Screening of sunflower genetic stocks for resistance to sunflower necrosis and incorporation of the trait in hybrid programme.

(c) Improvement of sunflower germplasm for resistance to pathogenic races of major diseases (rust and downy mildew) by utilizing wild species.

**3. *Quality aspects and special purposes*:** In North American and European countries breeding efforts are concentrated on the development of sunflower cultivars with high oleic acid content (80 to 90%). High oleic containing cultivars fetch premium price in the international market. In India research inputs in this direction have been scanty and hence more research efforts are needed in the coming years. Development of non oilseed (confectionery) sunflower cultivars has been neglected in the past. It offers large scope for export and domestic market and therefore it is worth while to accelerate breeding efforts to develop confectionery sunflower cultivars.

**4. *Biotechnological approaches*:** Bioengineering tools are becoming part of conventional breeding programmes. There is ample scope for utilizing modem techniques in the following areas of sunflower improvement.

(a) Genetic transformation for disease resistance.

(b) Gene tagging for high oleic production.

(c) Overcoming barriers to successful inter specific hybridization, and

(d) Molecular characterization of sunflower species and domestic cultivars.

Sunflower cultivation in India has bright future in the next millennium if the challenges enumerated above are met with success.

## REFERENCES

Agrawat, J.M., Chippa, H.P. and Mathur, S.J. (1979). Screening of sunflower germplasm against *Alternaria helianthi. Indian J. Mycology and Plant Path.* 9: 85–86.

Alba, E. and Greco, I. (1979). An analysis of the association of factors influencing seed yield in sunflower (*Helianthus annuus* L.). *Sunflower Newslett.* 3(2): 13–15.

Alba, E., Barsanti, P. and Carrozzo, G. (1985). Analysis of combining ability in new cytoplasmically male sterile lines and in fertility restorer lines of sunflower. *Annali délia Facoita de Agraria,* 31: 363–370.

Alba, E., Benvenuti, A., Tuberosa, R. and Vannozzi, G.P. (1979). A path coefficient analysis of some yield components in sunflower. *Helia 2:* 25–29.

Anand, I.J. and Chandra, S. (1979). Genetic diversity and interrelationships of oil yielding traits in sunflower. *Sunflower Newslett.* 4(1): 5–8.

Anfinrud, M.N. (1997). Planting hybrid seed production and seed quality evaluation. *In*: *Sunflower technology and production* (*Ed*., Schneiter, A.A.). ASA, CSSA, SSSA, Madison, WI, USA. pp. 697–708.

Anilkumar, T.B., Urs, S.D., Seshadri, V.S. and Hegde, R.K. (1974). *Alternaria* leaf spot of sunflower. *Curr. Sci.,* 43: 93–94.

Asthana, A.N. (1973). Selfing studies in sunflower (*Helianthus annuus* L.) using self and foreign pollen. *Sci. Cult.,* 39: 268–269.

Badigannavar, A.M. and Kuruvinashetti, M.S. (1996). Callus induction and shoot bud formation from cultured anthers in sunflower (*Helianthus annuus* L.) *Helia* 19(25): 35–38.

Badwal, S.S., Raheja, R.K., Anuja, K.L. and Bawa, B.S. (1993). Path analysis of oil yield in sunflower (*Helianthus annuus* L.) hybrids. *Indian J. Genet.,* 53: 387–390.

Balasubrahmanyam, N. and Kolte, S.J. (1980). Effect of *Alternaria* blight on yield components, oil content and seed quality of sunflower. *Indian J. Agric. Sci.,* 50: 701–706.

Baldini, M., Cecconi, F. and Vannozzi, G.P. (1993). Influence of water deficit on gas exchange and dry matter accumulation in sunflower cultivars and a wild species (*Helianthus argophyllus* T & G). *Helia,* 16(19): 1–10.

Baldini, M., Cecconi, F. and Vannozzi, G.P. and Benvenuti, A. (1991). Effect of drought on yield reduction in different sunflower hybrids. *Helia,* 14(15): 71–76.

Berretta de berger, A.M. and Miller, J.E. (1985). Estudio genetico de seis fluentes de estatura reducida de plants en girasol. *In Proc. Il'"* Int. Sunflower Conf. Mar del Plata, Argentina. pp. 651–657.

Berry, S.T., Leon, A.J., Hanfrey, C.C., Challis, P., Burkholz. A., Barnes, S.J., Rufener, G.K., Lee.M. and Caligari P.D.S. (1995). Molecular marker analysis of *Helianthus annuus* L 2. Construction of an RFLP linkage map for cultivated sunflower. *Theor Appl. Genet.* 91: 195–199.

Berry, ST., Allen, R.J., Barnes, S.P. and Caligari, P.D.S. (1994). Molecular marker analysis of *Helianthus annuus L.* 1. Restriction fragment length polymorphism between inbred lines of cultivated sunflower. *Theor. Appl. Genet.,* 89: 435–441.

Bhatt, J.G. and Indirakutty, K.N. (1973). Salt uptake and salt tolerance by sunflower. *Plant Sci., 39:* 457–460.

Bidney, D.L. and Scelonge, C.J. (1997). Sunflower biotechnology. *In*: *Sunflower technology and production.* (*Ed.* Schneiter, A.A.). ASA, CSSA, SSSA, Madison, WI, USA. pp. 559–593.

Block, C.C. (1992). Screening for *Alternaria* leaf blight resistance in the USDA germplasm collection. In *Proc. Sunflower Res. workshop,* Fargo, ND, National Sunflower Assoc. Bismarck, ND pp. 64–66.

Burlov, V.V. (1974). Utilization of male sterility in sunflower breeding for heterosis. *In*: *Proc* 6th Int. Sunflower Conf., Bucharest, Rumania, pp. 353–360.

Burns, R.E. (1970). Head size of sunflower as an indicator of plot yields. *Agron. J.*, 62: 112–113.

Canvin, D.T. (1965). The effect of temperature on the oil content and fatty acid composition of the oils from several oilseed crops. *Can. J. Bot.,* 43: 63–69.

Cardon, P.V. (1922). Sunflower studies. *J. Amer. Soc. Agron.,* 14: 69–72.

Chandler, J.M. and Beard, B.H. (1983). Embryo culture of *Helianthus* hybrids. *Crop Sci.,* 23: 1004–1007.

Chandler, J.M. and Beared, B.H. (1978). Sunflower interspecific hybridization using embryo culture. In *Proc.* 8'h Int. Sunflower Conf., Minneapolis, MN. pp. 510–516.

Chandler, J.M. and Jan, C.C. (1984). Identification of salt–tolerant germplasm sources in the *Helianthus* species. *Agron. Abstr.* Amer Soc. Agron. Madison, WI, p. 61.

Chaudhary, S.K. and Anand, I.J. (1981). Seasonal influence on seed filling in sunflower. In *Proc. 4th Int. SABRAO Cong.* Kaulalumpur. pp. 22–24.

Chaudhary, S.K. and Anand, I.J. (1984). Heterosis and inbreeding depression in sunflower. *Crop Improv.,* 11: 15–19.

Chaudhary, S.K. and Anand, I.J. (1985) Influence of various characters on yield of sunflower. *J. Oilseeds Res.,* 2: 78–85.

Chaudhary, S.K. and Anand, I.J. (1993). Correlation and path coefficient analysis in F1 and F2 generations in sunflower (*Helianthus annuus* L.) *Int. J. Trop. Agric.,* 11: 204–208.

Connor, D.J. and Hall, A.J. (1997). Sunflower physiology. *In*: *Sunflower technology and production* (ed.A.A.Schneiter). ASA, CSSA, SSSA, Madison, WI, USA. pp. 113–182.

Dedio, W. (1982). Variability in hull content, kernel oil content and whole seed oil content of sunflower hybrids and parental lines. *Canadian J. Plant Sci.,* 62: 51–54.

Demurin, Y. (1993). Genetic variability of tocopherol composition in sunflower seeds. *Helia* 16(18): 59–62.

Deokar, A.B. and Patil, F.B. (1975). Inheritance of some qualitative characters in sunflower–cases of linkage. *Indian J. Hered.,* 7: 31–38.

Deshpande, S.K. and Giriraj, K. (1997). Induced polygenic variation for economic traits in two restorer lines of sunflower (*Helianthus annuus* L.). *Helia,* 20(26): 89–94.

Dhaduk, L.K., Desai, N.D., Patel, R.H. and Kukadia, M.U. (1985). Correlation and Path analysis in sunflower. *Indian J. Agric. Sci. 55:* 52–54.

Dominguez–Giminez, J. and Fick, G.N. (1975). Fertility restoration of male–sterile cytoplasm in wild sunflowers. *Crop Sci.,* 15: 724–726.

Dorrell, D.G. (1976). Chlorogenic acid content of meal from cultivated and wild sunflowers. *Crop Sci.,* 16: 422–424.

Dorrell, D.G. and Whelan, E.D.P. (1978). Chemical and morphological characteristics of seeds of some sunflower species. *Crop Sci.,* 18: 969–971.

Dua, R.P. and Yadava, T.P. (1983). Gene effects for some quantitative characters in sunflower. *Indian J. Agric. Sci.* 52: 439–443.

Dua, R.P. and Yadava, T.P. (1985). Genetics of seed yield and its components in sunflower (*Helinathus annuus* L.). In *Proc. 11th Int. Sunflower Conf.* Mar del Plata, Argentina. pp. 627–632.

Enns, H., Dorrell, D.G., Hoes, J.A. and Chubb, W.O. (1970). Sunflower research, a progress report. In *Proc. 4th Int sunflower conf.* Memphis, Tennessee, pp. 162–167.

Espinasse, A., Volin, J., Dybing, C.D. and Lay, C. (1991). Embryo rescue through in ovulo culture in *Helianthus. Crop. Sci.,* 31: 102–108.

Fambrini, M. and Pugliesi, C. (1996). Inheritance of a Chlorina–apicalis mutant of sunflower. *Helia* 19(25): 29–34.

Fereres. E., Giminez, C., Berengena, J., Fernandez–Martinez, J. and Dominguez, J. (1983). Genetic variability of sunflower cultivars in response to drought. *Helia,* 6: 17–21.

Fernandez–Martinez, J. and Knowles, P.F. (1976). Variability in fatty acid composition of the seed oil of *Helianthus* species. in Proc. 7th Int. Sunflower Conf. Krasnodar, Russia, pp. 401–409.

Fernandez–Martinez, J., Jimenez, A., Dominguez, J., Garcia, J., Garces, R. and Mancha, M. (1989). Genetic analysis of high oleic acid content in cultivated sunflower. *Euphytica,* 41: 39–51 .

Fernandez–Martinez, J., Munoz, J. and Gomez–Arnau, J. (1993). Performance of near–isogenic high and low oleic acid hybrids of sunflower. *Crop Sci.* 33: 1158–1163.

Fick, G.N. (1975). Hertiability of oil content in sunflower. *Crop. Sci.,* 15: 77–78.

Fick, G.N. (1976). Genetics of floral color and morphology in sunflowers. *J. Hered.,* 67: 227–230.

Fick, G.N. (1978). Breeding and genetics. *In: Sunflower Science and Technology* (*Ed.* Carter, J.E.) ASA, CSSA, SSSA, Madison, WI pp. 279–338.

Fick, G.N. (1984). Inheritance of high oleic acid in the seed oil of sunflower. In *Proc. 6th Sunflower Res. Workshop,* Bismarck ND, pp. 9.

Fick, G.N. and Swallers, C.M. (1972). Higher yields and greater uniformity with hybrid sunflowers. *N. Dak. Farm Res.* 29(6): 7–9.

Fick, G.N. and Zimmer, D.E. (1974). Fertility restoration in confectionery sunflowers. *Crop Sci.*, 14: 603–604.

Fick, G.N. and Zimmer, D.E. (1976). Yield stability of sunflower hybrids and open pollinated varieties. *In*: *Proc. 7th Int. Sunflower Conf.* Krasnodar, Russia. pp. 253–258.

Fick, G.N. and Zimmer, D.E. and Thompson, T.E. (1976). Wild species of *Helianthus* as a source of variability in sunflower breeding. In *Proc. Sunflower Res. Workshop,* National Sunflower Association, ND. pp. 4–5.

Fick, G.N. and Zimmer, D.E. and Zimmerman, D.C. (1974). Correlation of seed oil content in sunflowers with other plant and seed characteristics. *Crop Sci.,* 14: 755–757.

Fick, G.N. and Zimmer, D.E., Dominguez–Giminez, J. and Rehder, D.A. (1974). Fertility restoration and variability for plant and seed characteristics in wild sunflower. *In*: *Proc. 6th Int. Sunflower Conf.* Bucharest, Romania. pp. 333–338.

Francois, L.E. (1996). Salinity effects on four sunflower hybrids. *Agron. J.,* 88: 211–229

Freyssinet, M. and Freyssinet, G. (1988). Fertile plant regeneration from sunflower (*Helianthus annuus* L.) immature embryos. *Plant Sci.,* 56: 177–181.

Friedt, W. (1992). Present state and future prospects of bio–technology in sunflower breeding. *Field Crops Res.,* 30: 425–442.

Gangappa, E., Channkrishnaiah, K.M., Harini, M.S. and Ramesh, S. (1997). Studies on combining ability in sunflower (*Helianthus annuus* L). *Helia,* 20(27): 73–84.

Gentzbittel, L., Mestries. E., Mouzeyar, S., Mazeyrat. F., Badaoui, S., Vear, F., Tourvieille de Labrouhe, D. and Nicolas, P. (1999). A composite map of expressed sequences and phenotypic traits of the sunflower (*Helianthus annuus* L.) genome. *Theor. Appl. Genet.,* 99: 218–234.

Gentzbittel, L., Mouzeyar S., Badaoui, S., Mestries, E., Vear, F., Tourvieille de Labrouhe, D. and Nicolas, P. (1998). Cloning of molecular markers for disease resistance in sunflower. *Helianthus annuus* L. *Theor. Appl. Genet.,* 96: 519–525.

Gentzbittel, L., Vear, F., Zhang, Y–X., Berville, A. and Nicolas, P. (1995). Development of a consensus linkage RFLP map of cultivated sunflower (*Helianthus annuus* L.). *Theor. Appl. Genet.,* 90: 1079–1086.

Gentzbittel, L., Zhang, Y–X., Vear, F., Griveau, B. and Nicolas, P. (1994). RFLP studies of genetic relationships among inbred lines of the cultivated sunflower, *Helianthus annuus* L., evidence for distinct restorer and mintainer germplasm pools. *Theor Appl. Genet.* 89: 419–425.

George, D. and Shein, S. (1980). Effect of pollination and compatibility on seed set. The Sunflower, USA. pp. 12–14.

Ghanavathi, V.N. and Nahavandi, E. (1981). Breeding sunflower for semi–arid regions. *J. Agric. Sci.* (UK), 96: 447–450.

Gill, H.S. and Punia, M.S. (1996). Expression of heterosis in single, double and three–way cross hybrids of sunflower (*Helianthus annuus* L.). *Helia,* 19(25): 111–118.

Giminez, C. and Fereres, E. (1986). Genetic variability in sunflower cultivars under drought. II. Growth and water relations. *Aust. J. Agric. Res.,* 37: 583–597.

Giriraj, K. (1996). Issues related to sunflower breeding and seed production in India. In *Proc.* 14th *Int. Sunflower Conf.,* Beijing, China, pp. 111–115.

Giriraj, K., Hiremath, S.R. and Seenappa, K. (1987). Combining ability of converted male sterile lines of sunflower (*Helianthus annuus* L.). *Indian J. Genet.,* 47: 315–317.

Giriraj, K., Hiremath, S.R. and Seenappa, K. (1988). Stability of sunflower genotypes for seed yield. *In*: Proc. *12th Int. Sunflower Conf.,* Novisad, Yugoslavia. pp. 537–541.

Giriraj, K., Hiremath, S.R., and Seetharam, A. (1990). Induced variability for flowering, seed weight and oil content in parental lines of sunflower hybrid BSH–1. *Indian J. Genet.,* 50: 1–7.

Giriraj, K., Hiremath, S.R., Ashok kumar, T.N. and Shambulingappa, K.G. (1985a). Performance of different seed categories of sunflower for seed yield and oil content. *Seeds and Farms.* 11(8): 61–62.

Giriraj, K., Shivaraju, N. and Hiremath, S.R. (1986). Studies on heterosis and inbreeding depression in selected cross combination of sunflower. *J. Oilseeds Res.,* 3: 67–72.

Giriraj, K., Ujjinaiah, U.S. and Hiremath, S.R. (1985b). Response to cyclic selection for seed yield and oil content in sunflower population–Armaviriski–3497. *In*: *Proc.* 11th *Int. Sunflower Conf.,* Mar del Plata, Argentina. pp. 661–664.

Giriraj, K., Vidyashankar, T.S., Venkataramu, M.N. and Seetharam, A. (1979). Path coefficient analysis of seed yield in sunflower. *Sunflower Newslett.* 3(3): 10–12.

Gopalkirishnan, K., Naidu, M.R. and Sreedhar, D. (1993). Shortening breeding cycle through immature embryo culture in sunflower (*Helianthus annuus* L.) *Helia,* 16(19): 61–68.

Graciela, N., Roxana, Z., Luis, M. and Liliana, P. (1996). Plant regeneration from cotyledons derived from mature sunflower seeds. *Helia,* 19(24): 107–112.

Grafius, J.E. (1964). A geometry for plant breeding. *Crop Sci.,* 4: 241–246.

Gundaev, A.I. (1971). Basic principles of sunflower selection. *In*: *Genetic Principles of Plant Selection.* Nauka, Moscow. pp. 417–65.

Gupta, K.K. and Khanna, K.R. (1982). Gene action and heterosis for oil yield and component characters in sunflower. *Indian J. Genet.,* 42: 265–271.

Habura, E.C. (1957). Parasterilat bei der Sonnenblumen. *Pflanzenzucht,* 3: 280–298.

Hamilton, R.E. (1926). Improving sunflowers by inbreeding. *Sa. Agri.,* 6: 190–192.

Heiser, C.B. (1951). The suflower among the North American Indians. *Proc. Am. Phil. Soc.,* 95: 432–448.

Heiser, C.B. (1982). Registration of Indiana–1 CMS sunflower germplasm. *Crop Sci.,* 22: 1989.

Heiser, C.B. Smith, D.M., Clevenger, S.B. and Martin, W.C. (1969). The North American Sunflowers (*Helianthus*). *Memoirs Torr. Bot. Ce,* 22: 1–218.

Hendrickson, C.E. (1954). The flowering of sunflower explants in aseptic culture. *Plant Physiol.,* 29: 536–538.

Hennessy, C.M.R. and Sackston, W.E. (1972). Studies on sunflower rust. X Specialization of *Puccinia helianthi* on wild sunflower in Texas. *Can. J. Bot.,* 50: 1871–1877.

Hiremath, S.R. and Giriraj, K. (1984). Inheritance of ray floret shape in sunflower. *J. Oilseeds Res.* 1: 89–90.

Hockett, E.A. and Knowles, RE (1970). Inheritance of branching in sunflowers, *Helianthus annuus L. Crop Sci.,* 10: 432–436.

Hoes, J.A. and Putt, E.D. (1962). Races of *Puccinia helianthi. Phytopathology, 52:* 736–737.

Hongtrakul, V., Huestis, G.M. and Knapp, S.J. (1997). Amplified fragment length polymorphism as a tool for DNA finger printing sunflower germplasm: genetic diversity among oilseed inbred lines. *Theor. Appl. Genet.,* 95: 400–407.

Horn, R., Kohler, R.K. and Zetsche, K. (1991). A mitochondrial 16 k Da protein is associated with cytoplasmic male sterlity in sunflower. *Plant Mol. Bio.,* 17: 29–36.

Hussain, M.K. and Rehman, O. (1993). Breeding sunflower for salt tolerance: Physiological basis for salt tolerance in sunflower (*Helianthus annuus* L.). *Helia,* 16(18): 77–84.

Ilyas Ahmed, M. and Goud, J.V. (1978). Some interesting macromutants of sunflower. *Curr. Sci.,* 47: 58–59.

Ivanov, I.G. (1975). Study on compatibility and incompatibility display in crossing selfed sunflower lines. *Rastenievud Nauk,* 12(9): 36–40.

Jain, K.K., Vaish, D.E, Gupta, H.K. and Mathur, S.S. (1978). Studies on hollow seedness in sunflower. In *Proc. 8th Sunflower Conf.* Minneapolis, USA. pp. 138–147.

Jambhulkar, S.J. (1994). Inheritance of genetic male sterility obtained by immature embryo culture in sunflower cv. Morden. *Helia,* 17(21): 23–26.

Jambhulkar, S.J. (1995). Rapid cycling through immature embryo culture in sunflower (*Helianthus annuus* L). *Helia,* 18(22): 45–50.

Jan, C.C. (1997). Cytology and inter specific hybridization. *In*: *Sunflower technology and production* (*Ed.* Schneiter, A.A.). ASA, CSSA, SSSA, Madison, WI, pp. 497–558.

Jan, C.C., Vick, B.A., Miller, J.E, Kahler, A.L. and Butler, E.T.I. (1998). Construction of an RFLP linkage map for cultivated sunflower. *Theor. Appl. Gent.,* 96*:* 15–22.

Javed, N. and Aslam, M. (1995). Combining ability effects in sunflower F1 hybrids. *Helia,* 18(3): 41–46.

Joshi, S.S. and Giriraj, K. (1995). Inheritance of *Chlorina–leaf* colour mutant in sunflower. *Crop Res.,* 10: 221–222.

Joshi, S.S., Basavalingappa and Giriraj, K. (1994). Pleiotropy in sunflower (*Helianthus annuus* L.). *Helia,* 17(20): 1–6.

Joshi, S.S., Ramesh, S., Gangappa, E., Jagannath, D.P and Chikkadevaiah. (1997). Limits to parental divergence for the occurrence of heterosis in sunflower. *Helia,* 20(27): 95–100.

Kadkol, G.P., Anand, I.J. and Sharma, R.P. (1984). Combining ability and heterosis in sunflower. *Indian J, Genet.,* 44: 447–451.

Kandhola, S.S., Behl, R.K. and Punia, M.S. (1995). Combining ability in sunflower. *Annals Biol.,* 11: 103–106.

Khanna, R.K. (1972). Factors affecting the production of filled seeds in sunflower. *Euphytica,* 21: 384–387.

Kini, A.V, and Seetharam, A. (1994). Can achene characters of sunflower hybrids be predicted based on F0 values. *J. Oilseeds Res.,* 11: 130–131.

Kinman, M.L. (1970). New developments in the USDA and state experiment station sunflower breeding programs. In: *Proc. 4th Int. Sunflower Couf.* Memphis, Tennessee, pp. 181–183.

Kinman, M.L. and Earle, F.R. (1964). Agronomic performance and chemical composition of the seed of sunflower hybrids and introduced varieties. *Crop Sci.* 4: 417–420.

Kohler, R., Hom, R., Lossl, A., and Zetsche, K. (1991). Cytoplasmic mâle sterility in sunflower is correlated with the co–transcription of a new open reading frame with the *atp* A gene. *Molecular* and *General Genet.,* 227*:* 369–376.

Kolte, S.J. (1985). Diseases of annual edible oil seed crops. Vol. III: Sunflower, safflower and niger seed diseases. CRC Press. Inc. Boca Raton, Florida.

Korell, M., Brahm, L., Friedt, W. and Horn, R. (1996b). Interspecific and intergeneric hybridization in sunflower breeding. II. Specific use of wild germplasm. *Plant Breed. Abstr.,* 66(8): 1081–1091.

Korell, M., Brahm, L., Hom, R. and Friedt, W. (1996a). Interspecific and intergeneric hybridization in sunflower breeding. I. General breeding aspects. *Plant Breed. Abstr.,* 66(7): 925–931.

Kovacik, A. and Skaloud, V. (1972). The proportion of the variability component caused by the environment and the correlations of economically important properties and characters of the sunflower (*Helianthus annuus* L.). *Sci. Agric. Bohemoslov* 4: 249–261.

Kovacik, A. and Skaloud, V. (1978). A study of combining ability of sunflower lines and heterosis effects on crossing them. *Plant Breed. Abstr.* 48(2): 1040.

Kovacik, A. and Skaloud, V. (1980). Investigations on yield components in heterosis breeding of sunflower (*Helianthus annuus* L.). *Archiv. fur Zucht.,* 10: 145–153.

Krauter, R. and Friedt, W. (1991). Propagation and multiplication of sunflower lines (*Helianthus annuus* L.) by tissue culture *in vitro*. *Helia,* 14(14): 117–122.

Krauter, R., Steinmetz, A. and Friedt, W. (1991). Efficient interspecific hybridization in the genus *Helianthus via* "embryo rescue" and characterization of the hybrids. *Theor. Appl. Genet* 82: 521–525.

Kshirsagar, A.R., Deshmukh D.T. and Duhe, R.S. (1995). Study on genetic variability in sunflower. *PKV Res. T.,* 19: 175.

Lakshmanaiah, V.H. (1980). Genetic variability and association of morphological characters with seed yield and oil content in sunflower. (*Helianthus annuus* L.). *Mysore J. Agric. Sci.,* 14: 259–261.

Lakshmanrao, N.G., Shambulingappa, K.G. and Kusumakumari, P. (1985). Studies on path–coefficient analysis in sunflower. *In*: *Proc.* 11th Int. Sunflower Conf., Mar del Plata, Argentina, pp. 733–736.

Lakshminarayana, M.R., Giriraj, K., Ramanathan, K.V. and Khetrapal, C.L. (1984). Oil build up and quality in developing sunflower seeds. *La Rivista italiana Delie Sostanze Grasse,* 61: 487– 490.

Leclercq, P. (1968). Inheritance of some qualitative characters in sunflower. *Ann Amel. Plant,* 18: 307–315.

Leclercq, P. (1969). Une sterilite male cytoplasmique chez le tournesol. *Ann Amel. Plant,* 19: 99–106.

Leclercq, P. (1971). La sterilite male cytoplasmique du la fertilite. *Ann Amel. Plant,* 21: 45–54.

Leon, A.J., Lee, M., Rufener, G.K., Berry, S.T., and Mowers, R.P. (1995). Use of RFLP markers for genetic linkage analysis of oil percentage in sunflower seed. *Crop Sci.,* 35: 558–564.

Lipps, P.E. and Herr, L.J. (1986). Reactions of *Helianthus annuus* and *H. tuberosus* plant introductions to *Alternaria helianthi. Plant Dis.,* 70: 831–835.

Lofgren, J.R. (1997). Sunflower for confectionery food, bird food and pet food. *In*: *Sunflower technology and production (Ed.* Schneiter, A.A.*)*. ASA, CSSA, SSSA, Madison, WI, USA, pp, 747–764.

Luchkiewicz, T. (1975). Inheritance of some characters and properties in sunflower. *(Helianthus annuus* L.). *Genet. Pol.,* 16: 167–184.

Luciano, A., Kinman, M.L. and Smith, D. (1965). Heritability of self incompatibility in the sunflower *(Helianthus annuus* L.). *Crop Sci.,* 5: 529–532.

Madrap, I.A. and Makne, V.G. (1993). Heterosis in relation to combining ability effect and phenotypic stability in sunflower *(Helianthus annuus* L.). *Indian J. Agric. Sci.,* 63: 484–488.

Mandal, S. and Singh, R. (1993). Oil and protein contents in sunflower genotypes. *J. Oilseeds Res.,* 10: 161–162.

Manjula, K. (1997). Genetic variability and diversity studies of sunflower *(Helianthus annuus* L.). genotypes for confectionery purpose. M.Sc.Agri. Thesis, University of Agricultural Sciences, Dharwad.

Manjunath, A. (1978). Genetics of seed yield, oil content and other quantitative characters in sunflower. *Mysore J. Agric. Sci.,* 12: 667–668.

Manjunath, A. and Goud, J.V. (1983). Genetics of quantitative characters in sunflower. II. Days to flower and days to maturity. *Genetica Ibcrica,* 35: 13–23.

Marinkovic, R. (1993). Components of genetic variability for characters affecting oil of sunflower. *(Helianthus annuus* L.). *J. Genet. and Breed.* 47: 289–294.

Mayee, C.D. and Patil, M.A. (1986). Downy mildew of sunflower in India. *Trop Pest Mgmt.* 33: 81–82.

Mc Carter, S.M. (1993). Reaction of Jerusalem artichoke genotypes to two rusts and powdery mildew. *Plant Dis.,* 77: 242–245.

Mestries, E., Gentzbittel, L., Tourvieille de Labrouhe, D., Nicolas, P. and Vear, F. (1998). Analysis of quantitative trait loci associated with resistance to *Sclerotinia sclerotiorum* in sunflowers *(Helianthus annuus* L.) using molecular markers. *Mol. Breed.,* 4: 215–226.

Miller, J.F. (1995). Inheritance of salt tolerance in sunflower. *Helia,* 18(23): 9–16.

Miller, J.F. (1996). Inheritance of restoration of *Helianthus petiolaris* subsp. *fallax* (PEF1) cytoplasmic male sterility. *Crop Sci.,* 36: 83–86.

Miller, J.F. and Fick, G.N. (1997). The Genetics of sunflower. In *Sunflower technology and production* (*Ed.* Schneiter, A.A.), ASA, CSSA, SSSA, Madison, WI, USA, pp. 441–495.

Miller, J.F. and Gulya, T.J. (1987). Inheritance of resistance to race 3 downy mildew in sunflower. *Crop Sci.,* 27: 210–212.

Miller, J.F. and Gulya, T.J. (1988). Registration of six downy mildew resistant sunflower germplasm lines. *Crop. Sci.,* 28: 1040–1041.

Miller, J.F. and Gulya, T.J. (1991). Inheritance of resistance to race 4 of downy mildew derived from interspecific cross of sunflower. *Crop Sci.,* 31: 40–43.

Miller, J.F. and Hammond, J.J. (1991). Inheritance of reduced height in sunflower. *Euphytica* 53: 131–136.

Miller, J.F. and Wolf, S.L. (1991). Registration of three cytoplasmic male–sterile and three restorer sunflower germplasm lines. *Crop Sci.,* 31: 500.

Miller, J.F., Zimmerman, D.C. and Vick, B.A. (1987). Genetic control of high oleic acid content in sunflower oil. *Crop Sci.,* 27: 923–926.

Mishra, R., Shrivastava, A.N., Chandra, D.R. and Singh, P. (1985). Path analysis for yield components in sunflower *(Helianthus annuus* L.). *Agric. Sci. Digest.,* 5: 38–40.

Morris, J.B., Yang, S.M. and Wilson, L. (1983). Reaction of *Helianthus* species to *Alternaria helianthi. Plant Dis.,* 67: 539–540.

Mouzeyar, S., Roeckel–Drevet, P., Gentzbittel, L., Phillippon, J., Tourvieille de Labrouhe, D., Vear, F. and Nicolas, P. (1995). RFLP and RAPD mapping of the sunflower ph locus for resistance to *Plasmopara halstedii* race I. *Theor Appl. Genet.,* 91: 733–737.

Naik, N.M., Pawar, B.B. and Dumbre, A.D. (1988). Heterosis in sunflower. *J.Maharashtra Agric. Univ.,* 13; 39–42.

Nemeth, G. and Frank, J. (1992). Callus formation, embryogenesis and plantlet regeneration in wild *Helianthus* species. *Helia,* 15(16): 1–8.

Niranjanmurthy and Shambulingappa, K.G. (1989). Path analysis for seed yield in sunflower. *J. Oilseeds Res.,* 6: 22–25.

Paterson, K.E. and Everett, N.P. (1985). Regeneration of *Helianthus annuus* inbred plants from callus. *Plant Sci.,* 42: 125–132.

Pathak, A.R., Basudeo Singh and Kukadia, M.V. (1985). Genetic architecture of yield and economic characters in sunflower. *Oilseeds J.,* 15: 14–18.

Pathak, A.R., Kukadia, M.U. and Kunadra, B.A. (1983). Path coefficient analysis in sunflower. *Indian J. Agric. Sci.,* 53: 607–608.

Pathak, H.C. and Dixit, S.K. (1984). A correlation and path coefficient analysis of components of seed yield in sunflower. *(Helianthus annuus* L.). *Sunflower Newslett.,* 7: 36–40.

Pathak, R.S. (1974). Yield components in sunflower. *In*: *Proc. 6th Iut. Sunflower Conf.* Bucharest, Romania. pp. 271–281.

Patil, M.A. and Mayee, C.D. 1990. Race identity of Indian *Plasmopara halstedii,* cause of downy mildew of sunflower. *Indian Phytopath.* 43: 517–519.

Patil, M.S., Ramaswamy, N.M. and Sree Rangasamy, S.R. (1993). *In vitro* flowering in sunflower (*H. annuus L.). Curr. Sci.,* 65(7): 565–566.

Patil, P.V. and Anahosur, K.H. (1997). Identification of virulent races of sunflower rust *(Puccinia helianthi).* In: *Proc. 49th Annual Meeting and National Symp,* on *"Emerging issues in plant pahology".* Jabalpur. Abstr. p. 70.

Piquemal, G. (1970). How to produce hybrid sunflower seeds by inducing male sterility with gibberellic acid. *In*: Proc. *4th Int. Sunflower Conf.* Memphis. Tennesse. pp. 127–135.

Punia, M.S. and Gill, H.S. (1994). Correlations and path coefficient analysis for seed yield traits in sunflower. *Helia,* 17(20): 7–12.

Pustovoit, G.V. and Gubin, I.A. (1974). Results and prospects in sunflower breeding for group immunity by using the interspecific hybridization method. *In*: *Proc. 6th Int. Sunflower Conf.,* Bucharest. Romaina. pp. 373–381.

Pustovoit, G.V., Ilatovsky, V.P. and Slyusar, E.L. (1976). Results of prospects of sunflower breeding for group immunity by interspecific hybridization. *In*: *Proc. 7th Sunflower Conf.* Krasnodar, USSR, pp. 193–204.

Putt, E.D. (1940). Observations on morphological characters and flowering processes in the sunflower *(Helianthus annuus* L.). *Sci. Agric.,* 21: 167–169.

Putt, E.D. (1941). Investigations of breeding technique for the sunflower. *(Helianthus annuus* L.). *Sci. Agric.,* 21: 689–702.

Putt, E.D. (1943). Association of seed yield and oil content with other characters in sunflower. *Sci. Agric.,* 21: 377–383.

Putt, E.D. (1966). Heterosis, combining ability and predicted synthetics from a diallel cross in sunflowers. *(Helianthus annuus* L.) *Can. J. Plant Sci.,* 46: 59–67.

Putt, E.D. and Heiser, C.B. Jr. (1966). Male sterility and partial male sterility in sunflowers. *Crop Sci.,* 6: 165–168.

Putt, E.D. and Sackston, W.E. (1963). Studies on sunflower rust. IV. Two genes R1 and R2 for resistance in the host. *Can. J. Plant Sci.,* 43: 490–496.

Quresh, Z., Gulya, T.J. and Jan, C.C. (1989). New sources of rust resistance in wild *Helianthus annuus* accessions. *In*: Proc. *Sunflower Res. Workshop,* National Sunflower Assoc., Bismarck, ND. pp. 18–19.

Rajanna, M.P., Seetharam, A. and Virupakshappa, K. (1998). Stability of male steriliy in diverse cytosterile sources of sunflower *(Helianthus annuus* L.). *J. Oilseeds Res.,* 15: 46–49.

Rao, N.G.L. (1987). Studies on correlation and path coefficient analysis in sunflower *(Helianthus annuus* L.). *Mysore J. Agric. Sci.,* 21: 94–95.

Rao, N.M. and Singh, B. (1977). Inheritance of some quantitative characters in sunflower. *(H.annuus* L). *Pantnagar J. Res.,* 2: 144–146.

Rao, U.R., Pawar, B.B. and Dhumre, A.D. (1992). Combining ability studies in sunflower through diallel analysis. *J. Maharashtra Agric. Univ.,* 17: 149–150.

Rather, A.G. Sandha, G.S., Shafiq, Wani, A. and Sheikh, F.A. (1998). Correlation and path analysis in sunflower *(Helianthus annuus* L.). *J.Oilseeds Res.,* 15: 67–70.

Ravikumar, R.L. (1997). Effects of *Alternaria helianthi* toxin on sunflower pollen. *Helia,* 20(26): 29–34.

Ravikumar, R.L. and Chikkodi, S.B. (1998). Association between sporophytic reaction to *Alternaria helianthi* and gametophytic tolerance to pathogen culture filtrate in sunflower. *(Helianthus annuus* L.). *Euphytica,* 103: 173–180.

Ravikumar, R.L. Doddamani, I.K. and Kulkarni, M.S. (1995). Reaction of selected germplasm lines and *Helianthus tuberosus* derived introduction to *Alternaria helianthi. Helia,* 18(23): 67–72.

Ravishankar, K.V., Umashanker, R., Ravishankar, H.M., Udayakumar, M. and Prasad, T.G. (1991). Development of drought tolerant sunflower for semi–arid tracts of India: Duration of genotypes influence their performance under imposed moisture stress. *Helia,* 14(15): 77–86.

Reddy, M.J., Banerjee, A., Prakash, H. and Shetty, H.S. (1990). Differential response of sunflower and maize cultivars to the culture filtrate of *Alternaria alternata. Adv. Plant Sci.,* 3: 207–212.

Reddy, P.C. and Gupta, B.M. (1977). Disease loss appraisal due to leaf blight of sunflower incited by *Alternaria helianthi*. *Indian Phytopath*, 30: 569–570.

Reddy, P.S. and Thammiraju, B. (1977). Inheritance of fertility restoration in sunflower *(Helianthus annuus* L.). *Euphytica*, 26: 409–412.

Reddy, T.N. and Reddy, P.S. (1979). Studies in certain hybrids of sunflower *(Helianthus annuus* L.) *Indian J. Hered.*, 11: 21–23.

Roath, W.W. and Miller, J.F. (1982). Environmental effects on seed set in oilseed sunflower *(Helianthus annuus* L.). *Can. J.Plant Sci.*, 62: 867–873.

Rodriguez, R.H., Salaberry, M.T. and Encheverria, M.M. (1998). Inheritance of chlorophyll–deficiency in sunflower. *Helia*, 21(29): 109–114.

Roeckel–Drevet, P., Gagne, G., Mouzeyar, S., Gentzbittel, L., Philippon J., Nicolas, P., Tourvieille de Labrouhe, D. and Vear, F. (1996). Colocation of downy mildew *(Plasmopara halstedii)* resistance gènes in sunflower *(Helianthus annuus* L.) *Euphytica*, 91: 225–228.

Rogers, C.E., Thompson, T.T. and Seiler, G.J. (1982). Sunflower species of the United States. National Sunflower Association, Bismarck. N.D.

Russell, W.A. (1953). A study of the inter–relation of seed yield, oil content and other agronomic characters with sunflower inbred lines and their top crosses. *Can. J. Agric. Sci.*, 33: 291–314.

Sackston, W.E. (1962). Studies on sunflower rust. III. Occurrence, distribution and significance of races of *Puccinia helianthi* Schw. *Can. J. Bot.*, 40: 1449–1458.

Sackston, W.E., Gulya, T.J. and Miller, J.F. (1990). A proposed international system for designating races of *Plasmopara halstedii*. *Plant Dis.*, 74: 721–723.

Satyanarayana, A.R. and Seetharam, A. (1983). Method of hybrid seed production in sunflower *(Helianthus annuus* L.). II. Effect of planting ratios and method of pollination on seed quality. *Seed Res.*, 11: 8–12.

Schilling, E.E. and Heiser, C.B. (1981). Intrageneric classification of *Helianthus* (Compositae). *Taxonomy*, 30: 393–403.

Schuster, E. (1964). Inbreeding and heterosis in sunflower *(Helianthus annuus* L.). (Plant Breed. Abstr. 37: 1207). In *Wilhech Schmitz Verlag Ciessen*. p. 135.

Schuster, W. (1970a). Fertility of sunflower after enforced selfing. *Angeiv Bot.*, 40: 87–102.

Schuster, W. (1970b). Effects of continued inbreeding from Io to I18 on various characters of sunflower. Z. *Pflanzenzucht*, 64: 310–314.

Schuster, W. (1980). Investigations of the effects of continued inbreeding from the I0 to the I25 on different characters in the sunflower *(Helianthus annuus* L.). *Zeit. Fur. Pfanzen.*, 84(2): 148–167.

Schuster, W. and Friedt, W. (1988). Results and trends in breeding and cultivation of sunflower *(Helianthus annuus L.)* in West Germany. *Helia*, 11: 85–91.

Seetharam, A. (1981). Sunflower cultivation. *Indian Fmg.*, 25: 1–4.

Seetharam, A. (1982). Breeding strategy for developing high yielding varieties of sunflower. In Research and Development Strategies for Oilseed Productions in India. *Proc. Nat. Symp.* IARI, New Delhi, 143–152.

Seetharam, A. and Kusuma Kumari, P. (1975). Induction of male sterility by gibberellic acid in sunflower. *Indian J. Genet.*, 35: 136–138.

Seetharam, A. and Ravikumar, R.L. (1996). Sunflower. *In*: *Genetics, cytogenetics and breeding of crop plants*, (*Eds*. Bahl, P.N. and Salimath, P.M.), Oxford & IBH Publishing Co. New Delhi, pp. 283–310.

Seetharam, A. and Satyanarayana, A.R. (1983). Method of hybrid seed production in sunflower *(Helianthus annuus* L.) 1. Effect of parental ratios and method of pollination on hybrid seed yield and its attributes. *Seed Res.*, 11: 1–7.

Seetharam, A. and Virupakshappa, K. (1993). Present status and future directions of sunflower breeding in India. *In*: *Proc. National Seminar on Oilseeds Research and development in India: Status and stratégies,* Indian Society of Oilseeds Research. pp. 13–15.

Seetharam, A., Giriraj, K and Kusuma Kumari, P. (1980). Phenotypic stability of seed yield in sunflower hybrids. *Indian J. Genet.,* 40:102–104.

Seetharam, A., Giriraj, K. and Kusuma Kumari, P. (1978). Cernianka–66–A dwarf, early variety of sunflower. *Curr. Res.* 7: 164–165.

Seetharam, A., Kusuma Kumari, P., Patil, N.M. and Sindagi, S.S. (1977). Performance of hybrids of sunflower produced by means of cytoplasmic male sterility. *SABRAO J,* 9: 51–55.

Seiler, G.J. (1982). Variation in oil and oil quality of wild annual sunflower *(Helianthus annuus* L.) populations in a uniform environment. *In*: *Proc.* 10th *Int. Sunflower Conf.* Surfer's Paradise, Australia, pp. 212–215.

Seiler, G.J. (1983). Effect of genotype, flowering date, and environment on oil content and oil quality of wild sunflower seed. *Crop Sci.,* 23: 1063–1068.

Seiler, G.J. (1984). Variation in agronomic and morphological characteristics of several populations of wild annual sunflower (*Helianthus annuus* L.). *Helia,* 7: 29–32.

Seiler, G.J. (1985a). Evaluation of seeds of sunflower species for several chemical and morphological characteristics. *Crop Sci.,* 25: 183–187.

Seiler, G.J. (1985b). Interrelation of fatty acids in oil of wild annual sunflower *(Helianthus annuus* L.). *In*: Proc. *11th Int. Sunflower Conf.* Mar del Plata, Argentina, pp. 529–534.

Seiler, G.J. (1988). The genus *Helianthus* as a source of genetic variability for cultivated sunflower. *In*: *Proc.* 12th *Int. Sunflower Conf.* Novi Sad, Yugoslavia, 12: 17–58.

Seiler, G.J. (1991a). Registration of six interspecific sunflower germplasm lines derived from wild perennial species. *Crop Sci.,* 31: 1097–1098.

Seiler, G.J. (1991b). Registration of 15 interspecific sunflower germplasm lines derived from wild annual species. *Crop Sci.,* 31: 1389–1390.

Seiler, G.J. (1992). Utilization of wild sunflower species for the improvement of cultivated sunflower. *Field Crops Res.,* 30: 195–230.

Seiler, G.J. (1994). Oil concentration and fatty acid composition of achenes of North America *Helianthus* (Asteraceae) species. *Econ. Bot.,* 48: 271–279.

Seiler, G.J. and Rieseberg, L.H. (1997). Systematics, origin, and germplasm resources of the wild and domesticated sunflower. *In*: *Sunflower technology and production* (*Ed.* Schneiter, A.A.). ASA, CSSA, SSSA, Madison, WI, USA pp. 21–65.

Serieys, H.A. (1987). FAO subnetwork report 1984–1986. *In*: Skoric, D. (*Ed.*), Genetic evaluation and use of *Helianthus* wild species and their use in breeding programmes. FAO, Rome, Italy, pp. 1–23.

Serieys, H.A. and Vincourt, P. (1987). Characterization of some new cytoplasmic male sterility source from *Helianthus* genus. *Helia,* 10: 9–13.

Setty, K.L.T. and Singh, B. (1977): Line x tester analysis of combining ability in sunflower. *Pantnagar J. Res.,* 2: 23–26.

Shabana, R. (1974). Genetic variability of sunflower varieties and inbred lines. In Proc. *6th Int. Sunflower Conf.,* Bucharest, Romania. pp. 263–269.

Sheriff, N.M. and Appadurai, R. (1985). Genetic variability in some quantitative traits of sunflower. *Madras Agric. J.,* 72: 539–540.

Sheriff, N.M., Appadurai, R. and Rangaswamy, M. (1985). Combining ability in sunflower. *Indian J. Agric. Sci.,* 55: 315–318.

Shinde, Y.M., Wattamwar, M.J. and Patil, G.D., (1983). Variability and corrélation studies in sunflower. *J. Maharashtra Agric. Univ.,* 8: 122–123.

Shivaraju, N., Giriraj, K., Hiremath, S.R. and Seetharam, A. (1987). Autogamy in sunflower. *J. Oilseeds Res.,* 4: 292–294.

Sindagi, S.S., Kulkarni, R.S. and Seetharam, A. (1979). Line X tester analysis of combining ability in sunflower (*Helianthus annuus* L.). *Sunflower Newslett.* 3(2): 11–12.

Singh, B., Sachan, J.N. and Singh, D. (1977). Variability and correlations in sunflower (*Helianthus annuus* L.).. *Pantnagar J. Res.,* 2: 22–30.

Singh, S.B. and Labana, K.S. (1990). Correlation and path analysis in sunflower. Crop *Improv.,* 17: 49–53.

Skaloud, V. and Kovacik, A. (1974). Inheritance of some heteromorphic characters in sunflower. (*Helianthus annuus* L.). *In*: Proc. *6th Int. Sunflower Conf.,* Bucharest. Romania, pp. 291–295.

Skaloud, V. and Kovacik, A. (1994). Findings of sunflower self–fertility in connection with line hybridization. *Helia,* 17(20): 13–20.

Skoric, D. (1974). Correlation among the most important characters of sunflower in F1, generation. *In*: Proc. *6th Int. Sunflower Conf.* Bucharest, Romania. pp. 283–289.

Skoric, D. (1987). FAO subnetwork report. *In:* Skoric, D. (*Ed.*) Genetic evaluation and use of *Helianthus* wild species and their use in breding programmes. FAO, Rome, Italy pp. 1–17.

Skoric, D. (1992). Achievements and future directions of sunflower breeding. *Field Crops Res.,* 30: 231–270.

Soldatov, K.I. (1976). Chemical mutagenesis in sunflower breeding. In Proc. 7th *Int., Sunflower Conf.* Krasnodar, USSR, pp. 352–357.

Spirova, M. (1978). Inheritance of nuclear male sterility obtained by inbreeding sunflower (H.*annuus*). *Cenetika Selektsiya,* 11: 391–398.

Srinivas, T., Chandrasekhararao, K. and Chattopadhyay, C. (1998). Effect of *Alternaria* blight (*Alternaria helianthi; Alternaria alternata*) on yield of sunflower (*Helianthus annuus* L.). in India. *Helia,* 21(28): 75–80.

Srivastava, A.N. and Mishra, R. (1976). Genotypic and phenotypic variability in quantitative characters in sunflower. *Madras Agri. J.,* 63: 209–210.

Sudhakar, D., Seetharam, A. and Sindagi, S.S. (1984). Analysis of combining ability in sunflower. *J. Oilseeds Res.,* 1: 157–166.

Sujatha, M. and Prabhakaran, A.J. (1997). Propagation and maintenance of wild sunflower *in vitro. Helia,* 20(27): 107–114.

Sujatha, M., Prabhakaran, A.J. and Chattopadhyay, C. (1997). Reaction of wild sunflowers and certain interspecific hybrids to *Alternaria helianthi. Helia,* 20(27): 15–24.

Swamygowda, and Giriraj, K. (1989). Evaluation of sunflower inbreds, hybrids and populations for self–compatibility over seasons. *Indian J. Genet.,* 49: 1–7.

Tanimu, B. and Ado, S.C. (1988). Relationships between yield and yield components in forty populations of sunflower. *Helia,* 11: 17–20.

Thompson, T.E., Rogers, C.E., Zimmerman, D.C., Huang, H.C., Whelan, E.D.P. and Miller, J.F. (1978). Evaluation of *Helianthus* speices for disease resistance and oil content and quality. *In*: *Proc. 8th Int Sunflower Conf.* Minneapolis, MN. pp. 501–509.

Thompson, T.E., Zimmerman, D.C. and Rogers, C.E. (1981). Wild *Helianthus* as a genetic resource. *Field Crops Res.,* 4: 333–343.

Toms, E.M. and Pooni, H.S. (1995). An evaluation of crosses between some French male sterile and UK restorer lines of the sunflower. *Helia,* 18(22): 51–58.

Tuberosa, R., Alba, E., Greco, I. and Paradisi, V. (1982). Evaluation of combining ability in pure lines of sunflower. *Sementi Elette* 28; 19–22.

Tunwar, N.S. and Singh, S.V. (1988). *In*: *Indian minimum seed certification standards.* CSCB New Delhi, pp. 119–121.

Udayakumar, M., Ramarao, S., Prasad, T.G. and Sastry, K.S.K. (1976). Translocation of I4C metabolites to the head in sunflower. *Indian J. Exptl. Biol..* 15; 302–304.

Unrau, J. and White, W.J. (1944). The yield and other characters of inbred lines and single crosses of sunflowers. *Sci. Agric..* 24: 516–528.

Urie, L. (1985). Inheritance of high oleic acid in sunflower. *Crop Sci. 25:* 986–989.

Vanishree, G., Ananthasayana, K., Nagabhushanam, G.V.S. and Jagadish, C.A. (1988). Correlation and path coefficient analysis in sunflower *(Helianthus annuus* L). *J. Oilseeds Res.* 5: 46–51.

Varshney, S.K. and Singh, B. (1977). Correlation and path coefficient analysis in sunflower. *Pantnagar J. Res.,* 2: 147–149.

Vear, F, (1974). Studies on resistance to downy mildew in sunflower *(Helianthus annuus* L.). In *Proc. 6th Sunflower Conf.* Bucharest, Romania pp. 297–302.

Vear, F., Gentzbittel, L., Philippon, J., Mouzeyar, S., Mestries, E., Roeckel–Drevet, P., Tourvieille de Labrouhe, D. and Nicolas, P. (1997). The genetics of resistance of five races of downy mildew *(Plasmopara halstedii)* in sunflower *(Helianthus annuus* L.). *Theor. Appl. Genet.,* 95: 584–589.

Venkateswaralu, V., Reddy, P.S. and Rao, D.V.M. (1980). Heritability studies in sunflower. *Sunflower Newslett,* 4: 10–11.

Virupakshappa, K. (1995). Heterosis breeding in sunflower: Historical development, present status and future perspective. *In*: *Hybrid Research and Development* (*Eds*. Rai. M. and Mauria, S.). Indian Society of Seed Technology, pp. 81–91.

Virupakshappa, K. and Sindagi, S.S. (1988). A note on germplasm collections in sunflower. *J. Oilseeds Res.,* 5: 119–120.

Virupakshappa, K., Ranganatha, A.R.G. and Reddy, B.N. (1998). Hybrid sunflower seed production technology, Directorate of Oilseeds Research, Hyderabad. pp. 1–99.

Virupakshappa, K., Seetharam, A., Jayarame Gowda and Ravikumar, R.L. (1991). Maintainer and restorer behaviour of some sunflower lines on new cytoplasmic male sterile sources. *J. Oilseeds Res.,* 8: 195–198.

Vranceanu, A.V. Stoenescu, F.M. and Caramangiu (1974). Maintenance of the biological and genetic value of inbred lines in sunflower hybrid seed production. In: *Proc. 6th Int. Sunflower Conf.* Bucharest, Remania. pp. 427–433.

Vranceanu, A.V. (1970). Advances in sunflower breeding in Romania. In *Proc. 4th Int. Sunflower Conf.,* Memphis, Tennessee, pp. 136–148.

Vranceanu, A.V. and Stoenescu, F.M. (1970). Testing sunflower cytoplasm in relation to genes for mâle sterility. *Plant Breed. Abstr.,* 43; 3837.

Vranceanu, A.V. and Stoenescu, F.M. (1972). Producing hybrid sunflower seed on the basis of genetic male sterility. *Probl. Agric.,* 24: 69.

Vranceanu, A.V. and Stoenescu, F.M. (1978). Genes for pollen fertility restoration in sunflowers. *Euphytica,* 27: 617–627.

Vranceanu, A.V. and Stoenescu, F.M. (1982). Achievements and prospects of sunflower genetics, breeding and induced mutation utilization. In *Improvement of oilseed and industriel crops by induced mutations.* IAEA, Vienna pp. 81–87.

Vranceanu, A.V. Stoenescu, F.M. and Scarlet, A. (1978). The influence of different genetic and environmental factors on pollen self–compatibility in sunflower. *In*: *Proc. 8th Int. Sunflower Conf.* Minneapolis, MN. pp. 453–465.

Vranceanu, A.V., luras, M. and Stoenescu, F.M. (1986). A contribution to the diversification of the CMS sources in sunflower. *Helia,* 9*:* 21–25.

Vranceanu, A.V., Pirvu, N. and Stoenescu, RM. (1981a). New sunflower downy mildew resistance genes and their management. *Helia,* 4: 23–27.

Vranceanu, A.V., Pirvu, N., Stoenescu, F.M., Iliescu, H. and Lascu, I. (1981b). Genetic aspects of the resistance of sunflower to *Sclerotinia sclerotiorum* (Lib) de By (abstr). *Plant Breed. Abstr.,* 53: 9002.

Whelan, E.D.P. (1980). A new source of cytoplasmic male sterility in sunflower. *Euphytica,* 29*:* 33–46.

Whelan, E.D.P. (1981). Cytoplasmic male sterility in *Helianthus giganteus* L. x H. *annuus* L. interspecific hybrids. *Crop Sci.,* 21: 855–856.

Zali, A A., Yazdi, S.B. and Amirshahi, M.C. (1977). Multiple regression analysis for different quantitative characters in sunflower. *Agron. J.,* 18: 78–79.

Zimmer, D.E. and Kinman, M.I. (1972). Downy mildew resistance in cultivated sunflower and its inheritance. *Crop Sci.,* 12: 749–751.

Zimmer, D.E. and Rehdar, D.A. (1976). Rust resistance of wild *Helianthus* species of the North Central United States. *Phytopathol.,* 66: 208–211.

# 13

# Groundnut

## 1. INTRODUCTION

Groundnut (*Arachis hypogaea* L.) is the most important oilseed and a very important exportable agricultural commodity in our country. Groundnut is grown in about 84 countries on an area of 23.71 million ha with the production of 30.92 million tonnes and an average productivity of 1304 kg/ha. Among the groundnut producing nations, India shows the highest area under this crop and is the second largest producer, next to China (Fig. 1).

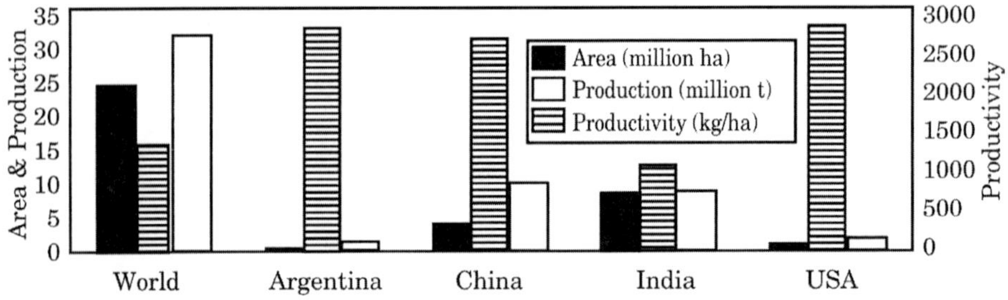


**Fig. 1:** Area, production and productivity of groundnut in world and major groundnut growing countries.

In India, groundnut occupies about 8 million ha with a production of about 8 million tonnes. It is cultivated in four seasons *viz.*, *kharif*, rabi, summer, and spring. The distribution of groundnut in India is presented in Fig. 2. About 19% of the total area under groundnut is irrigated. Around 6.8 million ha of the crop is rainfed where productivity

V.L. Chopra (Ed.): Breeding Field Crops I: Practices, Studium Press (LLC), USA.

fluctuates between 500 and 1500 kg/ha. The national average productivity is about 1000 kg/ha. In the rabi/summer season almost the entire crop is grown with assured moisture with an average yield of about 1500 kg/ha. About 91% of total groundnut area and production are confined to the states of Andhra Pradesh, Gujarat, Karnataka, Tamil Nadu, Maharashtra and Orissa (Fig. 2). The rest of the area and production is scattered mainly in the states of Rajasthan, Uttar Pradesh, Madhya Pradesh and Punjab.

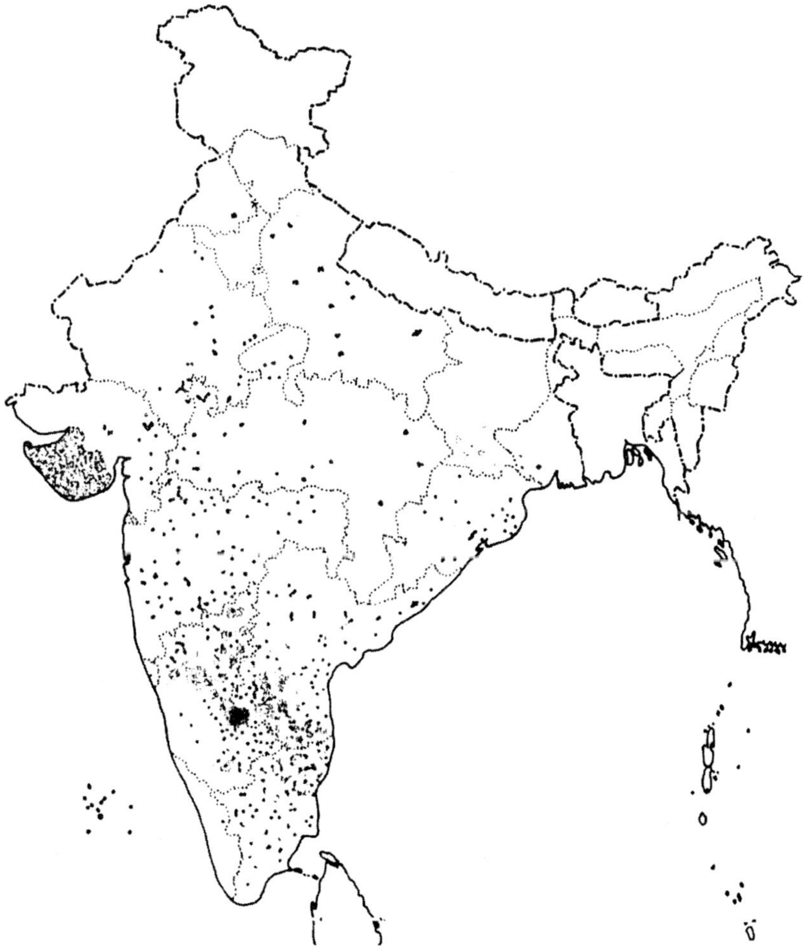

**Fig. 2:** Distribution of groundnut in India (The dots depict approximate spread and density)

Groundnut cultivation in the world is spread over a geographic area falling between 40°N and 40°S latitudes. It is not sensitive to day length in the classical sense. Because of this, groundnut is grown in India all the year round except when the temperature is very low (< 15°C). However, longer days tend to produce more vegetative growth and flowers. According to Williams *et al.* (1975), about 1600 heat units are required to harvest a good crop of groundnut. Although groundnut is a $C_3$ plant, some of its physiological characteristics like photosynthetic efficiency approaches the $C_4$ plants. It has been reported that 60% solar radiation for 60 days after emergence is critical for groundnut (Ono and Ozaki, 1971). Groundnut has been found to grow and yield well in areas receiving 50-125 cm of well-distributed rainfall. According to John (1949) the ideal rainfall for a successful crop of rainfed groundnut would be about 8-12 cm during summer months just preceding the sowing to facilitate the preparatory cultivation, about 10-12 cm at sowing, about 20 cm from early pod development to pod maturity. Variability in the amount and distribution of rainfall is the most important factor limiting yield of rainfed groundnut.

Well drained, light coloured, loose, friable, sandy loam soils well supplied with calcium and moderate amount of organic matter are best suited for groundnut cultivation. In India, groundnut is grown on a variety of soils but more extensively on light textured red sandy, red loamy, alluvial and coastal alluvial soils. Considerable area is also found on medium black and mixed black and red soils. Soil texture is an important consideration for growing groundnut. Heavy and stiff clays are unsuitable for cultivation of rainfed groundnut as they cause difficulties in pod growth and harvesting.

About 83% area is grown in the *kharif* season and is mainly rainfed. The rest of the area is grown in rabi, summer and spring seasons. In areas where winter is not severe and night temperatures do not fall below 15°C, groundnut is grown in the rabi season on a limited scale (12.23% area), a big chunk of which is in the rice fallows. The main rice fallow areas are in the coastal belts of Tamil Nadu, Andhra Pradesh, Karnataka and Orissa where groundnut is cultivated to utilize the residual moisture after harvest of rice or with minimal irrigation. Summer groundnut is mainly grown in the states of Orissa, Tamil Nadu, Andhra Pradesh, Karnataka, Gujarat and Maharashtra under irrigated conditions. Spring groundnut is cultivated at a very limited scale mainly in Uttar Pradesh, the Punjab and West Bengal. The parts of our country where groundnut has a good potential as a relatively new commercial crop are West Bengal, Assam and the Northeastern Hill states.

Although about 60% of *kharif* groundnut is grown as a sole crop, year after year, on the same piece of land in which no other crop is grown, a sustainable system involves well planned alternate use of the land through sequential cropping, intercropping, relay cropping etc. keeping groundnut as the central commodity of the system. The major groundnut-based cropping systems, which are either practiced, or can potentially be practiced, are the following:

1. *Sequential cropping*: The promising crop sequences for different parts of India are groundnut-wheat, groundnut-sunflower, groundnut-chickpea, groundnut-horse gram and rice-groundnut.
2. *Intercropping*: This system gives some safety to farmers against natural calamities and helps in better utilization of farm resources. The most promising intercropping systems identified in the recent years are, inter-cropping of groundnut with pigeonpea followed by inter-cropping of groundnut with sunflower and groundnut with cereals (bajra, maize and sorghum).

Groundnut has a distinct position among the oilseeds as it can be consumed and utilized in diverse ways. In India, it is also known as a poor man's almond. Mahatma Gandhi, the Father of the Nation, used to consume a few groundnut kernels and goat milk as a substitute for a meal. The pattern of utilization of groundnut in India has been presented in Fig. 3. In addition to being a source of edible oil and food, groundnuts and its products are used in other ways also as shown in the Fig. 3 (% of uses).

All parts of groundnut plant can be utilized. The vines with leaves make an excellent fodder for livestock. The shells are used for making particleboards and also as boiler fuel. The shells are a potential resource of some costly chemicals like the furfurals. Attempts are on to utilize them for organic farming. The kernels have many uses in the human and animal diet. It can be used directly for table purposes or crushed to produce oil and a high protein meal. Groundnut oil is used in cooking, lighting and as a food constituent. Groundnut meal (cake) is an excellent source of protein to balance the diet and to supplement animal feed. In the western countries the major use of groundnut is for peanut butter, direct dried and roasted products, making cookies and candies and other snack foods. Boiled and salted groundnut pods are popular in the near eastern countries. Quality of groundnut seed is affected by many factors like drying, storage and pest infestation. The ratio of oleic/linoleic acid determines the shelf life of groundnut; higher quantities of later lead to poor keeping qualifies but from nutrition point of view a lower ratio is preferable.

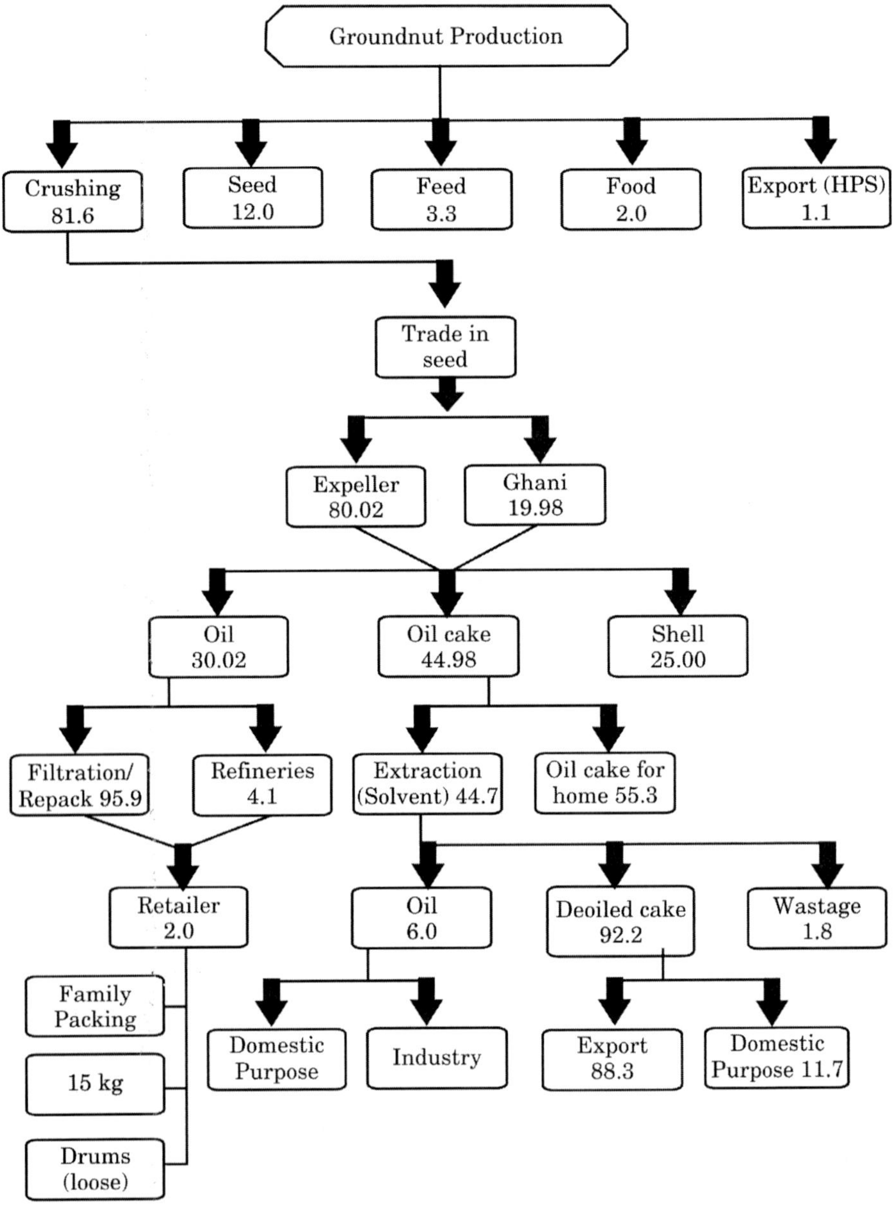


**Fig. 3:** Groundnut utilization pattern in India

## 1.1. Nutritional qualities of groundnut

1. Groundnut kernel contains 44-55% oil, 22-32% protein and 8-14% soluble sugars.

2. Raw groundnut oil can be stored for up to 2 years.

3. It has a smoking point (temperature at which smoke appears first) of around 240°C, making it a good medium for deep fat frying. The quality of oil does not deteriorate even after 20 hours of deep fat frying.

4. The oil contains about 30% linoleic acid, which is an essential fatty acid for human beings. It is rich, nutritious good quality edible oil.

5. Cake contains 45-50% protein. Groundnut protein is rich in all amino acids except leucine and methionine.

6. An adult human being requires about 55 g of protein per day. Groundnut alone can contribute on an average about 10% (5-6 g) of this requirement in India.

7. Sucrose is the major carbohydrate of groundnut. It also contains two undesirable sugars *viz.*, stachyose and raffinose.

8. Each 100 g of groundnut kernel can furnish about 564 calories of energy.

9. It is a rich source of oil (47 g/100g).

10. It is sufficiently endowed with protein, calcium, iron and vitamin $B_1$ and E.

11. It is, however, poor in constituent like iron, vitamins A, C and D and essential amino acids like lysine and methionine. These deficiencies can easily be made up if food is properly balanced.

12. Groundnut contains some anti-nutritional factors like trypsin inhibitor and phytic acid. Mild treatments like boiling and roasting generally inactivate anti-nutritional factors and hence these do not pose much problem. Aflatoxin development also can be prevented by proper handling and storage methods. The upper limit of aflatoxins in groundnut for edible use is 30 μg/kg.

## 2. ORIGIN AND EVOLUTION

Early explorers found evidence of groundnut being cultivated extensively in both Meso-America and South America. Remnant pericarp tissue recovered from archaeological sites in Fera dates its purposeful agricultural use there at approximately 3900-3750 years before the present. Its domestication probably first took place in the valleys of the Parana and Parguay river systems in the Gran Chaco area of South America. All wild species in the genus *Arachis* are found only in South America. The centre of diversity of *Arachis* could be in the Mato Grosso or Planalto profile from Corumba to Joazeiro (Gregory *et al.,* 1980) in Brazil.

From South America, Portuguese explorers and traders are thought to have carried groundnut to Europe, Asia, both coasts of Africa and Pacific islands. Much later, groundnut was introduced into the USA from Africa through slave trade. Groundnut was then transported along the American west coast to Mexico and then across the Pacific to the Philippines, from where it spread to China, India, Malaysia and Indonesia.

In India, groundnut first reached on the east coast of the then Madras province (present Tamil Nadu and parts of Andhra Pradesh and Karnataka). Available records tell that groundnut was first cultivated with turmeric in the Mysore State (Karnataka) around 1800 A.D. But the first large-scale cultivation was reported in 1850-51 in the South Arcot district of Madras State. It moved to the northwest around 1879 and was cultivated in erstwhile Bombay (present Maharashtra and Gujarat) and Madras State. Groundnut was introduced into the Saurashtra region of Gujarat State from Tamil Nadu in the year 1910 by one Shri Padmabhai Patel of Pipalia village of Rajkot district. Subsequently, the crop spread to other states in the country.

## 3. TAXONOMY

Bentham (1841) associated *Arachis* with the genera *Stylosanthes* and *Chapmannia* in the tribe *Hedysaria* of the family Leguminosae. Taubert (1894) subdivided the tribe *Hedysariae* into six subtribes and placed *Arachis* in the subtribe *Stylosanthineae.* The genera *Chapmannia, Stylosanthes* and *Arachis* of the subtribe *Stylosanthineae* are characterized by a distinct tubular hypanthium, pinnate leaves and straight embryo. The genus *Arachis* differs from the other two genera by having a geocarpic peg, an underground fruiting habit and by producing most of its flowers at the lower nodes (Taubert, 1894; Burkart, 1939; Hoehne, 1940). Rudd (1981) placed *Arachis* in the tribe *Aeschynomeneae,* which was considered to be a subtribe of Hedysariae. The classification of the genus *Arachis* is, to large extent, still incomplete. Similarly the exploration and documentation of genus *Arachis* is still incomplete.

The genus *Arachis* is subdivided into seven sections (*nom.nud.*) *viz.*, *Arachis, Erectoides, Caulorhizae, Rhizomatosae, Ambinervosae, Extranervosae,* and *Triseminlae.* The sections *Arachis, Erectoides, Rhizomatosae* have 1-3 series also. Each section has different species except for the section *Ambinervosae* in which no species name have been given so far (Table 1).

**Table 1:** Section series and the number of species in *Arachis*

| ***Section*** | ***Series*** | ***Ploidy level code*** | ***Section/Series described*** | ***No. of species*** |
|---|---|---|---|---|
| *Arachis* | Annuae | 2n | Al | 5 |
| | Perennes | 2n | A2 | 6 |
| | Amphiploides | 4n | A3 | 3 |
| *Erectoides* | Trifoliolatae | 2n | E1 | 2 |
| | Tetrafoliatae | 2n | E2 | 4 |
| | Procumbensae | 2n | E3 | 2 |
| *Caulorhizae* | | 2n | C | 2 |
| *Rhizomatosae* | Prorhizomatosae | 2n | R1 | 1 |
| | Eurhizomatosae | 4n | R2 | 2 |
| *Extranervosae* | | 2n | EX | 7 |
| *Ambinervosae* | | 2n | AM | – |
| *Triseminalae* | | 2n | T | 1 |

Modified after Krapovickas (1973) and Gregory *et al.* (1973)

Inter-specific cross-compatibility studies both between and within section of the genus *Arachis* shed some light on sectional relationships. The gene pool of the genus *Arachis* is classified into primary, secondary and tertiary based on cross-compatibility relationship (Table 2).

**Table 2:** Gene pool of *Arachis*

| ***Gene pool*** | ***Section*** |
|---|---|
| Primary | *Arachis hypogaea* and *A. monticola* Krap. *et,* Rig. |
| Secondary | All the diploid species of section *Arachis nom.nud.* |
| Tertiary | *A. glandulifera (Arachis)* and species of sections *Erectoides* Krap. *et* Greg. *nom. nud.* *Ambinervosae* Krap. *et.* Greg. *nom.nud.* *Caulorhizae* Krap. *et.* Greg. *nom.nud.* *Rhizomatosae* Krap *et* Greg *nom.nud.* *Extranervosae* Krap *et.* Greg. *nom.nud.* *Triseminlae* Krap. *et* Greg. *nom.nud.* |

The tetraploid species *A. monticola* is crossable with all four varietal forms of cultivated groundnut and produces fertile hybrids, because of which it does not deserve a separate specific name as proposed by Bhagat and Reddy (1988). It could be brought under *A. hypogaea* as a third subspecies, besides *hypogaea* and *fastigiata.* The secondary gene pool consists of all the species of section Arachis with a diploid chromosome number of 2n = 20, and which are crossable with all forms of cultivated groundnut. These diploid members form triploid hybrids with *A. hypogaea,* although most of the hybrids are sterile. The tertiary gene pool comprises *A. glandulifera* and the species belonging to the other six sections. The gene flow between different sections within the tertiary gene pool and between the tertiary and primary or secondary gene pools is much restricted.

Gregory *et al.* (1951) had given the following classification of cultivated groundnut on the basis of branching pattern, presence or absence of reproductive axes on main axis and the arrangement of reproductive and vegetative axes on the primary branches.

*Arachis hypogaea* sub-species *fastigiata:* Erect and bunch in habit, branching sequential, inflorescence usually present on the main axis and first branching on the cotylendonary laterals are reproductive, seed dormancy usually absent, foliage light green. It includes four varieties:

| | ***Branching*** | ***Infloresence*** | ***Other characters*** |
|---|---|---|---|
| var. *fastigiata* (Common name : Valencias) | Vegetative branches on primary branches absent or regularly placed at the distal end nodes | Usually simple, but may elongate to form a conspicuous long branch that may occasionally terminal leaves | Pods with two or two to four seeds; beak absent, slight or prominent, size medium to small, testa colour tan, red, white yellow, purple and variegated |
| var. *peruviana* | Long, strong reproductive branches (5-10 cm), with strong central axis and lateral branches | Usually simple | Fruits with very marked reticulation, and with prominent longitudinal ribs |
| var. *aequatoriana* | Long reproductive branches, mainly the lateral branches | Compound, Central axis mostly with short inflorescence and reproductive branches | Leaflets with a hairy (1-2 mm) dorsal surface of entire surface hairy |
| var. *vulgaris* (Common name: Spanish) | Vegetative branches occasional and irregularly placed | Inflorescence compound | Pods usually with 2 seeds, beak present or absent; size medium to small; testa colour tan, red, white or purple |

*Source*: Krapovickas and Gregory (1994)

*Arachis hypogaea* sub-species *hypogaea:* Semi-spreading or spreading in habit, branching alternate, inflorescence simple and absent on main axis, seed dormancy usually present, foliage dark green, first branch on cotylendonary lateral always vegetative. It includes two varieties:

| | ***Branching*** | ***Infloresence*** | ***Other characters*** |
|---|---|---|---|
| var. *hypogaea* (Common name: Virginia runner — more spreading Virginia bunch — more compact) | Vegetative and reproductive branches placed alternatively The first cotyledonary lateral is always vegetative | Usually simple and expands during maturation | Main axis in procumbent forms usually short; stem not very hairy; medium-late in maturity. Usually two-seeded, pod peak generally very prominent |
| var. *hirsuta* (Common name: Peruvian runner) | Habit procumbent, main axis may exceed 1 m, | Usually simple | Stem fairly hairy, very late in maturity |

There is full cross compatibility among the cultivars, with and between the subspecies.

The progenitors of *A. hypogaea* are as yet unidentified. With limited material at their disposal, various workers speculated that *A. pusilla, A. prostrata* and *A. sylvestris* could have been the ancestral forms of *A. hypogaea.* On cytogenetic grounds, Husted (1936) suggested that *A. hypogaea* had an amphidiploid origin. Mends (1947) concluded that the tetraploid cultivated groundnut could have arisen spontaneously by chromosome doubling of a diploid form. Krapovickas and Rigoni (1957) agreed with this. However, Gregory and Gregory (1976) suggested that the wild amphidiploids arose from a hybrid between annual and perennial species within the section *Arachis.* They also suggested that these parents could have been similar to *A. cardenasii nom.nud.* and *A. durenansis nom.nud.* On the basis of karyotype studies, Smartt *et al.* (1978) suggested that *A. batizocoi* and *A. cardenasii* were probable ancestral parents of *A. hypogaea.* Singh and Moss (1982) also suggested that *A. cardenasii* could be one of the ancestral parents for the tetraploid species. However, based on ribosomal gene families, and occurrence of centromeric bands, *A. villosa* and *A. ipaensis* were conjectured as the diploid progenitors of *A. hypogaea* and *A. monticola* (Raina and Mukai, 1999). This study excludes *A. batizocoi* as the B genome donor species for *A. hypogaea* and *A. monticola.*

Very recently Chandran *et al.* (2000) studied the numerical taxonomy in 35 accessions belonging to 13 species of *Arachis* section using morphological, palynological, and anatomical characters. The species of the section *Arachis* possessed high intra and inter-specific variation for most of the morphological and anatomical traits. Accessions of the species, *A. batizocoi, A. correnentina, A. stenosperma, A. monticola, and A. hypogaea* clustered together indicating their similarity. However, the accessions of *A. duranensis* formed four clusters. *A. kempf-mercadoi* formed two clusters, which were distinct in their morphological, anatomical and palynological traits. *A. batizocoi* was found to be closely related to *A. duranensis* accessions. The annual species, *A. stenosperma* showed more similarities with the perennial species *A. correntina, A. diogoi, A. khulmanii* and *A. kempf-mercadoi* in its long lateral branches, long hypanthium with bigger standard petal and leaflet shape and size. *A. monticola* was found to be closely related to *A. duranensis* accession (ICG 8208). The diploid species *A. cardenasii* like the tetraploid *A. monticola* and *A. hypogaea* showed a close resemblance in having triangular oblate shape of the pollen grains at polar view. The presence of triangular oblate shape of the pollen grains in the diploid species, *A. cardenasii* and *A. correntina,* indicated that one of the species might have contributed to the evolution of the amphiploid species, *A. monticola* and *A. hypogaea.* However, as Stalker (1980) indicated, many species still need to be collected and more basic information is required before the question of the putative parents of the cultivated groundnut can be resolved.

The genus has basic chromosome number of $x = 10$ and comprises diploid ($2n = 20$), and tetraploid ($2n = 40$) species. Cultivated groundnuts are allotetraploids ($2n=40$) in contrast to the wild diploid species ($2n=20$). The wild species of this section can be hybridized well and through ploidy and genomic manipulations desirable genes can be introgressed into the cultivated form. Very low level of variability was found in cultivated groundnut, while abundant variability was present among wild diploid species (Halward *et al.,* 1991).

## 4. MAINTENANCE OF GENETIC RESOURCES

International Crops Research Institute for Semi-Arid Tropics (ICRISAT), Hyderabad has been identified by the Food and Agricultural Organization (FAO) as the world repository of groundnut. They are engaged in collection, characterization, conservation and distribution of groundnut germplasms. There are about 15342 accessions including 197 wild *Arachis* accessions maintained at the ICRISAT.

National Research Centre for Groundnut of the Indian Council of Agricultural Research at Junagadh has been identified as an active collection centre by the International Plant Genetic Resources Institute, where the working collections of the groundnut are maintained and characterized. The base collection of groundnut germplasm available in India is maintained in the long-term storage facility of the NBPGR (ICAR), New Delhi. NRCG regularly publishes catalogues based on characterization of the germplasm for the benefit of the breeders.

## 5. FLOWER STRUCTURE AND FLORAL BIOLOGY

An inflorescenc in groundnut is either represented by a solitary flower (simple inflorescence) or by a raceme containing two to five flowers (compound inflorescence) in the axils of the cataphylls. Flower number per inflorescenc varies with cultivars. A flowering branch never occurs at the same node as a vegetative branch, although they may appear to do so because of the shortness of the internodes below the first cataphyll of a branch.

In the variety *hypogaea,* the inflorescences are simple and expand slightly in length during maturation. In the variety *vulgaris,* the inflorescences are compound and expand moderately. In the variety *fastigiata,* the inflorescences are simple, but may elongate to form a conspicuous long branch that may occasionally terminate in leaves. The length of the inflorescence is also dependent on the cultivar and may exceed 10 cm in some cultivars (Ramanantha Rao, 1988).

Groundnut flowers are typically papilionaceous and zygomorphic with a reduced pedicel. What appears to be a pedicel is actually an elongated hypanthium. The calyx has five lobes; in two groups of one and four. The single sepal is juxtaposed to the keel while the other four are fused except at their tips. The standard petal has a range of colours from yellow to orange to dark orange or garnet, and in rare cases, it is white or creamy white. It has a central area called the standard crescent, which has darker Unes (or markings) radiating from the base to the periphery of the standard in most cultivars. The wings are generally yellow and wrap around the keel. The keel is pale yellow, and closely wraps around the stamens and the upper parts of the style and stigma. There are 10 monadelphous stamens of which two are staminodes (sterile) represented only by filaments. The remaining eight are dimorphic. Of these, four are with globose, dorsi-fixed and monothecous anthers, alternating with four having adnate, notrorse, oblong anthers, three of which are bithecous and one, opposite the standard, monothecous. The basal two-third length of the filaments is fused. The filaments of the globose anthers are initially shorter than those of the oblong ones, but they elongate and become equal to or longer than them a few hours after pollination. The ovary is situated at the base of the hypanthium; it is superior, about 1.5 mm long, and normally has two to four ovules, occasionally five, and rarely six. The style is long and filiform with two bends; the first bend is closed to the upper end of the hypanthium, and the second one occurs along with the bend in the keel petal. The style has upward-slanting hairs on its distal portion. The stigma is club-shaped and usually on level with, or slightly above, the anthers.

Flowering begins 17-35 days after seedling emergence, depending on the cultivar and environmental conditions. Low temperatures generally delay flowering. The flowering pattern varies among and within the botanical varieties. Generally the valencias flower before the other types and have short time of flowering. The spanish types also flower early, but the first flowering peak may be broader than that in the valencias and some cultivars have multiple peaks. The virginia types take more time than the other two types to start flowering and have multiple flowering peaks.

The flower bud is 6-10 mm long 24 h before anthesis and, during the day, the hypanthium elongates slowly and the bud attains a length of 10-20 mm. During the night, elongation of the hypanthium is faster. The flower reaches maximum length of 50-70 mm at the time of anthesis. Flower opening is normally at sunrise, but may be delayed by low temperatures. Anthers may dehisce 7-8 h before flowers open in some genotypes; in others they may not do so even at flower opening. Stigma becomes receptive about 24 h before anthesis and its receptivity persists for about 12 hours after anthesis. Pollen grains are smooth, oval and sticky. Fertilization occurs about 6 h after pollination.

## 6. GENETICS OF QUALITATIVE AND QUANTITATIVE TRAITS

The work on genetics of groundnut was initiated by Vander Stok in 1910. Since then the genetics of numerous traits has been analyzed and reviewed (Seshadri, 1962; Hammons, 1973; Wynne and Cofelt, 1982; Reddy, 1988; Murthy and Reddy, 1996; Murthy and Ghewande, 1996). For details on this subject the reader may refer to the above-mentioned reviews. Some sample literature on inheritance studies is summarized below. It must be kept in mind that the results in these studies on inheritance pattern depend on the genetic differences between parents used in the studies. Hence a report cannot be taken as universal, but only as a guideline.

### 6.1. Genetics of qualitative traits

**Table 3:** The genetics of important qualitative traits in groundnut

| *Trait* | *Type of gene action* | *Reference(s)* |
|---|---|---|
| Growth habit | Spreading type dominant over bunch, and governed by one pair of genes | Higgins, 1938; Jadhav and Sinde, 1979 |
| | Spreading type dominant over bunch, two pair of genes | Coffelt, 1974 |
| | Bunch type dominant over Spreading, single pair of factors | Balaiah *et al.*, 1977 |

**Table 3:** (*Contd...*)

**Table 3:** (*Contd...*)

| *Trait* | *Type of gene action* | *Reference(s)* |
|---|---|---|
| | Semi-spreading dominant over bunch, single pair of factors | Balaiah *et al.,* 1977 |
| Main stem inflorescence | Two sets of duplicate loci with epistasis between sets | Wynne, 1975 |
| Sequential flowering | Sequential monogenic recessive to alternate | Chandramouli *et al.,* 1986 |
| Plant maturity | Perennial growth habit dominant to annual | Seshadri, 1962 |
| | Earliness recessive to late maturity, single factor | Badami, 1928 |
| Dwarfism | Dwarf recessive to tall, single gene | Bhuiyan, 1984 |
| | Dwarf recessive to tall, 2 genes | Balaiah *et al.,* 1977 |
| | Dwarf recessive to tall, 3 genes | Ashri, 1968 |
| | Dwarf recessive to tall, 4 genes with complementary-duplicate action | Coffelt and Hammons, 1973 |
| Stem pigmentation | Dark or Purple colour dominant to light with monogenic inheritance | Balaiah *et al.,* 1977 |
| Pod size | Large pod dominant to small pod size | Balaiah *et ai,* 1977 |
| | Controlled by three genes | Badami, 1928 |
| Pod reticulations | Deep pod reticulation dominant to shallow reticulations, single gene | Jadhav and Sinde, 1979 |
| Pod beak | Non-beaked pod dominant to beaked, single gene | Balaiah *et al.,* 1977 |
| | Pod beak was dominant over the beakless | Patel *et al.,* 1997 |
| Seed shape | Long seed shape dominant to short, two genes | Hayes, 1933 |
| Testa colour | Duplicate recessive loci model for red testa colour | Branch, 1995 |
| Leaf let size | Two types of alleles, one of which would be responsible for large leaflet size, while the other would be responsible for small leaflet size | Essomba *et al.,* 1995 |
| Narrow leaf | Single recessive gene | Mathur *et al.,* 2000 |
| Male sterility | Two recessive genes ($ms_1$ and $ms_2$) | Upadhyaya and Nigam, 1996 |
| Shrivelled seed | Single recessive gene | Jakkula *et al.,* 1997 |
| Black pod | Single dominant gene | Branch *et al.,* 1997 |
| Leaflet traits | Leaflet crinkling, leaflet bending and leaflet shape were all monogenic traits, while 2 recessive genes controlled albinism. | Tiwari *et al.,* 1990 |
| Albinism | 2 duplicate loci interacting with a third locus in an epistatic manner | Upadhyaya and Gopal, 1995 |
| Puckered-leaf | Two genes designated NI1 and NI2, which interact in a epistatic manner. | ICRISAT, 1992 |
| Aerial podding | Dominant monogenic and recessive monogenic. (Genetic background of alternative branching types modifies the expression of the aerial podding) | Vanisree and Prasad, 1995 |
| Non-nodulations | Recessive gene | Dashiell and Gorbet, 1982 |

**Table 3:** (*Contd...*)

**Table 3:** (*Contd...*)

| *Trait* | *Type of gene action* | *Reference(s)* |
|---|---|---|
| | Duplicate genes | Dashiell and Gorbet Nigam *et al.*, 1980 and 1982 |
| | Trigenic model with two genes expressing the nodulation and a third gene inhibiting nodulation when it is in a dominant condition and the former two genes are in recessive homozygous conditions | Dutta and Reddy, 1988 |
| | Non-nodulating lines originating from NC 17 X PI 259747 and Shantung No. 203 X PI 259747 crosses did not show allelic differences for non-nodulation | Brandi *et al.*, 1984 |

## 6.2. Genetics of Quantitative Traits

Many important traits of groundnut, such as yield, as in other species, are quantitatively inherited. The exploitation of genetic variability of quantitative traits through hybridization, inbreeding, and selection is an important feature of a groundnut breeding programme. The quantitative genetic research on (1) nature of genetic variability, (2) type of gene action, (3) heritability, (4) genetic advances and (5) correlation among traits are most significant to plant breeders. Results of some studies are summarized in Table 4.

**Table 4:** The genetics of important quantitative traits in groundnut

| *Trait* | *Type of gene action* | *Reference(s)* |
|---|---|---|
| Oil content | Non-additive gene effects | Basu *et al.*, 1988 |
| Soluble sugar | Additive gene effects | Basu *et al.*, 1988 |
| Brachytic sterilty | Duplicate, complementary, triplicate and quadriplicate factors | Gupta, 1988 |
| Pod yield | Epistasis with negative dominance Non-additive | Vindhiyavarman and Raveendran, 1994 |
| Number of pods per plant | Non-additive | Vindhiyavarman and Raveendran, 1994 |
| Harvest index | Additive and non-additve gene action | Vindhiyavarman and Raveendran, 1994 |
| Shelling outturn | Additive and non-additive gene action | Vindhiyavarman and Raveendran, 1994 |
| Sound mature kernels | Additive and non-additive gene action | Vindhiyavarman and Raveendran, 1994 |
| Height of main stem | Epistasis with negative dominance; duplicate epistasis | Sangha *et al.*, 1990 |
| Colour of stem | Purple stem and peg colour was dominant | Senapati and Roy, 1990 |
| Flower colour | Red flowers were incompletely dominant over yellow | Senapati and Roy, 1990 |
| First flowering | 2 recessive alleles acting in an additive fashion | Vindhiyavarman and Raveendran, 1996 |

**Table 4:** (*Contd...*)

**Table 4:** (*Contd...*)

| ***Trait*** | ***Type of gene action*** | ***Reference(s)*** |
|---|---|---|
| Days to first flower | Single gene with additive gene action. | Upadhyaya and Nigam, 1994 |
| Days to accumulation of 25 flowers from the appearance to first flower | Three independent genes with complete dominance at each locus | Upahyaya and Nigam, 1994 |
| 100-seed weight | Additive gene action | Manoharan and Ramalingam, 1993 |
| Height of the main stem | Additive gene action | Manoharan and Ramalingam, 1993 |
| Pod and seed size | Additive gene action; dominance toward smaller pods | Anderson *et ai,* 1993 |

Understanding the genetic nature of disease is useful to choose parents for the breeding programme. However, studies on genetics of disease resistance in groundnut are scattered and scanty.

**Table 5:** Genetics of disease resistance in groundnut

| ***Disease*** | ***Genetic nature*** | ***Reference(s)*** |
|---|---|---|
| Late Leaf Spots (LLS) | Non-additive, LLS governed by 5 recessive genes | Nevill, 1980, 1982 |
| | Non-additive, LLS governed by 5 recessive genes | Kornegay *et al.,* 1980 |
| | Duplicate recessive | Tiwari *et al.,* 1984 |
| | Additive | Walls and Wynne, 1985 |
| | Additive | Jogloy *ct al.,* 1987 |
| Early Leaf Spot (ELS) | Dominant | Company *et al.,* 1982 |
| ELS and LLS | Additive | Anderson *et al.,* 1986 |
| | Additive | Coffelt and Porter, 1986 |
| | Duplicate recessive | Soriano, 1988 |
| Rust resistance | Duplicate recessive | Bromfield and Bailey, 1972 |
| | More than 2 genes | Nigam *et al.,* 1980 |
| | Duplicate recessive | Cook, 1975 |
| | Digenic, trigenic | Kishore, 1981 |
| | Duplicate | Knauft and Norden, 1983 |
| | Recessive | Knauft, 1987 |
| | Multigenic | Knauft, 1987 |
| | Recessive | Tiwari *et al.,* 1984 |
| | Monogenic | Kalekar *et al.,* 1984 |
| | Duplicate recessive | Deokar *et al.,* 1986 |
| | Partially dominant or dominant | Middleton and Shorter, 1987 |
| | Recessive | Zheng, 1987 |
| | Recessive | Liao *et al.,* 1988 |
| | Dominant | Singh *et al.,* 1984 |

**Table 5:** (*Contd...*)

**Table 5:** (*Contd...*)

| *Disease* | *Genetic Nature* | *Reference(s)* |
|---|---|---|
| | 2 recessive genes | Vindhya varman *et al.*, 1993 |
| Cylindrocladium | Additive | Hadley *et al.*, 1979a, b |
| block rot | Additive | Green *et al.*, 1983 |
| Verticillium wilt | Monogenic recessive | Khan *et al*, 1973 |
| Bacterial wilt | Partially dominant (nucleo-cytoplasmic interaction may affect the inheritance of resistance | Liao *et al*, 1990 |
| | Additive | Rao *et al.*, 1989 |
| Groundnut rosette | Duplicate recessive | Bock, 1987 |
| virus | Abnormal $F_2$ ratios | Bock, 1987 |
| Multiple resistance | Additive resistance to ELS, LLS, rust, PStV, TSWV, damage by leaf miner | Anderson *et al.*, 1990a, b |

## 7. THE MAJOR BREEDING OBJECTIVES AND PROGRESS

The objectives of breeding in groundnut like in any other crop, depend on the cropping system in which it has to fit and its use by the consumer. High yield, high oil content, seed size and shelling percentage, maturity (early, medium and late), plant type, seed dormancy, seed viability, resistance to biotic stresses like diseases, insect pests, and moulds producing mycotoxins including aflatoxins, and abiotic stresses like drought, cold, salinity, acidity and aluminum toxicity, and increased iron efficiency, development of cultivars for different cropping system, fodder quality, nutrient-use-efficiency and large seeds with confectionery qualifies are the major objectives of groundnut breeding in India.

### 7.1. Plant Type Concept

Since groundnut breeders know the performance of their best available cultivars in terms of usual metric traits in optimal population densities, they should visualize an ideal groundnut plant in terms of plant habit, branches, pods, kernels and kernel weight and reaction to insect pests and diseases, so that a cultivar optimizing these traits can be developed. This mental visualization translated into a quantitative entity defines the "Plant type" for a crop.

Difficulty in exact definition of plant type stem from the fact that groundnut cultivars belong to three distinct botanical types defined earlier with different niches of adaptability. The difficulty is further compounded by the fact that many of the present day cultivars are derivatives of crosses between the botanical types. Some results from available studies point to the following common features:

1. The plants should have high partitioning efficiency with high total dry matter
2. Intermediate degree of compactness similar to the Virginia bunch types will be desirable
3. The proportion of flowers resulting in mature pods (called reproductive efficiency) should be as high as possible
4. More determinate habit with proportionately lesser duration from flowering to maturity will be desirable.

### 7.1.1. *Breeding for higher yield*

Pod and seed yield are ultimately what the groundnut breeder wants to increase. Even though four to five tonnes per hectare of pod yield have been achieved in India with existing groundnut cultivars at times, the average veers around 1 tonnes. In other words although the potential is high the realization has been very low because of poor management under rainfed conditions by resource poor farmers. Thus breeding for higher yield will mean, i) building stability of yield expression through incorporation of resistance to stresses both biotic and abiotic and ii) taking the potential yield itself to a higher level *so* that the fraction of the potential expressed is higher in sub-optimal situations. It must always be remembered that yield is the result of complex interaction of events in a plant's life and requires more location specific attention for breeding plans. Number of pods per plant, shelling percent and seed size are the major components that determine the yield. Some of the Virginia types have larger kernels than Spanish types and increasing seed size while maintaining pod/kernel number can substantially add to the final yield. Most of the yield increases in this crop in all countries so far have resulted from higher harvest index brought about by reducing vegetative growth. Hence, breeding for increase in the total biomass while retaining the present level of harvest index can be one of the main strategies for increasing yield potential.

### 7.1.2. *Breeding for moisture stress (drought)*

This is an objective applicable to majority of groundnut growig situations of the world. Drought is by far the most important problem of groundnut in India where, about 80% of the crop is rainfed. Effort put in to breed for drought resistance has been substantial but tangible results have not been obtained, possibly because treating "drought resistance" as a character with its own identity in terms of inheritance may not work. In an unpredictable situation different combinations of several traits may confer drought resistance (Ceccarelli *et al.,* 1991) because moisture deficit stress can occur in various phases of crop life (early-, mid- and end season) in combination with various temperatures. Resistances to these stresses are available in both the cultivated and alien germplasm but the complexities of response to stress make breeding for resistance to moisture deficiency-stress difficult. Considerable genetic variability has been reported for water-use efficiency traits (Jayalakshmi *et al.,* 1998). The work is in progress in screening for drought tolerance under *in-vitro* conditions (Puroshotham *et al.,* 1998; Venkateswarlu *et al,* 1998).

The various selection criteria being used for drought resistance breeding are as follows :

- Water use efficiency (WUE) *i.e.* amount of biomass produced per unit mass of water used by the plant, is a very important component of moisture stress deficit tolerance.
- Certain physiological and morphological parameters like membrane thermo stability at high temperature, waxiness of leaves, and diffusive resistance of stomata.
- Transpiration efficiency and harvest index under moisture stress (Nageswara Rao *et al.,* 1992; Nigam *et al.,* 1991) and relative water content of leaves have been found to be highly related to WUE (Nautiyal, personal communication).
- Carbon isotope discrimination (delta) during photosynthesis *i.e.* ratio between the $^{12}C$ and $^{13}C$ atoms taken up by groundnut plants have been found to be correlated with WUE. Specific leaf area (SLA) in turn has been found to be reasonably well correlated (-vely) with delta and WUE.

Variability among genotypes is available for all these traits *i.e.* WUE, delta, and SLA. Attempts are being made now to use SLA for selecting for WUE in groundnut. If it is successful, breeding for resistance to moisture deficit stress will be accelerated.

### 7.1.3. *Breeding for earliness*

Early maturing cultivars are useful for many reasons such as,

i Avoiding end-season-drought,

ii. Avoiding *in-situ* germination by escaping being caught in rains especially for rabi/summer groundnut,

iii. Fitting various cropping sequences like those based on residual moisture.

Breeding for early-maturing cultivars is an important objective of most breeding programmes. However, accurate maturity determination in groundnut is constrained by its indeterminate flowering nature, subterranean pod production, significant maturity × environment interaction and the subjective nature of most maturity determination methods (Sanders *et al.,* 1982). An alternative suggested to overcome this problem is the concept of cumulative thermal degree-days. It is calculated as the sum of the average of mean maximum and mean minimum temperature (in °C days) that a crop has experienced since it was sown. The crop is harvested when a predetermined sum (degree days) is reached. The concept can be subjected to criticism but is the only acceptable objective criterion for selection available so far.

### 7.1.4. *Breeding for disease resistance*

The following are the major disease of groundnut in India:

*Fungal diseases*

*Foliar diseases*:

- Early leaf spot *(Cercospora arachidicola)*
- Late leaf spot *(Phaeoisariopsis personata)*
- Rust *(Puccinia arachidis)*
- *Alternaria* leaf spot and Veinai necrosis *(Alternaria alternata)*
- Powdery mildew *(Oidium arachidis)*
- Sclerotium leaf spot *(Sclerotium rolfsii)*
- Pepper spot and leaf scorch *(Leptosphaerulina crassiasca)*
- *Alternaria* leaf blight *(Alternaria arachidis)*

*Seed and seedling diseases*

- Collar rot *(Diplodia gossypina)*
- Crown rot *(Aspergillus niger, A. pulverulentus)*
- Stem rot *(Sclerotium rolfsii)*
- Fusarium wilt (*Fusarium oxysporum)*
- Dry root rot *(Macrophomina phaseolina)*
- Pod rot *(Pythium myriotylum* and *Rhizoctonia solani)*
- Aflarot *(Aspergillus flavus)*

Bacterial diseases

- Bacterial wilt (*Pseudomonas solancearum*)
- Bacterial leaf spot (*Xanthomonas* spp.)

Virus diseases

- Peanut bud necrosis (caused by peanut Bud Necrosis Virus of Poty group)
- Peanut yellow spot
- Indian peanut clump virus
- Peanut mottle virus
- Groundnut rosette virus
- Tomato spotted wilt virus

Diseases caused by nematodes

- Root knot (*Meliondogyne*™ sp.)
- Kalahasti malady

Of the fungal diseases, early leaf spot, late leaf spot and rust have widespread occurence and are of economic importance (Bunting *et al.,* 1985) through out the world. The aflatoxin problem associated with the fungi *Aspergillus flavus* and *A. parasiticus* is also of great economic importance.

Because of the high value of the crop and availability of chemicals for disease control, breeding for disease resistance was not given high priority until the late 1970's. For the past 15 years, numerous germplasm accessions among cultivated groundnut have been identified as sources of disease resistance. Moreover, the importance of wild species as sources of resistance/immunity to most of the diseases has been realized. Breeding for disease resistance has received high priority since the late 1970's (Subrahmanyam *et al.,* 1989; Waliyar and McDonald, 1988; Rajgopal and Bandyopadhyay, 1999). Breeders have tended to focus on the major foliar diseases of groundnut, although breeding for locally important diseases has also received attention.

Subrahmanyam *et al.* (1995) have described the screening methods and sources of resistance to two important diseases, rust and late leaf spot of groundnut in a bulletin. It provides a comprehensive, well-illustrated guide to resistance screening, including screening methodologies, inoculums production, field layout, field inoculation, disease assessment, and the best resistance sources.

Variability of peanut pathogen is still inadequately understood and much additional research is needed to optimize breeding efforts. Major genes have not been clearly demonstrated in groundnut, however, for most pathogens. Effectiveness of minor gene resistance in groundnut (oligogenic or polygenic; additive effects) is strongly influenced by inoculum density (Black and Beute, 1984) and physical environments that influence host-defensive responses and/ or pathogen activity (Black and Beute, 1985). In addition to pathogen aggressiveness, other "fitness" characteristics (geographie adaptation, inoculum survival, etc.,) are of concern to the breeder (Bashi and Rosen, 1974).

Not much success has been achieved in breeding for resistance to the major foliar diseases by using the sources of resistance in the cultivated species, since of a few cultivars released (see table 7), none has been popular. This is mainly because of the complexity of inheritance of resistance and undesirable linkages like unacceptable pod shape, size and shelling percent etc., (see for example, Miller *et al.,* 1990).

Relatively less effort has been devoted to identify resistance to the soil-borne fungi. Reliable sources of resistance to the viruses are not available in the cultivated germplasm and the wild species are the only sources. Some degree of field resistance to PBND has been reported in the. cultivars ICGV 87123, ICGV 87128 and Kadiri 3.

Faster progress in breeding for disease resistant groundnut can be expected in the next decade. Many sources of disease resistance among cultivated germplasm have been identified and are being used. Advanced breeding lines with disease resistance are currently being evaluated at many locations and breeding for disease resistance has become a priority in most groundnut breeding programmes. Considerable attention is also being devoted to using wild species of *Arachis* for disease resistance. The high level of resistance or immunity to early and late leaf spot, rust, and other diseases can be transferred to cultivated groundnut from wild species (Stalker and Moss, 1987).

For introducing resistance to viruses, the main course being followed now is the introduction of coat protein genes or replicase genes by biotechnological means. These proteins when expressed in the plant prevent further infection by the virus. Some advancement has already been achieved in transferring coat protein gene of PStV (Higgins *et al.,* 1998). For the management of fungal disease, introduction of chitinases and glucanases is underway especially against the onslaught of soil-born pathogens.

### 7.1.5. *Breeding for insect stresses*

The major groundnut insect pests in India are the following:

Sucking pests:

- Leaf miner *(Aproaerema modicella)*
- Aphids *(Aphis craccivora* Koch.)
- Jassids *(Empoasca kerri pruthi)*
- Thrips *(Calliothrips* spp.)

Leaf eaters

- Red hairy caterpillar *(Amsacta albistriga)*
- Tobacco caterpillar *(Spodoptera litura)*
- White grub *(Holotrichia* sp.)
- Gram pod borer *(Helicoverpa armigera)*

Storage pests

- Bruchid beetle *(Caryedon serratus)*

Soil pests

- White grubs *(Apogonia* spp.)
- Termites *(Microtermes* spp. and *Nasutitermes* spp.)

The changing scenarios of cropping pattern and multiple cropping seasons have aggravated the insect pest problems. Leaf miner, white grub, hairy caterpillar and termites are the four economically most important pests (Rai, 1976). Achievements in breeding for resistance to insect pests have been limited and that too for a few sucking insects only. Though moderate degrees of resistance to the sucking insects like aphids, jassids and thrips and leaf miner are available in the cultivated germplasm, the transfer of these into high yielding backgrounds has not been very successful due to lack of genetic information either on the host resistance or on the virulence of the pest. White grubs is a complex group of polyphagous species. It may not be possible to breed for resistance to them in the near future at least by conventional means. Generalized protection through Bt or similar genes may be helpful.

Amin (1984) explained the methodology of screening for resistance to insect pests of groundnut. Mahadevan *et al.* (1988) screened 155 genotypes for resistance to leaf miner under unprotected field condition and reported that the spanish bunch genotypes ICG nos. 10361, 9212, 1458, and 1989 showed some resistance (scored 3 in 1-9 scale). The wild species are the potential sources of resistance for insect pests. The inter-specific derivatives ICGS 50 (Mahadevan *et al.*, 1988), and VG 101 were reported as resistant genotypes for leaf miner (Kalaimani *et al.*,

1989). Some sources of resistance to leaf miner, jassids, *Spodoptera litum,* Ash-weevil, root knot nematode were reported by Rajgopal and Bandyopadhyay (1999).

A groundnut line, ICGV 50 has been found to be highly resistant to leaf miner and tobacco caterpillar. Two cultivars (ICGV 86031, ICGV 86699) developed by ICRISAT were also found to be highly resistant to leaf miner. A cultivar, Girnar 1 developed by the NRCG during 1988 was found to possess high level of resistance to leaf hopper (*B. hartensis*). To develop a resistant cultivar for all the insect pests occurring in a locality is rather difficult as the feeding behaviour of various insects differs considerably.

### 7.1.6. *Breeding for fresh seed dormancy*

Sprouting of seeds when caught in the end season rains is a problem in *rabi*/summer groundnut in India (Nautiyal *et al.,* 2000), which account for over 14% of the total groundnuts produced. *In-situ* sprouting is especially the problem in spanish cultivars, which lack fresh seed dormancy as a rule. Very little has been done for inducing dormancy in Spanish types (Bandyopadhyay *et al.,* 1999). Though variation exists, at present none of the released truly spanish cultivars, except TG 17 (not bred for dormancy), possess fresh seed dormancy. The factors responsible for seed dormancy appear to be complex and associated to various degrees, with the testa (the maternal tissue), cotyledons and the embryo axis (zygotic tissues) of the seed making fresh seed dormancy a difficult character to breed for (Bandyopadhyay *et al.,* 1999). Also high inter-and within plant variations and degree of maturity have confounding effects on dormancy. Thus understanding the genetic mechanism and breeding for seed dormancy is difficult because classification of a plant in a segregating generation as having dormancy is not easy. The main strategy being followed now is to derive true spanish type cultivars from derivatives of spanish × virginia crosses because virginias generally have fresh seed dormancy.

### 7.1.7. *Breeding for increased seed viability*

The produce of robi/summer rapidly loses viability because high drying temperature and high humidity during the storage lead to loss of intergrity of seed testa and cause efflux of crucial enzymes and other solutes of soaking. Hence, use of the produce of one *rabi*/summer for sowing the next *rabi*/summer season crop results in poor plant stand, reduced crop vigour and finally loss in yield. Variation among groundnut genotypes in retention of seed viability of rabi/summer produce has been detected (Nautiyal *et al.*, 1989) and genotypes retaining over 70% seed viability after 8 months of storage under ambient conditions have now been identified at NRCG. However, systematic genetic and breeding studies on this important character have just been initiated.

### 7.1.8. *Breeding for cold tolerance*

Seed germination and seedling growth of *rabi*/summer-sown crop is affected because of low temperature. It is one of the main constraints of groundnut growing in a large potential area in northern India. The work done on breeding for tolerance to cold temperature has been meagre. Groundnut requires a minimum base temperature of 11°C for germination and sustained growth. Joshi *et al.* (1996) have identified germplasm lines that can germinate and show seedling growth at less than 12/18°C temperature cycles. However, more detailed studies on physiology and genetics of cold tolerance are required before a full-fledged breeding programme can be initiated on this aspect.

### 7.1.9. *Breeding for salinity tolerance*

Soil salinity is a problem of the coastal areas and the heavily irrigated light soil areas like that under the IGNP in Rajasthan and Kutch-Bhuj areas of Gujarat. Groundnut cannot germinate and grow at salinity levels exceeding 8 EC. A large number of genotypes have been screened *in vitro* at NRCG (Joshi *et al.*, 1994) and those that can germinate at high salinity levels have been identified. Planned efforts for breeding for salinity tolerance are needed to tackle this problem.

### 7.1.10. *Breeding for high temperature tolerance*

The optimum temperature at which groundnut can efficiently grow is 30-35°C. Higher temperature affects photosynthesis, water use and reproductive growth. High temperature stress is faced by the rabi/summer groundnut at the time of peak flowering and pod filling. In Rajasthan the kharif crop also faces high temperature. Not many studies have been made on this stress. The genetic differences in heat acclimation potential have been reported to be small and unrelated to growth differences (Talwar *et al.*, 1999). The genotypic differences in the response of groundnut yield to episodes of high temperature stress were due to differences in the timing of seed filling rather than to genotypic differences in the rate of dry matter partitioning to fruits (Wheeler *et al.,* 1997).

### 7.1.11 *Breeding for Aluminium (Al) toxicity tolerance*

Aluminium stress is generally a consequence of high soil acidity. It affects growth of roots and shoots and yield/plant through several yield components. Al toxicity differs significantly among the genotypes studied. It is recommended that root traits (tap root length, root size and fresh and dry weight) be considered as important criteria for evaluating Al toxicity to groundnut plants and the potential Al tolerance of the genotypes (Zhou *et al.,* 1998). Pal *et al.* (1999) have developed a very easy *in vitro* selection method for testing tolerance of Al toxicity. Breeding efforts have just been initiated.

#### 7.1.11.1 *Breeding for increased biological nitrogen fixation (BNF)*

Groundnut fixes atmospheric nitrogen in symbiosis with rhizobia *(Bradyrhizobia* more precisely). Groundnut is promiscuous in the sense that it can be nodulate by a whole group of *rhizobium* spp. known as "cowpea miscellany". It is reported that 124 kg per annum is fixed by groundnuts (Nutman, 1976). The efficiency of BNF can be increased substantially by a proper choice of the combination of host genotypes and *rhizobium* strain. The breeding approaches for increased nitrogen fixation needs the variability in the host, rhizobium, and their interaction. A large variability is available for host genotypes from germplasm collections (Nambiar and Dart, 1980; Wynne *et al.,* 1981). Nitrogenase activity, nodule mass and nodule number are the important components of BNF efficiency. At the global level not many breeders are engaged in breeding for increased $N_2$ fixation. The results are positive where both nitrogen fixation and yield has been combined. The possible two approaches to breeding for high BNF are:

1. Identify host genotypes or rhizobium genotypes with generalized responses
2. Identify a specific combination that gives best response.

It is accepted now that efforts to enhance the BNF efficiency of the host over a range of *rhizobium* strains is likely to yield better results because a selected *rhizobium* strain has to face competition with native rhizobia but a selected host with generalized response need not face this competition. But such acceptance has not made breeding cultivars with high BNF efficiency any easier. The most important reasons for this are that i) there is no technique available to select for BNF ability in the segregating generations and ii) the character has high and unpredictable temporal variability within a plant. Usable genetic variability for this character is available within the cultivated germplasm.

### 7.1.12. *Breeding for resistance to lime-induced chlorosis*

In calcareous and alkaline soils, lime-induced iron deficiency chlorosis is of common occurence in crop plants (Brown and Jolley, 1989). In groundnut, such chlorosis is very common in the Saurashtra region of Gujarat, Marathwada of Maharashtra and parts of Tamilnadu and Karnataka (Kannan, 1984). Generally a strong association between iron-efficiency and productivity has been observed. Samdur *et al.* (1999) reported that the relationship between Fe-deficiency chlorosis and yield were not always clear possibly because of compensation mechanisms in some genotypes. The development of Fe-efficient genotypes (tolerant), which can tolerate Fe deficiency chlorosis, could be the solution to this problem as iron is found to be in abundance in soil. Groundnut genotypes differ in their response to Fe stress (Singh and Chaudhari, 1991; Samdur *et al.,* 1999). Screening for resistance to iron deficiency is done by using a visual chlorotic rating (Singh and Chaudhari, 1991). Wide ranges of variability and resistance sources have been reported for this trait. Genetics of the resistance and systematic breeding efforts are going on.

### 7.1.13. *Breeding for quality characteristics*

*Large seeded / confectionery types (HPS)*

Large seeded groundnuts are in good demand for table purpose and fetch high premium in the export market.

Export of groundnut from India is generally done under categories, based in counts/ounce. (28.4g.)

| *Grade* | *Counts/Ounce*[1] | *Seed shape* |
|---|---|---|
| Virginia Extra-large | 28/32 | Elongated |
| Virginia Medium | 38/42 | Elongated |
| Virginia no. 1 | 45/55 | Elongated |
| Runner Jumbo | 38/42 | Round |
| Runner Medium | 40/50 | Round /elongated |
| Spanish Jumbo | 60/70 | Elongated |
| Spanish no. 1 | 70/80 | Round / elongated |

*Source :* National Peanut Council of America (1986)

Every size has a niche for different end uses but large seeded types (>60 g/100 seeds) with good colour fetch a premium. But generally the large seed cultivars tend to be long duration (145-150 days) type, with dormancy (45-60 days), and low shelling outturn (60-65%). Moreover they require higher seed rate (140 kg/ha) for sowing and give the best results in light soils, assured irrigation and higher nutrition regimes. However, progress has been made in developing relatively shorter duration large seeded types, such as the released cultivar ICGS 49.

With increasing competition from cheaper oils and the more open world market, groundnut has to capitalize on its being highly nutritious food in addition to being a source of oil. Some of the desirable qualities in groundnut for consumption as food or confectionery are high protein content, low oil content (<45%), higher sucrose content, lower content of undesirable sugars like stachyose and raffinose, higher portion of linoleic acid content. However, for stability, higher oleic/linoleic acid ratio (>2) is desired. The most important export requirement in groundnut is very low or nil aflatoxin content. The lowest aflatoxin content is demanded by the European Union countries (≤ 8 and ≤ 15 μg/kg for B1 and total aflatoxins respectively, for groundnut to be processed further and ≤ 2 and ≤ 4 μg/kg for B and total aflatoxins respectively for groundnut to be directly consumed.

Directed breeding efforts for confectionery quality groundnut have yet to be started in our country, because till now market premium is not available for better quality. It is available only for large seed size and low aflatoxin content. Some available information on quality attributes is given below.

### *Oil content*

In India, oil is still the most important ultimate product of the groundnut crop and so oil content is an important aspect of yield potential. But very little systematic breeding has been done to increase the oil percentage in spite of availability of variability among cultigens. The reasons for this lack of interest are possibly the following:

1. Oil content is highly variable and measurement especially in the segregating generations, is very difficult if not impossible, in the existing situation. So, one may ask whether it is more worthwhile to increase 10% seed yield than increasing 2% oil content.
2. Farmers generally do not get any incentive for high oil content.

However, if a part of the extremely high oil content (up to 63% reported in *Arachis appressipila*) found in some wild species could be transferred to the cultivars so that the oil percentage is increased by 5-6% the efforts may be worthwhile.

*Oil quality*

The ratio of oleic to linoleic acid (O/L ratio) is also a measure of oil stability (Young and Waller, 1972). Selection for this trait should be relatively straight forward, since selection for higher levels of oleic results in lower levels of linoleic. Studies have suggested that fatty acid content might be relatively easy to manipulate in a breeding programme (Tai and Young, 1975). Thus breeding should be able to extend the shelf life of oil and other groundnut products by genetically altering the fatty acid composition. Knauft *et al.* (1993) suggested that incorporation of high oleic acid into groundnut cultivars should be simple and straightforward.

*Other qualities*

In the past two decades, with the growth of other conventional, and the introduction of non-conventional vegetable oilseed crops, the pressure on groundnut crop as a source of vegetable oil has eased considerably and it can now be looked upon as an item of highly nutritive food. However, for diverting bulk quantities of groundnut and its value added products as food in domestic as well as export markets, it would be necessary to develop groundnut cultivars more suitable for direct consumption and processing. For direct consumption as an item of food, bold kernels having low calorie (oil) and high protein contents are preferred. Low free amino acid and reducing sugar contents are considered desirable from processing point of view, whereas high sucrose levels improve the organoleptic properties. Variability for these quality traits is available in the released cultivars (NRCG, 1997 and 1998) and breeding materials (Manivel *et al.*, unpublished data). However, systematic genetic and breeding approaches for improving these qualities are yet to be initiated.

***Resistance to aflatoxin contamination***

Aflatoxins are a group of toxins belonging to the genera of mycotoxins *i.e.*, toxins produced by fungi. Aflatoxins are produced by fungi *Aspergillus flavus* and *Aspergillus parasiticus*. They are known to cause various diseases especially liver cirrhosis, cancer in many animals including human being and affect the immune system of the body. They also pose a very important consideration for export as mentioned earlier. The fungi causing aflatoxin can invade the groundnut pods before and after harvest and during storage and transit. Because they are basically facultative saprophytic fungi the damaged pods are predisposed to their invasion. Hence, drought at the time of formation of pod, which causes fine cracks in the pods and insect damage to the pods are highly predisposing to aflatoxin contamination. Thus drought tolerance and resistance to damage of pods by insect can reduce the extent of aflatoxin contamination.

Resistance of aflatoxin production is quite complex in which different plant organs such as pod, the shell, the testa and the cotyledons are involved. Moreover, resistance to colonization of seeds by fungus need not necessarily be correlated with the degree of aflatoxin production. Although a number of genotypes have been identified to be resistant to *in-vitro* colonization by aflatoxin producing fungi, they do not necessarily show resistance to aflatoxin production. Among the genotypes tested so far, the ones which shown some degree of resistance are ICGV Nos. 86168 to 86171, 86173 to 86177, Jll and UF 71513 (Rao *et al.,* 1989).

Very little success has been achieved for incorporating resistance to aflatoxin contamination, mainly because of the following :

1. Complexity of nature of resistance
2. Non-availability of any genotypes in which all the seeds can be free from infection of the aflatoxin producing fungi. As a result, even a single highly infected seed in a seed lot can lead to an aflatoxin level, which is beyond the acceptable levels.
3. No method is available for selection in segregating generations.

In groundnut, different genes appear to confer resistance to seed colonization, pre-harvest seed infection, and aflatoxin production. Efforts to combine resistance to pre-harvest seed infection and post-harvest seed colonization or aflatoxin production have to be made. For better crop improvement strategies, genetic markers for resistance to fungal infection and aflatoxin production in these crops are needed. New molecular techniques to develop resistance to aflatoxigenic fungi/ aflatoxin should be developed for groundnut. Aspergillus-resistant or aflatoxin-resistant transgenic plants should be an effective genetic approach to the aflatoxin problem (Mehan, 1992). But breeding for resistance to aflatoxin contamination has to be seen as only a part of aflatoxin management system and not as an exclusive approach.

### 7.1.14. *Breeding for efficient adaptation to different cropping systems*

As mentioned earlier, groundnut is grown in four seasons in India. But breeding effort have been made especially for the *kharif* season. The cultivars released for rabi/summer seasons are actually spin offs. Advantage of rabi/summer season is that the crop is almost fully irrigated and relatively free from biotic stresses. In these two seasons the vegetative growth is also limited. Hence the crop can be treated as high in-put, high return crop, if cultivars can be developed which can respond to higher level of nutrients and attempts are made to breed for adaptability to these seasons.

Although groundnut is mainly grown as a sole crop in majority of the area, groundnut-based inter cropping is slowly increasing in popularity. Inter cropping with pigeon pea and castor is getting popular with the farmers. Groundnut is also grown in other crop sequences. No attempt has been made to breed for the existing or other potential system of groundnut based cropping systems. Studies have shown that system specific cultivars will yield results. Preliminary results have shown that bushy, tall and late maturing pigeon pea in combination with Virginia runner types of groundnut performed better than the erect, short, and early-maturing types in intercropping systems (Ghosh *et al.,* 1999). More systematic efforts in this direction are required.

### 7.1.15. *Breeding for nutritient use efficiency*

This is an objective, which requires special attention but has not received any so far. Groundnut is mainly grown under rainfed situation by resource poor farmers. In such conditions, application of required nutrients by the farmers is difficult. It is thus essential that the crop uses the applied nutrient most efficiently. But very little work has been done to understand the variability available in germplasm with respect to nutrient use efficiency and utilize it for breeding. Indications are that such variation is indeed available. Wissuwa and Ae (1998) assessed the genotypic variation for phosphorus (P) uptake from Fe-P in groundnut and concluded that genotypic variation for uptake of Fe-P exists and that direct P uptake through fruiting organs, as facilitated by the presence of root hair on the pegs of some genotypes, contributes to this variation. Reddy *et al.* (1991) reported that shoot weight was the most sensitive to P deficiency. There were cultivar differences in P use efficiency, measured as mg dry weight produced/mg P absorbed; 3 cultivars were classed as efficient, 11 as moderately efficient, and 6 as inefficient.

### 7.1.16. *Breeding groundnut for fodder*

Wherever groundnut is grown in India, groundnut haulms are used as cattle feed. Also, wild vegetatively propagated species like *Arachis pintoi* and *A. glabrata* are valued forage crops. In our country, no concerted efforts have yet been made either to improve groundnut haulm for nutrition of cattle or on allied groundnut species as forage/fodder crops. The work in this area has to be initiated.

## 8. BREEDING METHODS

The general breeding methods for other highly self-pollinated crops, *viz.*, (i) introduction and selection, (ii) hybridization and selection and (iii) mutation breeding are equally applicable to groundnut breeding. In this chapter we shall discuss the various methods advocated for groundnut.

### 8.1. Introduction and Selection

It is interesting to note that till the seventies most of the groundnut cultivars were the result of selection from introductions. For example M 13, a widely adapted spreading type with very high oil content, is a reselection from the US cultivar NC 13 and TMV 10, the bold seeded Virginia type is a selection from an Argentinian cultivar.

### 8.2. Hybridization and Selection

Artificial hybridization between parental lines to bring together desirable combination of genes is an integral component of any crop improvement programme. Groundnut is essentially self-pollinating, but as in most self-pollinating species some out crossing usually occurs. For controlled hybridization, rainy season is the best as atmospheric humidity is high. In greenhouses or growth chambers where it is possible to control light, humidity, and temperature, hybridization can be carried out at any time of the year (Nigam *et al.*, 1990). Hybridization should be restricted to the early phase of flowering because the success rate for mature pod recovery from early-formed flowers is higher (Muhammad and Dorairaj, 1969; Bear and Bailey, 1973; Ramanantha Rao, 1988). The skill of operator and environmental condition (high humidity is required) influence the success rate (Nigam *et al.,* 1990).

Norden (1973) described the conventional technique of hybridization in groundnut. Equipments required for hybridization includes forceps with fine points, coloured nylon threads, petri dishes, and alcohol for rinsing forceps between pollinations. Emasculation (removal of anthers from buds/ flowers before their dehiscence to avoid self-pollination) is carried out between 1330 hrs and 1730 hrs depending upon the prevailing environment conditions. Once a well-developed bud is selected, all other buds at that node are removed with forceps. The bud is held gently between the thumb and index finger of the left hand (in case of right handed person.) Using the forceps held in the right hand, the single sepals opposite the standard petal is pulled down. The fused sepal is also folded down and held back. The standard is then gently and carefully opened with forceps and is held back by the thumb and index finger. The wing petals are pulled down locking them with the standard. The keel is pulled outwards by its ridge with forceps to expose the anthers. All the anthers are removed with the filaments from their bases. This leaves only the stigma and style, which are now well exposed. The standard, wing, and keel petals usually return to their normal position after emasculation to cover the style and stigma. The internode just above the emasculated bud is then marked with a date-coded coloured nylon thread. A thread of different colour is used every day to help identify the buds for pollination on the next day.

Pollination (transference of pollen grains from the anthers of one flower to the stigma of another flower) is carried out the day after emasculation. Normally, buds start opening at sunrise. Pollination soon after buds open is best to achieve a high success rate. All flowers except those that have been artificially pollinated should be removed every day soon after pollination from the base of the hypanthium. This flower-removal operation should be carried on for at least 2 weeks after completing the last pollination of the season. It is necessary to find out the time in the morning at each location by which all non-emasculated buds are removed so that self-pollinated pods are eliminated. Some breeders have modified the conventional technique to increase the success rate (Schulz, 1947; Reddy *et al.,* 1970; Norden and Rodriguez, 1971; Hildebrand, 1974; Banks, 1976; Nigam *et al.,* 1980; Kale and Mouli, 1984).

### 8.2.1. *Selection of parents*

Selection of parents is the first and the most important step in hybridization for various breeding objectives. Parents are chosen for various reasons — as locally adapted cultivars, gene donors for resistance, or for specific morphological or physiological traits or quality traits. A breeder's knowledge of the parental lines and their behaviour in segregating generations helps in making a suitable choice of the parents and the direction of cross.

The reported work on groundnut regarding the choice of parents stresses on intermediate degree of diversity between the parents for achieving the best chances of useful transgressive segregants (Arunachalam *et al.,* 1984; Prasad, 1993). The usefulness of within botanical type crosses in addition to between types crosses has been pointed out by different breeders for combining productivity with earliness (Arunachalam *et al.,* 1984; Bandyopadhyay *et al.,* 1984; Durgaprasad *et al.,* 1985). The choice of parents on the basis of heterosis that is based on high general combining ability of parents has been advocated by Arunchalam *et al.* (1984).

Corley and Holbrook (1990) examined the utility of early generation diallel analysis for predicting parental potential for yield and yield components and found that general combining ability estimates from $F_1$ progeny were not effective in predicting performance in subsequent generations. They reported that parental performance *per se* was highly correlated with performance across cross combinations in the $F_2$ and $F_3$ progeny. But it must be kept in mind that the performance of a pair of parents is very difficult to generalise even from a very basic probabilistic genetics in view. This involves empiricism.

### 8.2.2. *Handling of segregating generation*

One of the greatest problems of the groundnut breeder is that he has to be content with small sizes of the $F_2$ populations, because of difficulty in successful hybridization and very low multiplication ratio. Thus, the quantum of recombination events available to him for selection is low. To over come this difficulty, different routes are being explored.

1. Fast vegetative multiplication of $F_1$ plants through *in-vitro* nodal culture: The protocols for *in-vitro* mass multiplication have been established at NRCG. Lab grown ex-plants are the best for this purpose. Interestingly 66% and 71% success in Spanish and virginia types respectively are available. A large number of $F_1$ plants can be generated from one hybrid seed by nodal culture and as a resuit a large $F_2$ generation can be obtained.
2. The possibility of increasing natural out crossing through induction of transient male sterility in the plants of the segregating generations exists. Interestingly, Dutta *et al.* (1987) reported that low doses of radiations can be utilized to induce pollen sterility and increase the levels of outcrossing in groundnut. They observed

that pollen sterility induced through gamma irradiation (5 kR) could produce as high as 33% outcrossing in a groundnut cultivar, M 13. Chemical sterilants can also be explored for this purpose.

Selection in groundnut is complicated owing to the fact that the produce is below the ground and the assessment based on yield has to be done only at harvest time. The evaluation of characters, which are correlated with yield, is of particular importance in this crop. Breeding approaches suggested by different workers are mentioned below.

The cultivars released so far in India are through some variant of pedigree breeding including the bulk-pedigree method in which the segregating generations are forwarded as a bulk with some culling of undesirable types till $F_4$ and $F_5$ generation and then plant-to-progeny pedigree breeding is resorted to. In single seed descent method (SSD) up to a certain generation, a pod from each plant in a segregating generations is taken and bulked, so that the bulk may represents the range of variation in that particular generation. However, whether the presumption is true can be argued against and for. In view of practical problems it is advisable to follow a kind of bulk-pedigree method rather than pure pedigree method. However, there are pros and cons to early generation selection as discussed below. It appears that early generation selection based on index involving a number of physiological characters may lead to success of conventional pedigree breeding and hence economy of efforts in later generation. Crop simulation and analytical models will be useful tools in developing index selection, because groundnut crosses are known to throw up segregants till as late generations as $F_9$-$F_{10}$ especially when inter-botanical crosses are dealt with. Reddy *et al.* (1993) however, found pedigree method to be superior over bulk method.

### 8.2.3. *Mutation breeding*

One of the earliest attempts on mutation breeding for crop improvement was by Gregory (1965) with groundnut. Groundnut is known to throw a wide range of variation through mutagens, both physical (gamma rays and x-rays) and chemical (DES, EMS, Sodium azide, etc.,). A number of cultivars have been released by Bhaba Atomic Research Centre, Trombay, Mumbai through direct mutation breeding or through use of mutants in hybridization programmes. Fig. 4 depicts how mutation breeding and classical breeding can be efficiently combined for obtaining useful results.

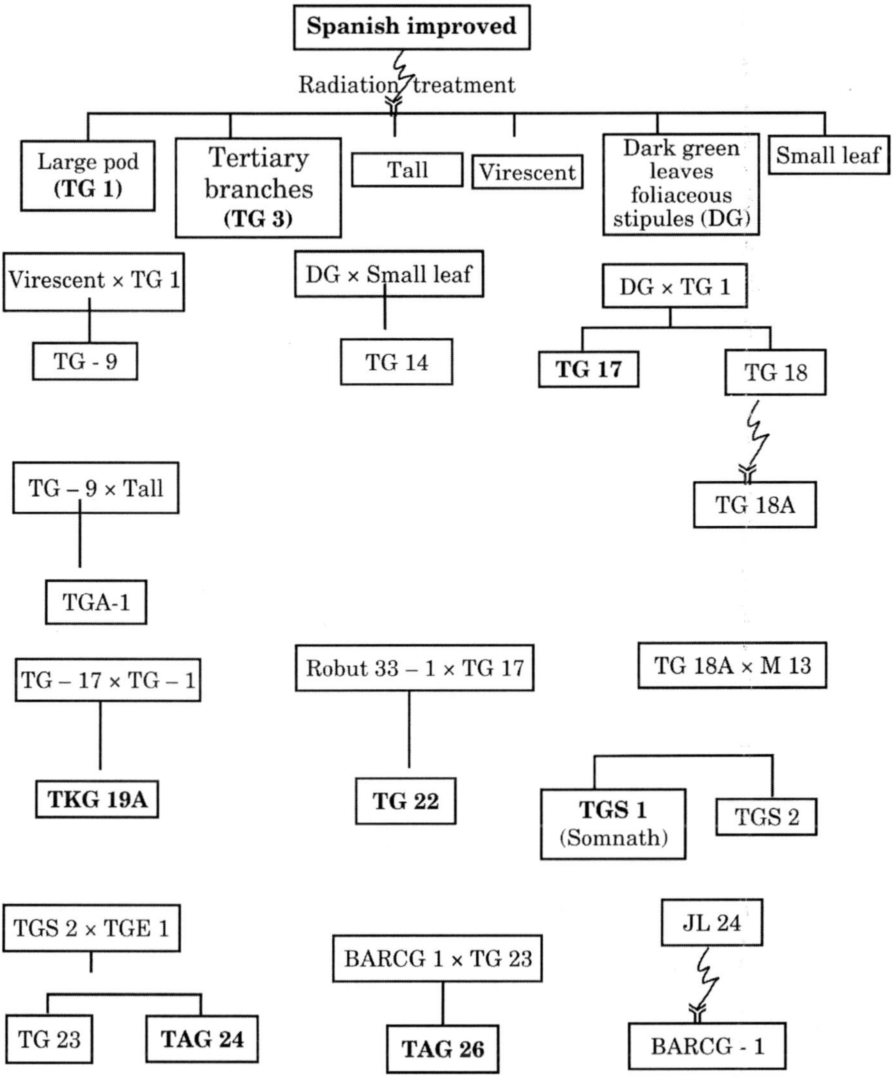


**Fig. 4:** Evolution of Trombay groundnut (TG) cultivars (Released and notified TG cultivars are in bold letters)

### 8.2.4. *Breeding for yield stability*

Resort to breeding homozygous productive genotypes entails a higher risk of genetic vulnerability. With achievement of higher productivity by breeding, the number of diseases and pest has also increased. This has jeopardized stability of production. To counter this situation, efforts were directed towards producing populations containing a number of co-adapted genotypes, termed "heterogeneously homozygous" (Hammons, 1976).

Early bunch, which has been for long a successful cultivar in the USA, was made of five sister lines, all of Virginia bunch type. The lines were derived from a cross between two Florida lines, which were themselves derivatives from single crosses. The long ruling high yielding cultivar, Florunner, in the USA is another example. Such populations are adapted to wide geographical areas, give more stable yield over seasons and afford broad protection against diseases. But they are less uniform than pure line cultivars and are more difficult to maintain and to certify the seed stock. When the seed are used for crushing purposes, the lack of uniformity of seed can be tolerated to a large extent. The very old cultivar AK-12-24, largely cultivated in the states of Orissa and West Bengal, is believed to be a mixture of some lines. It is known for its stability over years and is still a popular cultivar in the above-mentioned states.

Yield is under multi-genic control and cultivated groundnut is an allotetraploid. The genetic logic of breeding approach based on mixture of genotypes has been succinctly given in the following quotations. "Heterotic effects between alleles within a locus of a given genome are lost rapidly with selfing. With multiple genes controlling a trait and final selection of lines in the early generations, a moderate level of residual heterosis could be retained for several generations. Heterosis due to the interactions of genes at similar loci on different genomes could also be utilized and would be retained if the genes are in the homozygous conditions when the lines are composited (Norden, 1977). Thus both the genetic diversity of multi-lines and heterosis available through early generation selection might contribute significantly to stability of yield" (Norden *et al.,* 1982). More research on these lines is warranted.

### 8.2.5. *Multiple crosses*

The number of parents used for developing a cultivar in groundnut have been limited. But good variability is available in the germplasm studied. Unless variation is brought in for reshuffling the gene pool, the present stagnant level of yield cannot be overcome. One of the best ways to bring in a large number of selected germplasm lines together is through use of multiple crosses. In groundnut, the most practicable and tested are the three way and double crosses. In addition to developing enhanced gene pool, such crosses can be directly utilized for developing cultivars with pyramided genes for resistance to stresses, especially biotic stresses. It has been reported by Bandyopadhyay *et al.* (1985) that the frequencies of desirable selections were higher in three way crosses than in single crosses.

Double and single crosses were superior for generating desirable segregants for late leaf spot resistance as measured by green leaf area percentage. Three-way crosses followed by backcrosses were superior for releasing desirable segregants for pod yield and shelling percentage. Simultaneous selection of these characters based on the index showed that most of the desirable lines appeared in three-way and back crosses which constituted better foundation populations for further improvement (Gowda *et al.,* 1997). Multiple crosses (three-way crosses, double crosses and intermating of $F_2$ segregants) may be more effective than conventional single crosses for the production of cultivars with acceptable levels of shelling percentage and quality traits and for incorporating rust resistance (Vindhyavarman *et al.,* 1992).

### 8.2.6. *Natural out crossing : its avantages and limitations in breeding*

In a self pollinating crop, even a small amount of out crossing poses problems for maintaining the genetic purity of cultivars, but natural out crossing generates additional variability which breeders can capitalize on (Hammons, 1964; Nigam *et al.,* 1983). This concept has been successfully utilized in groundnut. The maximum natural out crossing in groundnut is about 2% only. ICRISAT, by utilizing natural hybrids, developed four groundnut cultivars, ICGS 11, ICGS 44, ICGS 37 and ICGS 1, which have been released for cultivation in India. Similarly in Zimbabwe, a groundnut cultivar 'Egret' was developed from natural outcrossing in the 'Makulu red' cultivar (Hildebrand, 1975). Generally spanish and valencia types show slightly higher percentages of outcrossing compared to the Virginia bunch and runner types (Culp *et al.,* 1968; Gillier and Silvesto, 1969; Reddy *et al.,* 1993).

It may not be necessary to use unadapted parents with distinct genetic markers to identify genuine $F_1$ hybrids. Instead, several commonly present simply inherited traits such as testa colour can be employed. Also, hybrid indices involving some quantitative characters can be used. However, more land and labour may be required for identification of hybrids. The land and labour requirements can be drastically reduced if outcrossing rates can be enhanced. This may be achieved by growing bee-attractant crops such as sunhemp and sunflower in the groundnut crossing blocks as suggested by Gibbons and Tattersfield (1969). Dutta *et al.* (1987) reported that low doses of radiations could be utilized to increase the levels of outcrosssing in groundnut. They observed that pollen sterility induced through gamma irradiation (5 kR) could produce as high as 33% outcrossing in a groundnut cultivar, M 13. So, if proper male gametocides are identified, the enhanced outcrossing rates can be utilized in groundnut improvement programmes.

In groundnut, artificial hybridization is difficult and the number of hybrid seeds a breeder gets from a cross is always limited. Further the number of $F_2$ seeds that a breeder gets from $F_1$ plants is also limited. As such the $F_2$ population is also limited which allows limited chances of recombination events. Enhanced natural out crossing among the $F_2$ plants will thus enhance number of recombination events. Another very important use of such enhancement may be in increasing the recombination frequencies in the segregating generations of groundnut.

### 8.2.7. *Early generation testing and selection*

When and how to select for productive derivatives in segregating generation is still an open topic in groundnut breeding. There are reports advocating early selection (Coffelt and Hammons, 1974; Kolesnikove, 1979; Kibite, 1981; Gebre-Mariam, 1982) and against it (Wynne, 1976; McNeal *et al.,* 1978; Whan *et al.,* 1981, 1982). The theoretical studies of Yaonezawa and Yamagata (1981) supported early generation selection as a cost- and time-efficient breeding strategy. Experimental evidence in groundnut based on extensive evaluation of $F_1$ to $F_5$. generations (Pungle, 1983; Koteswara Rao, 1984) has further shown that selection of heterotic $F_1$'s followed by index selection in $F_2$ are valuable components of a resource-efficient breeding strategy. Bandyopadhyay *et al.* (1985) used the $F_2$ generation of single crosses and the $F_2$ generation of a set of three way crosses and followed selection indices based on only direct yield components and combination of physiological parameters and yield components for predicting the performance of the $F_3$. The frequency of selection was higher in three-way than single crosses. Selection index, based on physiological and yield component, was more efficient in trapping $F_2$ plants providing selections in $F_3$ than index based on yield components only. Nagabhusanam *et al.* (1992) also advocated selection based on physio-morphological traits. Family selection was superior for all disease resistance and productivity parameters. However, single plant selection was effective for shelling percentage, percentage leaf area affected by disease, pod length and pod width. Early generation selection was ineffective for pod yield (Bhat *et al.,* 1996).

In pedigree breeding for productive pure lines, generations are usually advanced by selfing. This results in rapid reduction of heterozygosity, and in the small populations handled by the breeder in each generation, this further narrows down the genetic variability available for selection. Dutta *et al.* (1986) suggested that early generation intermating in groundnut produced higher frequency of superior plants than $F_1$. The reason for such superiority was suggested to be the recombination of genes from the upper and lower ends of the genotypic distribution under intermating.

### 8.2.8. *Interspecific hybridization in groundnut improvement*

Wild relatives of groundnut have been found to be important sources of resistance to many pest and diseases that cause severe yield losses round the world. Genetically uniform *A. hypogaea* — like derivatives from the section *Arachis* with high pod and haulm yield and resistance to disease have been produced and are now being used in various breeding programmes worldwide. It has been difficult to cross incompatible species classified into six other sections of genus *Arachis,* with *A. hypogaea,* However, progress has been made in understanding the barriers to hybridization, and establishing some rare hybrids ($F_1$) using *in-vitro* embryo rescue techniques, to incorporate the genomes of some accessions of sections *Erectoides* and *Rhizometosa.*

Sastri *et al.* (1992) obtained a large number of hybrid plants from embryo culture derived calli obtained from culture of hybrid embryos *(A. hypogaea X A. Sp* 276233 (Rhizomantosae)) through hormone-aided pollination followed by *in vitro* culture of immature ovules and embryos.

### 8.2.9. *Biotechnology in groundnut improvement*

The availability of biotechnological tools including marker assisted selection and gene transfer açross the species barrier has opened up novel opportunities for enhancing and stabilizing yield and improving quality. Using these techniques, phenomenal success has been achieved in manipulation of fatty acid composition of vegetable oils by expressing either a foreign gene or antisense of a native gene in the target species (Ohlrogge, 1994). A brief report on what has been done and what can be done in groundnut is given here.

### 8.2.10. *Tissue and organ culture and regeneration*

Successful exploitation of plant biotechnology depends on establishment of efficient regeneration system. Regeneration system is based on identifying a plant somatic tissue, which can be relatively easily used for transformation, and then whole plants can be generated from the transformed tissue. It must be kept in mind that the incorporated gene has to be transmitted to the progeny generations also. Groundnut is an inherently difficult material for meeting these requirements.

A range of tissues and organs from *Arachis hypogaea* and some of its wild relatives have been cultured on different media (Sastri *et al.*, 1981). Callus was obtained when the medium was supplemented with a combination of NAA (Naphthalene acetic acid) and BAP (Benzyl adeno purine) for culture of a range of seedling explants, root discs, shoot meristems, immature leaflets and epicotyls, and cotyledons from mature seeds (Nalini Mallikarjuna *et al.*, 1992). All these explants produced shoot-forming calli from *A. hypogaea, A. pusilla, A. villosulicarpa,* and *A. correntina* on MS semisolid medium with NAA (0.01-10.0 mg/1) and BAP (0.1-25.0 mg/1).

De-embryonated cotyledons (this terminology is accepted in *in vitro* culture parlance though truly speaking cotyledons are part of the embryo) have been widely used for *in vitro* regeneration because of their easy availability and ease of handling. A large number of shoots can be regenerated directly with out the intervention of a callus phase from a single cotyledon within a short time thus making them good candidates for use in genetic engineering (Moss *et al.,* 1992; Radhakrishnan *et al.*, 2000) mainly through *Agrobacterium* mediated transformation. The cotyledons are a good source of shoots for *in vitro* manipulation, and their own nutrient storage is sufficient for initiation of shoots in large numbers. Cotyledonory leaves have also been used for direct regeneration of shoots.

Another route of regeneration, which has been widely used in groundnut, is through direct somatic embryogenesis *i.e.,* generation of embryos from the somatic tissues, (mainly de-embryonated cotyledon have been used) without an intervening callus phase. Such somatic embryos are either further multiplied to form secondary somatic embryos and then single shoots are generated from these embryos or they are directly used for generating seedlings. A novel genotype-independent technique for generating multiple shoots from each somatic embryo has been developed by Radhakrishnan *et al.* (1997). This approach overcomes the problem of getting a big proportion of abnormal secondary embryos. Somatic embryos are a favourite material for transformation work through the use of particle bombardment (biolistic) methods because of easy incorporation and higher chances of transformed embryogenic cells becoming transformed differentiated organs.

A much less preferred and less successful tissue for transformation has been protoplasts derived from leaf cells. In this method, protoplast are isolated from leaf cells through enzymatic digestion of cell walls. The protoplasts are then used for transformation mainly through a method known as electroporation and then the protoplast is coaxed into regeneration into whole plant. This step is yet to be successfully achieved.

***Transformation of groundnut and identification of genes with potential for utilization in transformation***

Plant transformation is the introduction and stable integration of alien genes into the genome of a recipient plants. With transformation, the gene pool available for improvement of a crop is essentially unlimited, and could include genes from virtually any organism. This technology could be especially useful for the modification of certain traits in cultivated groundnut. It could also aid the transfer of useful genes from the diploid wild species into the allotetraploid cultivated species. Transgenics hold promise mainly for improvement of genotypes for resistance to pests and improving nutritional qualities.

Different transformation protocols have now been successfully used for developing transgenic groundnut expressing various desirable foreign genes. An update of the recent developments in this area is given in the Table 6.

**Table 6:** Update on transformation of groundnut *(Arachis hypogaea* L.)

| ***Gene(s) introduced*** | ***Gene delivery system employed*** | ***Target tissue i.e. tissue used for transformation*** | ***Regeneration status*** | ***Reference(s)*** |
|---|---|---|---|---|
| Gus with *Soyabean* | Biolistic | Embryogenic cultures | Transgenic plants up to $R_1$ generation | Wang *et al.,* 1998 |
| *Promotor-uidA chimeric gene* | | | | |
| *GUS* | *Agrobacterium tumefaciens.* | Leaf, cotyledon | Transformed callus in leaf explants; Gus expression in parenchymatous cells of cotyledon explants. | Freitas *et al.,* 1998 |
| Wild strain of *A. rhizogenes* | *Agrobacterium rhizogenes* | Hypocotyles | Transgenic plants | Akasaka *et al.,* 1998 |
| GUS and *nptII* | *Agrobacterium* | Stem internode, seedling explants | Tumors | Lacorte *et al.,* 1991 |
| GUS and *hph* | Biolistic | Embryogenic callus | Transgenic plants | Ozias-Akins *et al.,* 1993 |
| GUS and *nptII* | *Agrobacterium* | Leaf disc | Transgenic plants with shrivelled seeds | Eapen and George, 1994 |

**Table 6:** (*Contd...*)

**Table 6:** (*Contd...*)

| ***Gene(s) introduced*** | ***Gene delivery system employed*** | ***Target tissue i.e. tissue used for transformation*** | ***Regeneration status*** | ***Reference(s)*** |
|---|---|---|---|---|
| GUS, *bar* and TSWV nucleo capsid protein | Biolistic | Shoot meristem of embryonic axis | Transgenic plants, upto $R_2$ generation | Brar *et al.*, 1994 |
| GUS and *nptll* | *Agrobacterium* | Cotyledon explants | $T_2$ generation, viable seeds | ICRISAT 1994 |
| *Bar* and PStV genome | *Agrobacterium* | Embryonic axis | Putative transformants | Cassidy and Ponsamuel, 1996 |
| Gus and Npt II | *Agrobacterium* | Leaflet explants | Gus expression in explant tissues | Sarker and Chodhury, 1996. |
| GUS and *npt II* | *Agrobacterium* | Seedling explants | Second generation fertile plants | Li *et al.*, 1996 |
| GUS and *nptll* | Electroporation | Protoplast | Protoplast derived callus colonies | Li *et al.*, 1996 |
| PStV coat protein | Electroporation | Protoplast | Protoplast derived callus colonies | Li *et al.*, 1996 |
| GUS and *nptll* | *Agrobacterium* | Leaf explant | Fertile transgenic and mature $T_1$ plants | Cheng *et al.*, 1996 |
| GUS, *nptll* and PCV coat | *Agrobacterium* | Cotyledon and leaf explants | $T_2$ generation with viable seeds | ICRISAT, 1996 |
| GUS, *npt 11* and TSWV nucleo capsid protein | *Agrobacterium* | Leaf explants | Transgenic plants, upto $T_1$ generation | Li *et al.*, 1997 |
| GUS and 2S Brazil-nut protein | Biolistic | Seed explants | Transient expression | Lacorte *et al.*, 1997 |
| *hph* and *Bt CrylA(c)* gene | Biolistic | Somatic embryos | Transgenic plants, upto $T_1$ generation | Singsit *et al.*, 1997 |

*Source:* Updated from Misra, 1998

### 8.2.11. *Mechanism of introducing gene*

*Agrobacterium* mediated gene transfer bas been used by most earlier workers and is still being used even as other techniques like particle bombardment (biolistic), electroporation are becoming popular. Fertile transgenic plants upto $T_2$ generation have been obtained by both *Agrobacterium* mediated gene transfer and particle bombardment. Use of electroporation bas been restricted to protoplasts alone which developed into calli.

### 8.2.12. *Marker assisted selection (MAS)*

Markers based on DNA sequence variations are increasingly being utilized in crops for construction of genetic maps and marker-assisted selections. Application of molecular markers in plant breeding programme has established the need for information on variation in DNA sequences even in those crops in which little classical genetic and cytogenetic information is available. MAS should be most effective in the early generations of selection among progeny from crosses between inbred lines and for incorporation of resistance genes for various stresses.

Knowledge of the groundnut genome has so far been limited and only in the recent years have molecular techniques been used. A comprehensive and rigorous examination of the material available in the groundnut world collection, either by improving current techniques, or by using such advanced techniques as simple sequence repeats and amplified fragment length polymorphism could well reveal polymorphism at the molecular level (Singh *et al.,* 1998). From nil to low level of polymorphic variability, depending on the material and method used, in cultivated types to very high level of polymorphic variability in wild *Arachis* species have been reported in groundnut (Lanham *et al.,* 1992; He and Prakash, 1997; Bhagawat *et al.,* 1997). However, sufficient diversity in DNA profiles of some of the diseases resistant germplasm has been reported (Dwivedi *et al.,* 1999). Abundant restricted fragment length polymorphism (RFLP) has been detected among wild diploid species (Paik-Ro *et al.,* 1992). The first RFLP linkage map of groundnut was constructed using inter-specific hybridization between two related diploid wild species: *Arachis stenosperma* and *A. cardenasii* (Halward *et al.,* 1993). Using this framework map, introgression analysis was done (Garcia *et al.,* 1995) of the *A. cardenasii* genome into the tetraploid *A. hypogaea.* Garcia *et al.* (1996) later reported the first molecular marker linked with nematode resistance in groundnut. Concerted and wide research efforts on this line are expected in future.

## 8.3. Cultivars Developed

In the crop improvement history of groundnut in India, two years, 1905 and 1961, represent important landmarks. Groundnut cultivars 'Spanish Improved' a pure line selection from spanish peanut made at Dharwad, was released in 1905 for cultivation in bunch tract of Bombay-Karnataka region. This was the first official release of groundnut in India. In 1961, C 501, a Virginia bunch cultivar derived from a cross between D3 and Ah 477 at Ludhiana, was released for cultivation in Punjab state. This was the first groundnut cultivar in India derived through hybridization. The list of cultivars released over years in India is presented in the Table 7.

Between 1906 and 1960, twelve cultivars were released in different parts of the country. These cultivars were developed either by pure line selection or mass selection in local/introduced cultivars. Prominent among these were AK 12-24 and TMV 2 (both spanish and released in 1940), Karad 4-11 (virginia runner, released in 1957), and T 28 (virginia runner released in 1960). During 1961-79, 28 more cultivars were released. Of these, 11 originated from hybridization and 17 were mass/pure line selections.

Groundnut breeding in India received a real impetus in the 1980's when 30 new cultivars were released. The new cultivars included 20 spanish, seven virginia bunch and three virginia runner types. Contrary to previous decades where heavy reliance for varietal development was placed on mass/pure line selections in local and introduced materials, in the 80's, 80% of the new cultivars were cross derivatives. This decade also saw a shift in breeding objectives when greater emphasis was laid on stress resistance breeding. Three foliar disease resistant cultivars, (Girnar 1, ICGS (FDRS) 10, and ICGV 86590), were released during this period. Similarly cultivars like ICGS 11, ICGS 37 and ICGS 44, were specifically released for post-rainy season cultivation in different parts of the country.

From 1990 to 1999 about 30 cultivars have been released, almost all of which were developed through hybridization followed by selections besides mutation followed by hybridization. During this period the emphasis was given not only for yield and resistance but also for large seeded types. Till the end of 1999, about 104 cultivars were released in India giving a wide array of choice to farmers. An exercise conducted with the recently released cultivars in India indicated a genetic gain of 1.3-3.2% per year for pod yield under rainfed cultivation (Nigam *et al.*, 1991). However, the gain in productivity at farm level does not truly reflect the genetic gains which have been made experimentally. The gain in productivity obtained so far, needs to be sustained by incorporating resistance/tolerance to prevailing biotic and abiotic stresses. To increase the production further, cultivars suited to specific production systems are required.

**Table 7:** List of released groundnut cultivars in India

| ***Sr. no.*** | ***Name of the cultivar*** | ***Pedigree*** | ***Breeding meth*** | ***Habit group*** | ***Year of release*** | ***Area for released*** | ***Originating centre*** | ***Pod yield kg/ha*** | ***Shelling per cent*** | ***Oil (%)*** | ***100 kernel weight*** | ***Salient features*** |
|---|---|---|---|---|---|---|---|---|---|---|---|---|
| ***S. no.*** | ***(1)*** | ***(2)*** | ***(3)*** | ***(4)*** | ***(5)*** | ***(6)*** | ***(7)*** | ***(8)*** | ***(9)*** | ***(10)*** | ***(11)*** | ***(12)*** |
| 1. | Gangapuri | – | S | VL | – | Madhya Pradesh and entire country | Khargaon | 2000 | 59.7 | 49.5 | 36.8 | 3-4 seeded pod with purple testa colour, susceptible to aphid and jassids |
| 2. | Spanish Improved | Selection from Spanish peanut | S | SB | 1905 | Tract of Bombay & Kamataka region | Dharwad | 2400 | 67.0 | 44.0 | 29.6 | Less prominent beak and constriction; kernels with round ends |
| 3. | Kopergoan 1 | Selection from local | S | SS | 1933 | Sangali and district of Maharashtra | Kopergaon | 1250 | 72.0 | 47.0 | 44.8 | Pod medium in size |
| 4. | Kopergoan 3 | Selection from local | S | VL | 1933 | Western Maharashtra | Kopergaon | 1900 | 69.0 | 47.0 | 35.1 | Early maturity (90 days); 3 seeded red testa preferred |
| 5. | Ak 12-24 | Selection from local | S | SB | 1940 | Vidharbha region of Maharashtra but grown in the states of Orissa, Madhya Pradesh and Rajasthan | Akola | 1250 | 75.0 | 48.5 | 29.4 | Wider adaptability; suited for medium to heavy soils |
| 6. | TMV 1 | Mass selection from Salom | S | VR | 1940 | Tamil Nadu | Tindivanam | 1450 | 73.5 | 50.0 | 32.3 | Pod 1-3 seeded |

**Table 7:** (*Contd...*)

**Table 7:** *(Contd...)*

| Sr. no. | Name of the cultivar | Pedigree | Breeding meth | Habit group | Year of release | Area for released | Originating centre | Pod yield kg/ha | Shelling per cent | Oil (%) | 100 kernel weight | Salient features |
|---|---|---|---|---|---|---|---|---|---|---|---|---|
| S. no. | (1) | (2) | (3) | (4) | (5) | (6) | (7) | (8) | (9) | (10) | (11) | (12) |
| 7. | TMV 2 | Mass selection from Gudh-iatham bunch | S | SB | 1940 | Tamil Nadu, Currently grown in Andhra Pradesh & Karnataka | Tindivanam | 1025 | 76.7 | 49.0 | 32.7 | Widely adapted; well suited for summer season |
| 8. | TMV 3 | Selection | S | VR | 1943 | Tamil Nadu | Tindivanam | 1450 | 76.7 | 49.6 | 36.6 | Pod short 1-3 seeded with reticulation and constriction |
| 9. | TMV 4 | Selection from North Carolina | S | VR | 1947 | Tamil Nadu | Tindivanam | 1450 | 75.5 | 50.0 | 36.3 | High percentage of 3-4 seeded pods |
| 10. | Punjab 1 | Selection from Samrla local | S | VR | 1953 | Punjab but grown in Gujarat and Rajasthan | Ludhiana | 1900 | 69.0 | 49.0 | 46.8 | Wider adaptability |
| 11. | RS 1 | Selection from local callection | S | VR | 1953 | Rajasthan | Durgapura | 1300 | 71.0 | 45.0 | 40.0 | Kernel medium bold |
| 12. | Karad 4-11 | Selection from local callection | S | VR | 1957 | Satara, Sangali, Kolhapur, Solapur and Pune district of Maharashtra | Karad | 1000 | 72.0 | 48.0 | 42.4 | Medium to long pod 1-3 seeded |

**Table 7:** *(Contd... )*

**Table 7:** (*Contd...*)

| *S. no.* | *(1)* | *(2)* | *(3)* | *(4)* | *(5)* | *(6)* | *(7)* | *(8)* | *(9)* | *(10)* | *(11)* | *(12)* |
|---|---|---|---|---|---|---|---|---|---|---|---|---|
| 13. | T 28 | Selection from Bombay collection | S | VB | 1960 | Uttar Pradesh | Mainpuri | 1900 | 74.0 | 47.5 | 32.6 | Pod 3 seeded with promiment beak and retic-ulation kernel medium, spherical with light red testa |
| 14. | RSB 87 | Selection from Brazilian collection | S | VB | 1961 | Kota division and other heavy soil area of Rajasthan | Durgapur | 1750 | 66.0 | 50.0 | 49.7 | Small dark green leaflets; 3 seeded with dark red kernels |
| 15. | TMV 5 | Gross between Native Tangani-yaka & Gudha-tham bunch | HS | SB | 1961 | Tamil Nadu | Tindivanam | 1250 | 74.6 | 50.5 | 33.3 | Matures in 110 days; partial dormant |
| 16. | TMV 6 | Selection from Virginia Bunch | S | VB | 1961 | Tamil Nadu | Tindivanam | 950 | 73.0 | 48.0 | 40.3 | Suited for table purpose; pods 1-3 seeded with shallow to medium construction; prominent reticulation |
| 17. | C 501 | D 3 × Ah 477 | HS | VB | 1961 | Punjab | Ludhiana | 1750 | 68.0 | 48.0 | 40.4 | 1-3 seeded pod; well suited for |

**Table 7:** (*Contd...*)

**Table 7:** *(Contd...)*

| *Sr. no.* | *Name of the cultivar* | *Pedigree* | *Breeding meth* | *Habit group* | *Year of release* | *Area for released* | *Originating centre* | *Pod yield kg/ha* | *Shelling per cent* | *Oil (%)* | *100 kernel weight* | *Salient features* |
|---|---|---|---|---|---|---|---|---|---|---|---|---|
| ***S. no.*** | ***(1)*** | ***(2)*** | ***(3)*** | ***(4)*** | ***(5)*** | ***(6)*** | ***(7)*** | ***(8)*** | ***(9)*** | ***(10)*** | ***(11)*** | ***(12)*** |
| | | | | | | | | | | | | sandy loam soil under irrigation; matures in 123 days |
| 18. | J 11 | Ah 4218 × Ah 4354 | HS | SB | 1964 | Gujarat state, suitable for state other also | Junagadh | 1300 | 75.0 | 49.0 | 36.7 | Wider adaptability; resistant to collar rot and *Aspergillus flavus* invasion; suitable for summer season also |
| 19. | SB XI | Ah 4213 × Ah 4354 | HS | SB | 1965 | Maharashtra | Originally at Junagadh but finally tested at Jalgaon | 1300 | 75.0 | 49.0 | 35.2 | Suitable for cultivation in summer season also |
| 20. | T64 from EC 1664 | Selection | S | VB | 1966 | Uttar Pradesh | Mainpuri | 2100 | 70.0 | 48.0 | 37.2 | Bold pods, HPS category with prominent reticulation and beak; kernels elliptical with light red testa |

**Table 7:** *(Contd... )*

**Table 7:** (*Contd...*)

| S. no. | (1) | (2) | (3) | (4) | (5) | (6) | (7) | (8) | (9) | (10) | (11) | (12) |
|---|---|---|---|---|---|---|---|---|---|---|---|---|
| 21. | TMV7 | Selection from Teneese white | S | SB | 1967 | Tamil Nadu | Tindivanam | 1400 | 75.2 | 49.6 | 35.8 | Bold pod; dark green foliage |
| 22. | Pollachil 1 | Selection from Malaya-dian Bunch | S | SB | 1968 | Pollachi tract of Tamil Nadu | Pollachi | 1450 | 76.6 | 48.2 | 31.1 | Fit for HPS types |
| 23. | TMV 8 | Selection from Manapuri local | S | VB | 1968 | Southern and central region of Tamil Nadu | Tindivanam | 1600 | 74.4 | 50.1 | 34.0 | Mostly 3 seeded pod; dormant upto 60 days . |
| 24. | M 145 | A1-1 × D3 | HS | VB | 1968 | Punjab | Ludhiana | 2200 | 76.0 | 50.5 | 40.6 | Light green leaves;1-3 seeded pods; purple coloured testa; smaller, lateral spread |
| 25. | S 230 | Selection from Tandur local | S | SB | 1969 | Northern Karnataka | Raichur | 1280 | 70.0 | 50.0 | 41.2 | – |
| 26. | S 206 | Selection from Manvi local | S | SB | 1969 | Northern Karnataka | Raichur | 1900 | 73.0 | 49.5 | 33.8 | Reticulated pod with slight beak and constriction |
| 27. | TMV 9 | Ah 3490 × Ah 477 | HS | SB | 1970 | Tamil Nadu | Tindivanam | 1150 (rainfed) | 75.6 | 51.4 | 33.3 | Dormancy up to 15 days |

**Table 7:** (*Contd...* )

**Table 7:** *(Contd...)*

| *Sr. no.* | *Name of the cultivar* | *Pedigree* | *Breeding meth* | *Habit group* | *Year of release* | *Area for released* | *Originating centre* | *Pod yield kg/ha* | *Shelling per cent* | *Oil (%)* | *100 kernel weight* | *Salient features* |
|---|---|---|---|---|---|---|---|---|---|---|---|---|
| ***S. no.*** | ***(1)*** | ***(2)*** | ***(3)*** | ***(4)*** | ***(5)*** | ***(6)*** | ***(7)*** | ***(8)*** | ***(9)*** | ***(10)*** | ***(11)*** | ***(12)*** |
| | | | | | | | | 2000 (irrigated) | | | | |
| 28. | TMV 10 | Natural mutant from Argentina | M | VB | 1970 | Tamil Nadu but suitable for entire country | Tindivanam | 1700 | 77.7 | 54.4 | 54.0 | Testa varigated; high oil content |
| 29 | Kadiri 71-1 | Selection from Ah 288 | S | VB | 1971 | Rayalseema region of Andhra Pradesh | Kadiri | 1390 | 74.0 | 47.0 | 38.0 | Efficient in fixing atmospheric nitrogen |
| 30 | Jyoti | Selection from exotic 7 | S | SB | 1971 | Madhya Pradesh | Khargaon | 1600 | 77.8 | 53.3 | 31.5 | Less incidence of root and from collar rot |
| 31. | M 13 | Selection from NC13 | S | VR | 1972 | Entire country | Ludhiana | 2750 | 68.0 | 49.0 | 58.1 | Leaves dark green with waxy coating; Large size pod, HPS category; prominent reticulation and medium constriction; tolerant to leafspot |
| 32. | GAUG1 | Ak 10 × Ak 12-24 | HS | SB | 1973 | Gujarat | Junagadh | 1500 | 76.0 | 50.0 | 34.0 | Small thin shelled pods having prominent beak |

**Table 7:** *(Contd... )*

**Table 7:** *(Contd...)*

| *S. no.* | *(1)* | *(2)* | *(3)* | *(4)* | *(5)* | *(6)* | *(7)* | *(8)* | *(9)* | *(10)* | *(11)* | *(12)* |
|---|---|---|---|---|---|---|---|---|---|---|---|---|
| 33. | Pollachi 2 | Pollachi Red x Ah 2105 | HS | SB | 1973 | Coimbator, Salem & Trichi dist., of T. N. | Pollachi | 1500 (rainfed) 2700 (irrigated) | 78.6 | 48.6 | 35.0 | High shelling per cent |
| 34. | TG1 (Vikaram) | X-ray mutant from Spanish improved | M | VB | 1973 | Entire country | BARC Trombay | 2695 | 68.0 | 46.5 | 72.0 | Bold pod; HPS Grade; profuse branching but late maturity |
| 35. | GAUG 10 | G 224-3 × GO 343 | HS | VR | 1973 | Gujarat | Junagadh | 1800 | 74.0 | 50.0 | 45.4 | Plant well branched; stem thin; medium sized pod 2-1 seeded with rose testa |
| 36. | Dh-3-30 | Spanish Improved × US4 | HS | SB | 1975 | Northern Karnataka | Dharwad | 2800 | 77.6 | 46.5 | 40.0 | Pod with prominent beak and constriction; bold kernels, HPS category; tolerant to drought |
| 37. | MH 1 | Selection from Faizpur 1-5 | S | SB | 1975 | Haryana | Hisar | 2000 | 70.0 | 50.0 | 40.8 | Light green leaves and light rose kernels; small pods |
| 38. | TMV 11 | Selection from East Africa | S | VL | 1977 | Tamil Nadu | Tindivanam | 1200 | 73.0 | 50.2 | 33.6 | Big pod; 1-3 seeded; thick shelled; purple testa |

**Table 7:** *(Contd...)*

**Table 7:** (*Contd...*)

| Sr. no. | Name of the cultivar | Pedigree | Breeding meth | Habit group | Year of release | Area for released | Originating centre | Pod yield kg/ha | Shelling per cent | Oil (%) | 100 kernel weight | Salient features |
|---|---|---|---|---|---|---|---|---|---|---|---|---|
| S. no. | (1) | (2) | (3) | (4) | (5) | (6) | (7) | (8) | (9) | (10) | (11) | (12) |
| 39. | Chandra | Selection from Ah 114 | S | VR | 1977 | Uttar Pradesh | Mainpuri | 2500 | 70.0 | 47.7 | 40.2 | Bold pod; kernel light rose, big oval shaped |
| 40. | Kadiri 2 | Nigerian culture MK374 | I/S | VB | 1978 | Srikakulam, Vishakhapatnam & Chittor district of Andhra Pradesh | Kadiri | 1800 | 78.0 | 47.0 | 50.9 | Efficient in fixing atmospheric nitrogen; maturing in 115-120 days; Bold seeded brownish testa |
| 41. | Kadiri 3 | Selection from Robut 33-1 | S | VB | 1978 | Andhra Pradesh but adopted to entire country | Kadiri | 2100 | 75.0 | 49.0 | 41.0 | Clustered bearing; smooth and short pod; rose testa; early maturing (105 days); suitable for summer season also |
| 42 | MH2 | Selection from Gujarat Dwarf Mutant (GDM) | S | VL | 1978 | Haryana | Hissar | 3000 | 72.0 | 49.0 | 27.2 | Very dwarf plant; pod 1-4 seeded; red testa; responsive to closer spacing 15×15 cm |
| 43. | JL24 (Phule | Selection from | S | SB | 1978 | Maharashtra but suitable | Jalgaon | 1800 | 75.0 | 50.7 | 53.7 | Large dark green leaves; |

**Table 7:** (*Contd...* )

**Table 7:** (*Contd...*)

| *S. no.* | *(1)* | *(2)* | *(3)* | *(4)* | *(5)* | *(6)* | *(7)* | *(8)* | *(9)* | *(10)* | *(11)* | *(12)* |
|---|---|---|---|---|---|---|---|---|---|---|---|---|
| | Pragati) | EC 94943 | | | | for other states | | | | | | Early (95 days); smooth pod; compact bea-ring; widely adopted |
| 44. | TMV12 | Pureline selection from Uganda n culture | S | SB | 1978 | Tamil Nadu | Tindivanam | 1250 (rainfed) 2100 (irriga-ted) | 72.0 | 51.2 | 35.3 | Medium to bold pods; shallow constriction |
| 45. | CO 1 | Ah 6279 × TMV3 | HS | SB | 1979 | Tamil Nadu | Coimbatore | 1300 (rainfed) 2200 (irrigated) | 47.0 | 50.4 | 34.0 | High harvest index; suited for Rabi/summer cutltivation also |
| 46. | BG 1 | X-ray mutant of 41-C | M | VB | 1979 | Bihar | Kanke | 2000 | 70.0 | 48.0 | 50.0 | Bold pod; SMK % 93-95 |
| 47. | BG2 | X-ray mutant of 41-C | M | VB | 1979 | Bihar | Kanke | 2200 | 69.0 | 49.3 | 51.0 | Bold pod; SMK % 93-95 |
| 48. | Kisan | Spanish Improved × B31 | HS | SB | 1980 | Orissa | Chiplima | 1600 | 70.8 | 49.9 | 35-2 | Small pod with prominent reticualtion |
| 49. | M 37 | A 1 × C 6-4-7-2 | HS | VR | 1980 | Punjab | Ludhiana | 1650 | 69.0 | 50.5 | 47.4 | Pod two seeded with small beak; kernels with light brown testa |
| 50. | KRG 1 | Selection from Argentina | S | SB | 1981 | Raichur, Bellary & Gulbarga | Raichur | 1200 (rainfed) 2230 | 73.0 | 49.0 | 42.0 | Medium sized; pod 2 seeded; suitable for |

**Table 7:** (*Contd...* )

**Table 7:** (*Contd...*)

| **Sr. no.** | ***Name of the cultivar*** | ***Pedigree*** | ***Breeding meth*** | ***Habit group*** | ***Year of release*** | ***Area for released*** | ***Originating centre*** | ***Pod yield kg/ha*** | ***Shelling per cent*** | ***Oil (%)*** | ***100 kernel weight*** | ***Salient features*** |
|---|---|---|---|---|---|---|---|---|---|---|---|---|
| **S. no.** | ***(1)*** | ***(2)*** | ***(3)*** | ***(4)*** | ***(5)*** | ***(6)*** | ***(7)*** | ***(8)*** | ***(9)*** | ***(10)*** | ***(11)*** | ***(12)*** |
| | | | | | | district of Karnataka | | (irrigated) | | | | summer season also |
| 51. | TG 17 | Dark green mutant × TGl | M/HS | SB | 1982 | Maharashtra state for summer season | BARC Trombay | 2000 | 69.0 | 49.0 | — | Bold podded; pinkish kernel; high harvest index; fresh seed dormancy upto 30 days |
| 52. | M 197 | C 501 × U 4-7-2 | HS | VR | 1982 | Punjab state | Ludhiana | 1800 | 67.4 | 51.2 | 48.7 | Leaves dark green; pod with smooth veination; bold kernel |
| 53. | GG 2 | J11 × EC 16659 | HS | SB | 1983 | Saurashtra region of Gujarat for summer season | Junagadh | 3100 | 70.5 | 49.0 | 36.0 | Early flowering; dark green leaves; reticulated; 2 seeded |
| 54. | Jawan | J11 × Asiriya Mwitunde | HS | SB | 1983 | Orissa | Chiplima | 1230 (rainfed) 2000 irrigated) | 66.3 | 47.6 | 36.5 | Elongated pod with slight larger beak; medium rose kernel |
| 55. | CO 2 | EMS mutant | M | SB | 1983 | Tamil Nadu | Coimbatore | 1650 (rainfed) | 77.0 | 51.4 | 40.0 | Medium pod; 1-2 seeded; |

**Table 7:** (*Contd...* )

**Table 7:** (*Contd...*)

| *S. no.* | *(1)* | *(2)* | *(3)* | *(4)* | *(5)* | *(6)* | *(7)* | *(8)* | *(9)* | *(10)* | *(11)* | *(12)* |
|---|---|---|---|---|---|---|---|---|---|---|---|---|
| | | from Pol 1 | | | | | | 2700 (irriga-ted) | | | | plumpy rose colour testa |
| 56. | Dh 8 | Selection from RS 144 | S | SB | 1984 | Transitional tract of northern Karnataka | Dharwad | 3200 | 71.1 | 46.0 | 33.0 | Dark green leaves; compact plant; tolerant to late leaf spot; small pod; smooth kernel; rose rounded at one end and sharply pointed at the other |
| 57. | Chitra | Spanish 58-1 × EC 1688 | HS | VR | 1984 | Uttar Pradesh | Mainpuri | 2000 | 71.0 | 49.0 | 32.0 | Leaves dark green; testa varigated on rose back ground |
| 58. | Kaushal (G 201) | Selection from T 28 | S | VR | 1984 | All India | Mainpuri | 1700 | 71.0 | 49.0 | 40.4 | Compact plant; dark green leaves even at maturity; early (108-112 days); 1-3 seeded pod |
| 59. | UF 70-103 | Intro-duction from USA | I | VR | 1984 | Vidharbha and western region of Maharashtra | Akola | 2000 | 71.3 | 52. | 31.2 | Suitable for summer |
| 60. | GG 11 | M13 × GAUG 10 | HS | VR | 1984 | Entire Gujarat | Junagadh | 2050 | 72.6 | 48.6 | 52.0 | Leaflet and pod bigger than |

**Table 7:** (*Contd...* )

**Table 7:** (*Contd...*)

| Sr. no. | Name of the cultivar | Pedigree | Breeding meth | Habit group | Year of release | Area for released | Originating centre | Pod yield kg/ha | Shelling per cent | Oil (%) | 100 kernel weight | Salient features |
|---|---|---|---|---|---|---|---|---|---|---|---|---|
| S. no. | (1) | (2) | (3) | (4) | (5) | (6) | (7) | (8) | (9) | (10) | (11) | (12) |
| | | | | | | | | | | | | GAUG 10; 4.9% higher yield than GAUG 10 and 14.3% higher yield than M13 |
| 61. | TG 3 | Mutant of M Spanish Improved | M | SB | 1985 | Kerala | BARC Trombay | 1200 (R) | — | 48.5 | — | Bold pod HPS Grade; profuse branching but late maturity |
| 62. | M 335 | M13× F7 | HS | VR | 1986 | Sandy area of Punjab under irrigated condition during kharif season | Ludhiana | 2300 | 67.0 | 49.0 | 71.0 | Plant has less lateral spread; leaflets large and dark green in colour; pod bold with 1-2 seeded and rarely 3 seeded; reticulation prominent; constriction medium; kernels bold with light brown testa |
| 63. | ICGS 11 | Selection from | S | SB | 1986 | Zone III comprising | ICRISAT | 2000 | 70.0 | 48.7 | 42.0 | Dark green leaflet; compact |

**Table 7:** (*Contd...*)

**Table 7:** (*Contd...*)

| S. no. | (1) | (2) | (3) | (4) | (5) | (6) | (7) | (8) | (9) | (10) | (11) | (12) |
|---|---|---|---|---|---|---|---|---|---|---|---|---|
| | | Robut 33-1 | | | | parts of M.P. and M.H. and zone V comp., A.P., Karna., & parts of M.H. for Rabi/Summer cultivation. | | | | | | plant; pod 2 seeded; constriction reticulation less prominent and beak absent |
| 64. | SG 84 | Selection from ICGS 1 | S | SB | 1986 | Loamy soil of Punjab under irrigation for spring season | Ludhiana | 2062 | 64.0 | 50.0 | 49.0 | Plant grows erect with medium sized dark green leaves; pod 2 seeded with medium constriction and slight beak; testa light brown |
| 65. | VRI 1 | TMV 7 × FSB7 | HS | SB | 1986 | Tamil Nadu | RRS Vridhacha-lam | 1590 (K) 1877 (R) | 74.0 | 48.0 | 36.0 | Suitable for rainfed and irrigated condition with high shelling; fresh seed dormancy for a week |
| 66. | BG3 | Early Runner × Asiriya Mwitunde | HS | VB | 1986 | Bihar | BAU,Kanke | 2500 | 72.0 | 49.0 | 52.0 | Virginia Bunch cultivar with early maturity |
| 67. | MA 16 | Selection from | S | VB | 1986 | Uttar Pradesh | Mainpuri | 1500 (R) | — | — | — | Bold seeded; suitable for |

**Table 7:** (*Contd...* )

**Table 7:** *(Contd...)*

| *Sr. no.* | *Name of the cultivar* | *Pedigree* | *Breeding meth* | *Habit group* | *Year of release* | *Area for released* | *Originating centre* | *Pod yield kg/ha* | *Shelling per cent* | *Oil (%)* | *100 kernel weight* | *Salient features* |
|---|---|---|---|---|---|---|---|---|---|---|---|---|
| ***S. no.*** | ***(1)*** | ***(2)*** | ***(3)*** | ***(4)*** | ***(5)*** | ***(6)*** | ***(7)*** | ***(8)*** | ***(9)*** | ***(10)*** | ***(11)*** | ***(12)*** |
| | | EC 16664 | | | | | | | | | | HPS; moderately resistant to leafspot |
| 68. | ALR1 | Pol 2 × PPG 4 | HS | VB | 1987 | Pollachi tract of Tamil Nadu | ARS, Aliyarnagar | 1840 (K) 2000 (R) | 70.0 | 49.0 | 33.0 | Suitable for rust endemic areas (Pollachi tract) |
| 69. | Girnar 1 | X14-4-B-19-B xNC-Ac 17090 | HS | SB | 1988 | Western M.H., A.P., T.N. | NRCG, Junagadh | 2000 (R) | 70.9 | 50.0 | 33.0 | Early maturing multiple resistant cultivar suitable for rainfed conditions |
| 70. | ICGS44 | Selection from Robut 33-1 | S | SB | 1988 | Gujarat, M.H. & M.P. | ICRISAT | 2500 (R/S) | 70.0 | 49.0 | 60.0 | Suitable for Rabi/Summer; tolerant to BND |
| 71. | RG141 | Robut 33-1 × NCAc 2821 | HS | SB | 1989 | Black soils Rajasthan | RAU, Durgapura | 2100 | 72.0 | 50.8 | 42.0 | Cultivar with dark green foliage |
| 72. | RS138 | Selection from Brazilian | S | SB | 1989 | Durgapura, Rajasthan | RAU, Durgapura | 2100 | 72.0 | 50.0 | 56.0 | Cultivar resembling RSB 87 |
| 73. | ICGS 76 | TMV 10 × Chico | HS | VB | 1989 | Souther M.H., A.P., T.N. & Karnataka | ICRISAT | 1300 (R) | 72.0 | 42.5 | 44.0 | A cultivar with two seeded pods; tan colour testa |
| 74. | VRI2 | JL 24 x | HS | SB | 1989 | Vridhachalam | RRS | 1500 | 74.0 | 48.0 | 50.0 | Bold podded |

**Table 7:** *(Contd... )*

**Table 7:** (*Contd...*)

| *S. no.* | *(1)* | *(2)* | *(3)* | *(4)* | *(5)* | *(6)* | *(7)* | *(8)* | *(9)* | *(10)* | *(11)* | *(12)* |
|---|---|---|---|---|---|---|---|---|---|---|---|---|
| | | CO 2 | | | | Tamil Nadu | Vridhachalam | | | | | with medium constrictions suitable to both rainfed and irrigated conditions |
| 75. | Somnath | TG 18 A (Induced mutant of TG 18 A × M 13) | M/HS | VR | 1990 | Gujarat and Rajasthan | BARC, Bombay | 1900 | 72.3 | 50.1 | 62.0 | High yielding; Early maturing; Bold seeded; HPS grade; for kharif season |
| 76. | ICGS1 | Selection from Robut 33-1 | S | SB | 1990 | Haryana, U.P., Punjab, Bihar and Rajasthan | ICRISAT | 2300 | 70.0 | 51.4 | 35.0 | Cultivar suitable for both kharif and spring season |
| 77. | ICG (FDRS) 10 | Ah 65 × NCAc 17090 | HS | SB | 1990 | Peninsular India | ICRISAT | 2200 | 67.0 | 47.8 | 36.0 | Suitable for kharif season, where rust and LLS diseases are problem |
| 78. | VRI3 | J 11 × Robut 33-1 | HS | SB | 1990 | Tamil Nadu | RRS Vridhachalam | 1668 | 75.0 | 48.7 | 33.0 | Pods and seed are small; Pods have slight to moderate constriction with little or no beak; Highly suitable for situation of delayed south west monsoon |

**Table 7:** (*Contd...* )

**Table 7:** *(Contd...)*

| Sr. no. | Name of the cultivar | Pedigree | Breeding meth | Habit group | Year of release | Area for released | Originating centre | Pod yield kg/ha | Shelling per cent | Oil (%) | 100 kernel weight | Salient features |
|---|---|---|---|---|---|---|---|---|---|---|---|---|
| S. no. | (1) | (2) | (3) | (4) | (5) | (6) | (7) | (8) | (9) | (10) | (11) | (12) |
| 79. | ICGS 37 | Selection from Robut 33-1 | S | SB | 1990 | Gujarat | ICRISAT | 3000 | 70.0 | 48.0 | 53.0 | Seqential flowering |
| 80. | RSHY1 | GDM × TMV 2 | HS | — | 1991 | Orissa and Coasatal A.P. | IARI, Hyderabad | 2480 | 73.0 | 50.0 | 27.0 | Suitable for Rabi residual moisture |
| 81. | TAG24 | Selection from TGS 2 | S | SB | 1991 | Maharashtra | BARC Trombay | 1683 | 70.0 | 51.0 | 38.0 | Early with 2-3 seeded; tolerant to BND leaf spot jassid and cater-pillar |
| 82. | Tirupati 2 | GAUG 1 × NCAc FLA-14 | HS | SB | 1991 | Andhra Pradesh | APAU, Tirupati | 2100 (K) 3500 (R) | 77.0 | 49.0 | 34.0 | Suitable for both seasons : possesses high peg strength and tolerant to kala husthi melody. |
| 83. | ICGV 86590 | X14-4-B-19-B x PI 259747 | HS | SB | 1991 | Peninsular India | ICRISAT | 1785 | 62.0 | 41.6 | 33.0 | Multiple disease and insect pest resistant |
| 84. | CSMG 84-1 | Selection from MA 10 | S | VR | 1992 | Rajasthan, U.P., and Haryana | CSAU A&T Mainpuri | 2704 | 64.0 | 50.4 | 48.0 | Tolerant to thrips, termites; pod borer & foliar diseases |
| 85. | BAU 13 | BAU 6 × | HS | VB | 1993 | Bihar, | Kanke | 2191 | 63.0 | 48.0 | 71.0 | Higher yield |

**Table 7:** *(Contd... )*

Table 7: (*Contd...*)

| S. no. | (1) | (2) | (3) | (4) | (5) | (6) | (7) | (8) | (9) | (10) | (11) | (12) |
|---|---|---|---|---|---|---|---|---|---|---|---|---|
| | | M 13/ | | | | UP, Rajasthan, Gujarat, Maharashtra and T.N. | | | | | | with bold seeded suitable for HPS export |
| 86. | TKG 19A | TG 17× TG 1 | M/HS | VB | 1993 | Konkan region R/S and kharif | K.K.V. Dapoli | 2260 | 63.0 | 45.0 | 60.5 | Bold and attractive kernel seed quality for HPS grade |
| 87. | B 95 | M 13 × Sulamith | HS | VB | 1993 | Soutern Maharashtra | MPKV Rahuri | 3345 | 68.0 | 48.0 | 90.0 | Suitable for summer, extra bold seeded, HPS grade |
| 88. | K 134 | Kadiri 3 × JL24 | HS | VB | 1993 | A.P. and T.N. | ARS Kadiri | 1677 | 71.0 | 45.0 | 34.0 | Early maturing; high yielding; tolerant to leaf spot and drought |
| 89. | ICGV 86325 | ICGS20× G201 | HS | VB | 1994 | Southern Maharashtra, A.P., T.N., Karnataka and Kerala | ICCRISAT | 2700 | 70.0 | 45.0 | 35.0 | High yielding under rainfed condition; tolerant to BND |
| 90. | GG 3 | GAUGI× JL24 | HS | SB | 1994 | M.P., and Northern Maharastra | GAV Jhangadh | 1283 | 68.7 | 51.0 | 32.0 | Early maturing; green foliage at harvest |
| 91. | DRG 17 | R-33-1- × TAP5 | HS | VB | 1994 | Rajasthan, Haryana, and U.P. | DOR Hyderabad | 2100 | 65.0 | 49.0 | 49.0 | High yielding; for kharif rainfed; tolerant to moisture |

Table 7: (*Contd...* )

**Table 7:** *(Contd...)*

| Sr. no. | Name of the cultivar | Pedigree | Breeding meth | Habit group | Year of release | Area for released | Originating centre | Pod yield kg/ha | Shelling per cent | Oil (%) | 100 kernel weight | Salient features |
|---|---|---|---|---|---|---|---|---|---|---|---|---|
| S. no. | (1) | (2) | (3) | (4) | (5) | (6) | (7) | (8) | (9) | (10) | (11) | (12) |
| | | | | | | | | | | | | stress |
| 92. | DRG 12 | R33-1-MP –1 × TAP5 | HS | SB | 1994 | Rabi-summer area of A.P., T.N., Karna., and Mahar., | DOR Hyderabad | 2604 | 69.0 | 47.0 | 39.0 | High yielding; tolerant to foliar disease and BND |
| 93. | TG 26 | BARCG 1 | M/HS | SB | 1995 | Rabi-summer area of Guja., north Mahar., and M.P. | BARC | 1596 (K) | 65 | 49.0 | 35.0 | High yielding; earliness with fresh seed dormancy |
| 94. | M 552 | PG 1 × M334-AB14 | HS | VR | 1995 | Punjab | Ludhiana | 2525 | 68.0 | 50.7 | 65.0 | Early maturing compared to M 335; high oil content |
| 95. | G 8808 | ICGS 11× Chico | HS | SB | 1997 | Karnataka, A.P. and T.N. | Raichur | 2486 | 69.0 | 48.5 | 38.0 | Highly suitable for cultivation in the hot spot of bud necrosis diseases |
| 96. | VRI 4 | VG 5 × NCAc 17090 | HS | SB | 1997 | Tamil Nadu | Vridhachlam | 2170 | 72.0 | 47.0 | 41.0 | Suitable for irrigated and rainfed cultivation |
| 97. | Kadiri 4 | Dh 3-30 × NCAc 2230 | HS | SB | 1997 | A.P. | Kadiri | 2259 | 74.0 | 48.0 | 32.0 | Tolerant to bud necrosis and late leaf spot, suitable for both kharif and rabi-summer |

**Table 7:** *(Contd... )*

**Table 7:** *(Contd...)*

| *S. no.* | *(1)* | *(2)* | *(3)* | *(4)* | *(5)* | *(6)* | *(7)* | *(8)* | *(9)* | *(10)* | *(11)* | *(12)* |
|---|---|---|---|---|---|---|---|---|---|---|---|---|
| 98. | DSG 1 | Selection from local condition | S | VR | 1997 | Karnataka | Dharwad | | | | | Spreading type with dark green and small size leaves |
| 99. | ALR 2 | Selection from ICGV 86011 | S | SB | 1197 | Tamil Nadu Pollachi tract | Aliyar nagar | 1740 | | | | Field tolerance of leaf miner, rust and leaf spots suilable for both irrigated and rainfed condition |
| 100. | BSR 1 | 1CGS 44 (Robut 33-1 × NC-Ac 2821) | HS | SB | 1997 | Tamil Nadu | Bhavani-sagar | 2845 (K) 3625(R) | 70.0 | 48.0 | | Resistant to collar rot, stem rot, rust and leaf spot. moderately resistant to aphids, jassids and leaf miner |
| 101. | JCC 88 | J 11 × TG (E)-1 | HS | SB | 1998 | A.P. | Jagtial | 1396 | 74.0 | 48.0 | | Resistant to bud necrosis |
| 102. | HNG 10 | | HS | VB | 1999 | Zone I | Hanum-angadh | 1918 | 70 | | 45 | Resistant to collar rot and ELS |
| 103. | CMSG 884 | | HS | VB | 1999 | Zone 1 | Mainpuri | 2281 | 71 | 49.0 | 59 | Moderately resistant to ELS, LLS, BND |

S = Selecion HS = Hybridization and selection, M = Mutation Breeding
SB = Spanish bunch VL = Valencia SS = Semi-Spreading VR = Virginia runner VB = Virginia bunch

### 8.4. Future Thrusts

- Stability of yield and realization of yield potential will be the main priority concerns for groundnut breeders. As such, breeding for resistance to stresses should have the highest priority. In addition, a system specific approach to breeding, keeping the input use efficiency as an important component, has to receive the required thrust now. The use of transgenics will be an important tool in breeding for stress resistance.
- Enhancement of the gene pool through an extensive use of the whole gamut of core germplasm variability has to be undertaken so that the genes available in the pool are utilized fully in a large number of combinations. Multiple crosses and means to enhance natural cross-pollination will be useful in developing the gene pool. Identification of molecular markers can be an important component of gene pool enhancement, which can be used further for marker assisted selection.
- Groundnut oil faces a very stiff competition today from other cheaper, edible oils like palm oil and even cotton seed oil. On the other hand groundnut is a very nutritious food having the capacity to meet nutritional and fancy snacks needs. It also has a very potential export nich. Therefore, breeding groundnut for qualities fulfilling the needs as a food has started getting attention and in future a far greater stress will be given to this aspect
- The use of alien germplasm in groundnut breeding in our country has been at a very low key whereas the alien germplasm holds the key to resistance to many of the stresses and as a good source of fodder. A strong programme to utilize alien germplasm is urgently needed.

## 9. ACKNOWLEDGEMENTS

Sincere gratitude is expressed to all the groundnut research workers whose contributions and work has been freely referred to in this chapter. The supply of list of cultivars developed through mutation breeding by BARC, Trombay is acknowledged.

## REFERENCES

Akasaka, Y., Mii, M., and Daimon, H. (1998). Morphological alterations and root nodule formation in *Agrobacterium rhizogenes*–mediated transgenic hairy roots of peanut (*Arachis hypogaea* L.). *Annals of Botany,* 81: 355–362.

Amin, P.W. (1984). Metholodogy of screening for resistance to insect pests of groundnut. Patancheru, A.P. 502 324, India International Crops Research Institute for Semi–Arid Tropics p. 23. (Limited distribution).

Anderson, W.F., Beute, M.K., Wynne, J.C. and Wongkaew, S. (1990b). Statistical procedures for assessment of resistance in multiple foliar disease complex of peanut. *Phytopathology,* 80: 1451–1459.

Anderson, W.F., Fitzner, M.S. Isleib, T.G., Wynne, J.C. and Phillips, T.D. (1993). Combining ability for large pod and seed traits in peanut. *Peanut–Sdence.* 20: 49–52.

Anderson, W.F., Patanothai, A., Wynne, J.C. and Gibbons, R.W. (1990a). Assessment of a diallel cross for multiple foliar pest resistance in peanut. *Oleagineux,* 45: 373–378.

Anderson, W.F., Wynne, J.C., Green, C.C. and Beute, M.K. (1986). Combining ability and heritability of resistance to early and late leaf spot of peanut. *Peanut Sci.,* pp. 10–14

Arnon, D.I. (1949). Copper enzymes in isolated chloroplasts, polyphenol oxidase in *Beta vulgaris. Plant Physiology,* 24: 1–15.

Arunachalam, V., Bandyopadhyay, A., Nigam, S.N. and Gibbons, R.W. (1982). Heterotic potential of single cross in groundnut (*Arachis hpogaea* L.). *Oleagineux,* 37: 415–418.

Arunachalam, V., Bandyopadhyay, A., Nigam, S.N. and Gibbons R.W. (1984). Heterosis in relation to genetic divergence and specific combining ability in groundnut *(Arachis hypogaea* L.). *Euphytica,* 33: 33–39.

Ashri, A. (1968) Morphology and inheritance of sterile branchytic dwarfs in peanuts, *Arachis hypogaea. Crop Sci.,* 8: 413–415.

Badami, V.K. (1928). *Arachis hypogaea–(the* groundnut) PhD thesis, Cambridge University. Cited in H. Hunter, and H.M. Lecke (1933). *Recent Advance in Agric. Plant Breeding.* Blakiston, Philadephia.

Balaiah, C., Reddy, P.S. and Reddy, M.V. (1977). Genetic analysis in groundnut I. Inheritance studies on 18 morphological characters in crosses with "Gujarat Narrow Leaf Mutant". *Proc, Indian Acad. Sci.,* 85B: 340–350.

Bandyopadhyay, A., Nautiyal, P.C., Radhakrishnan, T. and Gor, H.K. (1999). Role of testa, cotyledons and embryonic axis in seed dormancy of groundnut *(Arachis hypogaea* L.). *J. Agronomy and Crop Science* 182: 37–41.

Bandyopadhyay, A.V. Arunchanalam, and Venkaih, K. (1985). Efficient selection intensity in early generation index selection in groundnut *(Arachis hypogaea* L.). *Theor. Appl. Genet.,* 71: 300–304.

Banks, D.J. (1976). Hybridization of Peanuts in growth chambers. *Peanut Science,* 3: 66–69.

Bashi, E and Rosen, J. (1974). Adaptation of four pathogens to semiarid habitats as conditioned by penetration rate and germinating spore survival. *Phytopathology,* 64: 1035–39.

Basu, M.S., Nagaraj G., Reddy, P.S. (1988). Genetics of oil and other major biochemical components in groundnut (*Arachis hypogaea* L.). *International Journal of Tropical Agriculture,* 6(1–2): 106–110.

Bear, J.E. and Bailey, W.K. (1973). Earliness of flower opening and potential for pod development in peanuts, *Arachis hypogaea. Journal of the American Peanut Research and Education Association,* 5: 26–31.

Bentham, G. (1841). On the structure and affinities of *Arachis* and Voandzeia. *Trans. Linn. Soc. Lond.,* 18: 155–162.

Bhagat, N.K. and Reddy, P.S. (1988). Utilization of genetic diversity in *Arachis* and its related wild species. *In*: Paroda, R.S., Arora, R.K. and Chandel, K.P.S. (*Eds*.), Proceedings of a National Symposium on Plant Genetic Resources–Indian Perspective. NBPGR, New Delhi, India, pp. 210–219.

Bhagawat, A., Krishna, T.G. and Bhatia, C.R. (1997). RAPD analysis of induced mutants of groundnut (*Arachis hypogaea* L.). *J. Genet.,* 76: 201–208.

Bhat, R.S., Gowda, M.V.C., and Khader, K.M.A. (1996). Early generation selection for late leaf spot resistance and productivity in groundnut *(Arachis hypogaea* L.) *Indian journal of Genetics* and *Plant Breeding,* 56(3): 352–356.

Bhuiyan, S.A. (1984). Inheritance of plant type in groundnut. *India J. Genet. Plant Breed.,* 44: 215–217.

Black, M.C. and Beute, M.K. (1985). Soil components that affect severity of *Cylindrocladium* black rot of peanut. *Plant Dis.,* 69: 36–39.

Black, M.C., and Beute, M.K. (1984). Relationship among inoculum density, microsclerotium size and inoculum efficiency of *Cylindrocladium crotolariae* causing root rot on peanut. *Phytopathohgy,* 74: 1128–32.

Bock, K.R. (1987). Rosette and early leaf spot diseases: A review of research progress, 1984/85. In Proceedings of the Second Regional Groundnut Workshop for Southern Africa, Harare, Zimbabwe, 10–14 February 1986, ICRISAT, Patancheru, India. pp. 5–14.

Branch, W.D. (1995). Inheritance of peanut testa colors involved in market acceptability. *Crop Science.* 35: 270–271.

Branch, W.D., Hammons, R.O. and Kvien, C.S. (1984). Non–nodulating allelism test in *Arachis hypogaea* (L.). Crop *Science* 39: 487–488.

Branch, W.D., Williams, D.E. and Williams, E.J. (1997). Inheritance of black pod colour in peanut. *Journal of Heredity,* 88: 156–158.

Brar, G.S., Cohen, B.A., Vick, C.L. and Johnson, G.W. (1994). Recovery of transgenic peanut (*Arachis hypogaea* L.) plants from elite cultivars utilizing ACCELL technology. *The Plant Journal,* 5: 745–753.

Bromfield, K.R. and Bailey, W.K. (1972). Inheritance of resistance to *Puccinia arachidis* in peanut. *Phytopathology,* 62: 748.

Brown, J.C. and Jolley, V.D. (1989). Plant metabolic responses to iron–deficiency stress. *Biosciences,* 39: 549–551.

Bunting, A.H., Gibbons, R.W. and Wynne, J.C. (1985). Groundnut *(Arachis hypogaea* L.). In Grain Legume Crops, *Eds.* Summerfield, R.J. and Roberts, E.H. pp. 747–800. London: Collins.

Burkart, A. (1939). Estudios sistematicos sobre las Leguminosas Hedisareas de al Republica Argentina yregions adyacontes (In Es.) *Darwiniana,* 3: 117–302.

Cassidy, B., and Ponsamuael, J. (1996). Update on groudnut transformation and evidence for mechanism of induced pathogen–derived resistance to peanut stripe virus in *Nicotiana benthamiana. In*: *Groundnut Virus Diseases in the Asia–Pacific Region:* Summary and recommendations of the Fourth Meeting of the International Working Group, 12–14 March, 1995, Kohn Kaen University, Thailand. p. 14. Patancheru 502 324, Andhra Pradesh, India: International Crops Research Institute for Semi–Arid Tropics. p. 44.

Ceccarelli, S., Acevedo, E. and Grando, S. (1991). Breeding for yield stability in unpredictable environments: Single traits, interaction between traits, and architecture of genotypes. *Euphytica.,* 56: 169–185.

Chandramouli, Kale, D.M., and Patil, S.H. (1986). Inheritance of sequential flowering pattern in the mutants of groundnut cultivar Robut 33–1. *Current Science,* 55: 1185–87.

Chandran, K., Rajgopal, K. and Pandya, S.M. (2000). Numerical taxonomic studies in *Arachis species* of the section *Arachis. Abstract* in National Seminar on Oilseeds and oils–research development needs in the millenium. 02–04th February, 2000 at the Directorate of Oilseed Research, Hyderabad (A.P.) p. 1.

Cheng, M., Jarret, R.L., Li, Z., Xing, A., and Demaski, J.W. (1996). Production of fertile transgenic peanut (*Arachis hypogaea* L.) plants using *Agrobacterium tumefaciens. Plant Cell Reports,* 15: 653–657.

Coffelt, T.A. and Hammons, R.O. (1973). Influence of sizing peanut seed on two phenotypic ratios. *J. Hered.* 64: 39–42.

Coffelt, T.A. and Porter, D.M. (1986). Field screening of reciprocal Chico x Florigiant peanut populations for resistance to leaf spot in Virginia. *Peanut Sci.,* 13: 57–60.

Coffelt, T.A., and Hammons, R.O. (1974). Inheritance of pod constriction in peanuts. *J. Hered.,* 65: 94–96.

Company, M., Stalker, H.T. and Wynne, J.C. (1982). Cytology and leaf spot resistance in *Arachis hypogaea* × wild species hybrids. *Euphytica,* 31: 885–893.

Cook, M. (1975). Rust and leaf spot resistance in peanut cultivars. Ph.D thesis, University of the West Indies, Kingston, Jamaica, p. 539.

Corley Holbrook, C. (1990). Utility of early generation analysis for predicting parental potential for yield components in Peanuts. *Peanut Sci.,* 17: 9–11.

Culp, T.W., Bailey, W.K., and Hammons, R.O. (1968). Natural hybridization of peanuts (*Arachis hypogaea*) in Virginia. *Crop Sri.,* 8: 109–110.

Dashiell, K.E., and Gorbet, D.W. (1982). Genetic analysis of a non–nodulating peanut. Agronomy Abstracts ASA, Madison, WI. p. 63.

Deokar, A.B., Kalekar, A.R. and Patil, R.C. (1986). Inheritance of rust resistance in groundnut. *J. Maharashtra Agric. Univ.,* 11: 234.

Durgaprasad, M.M.K., Arunchalam, V, and Bandyopadhyay, A. (1985). Diversity pattern elucidating choice of parents for hybridization in varieties of groundnut (*Arachis hypogaea* L.). *Trop. Agric.,* 62: 237–42.

Dutta, M., and Reddy, L.J. (1988). Further studies on genetics of non–nodulation in peanut. *Crop Science,* 28: 60–62.

Dutta, M., Arunchalam, V., and Bandyopadhyay, A. (1987). Enhanced cross–pollination to widen the scope of breeding in groundnut (*Arachis hypogaea* L.) *Theor. Appl. Genet.,* 74: 466–470.

Dutta, M., Arunchanalam, V., Bandyopadhyay, A. and Vinod Prabu, K. (1986). Early generation intermating for yield improvement in groundnut (*Arachis hypogaea* L.). *Theor. Appl. Genet.,* 71: 662–666.

Dwivedi, S.L., Gurtu, S., Chandra, S., Weng Yuejin, and Nigam, S.N. (1999). Genetic diversity in groundnut (*Arachis hypogaea* L.) according to DNA profiles ensuing from RAPD analysis. (Submitted to Euphytica).

Eapen, S., and George, L. (1994). *Agrobacterium tumefaciens* mediated gene transfer in groudnut (*Arachis hypogaea* L.). *Plant Cell Reports,* 13: 582–586.

Essomba, N.B., Coffelt, T.A., Branch, W.D., Scoyoc, S.W. and Van–Scoyoc. S.S. (1993). Inheritance of leaflet size in peanut (*Arachis hypogaea* L.). *Peanut–Sdence,* 20: 90–93.

Freitas, V.G. De, Lacorate, C, Sachetto–Martins, G., Krul, W.R., Oliveira, D.E. de, Neves. L.J. and Mansur, E. (1997). Identification of competent cells for *Agrobacterium–* transformation and *in vitro* regeneration in peanut leaf and cotyledon explants. *Revista Brasileira de Fisiologia Vegetal,* 9: 157–167.

Garcia, G.M., Stalker, H.T., and Kochert, G. (1995). Introgression analysis of an interspecific hybrid population in peanuts (*Arachis hypogaea* L.). using RFLP and RAPD markers. *Genome,* 38: 166–176.

Garcia, G.M., Stalker, H.T., Schroeder, E., and Kochert, G. (1992). Identification of RAPD, SCAR AND RFLP markers tightly linked to nematode resistance genes introgressed from *A. cardensii* into *A. hypogaea. Genome,* 39: 836–85.

Gebre–Mariam, M. (1982). Index selection for genetic improvement of yield, kernel weight and protein content in wheat. Dissertation *Abstracts International* B 42 (12, I) 4679 B.

Ghosh, P.K., Mathur, R.K., Bandyopadhyay, A., Devi Dayal, Gor, H.K. and Naik, P.R. (1999). Genotypic compatibility in groundnut/pigeonpea intercropping system. International *Arachis News letter,* 19: 53–55.

Gibbons, R.W. and Tattersfield, J.R. (1969). Outcrossing trails with groundnut *(Arachis hypogaea). Rhod. J. Agric Res.,* 7: 71–85.

Gillier, P. and Silvestre, P. (1969). L arachide. Paris, Maisonneuve et Larose. *Techniques Agricoles et Productions Tropicales,* 15: 292.

Gowda, M.V.C., Bhat, R.S. and Khadar, K.M.A. (1997). Comparison of single and multiple crosses for combining resistance of late leaf spot and productivity in groundnut *(Arachis hypogaea* L.) *Crop–Improvement,* 24: 55–60.

Green, C.C., Wynne, J.C., and Beute, M.K. (1983). Genetic variability and heritability estimates based on the F2 generation from crosses of large seeded Virginia type peanuts with lines resistant to *Cylindrocladium* black rot. *Peanut Sci.,* 10: 47–51.

Gregory, W.C, Krapovickas, A., and Gregory, M.P. (1980). Structures, variation, evolution and classification in *Arachis. In*: Summerfield, R.J. and Bunting, A.H. (*Eds.*). Advances in Legume Science, Royal Botanic Gardens, Kew, UK, pp. 469–481.

Gregory, W.C. (1965). Mutation frequency, magnitude of change and the probability of improvement in adaptation. The use of Induced Mutations in Plant Breeding. *Radiat. Bot.,* 5(Suppl.): 429–441.

Gregory, W.C. and Gregory, M.P. (1976). Groudnut *Arachis hypogaea* (Leguminosae Haplionatae). *In*: Simmonds, N.W. (*Ed.*) Evolution of Crop Plants. Longman, London, pp. 151–154.

Gregory, W.C., Gregory, M.P., Krapovickas, A., Smith, B.W. and Yarbrough, J.A. (1973). A structure and genetic resources of Peanut. *In*: Peanut–Culture and Uses. American Peanut Research and Education Association Inc., Still water, Oklahoma. 3: 43–133,

Gregory, W.C., Smith, B.W. and Yarbrough, J.A. (1951). Morphology, genetics and breeding. In The Peanut, the Unpredictable Legume, National Fert. Assoc. Washington, USA, pp. 28– 88.

Gupta, R.B. (1988). Genetics of brachytic sterility in groundnut *(Arachis hypogaea L.) Indian J. Agric. Res.,* 22: 41–50.

Hadley, B.A., Beute, M.K. and Leonard, K.J. (1979b). Heritability of *Cylindrocladium* black rot resistance in peanuts. *Peanut Sci., 6:* 51–54.

Hadley, B.A., Beute, M.K. and Leonard, KJ. (1979a). Variability of *Cylindrocladium crotalariae* response to resistant host plant selection pressure in peanut. *Phytopathology,* 69: 1112–1114.

Halward, T., Stalker, H.T., and Kochert, G. (1993). Development of an RFLP linkage map in diploid peanut species. *Theor, Appl. Genet.,* 87: 379–384.

Halward, T.M., Stalker, H.T., LaRue, E.A. and Kochert. G. (1992). Use of single–primer DNA amplifications in genetic studies of peanut *(Arachis hypogaea* I.). *Plant Molecular Biology,* 18: 315–325.

Halward, T.M., Stalker, H.T., LaRue, E.A., and Kochert, G. (1991). Genetic variation detectable with molecular markers among unadapted germplasm resources of cultivated peanut and related wild species. *Genome,* 34: 1013–1020.

Hammons, R.O. (1964). Pedigreed natural crossing– a new genetic technique, *In*: Proceedings of the Third National Peanut Research Conference, Auborn, Alabama, USA. pp. 49–53.

Hammons, R.O. (1973). Genetics of *Arachis hypogaea. In*: Peanuts: Culture and Uses. Amer. Peanut Res. Educ. Soc., Stillwater, Oklahoma, USA., pp. 135–173.

Hammons, R.O. (1976). Peanut breeding strategy: Modified composite cross. *Proc. Amer. Peanut Res. and Educ. Assoc.,* 8: 48–53.

Hayes, T.R. (1933). The classification of groundnut varieties with preliminary note on the inheritance of some characters. *Trop. Agric.,* 10: 318–327.

He, G., and Prakash, C.S. (1997). Identification of polymorphic DNA markers in cultivated peanut *(Arachis hypogaea* L.). *Euphytica,* 97: 143–49

Higgins, B.B. (1938). Peanut breeding. *In*: Proceedings of the 39th Annual Convention Assoc. South Agric. Workers, Atlanta Georgia, USA. pp. 57–58.

Hildebrand, G.L. (1974). A note of artificial hybridization of the groundnut. *Rhodesian Journal of Agriculture Research,* 12: 195–196.

Hildebrand, G.L. (1975). Egret groundnut. *Rhodesia Agric. J.,* 72: 154.

Hoehne, F.C. (1940). Leguminosae–Papilionadae. *Genera Arachis. Flora* Brasilica 25 (II) 122: 1–20.

Husted, L. (1936). Cytological studies of the peanut *Arachis* II. Chromosome number, morphology and behaviour, and their application to the origin or cultivated forms. *Cytologia,* 7: 396–423.

ICRISAT (International Crops Research Institute for Semi–Arid Tropics), (1992) and (1996). ICRISAT Asia Region Annual Report 1995. Patancheru 502 324, Andhra Pradesh. India: ICRISAT.

ICRISAT, Legumes Program. (1994). Annual Report 1993. Patancheru 502 324, A.P., India Legumes Program, International Crops Research Institute for Semi–Arid Tropics. p. 260.

Jadhav, G.D., and Shinde, N.N. (1979). Genetic studies in groundnut *(Arachis hypogaea* L.,). *Indian J. Agric. Res.,* 13: 93–86.

Jakula, L.R., Knauft, D.A. and Gorbet. D.W. (1997). Inheritance of a shriveled seed trait in peanut. *Journal of Heredity.* 88: 47–51.

Jayalakshmi, V., Reddy, P.V., Asalatha, M. and Vasanthi, R.P. (1998). Genetic variability for water use efficiency traits in groundnut. *Legume Res.,* 21: 8–12.

Jogloy, S., Wynne, J.C., and Beute, M.K. (1987). Inheritance of late leaf spot resistance and agronomic traits in peanut. *Peanut Sci.,* 14: 86–90.

John, C.M. (1949). Report on research on Oilseed crops in India. The Indian Central Oilseeds Committe, New Delhi, Appendix III, P, XIX.

Joshi, Y.C., Nautiyal, P.C., and Ravidra, V. (1994). Screening for salinity in groundnut *(Arachis hypogaea L.).* Food Legume News Letter, Australia, p. 7.

Joshi, Y.C., Nautiyal, P.C., and Ravidra, V. (1996). Screening for cold tolerance and osmoconditioning to enhance germination of groundnut in sub–optimal temperatures. *Tropical Sci.,* 36: 224–228.

Kalaimani, S., Mahadevan, N.R., Manoharan, V. and Sethupathi Ramalingam, R. (1989). Screening of inter–specific derivatives for leaf miner, *(Aproacerema modicella* Deventer) resistance in groudnut. International *Arachis Newsletter* No. 5: 15–16.

Kale, D.M. and Mouli, C. (1984). Hybridization techique in groundnut. *Indian Journal of Genetics and Plant Breeding,* 44: 379–384.

Kalekar, A.R., Patil, B.C., and Deokar, A.B. (1984). Inheritance of resistance to rust in groundnut. *Madras Agric. J.,* 71: 125–126.

Karman, S. (1984). Problems of iron deficiency in different crop plants in India. Causative factors and control measures. *Journal of Plant Nutrition,* 7: 187–200.

Khan, B.M., Kirby, J.S. and Wadsworth, D.F. (1973). Breeding peanuts *(Arachis hypogaea* L.) for resistance to Verticillium wilt. *J. Amer. Peanut Res. Educ. Soc.,* 5: 193.

Kibite, S. (1981). Genetic studies on the simultaneous improvement of grain yield and grain protein content in wheat *(Triticum aestivum* L. em Thell). *Dissertation Abstracts Ineternational B,* 41: 3263B

Kishore, B. (1981). Rust inheritance studies in groundnut *(Arachis hypogaea* L.) M.Sc. (Ag.) thesis, Andhra Pradesh Agricultural University, Hyderabad India.

Knauft, D.A. (1987). Inheritance of rust resistannce to groundnut. *In*: Groundnut Rust Disease, Proceedings of a Discussion Group Meeting. ICRISAT, Patancheru, India, pp. 183–187.

Knauft, D.A. and Norden, AJ. (1983). Inheritance of rust resistance in peanuts. *Proc. Amer. Peanut Res. Educ. Soc.,* 15–96.

Knauft, D.A., Moore, K.M. and Gorbet, D.W. (1993). Further studies on the inheritance of fatty acid composition in peanut. *Peanut–Science,* 20: 74–76.

Kornegay, J.L., Beute, M.K. and Wynne, J.C. (1980). Inheritance of resistance to *Cercospora arachidocola* and *Cercosporidium personatum* in six Virginia type peanut lines. *Peanut Sci., 7:* 4–9.

Koteswara Rao, M.V. (1984). Realized genetic advance by early generation selection for physiological and for yield components in groundnut *(Arachis hypogaea* L.) Ph.D thesis. Andhra Pradesh Agricultural University, Hyderabad, India.

Krapovickas, A. (1973). Evolution of the genus Arachis. In Moav, R. (ed.) Agricultural Genetics: Selected tropics. John Wiley, New York, pp. 135–151.

Krapovickas, A. and Gregory, W.C. (1994). Taxonomia del genero Arachis (Leguminosae). *Bonplandia,* 8: 1–187.

Krapovickas, A. and Rigoni, V.A. (1957). Neuvas especies de *Arachis* vinculadas al problem del origen del mani. *Darwiniana,* 11: 431–455.

Lacorte, C., Aragao, F.J.L., Almeida, E.R., Mansu, E., and Rech, E.L. (1997). Transient expression of GUS and 25 ablumin gene from Brazil–nut in peanut *(Arachis hypogaea* L.) seed explants using particle bombardment. *Plant Cell Reports,* 16: 619–623.

Lacorte, C., Mansur, E., Timmerman, B., and Cordeiro, A.R. (1991). Gene transfer into peanut *(Arachis hpogaea* L.) by *Agrobacterium tumefaciens. Plant Cell Reports,* 10: 354–357.

Lanham, P.G., Fennell, S., Moss, J.P. and Powell., W. (1992). Detection of polymorphic loci in *Arachis* germplasm using random amplified polymorphic DNAs. *Genome,* 35: 885–889.

Li, Z., Cheng, M., Xing, A., Jarret, R.L., Pittman, R., and Demski, J.W. (1996). Groundnut transformation research in Griffin, Georgia. In *Groundnut Virus diseases in the Asia Pacific Region*: Summary and recommendations of the Fourth Meeting of the International Working Group, 12–14 March, 1995, Kohn Kaen University. Thailand. pp. 9–10. Patancheru 502 324, Andhra Pradesh, India: International Crops Research Institute for Semi–Arid Tropics, p. 44.

Li, Z., Jarret, R.L., and Demski, J.W. (1997). Engineered resistance to tomato spotted wilt virus in transgenic peanut expressing the viral nucleocapsid gene. *Transgenic Research,* 6: 297–305.

Liao, B., Wang, Y., Xia, X., Tang, G., Tan, Y, and Sun, D. (1990). Genetic and breeding aspects of resistance to bacterial wilt in groundnut. *Proc. ACIAR No,* 31: 39–43.

Liao, B.S., and Wang, Y.Y. (1988). Inheritance of resistance to rust *(Puccinia arachidis* Speg.) in peanuts *(Arachis hypogaea* L.). *Oil Crops of China,* 3: 13–17.

Mahadevan, N.R., Sethupathi Ramalingam, R. and Manoharan, V. (1988). Screening for resistance to groundnut leaf–miner, *Aproacerema modicella* Deventer. International *Arachis Newsletter No.,* 4: 20–21.

Manivel, P., Bandyopadhyay, A., Mathur, R.K. and Rajgopal, K. (2000). Trend in yield components of cultivars of groundnut in India released over year. *Abstrnct* in National Seminar on Oilseeds and oils–research development needs in the millenium. 02–04 February, 2000 at the Directorate of Oilseeds Research, Hyderabad (A.P.) p. 106.

Manoharan, V. and Sethupalhi Ramalingam, R. (1993). Genetic parameters of quantitative traits in Virginia groundnuts. *Madras Agricultural–Journal.* 80: 716–718.

Mathur, R.K., Manivel, P. and Samdur, M.Y, (1999). Girnar 1 nlm – A new chemically induced narrow leaf mutant of groundnut. *Indian Journal of Genetics and Plant Breeding,* 56: 527–530.

McNeal, F.H., Qualset, C.O., Baldridge, D.E., and Stewart, V.R. (1978). Selection for yield and yield components in wheat. *Crop Sa.* 18: 795–798.

Mehan, V.K. (1992). Control of aflatoxin contamination in groundnut and maize genetic approach Presented at: Symposium on Mycotoxins, 18th Annual Meeting of the Mycological Society of India, NIN, Hyderabad, Andhra Pradesh, India.

Mendes, A.J.T. (1947). Estudos citologicos no genero Arachis. *Bragantia,* 7: 257–267

Middleton, K. and Shorter, R. (1987). Occurrence and management of groundnut rust in Australia. In Groundnut Rust Disease, Proceedings of a Discussion Group Meeting, ICRISAT, Patancheru, India, pp. 73–75.

Miller, I.L., Norden, A.J., Knauft D.A. and Gorbet, D.W. (1990). Influence of maturity and fruit yield on susceptibility of peanut to *Cercosporidium personatum* (late leaf spot pathogen).*Peanut–Sci.,* 17: 52–58.

Misra, J.B. (1997). Update on transformation of groundnut and potential genes for enhancement of quality. *International Arachis Newsletter*, 17: 18–21.

Moss, J.P., Reena, M.J.T. Reena, N.R.G. Dutt and Sastri, D.C. (1992). Regeneration in *Arachis hypogaea. In*: Biotechnology and crop improvement in Asia (Moss, J.P., *Ed.*). Patancheru, A.P. 502 324, India: International Crops Research Institute for Semi Arid Tropics pp. 157–158.

Muhammad, V., and Dorairaj, M.S. (1969). Flowering pattern and reproductive efficiency in bunch varieties of*Arachis hypogaea* L. *Madras Agricultural Journal,* 56: 239–243.

Murthy, T.G.K. and Reddy P.S. (1996). Genetics of qualitative traits in groundnut *(Arachis hypogaea* L.) In: Genetic Improvement of Oilseed crops". (*Eds* Nizam and Editors: Farook, S.A. and Irfan Khan, A.). Ukaaz publications, Hyderabad 500 036.

Nagabhushanam, G.V.S., Prasad, M.V.R. and Jagadish, C.A. (1992). Studies on association among canopy and reproductive attributes in F1 and F2 generations of intraspecific and intersubspecific crosses m groundnut *(Arachis hypogaea* L.). *J. of Genet, and Breed,* 46: 155–162.

Nageswara Rao, R.C., Williams, J.H., Wadia K.D.R., Hubick, K.T., and Farquhar, G.D. (1992). Crop growth, water–use efficiency and carbon isotope discrimination in groundnut *(Arachis hypogaea* L.) genotypes under end–of–season drought conditions. *Annals of Applied Biology,* 122(2): 357–367.

Nalini Mallikarjuna, Amar Kumar, Powell, W., Moss, J.P. and Sastri, D.C. (1992). Preliminary experiments on transformation of tissues and organs of *Arachis* species in Biotechnology and crop improvement. *In* Asia (Moss, J.P. *Ed.*). Patancheru, A.P. 502 324, India: International Crops Research Institute for Semi–Arid Tropics. p. 205

Nambiar, P.T.C., and Dart, P.J. (1980). Studies on nitrogen fixation on groundnuts at ICRISAT. *In*: Proceeding of International Workshop on Groundnut. ICRISAT, Patancheru, India, pp. 110–124.

Nambiar, P.T.C., and Rego, T.J. (1986). Comparison of requirements and utilization of nitrogen by genotypes of sorghum *(Sorghum bicolor* (L.) Monech), and nodulating and non–nodulating groundnut *(Arachis hypogaea* L.). *Field Crops Research,* 15: 165–179.

National Peanut Council of America. (1986). USA peanuts 1986. 101, S. Peyton street, Suite 301, Alexandria, VA 22314, USA, Export Committee, National Peanut Council of America. (Limited distribution).

Nevill, D.J. (1980). Studies on resistance to foliar pathogens. *In*: Proceedings of International Workshop on Groundnut, ICRISAT, Patancheru, India, pp. 199–202.

Nevill, D.J. (1982). Inheritance of resistance to *Cercosporidium personatum* in groundnuts: A genetic model and its implications for selection. *Oleagineux,* 37: 355–366.

Nigam, S.N., Arunachalam, V., Gibbons, R.W., Bandyopadhyay, A. and Nambiar, P.T.C. (1980). Genetics of non–nodulation in groundnut *(Arachis hypogaea* L.). *Oleagineux,* 35: 453–455.

Nigam, S.N., Dwivedi, S.L. and Gibbons, R.W. (1991). Groundnut breeding: Constraints, achievements and future possibilities. *Plant Breeding Abstracts,* 61: 1127–1136.

Nigam, S.N., Dwivedi, S.L., and Gibbons, R.W. (1980). Groundnut breeding at ICRISAT. Pages 62–68 in Proceedings of the International Workshop on Groundnuts, 13–17 Oct 1980, ICRISAT Centre, India. Patancheru, A.P. 502 324, India: International Crops Research Institute for the Semi–Arid Tropics.

Nigam, S.N., Nambiar, P.T.C., Dwivedi, S.L., Gibbons, R.W. and Dart. P.J. (1982). Genetics of non–nodulation in groundnut *(Arachis hypogaea* U). Studies with single and mixed *Rhizobium* strains. *Euphytica,* 31: 691–693.

Nigam, S.N., Rao, V.R. and Gibbons, R.W. (1983). Utilization of natural hybrids in the improvement of groundnut (*Arachis hypogaea). Expl. Agric.,* 19: 355–359.

Nigam, S.N., Vasudeva Rao, M.J., and Gibbons, R.W. (1990). Artificial hybridization in groundnut ICRISAT Information Bulletin no.29. International Crops Research Institute for the Semi–Arid Tropics, Patancheru, Andhra Pradesh 502 324, India p. 27.

Norden, A.J. (1973). Breeding of cultivated peanuts. In: Peanuts–culture and uses (Pattee, H.E. and Young, C.T. *Eds.*) Yoakum, Texas, USA:American Peanut Research and Education Association. pp. 175–208

Norden, A.J. (1977). Genetic basis for utilizing early generation multiline cultivars in peanut breeding. *Amer. Soc. Agron. Abstr.,* pp. 62–70.

Norden, A.J. (1982). Breeding of the cultivated peanut. *In*: Peanut Science and Technology, pp.95–122 American Peanut Research and Education Society, Yoakum, Texas

Norden, A.J., and Rodroguez, VA. (1971). Artificial hybridization of peanuts. *Oleagineux* 26: 159–162.

NRCG, (1997). Vision–2020, NRCG perspective plan, National Research Centre for groundnut, (ICAR), Junagadh, Gujarat, India.

NRCG, (1998). Annual Report, National Research Centre for groundnut, (ICAR), Junagadh, Gujarat, India.

Nutman, P.S. (1976). In Current Perspectives in Nitrogen Fixation. Proc. Fourth Int. Symp. on Nitrogen Fixation Canberra pp. 194–204.

Ohlrogge, J.B. (1994). Design of new plant products: Engineering fatty acid metabolism. *Plant Physiology,* 104: 821–826.

Ono, Y. and Ozaki, K. (1971). Effect of shading treatment at early growth stage on growth and yield of peanut plants. *Proceedings of Crop Science Society of Japan,* 20: 480–85.

Ozias–Akins, P., Schnall, J.A., Andersen, W.F., Singsit, C., Clemente, T.E., Adang, M.J. and Weisinger, A.K. (1993). Regeneration of transgenic peanut plants from stably transformed embryonic callus. *Plant Science,* 93: 185–194.

Paik–Ro, O.G., Smith, R.L. and Knauft. D.A. (1992). Restriction fragment length polymorphism evaluation of six peanut species within the Arachis section. *Theoretical and Applied Genetics* 84: 201–208.

Pal, K.K. and Rinku, Dey. (1999). A simple, rapid, and nondestructive method for screening Aluminum tolerance in groundnut. *International Arachis Newsletter,* 19: 44–46.

Patel, J.A., Patel, S.A., Chaudhary, D.N. (1997). Inheritance of pod beak and pod constriction in groundnut. *Indian J. Genet and PI. Breed.,* 57: 229–232.

Prasad, M.V.R. (1993). Genetic enhancement of groundnut for higher productivity based on canopy development. National Seminar on Oilseeds Research and Development in India: Status and Strategies, Hyderabad, Andhra Pradesh, India, 2–5 Aug 1993. pp. 2–3.

Pungle, G.D. (1983). Genetic investigation of characters related to growth, biological nitrogen fixation and yield in groundnut (*Arachis hypogaea* L.). PhD thesis. Indian Agricultural Research Institute, New Delhi, India.

Puroshotham, M.G., Vajranabhaiah, S.N., Patil, V.S., Reddy, P.C., Prasad, T.G. and Prakash, A.H. (1998). Development of drought tolerant cell lines in groundnut (Arachis *hypogaea* L.) genotypes *in–vitro. Indian J. PI. Phys.* 3: 283–286.

Radhakrishnan, T., Murthy, T.G.K. and Bandyopadhyay, A. (1997). Somatic embryogenesis in groundnut. Tropical Crop Research and Development, India–international, held at Trichur, Kerala.

Radhakrishnan, T., Murthy, T.G.K., Chandran, K., Bandyopadhyay, A. (2000). Micropropagation in groundnut. *Biologia plantarum.* (In press)

Rai, K. (1976). Pests of oilseed crops in India and their control. New Delhi, India: Indian Council of Agricultural Research p. 121.

Raina, S.N., and Mukai, Y. (1999). Detection of variable number of 18S–5 8S–26S and 5S ribosomal DNA loci by fluorescent *in situ* hybridization in diploid and tetraploid *Arachis* species. *Genome,* 42: 52–59.

Rajgopal, K. and Bandyopadhyay. A. (1999). Elite groundnut germplasm—A ready reference. Technical Bulletin. NRCG, Junagadh. p. 35.

Ramanantha Rao, V. (1988). Botany. *In*: Groundnut (Reddy, P.S. ed.) New Delhi, India: Indian Council of Agricultural Research pp. 24–64.

Rao, M.J.V., Nigam, S.N., Mehan, V.K. and McDonald, D. (1989). *Aspergillus flavus* resistance breeding in groundnut: Progress made at ICRISAT Centre. in Aflatoxin contamination of groundnut: Proceedings of the International Workshop, 6–9 October, 1987, ICRISAT Centre, India, Patancheru, A.P. 502 324, India: International Crops Research Institute for Semi–Arid Tropics. pp. 345–356

Reddy, G.P., Reddy, P.S. and Murthi, A.N. (1970). An improved crossing technique in groundnut. *Andhra Agricultural Journal,* 17: 124–127.

Reddy, K.B., Reddy, O.S., Reddy, CM. (1991). Evaluation of groundnut genotypes for phosphorus use efficiency. *Indian Journal of Plant Physiology,* 34: 228–234.

Reddy, K.H.P., Reddy, G.L.K. and Reddy, K.R. (1993). Comparison of pedigree and bulk methods in *F6* generation of groundnut *(Arachis hypogaea* L.). *Annals of Agricultural Research,* 14: 119–121.

Reddy, L.J., Nigam, S.N. and Reddy, A.G.S. (1993). Natural outcrossing in groundnut and its implications in groundnut breeding. *J. Oilseeds Res.,* 10: 99–104.

Reddy, P.S. (1988). Genetics, Breeding and Varieties *In*: Groundnut *Ed.* by Reddy, P.S. Indian council of Agricultural Research, New Delhi, pp. 200–317.

Rudd, V.E. (1981). Aeshynomeneae. *In*: Polhill, R.M. and Raven, P.H. (*Eds*). Advances in Legume Systematics. Volume 2 of International Legume Conference, 24–29 July 1978, Kew, UK, pp. 347–354.

Samdur, M.Y., Mathur, R.K., Manivel, P., Singh, A.L., Bandyopadhyay, A., and Chikani, B.M. (1999). Screening of advance breeding lines for tolerance to lime–induced iron deficiency chlorosis. *Indian Journal of Agricultural Sciences,* 69: 31–35.

Sanders, T.H., Schubert A.M. and Pattee, H.E. (1982). Post harvest physiology and methodologies for estimation maturity. *In*: Pattee, E.E. and Young, C.T. (*Eds.*), Peanut Science and Technology. American Peanut Res. and Education Society, Inc. Yoakum, Tx., USA pp. 624–654.

Sangha, A.S., Labana, K.S. and Singh, Mohinder (1990). Genetic analysis in a cross of runner and bunch groundnut types. *Crop Improvement,* 17: 186–187.

Sarkker, R.H., and Chowdhury, A.P. (1996). Preliminary studies on agrobacterium–mediated genetic transformation of peanut *(Arachis hypogaea* L.) In: Abstracts of poster sessions. 2nd International Crop Science Congress: Crop Productivity and sustainability– Shaping the Future, New Delhi, India, 17–24 Nov. 1996. New Delhi, India: National Academy of Agricultural Sciences; Indian Council of Agricultural Research p. 203.

Sastri, D.C., Nalini, M.S. and Moss, J.P. (1981). Tissue culture and prospects for improvement of *Arachis hypogaea* and other oilseed crops. *In*: Proceedings of COSTED Symposium on Tissue Culture of Economically Important Plants pp. 42–57,

Sastri, D.C., Singh, A.K., Moss, J.P., Nalini Mallikarjuna, and Zhang, X. (1992). Wide hybridization and crop improvement in the genus *Arachis, In*: Biotechnology and crop improvement in Asia (Moss, J.P., *Ed.*). Patancheru, A.P. 502 324, Indian: International Crops Research Institute for Semi–Arid Tropics p. 165.

Schultz, E.E Jr. (1947). An attempt to isolate and measure some of the factors influencing fertilization of artificially cross pollinated peanuts flowers. MS thesis, North Carolina State University, Releigh, North Carolina, USA. p. 24.

Senapati, B.K. and Roy, K. (1990). Genetics of colour in groundnut *(Arachis hypogaea* L.). *Legume Research* 13: 188–190.

Seshadri, C.R. (1962). Groundnut. Indian Central Oilseeds Committee. Hyderabad.

Singh, A.K. and Moss, J.P. (1982). Utilization of wild relatives in genetic improvement of *Arachis hypogaea L. 2.* Chromosome complements of species in section Arachis. *Theor. Appl. Genet.,* 61: 305–314.

Singh, A.K., Smartt, J., Simpson, C.E., and Raina, S.N. (1998). Genetic variation vis–à–vis molecular polymorphism in groundnut, *Arachis hypogaea* L. *Genetic Resource and Crop Evolution,* 45: 119–126.

Singh, A.K., Subrahmanyam, P. and Moss, J.P. (1984). The dominant nature of resistance to *Puccinia arachidis* in certain wild *Arachis* species. *Oleagineux,* 39: 535–538.

Singh, A.L., and Chaudhari, V. (1991). Screening of groundnut *(Arachis hypogaea)* varieties tolerant to iron chlorosis. *Indian Journal of Agricultural Sciences,* 61: 925–27.

Singsit, C, Adang, M.J., Lynch, R.E., Andersen, W.F., Wang, A., Cardineau, G. and Ozias–Akins, P. (1997). Expression of a *Barillus thuringiensis crylA(c)* gene in transgenic peanut plant and its efficacy against lesser cornstalk borer. *Transgenic Research,* 6: 169–176.

Smartt, J., Gregory, W.C., and Gregory, M.P. (1978). The genomes of *Arachis hypogea.* I. Cytogenetic studies of putative genome donors. *Euphytica,* 27: 665–675.

Soriano, J.D. (1988). Radiation induced mutations for leaf spot resistance in peanut. III. Field tests and inheritance studies. In improvement of Grain Legume Production Using Induced Mutations, Proceedings of workshop, 1–5 July 1986, Pullman, Washington, USA, pp. 485–493.

Stalker, H.T. (1980). Cytogenetic investigations in the genus *Arachis. In*: Proceedings of International Workshop on Groundnuts 13–17 October 1980. ICRISAT, Patancheru, India, pp. 73–81.

Stalker, H.T. and Moss, J.P. (1987). Speciation, cytogenetics, and utilization of *Arachis* species. *Adv. Agron.* 41: 1–40.

Subrahmanyam, P., McDonald, D., Waliyar, F., Reddy, L.J., Nigam, S.N., Gibbon, R.W., Ramanantha V. Rao, Singh, A.K. Pande, S. Reddy P.M. and Subba Rao, P.V. (1995). Screning methods and sources of resistance to rust and late leaf spot of groundnut. Information Bulletin No. 47. Patancheru 502 324, Andhra Pradesh, India International Crops Research Institute for Semi–Arid Tropics. p. 20.

Subrahmanyam, P., Ramanantha Rao, V., McDonald., D., Moss, J.P. and Gibbons. R.W. (1989). Origin of resistances to rust and late leaf spot in peanut *(Arachis hypogaea,* Fabaceae). *Economie Botany,* 43: 444–445.

Tai, Y.P. and Young, C.T. (1975). Genetic studies of peanut proteins and oils. *Amer. OU Chem. Soci.,* 52: 377–385.

Talwar, H.S., Takeda, H., Yashima, S. and Senboku, T. (1999). Growth and photosynthetic responses of groundnut genotypes to high temperature. *Crop Sci.,* 39: 460–466.

Taubert, P. (1894). Leguminosae. *In*: Engler, A. and Prantl, K. (*Eds.*), Die Naturlichen Pflanzenfamilien. *III. Teil. Abst.,* 3: 70–338 *(Arachis,* pp. 322–325).

Tiwari, S.P., Ghewande, M.P. and Misra, D.P. (1984). Inheritance of resistance to rust and late leaf spot in groundnut *(Arachis hypogaea* L.). *J. Cytol. Genet.,* 19: 97–101.

Tiwari, S.P., Murthy, T.G.K., Johnson, G.K., and Reddy, P.S. (1990). Genetics of some and development of marker stocks in groundnut. *Legume Research,* 13: 197–199.

Upadhyaya, H.D. and Gopal, K. (1995). Inheritance of albinism in certain crosses of groundnut *(Arachis hypogaea* L.). *Journal of Oilseed Research,* 12: 167–170.

Upadhyaya, H.D., and Nigam, S.N. (1994). Inheritance of two components of early maturity in groundnut *(Arachis hypogaea* L.) *Euphytica,* 78: 59–67.

Upadhyaya, H.D., and Nigam, S.N. (1996). Identification and inheritance of male sterility in groundnut *(Arachis hypogaea* L.). *Euphytica,* 88: 227–230.

Van der Stok, J.E. (1910). Onderzockingen omirent, *Arachis hypogaea* L. (Katang–Tanah). *Mededelingen Yen het Department Van Landbouw,* 12: 176–221 (cf. Hull, 1937).

Vanisree, G. and Prasad, M.V.R. (1995) Genetics of aerial podding attribute in groundnut *(Arachis hypogaea* L.) *Journal of Oilseeds Research,* 12: 301–303.

Venkateswarlu, B.K. Mukhopadhyay, and Chiydhuri, J. (1998). An *in–vitro* regeneration protocol for screening groundnut plants for water stress tolerance. *Legume Res.,* 21: 1–7.

Vindhiyavarman, P. and Raveendran, T.S. (1994). Line X tester analysis of combining ability in groundnut. *Madras Agricultural Journal,* 81: 529–532.

Vindhiyavarman, P., and Raveendran, T.S. (1996). Genetics of period from seedling emergence to first flowering in groundnut. *Madras Agricultural Journal,* 83: 317–318.

Vindhiyavarman, P., Raveendran, T.S. and Ganapathi, T. (1993). Inheritance of rust resistance in groundnut. *Madras Agricultural Journal,* 80: 175–176.

Vindhyavarman, P., and Paramasivam, K. (1992). Genetic architecture of yield and quality characters in groundnut. *Madras Agricultural Journal,* 79: 688–694.

Waliyar, F. and McDonald, D. (1988). Improving field screening of groundnut genotypes for resistance to foliar fungal diseases. *International Arachis Newsletter,* 4: 18–19.

Walls, S.B. and Wynne, J.C. (1985). Combining ability for resistance to *Cercosporidium personatum* for late leaf spot resistant peanut germplasm lines. *Oleagineux,* 40: 389–394.

Wang, A.M., Fan, H.L., Chong, S.S., and Ozias–Akins, P. (1988). Transformation of peanuts with a soyabean vspB promoter–uidA chimeric gene. I. Optimization of a transformation system and analysis of GUS expression in primary transgenic tissues and plants. *Physiologia Plantarum,* 102: 38–48.

Whan, B.R., Knight R. and Rathijen A. (1982). Response to selection for grain yield and harvest index in F2, F3, F4 derived lines of rwo wheat crosses. *Euphytica,* 31: 139–150.

Whan, B.R., Rathijen A. and Knight R. (1981). The relation between wheat lines derived from the F2, F3 and F4 generations for grain yield and harvest index. *Euphytica,* 30: 419–430.

Wheeler, T.R., Chatzialioglou, A., Craufurd, P.Q., Ellis, R.H. and Summerfield, R.J. (1997). Dry matter partitioning in groundnut exposed to high temperature stress. *Crop–Sdence,* 37: 1507–1513.

Williams, J.H., Wilson, J.H.H., and Bate, G.C. (1975). The growth of groundnut *(Arachis hypogaea* cv. Makulu Red) at three altitudes in Rhodesia. *Rhodesian Journal of Agricultural Research,* 13: 33–43.

Wissuwa, M and Ae. N. (1998). Genotypic variation for phosphorus uptake from hardly soluble iron–phosphate in groundnut *(Arachis hypogaea* L.). *Plant and Soil,* 206: 163–171.

Wynne, J.C. (1975). Inheritance of branching pattern in *Arachis hypogaea. Peanut Science,* 2: 1–5.

Wynne, J.C. (1976). Evaluation of early generation testing on peanuts. *Peanut Sci.,* 3: 62–66.

Wynne, J.C. and Cofelt. T.A. (1982) Genetics of *Arachis hypogaea* L. *In*: Peanut Science and Technology,American Peanut Research and Education Society pp. 50–96.

Wynne, J.C., Elkan, G.H., Meisner, C.M., Schneeweis, T.J. and Ligon, J.M. (1981). Green house evaluations of strains of Rhizobium for peanuts. *Agron J.,* 72: 645–649

Yoakum Texas. Yonezwa, K. and Yamagata, H. (1981). Selection strategy in breeding of self–fertilizing crops.3. Evaluation of delayed selection System in consideration of repulsion linkage between desirable alleles. *Japn J. Breed.* 31: 360–366.

Young, C.T. and Waller. G.R. (1972) Rapid oleic/linoeic micro–analytical procedure for peanuts. *J.Agr. Food Chem.,* 20: 116–118.

Zheng, G. (1987). Breeding for resistance to groundnut rust in the People's Republic of China. *In*: Groundnut Rust Disease, Proceedings of discussion Group Meeting, 24–28 September 1984. ICRISAT, Patancheru, India, pp. 107–108.

Zhou, R., Liao, B.S., Chen, X.M., Lei Y., Li, D., and Jin, H.B. (1998). Effects of Al stress on growth and development in groundnut genotypes. *Chinese Journal of Oil Crop Sciences,* 20: 48–51.

# 14

# Cotton

## 1. INTRODUCTION

Cotton is a major fibre crop of global importance and has high commercial value. The cotton seed coat extends into tubular fibre and is spun into yarn. Four out of the 50 recognized cotton species in the world are cultivated. Two of them (*Gossypium arboreum* and *G. herbaceum*) are diploid, and remaining two (*G. hirsutum* and *G. barbadense*) are tetraploids. More than 80 per cent of the world cotton area is covered by *G. hirsutum* and *G. barbadense*. However, diploid cottons are also in cultivation in Asia and middle East. India is the only country where all the cultivated species and some of their hybrid combinations are commercially grown. The diversity of cotton cultivars and cotton agroclimatic zones in India is considerably larger when compared to other major cotton growing countries in the world.

Cotton is cultivated in 70 countries of the world with the total coverage of 34 million ha. Over a quarter of the world cotton area is in India (Table 1) followed by USA (16%), China (14%) and Pakistan (8%). About 19 m tonnes of cotton is produced globally and the contribution of individual countries is : USA (22%); China (21%); India (12%); Pakistan (8%) and Uzbekistan (6%). The remaining production comes from, Turkey, Australia, Greece, Brazil and Egypt.

Among the five major cotton growing countries, China (830 kg/ha) holds highest productivity level followed by USA (783 kg/ha), Uzbekistan (762 kg/ha), Pakistan (505 kg/ha) and India (316 kg/ha). During the decade of nineties no spectacular productivity gains have been recorded in any of the major cotton growing countries in Table 1.

V.L. Chopra (Ed.): Breeding Field Crops I: Practices, Studium Press (LLC), USA.

**Table 1:** Area and production of cotton in the world between 1996-98 and productivity comparison during 1990s (Average of 1996-98)

| *Sl. no.* | *Country* | *Area* | *Production (m. tonnes)* | *Productivity (kg/ha)* | | | *No. of major varieties grown* |
|---|---|---|---|---|---|---|---|
| | | | | *1996-98* | *1993-95* | *1989-91* | |
| 1. | China | 4.70 | 3.90 | 830 | 805 | 810 | 20 |
| 2. | USA | 5.09 | 3.98 | 783 | 692 | 710 | 20 |
| 3. | India | 8.65 | 2.73 | 316 | 300 | 283 | 45 |
| 4. | Pakistan | 3.21 | 1.62 | 505 | 545 | 648 | 25 |
| 5. | Uzbekistan | 1.50 | 1.14 | 762 | 821 | 850 | 12 |
| 6. | Turkey | 0.74 | 0.79 | 1071 | 1090 | 936 | 10 |
| 7. | Australia | 0.35 | 0.53 | 1543 | 1448 | 1578 | 14 |
| 8. | Brazil | 0.92 | 0.34 | 376 | 382 | 368 | 8 |
| 9. | Egypt | 0.36 | 0.33 | 421 | 919 | 733 | 10 |
| 10. | Greece | 0.43 | 0.38 | 887 | 960 | 876 | 8 |
| 11. | Argentina | 0.96 | 0.43 | 453 | 480 | 483 | 10 |
| 12. | Others | 6.96 | 2.98 | 565 | 564 | 574 | — |
| | World total | 33.91 | 19.14 | 565 | 564 | 574 | — |

*Sources:* ICAC 1996, Khadi 1997.

## 1.1. Cultivation of Cotton in India

Indian cotton scenario has shown a positive trend with consistent increase in area, production and productivity during 1950-51 to 1997-98 (Table 2).

**Table 2:** Cotton cultivation scenario past and present in India

| *Year* | *Area (mha)* | *Production (m.bales)* | *Productivity (kg/ha)* |
|---|---|---|---|
| 1950-51 | 5.88 | 3.04 | 88 |
| 1960-61 | 7.61 | 5.60 | 106 |
| 1970-71 | 7.61 | 5.60 | 125 |
| 1980-81 | 7.82 | 7.01 | 152 |
| 1990-91 | 7.40 | 11.50 | 224 |
| 1992-93 | 7.68 | 12.50 | 285 |
| 1993-94 | 7.33 | 12.15 | 228 |
| 1994-95 | 7.92 | 13.50 | 257 |
| 1995-96 | 9.10 | 16.00 | 246 |
| 1996-97 | 8.80 | 17.87 | 343 |
| 1997-98 | 8.87 | 15.32 | 294 |

(1 bale = 170 kg)

Based on agroclimatic situations, cotton growing area has been classified into four zones (Table 3, Fig. 1)

Among nine major cotton growing states, Maharashtra (30 lakh/ha) has the largest area followed by Gujarat (15 lakh ha) and Andhra Pradesh (10 lakh ha). The three states contribute approximately 50 per

**Table 3:** Cotton growing zones in India

| | *Zones* | *States* | *Species grown* | *% of cotton area* | *% of cotton production* |
|---|---|---|---|---|---|
| 1. | Northern hirsutum arboreum zone. | Punjab, Haryana, Rajasthan. | *G. hirsutum*, *G. arboreum* | 20 (0.5)* | 27.0 (450)" |
| 2. | Central hirsutum arboreum and herbaceum zone | Madhya Pradesh, Maharashtra, Gujarat | *G. hirsutum*, *G. arboreum*, *G. herbaceum* Intra hirsutum Interspecific diploid hybrids. | 56.5 (63.7) | 47.0 (270) |
| 3. | Southern hirsutum herbaceum, arboreum and barbadense zone. | Andhra Pradesh Karnataka | All four species Intra hirsutum and Interspecific hybrids | 23.0 (55.0) | 26.0 (367) |
| 4. | Eastern arboreum zone | Orissa, Bihar, West Bengal and North Eastern states. | *G. arboreum* | 0.5 (40.0) | 1.0 (340) |

* Percentage rainfed area
** Productivity (lint kg/ha)

cent of lint to the Indian cotton basket (Table 4). High productivity has been obtained in Madhya Pradesh (600 kg/ha), Andhra Pradesh (450 kg/ha) and Gujarat (410 kg/ha). These states cultivate hybrid cotton in approximately 50 per cent of their cotton area.

**Table 4:** State wise area, production and productivity of cotton lint for 1996-97 and 1998-1999

| *States* | *% Irrigated area* | *Area (lakh ha)* | | | *Production* | | | *Productivity* | | |
|---|---|---|---|---|---|---|---|---|---|---|
| | | *1995-96* | *1996-97* | *1997-98* | *1995-96* | *1996-97* | *1997-98* | *1995-96* | *1996-97* | *1997-98* |
| Punjab | 100 | 7.50 | 7.00 | 7.25 | 14.80 | 16.35 | 9.00 | 335 | 397 | 211 |
| Haryana | 98 | 6.46 | 5.49 | 6.55 | 11.45 | 13.90 | 10.50 | 301 | 430 | 273 |
| Rajasthan | 100 | 6.06 | 6.20 | 5.42 | 13.65 | 15.25 | 11.50 | 382 | 418 | 360 |
| Gujarat | 45 | 14.10 | 15.24 | 16.02 | 31.80 | 36.80 | 39.00 | 383 | 410 | 414 |
| Maharashtra | 13 | 30.65 | 29.63 | 31.39 | 28.60 | 33.50 | 15.00 | 159 | 192 | 81 |
| Madhya Pradesh | 25 | 5.37 | 5.27 | 5.35 | 14.40 | 19.80 | 19.00 | 455 | 639 | 603 |
| Andhra Pradesh | 60 | 10.74 | 10.07 | 8.04 | 28.57 | 21.60 | 22.00 | 462 | 441 | 465 |
| Karnataka | 25 | 6.74 | 6.68 | 4.45 | 10.30 | 10.00 | 9.00 | 259 | 254 | 344 |
| Tamil Nadu | 35 | 2.65 | 2.52 | 2.03 | 5.00 | 5.50 | 6.00 | 321 | 371 | 502 |
| Others | 40 | 0.53 | 0.50 | 0.76 | 1.25 | 1.00 | 1.00 | 400 | 340 | 224 |
| Loose supply | – | – | – | – | – | 0.5 | 6.00 | – | | |
| All India | 36 | 90.63 | 88.60 | 87.26 | 160.0 | 178.7 | 148.0 | 300 | 343 | 288 |

*Source* : Venugopal *et al.*, 1998.

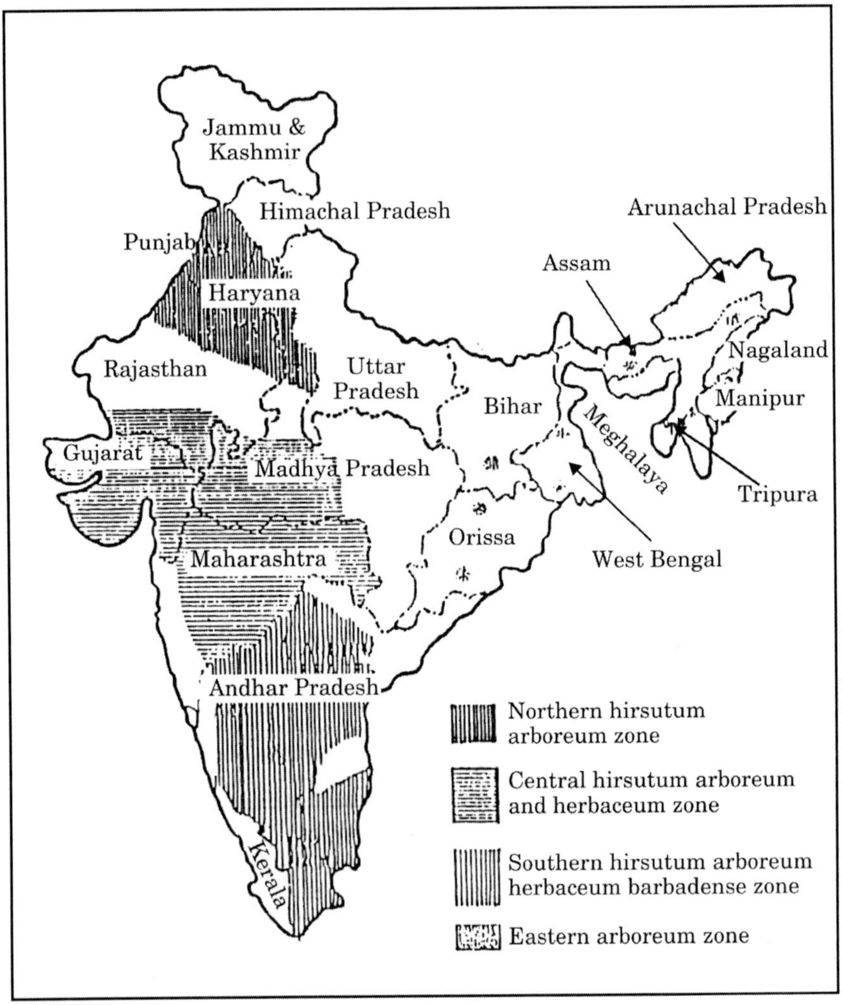


**Fig. 1 :** Cotton growing zones in India.

Species composition of cultivated cotton in India has changed over the years (Table 5). In 1947, 97 per cent area was sown to *G. arboreum* and *G. herbaceum; G. hirsutum* contributed only 3 per cent. Now, 72 per cent of area is occupied by *G. hirsutum, intrahirsutum* and *hirsutum-barbadense* hybrids. The *per se* contribution of *G. barbadense* is negligible but as male parent of interspecific hybrids, it is the chief source of extra long staple cotton in India. The present species composition with about 28 per cent (27 lakh ha) under *G. arboreum* and *G. herbaceum* varieties should be maintained, so that the genetic base for tolerance to abiotic and biotic stresses like moisture stress, resistance to leaf curl virus disease and jassids is not depleted.

**Table 5:** Species composition of cultivated cottons in India

| ***Species*** | ***Percent area covered*** | | |
|---|---|---|---|
| | ***1947-48*** | ***1975-76*** | ***1996-97*** |
| ***Diploid*** | | | |
| *G. herbaceum* | 32.0 | 20.2 | 11.0 |
| *G. arboreum* | 65.0 | 27.1 | 17.0 |
| ***Tetraploid*** | | | |
| G. *hirsutum* | 3.0 | 52.5 | 35.9 |
| *G. barbadcnse* | – | 1.2 | 0.10 |
| Hybrids | – | – | 36.0 |

Staplewise production of cotton in India has also witnessed a significant change (Table 6). During 1960-61 all the cotton produced in India had fibre length below 24 mm. At present approximately 40 per cent of cotton produced in India has more than one inch (24.5 mm) staple length. The reason for increase in diversity of staple classes and net staple length of Indian cotton is attributed to the introduction of tetraploids from New world. The variability in spinning potential in India has also increased and ranges between 6s and 120s, which is largely due to hybrid cotton (Narayanan *et al.,* 1990).

**Table 6:** Staplewise production of cotton in India

| ***Year*** | ***Staple length and class**** | | | | | ***Total*** |
|---|---|---|---|---|---|---|
| | ***Superior long (>27.0 mm)*** | ***Long (24.5-26 mm)*** | ***Superior medium (22-24 mm)*** | ***Medium (20-21.5 mm)*** | ***Short (<19 mm)*** | |
| 1960-61 | – | – | 25.5 | 23.20 | 7.8 | 56.5 |
| 1970-71 | 1.6 | 23.2 | 36.4 | 11.20 | 8.1 | 80.5 |
| 1985-86 | 28.6 | 15.6 | 31.85 | 5.60 | 5.6 | 87.3 |
| 1990-91 | 29.1 | 9.43 | 48.45 | 1.40 | 10.70 | 99.14 |
| 1992-93 | 33.8 | 9.56 | 58.29 | 0.80 | 13.40 | 115.83 |

*Source :* Anonymous 1998. *Old classification and New classification ,<20 mm-Short; 20.5 - 24.5 mm. Medium; 25 - 27 mm-Medium Long 27.5 - 32 mm - Long; >32.5-Extralong.

In India, cotton research activities are being carried out under the umbrella of All India Co-ordinated Cotton Improvement Project (AICCIP) operating in 11 main centres and 16 subcentres located in different cotton growing states with headquarters at Coimbatore. There are two central institutes which play a pivotal role in cotton research.

1. Central Institute for Cotton Research (CICR) located at Nagpur (MS) has regional stations at Coimbatore (TN) and Sirsa (Haryana). CICR, apart from maintaining germplasm, concentrates on basic research on cotton.

2. Central Institute for Research on Cotton Technology (CIRCOT) located at Mumbai has regional stations at 13 locations spread over India. CIRCOT deals with various aspects of fibre technology and cotton by-products.

## 2. HISTORY AND TAXONOMY

The first reference to cotton is found in *Rig-Veda* hymn which was written about 15 centuries BC. The use of cotton in about 800 BC is recorded in Manu's "Dharmashastra". The Sanskrit word *karpasa-i* was used in ancient literature which is connected to kapas of modern Hindustani. The technological and agricultural term in English, Cotton, which describes cultivated species of *Gossypium* comes from Arabic word *qutum* or *kutum* (Brovvn, 1958). Systematic taxonomic study of cotton started with description of *Gossypium* by Linnaeus during 1753.

The work of Sir George Watt entitled "The wild and cultivated cotton plants of the world" provided new dimension to the taxonomic studies. The cytological studies of Zaitzev (1928) cited in the paper "A contribution to the classification of genus *Gossypium*" was a landmark in cotton classification.

Classification of the genus *Gossypium,* belonging to family *Malvaceae* and tribe *Gossypieae* has been presented in Table 7. This dicotyledonous genus comprises approximately 50 species of which 45 are diploid and five are allopolyploid (Fryxell, 1992). The diploid *Gossypium* species

**Table 7:** Classification of genus *Gossypium*

| *Primary distribution* | *Subgenus* | *Section* | *Subsection* | *Examples of species* |
|---|---|---|---|---|
| Australia | *Sturtia* | *Sturtia* | – | G. *sturtianum* |
| | | *Grandi calys* | – | *G. costulatum* |
| | | *Hibiscoidea* | – | *G. australe* |
| America | *Houzingenia* | *Houzingenia* | *Houzingenia* | *G. thurberi* |
| | | | *Integrifolia* | *G. davidsonii* |
| | | | *Caducibractealata* | *G. harknessii* |
| | | *Erioxylum* | *Erioxylum* | *G. aridum* |
| | | | *Selera* | *G. gossypioides* |
| | | | *Astromericana* | *G. raimondii* |
| Africa | *Gossypium* | *Gossypium* | *Gossypium* | *Asiatic diploids* |
| | | | *Anamola* | *G. anomalum* |
| | | *Pseudopambak* | *Pseudopambak* | *G. stockssii* |
| | | | *Longibola* | *G. longicalyx* |
| New World | *Karpas* | – | – | All tetraploid species including New World cultivar. |

consist of eight cytological groups or genomes (Beasley, 1940; Endrizzi *et al., 1985;* Phillips and Strickland, 1966). The remaining five allotetraploid species are united version of Old World A and New World D genome in A genome cytoplasm (Skovsted, 1937; Endrizzi, 1962; Phillips, 1963; Wendel, 1989; Wendel and Albert, 1992; Brubaker *et al.,* 1999). The present list of species of genus *Gossypium* grouped according to genomic affinities has been given in Table 8, which is based on literature of Fryxell (1992), Vollesen (1987), Craven *et al.* (1995).

**Table 8:** List of *Gossypium* species grouped according to germplasm pool

| *Pool* | *Species* | *Genome* | *Seed* | *Notes* |
|---|---|---|---|---|
| Primary | *G.hirsutum* | $AD_1$ | + | Current and obsolete cultivars, breeding stock, landraces, feral and wild accessions. |
| | *G. barbadense* | $AD_2$ | + | Ibid. |
| | G. *tomentosum* | $AD_3$ | + | Hawaiian Islands |
| | *G. mustelinum* | $AD_4$ | + | NE Brazil |
| | *G. darwinii* | $AD_5$ | + | Galapagos Islands |
| Secondary | *G. herbaceum* | $A_1$ | | Cultivars, landraces of Africa and Asia Minor, one wild from Southern Africa |
| | *G. arboreum* | $A_2$ | + | Cultivars, landraces from Asia Minor to SE Asia and China; some African |
| | *G. anomalum* | $B_1$ | + | Two subspecies, Sahel and SW Africa |
| | *G. triphyllum* | $B_2$ | + | SW Africa |
| | *G. capitis-viridis* | $B_3$ | + | Cape Verde Islands |
| | *G. trifurcatum* | $B_?$ | – | NE Somalia |
| | *G. longicalyx* | $F_1$ | + | Trailing shrub, Sudan, Uganda, Tanzania |
| | *G. thurberi* | $D_1$ | + | Sonora Desert, North America |
| | *G. armourianum* | $D_{2-1}$ | + | Baja California (San Marcos Island) |
| | *G. harknessii* | $D_{2-2}$ | + | Central Baja California |
| | *G. davidsonii* | $D_{3-d}$ | + | Southern Baja California |
| | *G. klotzschianum* | $D_{3-k}$ | + | Galapagos Islands |
| | *G. aridum* | $D_4$ | + | Arborescent, Pacific slopes of Mexico |
| | *G. raimondii* | $D_5$ | + | Pacific slope valleys of Peru |
| | *G. gossypioides* | $D_6$ | + | Central Oaxaca, Mexico |
| | *G. lobatum* | $D_7$ | + | Arborescent, Central Michoacan, Mexico |
| | *G. trilobum* | $D_8$ | + | West central Mexico |
| | *G. laxum* | $D_9$ | + | Arborescent, Canon del Zopilote, SW Mexico |
| | *G. tumeri* | $D_{10}$ | + | NW Mexico, coastal |
| | *G. schwendimanii* | $D_{11}$ | + | Arborescent, El Infiernillo Valley, SW Mexico |
| Tertiary | G. *sturtianum* | $C_1$ | + | Ornamental, Transcentral Australia arid zone |
| | G. *robinsonii* | $C_2$ | + | Western Australia |
| | G. *bickii* | $G_1$ | + | Central Australia arid zone |
| | G. *australe* | G | + | Transaustralia, north arid zone |
| | *G. nelsonii* | G | + | Central Australia |

**Table 8:** *Contd...*

**Table 8:** *Contd...*

| *Pool* | *Species* | *Génome* | *Seed* | *Notes* |
|---|---|---|---|---|
| | *G. costulatum* | K | + | North Kimberley (wet-dry tropical), Western Australia |
| | *G. cunninghamii* | K | + | Northern NT, Australia |
| | *G. enthyle* | K | + | North Kimberley, WA |
| | *G. exgiuum* | K | + | Prostrate, North Kimberley, WA |
| | *G. nobile* | K | + | North Kimberley, WA |
| | *G. pilosum* | K | + | Trailing, Nort Kimberley, WA |
| | *G. populifolium* | K | + | North Kimberley, WA |
| | *G. pulchellum* | K | + | North Kimberley, WA |
| | *G. rotundifolium* | K | + | Prostrate, North Kimberley, WA |
| | *G. sp. nov.* | K | + | North Kimberley, WA |
| | *G. stocksii* | $E_1$ | + | Arabian Peninsula & Horn of Africa |
| | *G. somalense* | $E_2$ | + | Horn of Africa to Chad |
| | *G. areysianum* | $E_3$ | + | Yemen |
| | *G. incanum* | $E_4$ | + | Yemen |
| | *G. benadirense* | E | – | Ethiopia, Somalia, Kenya |
| | *G. bricchetti* | E | – | Somalia |
| | *G. vollesenii* | E | – | Somalia |

Adopted from Stewart 1995, +seeds are preserved ex *situ* for most species although in very limited quantity for some.

## 3. ORIGIN AND DISTRIBUTION

The concept of organismal and genome relationships of diploid and allopolyploid taxa in the genus *Gossypium* have been given by Cronn and Wendel in 1998 (Fig. 2). The diploid ancestral A and D genomes of extant allotetraploid are thought to have diverged from a common ancestor about 4 or 6 to 11 million years ago giving rise to two lineages

Diploid ancestor
(6 – 11 million years ago)
↓ ↓
AA × DD
Old World | New World
n=13 | n=13
(Big Chromosomes) (Small Chromosomes)
↓
Polyploidization
(1-2 million years ago)
↓
AADD
New world tetraploid
n=26 (13 big + 13 small)

**Fig. 2:** Evolution and Phylogenetic relationships among *Gossypium* genus (Endrizzi *et al.*, 1985; Wendel, 1989)

(Wendel, 1989; Cronn and Wendel, 1998). The five polyploid *Gossypium* species recognized today, including cultivated cottons of *G. hirsutum* and *G. barbadense,* are thought to have originated 1 to 2 million years ago by transoceanic migration of Old World A genome progenitor, followed by hybridization with New World D genome progenitor (Endrizzi *et al., 1*985; Wendel, 1989; Cronn and Wendel, 1998). This hypothesis proposed by Wendel and his group is a polished version of simple origin of Old World and New World diploids and their hybridization in the new world before 1-2 million years ago. Despite intensive study, the identity of the parental diploids and the antiquity of polyploidisation remain unresolved. Nevertheless, the established and accepted facts are briefed below.

## 4. ORIGIN AND DISTRIBUTION OF DIPLOIDS

According to Hutchinson (1959), The cultivated *G. herbaceum* was derived from the truly wild form of the diploid, *G. herbaceum* race *africanum* which has distribution in South Africa. He assumed that traders sailing between Mozambique and Western India introduced this wild form of *G. herbaceum* into Southern Arabia where the first domestication in the Old World cotton took place. From here, the spread of the species lead to the development of new races. *G. herbaceum* consists of five races: 1. *Africanum* 2. *Acerifolium* 3. *Persicum* 4. *Kuljianum* 5. *Wighitianum.*

The genome of *G. arboreum* is derived from that of *G. herbaceum* and these two species are set apart by a reciprocal translocation (Gerstel 1953). Genetically, both species are closely related and are good functional diploids. *G. arboreum* arose as an incipient species with the origin and fixation of the translocation. The accumulation of genes due to consistent isolation and selection supported by hybridization resulted into eventual reemergence of *G. arboreum* as a full fledged species (Fryxel 1984). The races evolved from *G. arboreum* are 1. *Indicum* 2. *Burmanicum* 3. *Sinense* 4. *Sudanense* 5. *Cernum.*

The wild diploid species belonging to B, E and F genome have distribution in Africa and Arabia and the entire D genome has distribution in South and Central America (Fryxell, 1992). Kimberly cottons belonging to *Grandicalyx* (K) and other diploids belonging to *Sturtia* (C) and *Hibiscoidea* (G) have been found distributed in Australian continent (Craven *et al.,* 1995*)* (Fig. 3).

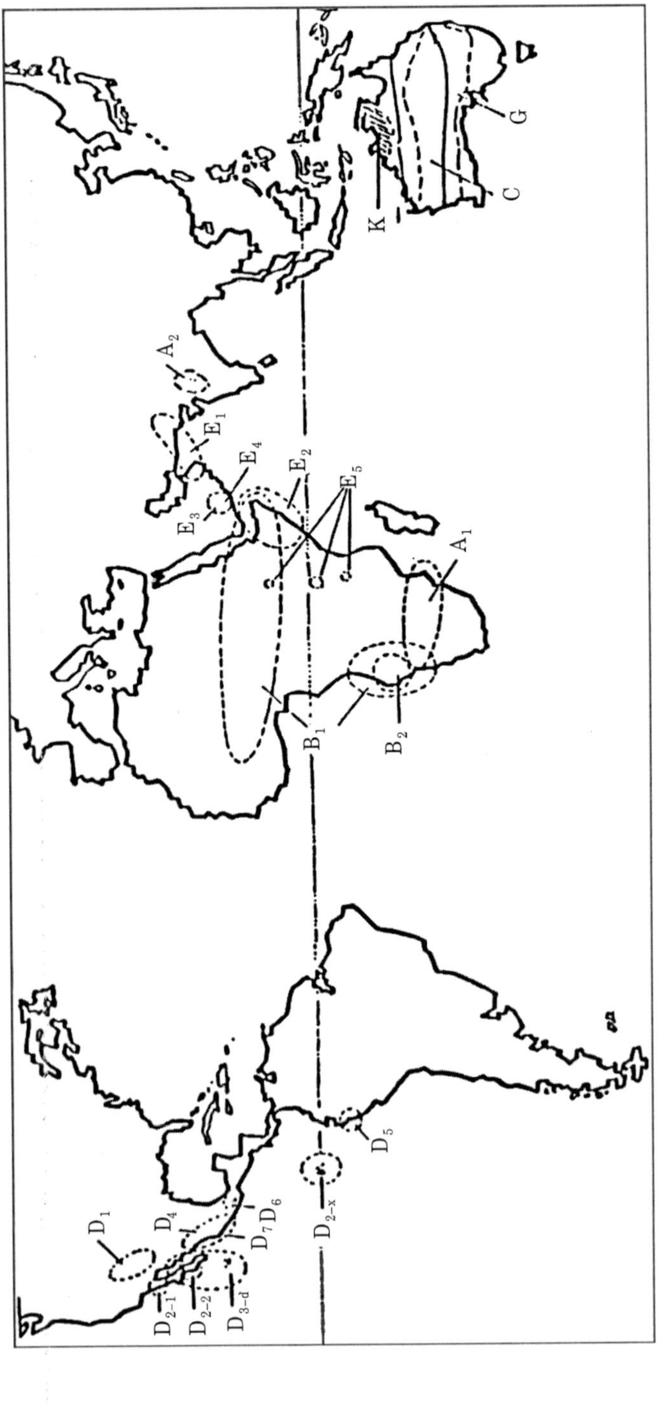


**Fig. 3:** Distribution of diploid wild species in the world (Fryxell 1992, Craven *et al.*, 1995, Stewart, 1995)

## 5. ORIGIN AND DISTRIBUTION OF ALLOTETRAPLOID COTTONS

Skovsted (1937), based on his cytogenetic studies on crosses between *G. hirsutum, G. barbadense* and diploids, showed existence of two sets of 13 chromosomes. He hypothesized that the chromosome complement of allotetraploid was made up of one set of 13 bigger size homologous chromosomes of Asiatic cottons and another set of 13 smaller homologous chromosomes of New World diploid species. Beasly (1940) and Hutchinson (1940) independently confirmed Skovsted's hypothesis.

Gerstel (1953) exhibited the contribution of *G. herbacewn* as A genome and *G. mimondii* as D genome in the development of allotetraploid based on the univalent frequencies in hexaploids of crosses between tetraploid, *G. hirsutum* with different diploids. Study of multivalent frequencies and genetic segregation ratios showed that *G. raimondii* ($D_5$) closely approached allotetraploid behaviour and must be related to the D sub genome contributor of the AD allotetraploid (Sarvella, 1958; Gerstel, 1963; Phillips, 1963). Further, the data on DNA content of A and D genomes and their near additivity in tetraploids also confirmed the polyploidisation between A and D genomes (Gomez *et al.,* 1993). The diploid like behaviour of allotetraploids was confirmed by Endrizzi and Phillips (I960), Endrizzi (1962), Mursal and Endrizzi (1976). The studies on cpDNA (chloroplast DNA) restriction indicated the presence of A genome cytoplasm in tetraploids ($A_1$) (Wendel, 1989).

For all practical purposes the progenitors of the New World allotetraploid cottons have now been fixed as $A_1$ (*G. herbaceum* var. *africanum)* and $D_5$ (G. *raimondii).* However, the studies on spread of dispersed repetitive DNA into the New World D genome supports the view that *G. gossypioids* rather than its sister *G. raimondii* may be the closest living descendant of the New World, D genome cotton ancestor (Reinisch *et al.,* 1994; Zhao *et al.,* 1998). On the basis of Slot-blot hybridization signals, about 400,000 copies of A genome specific dispersed repeats were found widely distributed through out the genome of *G. gossypioides* (Zhao *et al.,* 1998). This discovery adds support to a suggestion previously made, based on evidence from only a single genetic locus (Wendel *et al.,* 1995) that this species may be either the closest living descendent of the New World (D genome) cotton ancestor or an adulterated relic of polyploid formation. The present understanding of Cladogenetic relationships in *Gossypium* genus is presented in Fig. 4.

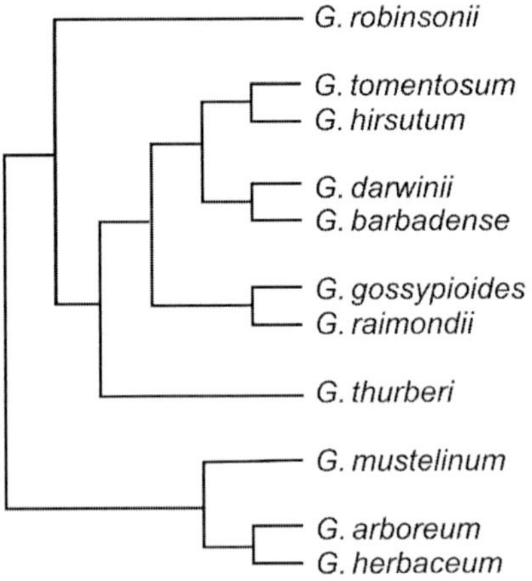


**Fig 4 :** Present understanding of cladogenetic relationship in *Gossypium* genus.

Based on the large body of cytological data indicating the similarity in chromosome end arrangement in all five tetraploid New World cottons and perfect meiotic pairing suggested monophyletic origin of allotetraploids. However, the existence of several diploid species in the New World coupled with their geographical distribution suggested a polyphyletic origin. This concept of polyphyletic origin was supported by

(a) Chromatographic studies of Parks *et al.* (1975)

(b) Studies on Electrophoretic banding pattern of seed protein by Johnson (1975)

(c) Investigation of RFLP data by Reinisch *et al.* (1994).

After polyploidation, the AD genome group diverged into three distinct lineages (Brubaker and Wendel, 1994; Small *et al.,* 1998) presently represented by five species, including economically important cottons of *G. hirsutum* and *G. barbadense* (Fig. 5).

*G. hirsutum* is considered to be native to Mexico and Central America. Since these were grown in upland sites they are called 'Upland cotton'. Similarly *G. barbadense* is considered to be native to South America and was adapted to the coasts of the Islands of Carolinas and Georgia, hence called 'Sea Island cotton'. The introductions of *G. barbadense* in Egypt during early 19th cenury brought the name 'Egyptian cotton'. Subsequent reintroduction of the Egyptian cotton into the South West USA added another synonym 'Pima cotton'. The two races developed in *G. barbadense* are *brasilliense* and *darwinii.* The seven races evolved in *G. hirsutum* are 1. *palmeri, 2. morilli, 3. richmondii* 4. *Yucatenanse*

*5. punctatum* 6. *marie galante* 7. *latifolium.* The race *Latifolium* is widely cultivated in the world.

**Fig. 5:** Distribution of allotetraploid species of *Gossypium*

## 6. GENERAL BOTANICAL DESCRIPTION OF *GOSSYPIUM*

***Habit*** **:** Annual, biennial or perennial, herbaceous to small tree 1-2 m tall. ***Root*** **:** Tap root system, deep rooted. ***Stem*:** Erect, branched, branches angled, *tomentose,* hairy or glabrous. Vegetative branches-Monopodia 1-3 or more. Reproductive branches—Sympodia. Whole plant dotted with oil glands. ***Leaves*** **:** Alternate, petiolate, 3-9 lobed and palmately veined, with varying size, shape, texture and hairiness. ***Flowers*** **:** Extra auxillary, terminal or solitary, opening of flower is spiralaceose in acropetal and centrifugal succession. Petal colour vary with colours white, yellow, cream yellow, purple. ***Bracteoles*** **:** Three in number, usually foliar and persistent, sometimes small or minute and cordate, toothed or entire, rarely caducous. ***Calyx*** **:** Cup shaped, truncate, undulate with five toothed and persistent. ***Corolla*** **:** Five in number, colour vary : white, cream, yellow or purple. In some species a spot of purple or dark red colour called 'Eye' is found on the claw of petal. ***Androecium*** **:** Staminal column, anthers unilocular, reniform and monadelphous. ***Gynoecium*** **:** Ovary vary with 3-5 locules, superior, ovules one to several in loculi. *style*-glandular, club shaped and clavate shortly into, as many lobes as loculi in the ovary. ***Fruit*** **:** A loculicidal capsule termed boll, 3-5 loculed. Seed : Covered with one or two coats of long unicellular hairs or naked. Seeds 1-9 are in each locule. Subglobose or angular pyriform.

## 7. GERMPLASM RESOURCES

Several centres maintain large collections of cotton germplasm. The major ones are:

**1. *United States of America: United States Department of Agriculture (USDA)*** **:** Maintains the following types of germplasm.

(a) Primitive types of *G. barbadense* and *G. darwinii* at Phoenix, Arizona.
(b) Obsolete cultivars of *G. hirsutum* at Stoneville, Missisipi.
(c) Primitive types and Genetic Markers of *G. hirsutum* and all other species at College Station Texas.
(d) National Seed Storage Laboratory at Fort Collins, Colorado has genetic stocks of all the above mentioned.

**2. *Central Institute for Cotton Research CICR Nagpur*** **:** In India its Regional Stations at Sirsa and Coimbatore maintain working collections. At present 4000 accessions of *G. hirsutum,* 390 of *G. barbadense,* 1700 of *G. arboreum,* 400 of *G. herbaceum,* 24 wild species and 400 perennials as race stocks, polyploids and their derivatives (totaling around 7000) are being maintained. Also collection of diploid cottons (*G. herbaceum* and *G. arboreum}* is maintained at Cotton Research Station in Surat, Gujarat.

**3. *Tashkent*** **:** Cotton germplasm collected from Central and South American area by Mauer and Bukasor are maintained.

**4. *Germplasm in China*** **:** Over 2300 accessions of various species introduced from 18 Asian, 17 African, 9 Latin American and 2 North American countries are maintained (Zhuang, 1994). They include 16 monosomic lines, 29 telosomic lines, 58 stable translocation lines and 11 lines with marker genes.

Stewart (1995), based on the model concept of germplasm pools described by Harland de Wet (1971), classified cotton gene pool as primary, secondary and tertiary according to ease with which genes could be transferred from source to the tetraploid cultivated cotton.

**Table 9:** Distinguishing features of cultivated species of *Gossypium L.*

| ***Feature*** | ***G. hirsutum*** | ***G. barbadense*** | ***G. arboreum*** | ***G. herbaceum*** |
|---|---|---|---|---|
| Chromosome number | 2n=52 | 2n=52 | 2n=26 | 2n=26 |
| Ploidy | Tetraploid | Tetraploid | Diploid | Diploid |
| Origin | Central America, Mexico (New World) | South America (New World) | Africa (Old World) | India and East Asia (Old World) |
| Popular names | American cotton, Upland cotton, Combodia cotton, Dharwad American | Egyptian cotton, Sea Island cotton, Pima cotton | Asiatic cotton, *Desi* cotton | Asiatic, *Desi* cotton |
| Habit | Small, annual, sub-shrub 1.5m tall | Perennial, shrub/ annual, sub-shurb. 1-3m tall | Perennial, branched, shrub /annual, sub-shrub 1.5 2m Tall | Sub-shrubs 1-1.5 m tall |
| Stem | Green or brown sparsely hairy or glabrous, fruiting branches many jointed | Green glabrous and rarely hairy, fruiting branches many jointed | Green, brown, hairy, fruiting branches two jointed | Green, rarely pigmented, hairy, rarely glabrous and fruiting branches many jointed |
| Leaves | Large cordate, 1/2 cut or less, 3-5 lobes not constricted, also overlapping lobes | 2/3 cut into 3-5 lobes, sinuses thrown into folds, lobes longs and tapering | 2/3 to 4/5 cut into 5-7 lobes long and narrow | 1/2 cut or less, 3-7 lobes only slightly constricted at the base |
| Bracteole | Triangular, 4-12 long teeth, longer than broad | 10-15 accuminate teeth, as long as broad | 3-4 teeth closely invested to bud flower, longer than broad | 6-8 teeth, flaring widely from the buds, flower and capsule |
| Petal | Cream, light yellow to yellow | Sulphur Yellow, deep | White to yellow, red | Medium yellow |
| Petal spot | Absent | Prominent, large dark | Present, prominent | Present, dark |
| Stamen/ Anthers stigma | Staminal column short, Anthers closely arranged, stigma united throughout, rarely divided at tip | Staminal column long, antheriferous closely packed, filaments short | Staminal column long, antheriferous, short anthers short style, united stigma | Staminal column throughout antheriferous, filament short style short, united top |

**Table 9:** *Contd...*

**Table 9:** *Contd...*

| *Feature* | *G. hirsutum* | *G. barbadense* | *G. arboreum* | *G. herbaceum* |
|---|---|---|---|---|
| Boll (capsules) | Rounded to mod, tapering 3-5 locular, 4 column smooth to mod pitted | Tapering longer than broad 3-4 but usually 3 locule, deeply pitted and glanded often rough | Mod. rounded to tapering, 3 to 4 loculi (3 common), smooth to deeply pitted, rough | Rounded, smaller 3, loculi smooth to mid pitted |
| Seeds | 5-11 Large size seeds/loculus, mod, large, Fuzzy to rarely naked | 5-8 long size seeds/loculus, tuft of frizz on seeds, seeds often without coat of fizz. very long fibre | 6-17, medium seeds/locules rarely naked, Fuzzy. | 8-11 medium size seeds/locules Fuzzy |
| Fibres | Moderate to long fibre | Very long fibre | Short to medium fibre | Short to medium fibres |
| Ginning out turn | More | Less | More | Less |

***Primary gene pool*** **:** The primary pool of cotton germplasm consists of all natural *Gossypium* allotetraploids (2AD) which cross with *G. hirsutum* lines resulting in direct genetic recombination between the parental genomes. Production of sexual hybrids requires no special technique in this pool other than synchronized flowering.

***Secondary gene pool*** **:** The secondary pool consists of mainly A and D diploid genomes because of their affinity towards corresponding A and D of tetraploid. It also comprise species of B and F genomes because of their affinity to A genome. Here production of fertile hybrids, between *G. hirsutum* and secondary pool require some degree of manipulation and some times special techniques. However, recombination potential of secondary pool is high in the hybrids with tetraploid gene pool.

***Tertiary gene pool*** **:** The tertiary germplasm pools comprise of all *Gossypium* species indigenous to Australia and a few from Africa belonging to C,G,K and E genomes that have reduced homology to the chromosomes of cultivated tetraploid cotton. The gene pools may or may not hybridize easily with tetraploid cotton and produce very low level of genetic recombination.

***Genetic studies of qulitative characters*** **:** Endrizzi *et al.* (1984, 1985) and Percival and Kohel (1991) have reviewed genetics of different qualitative traits in a comprehensive way. Kohel (1973) has addressed the description of genetic mutants based on the rules of the International Committee on Genetic Symbols and Nomenclature.

## 8. BREEDING OBJECTIVES

Breeding objectives are formulated by taking into consideration the species in which improvement is sought. However, in India all four species have equal importance in judging their genetic improvement programmes. By and large breeding objectives in India vary according to the cotton growing zones generally and different regions specifically. Nevertheless, increased productivity and fibre quality along with resistance to biotic and abiotic stresses assumes general importance in most situations. Genetic modification of seed oil content and gossypol free oil are also important.

## 9. BREEDING

Cotton is predominantly a self pollinated crop though varying degrees of cross pollination have been reported. In USA 30-50 per cent cross pollination has been reported and some workers (Richmond, 1950, 1951; Simpson, 1948) have reported as high as 81 per cent (California) and 50 per cent (Tennessee) cross pollination. In India, natural out crossing has been observed only upto 2 per cent. Hence, breeding methods employed for cotton involve procedures of both self and cross pollinated crops.

**Breeding and selection approaches utilized in cotton can be classified into the following**

**A. *General Selection Procedure***

1. Introductions
2. Mass selection
3 Pure line selection
4. Pedigree method
5. Texas method of bulked progeny selection
6. Type selection
7. Line test
8. Sudan technique
9. Honey comb method of selection

**B. *Methods to Exploit Heterosis or Recombination***

1. Breeding of cotton hybrid
2. Synthetics
3. Multilines

**C. *Population Improvement Approaches***

1. Disruptive mating
2. Biparental mating
3. Recurrent selection

**D. *Breeding Methods for Specific Purpose***

1. Back cross method
2. Mutation breeding
3. Utilization of wild species

**E. *Complex but Special Efforts***

1. Multi Adversity Resistance (MAR)
2. Multi Environment Stress Resistance (MESR)

Among the above methods of breeding, heterosis has been explained in detail and other methods are treated on their merit and extent of utilization.

## A. General Selection Procedures

**1. *Plant introduction* :** Introductions produced dramatic impact on cotton scenario of India. Sea Island Andrews, a variety of Egyptian cotton introduced from West Indies, was directly released for commercial cultivation in Tamil Nadu. *G. hirsutum* germplasm introduced from American continent has changed species composition of cultivated cottons in India. Introduction of American Nectariless has lead to the development of first commercial *intrahirsutum* hybrid and the introduction of Russian *barbadense* SB289E, resulted in production of interspecific hybrid. Most of the introductions were used as sources for many characters for cotton improvement rather than direct release of varieties.

**2. *Mass selection* :** Mass selection is usually practiced in indigenous or introduced genetic material in the initial phase of any breeding programme. It is also exercised in derived composite population for isolation of superior genotypes. Bikaneri Narma was the variety isolated from a nondescript G. *hirsutum* cotton. F414, H777 are reselections from Bikaneri Narma. The male parent of Savitha hybrid, M12, is a mass selection from LRA 5166. Narmada is another example of mass selection from Buri type. Some G. *arboreum* cultivars isolated by mass selection are G22, HD11, LD 133 and Saraswati.

**3. *Pure line selection*** : Pure line selection in cotton begins with individual plant selections and culminates into a uniform variety. This selection procedure has been widely used for genetic improvement of cotton. Several varieties in India namely MCU 5VT, $CO_2$ Kanchana (LPS-1) in *G. hirsutum,* a few Gourani varieties and Lohit in *G. arboreum* and Sujatha in *G. barbadense* are pure lines.

**4. *Pedigree method*** : In cotton, majority of the varieties were developed by this method of breeding. Segregating populations of single, double, three way, and multiple crosses have been handled in isolating varieties. Some notable varieties developed from pedigree method of breeding are as follows.

| | ***Varieties*** | ***Pedigree*** |
|---|---|---|
| **I.** | ***G. hirsutum*** | |
| | Laxmi | Gadag 1 × $Co_2$ |
| | LRA 5166 | Laxmi (Reba B 50 × Acala 122) |
| | Khandwa-3 | (68 Kh-33 x 1146A) × (56-34) × Acala44-2). |
| **II.** | ***G. arboreum*** | |
| | AKA 5 | H 253 × C 573 |
| | Eknath | AK235 × Sel.218 |
| | Rohini | (CJ 73 × C 875) × C J 73 |
| | Sanjay | C-520 × Jailla |
| **III.** | ***G. herbnceum*** | |
| | Digvijaya | Vijaya × (1027 ALF × Vijaya) |
| | V-797 | Kahyan × Vijaya |
| | G. cot 13 | 1802 × Kahyan |
| | Jaydhar | KFT-12-3-X l-A-14-3. |

**5. *Texas method of bulked progeny test system and single seed descent (SSD) method*** : The Bulk method or SSD have been rarely used in cotton breeding but principles of bulk method were utilized by Texas method of bulked progeny test system (Richmond, 1951). This breeding programme emphasises on conservation and maintenance of genetic variability in progeny tests extending over number of years. During segregating generation, progeny rows are grown in randomized block design with checks. Superior progenies are selected and random bolls harvested to advance the generations. $F_4$ onwards, they are grown in plots in RBD along with appropriate commercial checks and measurements on plot basis are made. Random bolls from superior progeny plots are harvested and seeds are used for next cycle of selection. By $F_6$ to $F_8$, the selected progeny will be really superior for yield and other traits. The random bolls sampled out, represent the family. Most of the plants of a family will have attained homozygocity and only a few of them may be heterozygotes. Reselection within the family may be practised for attaining uniformity; othewise family bulks can be straight way used as varieties.

**6. *Type selection*** : Cook (1932) advocated the need for maintaining varieties of uniform type especially for processing purposes. Uniformity can be obtained by a combination of progeny and type selection rather than selection for a specific set of varietal characteristics based on single homozygous plant. This practice serves to provide uniformity in fibre length, quality etc., and at the same time allows sufficient genotypic diversity for adaptability.

**7. *Line test*** : Trought and King (1934) described the method of testing small family bulk in which material is planted in two rows of 100 m length along with 100 m length of control variety on either side. Individual plants in family rows are compared with corresponding individual plants of control row that correspond exactly in position and spacing.

**8. *Sudan technique*** : This technique developed by Knight and Rose (1954) has been devised to combine the advantages of selfing and maintaining plasticity and potentiality for further advancement. Large number of individual plants are selected and grown in progeny rows and selfed to avoid contamination and also to 'lockup' some genes through attainment of homozygosity. Selfed seeds are retained. Superior progenies, based on statistical tests, are selected and allowed to outcross (panmixes) in areas where natural out crossing is present. This unlocks gene complexes. Bulked seeds of panmictic plot are then grown for one more year for releasing variability. The cycle is repeated. The chances of obtaining desirable character combination depends on the extent to which linkage blocks are broken and genetic recombination occurs.

**9. *Honeycomb method of selection*** : This selection design allocates entries to comparable growing conditions for effectively sampling environmental variation (Fasoulas, 1973). The name of the breeding method is derived from hexagonal arrangement of plots in the field.

Batzois *et al.* (1998) compared efficiency of honeycomb selection with pedigree selection and single seed descent methods in the cross Peed Dee × (71414 × 7146) in two locations. The superiority of honeycomb selection derived progenies for seed cotton yield, fibre length and boll weight was evident when compared to other two methods after 5 years of selection cycle at both the locations. The lines originating from pedigree selection and single seed descent method were comparable to each other. This procedure was used to build up resistance to *Verticillium* wilt in cotton.

## B. Methods to Exploit Heterosis and/or Recombination

**1. *Breeding cotton hybrids*:** The basic principles, genetic basis, mechanisms and other details are described later under the heading of "heterosis breeding".

**2. *Synthetic varieties*:** Synthetic varieties offer an opportunity to utilize a degree of heterosis in cross pollinated or often cross pollinated crop plants. Douglas and Weaver (1963) suggested that the components of synthetic varieties should have large general combining ability. Kohel and Richmond (1969), compared synthetic varieties produced under high (42%) and low (12%) levels of natural crossing. In each location, a few selected flowers were selfed and others were left for open pollination. In the first year, selfed and open pollinated seeds were harvested on individual plant basis. For subsequent generations seeds were taken from plants which had both selfed and open pollinated bolls to avoid possible divergence between the two. Population was grown to develop synthetics by harvesting in bulk and taking random sample of seeds. The assumption was that the heterosis present in the population would help in increasing genetic plasticity and seed cotton yield. Varieties produced at high level of natural out crossing areas were superior to those produced at lower level of natural crossing.

**3. *Multilines* :** Mechanical mixtures of cotton seeds from two or more selected lines are made to constitute a population intended for wide spread distribution.

Walker (1963), experimented on a multiline BP 52 in Uganda. When component lines of BP 52 were crossed in diallel fashion, substantial amount of heterozygosity was detected which conferred advantages because of heterosis and homeostasis. Significant interaction component was found among the components of BP 52 but the size of interaction was too small to explain the difference between the yield levels of multilines and weighted mean of its components. After successive growing for a few generations, the differences became more pronounced and multiline yield exceeded the yield of maximum yielding component. High degree of natural crossing is necessary for multilines to function properly.

Mechanical mixtures of different lines of cotton were also released for commercial cultivation in Tanzania during 1946-1958. Such mixtures were termed as multiline issues (Peat and Brown, 1961).

## C. *Population Improvement Approaches*

Population improvement approaches are aimed at increasing the frequency of desirable alleles. In cotton, procedures like recurrent selections, disruptive selection and biparental mating systems have been used to a limited extent.

1. ***Recurrent selection*** : Table 11 summarises reports where recurrent selection was practiced to improve particular characters.

**Table 11:** Traits improved through recurrent selection

| *Traits* | *Reference(s)* |
|---|---|
| Fibre strength | Massey, 1961; Shephered, 1965 |
| Lint percentage | Miller and Rawlings, 1967; Meredith and Bridge, 1973 |
| Earliness | Miller and Rawlings, 1967 |
| Seed per locule | Miller and Rawlings, 1967 |
| Seed cotton yield | Miller and Rawlings, 1967 |

2. ***Disruptive selection*** : Selection of the two extreme types of a character in segregating generation followed by intermating is called disruptive selection. Narayanan *et al.* (1987a, 1987b, 1988a, 1988b) practiced three cycles of disruptive selection to release vast genetic variability and for getting transgressive segregants for characters like boll weight, boll number, ginning percentage, halo length etc.,

3. ***Biparental mating*** : Singh *et al.* (1989) crossed randomly selected plants in $F_2$ and found it to be effective in breaking negative association of boll number and boll weight.

## D. Breeding Methods for Specific Purposes

These are methods used in cotton for transferring specific traits like male sterility, restorer genes, disease resistance, morphological characters, getting new phenotypes through mutations, getting introgression of selected traits from wild species and genetic transformation.

1. ***Back cross method*** : In cotton, this method is very effective for transfer of resistance, male sterility, interspecific gene transfer and development of multiline varieties. V797, Digvijaya and Vijalapa have been improved by backcross method. Some specific characters transferred through back cross method are given in Table 12.

**Table 12:** Traits transferred through back cross in cotton

| *Characters* | *Reference(s)* |
|---|---|
| Fregobract | Jones and Andries (1969) |
| Nectariless | Meyer and Meyer (1961) |
| Okra leaf | Andries *et al.* (1969) |
| Storm proof | Niles and Richmond (1962) |
| Male sterility | Meyer (1975) |

## Mutation breeding

Induced and spontaneous mutations have played significant role in the genetic improvement of cotton. Singh *et al.* (1994) have reviewed the role of induced mutations in cotton improvement. Besides development of breeding material, mutations could also provide some varieties and parental lines of cotton. The results of some trait modification by induced mutations are given in Table 13.

**Table 13:** Induced mutation studies conducted by different scientist using various mutagens to improve some characters in *Gosspium*.

| *Character* | *Mutagen* |
|---|---|
| 1. ***Earliness*** | |
| (a) *G. hirsutum* | Gamma irradiation Gamma rays, Ethyl methane sulphonate (EMS) X'rays |
| (b) *G. barbadense* | Sodium Azide Gamma irradiation and Dimethyl sulphonate (DMS). |
| (c) *G. arboreum* | Diethyl sulphonate (DES) |
| 2. ***Dwarfness and compactness*** | |
| *G. hirsutum* | Thermal neutrons and gamma irradiation |
| | Gamma irradiation of MCU 5 |
| | Ethylene Imine injection into base of ovary |
| | Gamma irradiation of Stoneville |
| | Gamma+EMS |
| 3. ***Boll weight improvement*** | |
| (a) *G. hirsutum* | Gamma irradiation |
| | Seed treatment with radioactive phosphorous |
| | Spontaneous mutant |
| | Gamma+EMS |
| (b) *G. barbadense* | Gamma irradiation and DMS |
| 4. ***Improvement of Ginning out turn and fibre length*** | |
| (a) *G. hirsutum* | Gamma irradiation |
| | Gamma+EMS |
| | X ray irradiation |
| (b) *G. barbadense* | Gamma irradiation |
| | Ethyl methane sulphonate |
| 5. ***Improvement in seed cotton yield*** | |
| (a) *G. hirsutum* | Gamma irradiation |
| | Radioactive phosphorous |
| | X ray irradiation |
| | Gamma+EMS |
| | Unknown source in tree cotton |
| (b) *G. barbadense* | Ethyl methane sulphonate |
| 6. ***Improvement of seed oil content*** | |
| *G. hirsutum* | Ethylene imine injection into floral buds |
| | X'ray irradiation |
| 7. ***Induction of sterility*** | |
| *G. hirsutum* | Gamma irradiation of pollen |
| | Gamma irradiation |
| | Gamma+EMS |
| | X'ray irradiated pollen |
| 8. ***Glandless character*** | |
| (a) *G. hirsutum* | X'ray irradiation |
| (b) *G. barbadense* | Ethyl methane sulphonate |

Apart from these traits, improvement in fibre properties was also noticed by many workers (Raafat, 1998; Badigannavar, 1999). Out of 16 improved varieties developed all over the world, six have been released for commercial cultivation in India. These varieties are Indore-2, MCU 7, Rashmi, DB 3-12 (spontaneous mutant), MCU 10 and $DS_1$ One mutant, namely SB(YF)425, has served as a parent of thé interspecific hybrid DCH-32.

## 2. Utilization of wild species in cotton improvement

More than 50 species of *Gossypium* have many special characters which have been transferred to either tetraploid or diploid cultigens (Table 14).

**Table 14:** Traits transferred through distant hybridization in cotton

| *Character* | *Trait transformed from* | *Transferred to* |
|---|---|---|
| Jassid resistance and nectariless | G. *tomentosum* | *G.hirsutum* and *G. barbadense* |
| Smoothness for boll weevil resistance, Canducous bract | *G. armorianum* | *G. hirsutum* |
| Rust resistance | *G. raimondii* | *G. hirsutum* |
| Bacterial blight resistance | *G. anomalum* | *G. hirsutum* |
| Black arm resistance, High ginning Out-Turn, Drought resistance | *G. arboreum* | *G. hirsutum* *G. barbadense* |
| Fibre length; Fibre strength | *G. thurberi* | *G. hirsutum* |
| Cytoplasmic male sterility and | *G. harknesii* | *G. hirsutum* |
| Restoration of fertility factors | *G. aridum* | *G. trilobum* |
| Fibre length | *G. barbadense* | *G. hirsutum* |
| Genetic male sterility | *G. anomalum* | *G. arboreum* |
| Fibre length; fibre fineness | *G. hirsutum* | *G. arboreum* |

Stewart (1995) has discussed the details of different introgression schemes based on the ease with which genes could be transferred from the donor source to the crop species.

The extent of success in production of a hybrid between two *taxa* is species specific. Hybridization among tetraploid species has no genetic barriers. Similarly, species such as *G. harknessii* and those from the Kimberly region of Australia, hybridize readily when *G. hirsutum* is used as the maternal parent. A few diploid species, namely *G. davidsonii, G. klotzschianum, G. gossypioides,* carry complementary lethal genes that cause necrosis of hybrid embryos or seedlings. Further, species such as *G. thurberi, G. bichii* and 'A' genome species are very difficult to hybridize with tetraploid cottons because of endosperm abortions. In such cases ovule culture (Stewart and Hsu, 1977, 1978; Gill and Bajaj, 1987; Altman, 1988) allowed those hybrids to be obtained that were rare or unattained by traditional crossing (*e.g.*, *G. bickii*) or allowed difficult hybrids to be obtained in quantity ('A' genome species). Colchicine is used in most cases as mitosis inhibitor and for chromosome doubling. Level of manipulation required to obtain fertile hybrids between A,D,B and F genomes and the former species varies (Stewart, 1995).

Interspecific hybridization has been utilized in India also to generate diverse genetic stocks for commercial hybrids (Table 15).

**Table 15:** Cotton varieties and hybrids developed through interspecific hybridization

| ***Species involved*** | ***Varieties/hybrids relased*** | ***Character imported*** |
|---|---|---|
| | ***A. Varieties*** | |
| *G. hirsutum* × *G. totnentosum* | Badnawar 1<br>Khandwa 1<br>Khandwa 2 | Hairyness, Jassid resistance |
| *G. hirsutum* × *G. arboreum* | Deviraj (170 Co2)<br>Gujarat 67. | Drought tolerance |
| *G. hirsutum* × G. *herbaceum* | Devitej (130 Co2M) | Drought tolerance |
| G. *hirsutum* × G. *barbadense* | MCU 2, MCU 5 | Fibre length and fibre fineness |
| G. *hirsutum* × *G. anomalum* | PKV 081 | — |
| *G. hirsutum* × *(G. thurberi* × G. *anomalum)* | Rajat | — |
| *G. arboreum* × *G. anomalum* | AKA 8401 | Fibre length |
| *G. hirsutum* × *G. anomalum* | Arogya | Bacterial blight resistance |
| | ***B. Hybrids*** | |
| *G. hirsutum* × *G. barbadense* | Varalaxmi<br>DCH-32<br>DHB 105, TCHB 213<br>HB 224 | Fibre length,<br>Fibre fineness and<br>Fibre strength |
| *G. herbaceum* × *G. arboreum* | DDH 2,<br>DH7, DH 9 | High yields, Drought tolerance |

Cotton breeding efforts in India have catered to the needs of location specific culivars. For this reason, India has about 45 cultivars in cultivation. Cultivar development and seed problems in India have been critically analyzed indicating essentiality of SWOT analysis (Strength, Weaknesses, Opportunities and Threats) of each cotton breeding programme in terms of genetic stocks, germplasm enhancement procedures adopted and prioritization of objectives. The necessity of maintenance breeding has been emphasized to prevent the genetic mix-up of the released varieties. The list of popular varieties and hybrids released and their properties have been provided in Table 16.

**Table 16:** Major popular stable varieties and hybrids of cotton in India

| *Stable variety or hybrid* | *Seed-cotton yield (tonnes/ha)* | *GP (%)* | *MFL (mm)* | *Spinning (HSC)* | *State or zone* |
|---|---|---|---|---|---|
| | | | ***Varieties*** | | |
| *G. hirsutum* | | | | | |
| F414 | 2.0 | 34.2 | 22.5 | 30s | Punjab |
| H777 | 2.8 | 34.6 | 22.5 | 30s | Haryana |
| GN Ageti | 2.5 | 36.0 | 23.5 | 30s | Rajasthan |
| LH 900 | 3.5 | 33.9 | 22.5 | 30s | Punjab |
| F 505 | 3.0 | 34.6 | 22.5 | 30s | Punjab |
| LH 886 | 3.8 | 35.5 | 23.0 | 35s | Punjab |
| HS 45 | 3.0 | 34.0 | 22.0 | 30s | Haryana |
| LH 1134 | 4.2 | 35.5 | 25.0 | 40s | Punjab |
| RST 9 | 2.6 | 36.0 | 22.5 | 30s | Rajasthan |
| DHY 286 7 | | | | | |
| B 1007 | 1.4 | 36.0 | 28.0 | 50s | Maharashtra |
| G. cot 12 | 1.8 | 6.0 | 24.0 | 24s | Gujarat |
| Khandwa 2/3 | 0.9 | 35.0 | 23.0 | 30s | Madhya Pradesh |
| AHH 081 | 2.0 | 36.0 | 24.0 | 34s | Maharashtra |
| LRA 5166 | 3.0/1.5 | 35.0 | 24.5 | 34s | Southern and Central zone |
| LRK 516 | 3.0 | 36.0 | 25.0 | 36s | Central zone |
| CNH36 | 3.0 | 35.5 | 25.5 | 40s | Maharashtra |
| MCU5/ MCU5VT | 3.0 | 34.0 | 29.5 | 50/60s | South zone |
| MCU 7 | 1.4 | 35.0 | 23.5 | 34s | Tamil Nadu (rainfed) |
| LK 861V L389 | 2.5 | 36.0 | 27.0 | 50s | Andhra Pradesh |
| Jhuard | 2.5 | 34.0 | 25.0 | 34s/40s | Punjab, Haryana |
| Abadita | 2.5 | 3.8 | 26 | 40s | South zone |
| Sahana | 2.5 | 39 | 27 | 40s | South zone |
| G. *barbadense* | | | | | |
| Suvin | 2.0 | 29.0 | 36.0 | 120s | Tamil Nadu, Andhra Pradesh |
| ***Desi cotton*** | | | | | |
| RG 8 | 2.5 | 40 | 16.5 | 10s | Rajasthan |
| LD 327 | 3.5 | 42 | 16.0 | 10s | Punjab |
| DS 5 | 2.5 | 40 | 16.0 | 40s | Haryana |
| AKA 8401 | 1.0 | 38 | 27.0 | 20s | Maharshtra |
| AKH 47 AKA5 | 0.7 | 39 | 23.0 | 20s | Maharshtra |
| G.cot 15 | 1.0 | 34 | 22.0 | 24s | Maharashtra |
| G.cot 11/G.cot 13 | 1.0 | 39 | 23.0 | 30s | Gujarat (Wagad) |
| DB 3-12 | 0.8 | 34 | 29.5 | 24s | Karnataka |
| K 10 | 0.7 | 36 | 27.0 | 26/30s | Tamil Nadu |
| Jayadhar | 1.0 | 33 | 21.0 | 20s | Karnataka |

**Table 16:** *Contd...*

**Table 16:** *Contd...*

| ***Stable variety or hybrid*** | ***Seed-cotton yield (tonnes/ha)*** | ***GP (%)*** | ***MFL (mm)*** | ***Spinning (HSC)*** | ***State or zone*** |
|---|---|---|---|---|---|
| | | | ***Hyrbrids*** | | |
| ***Intrahirsutum*** | | | | | |
| Hybrid 4 (H4) | 2.5 | 34 | 29 | 40/50s | Gujarat, Mahra-shtra, Andhra Pradesh |
| JKHY 1 | 2.3 | 33 | 27 | 40s | Madhya Pradesh, Maharashtra |
| H6 | 2.8 | 35 | 29 | 60s | Gujarat, Maharashtra, Andhra Pradesh |
| AHH 468 ('PKV Hy2') (also CAHH 468) | 1.2 | 35 | 25 | 40s | Maharashtra |
| MECH1 | 2.5 | 38 | 30 | 60s | Maharashra, Andhra Pradesh, Madhya Pradesh. |
| DHH 11 | 3.5 | 39 | 27 | 50s | Karnataka |
| NHH 44 | 2.4 | 35 | 25 | 30 /40s | Maharashtra |
| Savitha | 2.5 | 34 | 30 | 60s | Tamil Nadu, Andhra Pradesh, |
| H8 | 3.0 | 34 | 26 | 50/60s | Gujarat |
| CICR HH1 | 1.5(R) | 35 | 25.5 | 30/40S | Maharashtra |
| TM 1312 | 2.5 | 38 | 30 | 50/60s | Tamil Nadu, Andhra Pradesh, Karnataka |
| Fateh | 2.8 | 34 | 26 | 30s | Punjab |
| IIIIII 81 | 2.8 | 31 | 25 | 30 /40s | Haryana |
| Raj HH 16 | 2.6 | 34 | 25 | 30/40s | Rajasthan |
| MDCH 201 | 2.0 | 38 | 25 | 30s | Central zone |
| ***Interspecific*** | | | | | |
| DCH 32 | 3.0 | 34 | 33 | 80s | Andhra Pradesh, Tamil Nadu, Gujarat |
| DHB 105 | 3.3 | 34 | 32 | 80s | Maharashtra, Madhya Pradesh |
| TCHB 213 | 2.5 | 34 | 32 | 80s | Tamil Nadu, Andhra Pradesh |
| HB 224 | 2.5 | 33 | 31 | 80s | Tamil Nadu, Andhra Pradesh, Karnataka |
| ***Desi hybrids*** | | | | | |
| G.cot DH 7 | 1.0 | 37 | 22 | 20s | Central zone |
| G.cot DH 9 | 1.2 | 34 | 28 | 40/50s | Central zone |
| DDH2 | 1.0 | 34 | 22 | 20s | Andhra Pradesh, Karnataka, Tamil Nadu |

## E. Complex But Special Efforts

High level of resistance to insects, plant pathogens and abiotic stresses are important for stabilized production. To achieve this, two approaches were almost simultaneously started during 1970s in USA and India:

1. Multi Adversity Resistance Genetic improvement (MAR) (Bird 1982).
2. Multi Environment Stress Resistance (MESR).

Both required development of gene pools through composite crossing and achieving progressive improvement in the targeted characters. These gene pools were exposed to many biotic and abiotic stresses and careful selections were made for relevant morphological, physiological and biochemical characters for maintaining a strong agronomic base in the populations. At present Tormcot varieties produced from MAR system and CPD and JK series of lines from MESR system are cultivated in large areas. Still these gene pools are source of variability for many characters.

### *Heterosis breeding in cotton*

The success of heterosis breeding in maize provided an impetus to work on different species combinations of cotton for evaluating $F_1$ superiority over better parent (Heterobeltiosis) and commercial check variety (standard heterosis). Following combinations have been found to produce successful hybrids in cotton.

| *Cross* | *Common name* |
|---|---|
| G. *hirsutum* × *G. hirsutum* | Intrahirsutum hybrids |
| G. *hirsutum* × G. *barbadense* | Interspecific HB hybrids |
| *G. herbaceum* × G. *arboreum* | Interspecific Asiatic hybrids |
| G. *arboreum* × G. *herbaceum* | Interspecific Asiatic hybrids |
| *G. arboreum* × G. *arboreum* | Intra arboreum hybrids |

The hybrid vigour or heterosis in cotton has been critically reviewed by Davis (1978); Singh *et al.* (1980); Bhale (1987); Narayanan *et al.* (1989); Joshi (1997), and ICAC (1997). India has the distinction of spreading hybrid technology to 40 per cent of its cotton area which is mainly concentrated in South and Central India.

### *General features of hybrid vigour in cotton*

1. Heterosis is observed for many characters in different combinations of *Gossypium* (Table 17).
2. $F_1$ hybrids produce exceptionally high and uniform quality of fibre.

3. The parental lines G67, Laxmi, SB289E, Khandwa *2,* G.cot 10, AK 32, Bikaner Narma, LRA-5166 etc, have contributed to the production of high heterotic sustainable hybrids.
4. Very high range of fibre category requirements has been met by hybrids.
5. The degree of inbreeding depression is low and implies the potential of exploitation of $F_2$ heterosis also.
6. The extent of heterosis observed in interspecific hybrid was 10 to 138 per cent and in intrahirsutum hybrid 7 to 50 per cent. In both cases, under highly favourable environments, 80 per cent to 187 per cent heterosis has been observed in India.

**Table 17:** Heterosis structure over better parent in different classes of hybrids

| ***Characters*** | ***Tetraploid*** | | ***Diploid*** | |
|---|---|---|---|---|
| | ***Intrahirs-utum*** | ***Interspe-cific*** | ***Intrahir -sutum*** | ***Interspecific (G. arboreum x G. herbaceum) or reciprocal crosses*** |
| 1. Plant height | + | + | + | + |
| 2. Number of monopodia per plant* | + | + | + | + |
| 3. Number of sympodia per plant | + | + | + | + |
| 4. Days to 50% flowering | +/– | +/– | +/– | +/– |
| 5. No. of bolls/plant | + | + | + | + |
| 6. Boll weight* | +/– | – | + | + |
| 7. Seed index* | +/– | + | +/– | +/– |
| 8. Lint index | + | +/– | + | + |
| 9. Ginning out turn | +/– | – | + | +/– |
| 10. Seed cotton yield | + | + | + | + |
| 11. Lint yield | + | + | + | + |
| 12. Fibre length* | + | + | + | + |
| 13. Strength* | + | + | + | + |
| 14. Micronaire | +/– | – | – | – |
| 15. Uniformity ratio* | +/– | +/– | +/– | +/– |
| 16. Short fibre index | NA | + | – | – |

* Comparatively low level of heterosis observed.

Though, Mell (1894) and Balls (1908) reported heterosis in tetraploid cotton and Kulkarni and Khadilkar (1929) in diploid cotton, it was Patel (1971) who demonstrated heterosis at commercial level. The first hybrid cotton H4 (Shankar 4) developed by him was an intra-hirsutum (G-67 x American Nectariless). In the same year Katarki (1971) showed heterosis in interspecific tetraploid hybrid, through the release of Varalaxmi (Laxmi × SB 289E). The two events transformed the entire cotton scenario of India. C.T. Patel is called Father of Hybrid Cotton Technology.

## Hybrid seed production techniques in cotton

Methods of production of hybrid cotton seed can be classified as per the following scheme.

| *Emasculation* | *Pollination* |
|---|---|
| A. Hand emasculation | A. Hand pollination |
| B. Use of male sterility | B. Bee pollination. |
| (i) Genetic male sterility | (i) Employ bees, through reared colonies. |
| (ii) Cytoplasmic genetic male sterility | (ii) Pollination through natural populations of wild bees. (Limited scope because during cotton season there is abundance of other and more alternative sources of pollen). |
| C. Use of chemical induced male sterility. | |

The exploitation of heterosis in cotton depends on two factors:

1. Careful identification of good combiners
2. Success of hybrid seed production.

### 1. Identification of Good Combiners

Good general combining ability is mandatory for parents, while specific combining ability is the final measure in choice of parents. Apart from this, the female parent should have good boll weight, good seed index, more seeds per boll, ease of emasculation and availability of genetic marker for easy grow out test.

### 2. Hybrid Seed Production

***Hand emasculation and pollination*** **:** Doak's method (Doak, 1934) of hand emasculation and pollination is still being used with modifications in conventional hybrid seed production in India. Patel (1955), Srinivasan and Gururajan (1983), Mehta and Patel (1983), Mehta *et al.* (1983), and Rao (1993), have reviewed the literature and suggested modifications to basic Doak's method. Flower buds, that are likely to open the next day are emasculated during afternoon or evening hours by removing anther column. The emasculated flowers are tagged with red tissue paper bag or twine thread for identification of the bud for pollination the next day and to identify crossed boll at the time of harvest, respectively. The stigma is receptive between 8-12 AM. Pollen from one male flower is used to pollinate 4-5 emasculated female flowers. To maintain high genetic purity, uncrossed flowers are removed every day and uncrossed bolls (if any) are removed at the time of harvest. Similarly, male plants are removed after crossing period is over. Mehta and Patel (1983) have worked out equipment and materials required for 0.4 ha of seed production plot. During peak flowering period 25-30 persons are required for effective crossing operation.

### *Use of male sterility*

Hand emasculation and pollination is laborious and results in high cost of hybrid seed. Use of male sterility can make hybrid seed much cheaper. The sources of male sterility and its deployment has been discussed by many workers. Studying male sterility in tetraploids (*G. hirsutum*) and diploids (*G. arboreum)* for commercial hybrid production is a better approach.

### 1. Male Sterility in Tetraploid

***Genetic male sterility (GMS)*** **:** A total of 11 loci have been identified that condition GMS and 10 of them are in *G. hirsutum* and one in *G. barbadense.* Four genes, namely $Ms_4$, $Ms_7$, $Ms_{10}$ and $Ms_n$, are dominant and produce complete sterility while the remaining seven are recessive. Among the recessive genes, $ms_1$ $ms_2$ $ms_3$ cause male sterility when present singly while $ms_5$, / $ms_6$, $ms_8$, and $ms_9$ behave as duplicate recessive genes. GMS system involving $ms_5ms_5$ $ms_6ms_6$, found in Greg MS, is the only stable source, utilized in India, Pakistan and USA. All *G. hirsutum* genotypes which carry *Ms.* or $Ms_6$, (or both genes) are restorers. Any *G. hirsutum* line can be converted into GMS system by repeated back crossing with alternate selfing and selection. Maintenance of GMS lines involves sibmating between male sterile plants ($ms_5ms_5$, $ms_6ms_6$) and heterozygous male fertile plants ($ms_5ms_5$ $Ms_6ms_6$ or $ms_5Ms_5ms_6$ $ms_6$). The seed production plots of GMS female contains 50 per cent fertile plants which need to be rougued out during flowering but before pollination. For this reason GMS was considered non profitable mechanism for hybrid seed production.

***Cytoplasmic genetic male sterility*** **:** Interaction between nucleus of *G. hirsutum* and cytoplasm of *G. arboreum, G. anomalum, G. harknessii, G. longicalyx, G. aridum, G. trilobum* produces male sterility (Meyer, 1973, 1975; Meshram *et al.,* 1992). However, *G. harknessii* ($D_2$, CMS), *G. trilobum* ($D_8$ CMS) and *G. aridum* ($D_4$ CMS) are sources of cytoplasms which induce stable male sterility for practical hybrid seed production. Most of the *G. hirsutum* lines are maintainers (B lines) for these CMS lines (A lines). Any B line can be converted into MS line by repeated backcrossing and selection. Restorer line can also be converted through backcross method by alternate selfing and selection with the background of sterile cytoplasm.

The restoration in $D_2$ CMS involves monogenic dominant action with one enhancer gene (Sheetz and Weaver, 1980). Similarly in $D_8$ CMS, restoration is monogenic dominant. However, preliminary studies in $D_4$, CMS indicate action of one or two dominant genes.

It has been found that with the same set of parents, the performance of hybrids is superior, when $F_1$ seed is produced by emasculation and pollination as compared to seed produced by employing cytoplasmic genetic male sterility system.

## Male Sterility in Diploids

Asiatic hybrids between cultivated diploid species have produced very high level of exploitable heterosis (upto 200%) when crossed through conventional technique. The hybrids DDH 2, G.cot Dh 7 and G.cot DH 9 give high yields but have seed production problems. There are at present two sources of GMS.

**1. *Hissar source* :** The recessive GMS in *G. arboreum* cotton variety, DS 5 (GMS-1) has white small flowers with petal spot. The GMS-1 was isolated as a spontaneous mutation. Semiclosed corolla is drawn back in GMS-1 and it has been over come in GMS-2.

**2. *Akola source* :** The GMS line GAK-423A is developed by transferring the genome of *G. arboreum* (AKH 4) into *G. anomalum* cytoplasm (Meshram and Wadodkar, 1992). This source has yellow, larger flowers than DS 5 GMS and possesses dark petal spot.

Most of *G. herbaceum* and *G. arboreum* lines restore fertility when used as males. Using GMS, hybrid making in diploids has become easy to exploit high levels of heterosis.

High levels of useful heterosis (upto 185%) in GMS based hybrids has been reported by Rajput *et al.* (1998). Superior performance of diploid hybrids over tetraploid by 10 to 102 per cent was observed in the preliminary study conducted by Narayanan *et al.* (1989). Sufficient seed set by using GMS has been obtained and seed production can be made economical. India is the first country to release a GMS based hybrid (AAH-1) in diploids.

## Chemical Induced Male Sterility

Chemicals male sterilizing agents act by prohibiting anther dehiscence. Chemicals FW 450 (Sodium $\alpha$-dichloro-iso-butyrate) and TD 1123 (Chemical constituents not known) have been demostrated to possess male gametocide action. Gametocides must be sprayed at least two weeks before start of flower opening and they remain active for 2-3 weeks. Chemical sterility has two advantages over other sterility mechanisms: no fertile segregants occur and no deleterious effect of diploid cytoplasm is produced on kapas yield. However, their commercial viability has not been established so far.

## Bee Pollination

Cotton pollen need to be transported physically as wind dispersal is impeded because of its weight. Even when male sterility is employed, seed set is a limitation because other, more attractive, options distract bees form acting as pollinators. Studies on honey bee pollination showed less uniform transfer of pollen (Bhale and Bhat, 1989; Vaissiere *et al.*, 1984) resulting in lowering boll setting compared to hand emasculation and pollination.

## Breeding for Insect Resistance

Pest infestation is a major destabilizer of cotton production. The significance of pest control can be guaged by the fact that cotton accounts for 22.5% of all root insecticide sales worldwide because insect fauna inhabitating cotton has been estimated to number over 1326.

Cotton insects are classified into following two groups based on feeding behaviour.

**1. *Sucking pests*:** This group includes Jassids (*Amrasca bigutulla bigutulla*), Whitefly (*Bemicia tabaci*), Aphids (*Aphis gossypii*), Thrips (*Thrips tabaci*), and mites (*Tetranynchus* sp.).

**2. *Tissue feeders*:** This group includes bollworms and weevils including American bollworms *(Helicoverpa armigera* and *H. virescens),* Pink bollworm *(Pectinophora gossypiella),* Spotted bollworms (*Earias vitella* and *E. insulina*), Tobacco cutworm *(Spodoptera litura),* Bollweevil *(Anthonomous grandis), Red* bollworm *(Diparopsis castanea),* Shoot weevil *(Alcidodes affaber).* Among these Jassids, Aphids, Whitefly and Bollworms *(H. armigera* and *P. gossypiella* and *Earias* sp.) are serious pests in India. In general, losses due to sucking pests (5-10%) are much less than from bollworms (25 to 50%). During reproductive period bollworms cause not only reduction in the yield but also affect fibre properties. Sucking pests, active during reproductive period, are vectors of many pathogen and viruses, the best example is whitefly, the vector for Cotton Leaf Curl virus.

## Germplasm Enhancement for Pest Tolerance

There are two approaches for developing pure lines for pest tolerance:

1. Conventional breeding approach
2. Biotechnological approach

**I. *Conventional Breeding Approach*** : Involves manipulation of morphological traits and selection for levels of plant biochemical products that act as feeding deterrent. The concept of conventional breeding programme is based on three mechanisms of resistance :

A. Antixenosis (Non-preference) B. Antibiosis C. Avoidance.

Host plant resistance studies have been reviewed by many workers (Maxwell *et al.,* 1972; Thomson and Lee, 1980; Jenkins, 1989; Smith 1992; Jenkins, 1995; Khadi, 1996).

**(a) *Antixenosis (Non-preference)*:** It is mediated through morphological traits that are unacceptable or undesirable to the insect and inhibit their feeding and reprodution. In this mechanism, morphological and anatomical characters indicate tolerance to various pests (Table 18).

**Table 18:** Reaction of insects toward morphological features of cotton

| *Characters* | *Sucking pests (Jassids)* | *Whiteflies* | *Bollworms* | *Boll weevils* |
|---|---|---|---|---|
| Hairyness | R | S | S | R |
| Glabrous | S | R | T | N |
| Glabrous upper surface hairy lower surface | R | S | T | - |
| Red pigmentation | N | R | T | R |
| Nectariless | N | N | T | N |
| Fregobract | N | N | T | R |
| Thick bollring | N | N | T | R |
| Hardness of the boll | N | N | T | R |
| Okra leaf/small leaf | N | R | T | R |
| Thin lamina | R | R | N | N |
| Thick lamina | S | S | N | N |
| Pedicel length | N | N | T | R |
| Less bractiole teeth | N | N | T | R |
| Gossypol glands | R | R | T | R |

S=Susceptible T=Tolerant R=Resistant N=Neutral and/or not affected

The anatomical characters contributing to resistance are as follows :

1. Dense cortical cells per unit area of petiole, stemtip and midrib, compact mesophyll cells of leaves, thick coating of leaf–Resistance to sucking pests.

2. More collenchyma (mechanical tissue), more compact epidermal cells and less cell interspace – Resistance to sucking pests.
3. More collenchyma and compact cell arrangement with less cell interspace of bollrind – Tolerance to bollworms.
4. Long and compact palisade layer, more distance to the phloem and the presence of adaxial layer of palisade and epidermis in G. *arboreum* – Resistance to sucking pests.

***Antibiosis*** **:** This mechanism involves production of variable quantity of feeding deterrents or allelochemicals by host plants. The allelochemicals act as repellent, insect growth retardent or factor responsible for reduction in insect survivability. Allelochemicals like, Terpenoid Aldehyde (esp. Gossypol), phenols (esp. tannins), proteins, sugars are involved in pest tolerance. Bollworm tolerance is conferred by production of high levels of gossypol and tannin, high levels of proteins and sugars.

### C. *Avoidance or escapism*

This mechanism of insect resistance involves preponement of maturity or earliness so as to escape from insect damage.

In short duration cotton, the period available for insect development is reduced and so are the levels of overwintering populations. Such compact flowering period varieties are found to escape Bollweevil and Pink bollworm damage (Liu *et al.,* 1990; Walhood *et al.,* 1981). Escape from bollworms due to reduced boll period was indicated by Rao *et al.* (1996).

The conventional breeding approach in cotton for resistance to insect pests has yielded a variety of genetic stocks which are either tolerant to boll feeders or resistant to sucking pests. Genetic stocks which act as sources for insect pest tolerance are listed in Table 19.

**Table 19:** Genetic sources for tolérance/résistance to différent insects

| *Insect pests* | *G. hirsutum* | *Wild species* |
|---|---|---|
| Jassids | B 1007, Laxmi, Khandwa-2 SRT-1, Badnavar 1, DR6 (Restorer on CGMS with G. *herknessi* cytoplasm)., BN-1, T13, M12. | *G. anomalum, G. davidsonii, G. armorianum, G. tomentosum, G. lobatum, G. gossypoidis.* |
| Bollworms | Abadhita, Sharada, MCU 7, H777. LH 900, LRK 516, Sahana, CNH 120MB, CPD 423, CPD 428 | *G. somalense*<br>*G. sturtianum, G. australe*<br>*G. bickii*<br>*G. davidsonii,*<br>*G. thurberi, G. tomentosum.* |
| Whitefly | Kanchan, RS 875, LHH 144 | *G. longicalyx, G. armorianum.* |

In general, diploid cultivated species are comparatively more tolerant to many pests as compared to the tetraploid species.

## II. Biotechnological Approach

Recent developments in plant molecular biology permit the introduction and expression of alien genes in cotton to impart resistance against herbicides and some of the major insect pests. The alien gene is called a transgene and the cotton in which such a gene has been introduced and expressed is called as transgenic cotton. Transgenic cotton *(Bt* cotton) in which a gene *(Cry IA)* of *Bacillus thuringiensis* has been introduced and expressed for imparting in-built resistance to bollworm is a good example of the role that biotechnology application can play for improved practical agriculture. The *Bt* gene directs the synthesis of a crystal protein in the plant tissues and the insects that feed on these tissues are killed. In 1999, the global area under transgenic cotton was 3.7 m ha. The traits modified by transgenics and the area under respective transgenics was : insect resistance *(Bt),* 1.3 m ha; herbicide resistance 1.6 m ha; combination of insect resistance and herbicide resistance, 0.8 m ha. In India, transgenic *Bt* cotton is under experimental field testing trials by Mahyco Monsanto joint venture.

The cost saving in managing insect and weed free crops by cultivating transgenics is considerable. Development of transgenics also offers the advantage of environmental protection by reducing the load of residues from protection agro-chemicals like pesticides and weedicides. However, there are serious concerns about biosafety and socio-ethical issues connected with large scale application of genetic engineering technologies and a number of public interest groups are strongly opposed to biotechnology in agriculture in the developing country context. A lot will need to be done to educate the user community and gain their confidence before full benefits of this potentially useful tool are realized.

## Disease Resistance

Most fungal, bacterial and viral diseases in cotton are associated with cold, wet and humid condition. Some of the important diseases are given below :

| ***Seedling disease*** | ***Leaf blight and spots*** | ***Wilts*** | ***Bollrot*** | ***Viral diseases*** |
|---|---|---|---|---|
| *Rhizoctonia* | *Alternaria* | *Verticillium* | Many pathogens have been isolated | Curl viruses (CLCV); leaf roll virus. |
| *Collectotrichum* *Xanthomonas* | *Ramularia* *Cerospora* *Xanthomonas* | | | |

In *Xanthomonas campestris* pv *malvacearum (Xcm)* a total 32 races have been reported (Verma and Singh, 1974) and atleast 22 major genes (B) for resistance have been identified (El-zik and Thaxton, 1995). Majority of these genes are completely or partially dominant for resistance. Though a single B gène confers resistance to a few races of *Xcm* (vertical resistance), vulnerability to other races of pathogen remains. Combination of the B genes with modifiers is important to obtain stable resistance. The combination $B_2$,$B_3$ $Bs_m$ conferred immunity to all races found in USA and resistance has been stable for 22 years. An African strain, S 295 bred through recurrent selection in Chad is known to be resistant to all known races and isolates of *Xcm* including the highly virulent race *HV1* (Girardot *et al.,* 1986; Follin *et al.,* 1988; Wallace and El-zik, 1989). Comprehensive reviews on this disease have been published periodically (Weindling, 1948; Wickens, 1953; Brinkerhoff, 1970; Innes, 1983; Verma, 1986; Hillocks, 1992). Cultivars like Stoneville-20, Albar, MCU 10, RKR 4145 and Supriya are resistant sources for blight.

Vegetative compatibility (V-C.) tests and isozyme analysis of wilt caused by *Verticillium dahliae* have shown that there are four genetically isolated populations (V-C groups) within the species and that each V-C group has at least two sub groups (Straushbaugh *et al.,* 1992). However, the V-C groups and sub groups vary in geographical occurrence, virulance to cotton and other crops, and sensitivity to fungicide (Puhalla and Hummel, 1983; Struasbaugh *et al.,* 1992). Major terpenoid phytoalexins formed in xylem of upland cotton were found to be involved in active defense mechanism and Russian varieties like Tashkent 1, Tashkent 2 and Tashkent 3 are widely used resistance sources in the world against *V. dahliae. Verticillium* wilt is more pronounced in winter cotton area of Tamil Nadu where a resistant cultivar MCU 5VT has been recommended.

*Fusarium* wilt *(Fusarium oxyporium* f.sp. *vasinfectum)* is most prevalent in parts of USA, India, Tanzania and Sudan. Armstrong and Armstrong (1980) have reported six races across cultivars of different cotton species and other crops. In India, all the currently released diploid and most of the tetraploid varieties are resistant to *Fusarium* wilt. Detailed account of resistance sources for different fungal and bacterial diseases available in the germplasm of all four cultivated species in India is given by Sheoraj (1992).

Some wild species reported to be resistant to Bacterial Blight, *Fusarium* and *Verticillium* wilt ar listed in Table 20.

**Table 20:** Resistance sources in wild species of *Gossypium* for fungal and bacterial diseases

| ***Bacterial blight*** | ***Wilts*** | |
|---|---|---|
| | ***Fusarium*** | ***Verticillium*** |
| *G. anamalum* | *G. sturtianum* | *G. thurberi* |
| *G. armourianum* | *G. harknessii* | *G. bickii* |
| *G. davidsonii* | *G. thurberi* | *G. sturtianum* |
| | | *G. raimondii* |
| | | *G. harknessii* |

Among the viral diseases, cotton leaf curl virus (CLCuV) transmitted by adult whitefly *(Bemicia tabaci)* was devastating in North India and Pakistan during the nineties. During 1993, CLCuV disease affected almost the entire 5,54,000 acres cotton area in Pakistan (Rahaman, 1997) but in India the disease incidence was only in patches (Narula *et al.,* 1999). However, during 1997 the entire North Indian, cotton (2,18,610 ha) was found affected by CLCuV (Narula *et al.,* 1999).

Genetics of resistance in the resistant G. *barbadense* strains × 1530 and × 1230 was worked out and indicated monogenic dominant inheritance with modifiers. In India, the short compact *G. hirsutum* variety Rs. 875 was found resistant to CLCuV, and has been recommended for double cropping systems of North India. LHH 144, and intra hirsutum resistant hybrid has been recommended for cultivation in North India. LRA-5166 has also been found to be resistant to CLCuV. In Pakistan, LabAcala (69) 11, C 1743, FH 643, C1M 1100 and CIM 448 have been found resistant to CLCuV. All diploid *(desi)* cottons belonging to *G. herbaceum* and *G. arboreum* are immune to the CLCuV.

Another viral disease, called Blue disease, transmitted by *Aphis gossypii* prevails in Vietnam. When Indian *G. arboreum* and *G. hirsutum* cultures were screened against the disease, *G. arboreums* (GA) were found to be more resistant than *G. hirsutum.* GA, 10 to 13 lines exhibited immunity. Some intra hirsutum hybrids like Bioseed 7 and 2 were resistant to blue disease (Singh and Singh, 1999).

Incidence of root knot nematode *(Meloidogyne incognita)* has been seen in North India. G. *hirsutum* genotypes H 1185, LH 1832 exhibited resistant reaction to the nematode (Singh *et al.,* 1999).

## Fibre quality and its improvement

Quality of cotton refers to suitability of the fibre to produce better quality yarn and fabric. Improved fibre quality traits include length, strength, fineness, maturity and uniformity. Fibre quality norms to be kept in mind while breeding for specific spinning potential have been summarized in Table 21.

Tetraploid cultivated species possess longer and finer fibres. The diploid Asiatic species generally have shorter and coarse fibre. *G. barbadense* cultivars exhibit longest fibres of high fineness and are used to produce very fine fabrics. *G. herbaceum* and *G. arboreums* are used for coarse fabric manufacture. Fibre quality improvement in tetraploid cotton has reached high standard with release of MCU-5 in *G. hirsutum,* Suvin in *G. barbadense* and Varalaxmi, DCH-32, HB-224, DHB 105, TCH 213 as interspecific hybrids. The present day *G. hirsutum* varieties or hybrids have minimum spinning potential of 20s. Increase in length in G. *hirsutum* has also been due to introgression of genes from G. *barbadense.*

**Table 21:** CIRCOT norms for fibre properties in breeding

| *Count* | *2.5% Span length (mm)* | *Mic value* | *Minimum maturity (PM%)* | *Mininmum tenacity (g/t)* | *FQI* | *CSP* |
|---|---|---|---|---|---|---|
| | | | ***Carded yarns*** | | | |
| <10s | <20 | <7.0 | 90 | 16 | >110 | >1790 |
| 10s – 20s | 20 – 22 | 5.0 – 6.0 | 85 | 18 | 150 – 170 | 1860 – 1895 |
| 20s | 22 – 24 | 4.4 – 4.8 | 80 | 19 | 180 – 210 | 1910 – 1965 |
| 30s | 24 – 27 | 3.5 – 4.5 | 80 | 20 | 220 – 260 | 1980 – 2050 |
| 40s | 27 – 28 | 3.6 – 4.0 | 75 | 22 | 270 – 310 | 2070 – 2140 |
| 50s | 28 – 31 | 3.0 – 4.0 | 75 | 23 | 320 – 360 | 2155 – 2225 |
| 60s | 29 – 32 | 3.0 – 4.0 | 70 | 24 | 370 – 420 | 2240 – 2330 |
| 80s | 32 – 35 | 3.0 – 3.5 | 70 | 26 | 480 – 520 | 2435 – 2500 |
| 100s | >35 | 2.8 – 3.2 | 65 | 28 | >550 | >2550 |
| | | | ***Denim yarn*** | | | |
| <20s | 23 – 25 | 4.0 – 4.5 | 75 | 19 | – | – |
| 22s – 30s | 25 – 30 | 3.0 – 3.5 | 80 | 25 | – | – |

FQI = (2.5%SL x Tenacity) √Mic. Value ; Count C = 0.196 FQI–16 & CSP = 1.74 FQI+1600.

The diploid species, especially *G. arboreum,* have also been improved for their fibre traits through introgression of genes from *G. hirsutum* and upto 30 mm length has been achieved with 3.1 to 5.0 micronaire in the resultant lines. Some wild species as a sources of good fibre properties are given in Table 22 (Kairon *et al.,* 1998).

**Table 22:** Sources of quality parameters in the wild species of *Gossypium*

| *Species* | *Character* |
|---|---|
| G. *sturtanum* | Fibre strength, fibre yield |
| *G. australe* | High spinning |
| G. *thurberi* | Fibre strength |
| *G. harknessii* | Lustrous fibre |
| *G. aridum* | Fibre strength |
| *G. raimondii* | Fibre fineness, length and strength |
| *G. stocksii* | Fibre strength and elasticity |
| *G. areysianum* | Fibre strength and elasticity |
| *G. longicalyx* | Fibre fineness and strength |

## Value Addition for Cotton Through High oil Yield

Fibre is the primary product of cotton and oil is considered to be secondary. Cotton has distinct opportunity to become dual purpose crop for both fibre and oil as there is no major negative association reported between oil content, seed size, lint yield and quality. Though cotton seed is an inexpensive and rich source of edible oil and protein, breeding efforts in this direction are limited (Dani, 1990). Williams (1906) was the first to succeed in increasing the oil content in cotton seed from 16 per cent to 23 per cent. Genetic variability for oil content in cotton is considerable (Dani, 1984; Kohel, 1980).

Murthy and Achaya (1975) have reviewed cotton seed chemistry and technology as well as variation in seed oil and other characters in all the four cultivated species (Table 23).

**Table 23:** Summary of composition of cotton seed

| | *Range and mean values of* | | | | | |
|---|---|---|---|---|---|---|
| ***Species*** | ***Oil (%)*** | ***Hull (%)*** | ***Kernel (%)*** | ***Linters (%)*** | ***Protein (%)*** | ***Seed Index (g)*** |
| 1. *G. barbadense* (12)* | 16.6-21.2 (18.3) | 39.2-43.5 (41.3) | 56.5-60.4 (58.7) | 0.7-1.3 (1.0) | 18.9-23.4 (20.9) | 9.5-11.7 (10.4) |
| 2. *G. hirsutum* (245) | 13.2-22.3 (18.2) | 30.8-44.5 (38.0) | 43.5-60.4 (50.8) | 1.6-15.6 (10.0) | 16.9-22.4 (19.5) | 6.9-11.1 (8.3) |
| 3. *G. herbaceum* (144) | 12.6-23.0 (16.3) | 36.3-49.2 (44.40) | 46.0-53.3 (49.8) | 1.3-41.1 (4.5) | (13.2-21.5) (17.4) | 5.4-7.1 (6.0) |
| 4. *G. arboreum* (214) | 13.4-24.4 (17.4) | 42.2-50.9 (46.3) | 41.1-54.8 (49.5) | 1.0-12.4 (5.10) | (14.0-19.4) (16.5) | 4.3-6.9 (6.5) |

* No. of samples analysed.

Tetraploid cotton contains more oil than diploids (Murthy and Appu Rao, 1963). The percentages of kernel, protein, linters has been found to be very high in tetraploids. On the contrary, hul percentage was high in diploid varieties (Murthy and Appu Rao, 1975). Kohel (1980) reported variability of oil content from 15 to 33 per cent in the world representative collection of *G. hirsutum*. Possibilities of even greater genetic variability for oil content have been expressed by Narayanan *et al.* (1988a).

Heterosis for oil content in intrahirsutum hybrids was from 6.74 per cent to 22.47 per cent over commercial check (Dani, 1984); and crosses between genetically diverse parents appear to result in greater heterosis for oil content (Dani, 1990). Mutation breeding has also been found effective in increasing the oil content upto 24.7 per cent in *G. hirsutum.*

Seed and embryo size in cotton are determined predominantly by maternal parent (Von Heerden, 1969). Maternal effects as a source of variation in cotton seed oil were reported by Kohel (1980) and Dani (1992). Glandless genotypes possess marginally higher seed oil content than glanded genotype (Kohel, 1980; Harry and Richard, 1986). Glands on cotton seed which are called pigment glands are the main source of gossypol that imparts colour to the oil. Gossypol is toxic to the nonruminant animals (Murthy and Appu Rao, 1975). However, presence of gossypol glands on plant parts ensures tolerance to pests. The diploid Australian species *G. australe* and *G. sturtianum* having glandless seed (Gossypol free oil) and glanded foliage (pest tolerant) and are the best sources to produce dual purpose genotypes.

## Naturally Coloured Cotton

Some species of cotton produce naturally coloured cotton. The most common colours observed are different shades of brown and green. Varieties with brown and green are presently being cultivated in restricted area of USA (Foxsally, 1987a, 1987b). Different aspects of coloured cotton have been reviewed by Khadi and Kulkarni (1996) and Waghmore and Koranne (1998). Sunlight has profound influence on development of colour in the fibre (Khadi *et al.,* 1996).

Considering its ecofriendly nature, breeding efforts to produce coloured cottons are under way in many Cotton Research Institutes in India. Presently the coloured genotypes in India have inferior yielding ability and poor fibre properties. Sufficient heterosis has been observed in white × colour linted hybrids (Amudha and Raveendran, 1997; Singh *et al.,* 1996). Contamination of white cotton through outcrossing and during ginning are potential threat to thé development of Naturally Coloured Cottons.

## Molecular Marker Techniques Used in Cotton Improvement

A detailed RFLP map of cotton has been developed by Reinisch *et al.* (1994) using interspecific (*G. hirsutum* and *G. barbadense*) $F_2$ population and aneuploid lines. RFLP-QTL maps are also being drawn in cotton (Jiang *et al.,* 1998; Shappely *et al.,* 1998). Mapping of genes related to *Xcm* resistance and trichome density has also been worked out (Wright *et al.,* 1998, 1999). Sequence of restorer gene through the analysis of isogenic lines has also been completed (Lan *et al.,* 1999). These molecular techniques have been used in assessing genomic affinities, phylogeny etc., (Cronn and Wendel, 1998; Zhao *et al.,* 1998).

## Future Strategies

Cotton remains the chief raw material for textile industry. The demand for cotton textile products is increasing every day due to increasing global population. To meet the challenges ahead, viable strategies need to be designed. These can be classified under the following heads.

(a) Net productivity increase
(b) Quality improvement
(c) Resistance to biotic and abiotic stresses
(d) Utilisation of genetic engineering procedures
(e) Others

**(a) *Net productivity increase* :** The productivity increase sought may be in terms of seed cotton yield or lint yield. Manipulation of boll number, boll weight and sympodial branches provide opportunities of increasing productivity. In cotton, source is not a problem but sink is a constraint. Genetic variability for boll retention has to be exploited along with balance between boll number and boll weight. Fibre yield increase can be achieved through increasing ginning out turn. The possibilities of upgrading ginning out turn upto 39 per cent in *G. hirsutum* has been demonstrated by varieties like Sahana in South Zone.

**(b) *Quality improvement* :** Quality in terms of fibre properties and seed cotton oil are gaining importance. Innovations in spinning technology, such as open end spinning, jet spinning etc., require higher levels of fibre strength. Hence, high priority to breeding cotton for increased strength and maturity assumes importance. The potential of improving fibre properties especially length and fineness, of diploid cultivated cotton needs to be exploited.

The presence of gossypol in the oil is a negative attribute in terms of edible quality. The processing cost to remove gossypol from oil can be eliminated if the seeds have no gossypol glands. But gossypol is the main terpenoid aldehyde which imparts resistance against insects. Hence, balanced genotypes have to be produced which have no gossypol glands on seed but the glands are present on foliage. This can be done by either utilising wild diploids species like *G. australe* and *G. sturtianum* or through mutations. Simultaneously, genetic variability for increasing net oil content should be exploited for value addition to the crop.

**(c) *Abiotic stresses* :** Drought stress affects crop in rainfed areas and salinity in irrigated areas. Hence, resistance sources for both environments have to be utilised appropriately. Diploid cultivated cottons, which have stress tolerance capacities, occupy a sizable (27 lakh ha) area under rainfed conditions. Genetic improvement of these diploids (*G. arboreum* and *G. herbaceum*) needs to be given high and urgent priority so that these important genetic resources are not lost. Resistance breeding for salinity is as yet an untouched area.

Under the biotic stresses, insects, like bollworms and diseases like CLCuV need urgent consideration for sustainable cotton production. Resistance to whitefly, which is the vector of CLCuV, provides solution to two problems simultaneously. Search for characters in wild *taxa* is ideal for breeding against biotic stresses. Transfer of palisade layer from *G. arboreum* to *G. hirsutum* is the best option for developing resistance to sucking pests.

**(d) *Utilising genetic engineering procedures* :** Though *Bt* cottons are already in the field, they are associated with threats of insecticide resistance development against bollworms and instability in their bioefficacy. Hence, use of alternate sources of insecticidal proteins like *tea* complexes of *P. luminacence* and *multiple gene constructs (of* Cry genes) can be thought of, to overcome the negative points of *Bt* cotton technology. Sucking pests may also be brought under the umbrella of biotechnology, to build resistance in cotton genotypes. Exploitation of *chitinase* gene against diseases is another good option for breeding fungal disease resistance. Antisense technology can be employed to construct varieties resistant to leaf CLCuV disease.

**(e) *Miscellaneous* :** To achieve "Total Natural Fibre" concept, breeding naturally coloured cotton deserves consideration. Increasing spinnability of the coloured cottons in adddition to enhacing their productivity and range of colours are good areas for future work.

Cotton is mostly cultivated as sole crop but area under cotton-based cropping system is also large. Development of genotypes suitable for different cropping system under different soil conditions deserves attention for increasing the net income per unit area.

The concept of ultra narrow spacing is the talk of the day. Short compact genotypes amenable for machine picking are important. These genotypes not only reduce dependence on labour for cotton picking but also fit in various cropping systems. Accelerated efforts have to be made for the overall improvement of cotton to reach at least the world average of productivity.

## REFERENCES


Amudha, K. and Raveendran. S. (1997). Heterosis in cloured linted cotton G. *hirsutum L. J. Indian Soc. Cotton Improv.,* 22: 20–22.

Andries, J.A., Jones, J.E., Sloane, L.W. and Marshall, J.G. (1969). Effect of okra leaf on bollrot, yield and other important characters of upland cotton (*G. hirsutum* L.) *Crop Sci.,* 9: 705–710.

Balls, W.L. (1908). Mendelian studies in Egyptian cottons. *J. Agri. Sci.,* 2: 346–379.

Batzios, D., Roapakias, D., Kechagia, U. and Galano Poulou, S.S. (1998). Comparative efficiency of three selection methods for yield and quality in cotton. *Paper presented at World Cotton Research Conference–2* held at Athens, Greece. Abstract Book p. 36.

Beasley, J.O. (1940). The origin of American tetraploid *Gossypium* species. *Amer. Nat.* 74: 258–286.

Bhale, N.L. (1987). Hybrid cottons in India. FAO Consultancy Report CICR Nagpur India.

Bhale, N.L. and Bhat, M.G. (1989). Use of honey bee *(Apis cerana indica)* as pollinator in hybrid seed production on male sterile lines of upland cotton. *Indian J. Agril. Sciences,* 59(1): 74–77.

Bird, L.S. (1982). The MAR (multi–adversity resistance) system for genetic improvement of cotton. *Plant Dis.,* 66: 172–176.

Brinkerhoff, L.A. (1970) Variation in *Xanthomonas malvacearum* and its relation to control. *Annu Rev. Phytopathology,* 8: 85–110.

Brubaker, C. L., Paterson, A.H. and Wendel, J.F. (1999). Comparative genetic mapping of allotetraploid cotton and its diploid progenitors. *Genome,* 42; 184–203.

Brubaker, CL. and Wendel, J.F. (1994). Reevaluating the origin of domesticated cotton *(Gossypium hirsutum: Malvaceae)* using nuclear restriction fragment length polymorphism (RFLPS) *Amer. J. Bot.,* 81: 1309–1326.

Cook, O.F. (1932). Cotton improvement through type collection, with special reference to the Acala variety. *Tech. Bull. U.S. Dept., Agric.,* 302: 62.

Craven, L.A. Stewart, J.McD., Brown, A.H.D. and Grace, J.P. (1995). The Australian wild species of *Gossypium. In*: *Challenging thé Future: Proceedings of the World Cotton Research Conference– 2. Constable, G.A. and Forrester, N.W. (Eds.).* Brisbane Australia February 14–17 1994. CSIRO Melbourne pp. 278–281.

Cronn, R. and Wendel, J.F. (1998). Simple methods for isolating homologous loci from allopolyploid genomes. *Genomes,* 41:756–762.

Dani, R.G., (1984). Variability of seed–oil and productivity in some Indian Cottons tested in Texas. *Indian J. Agric. Sci.,* 54: 550–556.

Dani, R.G., (1992). Maternal effects of cotton seed oil. *Ami. Agric. Res.,* 13: 406–409.

Davis, D.D. (1978). Hybrid cotton: Specific problems and potentials, *Adv. Agron.,* 30: 129–150.

Doak, C.C., (1934). A new technique in cotton hybridizing suggested changes in existing methods of emasculation and bagging of cotton flowers. *J. Hered.,* 25: 201–204.

Douglas, A.G. and Weaver, J.B. Jr., (1963). Comparison of open pollinated seed with registered seed of three cotton varieties. *Crop Sci.,* 3: 515–516.

El–zik, K.M. and Thaxton, R.M. (1995), Breeding for resistance to bacterial blight of cotton in relation to races of pathogen. *In: Challenging the future: Proccedings of the Paper presented at World Cotton Research Conference–1,* Brisbane, Australia, February 14–17,1994. G.A. Constable and Forrester, N.W. (*Eds*.), CSIRO, Melbourne pp: 236–241.

Endrizzi, J.E., Turcotte, E.L. and Kohel, R.J. (1984). Qualitative genetics, cytology and cytogenetics. *In*: *Cotton–Agronomy Monograph* No. 24 (*Eds*. Kohel, R.J. and Lewis, F.C.) A SACSSA–SSSA. Wisconsin, USA, pp. 81–119.

Endrizzi, J.E., Turcotte, E.L. and Kohel, R.J. (1985) Genetics, cytology and evolution of *Gossypium. Adv. Genet.* 23: 271–327.

Endrizzi. J.E. (1962). The diploid like behaviour of tetraploid cotton. *Evolution* 16:325–329.

Fasoulas, A.C. (1973). A new approach to breeding superior yielding varieties, *Publ. 3. Dept. Genetic Plant Breeding. Aristotelian University of Agricultural sciences. Thessaloniki Greece.*

Follin, J.C., Giravdot, B., Mangano, V. and Benitez, R. (1998), New results on inheritance of immunity to bacterial blight *(Xanthomonas campestris pv. malvacearum.* Smith Dye, races 18–20) in the cotton plant (G. *hirsutum* L). *Cotton Fibres Trop,* 43: 167–174.

Foxsally (1987a). In search of coloured cotton SPINOFF, March pp. 29–31.

Foxsally (1987b). Naturally coloured cotton SPINOFF, December pp. 48–50.

Fryxell, P.A. (1984), Taxonomy and Germplasm resources in Cotton. *Agronomy monograph ASA–CSSA–SSSA, 677 South Segoe, Road Madison, WI 53711, USA* pp. 27–29.

Fryxell, P.A. (1992). A revised taxonomic interpretation of *Gossypium* L. *(Malvaceae).* Rheedea 2: 108–165.

Gerstel, D.U. (1953). Chromosome translocations in interspecific hybrids of the genus *Gossypium. Evolution,* 7: 234–244.

Gerstel, D.U. (1963). Evolutionary problems in some polyploid crop plants *Heriditas Suppl.,* 2: 481–504.

Girardot, B., Hequet, E., Yehouessi, M.T. and Guibordau, P. (1986). Finding a variety of *G. hirsutum* L. resistant to strains of *Xanthomonas campestris* pv. *Malvacearum* (Smith) Dye Virulent on associations of major genes (B2B3 or B9L–B10L). *Cotton Fibres Trop.,* 43: 167–174.

Gomez, M., Johnston, J.S., Ellison, J.R. and Price, H.J. (1993). Nuclear 2C DNA content of *Gossypium hirsutum* L. accessions determined by flow cytometary. *Biol Zentralbl.,* 112: 351–351.

Harry, B. and Richard, G. (1986). Result of first large scale growing of varieties in the Ivary Coast. *Cot. Fib. Trop.,* 4: 100–101.

Hillocks, R.J. (1992). Bacterial blight, *In:* Hillocks, R.J. *(Ed.) Cotton Diseases,* CAB International, Walling Ford, UK. pp: 39–85.

Hutchinson, J.B. (1940). New polyploids in cotton by use of colchicine. *Trop. Agri. (Trinindad)* 17: 53–54.

Hutchinson, J.B. (1959). *The Application of Genetics of Cotton Improvement.* Cambridge University Press London, New York.

ICAC, (1997). *Commercial cotton hybrids ICAC RECORDER,* pp. 3–14.

Innes, N.L. (1983), Bacterial blight of cotton. Cambridge *Philos. Soc. Biological Review,* 58: 157–176.

Jenkins, J.N. (1995). Host plant resistance to insects *In: cotton challenging the future: Proceedings of the World Cotton Research Conference–1* Brisbane Australia, Eds: G.A. Constable and N.W. Forrester CSIRO, Melbourne pp. 359–372.

Jenkins, J.N. (1989). State of the art in host plant resistance in cotton. *In: Pest Management in Cotton (Eds.* Green, M.B. and DeB. Lyon, D.J.). Ellis Harweed Ltd., Chichester, England, pp. 54–69.

Jiang, C.X., Wright, R.J., ELZIK K.M. and Paterson, A.H. (1998). Polyploid formation created unique avenues for response to selection in *Gossypium* (cotton). *Proc. Natl. Acad. Sci.* USA, 95. 4419–4424.

Johnson, B.L. (1975). *Gossypium palmeri* and polyphyletic origin of the New World cotions. *Bull. Torrey Bot. Club.,* 102: 340–349.

Jones, J.E. and Andries, J.A. (1969). Effect of frego on the incidence of cotton bollrot. *Crop Sci.,* 9: 426–428.

Joshi, M. (1997). *Hybrid cotton in India*. Kalyani Publisher Ludhiana. India pp. 1–18.

Kairon, M.S., Rao, M.R.K., Venugopalan, M.V. and Singh, M. (1998). Cotton (*Gossypium* spp) research, A pursuit towards self sufficiency and export. *Indian J. Agric Sci.*, 68: 460–467.

Khadi, B.M. (1996). Breeding for resistance to insects pests in relation to organic cotton production. *J. Ind. Soc. Cotton Improv.*, 21(2): 131–134.

Khadi, B.M. and Kulkami, V.N. (1996). Coloured cotton: Problems and prospects. *Indian Textile Journal*, 106:72–78.

Khadi, B.M., Katageri, I.S. and Nalini, A.S. (1994). Histological basis of CMS in Reba 50A cotton genotype. *J. Indian Soc. Cotton Improve.* 19: 25–25.

Khadi, B.M., Katageri, I.S., Vamadevaiah, H.M., Shirsat, S., Manjula, S.M, and Bijapur, R. (1996). Colour development in cotton fibres. *Indian Textile Journal*, 106: 78–80.

Knight, R.L. and Rose, M.F. (1954). A new approach to the technique of cotton selection. *Emp. Cott. Gr. Rev.*, 31: 162–170.

Kohel, R.J. (1973). Genetic nomenclature in cotton. *J. Hered.* 64: 291–295.

Kohel, R.J. (1980). Genetic studies of seed oil in cotton. *Crop Sci.* 20: 784–787.

Kohel, R.J. and Richmond, T.R. (1969). Evaluation of synthetic varieties of upland cotton developed under two levels of natural crossing. *Crop Sci.*, 9: 647–651.

Kulkarni, R.K. and Khadilkar, T.R. (1929). Studies on inheritance in cotton. The improvement of Dharwad American cotton by hybridization. *Bull. Agric. Res. Inst. Pusa* (India), p. 189.

Lan, T.H., Cook, C.G. and Paterson, A.H. (1999). Identification of a RAPD marker linked to a male fertility restoration gene in cotton (*Gossypium hirsutum* L). *Journal of Agri Genomics*, 1: 1–5.

Linnaeus, C. (1953). *Species Plantarum* vol. 1 1" edn. Stockholm.

Liu, S., Fan, X., He., B., Song, M., Cai, S., Jin, Z., Gu, S. and Hu, Q. (1990). A study on the insect and disease avoiding effects of a short season cotton variety. *China cotions*, 4: 40–42.

Manoharan, M., Doddayenkanna, K.H., and Rudramuniyappa, C.K. (1994). Histology of pollen degeneration in cytoplasmic male sterile (CMS) cotton (*Gossypium hirsutum* L). *Proc. Indian National Sci. Acad.*, 60(6): 565–570.

Maxwell, F.G., Jenkins, J.N. and Parrot, W.L. (1972). Resistance of plants to insects. *Adv. Agron.*, 24: 187–265.

McGregor, J.C. (1931). Prehistoric cotton fabrics of Arizona. *Mus. Notes. Mus. North Ariz.*, 4: 2.

Mehetre, S.S. (1988). Male sterility in cotton. *Agric Res.*, 9: 7–17.

Mehetre, S.S. and Thombre, M.V. (1982). Note on the reaction of some promising mutants of upland cotton to the attack of bollworm. *Indian J. Agric. Sci.*, 52(7): 474–476.

Mehta, N.P. and Patel, C.J. (1983). Hybrid seed production technique for exploitation of heterosis in cotton. *Indian Farm*, 33(9): 23–31.

Mehta, N.P., Badaya, S.N., and Patel, G.S. (1983). A modified hybrid seed production technique for Asiatic cotton. *J. Indian. Soc. Cotton. Improv.*, 7: 36–37.

Mell, P.H. (1984). Experiments of crossing for the purpose of improving the cotton fibre. *Alabama (US) Agri. Expt. Sta. Bull.* p. 56.

Meshram, L.D. and Wadodkar, M.B. (1992). Male sterility in Asiatic cotton *Gossypium arboreum* L. *Hybrid cotton News letter*, 2: 3.

Meyer, J.R., and Meyer, V.G., (1961). Origin and inheritance of nectariless cotton. *Crop. Sci.*, 1: 167–169.

Meyer, V.G. (1973). A study of reciprocal hybrids between upland cotton (*Gossypium hirsutum* L) and experimental lines with cytoplasm from seven other species. *Crop Sci.*, 13: 439–444.

Meyer, V.G. (1975). Male sterility from *Gossypium harknessii. J. Hered.,* 66(1):23–27.

Mohod, P., Bharad, S, Meshram, L.D. and Kalpande, H.V. (1998). Studies on isogenic cotton hybrids based on different cytoplasms. *J. Cotton. Res. Dev.,* 12: 151–155.

Mursal, I. El. Jack and Endrizzi, J.E. (1976). A reexamination of the diploid like meiotic behaviour of polyploid cotton. *Theor. Appl. Genetic.* 47: 171–181.

Murthy, K.S. and Achaya, K.T. (1975). *Cotton seed chemistry and Technology. Publication and Information Directorate,* CSIR. pp. 1–347.

Murthy, K.S. and AppuRao, B., (1963). Studies on the compositional and varietal characteristics of Indian Cotton Seed during decennium 1951–52 to 1961–62. *Indian Central Oilseeds Committee,* p. 13.

Narayanan, S.S., Bhat, M.G. and Singh, P. (1990). Role of hybrid cottons for quantum jump in yield and production. *In*: Cotton Scenario in India. A souvenir. 1CAR–CICR, Publication pp. 29–34.

Narayanan, S.S., Singh, P. and Singh, V.V. (1987a). Disruptive selection for earliness in upland cotton. *Indian J. Agric. Sci.,* 57(8): 544–546.

Narayanan, S.S., Singh, P. and Singh, V.V. (1988a). Effects of disruptive selection on seed oil contents in upland cotton. *Indian J. Agric. Sci.,* 58(5): 399–400.

Narayanan, S.S., Singh, P. and Singh, V.V. (1988b). Effects of disruptive selection on technological properties in upland cotton. *J. Cotton Res. Dev.,* 2(1): 8–11.

Narayanan, S.S., Singh, P., Singh, V.V. and Chauhan, S.K. (1987b). Disruptive selection for genetic improvement of upland cotton. *Indian J. Agric. Sci.,* 57(7): 447–450.

Narayanan. S.S., Singh, P. and Bhat, M.G. (1989). Heterosis breeding in cotton. *In:* Rakshit, R.C. *(Ed.) Heterosis Breeding* p.37–48. Bidhan Chandra Agric. Univ. Kalyani, West Bengal India.

Narula, A.M., Monga, D., Chauhan, M.S. and Sheo Raj (1999). Cotton leaf curl virus disease in India. The challenge ahead. *J. Cotton Res. Dev.* 13(2): 129–139.

Niles, G.A. and Richmond, T.R. (1962). Performance trials with selected strains of storm resistant cotton. *Texas Agric. Exp. Sta. Mise. Publ. 577* College Station, Texas.

Parks, C.R. Ezell, W.L., Williams, D.E. and Dreyer, D.L. (1975). VII. The application of flavonoid distribution to taxonomic problems in the genus *Gossypiun Bull. Torrey Bot. Club,* 102: 350–361.

Patel, C.T. (1955). Technique for hybrid seed production on commercial scale. *Former,* 7: 61–63.

Patel, C.T. (1971). Hybrid 4–a new hope towards self sufficiency in cotton in India. *Cot. Dev.* 1(2): 1–6.

Peat, J.E. and Brown, K.J. (1961). A record of cotton breeding for the lake province of Tanganyika. *Emp. J. Exp. Agric.,* 29: 119–135.

Percival, A.E. and Kohel, R.J. (1991), Distribution, collection and evaluation of *Gossypium. Adv. Agron.,* 44: 225–256.

Phillips, L.L. (1963). The cytogenetics of *Gossypium* and the origin of the New World Cottons. *Evolution,* 17: 460–469.

Phillips, L.L. and Strickland, M.A. (1966). The cytology of a hybrid between *Gossypium hirsutum* and *G. longicalyx. Can. J. Genet. Cytol.,* 8: 91–95.

Puhalla, J.E. and Hummel, M. (1983), Vegetative compatility groups within *Verticillium dalhiae. Phytopathology,* 73: 1305–1308.

Raafat, M.A.A. (1998). Study effect of mutagenesis on Egyptian cotton. *Paper Presented in World Cotton Research Conference–2* held at Athens Greece Abstract Book p. 31.

Rahaman, H. (1997). Breeding approaches to cotton leaf curl resistance *ICAC RECORDER* March 11–14.

Rao, P., Kadapa, S.N. and Khadi, B.M. (1996). Morphological and Biochemical characters association in pest tolerant and susceptible cotton genotypes. *J. Cotton Res. and Dev.,* 10(1): 68–75.

Rao, S.B.P. (1983). Cotton seed industry and scenario standard seeds. *Indian Textile Journal,* pp. 132–134.

Reinisch, A., Dong, J., Brubaker, C.L., Stelly, D.M., Wendel, J.F. and Paterson, A.H. (1994). A detailed RFLP map of cotton *(Gossypium hirsutum XG. barbadense):* Chromosome organization and evolution in disomic polyploid genome. *Genetics,* 138: 1–19.

Richmond, T.R. (1951). Procedures and methods of cotton breeding with special reference to American cultivated species. *Adv. Agron.,* 4: 213–245.

Richmond. T.R. (1950). Cotton IX Breeding and Improvement. *Adv. Agron.,* 2: 63–74.

Sarvella, P. (1958). Multivalent formation and genetic segregation in some allopolyploid *Gossypium* hybrids. *Genetics,* 43: 601–609.

Shappley, Z.W., Jenkins, J.N., Meredith, W.R. and Me. Carty, J.C. (1998). An RFLP linkage map of upland cotton *Gossypium hirsutum. Theor. Appl. Genet.,* 97: 756–761.

Sheetz. R.H. and Weaver, Jr. J.B. (1980). Inheritance of fertility enhancer factor from Pima cotton when transferred into upland cotton with *Gossypium harknessii* Brandegee cytoplasm. *Crop. Sci.,* 20: 272–275.

Sheo Raj (1992), Achievements in plant pathology. *In: All India Co–ordinated Cotton Improvement Project Achievements. Silver Jubilee.* Dr. Basu. A.K. and Narayanan, S.S. (*Eds.*) pp. 152–176.

Simpson, D.M. (1948). Hybrid vigour for natural crossing for improving cotton production. *J. Amer. Soc. Agron.,* 40: 970–979.

Singh, M. and Singh, R.P. (1999), Screening of cotton germplasm and hybrids for Blue Disease resistance in S.R. of Vietnam, *J. Indian Soc. Cotton. Improv.,* 24(1): 33–35.

Singh, M., Singh, V.P., Pal, K and Lal, C.B. (1989). Improvement of yield through increased boll weight in upland cotton (*G. hirsutum). Indian J. Agric. Sci.,* 54: 141–144.

Singh, P., Joshi, S.S. and Narayanan, S.S. (1994). Role of induced mutations in genetic improvement of cotton a review. *J. Indian Soc. Cot. Improvement,* 19: 113–123.

Singh, T.H., Chahal, G.S., Bharadwaj, H.L., and Tikku, P.L. (1980). Exploitation of heterosis in cotton –A review. J. *Indian Soc. Cotton Improv.,* 5: 46–56.

Singh, V.V., Punit Mohan and Kothandaraman, R. (1996). Naturally coloured linted genetic resources in National Cotton Gene Bank, their characteristics and utilisation. *J. Indian Soc.Cotton. Improv.,* 21(2): 151–158.

Skovsted, A. (1937). Cytological studies in cotton IV. chromosome conjugation in interspecific hybrids. *J. Genet.,* 34: 97–134.

Small, R.L., Rayburn, J.A. Cronn, R.C. Seelanan, T. and Wendel, J.F. (1998). The tortoise and the hare: Choosing between non coding plastome and nuclear *Adh* sequences for phylogeny reconstruction in a recently diverged plant group. *Amer. J. Bot.,* 85: 1301–1315.

Srinivasan, K. and Gururajan, K.N. (1983). Suguna medium staple hybrid cotton. *J. Indian Soc. Cotton Improv. J.,* 8(2): 83–86.

Stewart, J : McD. (1995). Potential for crop improvement with exotic germplasm and genetic engineering. *In: challenging the future: Proceedings of the World Cotton Research Conférence* – J. Brisbane Australia G.A., Constable and N.W. Forrester (Eds), LSIRO, Melbourne pp. 313–312.

Strausbaugh, C.A. Schroth, M.N., Weinhold, A.R. and Hancock, J.G. (1992), Assessment of vegetative compatibility of *Verticillium dalhiae* tester strains and isolated from California Potatoes. *Phytopathology,* 82: 61–68.

Strauss, E. (1998). Possible new weapon for insect control. *Science,* 280; 2050.

Thompson, N.J. and Lee, J.A. (1980), Insect resistance in cotton: A review and prospects for Australia. *J. Aust. Insti. Agric. Sci.,* 46: 75–86.

Trought, T. and King, H.E. (1934). Preliminary testing of new varieties of types of cotton. *2nd Conf. Cott. Gr. Probl. Emp. Cott. Gr. Corp.,* pp. 51–60.

Umbeck, P., Johnson, P., Barton, K. and Swain, W. (1987). Genetically transformed cotton *(Gossypium hirsutum* L) plants. *Bio / Technol.,* 5: 263–266.

Vaissiere, B.E., Moffet, J.O., and Loper, G.M. (1984). Honey bees as pollinators for hybrid cotton seed production on Texas high plains. *Agron. J.,* 76: 1005–1010.

Verma, J.P. (1986), Bacterial blight of cotton. CRC Press. Inc. Boca Raton, FI., p. 278.

Verma. J.P. and Singh, R.P. (1974), Recent studies on the bacterial diseases of fibre and oilseed crops in India. *In*: Raychaudhuri, S.P. and Verma, J.P. (*Eds.*) *Current trends in plant pathology* Lucknow University, India. pp: 134–145.

Vollesen, K. (1987). The native species of *Gossypium (Malvaceae)* in Africa, Arabia and Pakistan *Kew Bull.,* 42: 337–347.

Waghmore, V.N. and Koranne K.D. (1998). Coloured cottons in India. *Indian J. Genet.,* 158: 1–15.

Walhood, V, Henneberry, T., Bariola, L., Kittock, D. and Brown. C. (1981). Effect of short season cotton on overwintering pink bollworm larvae and spring moth emergence. *J. Economic Entomology,* 74: 297–302.

Walker, J.T. (1963). Multiline concept of intra varietal heterosis. *Emp. Cott. Gr. Rev.,* 40: 190–215.

Wallace, T.M. and El–zik, K.M. (1989). Inheritance of resistance in three cotton cultivars to the HVI isolates of bacterial blight. *Crop. Sci.,* 29: 1114–1119.

Watt, G. (1907). *The wild and cultivated cotton plants of the world.* Longmans, Green and Co., London.

Weindling, R. (1948), Bacterial Blight of cotton under conditions of artificial inoculation. *US. Dept. Agric. Tech. Bull.,* 956: 59.

Wendel, J.F. (1989). New World Tetraploid cottons contain Old World cytoplasm. *Proc. Natl.Acad. Sci.* USA, 86: 4132–4136.

Wendel, J.F. and Albert, V.A. (1992). Phylogenetics of the cotton genus *Gossypium :* Character state weighted parsimony analysis of chloroplast DN A restriction site data and its systematic and biogeographic implications. *Syst. Bot.,* 17:115–143.

Wendel, J.F. Schnabel, A. and Seelanan, T. (1995). An unusual ribosomal sequence from *Gossypium gossypioides* reveals ancient, cryptic, intergenomic introgression. *Mol. Phylogenet. Evol.,* 4: 298–313.

Wickens, G.M. (1953), Bacterial Blight. A survey of present knowledge, with particular reference to possibilities of control of the disease in African rain grown cotton. *Emp. Cation Grow. Rev.,* 30: 81–103.

Williams, B.C. (1906.) Cotton plant. *Bull N.C. State Broad Agric.,* 27: 1–27.

Wright R.S., Taxtan RM., EL–Zik, K.M. and Paterson, A.H. (1998). D–sub genome bias of *Xcm* resistance genes in tetraploid *Gossypium* suggest that polyploid formation has created novel avenue for evolution. *Genetics,* 149: 1987–1996.

Wright, R.J., Thaxton, P.M., El–zic, K.M. and Patterson, A.H. (1999). Molecular mapping of genes affecting pubescence of cotton. *J. Heredity,* 90: 215–219.

Zapata, C, Park, S.H., El–zik, K.M. and Smith, R.H. (1999). Transformation of a Texas cotton cultivar by using *Agrobacterium* and the shoot apex. *Theo. Appl.* Genet., 98: 252–256.

Zhao, X. Yang, S., Hanson, R.E., Crane, C.F. Price, J.H. Stelly, D.M., Wendel. J.F. and Patterson, A.H. (1998). Dispersed repetitive DNA has spread to new genomes since polyploid formation in cotton. *Genome,* 8: 479–492.

Zhuang, X. (1994). Introduction, studying and utilization of *Gossypium* germplasm resources. *Crop Gcnetic Resources,* 4: 43–45.

# Subject Index

## D



## E



## F



## G

## Q



## R



## S



## T



## V



## W